# DISTRIBUTED OPERATING SYSTEMS

Delayed write of fs cache = periodic write

Sprite – Wkstn.
Mach
Spring
Plan 9 – Proc. pool
Exokernel
Opal
Amoeba – Proc. pool
Taos
Choices
2/5
✓ – Wkstn-pool

Block level filetr.
File level filetr.

Zebra
DCE DFS
Sun NFS
Sprite LFS
AFS 2
AFS 3
xFS
CODA
Frangipani
Cedar – Immutable
CFS – "keep" param
file-level access

Acc Control ; Digi. Signs.
Deadlock

**Also from IEEE Press**

**Computer Communications and Networks, Second Edition**
John Freer
Copublished with UCL Press
1996 Hardcover 400 pp IEEE Order No. PC5654 ISBN 0-7803-1179-5

**Engineering Networks for Synchronization, CCS 7 and ISDN: Standards, Protocols, Planning, and Testing**
P. K. Bhatnagar
1997 Hardcover 528 pp IEEE Order No. PC5628 ISBN 0-7803-1158-2

**SONET-SDH: A Sourcebook of Synchronous Networking**
edited by Curtis A. Siller, Jr. and Mansoor Shafi
1996 Hardcover 406 pp IEEE Order No. PC4457 ISBN 0-7803-1168-X

# Distributed Operating Systems

## Concepts and Design

**Pradeep K. Sinha**

*Centre for Development of Advanced Computing*

IEEE COMPUTER SOCIETY PRESS

IEEE PRESS

IEEE Communications Society, *Sponsor*

**Prentice-Hall of India** Private Limited
New Delhi - 110 001
2001

**This Second Indian Reprint—Rs. 295.00**
(Original U.S. Edition—Rs. 4426.00)

**DISTRIBUTED OPERATING SYSTEMS: Concepts and Design**
by Pradeep K. Sinha



**ISBN-81-203-1380-1**

This Eastern Economy Edition is the authorized, complete and unabridged photo-offset reproduction of the latest American edition specially published and priced for sale only in Bangladesh, India, Pakistan, and Sri Lanka.

Reprinted in India by special arrangement with The Institute of Electrical and Electronics Engineers, Inc., 345 East 47th Street, New York, NY 10017-2394.

**Second Printing** ... ... **June, 2001**

Published by Asoke K. Ghosh, Prentice-Hall of India Private Limited, M-97, Connaught Circus, New Delhi-110001 and Printed by Mohan Makhijani at Rekha Printers Private Limited, New Delhi-110020.

# Contents

## Chapter 2: Computer Networks 46



## Chapter 3: Message Passing 114



## Chapter 4: Remote Procedure Calls 167

## Chapter 10: Naming 496



## Chapter 11: Security 565



## Chapter 12: Case Studies 642



## Index 731

# Preface

## Motivation

The excellent price/performance ratio offered by microprocessor-based workstations over traditional mainframe systems and the steady improvements in networking technologies have made distributed computing systems very attractive. While the hardware issues of building such systems have been fairly well understood for quite some time, the major stumbling block until now has been the availability of good distributed operating systems. Fortunately, recent research and development work in academic institutions and industries have helped us better understand the basic concepts and design issues in developing distributed operating systems. Distributed operating systems are no more only in research laboratories but are now commercially available.

With the proliferation of distributed computing systems, it has become increasingly important for computer science and computer engineering students to learn about distributed operating systems. As a result, a number of universities have instituted regular courses on distributed operating systems at the graduate level. Even in various undergraduate-level operating systems courses, the fundamental concepts and design principles of distributed operating systems have been incorporated.

However, there is still a lack of good textbooks that can provide a comprehensive and solid introduction to distributed operating systems in an orderly manner. Except for a few recently published books, almost all books in this area are research monographs. Therefore, for both an educator and a student, the creation of an overall image of distributed operating systems is currently a complicated and time-consuming task. Furthermore, computer professionals and starting researchers who want to get an overall picture of distributed operating systems so as to identify the various research and design issues have difficulty in finding a good text for their purpose.

Motivated by these factors, I decided to do research toward the preparation of a textbook on distributed operating systems. My primary objective was to concisely present a clear explanation of the current state of the art in distributed operating systems so that readers can gain sufficient background to appreciate more advanced materials of this field.

## Overview

The book is designed to provide a clear description of the fundamental concepts and design principles that underlie distributed operating systems. It does not concentrate on any particular distributed operating system or hardware. Instead, it discusses, in a general setting, the fundamental concepts and design principles that are applicable to a variety of distributed operating systems. However, case studies are included in the text to relate the discussed concepts with real distributed operating systems.

The material in the book has been drawn largely from the research literature in the field. Of the vast amount of research literature available in this field, effort was made to select and give more emphasis to those concepts that are of practical value in real systems, rather than those that are only of theoretical interest.

Each chapter contains carefully designed exercises that are meant to test the understanding of the materials in the text and to stimulate investigation.

An extensive set of references and a list of selected pointers to on-line bibliographies on the Internet have been provided at the end of each chapter to allow interested readers to explore more advanced materials dealing with finer details about each chapter's topics.

Throughout the book, the style of presentation used is motivational and explanatory in nature.

## Contents

Chapter 1 provides an introduction to distributed computing systems, distributed operating systems, and the issues involved in designing distributed operating systems. It also provides a brief introduction to Distributed Computing Environment (DCE), whose components are described as case studies of key technologies in several chapters of the book.

Chapter 2 presents a brief introduction to computer networks and describes the current state of the art in networking technology.

Chapters 3, 4, and 5 describe the various communication techniques used for exchange of information among the processes of a distributed computing system. In particular, these three chapters deal with the issues involved in the design of interprocess communication mechanisms and the commonly used practical approaches to handle these issues. Chapter 3 deals with the message-passing mechanism. Chapter 4 deals with the remote procedure call mechanism, and Chapter 5 deals with the distributed shared-memory mechanism for interprocess communication.

Synchronization issues to be dealt with in a distributed system, such as clock synchronization, mutual exclusion, deadlock, and election algorithms, are discussed in Chapter 6.

Chapter 7 presents a discussion of the commonly used approaches for resource management in distributed systems.

Chapter 8 deals with the process management issues. In particular, it presents a discussion of process migration mechanisms and mechanisms to support threads facility.

A discussion of the issues and the approaches for designing a file system for a distributed system is given in Chapter 9.

Chapter 10 deals with the issues and mechanisms for naming and locating objects in distributed systems.

The security issues and security mechanisms for distributed systems are discussed in Chapter 11.

Finally, Chapter 12 contains case studies of four existing distributed operating systems to relate the concepts discussed in the preceding chapters with real distributed operating systems.

## Audience

The book is suitable for anyone who needs a concise and informal introduction to distributed operating systems.

It can serve as an ideal textbook for a course on distributed operating systems. It can also be used for advanced undergraduate and postgraduate courses on operating systems, which often need to cover the fundamental concepts and design issues of distributed operating systems in addition to those of centralized operating systems.

The book can also be used as a self-study text by system managers, professional software engineers, computer scientists, and researchers, who either need to learn about distributed operating systems or are involved in the design and development of distributed operating systems or distributed application systems.

Advanced researchers will also find the rich set of references and the pointers to on-line bibliographies on the Internet provided at the end of each chapter very helpful in probing further on any particular topic.

Although full care has been taken to make the subject matter simple and easy to understand by a wide range of readers, I have assumed that the reader has a knowledge of elementary computer architecture and is familar with basic centralized operating systems concepts discussed in standard operating systems textbooks.

## About Pointers to Bibliographies on the Internet

In addition to a good number of references provided in the end-of-chapter bibliographies, I have also provided lists of selected pointers to the on-line bibliographies of interest on the Internet. The purpose of these pointers is twofold:

1. The end-of-chapter bibliographies contain only selected references. A large number of references on the topics covered in a chapter are not included in the chapter's bibliography due to space limitations. The pointers may be used by interested readers to locate such references.
2. The end-of-chapter bibliographies contain references to only already published documents. Distributed operating systems is currently an active area of research, and a large volume of new documents are published almost every month. Since the on-line bibliographies on the Internet are updated from time to time, interested readers may use the pointers to locate those documents that are published after the publication of this book. Thus, in addition to the information contained in it, the book also provides a way for its readers to keep track of on-going research activities on the topics covered and related topics.

Note that the end-of-chapter lists of pointers to on-line bibliographies are by no means exhaustive. I have provided pointers for only those on-line bibliographies that I knew about and I felt would be useful in easily locating references of interest. Moreover, it is often the case that there are many mirrors for an on-line bibliography (the same bilbiography exists on multiple sites). For such cases, I have provided only one pointer for a bibliography.

Also note that most of the on-line bibliographies are not about on-line documents, but about on-line references to documents. A vast majority of documents referenced in the on-line bibliographies only exist in hard-copy form. However, a few of the referenced documents do have an on-line version on the Internet. For such documents, the bibliographies normally contain URLs (Uniform Resource Locators) pointing to the on-line version of the document. If you find a reference containing such a URL, just follow the URL to access the on-line version of the corresponding document.

# Acknowledgments

Many people have contributed to this book, either directly or indirectly. To start with, I must thank all the researchers who have contributed to the fields of distributed computing systems and distributed operating systems because the book is based on their research results.

Mamoru Maekawa, my Ph.D. supervisor, provided me with the opportunity to do research in the area of distributed operating systems. Without this opportunity, this book would not have been possible.

Lively discussions with the members of the Galaxy distributed operating system project, including Kentaro Shimizu, Xiaohua Jia, Hyo Ashishara, Naoki Utsunomiya, Hirohiko Nakano, Kyu Sung Park, and Jun Hamano, helped a lot in broadening my knowledge of distributed operating systems.

Without the efforts of all the people who collected references and made them available on the Internet, it would not have been possible for me to provide the end-of-chapter pointers to the bibliographies on the Internet.

Several anonymous reviewers of my draft manuscript provided invaluable feedback concerning organization, topic coverage, typographical errors, and parts of the text that were not as clear as they are now.

My production editor at IEEE Press, Denise Phillip, did an excellent job in numerous ways to present the book in its current form. IEEE Press Director Dudley Kay, Senior

Acquisitions Editor John Griffin, and review coordinators Lisa Mizrahi and Lisa Dayne were of great help in improving the overall quality of the book and in bringing it out in a timely manner.

Finally, I thank my wife, Priti, for preparing the electronic version of the entire hand-written draft manuscript. I also thank her for her continuous patience and sacrifices during the entire period of this long project. Without her loving support and understanding, I would never have succeeded in completing this project.

**Pradeep K. Sinha**

# Abbreviations and Acronyms

| | |
|---|---|
| AAL | ATM Adaptation Layer |
| ACL | Access Control List |
| AFS | Andrew File System |
| ANSI | American National Standards Institute |
| API | Application Programming Interface |
| APPN | Advanced Peer-to-Peer Networking |
| ARP | Address Resolution Protocol |
| ARPANET | Advanced Research Projects Agency NETwork |
| ASN.1 | Abstract Syntax Notation |
| ATM | Asynchronous Transfer Mode |
| BIOS | Basic Input Output System |
| B-ISDN | Broadband Integrated Services Digital Network |
| CBR | Constant Bit Rate |
| CCITT | International Telegraph and Telephone Consultative Committee |
| CDS | Cell Directory Service/Server |
| CERN | European Centre for Nuclear Research |
| CFS | Cedar File System |
| CICS | Customer Information Control System |
| CLP | Cell Loss Priority |
| CMH | Chandy-Misra-Hass |
| CMIP | Common Management Information Protocol |
| COOL | Chorus Object-Oriented Layer |
| CSMA/CD | Carrier Sense Multiple Access with Collision Detection |
| CSRG | Computer Systems Research Group |
| DCE | Distributed Computing Environment |
| DDLCN | Distributed Double-Loop Computer Network |
| DEC | Digital Equipment Corporation |
| DES | Data Encryption Standard |

| | |
|---|---|
| DFS | Distributed File Service |
| DI | Directory Identifier |
| DIB | Directory Information Base |
| DIT | Directory Information Tree |
| DME | Distributed Management Environment |
| DN | Distinguished Name |
| DNS | Domain Name/Naming Service/System |
| DoD | Department of Defense |
| DSM | Distributed Shared Memory |
| DSVM | Distributed Shared Virtual Memory |
| DTS | Distributed Time Service |
| Email | Electronic Mail |
| ERB | Expanding Ring Broadcast |
| FDDI | Fiber Distributed Data Interface |
| FIFO | First-In First-Out |
| FLIP | Fast Local Internet Protocol |
| FTP | File Transfer Protocol |
| Gbps | Gigabits per second |
| GDA | Global Directory Agent |
| GDS | Global Directory Service/Server |
| GEOS | Geostationary Operational Environmental Satellites |
| GFC | Generic Flow Control |
| GNS | Global Name Service |
| GNU | Gnu's Not Unix |
| GPS | Global Positioning System |
| HEC | Header Error Control |
| HRPC | Heterogeneous Remote Procedure Call |
| IBM | International Business Machines |
| ICMP | Internet Control Message Protocol |
| IDL | Interface Definition Language |
| IEEE | Institute of Electrical and Electronics Engineers |
| IETF | Internet Engineering Task Force |
| IMS | Information Management System |
| INRIA | Institute National de Recherche en Informatique et Automatique |
| IP | Internet Protocol |
| IPC | Inter-Process Communication |
| ISDN | Integrated Services Digital Network |
| ISO | International Standards Organization |
| ITU | International Telecommunications Union |
| KDBMS | Kerberos Database Management Server |
| KDC | Key Distribution Center |
| LAN | Local Area Network |
| LEC | LAN Emulation Client |
| LES | LAN Emulation Server |
| LRPC | Lightweight Remote Procedure Call |
| MAN | Metropolitan Area Network |
| MBone | Multicast Backbone |
| Mbps | Megabits per second |
| MIG | Mach Interface Generator |
| MMU | Memory Management Unit |
| MTBF | Mean Time Between Failures |
| MTU | Maximum Transfer Unit |
| NCA | Network Computing Architecture |
| NCS | Network Computing System |
| NFS | Network File System |
| NIC | Network Information Center |
| NIST | National Institute for Standards and Technology |
| NRMB | Non-Replicated Migrating Block |
| NRNMB | Non-Replicated Non-Migrating Block |
| NSAP | Network Service Access Point |
| NTP | Network Time Protocol |
| NUMA | Non-Uniform Memory Access |
| OC-*n* | Optical Carrier level *n* |
| OLTP | On Line Transaction Processing |
| OPC | Output Port Controller |
| OSF | Open Software Foundation |
| OSI | Open System International |
| PCB | Process Control Block |
| PEM | Privacy Enhanced Mail |

| | |
|---|---|
| PKM | Public Key Manager |
| PMD | Physical Medium Dependent |
| POSIX | Portable Operating System Interface for Computer Environments |
| PRAM | Pipelined Random Access Memory |
| PSE | Packet Switching Exchange |
| PTI | Payload Type Identifier |
| RARP | Reverse Address Resolution Protocol |
| RDN | Relative Distinguished Name |
| RFS | Remote File Server |
| RFT | Request For Technology |
| RMB | Replicated Migrating Block |
| RNMB | Replicated Non-Migrating Block |
| RPC | Remote Procedure Call |
| RPCL | Remote Procedure Call Language |
| RR | Round-Robin |
| RSA | Rivest-Shamir-Adleman |
| RSS | Research Storage System |
| SDH | Synchronous Digital Hierarchy |
| SEAL | Simple and Efficient Adaptation Layer |
| SLIP | Serial Line Internet Protocol |
| SMTP | Simple Mail Transfer Protocol |
| SNA | System Network Architecture |
| SNMP | Simple Network Management Protocol |
| SONET | Synchronous Optical NETwork |
| STS-*n* | Synchronous Transport Signal level *n* |
| TC | Transmission Convergence |
| TCF | Transparent Computing Facility |
| TCP | Transport Control Protocol |
| TFTP | Trivial File Transfer Protocol |
| TI-RPC | Transport Independent-Remote Procedure Call |
| TP | Transport Protocol |
| TWFG | Transaction Wait-For-Graph |
| UCP | Unilateral Commit Protocol |
| UDP | User Datagram Protocol |
| UDS | Universal Directory Service |
| UNI | User Network Interface |
| UTC | Coordinated Universal Time |
| UUID | Universally Unique Identifier |
| VBR | Variable Bit Rate |
| VCI | Virtual Channel Identifier |
| VM | Virtual Memory |
| VMTP | Versatile Message Transfer Protocol |
| VPI | Virtual Path Identifier |
| WAIS | Wide Area Information Servers |
| WAN | Wide Area Network |
| WFG | Wait For Graph |
| WWW | World Wide Web |
| X-IPC | eXtented Inter-Process Communication |
| XDR | eXternal Data Representation |
| XDS | X/Open Directory Server |
| XNS | Xerox Networking System |
| XOM | X/Open Object Management |

# CHAPTER 1

# Fundamentals

## 1.1 WHAT IS A DISTRIBUTED COMPUTING SYSTEM?

Over the past two decades, advancements in microelectronic technology have resulted in the availability of fast, inexpensive processors, and advancements in communication technology have resulted in the availability of cost-effective and highly efficient computer networks. The net result of the advancements in these two technologies is that the price-performance ratio has now changed to favor the use of interconnected, multiple processors in place of a single, high-speed processor.

Computer architectures consisting of interconnected, multiple processors are basically of two types:

1. *Tightly coupled systems*. In these systems, there is a single systemwide primary memory (address space) that is shared by all the processors [Fig. 1.1(*a*)]. If any processor writes, for example, the value 100 to the memory location *x*, any other processor subsequently reading from location *x* will get the value 100. Therefore, in these systems, any communication between the processors usually takes place through the shared memory.

2. *Loosely coupled systems*. In these systems, the processors do not share memory, and each processor has its own local memory [Fig. 1.1(*b*)]. If a processor writes the value

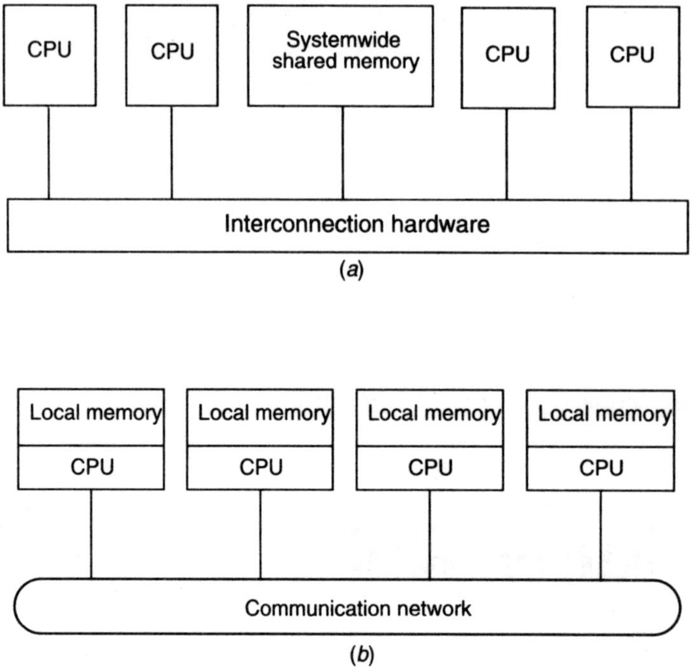


**Fig. 1.1** Difference between tightly coupled and loosely coupled multiprocessor systems: (*a*) a tightly coupled multiprocessor system; (*b*) a loosely coupled multiprocessor system.

100 to the memory location x, this write operation will only change the contents of its local memory and will not affect the contents of the memory of any other processor. Hence, if another processor reads the memory location *x*, it will get whatever value was there before in that location of its own local memory. In these systems, all physical communication between the processors is done by passing messages across the network that interconnects the processors.

Usually, tightly coupled systems are referred to as *parallel processing systems*, and loosely coupled systems are referred to as *distributed computing systems*, or simply distributed systems. In this book, however, the term "distributed system" will be used only for true distributed systems—distributed computing systems that use distributed operating systems (see Section 1.5). Therefore, before the term "true distributed system" is defined in Section 1.5, the term "distributed computing system" will be used to refer to loosely coupled systems. In contrast to the tightly coupled systems, the processors of distributed computing systems can be located far from each other to cover a wider geographical area. Furthermore, in tightly coupled systems, the number of processors that can be usefully deployed is usually small and limited by the bandwidth of the shared memory. This is not the case with distributed computing systems that are more freely expandable and can have an almost unlimited number of processors.

In short, a distributed computing system is basically a collection of processors interconnected by a communication network in which each processor has its own local memory and other peripherals, and the communication between any two processors of the system takes place by message passing over the communication network. For a particular processor, its own resources are *local*, whereas the other processors and their resources are *remote*. Together, a processor and its resources are usually referred to as a *node* or *site* or *machine* of the distributed computing system.

## 1.2 EVOLUTION OF DISTRIBUTED COMPUTING SYSTEMS

Early computers were very expensive (they cost millions of dollars) and very large in size (they occupied a big room). There were very few computers and were available only in research laboratories of universities and industries. These computers were run from a console by an operator and were not accessible to ordinary users. The programmers would write their programs and submit them to the computer center on some media, such as punched cards, for processing. Before processing a job, the operator would set up the necessary environment (mounting tapes, loading punched cards in a card reader, etc.) for processing the job. The job was then executed and the result, in the form of printed output, was later returned to the programmer.

The job setup time was a real problem in early computers and wasted most of the valuable central processing unit (CPU) time. Several new concepts were introduced in the 1950s and 1960s to increase CPU utilization of these computers. Notable among these are batching together of jobs with similar needs before processing them, automatic sequencing of jobs, off-line processing by using the concepts of buffering and spooling, and multiprogramming. *Batching* similar jobs improved CPU utilization quite a bit because now the operator had to change the execution environment only when a new batch of jobs had to be executed and not before starting the execution of every job. *Automatic job sequencing* with the use of control cards to define the beginning and end of a job improved CPU utilization by eliminating the need for human job sequencing. *Off-line processing* improved CPU utilization by allowing overlap of CPU and input/output (I/O) operations by executing those two actions on two independent machines (I/O devices are normally several orders of magnitude slower than the CPU). Finally, *multiprogramming* improved CPU utilization by organizing jobs so that the CPU always had something to execute.

However, none of these ideas allowed multiple users to directly interact with a computer system and to share its resources simultaneously. Therefore, execution of interactive jobs that are composed of many short actions in which the next action depends on the result of a previous action was a tedious and time-consuming activity. Development and debugging of programs are examples of interactive jobs. It was not until the early 1970s that computers started to use the concept of *time sharing* to overcome this hurdle. Early time-sharing systems had several dumb terminals attached to the main computer. These terminals were placed in a room different from the main computer room. Using these terminals, multiple users could now simultaneously execute interactive jobs and share the resources of the computer system. In a time-sharing system, each user is given the impression that he or she has his or her own computer because the system switches rapidly from one user's job to the next user's job, executing only a very small part of each job at a time. Although the idea of time sharing was demonstrated as early as 1960, time-sharing computer systems were not common until the early 1970s because they were difficult and expensive to build.

Parallel advancements in hardware technology allowed reduction in the size and increase in the processing speed of computers, causing large-sized computers to be gradually replaced by smaller and cheaper ones that had more processing capability than their predecessors. These systems were called *minicomputers*.

The advent of time-sharing systems was the first step toward distributed computing systems because it provided us with two important concepts used in distributed computing systems—the sharing of computer resources simultaneously by many users and the accessing of computers from a place different from the main computer room. Initially, the terminals of a time-sharing system were dumb terminals, and all processing was done by the main computer system. Advancements in microprocessor technology in the 1970s allowed the dumb terminals to be replaced by intelligent terminals so that the concepts of off-line processing and time sharing could be combined to have the advantages of both concepts in a single system. Microprocessor technology continued to advance rapidly, making available in the early 1980s single-user computers called *workstations* that had computing power almost equal to that of minicomputers but were available for only a small fraction of the price of a minicomputer. For example, the first workstation developed at Xerox PARC (called Alto) had a high-resolution monochrome display, a mouse, 128 kilobytes of main memory, a 2.5-megabyte hard disk, and a microprogrammed CPU that executed machine-level instructions at speeds of 2–6 μs. These workstations were then used as terminals in the time-sharing systems. In these time-sharing systems, most of the processing of a user's job could be done at the user's own computer, allowing the main computer to be simultaneously shared by a larger number of users. Shared resources such as files, databases, and software libraries were placed on the main computer.

Centralized time-sharing systems described above had a limitation in that the terminals could not be placed very far from the main computer room since ordinary cables were used to connect the terminals to the main computer. However, in parallel, there were advancements in computer networking technology in the late 1960s and early 1970s that emerged as two key networking technologies—*LAN* (*local area network*) and *WAN* (*wide-area network*). The LAN technology allowed several computers located within a building or a campus to be interconnected in such a way that these machines could exchange information with each other at data rates of about 10 megabits per second (Mbps). On the other hand, WAN technology allowed computers located far from each other (may be in different cities or countries or continents) to be interconnected in such a way that these machines could exchange information with each other at data rates of about 56 kilobits per second (Kbps). The first high-speed LAN was the Ethernet developed at Xerox PARC in 1973, and the first WAN was the ARPAnet (Advanced Research Projects Agency Network) developed by the U.S. Department of Defense in 1969. The data rates of networks continued to improve gradually in the 1980s, providing data rates of up to 100 Mbps for LANs and data rates of up to 64 Kbps for WANs. Recently (early 1990s) there has been another major advancement in networking technology—the *ATM* (*asynchronous transfer mode*) technology. The ATM technology is an emerging technology that is still not very well established. It will make very high speed networking possible, providing data transmission rates up to 1.2 gigabits per second (Gbps) in both LAN and WAN environments. The availability of such high-bandwidth networks will allow future distributed computing systems to support a completely new class of distributed applications, called *multimedia applications*, that deal with the handling of a mixture of information, including voice, video, and ordinary data. These applications were previously unthinkable with conventional LANs and WANs.

The merging of computer and networking technologies gave birth to distributed computing systems in the late 1970s. Although the hardware issues of building such systems were fairly well understood, the major stumbling block at that time was the availability of adequate software for making these systems easy to use and for fully exploiting their power. Therefore, starting from the late 1970s, a significant amount of research work was carried out in both universities and industries in the area of distributed operating systems. These research activities have provided us with the basic ideas of designing distributed operating systems. Although the field is still immature, with ongoing active research activities, commercial distributed operating systems have already started to emerge. These systems are based on already established basic concepts. This book deals with these basic concepts and their use in the design and implementation of distributed operating systems. Several of these concepts are equally applicable to the design of applications for distributed computing systems, making this book also suitable for use by the designers of distributed applications.

## 1.3 DISTRIBUTED COMPUTING SYSTEM MODELS

Various models are used for building distributed computing systems. These models can be broadly classified into five categories—minicomputer, workstation, workstation-server, processor-pool, and hybrid. They are briefly described below.

### 1.3.1 Minicomputer Model

The *minicomputer model* is a simple extension of the centralized time-sharing system. As shown in Figure 1.2, a distributed computing system based on this model consists of a few minicomputers (they may be large supercomputers as well) interconnected by a communication network. Each minicomputer usually has multiple users simultaneously logged on to it. For this, several interactive terminals are connected to each minicomputer. Each user is logged on to one specific minicomputer, with remote access to other minicomputers. The network allows a user to access remote resources that are available on some machine other than the one on to which the user is currently logged.

The minicomputer model may be used when resource sharing (such as sharing of information databases of different types, with each type of database located on a different machine) with remote users is desired.

The early ARPAnet is an example of a distributed computing system based on the minicomputer model.

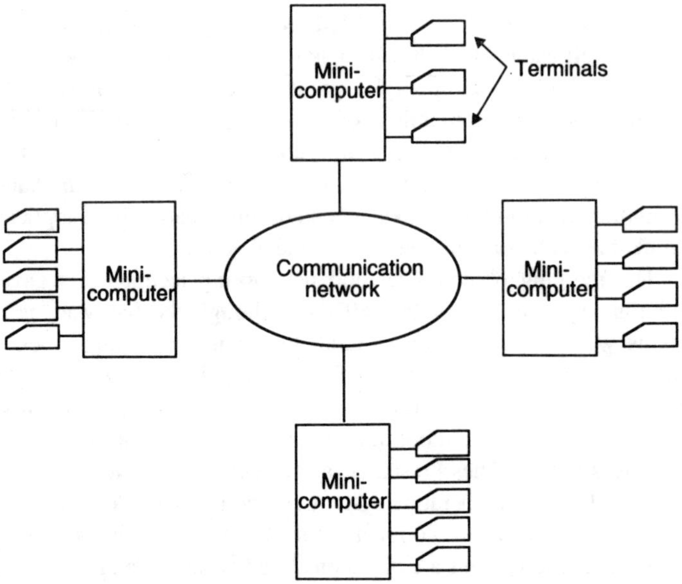


**Fig. 1.2** A distributed computing system based on the minicomputer model.

### 1.3.2 Workstation Model

As shown in Figure 1.3, a distributed computing system based on the *workstation model* consists of several workstations interconnected by a communication network. A company's office or a university department may have several workstations scattered throughout a building or campus, each workstation equipped with its own disk and serving as a single-user computer. It has been often found that in such an environment, at any one time (especially at night), a significant proportion of the workstations are idle (not being used), resulting in the waste of large amounts of CPU time. Therefore, the idea of the workstation model is to interconnect all these workstations by a high-speed LAN so that idle workstations may be used to process jobs of users who are logged onto other workstations and do not have sufficient processing power at their own workstations to get their jobs processed efficiently.

In this model, a user logs onto one of the workstations called his or her "home" workstation and submits jobs for execution. When the system finds that the user's workstation does not have sufficient processing power for executing the processes of the submitted jobs efficiently, it transfers one or more of the processes from the user's workstation to some other workstation that is currently idle and gets the process executed there, and finally the result of execution is returned to the user's workstation.

This model is not so simple to implement as it might appear at first sight because several issues must be resolved. These issues are [Tanenbaum 1995] as follows:

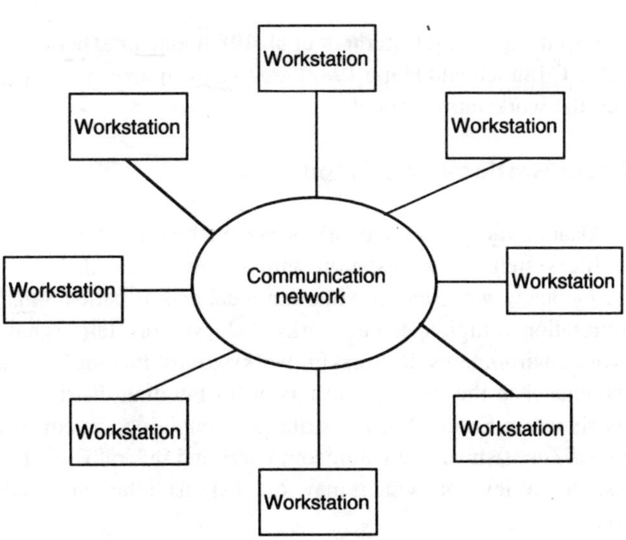


**Fig. 1.3** A distributed computing system based on the workstation model.

1. How does the system find an idle workstation?
2. How is a process transferred from one workstation to get it executed on another workstation?
3. What happens to a remote process if a user logs onto a workstation that was idle until now and was being used to execute a process of another workstation?

Ways to handle the first two issues are described in Chapters 7 and 8, respectively. Three commonly used approaches for handling the third issue are as follows:

1. The first approach is to allow the remote process share the resources of the workstation along with its own logged-on user's processes. This method is easy to implement, but it defeats the main idea of workstations serving as personal computers, because if remote processes are allowed to execute simultaneously with the logged-on user's own processes, the logged-on user does not get his or her guaranteed response.

2. The second approach is to kill the remote process. The main drawbacks of this method are that all processing done for the remote process gets lost and the file system may be left in an inconsistent state, making this method unattractive.

3. The third approach is to migrate the remote process back to its home workstation, so that its execution can be continued there. This method is difficult to implement because it requires the system to support preemptive process migration facility. The definition of preemptive process migration and the issues involved in preemptive process migration are given in Chapter 8.

The Sprite system [Ousterhout et al. 1988] and an experimental system developed at Xerox PARC [Shoch and Hupp 1982] are two examples of distributed computing systems based on the workstation model.

### 1.3.3 Workstation-Server Model

The workstation model is a network of personal workstations, each with its own disk and a local file system. A workstation with its own local disk is usually called a *diskful workstation* and a workstation without a local disk is called a *diskless workstation*. With the proliferation of high-speed networks, diskless workstations have become more popular in network environments than diskful workstations, making the workstation-server model more popular than the workstation model for building distributed computing systems.

As shown in Figure 1.4, a distributed computing system based on the *workstation-server model* consists of a few minicomputers and several workstations (most of which are diskless, but a few of which may be diskful) interconnected by a communication network.

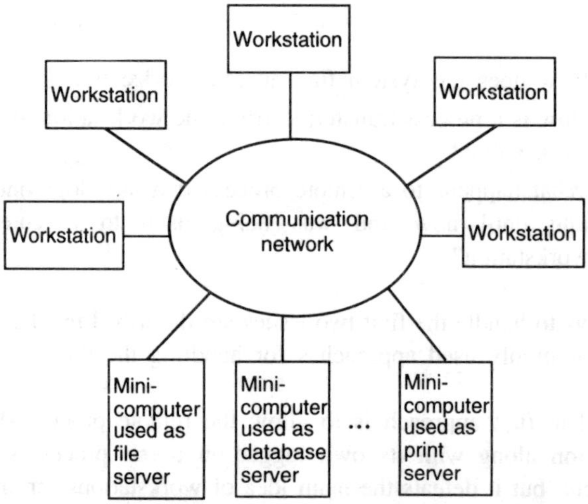


**Fig. 1.4** A distributed computing system based on the workstation–server model.

Note that when diskless workstations are used on a network, the file system to be used by these workstations must be implemented either by a diskful workstation or by a minicomputer equipped with a disk for file storage. The minicomputers are used for this purpose. One or more of the minicomputers are used for implementing the file system. Other minicomputers may be used for providing other types of services, such as database service and print service. Therefore, each minicomputer is used as a server machine to provide one or more types of services. Hence in the workstation-server model, in addition to the workstations, there are specialized machines (may be specialized workstations) for running server processes (called *servers*) for managing and providing access to shared resources.

For a number of reasons, such as higher reliability and better scalability, multiple servers are often used for managing the resources of a particular type in a distributed computing system. For example, there may be multiple file servers, each running on a separate minicomputer and cooperating via the network, for managing the files of all the users in the system. Due to this reason, a distinction is often made between the services that are provided to clients and the servers that provide them. That is, a *service* is an abstract entity that is provided by one or more servers. For example, one or more file servers may be used in a distributed computing system to provide file service to the users.

In this model, a user logs onto a workstation called his or her home workstation. Normal computation activities required by the user's processes are performed at the user's home workstation, but requests for services provided by special servers (such as a file server or a database server) are sent to a server providing that type of service that performs the user's requested activity and returns the result of request processing to the user's workstation. Therefore, in this model, the user's processes need not be migrated to the server machines for getting the work done by those machines.

For better overall system performance, the local disk of a diskful workstation is normally used for such purposes as storage of temporary files, storage of unshared files, storage of shared files that are rarely changed, paging activity in virtual-memory management, and caching of remotely accessed data.

As compared to the workstation model, the workstation-server model has several advantages:

1. In general, it is much cheaper to use a few minicomputers equipped with large, fast disks that are accessed over the network than a large number of diskful workstations, with each workstation having a small, slow disk.

2. Diskless workstations are also preferred to diskful workstations from a system maintenance point of view. Backup and hardware maintenance are easier to perform with a few large disks than with many small disks scattered all over a building or campus. Furthermore, installing new releases of software (such as a file server with new functionalities) is easier when the software is to be installed on a few file server machines than on every workstation.

3. In the workstation-server model, since all files are managed by the file servers, users have the flexibility to use any workstation and access the files in the same manner irrespective of which workstation the user is currently logged on. Note that this is not true with the workstation model, in which each workstation has its local file system, because different mechanisms are needed to access local and remote files.

4. In the workstation-server model, the request-response protocol described above is mainly used to access the services of the server machines. Therefore, unlike the workstation model, this model does not need a process migration facility, which is difficult to implement.

The request-response protocol is known as the *client-server model* of communication. In this model, a client process (which in this case resides on a workstation) sends a request to a server process (which in this case resides on a minicomputer) for getting some service such as reading a block of a file. The server executes the request and sends back a reply to the client that contains the result of request processing.

The client-server model provides an effective general-purpose approach to the sharing of information and resources in distributed computing systems. It is not only meant for use with the workstation-server model but also can be implemented in a variety of hardware and software environments. The computers used to run the client and server processes need not necessarily be workstations and minicomputers. They can be of many types and there is no need to distinguish between them. It is even possible for both the client and server processes to be run on the same computer. Moreover, some processes are both client and server processes. That is, a server process may use the services of another server, appearing as a client to the latter.

5. A user has guaranteed response time because workstations are not used for executing remote processes. However, the model does not utilize the processing capability of idle workstations.

The V-System [Cheriton 1988] is an example of a distributed computing system that is based on the workstation-server model.

### 1.3.4 Processor-Pool Model

The *processor-pool model* is based on the observation that most of the time a user does not need any computing power but once in a while he or she may need a very large amount of computing power for a short time (e.g., when recompiling a program consisting of a large number of files after changing a basic shared declaration). Therefore, unlike the workstation-server model in which a processor is allocated to each user, in the processor-pool model the processors are pooled together to be shared by the users as needed. The pool of processors consists of a large number of microcomputers and minicomputers attached to the network. Each processor in the pool has its own memory to load and run a system program or an application program of the distributed computing system.

As shown in Figure 1.5, in the pure processor-pool model, the processors in the pool have no terminals attached directly to them, and users access the system from terminals that are attached to the network via special devices. These terminals are either small diskless workstations or graphic terminals, such as X terminals. A special server (called a *run server*) manages and allocates the processors in the pool to different users on a demand basis. When a user submits a job for computation, an appropriate number of processors are temporarily assigned to his or her job by the run server. For example, if the user's computation job is the compilation of a program having $n$ segments, in which each of the segments can be compiled independently to produce separate relocatable object files, $n$ processors from the pool can be allocated to this job to compile all the $n$ segments in parallel. When the computation is completed, the processors are returned to the pool for use by other users.

In the processor-pool model there is no concept of a home machine. That is, a user does not log onto a particular machine but to the system as a whole. This is in contrast

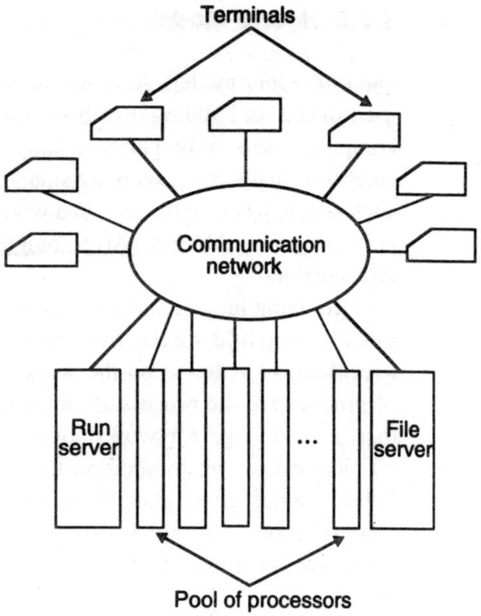


**Fig. 1.5** A distributed computing system based on the processor-pool model.

to other models in which each user has a home machine (e.g., a workstation or minicomputer) onto which he or she logs and runs most of his or her programs there by default.

As compared to the workstation-server model, the processor-pool model allows better utilization of the available processing power of a distributed computing system. This is because in the processor-pool model, the entire processing power of the system is available for use by the currently logged-on users, whereas this is not true for the workstation-server model in which several workstations may be idle at a particular time but they cannot be used for processing the jobs of other users. Furthermore, the processor-pool model provides greater flexibility than the workstation-server model in the sense that the system's services can be easily expanded without the need to install any more computers; the processors in the pool can be allocated to act as extra servers to carry any additional load arising from an increased user population or to provide new services. However, the processor-pool model is usually considered to be unsuitable for high-performance interactive applications, especially those using graphics or window systems. This is mainly because of the slow speed of communication between the computer on which the application program of a user is being executed and the terminal via which the user is interacting with the system. The workstation-server model is generally considered to be more suitable for such applications.

Amoeba [Mullender et al. 1990], Plan 9 [Pike et al. 1990], and the Cambridge Distributed Computing System [Needham and Herbert 1982] are examples of distributed computing systems based on the processor-pool model.

### 1.3.5 Hybrid Model

Out of the four models described above, the workstation-server model, is the most widely used model for building distributed computing systems. This is because a large number of computer users only perform simple interactive tasks such as editing jobs, sending electronic mails, and executing small programs. The workstation-server model is ideal for such simple usage. However, in a working environment that has groups of users who often perform jobs needing massive computation, the processor-pool model is more attractive and suitable.

To combine the advantages of both the workstation-server and processor-pool models, a hybrid model may be used to build a distributed computing system. The hybrid model is based on the workstation-server model but with the addition of a pool of processors. The processors in the pool can be allocated dynamically for computations that are too large for workstations or that require several computers concurrently for efficient execution. In addition to efficient execution of computation-intensive jobs, the hybrid model gives guaranteed response to interactive jobs by allowing them to be processed on local workstations of the users. However, the hybrid model is more expensive to implement than the workstation-server model or the processor-pool model.

## 1.4 WHY ARE DISTRIBUTED COMPUTING SYSTEMS GAINING POPULARITY?

From the models of distributed computing systems presented above, it is obvious that distributed computing systems are much more complex and difficult to build than traditional *centralized systems* (those consisting of a single CPU, its memory, peripherals, and one or more terminals). The increased complexity is mainly due to the fact that in addition to being capable of effectively using and managing a very large number of distributed resources, the system software of a distributed computing system should also be capable of handling the communication and security problems that are very different from those of centralized systems. For example, the performance and reliability of a distributed computing system depends to a great extent on the performance and reliability of the underlying communication network. Special software is usually needed to handle loss of messages during transmission across the network or to prevent overloading of the network, which degrades the performance and responsiveness to the users. Similarly, special software security measures are needed to protect the widely distributed shared resources and services against intentional or accidental violation of access control and privacy constraints.

Despite the increased complexity and the difficulty of building distributed computing systems, the installation and use of distributed computing systems are rapidly increasing. This is mainly because the advantages of distributed computing systems outweigh their disadvantages. The technical needs, the economic pressures, and the major advantages that have led to the emergence and popularity of distributed computing systems are described next.

### 1.4.1 Inherently Distributed Applications

Distributed computing systems come into existence in some very natural ways. For example, several applications are inherently distributed in nature and require a distributed computing system for their realization. For instance, in an employee database of a nationwide organization, the data pertaining to a particular employee are generated at the employee's branch office, and in addition to the global need to view the entire database, there is a local need for frequent and immediate access to locally generated data at each branch office. Applications such as these require that some processing power be available at the many distributed locations for collecting, preprocessing, and accessing data, resulting in the need for distributed computing systems. Some other examples of inherently distributed applications are a computerized worldwide airline reservation system, a computerized banking system in which a customer can deposit/withdraw money from his or her account from any branch of the bank, and a factory automation system controlling robots and machines all along an assembly line.

### 1.4.2 Information Sharing among Distributed Users

Another reason for the emergence of distributed computing systems was a desire for efficient person-to-person communication facility by sharing information over great distances. In a distributed computing system, information generated by one of the users can be easily and efficiently shared by the users working at other nodes of the system. This facility may be useful in many ways. For example, a project can be performed by two or more users who are geographically far off from each other but whose computers are a part of the same distributed computing system. In this case, although the users are geographically separated from each other, they can work in cooperation, for example, by transferring the files of the project, logging onto each other's remote computers to run programs, and exchanging messages by electronic mail to coordinate the work.

The use of distributed computing systems by a group of users to work cooperatively is known as *computer-supported cooperative working* (CSCW), or *groupware*. Groupware applications depend heavily on the sharing of data objects between programs running on different nodes of a distributed computing system. Groupware is an emerging technology that holds major promise for software developers.

### 1.4.3 Resource Sharing

Information is not the only thing that can be shared in a distributed computing system. Sharing of software resources such as software libraries and databases as well as hardware resources such as printers, hard disks, and plotters can also be done in a very effective way among all the computers and the users of a single distributed computing system. For example, we saw that in a distributed computing system based on the workstation-server model the workstations may have no disk or only a small disk (10–20 megabytes) for temporary storage, and access to permanent files on a large disk can be provided to all the workstations by a single file server.

### 1.4.4 Better Price-Performance Ratio

This is one of the most important reasons for the growing popularity of distributed computing systems. With the rapidly increasing power and reduction in the price of microprocessors, combined with the increasing speed of communication networks, distributed computing systems potentially have a much better price-performance ratio than a single large centralized system. For example, we saw how a small number of CPUs in a distributed computing system based on the processor-pool model can be effectively used by a large number of users from inexpensive terminals, giving a fairly high price-performance ratio as compared to either a centralized time-sharing system or a personal computer. Another reason for distributed computing systems to be more cost-effective than centralized systems is that they facilitate resource sharing among multiple computers. For example, a single unit of expensive peripheral devices such as color laser printers, high-speed storage devices, and plotters can be shared among all the computers of the same distributed computing system. If these computers are not linked together with a communication network, each computer must have its own peripherals, resulting in higher cost.

### 1.4.5 Shorter Response Times and Higher Throughput

Due to multiplicity of processors, distributed computing systems are expected to have better performance than single-processor centralized systems. The two most commonly used performance metrics are response time and throughput of user processes. That is, the multiple processors of a distributed computing system can be utilized properly for providing shorter response times and higher throughput than a single-processor centralized system. For example, if there are two different programs to be run, two processors are evidently more powerful than one because the programs can be simultaneously run on different processors. Furthermore, if a particular computation can be partitioned into a number of subcomputations that can run concurrently, in a distributed computing system all the subcomputations can be simultaneously run with each one on a different processor. Distributed computing systems with very fast communication networks are increasingly being used as parallel computers to solve single complex problems rapidly. Another method often used in distributed computing systems for achieving better overall performance is to distribute the load more evenly among the multiple processors by moving jobs from currently overloaded processors to lightly loaded ones. For example, in a distributed computing system based on the workstation model, if a user currently has two processes to run, out of which one is an interactive process and the other is a process that can be run in the background, it may be advantageous to run the interactive process on the home node of the user and the other one on a remote idle node (if any node is idle).

### 1.4.6 Higher Reliability

*Reliability* refers to the degree of tolerance against errors and component failures in a system [Stankovic 1984]. A reliable system prevents loss of information even in the event of component failures. The multiplicity of storage devices and processors in a distributed computing system allows the maintenance of multiple copies of critical information within the system and the execution of important computations redundantly to protect them against catastrophic failures. With this approach, if one of the processors fails, the computation can be successfully completed at the other processor, and if one of the storage devices fails, the information can still be used from the other storage device. Furthermore, the geographical distribution of the processors and other resources in a distributed computing system limits the scope of failures caused by natural disasters.

An important aspect of reliability is *availability,* which refers to the fraction of time for which a system is available for use. In comparison to a centralized system, a distributed computing system also enjoys the advantage of increased availability. For example, if the processor of a centralized system fails (assuming that it is a single-processor centralized system), the entire system breaks down and no useful work can be performed. However, in the case of a distributed computing system, a few parts of the system can be down without interrupting the jobs of the users who are using the other parts of the system. For example, if a workstation of a distributed computing system that is based on the workstation-server model fails, only the user of that workstation is affected. Other users of the system are not affected by this failure. Similarly, in a distributed computing system based on the processor-pool model, if some of the processors in the pool are down at any moment, the system can continue to function normally, simply with some loss in performance that is proportional to the number of processors that are down. In this case, none of the users is affected and the users cannot even know that some of the processors are down.

The advantage of higher reliability is an important reason for the use of distributed computing systems for critical applications whose failure may be disastrous. However, often reliability comes at the cost of performance. Therefore, it is necessary to maintain a balance between the two.

### 1.4.7 Extensibility and Incremental Growth

Another major advantage of distributed computing systems is that they are capable of incremental growth. That is, it is possible to gradually extend the power and functionality of a distributed computing system by simply adding additional resources (both hardware and software) to the system as and when the need arises. For example, additional processors can be easily added to the system to handle the increased workload of an organization that might have resulted from its expansion. Incremental growth is a very attractive feature because for most existing and proposed applications it is practically impossible to predict future demands of the system. Extensibility is also easier in a distributed computing system because addition of new resources to an existing system can be performed without significant disruption of the normal functioning of the system. Properly designed distributed computing systems that have the property of extensibility and incremental growth are called *open distributed systems*.

### 1.4.8 Better Flexibility in Meeting Users' Needs

Different types of computers are usually more suitable for performing different types of computations. For example, computers with ordinary power are suitable for ordinary data processing jobs, whereas high-performance computers are more suitable for complex mathematical computations. In a centralized system, the users have to perform all types of computations on the only available computer. However, a distributed computing system may have a pool of different types of computers, in which case the most appropriate one can be selected for processing a user's job depending on the nature of the job. For instance, we saw that in a distributed computing system that is based on the hybrid model, interactive jobs can be processed at a user's own workstation and the processors in the pool may be used to process noninteractive, computation-intensive jobs.

---

Note that the advantages of distributed computing systems mentioned above are not achieved automatically but depend on the careful design of a distributed computing system. This book deals with the various design methodologies that may be used to achieve these advantages.

## 1.5 WHAT IS A DISTRIBUTED OPERATING SYSTEM?

Tanenbaum and Van Renesse [1985] define an *operating system* as a program that controls the resources of a computer system and provides its users with an interface or virtual machine that is more convenient to use than the bare machine. According to this definition, the two primary tasks of an operating system are as follows:

1. To present users with a virtual machine that is easier to program than the underlying hardware.
2. To manage the various resources of the system. This involves performing such tasks as keeping track of who is using which resource, granting resource requests, accounting for resource usage, and mediating conflicting requests from different programs and users.

Therefore, the users' view of a computer system, the manner in which the users access the various resources of the computer system, and the ways in which the resource requests are granted depend to a great extent on the operating system of the computer system. The operating systems commonly used for distributed computing systems can be broadly classified into two types—*network operating systems* and *distributed operating systems*. The three most important features commonly used to differentiate between these two types of operating systems are system image, autonomy, and fault tolerance capability. These features are explained below.

1. *System image*. The most important feature used to differentiate between the two types of operating systems is the image of the distributed computing system from the point of view of its users. In case of a network operating system, the users view the distributed computing system as a collection of distinct machines connected by a communication subsystem. That is, the users are aware of the fact that multiple computers are being used. On the other hand, a distributed operating system hides the existence of multiple computers and provides a single-system image to its users. That is, it makes a collection

of networked machines act as a *virtual uniprocessor.* The difference between the two types of operating systems based on this feature can be best illustrated with the help of examples. Two such examples are presented below.

In the case of a network operating system, although a user can run a job on any machine of the distributed computing system, he or she is fully aware of the machine on which his or her job is executed. This is because, by default, a user's job is executed on the machine on which the user is currently logged. If the user wants to execute a job on a different machine, he or she should either log on to that machine by using some kind of "remote login" command or use a special command for remote execution to specify the machine on which the job is to be executed. In either case, the user knows the machine on which the job is executed. On the other hand, a distributed operating system dynamically and automatically allocates jobs to the various machines of the system for processing. Therefore, a user of a distributed operating system generally has no knowledge of the machine on which a job is executed. That is, the selection of a machine for executing a job is entirely manual in the case of network operating systems but is automatic in the case of distributed operating systems.

With a network operating system, a user is generally required to know the location of a resource to access it, and different sets of system calls have to be used for accessing local and remote resources. On the other hand, users of a distributed operating system need not keep track of the locations of various resources for accessing them, and the same set of system calls is used for accessing both local and remote resources. For instance, users of a network operating system are usually aware of where each of their files is stored and must use explicit *file transfer* commands for moving a file from one machine to another, but the users of a distributed operating system have no knowledge of the location of their files within the system and use the same command to access a file irrespective of whether it is on the local machine or on a remote machine. That is, control over file placement is done manually by the users in a network operating system but automatically by the system in a distributed operating system.

Notice that the key concept behind this feature is "transparency." We will see later in this chapter that a distributed operating system has to support several forms of transparency to achieve the goal of providing a single-system image to its users. Moreover, it is important to note here that with the current state of the art in distributed operating systems, this goal is not fully achievable. Researchers are still working hard to achieve this goal.

2. *Autonomy.* A network operating system is built on a set of existing centralized operating systems and handles the interfacing and coordination of remote operations and communications between these operating systems. That is, in the case of a network operating system, each computer of the distributed computing system has its own local operating system (the operating systems of different computers may be the same or different), and there is essentially no coordination at all among the computers except for the rule that when two processes of different computers communicate with each other, they must use a mutually agreed on communication protocol. Each computer functions independently of other computers in the sense that each one makes independent decisions about the creation and termination of their own processes and management of local

resources. Notice that due to the possibility of difference in local operating systems, the system calls for different computers of the same distributed computing system may be different in this case.

On the other hand, with a distributed operating system, there is a single systemwide operating system and each computer of the distributed computing system runs a part of this global operating system. The distributed operating system tightly interweaves all the computers of the distributed computing system in the sense that they work in close cooperation with each other for the efficient and effective utilization of the various resources of the system. That is, processes and several resources are managed globally (some resources are managed locally). Moreover, there is a single set of globally valid system calls available on all computers of the distributed computing system.

The set of system calls that an operating system supports are implemented by a set of programs called the *kernel* of the operating system. The kernel manages and controls the hardware of the computer system to provide the facilities and resources that are accessed by other programs through system calls. To make the same set of system calls globally valid, with a distributed operating system identical kernels are run on all the computers of a distributed computing system. The kernels of different computers often cooperate with each other in making global decisions, such as finding the most suitable machine for executing a newly created process in the system.

In short, it can be said that the degree of autonomy of each machine of a distributed computing system that uses a network operating system is considerably high as compared to that of machines of a distributed computing system that uses a distributed operating system.

3. *Fault tolerance capability.* A network operating system provides little or no fault tolerance capability in the sense that if 10% of the machines of the entire distributed computing system are down at any moment, at least 10% of the users are unable to continue with their work. On the other hand, with a distributed operating system, most of the users are normally unaffected by the failed machines and can continue to perform their work normally, with only a 10% loss in performance of the entire distributed computing system. Therefore, the fault tolerance capability of a distributed operating system is usually very high as compared to that of a network operating system.

The following definition of a distributed operating system given by Tanenbaum and Van Renesse [1985] covers most of its features mentioned above:

> A distributed operating system is one that looks to its users like an ordinary centralized operating system but runs on multiple, independent central processing units (CPUs). The key concept here is transparency. In other words, the use of multiple processors should be invisible (transparent) to the user. Another way of expressing the same idea is to say that the user views the system as a "virtual uniprocessor," not as a collection of distinct machines. [P. 419].

A distributed computing system that uses a network operating system is usually referred to as a *network system*, whereas one that uses a distributed operating system is usually referred to as a *true distributed system* (or simply a distributed system). In this book, the term *distributed system* will be used to mean a true distributed system.

Note that with the current state of the art in distributed operating systems, it is not possible to design a completely true distributed system. Completely true distributed systems are the ultimate goal of researchers working in the area of distributed operating systems.

## 1.6 ISSUES IN DESIGNING A DISTRIBUTED OPERATING SYSTEM

In general, designing a distributed operating system is more difficult than designing a centralized operating system for several reasons. In the design of a centralized operating system, it is assumed that the operating system has access to complete and accurate information about the environment in which it is functioning. For example, a centralized operating system can request status information, being assured that the interrogated component will not change state while awaiting a decision based on that status information, since only the single operating system asking the question may give commands. However, a distributed operating system must be designed with the assumption that complete information about the system environment will never be available. In a distributed system, the resources are physically separated, there is no common clock among the multiple processors, delivery of messages is delayed, and messages could even be lost. Due to all these reasons, a distributed operating system does not have up-to-date, consistent knowledge about the state of the various components of the underlying distributed system. Obviously, lack of up-to-date and consistent information makes many things (such as management of resources and synchronization of cooperating activities) much harder in the design of a distributed operating system. For example, it is hard to schedule the processors optimally if the operating system is not sure how many of them are up at the moment.

Despite these complexities and difficulties, a distributed operating system must be designed to provide all the advantages of a distributed system to its users. That is, the users should be able to view a distributed system as a virtual centralized system that is flexible, efficient, reliable, secure, and easy to use. To meet this challenge, the designers of a distributed operating system must deal with several design issues. Some of the key design issues are described below. The rest of the chapters of this book basically contain detailed descriptions of these design issues and the commonly used techniques to deal with them.

### 1.6.1 Transparency

We saw that one of the main goals of a distributed operating system is to make the existence of multiple computers invisible (transparent) and provide a single system image to its users. That is, a distributed operating system must be designed in such a way that a collection of distinct machines connected by a communication subsystem appears to its users as a virtual uniprocessor. Achieving complete transparency is a difficult task and requires that several different aspects of transparency be supported by the distributed operating system. The eight forms of transparency identified by the International Standards Organization's Reference Model for Open Distributed Processing [ISO 1992] are access transparency, location transparency, replication transparency, failure transparency, migration transparency, concurrency transparency, performance transparency, and scaling transparency. These transparency aspects are described below.

### Access Transparency

Access transparency means that users should not need or be able to recognize whether a resource (hardware or software) is remote or local. This implies that the distributed operating system should allow users to access remote resources in the same way as local resources. That is, the user interface, which takes the form of a set of system calls, should not distinguish between local and remote resources, and it should be the responsibility of the distributed operating system to locate the resources and to arrange for servicing user requests in a user-transparent manner.

This requirement calls for a well-designed set of system calls that are meaningful in both centralized and distributed environments and a global resource naming facility. We will see in Chapters 3 and 4 that due to the need to handle communication failures in distributed systems, it is not possible to design system calls that provide complete access transparency. However, the area of designing a global resource naming facility has been well researched with considerable success. Chapter 10 deals with the concepts and design of a global resource naming facility. The distributed shared memory mechanism described in Chapter 5 is also meant to provide a uniform set of system calls for accessing both local and remote memory objects. Although this mechanism is quite useful in providing access transparency, it is suitable only for limited types of distributed applications due to its performance limitation.

### Location Transparency

The two main aspects of location transparency are as follows:

1. *Name transparency.* This refers to the fact that the name of a resource (hardware or software) should not reveal any hint as to the physical location of the resource. That is, the name of a resource should be independent of the physical connectivity or topology of the system or the current location of the resource. Furthermore, such resources, which are capable of being moved from one node to another in a distributed system (such as a file), must be allowed to move without having their names changed. Therefore, resource names must be unique systemwide.

2. *User mobility.* This refers to the fact that no matter which machine a user is logged onto, he or she should be able to access a resource with the same name. That is, the user should not be required to use different names to access the same resource from two

different nodes of the system. In a distributed system that supports user mobility, users can freely log on to any machine in the system and access any resource without making any extra effort.

Both name transparency and user mobility requirements call for a systemwide, global resource naming facility.

### Replication Transparency

For better performance and reliability, almost all distributed operating systems have the provision to create replicas (additional copies) of files and other resources on different nodes of the distributed system. In these systems, both the existence of multiple copies of a replicated resource and the replication activity should be transparent to the users. That is, two important issues related to replication transparency are naming of replicas and replication control. It is the responsibility of the system to name the various copies of a resource and to map a user-supplied name of the resource to an appropriate replica of the resource. Furthermore, replication control decisions such as how many copies of the resource should be created, where should each copy be placed, and when should a copy be created/deleted should be made entirely automatically by the system in a user-transparent manner. Replica management issues are described in Chapter 9.

### Failure Transparency

Failure transparency deals with masking from the users' partial failures in the system, such as a communication link failure, a machine failure, or a storage device crash. A distributed operating system having failure transparency property will continue to function, perhaps in a degraded form, in the face of partial failures. For example, suppose the file service of a distributed operating system is to be made failure transparent. This can be done by implementing it as a group of file servers that closely cooperate with each other to manage the files of the system and that function in such a manner that the users can utilize the file service even if only one of the file servers is up and working. In this case, the users cannot notice the failure of one or more file servers, except for slower performance of file access operations. Any type of service can be implemented in this way for failure transparency. However, in this type of design, care should be taken to ensure that the cooperation among multiple servers does not add too much overhead to the system.

Complete failure transparency is not achievable with the current state of the art in distributed operating systems because all types of failures cannot be handled in a user-transparent manner. For example, failure of the communication network of a distributed system normally disrupts the work of its users and is noticeable by the users. Moreover, an attempt to design a completely failure-transparent distributed system will result in a very slow and highly expensive system due to the large amount of redundancy required for tolerating all types of failures. The design of such a distributed system, although theoretically possible, is not practically justified.

### Migration Transparency

For better performance, reliability, and security reasons, an object that is capable of being moved (such as a process or a file) is often migrated from one node to another in a distributed system. The aim of migration transparency is to ensure that the movement of the object is handled automatically by the system in a user-transparent manner. Three important issues in achieving this goal are as follows:

1. Migration decisions such as which object is to be moved from where to where should be made automatically by the system.
2. Migration of an object from one node to another should not require any change in its name.
3. When the migrating object is a process, the interprocess communication mechanism should ensure that a message sent to the migrating process reaches it without the need for the sender process to resend it if the receiver process moves to another node before the message is received.

Chapter 7 deals with the first issue. The second issue calls for a global resource naming facility, which is described in Chapter 10. Ways to handle the third issue are described in Chapter 8.

### Concurrency Transparency

In a distributed system, multiple users who are spatially separated use the system concurrently. In such a situation, it is economical to share the system resources (hardware or software) among the concurrently executing user processes. However, since the number of available resources in a computing system is restricted, one user process must necessarily influence the action of other concurrently executing user processes, as it competes for resources. For example, concurrent update to the same file by two different processes should be prevented. Concurrency transparency means that each user has a feeling that he or she is the sole user of the system and other users do not exist in the system. For providing concurrency transparency, the resource sharing mechanisms of the distributed operating system must have the following four properties:

1. An event-ordering property ensures that all access requests to various system resources are properly ordered to provide a consistent view to all users of the system.

2. A mutual-exclusion property ensures that at any time at most one process accesses a shared resource, which must not be used simultaneously by multiple processes if program operation is to be correct.

3. A no-starvation property ensures that if every process that is granted a resource, which must not be used simultaneously by multiple processes, eventually releases it, every request for that resource is eventually granted.

4. A no-deadlock property ensures that a situation will never occur in which competing processes prevent their mutual progress even though no single one requests more resources than available in the system.

Chapter 6 deals with the above-mentioned issues of concurrency transparency.

#### Performance Transparency

The aim of performance transparency is to allow the system to be automatically reconfigured to improve performance, as loads vary dynamically in the system. As far as practicable, a situation in which one processor of the system is overloaded with jobs while another processor is idle should not be allowed to occur. That is, the processing capability of the system should be uniformly distributed among the currently available jobs in the system.

This requirement calls for the support of intelligent resource allocation and process migration facilities in distributed operating systems. Chapters 7 and 8 deal with these two issues.

#### Scaling Transparency

The aim of scaling transparency is to allow the system to expand in scale without disrupting the activities of the users. This requirement calls for open-system architecture and the use of scalable algorithms for designing the distributed operating system components. Section 1.6.3 of this chapter and Section 2.6 of Chapter 2 focus on the issues of designing an open distributed system. On the other hand, since every component of a distributed operating system must use scalable algorithms, this issue has been dealt with in almost all chapters of the book.

### 1.6.2 Reliability

In general, distributed systems are expected to be more reliable than centralized systems due to the existence of multiple instances of resources. However, the existence of multiple instances of the resources alone cannot increase the system's reliability. Rather, the distributed operating system, which manages these resources, must be designed properly to increase the system's reliability by taking full advantage of this characteristic feature of a distributed system.

A *fault* is a mechanical or algorithmic defect that may generate an error. A fault in a system causes system failure. Depending on the manner in which a failed system behaves, system failures are of two types—fail-stop [Schlichting and Schneider 1983] and Byzantine [Lamport et al. 1982]. In the case of *fail-stop failure*, the system stops functioning after changing to a state in which its failure can be detected. On the other hand, in the case of *Byzantine failure*, the system continues to function but produces wrong results. Undetected software bugs often cause Byzantine failure of a system. Obviously, Byzantine failures are much more difficult to deal with than fail-stop failures.

For higher reliability, the fault-handling mechanisms of a distributed operating system must be designed properly to avoid faults, to tolerate faults, and to detect and recover from faults. Commonly used methods for dealing with these issues are briefly described next.

### Fault Avoidance

*Fault avoidance* deals with designing the components of the system in such a way that the occurrence of faults is minimized. Conservative design practices such as using high-reliability components are often employed for improving the system's reliability based on the idea of fault avoidance. Although a distributed operating system often has little or no role to play in improving the fault avoidance capability of a hardware component, the designers of the various software components of the distributed operating system must test them thoroughly to make these components highly reliable.

### Fault Tolerance

*Fault tolerance* is the ability of a system to continue functioning in the event of partial system failure. The performance of the system might be degraded due to partial failure, but otherwise the system functions properly. Some of the important concepts that may be used to improve the fault tolerance ability of a distributed operating system are as follows:

1. *Redundancy techniques*. The basic idea behind redundancy techniques is to avoid single points of failure by replicating critical hardware and software components, so that if one of them fails, the others can be used to continue. Obviously, having two or more copies of a critical component makes it possible, at least in principle, to continue operations in spite of occasional partial failures. For example, a critical process can be simultaneously executed on two nodes so that if one of the two nodes fails, the execution of the process can be completed at the other node. Similarly, a critical file may be replicated on two or more storage devices for better reliability.

Notice that with redundancy techniques additional system overhead is needed to maintain two or more copies of a replicated resource and to keep all the copies of a resource consistent. For example, if a file is replicated on two or more nodes of a distributed system, additional disk storage space is required, and for correct functioning, it is often necessary that all the copies of the file are mutually consistent. In general, the larger is the number of copies kept, the better is the reliability but the larger is the system overhead involved. Therefore, a distributed operating system must be designed to maintain a proper balance between the degree of reliability and the incurred overhead. This raises an important question: How much replication is enough? For an answer to this question, note that a system is said to be *k-fault tolerant* if it can continue to function even in the event of the failure of $k$ components [Cristian 1991, Nelson 1990]. Therefore, if the system is to be designed to tolerate $k$ fail–stop failures, $k$+1 replicas are needed. If $k$ replicas are lost due to failures, the remaining one replica can be used for continued functioning of the system. On the other hand, if the system is to be designed to tolerate $k$ Byzantine failures, a minimum of 2$k$+1 replicas are needed. This is because a voting mechanism can be used to believe the majority $k$+1 of the replicas when $k$ replicas behave abnormally.

Replication and consistency control mechanisms for memory objects are described in Chapter 5 and for file objects are described in Chapter 9.

Another application of redundancy technique is in the design of a stable storage device, which is a virtual storage device that can even withstand transient I/O faults and decay of the storage media. The reliability of a critical file may be improved by storing it on a stable storage device. Stable storage devices are described in Chapter 9.

2. *Distributed control.* For better reliability, many of the particular algorithms or protocols used in a distributed operating system must employ a distributed control mechanism to avoid single points of failure. For example, a highly available distributed file system should have multiple and independent file servers controlling multiple and independent storage devices. In addition to file servers, a distributed control technique could also be used for name servers, scheduling algorithms, and other executive control functions. It is important to note here that when multiple distributed servers are used in a distributed system to provide a particular type of service, the servers must be independent. That is, the design must not require simultaneous functioning of the servers; otherwise, the reliability will become worse instead of getting better. Distributed control mechanisms are described throughout this book.

### Fault Detection and Recovery

The fault detection and recovery method of improving reliability deals with the use of hardware and software mechanisms to determine the occurrence of a failure and then to correct the system to a state acceptable for continued operation. Some of the commonly used techniques for implementing this method in a distributed operating system are as follows:

1. *Atomic transactions.* An atomic transaction (or just *transaction* for short) is a computation consisting of a collection of operations that take place indivisibly in the presence of failures and concurrent computations. That is, either all of the operations are performed successfully or none of their effects prevails, and other processes executing concurrently cannot modify or observe intermediate states of the computation. Transactions help to preserve the consistency of a set of shared data objects (e.g., files) in the face of failures and concurrent access. They make crash recovery much easier, because a transaction can only end in two states: Either all the operations of the transaction are performed or none of the operations of the transaction is performed.

In a system with transaction facility, if a process halts unexpectedly due to a hardware fault or a software error before a transaction is completed, the system subsequently restores any data objects that were undergoing modification to their original states. Notice that if a system does not support a transaction mechanism, unexpected failure of a process during the processing of an operation may leave the data objects that were undergoing modification in an inconsistent state. Therefore, without transaction facility, it may be difficult or even impossible in some cases to roll back (recover) the data objects from their current inconsistent states to their original states. Atomic transaction mechanisms are described in Chapter 9.

2. *Stateless servers.* The client-server model is frequently used in distributed systems to service user requests. In this model, a server may be implemented by using any one of

the following two service paradigms—stateful or stateless. The two paradigms are distinguished by one aspect of the client-server relationship, whether or not the history of the serviced requests between a client and a server affects the execution of the next service request. The stateful approach does depend on the history of the serviced requests, but the stateless approach does not depend on it. Stateless servers have a distinct advantage over stateful servers in the event of a failure. That is, the stateless service paradigm makes crash recovery very easy because no client state information is maintained by the server. On the other hand, the stateful service paradigm requires complex crash recovery procedures. Both the client and server need to reliably detect crashes. The server needs to detect client crashes so that it can discard any state it is holding for the client, and the client must detect server crashes so that it can perform necessary error–handling activities. Although stateful service becomes necessary in some cases, to simplify the failure detection and recovery actions, the stateless service paradigm must be used wherever possible. Stateless and stateful servers are described in Chapters 4 and 9.

3. *Acknowledgments and timeout-based retransmissions of messages.* In a distributed system, events such as a node crash or a communication link failure may interrupt a communication that was in progress between two processes, resulting in the loss of a message. Therefore, a reliable interprocess communication mechanism must have ways to detect lost messages so that they can be retransmitted. Handling of lost messages usually involves return of acknowledgment messages and retransmissions on the basis of timeouts. That is, the receiver must return an acknowledgment message for every message received, and if the sender does not receive any acknowledgment for a message within a fixed timeout period, it assumes that the message was lost and retransmits the message. A problem associated with this approach is that of duplicate messages. Duplicate messages may be sent in the event of failures or because of timeouts. Therefore, a reliable interprocess communication mechanism should also be capable of detecting and handling duplicate messages. Handling of duplicate messages usually involves a mechanism for automatically generating and assigning appropriate sequence numbers to messages. Use of acknowledgment messages, timeout-based retransmissions of messages, and handling of duplicate request messages for reliable communication are described in Chapter 3.

The mechanisms described above may be employed to create a very reliable distributed system. However, the main drawback of increased system reliability is potential loss of execution time efficiency due to the extra overhead involved in these techniques. For many systems it is just too costly to incorporate a large number of reliability mechanisms. Therefore, the major challenge for distributed operating system designers is to integrate these mechanisms in a cost-effective manner for producing a reliable system.

### 1.6.3 Flexibility

Another important issue in the design of distributed operating systems is flexibility. Flexibility is the most important feature for open distributed systems. The design of a distributed operating system should be flexible due to the following reasons:

1. *Ease of modification*. From the experience of system designers, it has been found that some parts of the design often need to be replaced/modified either because some bug is detected in the design or because the design is no longer suitable for the changed system environment or new-user requirements. Therefore, it should be easy to incorporate changes in the system in a user-transparent manner or with minimum interruption caused to the users.

2. *Ease of enhancement*. In every system, new functionalities have to be added from time to time to make it more powerful and easy to use. Therefore, it should be easy to add new services to the system. Furthermore, if a group of users do not like the style in which a particular service is provided by the operating system, they should have the flexibility to add and use their own service that works in the style with which the users of that group are more familiar and feel more comfortable.

The most important design factor that influences the flexibility of a distributed operating system is the model used for designing its kernel. The *kernel* of an operating system is its central controlling part that provides basic system facilities. It operates in a separate address space that is inaccessible to user processes. It is the only part of an operating system that a user cannot replace or modify. We saw that in the case of a distributed operating system identical kernels are run on all the nodes of the distributed system.

The two commonly used models for kernel design in distributed operating systems are the monolithic kernel and the microkernel (Fig. 1.6). In the *monolithic kernel* model, most operating system services such as process management, memory management, device management, file management, name management, and interprocess communication are provided by the kernel. As a result, the kernel has a large, monolithic structure. Many distributed operating systems that are extensions or imitations of the UNIX operating system use the monolithic kernel model. This is mainly because UNIX itself has a large, monolithic kernel.

On the other hand, in the *microkernel* model, the main goal is to keep the kernel as small as possible. Therefore, in this model, the kernel is a very small nucleus of software that provides only the minimal facilities necessary for implementing additional operating system services. The only services provided by the kernel in this model are interprocess communication, low-level device management, a limited amount of low-level process management, and some memory management. All other operating system services, such as file management, name management, additional process, and memory management activities, and much system call handling are implemented as user-level server processes. Each server process has its own address space and can be programmed separately.

As compared to the monolithic kernel model, the microkernel model has several advantages. In the monolithic kernel model, the large size of the kernel reduces the overall flexibility and configurability of the resulting operating system. On the other hand, the resulting operating system of the microkernel model is highly modular in nature. Due to this characteristic feature, the operating system of the microkernel model is easy to design, implement, and install. Moreover, since most of the services are implemented as user-level server processes, it is also easy to modify the design or add new services. This also allows

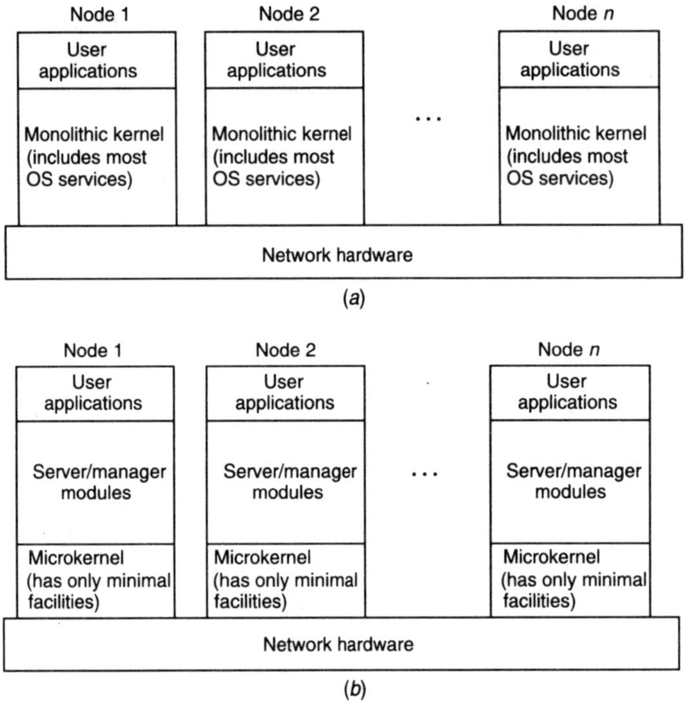


**Fig. 1.6** Models of kernel design in distributed operating systems: (*a*) The monolithic kernel model. The level above the kernel level can be partitioned by the users into whatever hierarchical levels are appropriate. (*b*) The microkernel model. Although the figure shows a two-level heirarchy above the kernel level, users can extend the hierarchy to whatever levels are appropriate.

those users who do not like a particular service provided by the operating system to implement and use their own service. Furthermore, for adding or changing a service, there is no need to stop the system and boot a new kernel, as in the case of a monolithic kernel. Therefore, changes in the system can be incorporated without interrupting the users.

The modular design of a system based on the microkernel model, however, is potentially subject to a performance penalty. This is because in the microkernel model each server is an independent process having its own address space. Therefore, the servers have to use some form of message-based interprocess communication mechanism to communicate with each other while performing some job. Furthermore, message passing between server processes and the microkernel requires context switches, resulting in additional performance overhead. In the monolithic kernel model, however, since all the services are provided by the kernel, the same address space is shared by all of them. Therefore, no message passing and no context switching are required while the kernel is performing the job. Hence a request may be serviced faster in the monolithic kernel model than in the microkernel model.

In spite of its potential performance cost, the microkernel model is being preferred for the design of modern distributed operating systems. The two main reasons for this are as follows:

1. The advantages of the microkernel model more than compensate for the performance cost. Notice that the situation here is very similar to the one that caused high-level programming languages to be preferred to assembly languages. In spite of the better performance of programs written in assembly languages, most programs are written in high-level languages due to the advantages of ease of design, maintenance, and portability. Similarly, the flexibility advantages of the microkernel model previously described more than outweigh its small performance penalty.

2. Some experimental results have shown that although in theory the microkernel model seems to have poorer performance than the monolithic kernel model, this is not true in practice. This is because other factors tend to dominate, and the small overhead involved in exchanging messages is usually negligible [Douglis et al. 1991].

Details of several distributed operating systems whose design is based on the microkernel model are presented in Chapter 12.

### 1.6.4 Performance

If a distributed system is to be used, its performance must be at least as good as a centralized system. That is, when a particular application is run on a distributed system, its overall performance should be better than or at least equal to that of running the same application on a single-processor system. However, to achieve this goal, it is important that the various components of the operating system of a distributed system be designed properly; otherwise, the overall performance of the distributed system may turn out to be worse than a centralized system. Some design principles considered useful for better performance are as follows:

1. *Batch if possible.* Batching often helps in improving performance greatly. For example, transfer of data across the network in large chunks rather than as individual pages is much more efficient. Similarly, piggybacking of acknowledgment of previous messages with the next message during a series of messages exchanged between two communicating entities also improves performance.

2. *Cache whenever possible.* Caching of data at clients' sites frequently improves overall system performance because it makes data available wherever it is being currently used, thus saving a large amount of computing time and network bandwidth. In addition, caching reduces contention on centralized resources.

3. *Minimize copying of data.* Data copying overhead (e.g., moving data in and out of buffers) involves a substantial CPU cost of many operations. For example, while being transferred from its sender to its receiver, a message data may take the following path on the sending side:

(a) From sender's stack to its message buffer
(b) From the message buffer in the sender's address space to the message buffer in the kernel's address space
(c) Finally, from the kernel to the network interface board

On the receiving side, the data probably takes a similar path in the reverse direction. Therefore, in this case, a total of six copy operations are involved in the message transfer operation. Similarly, in several systems, the data copying overhead is also large for read and write operations on block I/O devices. Therefore, for better performance, it is desirable to avoid copying of data, although this is not always simple to achieve. Making optimal use of memory management often helps in eliminating much data movement between the kernel, block I/O devices, clients, and servers.

4. *Minimize network traffic*. System performance may also be improved by reducing internode communication costs. For example, accesses to remote resources require communication, possibly through intermediate nodes. Therefore, migrating a process closer to the resources it is using most heavily may be helpful in reducing network traffic in the system if the decreased cost of accessing its favorite resource offsets the possible increased cost of accessing its less favored ones. Another way to reduce network traffic is to use the process migration facility to cluster two or more processes that frequently communicate with each other on the same node of the system. Avoiding the collection of global state information for making some decision also helps in reducing network traffic.

5. *Take advantage of fine-grain parallelism for multiprocessing*. Performance can also be improved by taking advantage of fine-grain parallelism for multiprocessing. For example, threads (described in Chapter 8) are often used for structuring server processes. Servers structured as a group of threads can operate efficiently because they can simultaneously service requests from several clients. Fine-grained concurrency control of simultaneous accesses by multiple processes to a shared resource is another example of application of this principle for better performance.

Throughout the book we will come across the use of these design principles in the design of the various distributed operating system components.

### 1.6.5 Scalability

*Scalability* refers to the capability of a system to adapt to increased service load. It is inevitable that a distributed system will grow with time since it is very common to add new machines or an entire subnetwork to the system to take care of increased workload or organizational changes in a company. Therefore, a distributed operating system should be designed to easily cope with the growth of nodes and users in the system. That is, such growth should not cause serious disruption of service or significant loss of performance to users. Some guiding principles for designing scalable distributed systems are as follows:

1. *Avoid centralized entities*. In the design of a distributed operating system, use of centralized entities such as a single central file server or a single database for the entire system makes the distributed system nonscalable due to the following reasons:

(a) The failure of the centralized entity often brings the entire system down. Hence, the system cannot tolerate faults in a graceful manner.
(b) The performance of the centralized entity often becomes a system bottleneck when contention for it increases with the growing number of users.
(c) Even if the centralized entity has enough processing and storage capacity, the capacity of the network that connects the centralized entity with other nodes of the system often gets saturated when the contention for the entity increases beyond a certain level.
(d) In a wide-area network consisting of several interconnected local-area networks, it is obviously inefficient to always get a particular type of request serviced at a server node that is several gateways away. This also increases network traffic. Local area and wide-area networking concepts are described in Chapter 2.

Therefore, the use of centralized entities should be avoided in the design. Replication of resources and distributed control algorithms are frequently used techniques to achieve this goal. In fact, for better scalability, as far as practicable, a functionally symmetric configuration should be used in which all nodes of the system have a nearly equal role to play in the operation of the system.

2. *Avoid centralized algorithms*. A centralized algorithm is one that operates by collecting information from all nodes, processing this information on a single node and then distributing the results to other nodes. The use of such algorithms in the design of a distributed operating system is also not acceptable from a scalability point of view. The reasons for this are very similar to those mentioned in the use of centralized entities. For example, a scheduling algorithm that makes scheduling decisions by first inquiring from all the nodes and then selecting the most lightly loaded node as a candidate for receiving jobs has poor scalability factor. Such an algorithm may work fine for small networks but gets crippled when applied to large networks. This is because the inquirer receives a very large number of replies almost simultaneously and the time required to process the reply messages for making a host selection is normally too long. Moreover, since the complexity of the algorithm is $O(n^2)$, it creates heavy network traffic and quickly consumes network bandwidth. Therefore, in the design of a distributed operating system, only decentralized algorithms should be used. In these algorithms, global state information of the system is not collected or used, decision at a node is usually based on locally available information, and it is assumed that a systemwide global clock does not exist (the clocks of all nodes are not synchronized).

3. *Perform most operations on client workstations*. If possible, an operation should be performed on the client's own workstation rather than on a server machine. This is because a server is a common resource for several clients, and hence server cycles are more precious than the cycles of client workstations. This principle enhances the scalability of the system, since it allows graceful degradation of system performance as the system grows in size, by reducing contention for shared resources. Caching is a frequently used technique for the realization of this principle.

Throughout the book, we will come across the use of these design principles in the design of the various distributed operating system components.

### 1.6.6 Heterogeneity

A heterogeneous distributed system consists of interconnected sets of dissimilar hardware or software systems. Because of the diversity, designing heterogenous distributed systems is far more difficult than designing homogeneous distributed systems in which each system is based on the same, or closely related, hardware and software. However, as a consequence of large scale, heterogeneity is often inevitable in distributed systems. Furthermore, often heterogeneity is preferred by many users because heterogeneous distributed systems provide the flexibility to their users of different computer platforms for different applications. For example, a user may have the flexibility of a supercomputer for simulations, a Macintosh for document processing, and a UNIX workstation for program development.

Incompatibilities in a heterogeneous distributed system may be of different types. For example, the internal formatting schemes of different communication and host processors may be different; or when several networks are interconnected via gateways, the communication protocols and topologies of different networks may be different; or the servers operating at different nodes of the system may be different. For instance, some hosts use 32-bit word lengths while others use word lengths of 16 or 64 bits. Byte ordering within these data constructs can vary as well, requiring special converters to enable data sharing between incompatible hosts.

In a heterogeneous distributed system, some form of data translation is necessary for interaction between two incompatible nodes. Some earlier systems left this translation to the users, but this is no longer acceptable. The data translation job may be performed either at the sender's node or at the receiver's node. Suppose this job is performed at the receiver's node. With this approach, at every node there must be a translator to convert each format in the system to the format used on the receiving node. Therefore, if there are $n$ different formats, $n - 1$ pieces of translation software must be supported at each node, resulting in a total of $n(n - 1)$ pieces of translation software in the system. This is undesirable, as adding a new type of format becomes a more difficult task over time. Performing the translation job at the sender's node instead of the receiver's node also suffers from the same drawback.

The software complexity of this translation process can be greatly reduced by using an intermediate standard data format. In this method, an intermediate standard data format is declared, and each node only requires a translation software for converting from its own format to the standard format and from the standard format to its own format. In this case, when two incompatible nodes interact at the sender node, the data to be sent is first converted to the standard format, the data is moved in the format of the standard, and finally, at the receiver node, the data is converted from the standard format to the receiver's format. By choosing the standard format to be the most common format in the system, the number of conversions can be reduced.

Various techniques to deal with heterogeneity in distributed systems are described in Chapters 2, 4, 5, and 8.

### 1.6.7 Security

In order that the users can trust the system and rely on it, the various resources of a computer system must be protected against destruction and unauthorized access. Enforcing security in a distributed system is more difficult than in a centralized system because of the lack of a single point of control and the use of insecure networks for data communication. In a centralized system, all users are authenticated by the system at login time, and the system can easily check whether a user is authorized to perform the requested operation on an accessed resource. In a distributed system, however, since the client-server model is often used for requesting and providing services, when a client sends a request message to a server, the server must have some way of knowing who is the client. This is not so simple as it might appear because any client identification field in the message cannot be trusted. This is because an intruder (a person or program trying to obtain unauthorized access to system resources) may pretend to be an authorized client or may change the message contents during transmission. Therefore, as compared to a centralized system, enforcement of security in a distributed system has the following additional requirements:

1. It should be possible for the sender of a message to know that the message was received by the intended receiver.
2. It should be possible for the receiver of a message to know that the message was sent by the genuine sender.
3. It should be possible for both the sender and receiver of a message to be guaranteed that the contents of the message were not changed while it was in transfer.

Cryptography (described in Chapter 11) is the only known practical method for dealing with these security aspects of a distributed system. In this method, comprehension of private information is prevented by encrypting the information, which can then be decrypted only by authorized users.

Another guiding principle for security is that a system whose security depends on the integrity of the fewest possible entities is more likely to remain secure as it grows. For example, it is much simpler to ensure security based on the integrity of the much smaller number of servers rather than trusting thousands of clients. In this case, it is sufficient to only ensure the physical security of these servers and the software they run. Chapter 11 deals with the commonly used techniques for designing secure distributed systems.

### 1.6.8 Emulation of Existing Operating Systems

For commercial success, it is important that a newly designed distributed operating system be able to emulate existing popular operating systems such as UNIX. With this property, new software can be written using the system call interface of the new operating system to take full advantage of its special features of distribution, but a vast amount of already existing old software can also be run on the same system without the need to rewrite them. Therefore, moving to the new distributed operating system will allow both types of software to be run side by side.

We will see in Chapter 12 how some of the existing distributed operating systems have been designed to support UNIX emulation facility.

## 1.7 INTRODUCTION TO DISTRIBUTED COMPUTING ENVIRONMENT (DCE)

Chapter 12 of the book presents case studies of four distributed operating systems: Amoeba, V-System, Mach, and Chorus. In addition, examples of key technologies of individual distributed operating system components that have either become or are poised to become de facto international standards are presented in individual chapters wherever such industry examples are available. In particular, the following technologies are presented as case studies:

- Ethernet, IEEE Token Ring, the Internet Protocol suite, and the Internet are presented as case studies of networking technologies in Chapter 2.
- The 4.3BSD UNIX interprocess communication mechanism is presented as a case study of message-passing technology in Chapter 3.
- SUN RPC and DCE RPC are presented as case studies of Remote Procedure Call (RPC) technology in Chapter 4.
- IVY and Munin are presented as case studies of Distributed Shared Memory (DSM) technology in Chapter 5.
- DCE Distributed Time Service (DTS) is presented as a case study of clock synchronization technology in Chapter 6.
- The DCE threads package is presented as a case study of threads technology in Chapter 8.
- DCE Distributed File Service (DFS) is presented as a case study of distributed file system technology in Chapter 9.
- The various components of DCE naming facility are presented as case studies of naming technology in Chapter 10.
- The Kerberos authentication system and DCE Security Service are presented as case studies of security technology in Chapter 11.

Notice from the above list that almost half of the key technologies presented as case studies in the various chapters of this book are tools and services that belong to DCE. This is because of the way in which DCE was created (described next). Therefore, for a better understanding of these key technologies, it will be useful to know something about DCE before going into the details of its key components. This section presents a brief introduction to DCE.

### 1.7.1 What Is DCE?

A vendor-independent distributed computing environment, DCE was defined by the Open Software Foundation (OSF), a consortium of computer manufacturers, including IBM, DEC, and Hewlett-Packard. It is not an operating system, nor is it an application. Rather, it is an integrated set of services and tools that can be installed as a coherent environment on top of existing operating systems and serve as a platform for building and running distributed applications.

A primary goal of DCE is vendor independence. It runs on many different kinds of computers, operating systems, and networks produced by different vendors. For example, some operating systems to which DCE can be easily ported include OSF/1, AIX, DOMAIN OS, ULTRIX, HP-UX, SINIX, SunOS, UNIX System V, VMS, WINDOWS, and OS/2. On the other hand, it can be used with any network hardware and transport software, including TCP/IP, X.25, as well as other similar products.

As shown in Figure 1.7, DCE is a middleware software layered between the DCE applications layer and the operating system and networking layer. The basic idea is to take a collection of existing machines (possibly from different vendors), interconnect them by a communication network, add the DCE software platform on top of the native operating systems of the machines, and then be able to build and run distributed applications. Each machine has its own local operating system, which may be different from that of other machines. The DCE software layer on top of the operating system and networking layer hides the differences between machines by automatically performing data-type conversions when necessary. Therefore, the heterogeneous nature of the system is transparent to the applications programmers, making their job of writing distributed applications much simpler.

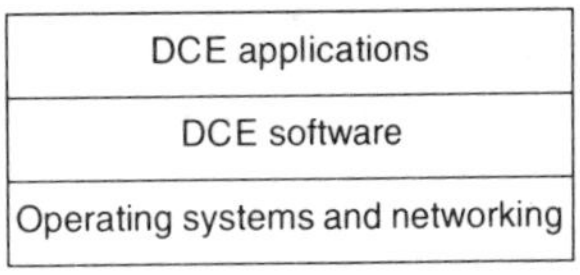


**Fig. 1.7** Position of DCE software in a DCE-based distributed system.

### 1.7.2 How Was DCE Created?

The OSF did not create DCE from scratch. Instead, it created DCE by taking advantage of work already done at universities and industries in the area of distributed computing. For this, OSF issued a request for technology (RFT), asking for tools and services needed to build a coherent distributed computing environment. To be a contender, a primary requirement was that actual working code must ultimately be provided. The submitted bids were carefully evaluated by OSF employees and a team of outside experts. Finally, those tools and services were selected that the members of the evaluation committee believed provided the best solutions. The code comprising the selected tools and services, almost entirely written in C, was then further developed by OSF to produce a single integrated package that was made available to the world as DCE. Version 1.0 of DCE was released by OSF in January 1992.

### 1.7.3 DCE Components

As mentioned above, DCE is a blend of various technologies developed independently and nicely integrated by OSF. Each of these technologies forms a component of DCE. The main components of DCE are as follows:

1. *Threads package.* It provides a simple programming model for building concurrent applications. It includes operations to create and control multiple threads of execution in a single process and to synchronize access to global data within an application. Details are given in Chapter 8.

2. *Remote Procedure Call (RPC) facility.* It provides programmers with a number of powerful tools necessary to build client-server applications. In fact, the DCE RPC facility is the basis for all communication in DCE because the programming model underlying all of DCE is the client-server model. It is easy to use, is network- and protocol-independent, provides secure communication between a client and a server, and hides differences in data requirements by automatically converting data to the appropriate forms needed by clients and servers. Details are given in Chapter 4.

3. *Distributed Time Service (DTS).* It closely synchronizes the clocks of all the computers in the system. It also permits the use of time values from external time sources, such as those of the U.S. National Institute for Standards and Technology (NIST), to synchronize the clocks of the computers in the system with external time. This facility can also be used to synchronize the clocks of the computers of one distributed environment with the clocks of the computers of another distributed environment. Details are given in Chapter 6.

4. *Name services.* The name services of DCE include the Cell Directory Service (CDS), the Global Directory Service (GDS), and the Global Directory Agent (GDA). These services allow resources such as servers, files, devices, and so on, to be uniquely named and accessed in a location-transparent manner. Details are given in Chapter 10.

5. *Security Service.* It provides the tools needed for authentication and authorization to protect system resources against illegitimate access. Details are given in Chapter 11.

6. *Distributed File Service (DFS).* It provides a systemwide file system that has such characteristics as location transparency, high performance, and high availability. A unique feature of DCE DFS is that it can also provide file services to clients of other file systems. Details are given in Chapter 9.

The DCE components listed above are tightly integrated. It is difficult to give a pictorial representation of their interdependencies because they are recursive. For example, the name services use RPC facility for internal communication among its various servers, but the RPC facility uses the name services to locate the destination. Therefore, the interdependencies of the various DCE components can be best depicted in tabular form, as shown in Figure 1.8.

| Component name | Other components used by it |
|---|---|
| Threads | None |
| RPC | Threads, name, security |
| DTS | Threads, RPC, name, security |
| Name | Threads, RPC, DTS, security |
| Security | Threads, RPC, DTS, name |
| DFS | Threads, RPC, DTS, name, security |

**Fig. 1.8** Interdependencies of DCE components.

### 1.7.4 DCE Cells

The DCE system is highly scalable in the sense that a system running DCE can have thousands of computers and millions of users spread over a worldwide geographic area. To accommodate such large systems, DCE uses the concept of cells. This concept helps break down a large system into smaller, manageable units called cells.

In a DCE system, a *cell* is a group of users, machines, or other resources that typically have a common purpose and share common DCE services. The minimum cell configuration requires a cell directory server, a security server, a distributed time server, and one or more client machines. Each DCE client machine has client processes for security service, cell directory service, distributed time service, RPC facility, and threads facility. A DCE client machine may also have a process for distributed file service if a cell configuration has a DCE distributed file server. Due to the use of the method of intersection for clock synchronization (described in Chapter 6), it is recommended that each cell in a DCE system should have at least three distributed time servers.

An important decision to be made while setting up a DCE system is to decide the cell boundaries. The following four factors should be taken into consideration for making this decision [Tanenbaum 1995, Rosenberry et al. 1992, OSF 1992]:

1. *Purpose*. The machines of users working on a common goal should be put in the same cell, as they need easy access to a common set of system resources. That is, users of machines in the same cell have closer interaction with each other than with users of machines in different cells. For example, if a company manufactures and sells various

types of products, depending on the manner in which the company functions, either a product-oriented or a function-oriented approach may be taken to decide cell boundaries [Tanenbaum 1995]. In the product-oriented approach, separate cells are formed for each product, with the users of the machines belonging to the same cell being responsible for all types of activities (design, manufacturing, marketing, and support services) related to one particular product. On the other hand, in the function-oriented approach, separate cells are formed for each type of activity, with the users belonging to the same cell being responsible for a particular activity, such as design, of all types of products.

2. *Administration*. Each system needs an administrator to register new users in the system and to decide their access rights to the system's resources. To perform his or her job properly, an administrator must know the users and the resources of the system. Therefore, to simplify administration jobs, all the machines and their users that are known to and manageable by an administrator should be put in a single cell. For example, all machines belonging to the same department of a company or a university can belong to a single cell. From an administration point of view, each cell has a different administrator.

3. *Security*. Machines of those users who have greater trust in each other should be put in the same cell. That is, users of machines of a cell trust each other more than they trust the users of machines of other cells. In such a design, cell boundaries act like firewalls in the sense that accessing a resource that belongs to another cell requires more sophisticated authentication than accessing a resource that belongs to a user's own cell.

4. *Overhead*. Several DCE operations, such as name resolution and user authentication, incur more overhead when they are performed between cells than when they are performed within the same cell. Therefore, machines of users who frequently interact with each other and the resources frequently accessed by them should be placed in the same cell. The need to access a resource of another cell should arise infrequently for better overall system performance.

Notice from the above discussion that in determining cell boundaries the emphasis is on purpose, administration, security, and performance. Geographical considerations can, but do not have to, play a part in cell design. For better performance, it is desirable to have as few cells as possible to minimize the number of operations that need to cross cell boundaries. However, subject to security and administration constraints, it is desirable to have smaller cells with fewer machines and users. Therefore, it is important to properly balance the requirements imposed by the four factors mentioned above while deciding cell boundaries in a DCE system.

## 1.8 SUMMARY

A distributed computing system is a collection of processors interconnected by a communication network in which each processor has its own local memory and other peripherals and communication between any two processors of the system takes place by message passing over the communication network.

The existing models for distributed computing systems can be broadly classified into five categories: minicomputer, workstation, workstation-server, processor-pool, and hybrid.

Distributed computing systems are much more complex and difficult to build than the traditional centralized systems. Despite the increased complexity and the difficulty of building, the installation and use of distributed computing systems are rapidly increasing. This is mainly because the advantages of distributed computing systems outweigh its disadvantages. The main advantages of distributed computing systems are (a) suitability for inherently distributed applications, (b) sharing of information among distributed users, (c) sharing of resources, (d) better price-performance ratio, (e) shorter response times and higher throughput, (f) higher reliability, (g) extensibility and incremental growth, and (h) better flexibility in meeting users' needs.

The operating systems commonly used for distributed computing systems can be broadly classified into two types: network operating systems and distributed operating systems. As compared to a network operating system, a distributed operating system has better transparency and fault tolerance capability and provides the image of a virtual uniprocessor to the users.

The main issues involved in the design of a distributed operating system are transparency, reliability, flexibility, performance, scalability, heterogeneity, security, and emulation of existing operating systems.

## EXERCISES

**1.1.** Differentiate among the following types of operating systems by defining their essential properties:
  (a) Time sharing
  (b) Parallel processing
  (c) Network
  (d) Distributed

**1.2.** In what respect are distributed computing systems better than parallel processing systems? Give examples of three applications for which distributed computing systems will be more suitable than parallel processing systems.

**1.3.** What were the major technological, economical, and social factors that motivated the development of distributed computing systems? What are some of the main advantages and disadvantages of distributed computing systems over centralized ones?

**1.4.** Discuss the relative advantages and disadvantages of the various commonly used models for configuring distributed computing systems. Which model do you think is going to become the most popular model in future? Give reasons for your answer.

**1.5.** Consider the case of a distributed computing system based on the processor-pool model that has $P$ processors in the pool. In this system, suppose a user starts a computation job that involves compilation of a program consisting of $F$ source files ($F < P$). Assume that at this time this user is the only user using the system. What maximum gain in speed can be hoped for this job in this system as compared to its execution on a single-processor system (assume that all the processors we are talking about are of equal capability)? What factors might cause the gain in speed to be less than this maximum?

**1.6.** Explain the difference between the terms *service* and *server.* In the design of a distributed operating system, discuss the relative advantages and disadvantages of using a single server and multiple servers for implementing a service.

**1.7.** Why are distributed operating systems more difficult to design than operating systems for centralized time-sharing systems?

**1.8.** What is *groupware*? Why is it considered to be a promising technology for software development?

**1.9.** What are the main differences between a network operating system and a distributed operating system?

**1.10.** What are the major issues in designing a distributed operating system?

**1.11.** A distributed operating system makes a collection of networked machines to act like a virtual uniprocessor. What are the main advantages of this virtual-machine architecture for a user? What issues are important for a distributed operating system designer in achieving this goal?

**1.12.** Concurrency transparency is an important issue in the design of a distributed operating system. Is it also an important issue in the design of an operating system for a centralized system? If no, explain why. If yes, list some mechanisms that are commonly used in operating systems for centralized systems to support this feature.

**1.13.** Discuss some of the important concepts that a distributed operating system designer might use to improve the reliability of his or her system. What is the main problem in making a system highly reliable?

**1.14.** Differentiate between the monolithic kernel and microkernel approaches for designing a distributed operating system. Discuss their relative advantages and disadvantages.

**1.15.** In the microkernel approach for designing a distributed operating system, what are the primary tasks that the kernel must perform?

**1.16.** Figure 1.6 indicates that a layered approach is used to design a distributed system. What are the main advantages of using this approach?

**1.17.** Discuss the main guiding principles that a distributed operating system designer must keep in mind for the good performance of his or her system.

**1.18.** Why is scalability an important feature in the design of a distributed system? Discuss some of the guiding principles for designing a scalable distributed system.

**1.19.** Why is heterogeneity unavoidable in many distributed systems? What are some of the common types of incompatibilities encountered in heterogeneous distributed systems? What are the common issues with which the designer of a heterogeneous distributed system must deal?

**1.20.** Suppose a component of a distributed system suddenly crashes. How will this event inconvenience the users when:

(a) The system uses the processor-pool model and the crashed component is a processor in the pool.

(b) The system uses the processor-pool model and the crashed component is a user terminal.

(c) The system uses the workstation-server model and the crashed component is a server machine.

(d) The system uses the workstation-server model and the crashed component is a user workstation.

**1.21.** Compare the following types of systems in terms of cost, hardware complexity, operating system complexity, potential parallelism, and programmability (how easily users can write efficient programs):

(a) A multiprocessor system having a single shared memory.

(b) A multiprocessor system in which each processor has its own local memory in addition to a shared memory used by all processors in the system.

(c) A multiprocessor system in which each processor has its own memory. All processors are kept in a big hall and are interconnected by a high-capacity communication line forming a network. Each processor can communicate with other processors only by exchanging messages.

(d) A multiprocessor system in which each processor has its own memory. The processors are located far from each other (may be in different cities of a country) and are interconnected by a low-capacity communication line forming a network. Each processor can communicate with other processors only by exchanging messages.

For comparing the systems, consider three cases—(a) number of processors is small (2–8); (b) number of processors is large (16–32); and (c) number of processors is very large (more than 100).

## BIBLIOGRAPHY

**[Accetta et al. 1986]** Accetta, M., Baron, R., Golub, D., Rashid, R., Tevanian, A., and Young, M., "Mach: A New Kernel Foundation for UNIX Development," In: *Proceedings of the Summer 1986 USENIX Technical Conference*, pp. 93–112 (July 1986).

**[Avresky and Pradhan 1996]** Avresky, D., and Pradhan, D. (Eds.), *Fault-Tolerant Parallel and Distributed Systems*, IEEE Computer Society Press, Los Alamitos, CA (1996).

**[Black et al. 1992]** Black, D. L., Golub, D. B., Julin, D. P., Rashid, R. F., Draves, R. P., Dean, R. W., Forin, A., Barrera, J., Tokuda, H., Malan, G., and Bohman, D., "Microkernel Operating System Architecture and Mach," In: *Proceedings of the USENIX Workshop on Microkernels and Other Kernel Architectures*, USENIX, pp. 11–30 (1992).

**[Boykin and LoVerso 1990]** Boykin, J., and LoVerso, J., "Recent Developments in Operating Systems," *IEEE Computer*, pp. 5–6 (May 1990).

**[Brazier and Johansen 1993]** Brazier, F., and Johansen, D. (Eds.), *Distributed Open Systems*, IEEE Computer Society Press, Los Alamitos, CA (1993).

**[Butler 1993]** Butler, M., *Client Server*, Prentice-Hall, London, UK (1993).

**[Casavant and Singhal 1994]** Casavant, T. L., and Singhal, M. (Eds.), *Readings in Distributed Computing Systems*, IEEE Computer Society Press, Los Alamitos, CA (1994).

**[Cheriton 1984]** Cheriton, D. R., "The V Kernel: A Software Base for Distributed Systems," *IEEE Software*, Vol. 1, No. 2, pp. 19–42 (1984).

**[Cheriton 1988]** Cheriton, D. R., "The V Distributed System," *Communications of the ACM*, Vol. 31, No. 3, pp. 314–333 (1988).

**[Coulouris et al. 1994]** Coulouris, G. F., Dollimore, J., and Kindberg, T., *Distributed Systems Concepts and Design*, 2nd ed., Addison-Wesley, Reading, MA (1994).

**[Cristian-1991]** Cristian, F., "Understanding Fault-Tolerant Distributed Systems," *Communications of the ACM*, Vol. 34, pp. 56–78 (February 1991).

**[Critchley and Batty 1993]** Critchley, T., and Batty, K., *Open Systems: The Reality*, Prentice-Hall, London, UK (1993).

**[Deitel 1990]** Deitel, H. M., *An Introduction to Operating Systems*, 2nd ed., Addison-Wesley, Reading, MA (1990).

**[Douglis et al. 1991]** Douglis, F., Ousterhout, J. K., Kaashoek, M. F., and Tanenbaum, A. S., "A Comparison of Two Distributed Systems: Amoeba and Sprite," *Computing Systems*, Vol. 4, pp. 353–384 (1991).

**[Ghafoor and Yang 1993]** Ghafoor, A., and Yang, J., "A Distributed Heterogeneous Supercomputing Management System," *IEEE Computer*, Vol. 26, No. 6, pp. 78–86 (1993).

**[Gien 1990]** Gien, M., "Micro-Kernel Architecture: Key to Modern Operating Systems Design," *UNIX Review*, p. 10 (November 1990).

**[Gien and Grob 1992]** Gien, M., and Grob, L., "Microkernel Based Operating Systems: Moving UNIX on to Modern System Architectures," In: *Proceedings of the UniForum'92 Conference*, USENIX, pp. 43–55 (1992).

**[Golub et al. 1990]** Golub, D., Dean, R., Forin, A., and Rashid, R., "UNIX as an Application Program," In: *Proceedings of the Summer 1990 USENIX Conference*, USENIX, pp. 87–95 (June 1990).

**[Goscinski 1991]** Goscinski, A., *Distributed Operating Systems, The Logical Design*, Addison-Wesley, Reading, MA (1991).

**[Hariri et al. 1992]** Hariri, S., Choudhary, A., and Sarikaya, B, "Architectural Support for Designing Fault-Tolerant Open Distributed Systems," *IEEE Computer*, Vol. 25, No. 6, pp. 50–62 (1992).

**[Hunter 1995]** Hunter, P., *Network Operating Systems: Making the Right Choice*, Addison-Wesley, Reading, MA (1995).

**[Islam 1996]** Islam, N., *Distributed Objects: Methodologies for Customizing Operating Systems*, IEEE Computer Society Press, Los Alamitos, CA (1996).

**[ISO 1992]** *Basic Reference Model of Open Distributed Processing, Part 1: Overview and Guide to Use*, ISO/IEC JTC1/SC212/WG7 CD10746–1, International Standards Organization (1992).

**[Jalote 1994]** Jalote, P., *Fault Tolerance in Distributed Systems*, Prentice-Hall, Englewood Cliffs, NJ (1994).

**[Khanna 1994]** Khanna, R. (Ed.), *Distributed Computing: Implementation and Management Strategies*, Prentice-Hall, Englewood Cliffs, NJ (1994).

**[Khokhar et al. 1993]** Khokhar, A., Prasanna, V. K., Shaaban, M. E., and Wang, C. L., "Heterogeneous Computing: Challenges and Opportunities," *IEEE Computer*, Vol. 26, No. 6, pp. 18–27 (1993).

**[Lampson 1983]** Lampson, B. W., "Hints for Computer System Design," In: *Proceedings of the 9th Symposium on Operating Systems Principles* (October 1983).

**[Lamport et al. 1982]** Lamport, L., Shostak, R., and Pease, M., "The Byzantine Generals Problem," *ACM Transactions on Programming Languages and Systems*, Vol. 4, No. 3, pp. 382–401 (1982).

**[Lelann 1981]** Lelann, G., "Motivations, Objectives, and Characterization of Distributed Systems," *Distributed Systems—Architecture and Implementation, Lecture Notes in Computer Science*, Vol. 105, Springer-Verlag, New York, NY (1981).

**[Lockhart Jr. 1994]** Lockhart Jr., H. W., *OSF DCE: Guide to Developing Distributed Applications*, IEEE Computer Society Press, Los Alamitos, CA (1994).

**[Marca and Bock 1992]** Marca, D., and Bock, G. (Eds.), *Groupware: Software for Computer-Supported Cooperative Work*, IEEE Computer Society Press, Los Alamitos, CA (1992).

**[Martin et al. 1991]** Martin, B. E., Pedersen, C. H., and Roberts, J. B., "An Object-Based Taxonomy for Distributed Computing Systems," *IEEE Computer*, Vol. 24, No. 8 (1991).

**[Milenkovic 1992]** Milenkovic, M., *Operating Systems: Concepts and Design*, 2nd ed., McGraw-Hill, New York (1992).

**[Mullender 1987]** Mullender, S. J.,"Distributed Operating Systems," *Computer Standards and Interfaces*, Vol. 6, pp. 37–44 (1987).

**[Mullender 1993]** Mullender, S. J. (Ed.), *Distributed Systems*, 2nd ed., Addison-Wesley, Reading, MA (1993).

**[Mullender and Tanenbaum 1984]** Mullender, S. J., and Tanenbaum, A. S., "Protection and Resource Control in Distributed Operating Systems," *Computer Networks*, Vol. 8, pp. 421–432 (1984).

**[Mullender et al. 1990]** Mullender, S. J., Van Rossum, G., Tanenbaum, A. S., Van Renesse, R., and Van Staverene, H., "Amoeba: A Distributed Operating System for the 1990s," *IEEE Computer*, Vol. 23, No. 5, pp. 44–53 (1990).

**[Needham and Herbert 1982]** Needham, R. M., and Herbert, A. J., *The Cambridge Distributed Computing System*, Addison-Wesley, Reading, MA (1982).

**[Nelson 1990]** Nelson, V. P., "Fault-Tolerant Computing: Fundamental Concepts," *IEEE Computer*, Vol. 23, No. 7, pp. 19–25 (1990).

**[Nicol et al. 1993]** Nicol, J. R., Wilkes, C. T., and Manola, F. A., "Object Orientation in Heterogeneous Distributed Computing Systems," *IEEE Computer*, Vol. 26, No. 6, pp. 57–67 (1993).

**[Notkin et al. 1987]** Notkin, D., Hutchinson, N., Sanislo, J., and Schwartz, M., "Heterogeneous Computing Environments: Report on the ACM SIGOPS Workshop on Accommodating Heterogeneity," *Communications of the ACM*, Vol. 30, No. 2, pp. 132–140 (1987).

**[Nutt 1991]** Nutt, G. J., *Centralized and Distributed Operating Systems*, Prentice-Hall, Englewood Cliffs, NJ (1991).

**[Nutt 1992]** Nutt, G. J., *Open Systems*, Prentice-Hall, Englewood Cliffs, NJ (1992).

**[OSF 1992]** *Introduction to OSF DCE*, Prentice-Hall, Englewood Cliffs, NJ (1992).

**[Ousterhout et al. 1988]** Ousterhout, J. K., Cherenson, A. R., Douglis, F., Nelson, M. N., and Welch, B. B., "The Sprite Network Operating System," *IEEE Computer*, Vol. 21, No. 2, pp. 23–36 (1988).

**[Pike et al. 1990]** Pike, R., Presotto, D., Thompson, K., and Trickey, H., "Plan 9 from Bell Labs," In: *Proceedings of the Summer 1990 UKUUG (UK Unix Users Group) Conference*, pp. 1–9 (July 1990).

**[Popek and Walker 1985]** Popek, G., and Walker, B., *The LOCUS Distributed System Architecture*, MIT Press, Cambridge, MA (1985).

**[Rashid 1985]** Rashid, R. F., "Network Operating Systems," In: *Local Area Networks: An Advanced Course, Lecture Notes in Computer Science*, Vol. 184, pp. 314–340, Springer-Verlag, New York, NY (1985).

**[Ritchie and Thompson 1974]** Ritchie, D., and Thompson, K., "The UNIX Time-Sharing System," Communications of the ACM, Vol. 17, No. 7, pp. 365–375 (1974).

**[Rosenberry et al. 1992]** Rosenberry, W., Kenney, D., and Fisher, G., *OSF DISTRIBUTED COMPUTING ENVIRONMENT, Understanding DCE*, O'Reilly, Sebastopol, CA (1992).

**[Schlichting and Schneider 1983]** Schlichting, R. D., and Schneider, F. B., "Fail-Stop Processors: An Approach to Designing Fault-Tolerant Computing Systems," *ACM Transactions on Computer Systems*, Vol. 1, No. 3, pp. 222–238 (1983).

**[Shoch and Hupp 1982]** Shoch, J. F., and Hupp, J. A., "The Worm Programs: Early Experiences with a Distributed Computation," *Communications of the ACM*, Vol. 25, No. 3, pp. 172–180 (1982).

**[Silberschatz and Galvin 1994]** Silberschatz, A., and Galvin, P. B., *Operating Systems Concepts*, 4th ed., Addison-Wesley, Reading, MA (1994).

**[Singhal and Shivaratri 1994]** Singhal, M., and Shivaratri, N. G., *Advanced Concepts in Operating Systems*, McGraw-Hill, New York, NY (1994).

**[Stalling 1995]** Stalling, W., *Operating Systems*, 2nd ed., Prentice-Hall, Englewood Cliffs, NJ (1995).

**[Stankovic 1984]** Stankovic, J. A., "A Perspective on Distributed Computer Systems," *IEEE Transactions on Computers*, Vol. C-33, No. 12, pp. 1102–1115 (1984).

**[Suri et al. 1994]** Suri, N., Walter, C. J., and Hugue, M. M. (Eds.), *Advances in Ultra-Dependable Distributed Systems*, IEEE Computer Society Press, Los Alamitos, CA (1994).

**[Tanenbaum 1995]** Tanenbaum, A. S., *Distributed Operating Systems*, Prentice-Hall, Englewood Cliffs, NJ (1995).

**[Tanenbaum and Van Renesse 1985]** Tanenbaum, A. S., and Van Renesse, R., "Distributed Operating Systems," *ACM Computing Surveys*, Vol. 17, No. 4, pp. 419–470 (1985). © ACM, Inc., 1985.

**[Umar 1993]** Umar, A., *Distributed Computing: A Practical Approach*, Prentice-Hall, Englewood Cliffs, NJ (1993).

**[Vaughn 1994]** Vaughn, L. T., *Client/Server System Design and Implementation*, IEEE Computer Society Press, Los Alamitos, CA (1994).

**[Wittie 1991]** Wittie, L. D., "Computer Networks and Distributed Systems," *IEEE Computer*, pp. 67–75 (1991).

## POINTERS TO BIBLIOGRAPHIES ON THE INTERNET

Bibliography containing references on *Operating Systems* can be found at:

ftp:ftp.cs.umanitoba.ca/pub/bibliographies/Os/os.html

Bibliography containing references on *Taxonomies for Parallel and Distributed Systems* can be found at:

ftp:ftp.cs.umanitoba.ca/pub/bibliographies/Parallel/taxonomy.html

Bibliography containing references on *Distributed Computing* can be found at:

ftp:ftp.cs.umanitoba.ca/pub/bibliographies/Distributed/Osser.html

Bibliographies containing references on *Distributed Systems* can be found at:

ftp:ftp.cs.umanitoba.ca/pub/bibliographies/Distributed/Dcs-1.0.html

ftp:ftp.cs.umanitoba.ca/pub/bibliographies/Distributed/dist.sys.1.html

Bibliography containing references on *Open Systems* and *Open Computing* can be found at:

ftp:ftp.cs.umanitoba.ca/pub/bibliographies/Os/opencomp.html

Bibliography containing references on *Fault Tolerant Distributed Systems* can be found at:

ftp:ftp.cs.umanitoba.ca/pub/bibliographies/Distributed/fault.tolerant.html

Bibliographies containing references on *Computer Supported Cooperative Work* (*CSCW*) can be found at:

ftp:ftp.cs.umanitoba.ca/pub/bibliographies/Distributed/CSCWBiblio.html

ftp:ftp.cs.umanitoba.ca/pub/bibliographies/Distributed/CSCW92.html

List of publications of the MIT Parallel & Distributed Operating Systems (*PDOS*) group can be found at:

http:www.pdos.lcs.mit.edu/PDOS-papers.html

List of publications of the Stanford Distributed Systems Group (DSG) can be found at:

http:www-dsg.stanford.edu/Publications.html

List of publications of the Distributed Systems Research Group (DSRG) at Oregon Graduate Institute can be found at:

http:www.cse.ogi.edu/DSRG/osrg/osrg.html#Current Paper

List of publications of the Distributed Systems Group at Trinity College, Dublin, can be found at:

http:www.dsg.cs.tcd.ie/dsgpublications/bibs

# CHAPTER 2

# Computer Networks

## 2.1 INTRODUCTION

A computer network is a communication system that links end systems by communication lines and software protocols to exchange data between two processes running on different end systems of the network. The end systems are often referred to as *nodes*, *sites*, *hosts*, *computers*, *machines*, and so on. The nodes may vary in size and function. Sizewise, a node may be a small microprocessor, a workstation, a minicomputer, or a large supercomputer. Functionwise, a node may be a dedicated system (such as a print server or a file server) without any capability for interactive users, a single-user personal computer, or a general-purpose time-sharing system.

As already mentioned in Chapter 1, a distributed system is basically a computer network whose nodes have their own local memory and may also have other hardware and software resources. A distributed system, therefore, relies entirely on the underlying computer network for the communication of data and control information between the nodes of which they are composed. Furthermore, the performance and reliability of a distributed system depend to a great extent on the performance and reliability of the underlying computer network. Hence a basic knowledge of computer networks is required for the study of distributed operating systems. A comprehensive treatment of computer networks will require a complete book in itself, and there are many good books available on this subject [Tanenbaum 1988, Black 1993, Stallings 1992b, Ramos et al. 1996].

Therefore, this chapter deals only with the most important aspects of networking concepts and designs, with special emphasis to those aspects that are needed as a basis for designing distributed operating systems.

## 2.2 NETWORKS TYPES

Networks are broadly classified into two types: *local area networks* (*LANs*) and *wide-area networks* (*WANs*). The WANs are also referred to as *long-haul networks*. The key characteristics that are often used to differentiate between these two types of networks are as follows [Abeysundara and Kamal 1991]:

1. *Geographic distribution*. The main difference between the two types of networks is the way in which they are geographically distributed. A LAN is restricted to a limited geographic coverage of a few kilometers, but a WAN spans greater distances and may extend over several thousand kilometers. Therefore, LANs typically provide communication facilities within a building or a campus, whereas WANs may operate nationwide or even worldwide.

2. *Data rate*. Data transmission rates are usually much higher in LANs than in WANs. Transmission rates in LANs usually range from 0.2 megabit per second (Mbps) to 1 gigabit per second (Gbps). On the other hand, transmission rates in WANs usually range from 1200 bits per second to slightly over 1 Mbps.

3. *Error rate*. Local area networks generally experience fewer data transmission errors than WANs do. Typically, bit error rates are in the range of $10^{-8}$–$10^{-12}$ with LANs as opposed to $10^{-5}$–$10^{-7}$ with WANs.

4. *Communication link*. The most common communication links used in LANs are twisted pair, coaxial cable, and fiber optics. On the other hand, since the sites in a WAN are physically distributed over a large geographic area, the communication links used are by default relatively slow and unreliable. Typical communication links used in WANs are telephone lines, microwave links, and satellite channels.

5. *Ownership*. A LAN is typically owned by a single organization because of its limited geographic coverage. A WAN, however, is usually formed by interconnecting multiple LANs each of which may belong to a different organization. Therefore, administrative and maintenance complexities and costs for LANs are usually much lower than for WANs.

6. *Communication cost*. The overall communication costs of a LAN is usually much lower than that of a WAN. The main reasons for this are lower error rates, simple (or absence of) routing algorithms, and lower administrative and maintenance costs. Moreover, the cost to transmit data in a LAN is negligible since the transmission medium is usually owned by the user organization. However, with a WAN, this cost may be very high because the transmission media used are leased lines or public communication systems, such as telephone lines, microwave links, and satellite channels.

Networks that share some of the characteristics of both LANs and WANs are sometimes referred to as *metropolitan area networks* (*MANs*) [Stallings 1993a]. The MANs usually cover a wider geographic area (up to about 50 km in diameter) than LANs and frequently operate at speeds very close to LAN speeds. A main objective of MANs is to interconnect LANs located in an entire city or metropolitan area. Communication links commonly used for MANs are coaxial cable and microwave links.

We saw in Chapter 1 that the performance of a distributed system must be at least as good as a centralized system. That is, when a particular application is run on a distributed system, its overall performance should not be appreciably worse than running the same application on a single-processor system. The data transmission rates of LANs and MANs are usually considered to be adequate to meet this requirement for many applications. However, with the current technology, the transmission rates of WANs cannot fully meet this requirement of distributed systems. Therefore, WAN-based distributed systems are used mainly for those applications for which performance is not important. Several inherently distributed applications that require information sharing among widely distributed users/computers belong to this category.

Although current WANs cannot fully meet the performance requirements of distributed systems, with the emergence of Broadband Integrated Services Digital Network (B-ISDN) [Kawarasaki and Jabbari 1991] and Asynchronous Transfer Mode (ATM) technologies [Vetter 1995], future WANs are expected to have data transmission rates that will be adequate for the construction of WAN-based distributed systems and the implementation of a wide range of applications on these distributed systems. ISDN [Helgert 1991] refers to telecommunication networks that transfer many types of data, such as voice, fax, and computer data, in digital form at data transmission rates that are multiples of a basic channel speed of 64 kilobits per second (Kbps). B-ISDN are ISDN networks that provide point-to-point data transmission speeds of 150 Mbps and above. B-ISDN networks are considered to be suitable for high-bandwidth applications, such as applications involving high-quality video and bulk data transmissions. ATM technology can provide data transmission rates of up to 622 Mbps. (ATM technology is described later in this chapter.)

## 2.3 LAN TECHNOLOGIES

This section presents a description of topologies, principles of operation, and case studies of popular LANs.

### 2.3.1 LAN Topologies

The two commonly used network topologies for constructing LANs are multiaccess bus and ring. In a simple *multiaccess bus network*, all sites are directly connected to a single transmission medium (called the bus) that spans the whole length of the network (Fig. 2.1). The bus is passive and is shared by all the sites for any message transmission in the network. Each site is connected to the bus by a drop cable using a T-connection or tap. Broadcast communication is used for message transmission.

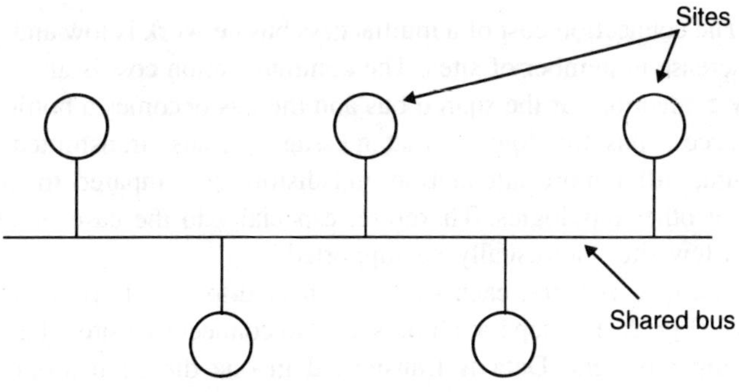


**Fig. 2.1** Simple multiaccess bus network topology.

That is, a message is transmitted from one site to another by placing it on the shared bus. An address designator is associated with the message. As the message travels on the bus, each site checks whether it is addressed to it and the addressee site picks up the message.

A variant of the simple multiaccess bus network topology is the multiaccess branching bus network topology. In such a network, two or more simple multiaccess bus networks are interconnected by using repeaters (Fig. 2.2). *Repeaters* are hardware devices used to connect cable segments. They simply amplify and copy electric signals from one segment of a network to its next segment.

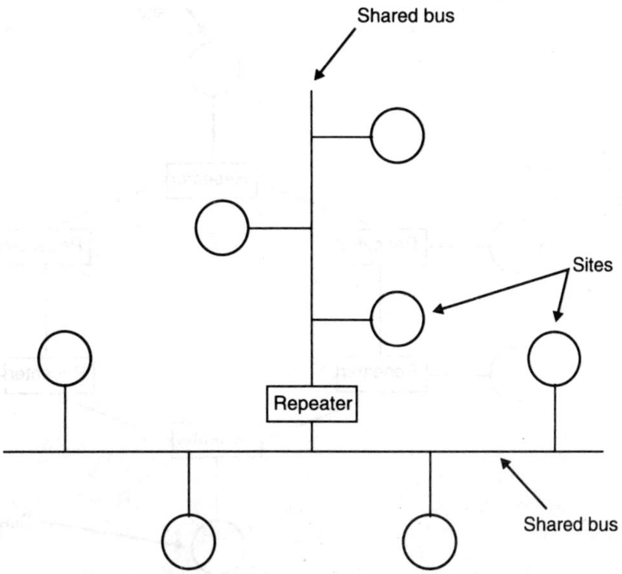


**Fig. 2.2** Multiaccess branching bus network topology.

The connection cost of a multiaccess bus network is low and grows only linearly with the increase in number of sites. The communication cost is also quite low, unless there is heavy contention for the shared bus and the bus becomes a bottleneck. A disadvantage of multiaccess bus topology is that message signals, transmitted over the single shared medium, suffer more attenuation and distortion compared to the shorter point-to-point links of other topologies. Therefore, especially in the case of fiber-optic bus networks, only a few sites can usually be supported.

In a *ring network*, each site is connected to exactly two other sites so that a loop is formed (Fig. 2.3). A separate link is used to connect two sites. The links are interconnected by using repeaters. Data is transmitted in one direction around the ring by signaling between sites. That is, to send a message from one site to another, the source site writes the destination site's address in the message header and passes it to its neighbor. A site that receives the message checks the message header to see if the message is addressed to it. If not, the site passes on the message to its own neighbor. In this manner, the message circulates around the ring until some site removes it from the ring. In some ring networks, the destination site (to which the message is addressed) removes the message from the ring, while in others it is removed by the source site (which sent the message). In the latter case, the message always circulates for one complete round on the ring. Generally, in ring networks, one of the sites acts as a *monitor site* to ensure that a message does not circulate indefinitely (that is, in case the source site or the destination site fails). The monitor site also perform other jobs, such as housekeeping functions, ring utilization, and handling other error conditions.

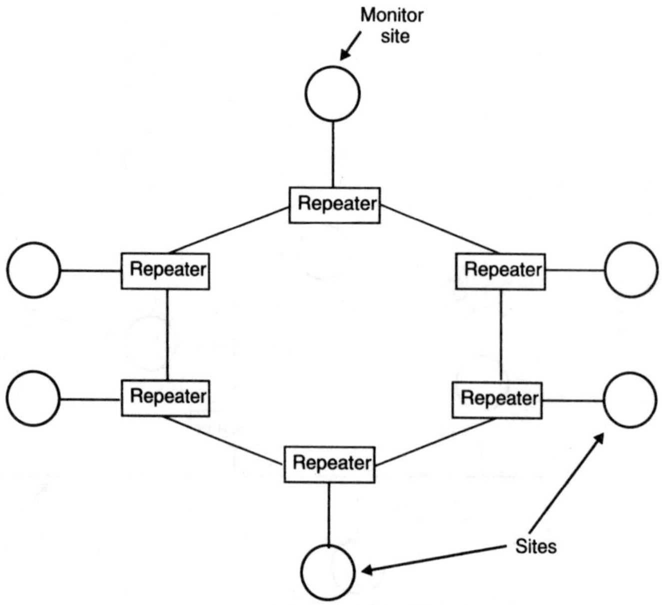


**Fig. 2.3** Ring network topology.

The connection cost of a ring network is low and grows only linearly with the increase in number of sites. The average communication cost is directly proportional to the number of sites in the network. If there are $n$ sites, at most $(n-1)$ links have to be traversed by a message to reach its destination. An often-quoted disadvantage of ring topology is the vulnerability of ring networks due to site or link failures; the network is partitioned by a single link failure. Variations of the basic ring topology, such as using bidirectional links, providing double links between two neighbors, and site skipping links with each site joined to its two immediate predecessors, have been considered to improve network reliability.

### 2.3.2 Medium-Access Control Protocols

In case of both multiaccess bus and ring networks, we saw that a single channel is shared by all the sites of a network, resulting in a multiaccess environment. In such an environment, it is possible that several sites will want to transmit information over the shared channel simultaneously. In this case, the transmitted information may become scrambled and must be discarded. The concerned sites must be notified about the discarded information, so that they can retransmit their information. If no special provisions are made, this situation may be repeated, resulting in degraded performance. Therefore, special schemes are needed in a multiaccess environment to control the access to a shared channel. These schemes are known as *medium-access control protocols*.

Obviously, in a multiaccess environment, the use of a medium having high raw data rate alone is not sufficient. The medium-access control protocol used must also provide for efficient bandwidth use of the medium. Therefore, the medium-access control protocol has a significant effect on the overall performance of a computer network, and often it is by such protocols that the networks differ the most. The three most important performance objectives of a medium-access control protocol are high throughput, high channel utilization, and low message delay. In addition to meeting the performance objectives, some other desirable characteristics of a medium-access control protocol are as follows [Abeysundara and Kamal 1991]:

1. For fairness, unless a priority scheme is intentionally implemented, the protocol should provide equal opportunity to all sites in allowing them to transmit their information over the shared medium.
2. For better scalability, sites should require a minimum knowledge of the network structure (topology, size, or relative location of other sites), and addition, removal, or movement of a site from one place to another in the network should be possible without the need to change the protocol. Furthermore, it should not be necessary to have a knowledge of the exact value of the end-to-end propagation delay of the network for the protocol to function correctly.
3. For higher reliability, centralized control should be avoided and the operation of the protocol should be completely distributed.

4. For supporting real-time applications, the protocol should exhibit bounded-delay properties. That is, the maximum message transfer delay from one site to another in the network must be known and fixed.

It is difficult to achieve all of the previously mentioned characteristics at the same time while achieving the performance objectives of high throughput, high channel utilization, and low message delay.

Several protocols have been developed for medium-access control in a multiaccess environment. Of these, the Carrier Sense Multiple Access with Collision Detection (CSMA/CD) protocol is the one most commonly used for multiaccess bus networks, and the token ring and slotted ring are the two commonly used protocols for ring networks. These medium-access control protocols are described next.

Note that for efficient and fair use of network resources, a message is often divided into packets prior to transmission. In this case, a *packet* is the smallest unit of communication. It usually contains a header and a body. The body contains a part of the actual message data, and the header contains addressing information (identifiers of the sender and receiver sites) and sequencing information (position of the packet data within the entire message data).

### The CSMA/CD Protocol

The CSMA/CD scheme [IEEE 1985a] employs decentralized control of the shared medium. In this scheme, each site has equal status in the sense that there is no central controller site. The sites contend with each other for use of the shared medium and the site that first gains access during an idle period of the medium uses the medium for the transmission of its own message. Obviously, occasional collisions of messages may occur when more than one site senses the medium to be idle and transmits messages at approximately the same time. The scheme uses collision detection, recovery, and controlled retransmission mechanisms to deal with this problem. Therefore, the scheme is comprised of the following three mechanisms and works as described next:

1. *Carrier sense and defer mechanism.* Whenever a site wishes to transmit a packet, it first listens for the presence of a signal (known as a *carrier* by analogy with radio broadcasting) on the shared medium. If the medium is found to be free (no carrier is present on the medium), the site starts transmitting its packet. Otherwise, the site defers its packet transmission and waits (continues to listen) until the medium becomes free. The site initiates its packet transmission as soon as it senses that the medium is free.

2. *Collision detection mechanism.* Unfortunately, carrier sensing does not prevent all collisions because of the nonzero propagation delay of the shared medium. Obviously, collisions occur only within a short time interval following the start of transmission, since after this interval all sites will detect that the medium is not free and defer transmission. This time interval is called the *collision window* or *collision interval* and is equal to the amount of time required for a signal to propagate from one end of the shared medium to the other and back again. If a site attempts to transmit a packet, it must listen to the shared

medium for a time period that is at least equal to the collision interval in order to guarantee that the packet will not experience a collision.

Collision avoidance by listening to the shared medium for at least the collision interval time before initiation of packet transmission leads to inefficient utilization of the medium when collisions are rare. Therefore, instead of trying to avoid collisions, the CSMA/CD scheme allows collisions to occur, detects them, and then takes necessary recovery actions.

A decentralized collision detection mechanism is used when a site transmits its packet through its output port, it also listens on its input port and compares the two signals. A collision is detected when a difference is found in the two signals. On detection of a collision, the site immediately stops transmitting the remaining data in the packet and sends a special signal, called a *jamming signal*, on the shared medium to notify all sites that a collision has occurred. On seeing the jamming signal, all sites discard the current packet. The sites whose packets collided retransmit their packets at some later time.

Note that, for ensuring that all collisions are detected, a lower bound on packet length is needed. To illustrate this, let us assume that the maximum propagation delay between two sites of a network is $t$. If the two sites start transmitting their packets almost at the same time, it will take at least time $t$ for the sites to start receiving the other site's packet data and to detect the collision. Hence if the packet size is so small that it takes less than time $t$ for a site to pump all its data on the network, the sites will not detect the collision because the two sites complete their packet transmission before they see the other site's packet data. However, any other site on the same network for which the propagation time from the two sites is less than $t$ will receive scrambled data of the packets of both the sites.

3. *Controlled retransmission mechanism.* After a collision, the packets that became corrupted due to the collision must be retransmitted. If all the transmitting stations whose packets were corrupted by the collision attempt to retransmit their packets immediately after the jamming signal, collision will probably occur again. To minimize repeated collisions and to achieve channel stability under overload conditions, a controlled retransmission strategy is used in which the competition for the shared medium is resolved using a decentralized algorithm.

Retransmission policies have two conflicting goals: (a) scheduling a retransmission quickly to get the packet out and maintain use of the shared medium and (b) voluntarily backing off to reduce the site's load on a busy medium. A retransmission algorithm is used to calculate the delay before a site should retransmit its packet. After a collision takes place, the objective is to obtain delay periods that will reschedule each site at times quantized in steps at least as large as a collision interval. This time quantization is called the *retransmission slot time*. To guarantee quick use of the medium, this slot time should be short; yet to avoid collisions it should be larger than a collision interval. Therefore, the slot time is usually set to be a little longer than the round-trip time of the medium. The real-time delay is the product of some retransmission delay $D$ (a positive integer) and the retransmission slot time ($S_t$).

A good example of the controlled retransmission mechanism is the binary exponential back-off algorithm used in Ethernet. This algorithm is described later in this chapter during the description of Ethernet (a case study of LAN technology).

The CSMA/CD scheme works best on networks having a bus topology with bursty asynchronous transmissions. It has gained favor for transmission media that have relatively low speeds (around 10 Mbps) mainly because of its ease of implementation and its channel utilization efficiency. Notice that the performance of the CSMA/CD scheme depends on the ratio of packet length to propagation delay. The higher the ratio, the better the performance because the propagation delay is the interval during which a packet is vulnerable to collision. After that interval, all sites will have "heard" the transmission and deferred. As this ratio diminishes, the collision frequency increases, causing significant performance degradation. Because this performance becomes more pronounced when the ratio of packet length to propagation delay is too low, CSMA/CD is unsuitable for high data rates and/or long distances. For instance, for a transmission medium having photonic speeds (hundreds of megabits per second or gigabits per second) the efficiency of CSMA/CD is often unacceptable.

In addition to being unsuitable for systems having high data rates, small-size packets, and long cable lengths, the CSMA/CD scheme has the following drawbacks: (a) It does not possess a bounded-delay property. Because the loading of the shared medium is variable, it is impossible to guarantee the delivery of a given message within any fixed time, since the network might be fully loaded when the message is ready for transmission. (b) It is not possible to provide priorities for the use of the shared transmission medium. Since all sites are equal, none have priority over others, even though some sites may require greater use of the facilities due to the nature of a particular application.

### The Token Ring Protocol

This scheme also employs decentralized control of the shared medium. In this scheme, access to the shared medium is controlled by using a single token that is circulated among the sites in the system. A *token* is a special type of message (having a unique bit pattern) that entitles its holder to use the shared medium for transmitting its messages. A special field in the token indicates whether it is free or busy. The token is passed from one site to the adjacent site around the ring in one direction. A site that has a message ready for transmission must wait until the token reaches it and it is free. When it receives the free token, it sets it to busy, attaches its message to the token, and transmits it to the next site in the ring. A receiving site checks the status of the token. If it is free, it uses it to transmit its own message. Otherwise, it checks to see if the message attached to the busy token is addressed to it. If it is, it retrieves the message attached to the token and forwards the token without the attached message to the next site in the ring. When the busy token returns to the sending site after one complete round, the site removes it from the ring, generates a new free token, and passes it to the next site, allowing the next site to transmit its message (if it has any). The free token circulates from one site to another until it reaches a site that has some message to transmit. To prevent a site from holding the token for a very long time, a token-holding timer is used to control the length of time for which a site may occupy the token.

To guarantee reliable operation, the token has to be protected against loss or duplication. That is, if the token gets lost due to a site failure, the system must detect the loss and generate a new token. This is usually done by the monitor site. Moreover, if a site $i$ crashes, the ring must be reconfigured so that site $i$–1 will send the token directly to site $i$+1.

An advantage of the token ring protocol is that the message delay can be bounded because of the absence of collisions. Another advantage is that it can work with both large and small packet size as well as variable-size packets. In principle, a message attached to the token may be of almost any length. A major disadvantage, however, is the initial waiting time to receive a free token even at very light loads. This initial waiting time could be appreciable, especially in large rings.

A variant of the token ring protocol described above is the IEEE 802.5 standard Token Ring protocol [IEEE 1985c]. This protocol is described later in this chapter during the description of IEEE Token Ring (a case study of LAN technology).

### The Slotted-Ring Protocol

In this scheme, a constant number of fixed-length message slots continuously circulate around the ring. Each slot has two parts—control and data. The control part usually has fields to specify whether the slot is full or empty, the source and destination addresses of the message contained in a full slot, and whether the message in it was successfully received at the destination. On the other hand, the data part can contain a fixed-length message data.

A site that wants to send a message first breaks down the message into packets of size equal to the size of the data part of the slots. It then waits for the arrival of an empty slot. As soon as an empty slot arrives, it grabs it, places one packet of its message in its data part, sets the source and destination addresses properly, sets the full/empty field to full, and puts it back on the ring. This slot then circulates on the ring and the site again waits for the arrival of another empty slot. The site continues doing this until it has transmitted all the packets of the message.

Each site inspects every full slot to check if it contains a packet addressed to it. If not, it simply forwards the slot to the next site on the ring. Otherwise, it removes the packet from the slot, properly alters the field in the slot showing that the message in the slot was successfully received at the destination, and then forwards the slot to the next site in the ring. When the slot returns back to its sender after completing its journey round the ring, the sender changes its full/empty field to *empty*, making it available for transmission of any other message in the system.

This scheme prevents hogging of the ring and guarantees fair sharing of the bandwidth of the shared medium among all sites. It also allows messages from multiple sites to be simultaneously transmitted (in the token ring scheme, only one site can transmit at a time). However, it requires a long message to be broken into smaller packets (this is not required in the token ring scheme).

The slotted-ring scheme is used in the Cambridge Ring [Wilkes and Wheeler 1979], which was developed at Cambridge University in the 1970s and is widely used in Britain. Further details of this protocol can be found in [King and Mitrani 1987].

### 2.3.3 LAN Technology Case Studies: Ethernet and IEEE Token Ring

#### Ethernet

Ethernet is the most widely used LAN technology for building distributed systems because it is relatively fast and economical. It was introduced by DEC (Digital Equipment Corporation), Intel, and Xerox in 1980, and subsequently, a slightly modified version of it was adopted by the IEEE as a standard LAN technology, known as the IEEE 802.3 standard [IEEE 1985a].

The network topology used for Ethernet is a simple multiaccess bus or a multiaccess branching bus topology. The communication medium used is low-loss coaxial cable having a data transfer rate of 10 Mbps.

A message is transmitted from one site to another by breaking it up into packets (called *frames* in Ethernet) and then by broadcasting the packets to the bus. An address designator is associated with each packet. As a packet travels on the bus, each site checks whether the packet is addressed to it and the addressee site picks up the message.

For medium-access control, Ethernet uses the CSMA/CD protocol with a *binary exponential back-off algorithm* as the controlled retransmission mechanism. In the binary exponential back-off algorithm of Ethernet, the value of retransmission delay ($D$) is selected as a random number from a particular retransmission interval between zero and some upper limit ($L$). That is, if the packets of two sites collide, one will retransmit after an interval of $X \times S_t$ ($S_t$ is the retransmission slot time) and the other will retransmit after an interval of $Y \times S_t$, where $X$ and $Y$ are likely to be different since they were chosen randomly. To control the shared medium and keep it stable under high load, the value of $L$ is doubled with each successive collision, thus extending the range for the random selection of the value of $D$. In Ethernet, on first collision, the value of $D$ is randomly chosen to be 0 or 1; on the second collision, it is randomly chosen to be 0, 1, 2, or 3; and on the $i$th successive collision, it is randomly chosen to be an integer in the range 0 and $2^i - 1$ (both inclusive). Thus, the more often that a sender fails (due to repeated collisions), the longer potential period of time it will defer before attempting to retransmit. This algorithm has very short retransmission delays at the beginning but will back off quickly, preventing the medium from becoming overloaded.

Notice that after some number of back-offs, the retransmission interval becomes large. To avoid undue delays and slow response to improved medium characteristics, the doubling of the retransmission interval is usually stopped at some point, with additional retransmissions still being drawn from this interval, before the transmission is finally aborted. This is referred to as the *truncated binary exponential back-off algorithm.*

The structure of a packet in Ethernet is shown in Figure 2.4. The destination and source addresses occupy 6 bytes each. The destination address may be a single-site address (specifies a single site), a multicast address (specifies a group of sites), or a broadcast address (specifies all sites). The address consisting of all 1's is the broadcast address. The sites that belong to a multicast address have their network interfaces configured to receive all packets addressed to the multicast address. Moreover, to distinguish multicast addresses from single-site addresses, the higher

| 6 bytes | 6 bytes | 2 bytes | 46 bytes ≤ length ≤ 1500 bytes | 4 bytes |
|---|---|---|---|---|
| Destination address | Source address | Type | Message data | Checksum |

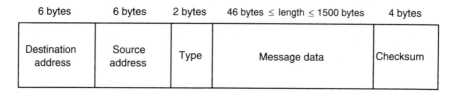

**Fig. 2.4** Structure of a packet in Ethernet.

order bit of a multicast address is always 1, whereas this bit of a single-site address is always 0.

The type field is used to distinguish among multiple types of packets. This field is used by higher layer communication protocols (communication protocol layers are described later in this chapter).

The message data field is the only field in the packet structure that may have variable length. It contains the actual message data to be transmitted. The length of this field may vary from 46 to 1500 bytes. The minimum length of 46 bytes for this field is necessary to ensure that collisions are always detected in the CSMA/CD scheme used for medium-access control. On the other hand, the maximum length of 1500 bytes for this field is used to allow each site in the network to allocate buffer space for the largest possible incoming packet and to avoid a sender site waiting for a long time for the communication channel to become free. Since there is no field to indicate the length of the message data field, an interval of 9.6 $\mu$s is used between the transmission of two packets to allow receiving sites to detect the end of transmission of a packet.

The last 4 bytes of a packet always contain a checksum generated by the sender and used by the receiver(s) to check the validity of the received packet. A receiver simply drops a packet that contains an incorrect checksum. Due to this, message delivery is not guaranteed in Ethernet. This is the reason why simple datagram protocols used in local networks are potentially unreliable. If guaranteed message delivery is needed, the upper layer of the communication protocol (communication protocol layers are described later in this chapter) must use acknowledgments for the receipt of each packet and timeout-based retransmissions for unacknowledged packets.

Every Ethernet hardware interface is assigned a unique address by the manufacturer. This allows all the sites of a set of interconnected Ethernets to have unique addresses. IEEE acts as an allocation authority for Ethernet addresses. A separate range of 48-bit addresses is allocated to each manufacturer of Ethernet hardware interfaces.

### IEEE Token Ring

Another commonly used LAN technology for building distributed systems is the IEEE Token Ring technology, known as the IEEE 802.5 standard [IEEE 1985b]. IBM has adopted this technology as a basis for its distributed system products.

The network topology used in the IEEE Token Ring technology is ring topology, and the medium-access control protocol used is the token ring protocol. Initially it operated at a speed of 4 Mbps but was later upgraded to 16 Mbps. It can use a cheap twisted pair or optical fiber as the communication medium and has almost no wasted bandwidth when all sites are trying to send.

A single token of 3 bytes keeps circulating continuously around the ring. The token may either be busy or free. A site willing to send a message attaches its message to the token and changes its status to busy, when the circulating token arrives at the sender's site with free status. Therefore, a busy token has a message packet attached to it whose structure is shown in Figure 2.5.

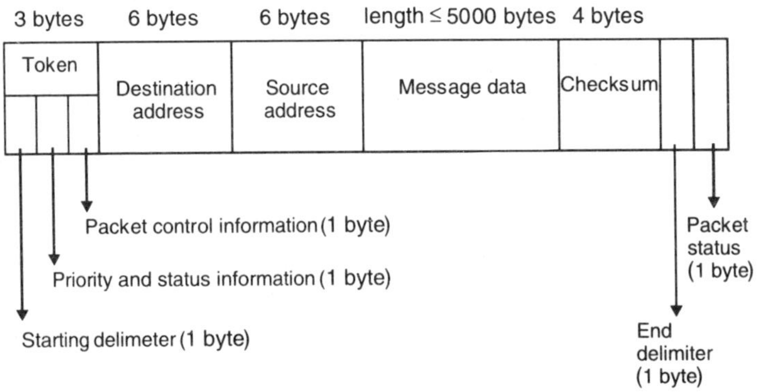


**Fig. 2.5** Structure of a packet in IEEE Token Ring.

The first byte of the token contains a fixed bit pattern that enables sites to recognize the start of a packet and synchronize to the data transmission rate. The second byte contains priority and token status (free/busy) information. The third byte contains packet control information. The priority field can be used to implement a variety of methods for sharing the channel capacity among the sites on the network.

In addition to the token, a packet in the IEEE Token Ring has fields for source and destination addresses (each 6 bytes long), message data (*length* ≤ 5000 *bytes*), checksum (4 bytes), end delimiter (1 byte), and packet status (1 byte). The source address and destination address fields respectively contain the addresses of the sending and receiving sites. The message data field contains the data to be transmitted. This field is of variable length and allows packets to be of almost any length. The upper bound of 5000 bytes for the length of this field is a default value for a parameter that can be configured on a per-installation basis. The checksum field contains a checksum generated by the sender and used by the receiver to check the validity of the received packet. The end-delimiter field contains a fixed bit pattern that enables sites to recognize the end of a packet. Finally, the packet status field specifies whether the packet was successfully received by the receiving site. This field helps the sending site in knowing whether its packet was received by the receiver. The sending site is responsible for removing its packet from the ring when it returns after one rotation.

## 2.4 WAN TECHNOLOGIES

A WAN of computers is constructed by interconnecting computers that are separated by large distances; they may be located in different cities or even in different countries. In general, no fixed regular network topology is used for interconnecting the computers of a WAN. Moreover, different communication media may be used for different links of a WAN. For example, in a WAN, computers located in the same country may be interconnected by coaxial cables (telephone lines), but communications satellites may be used to interconnect two computers that are located in different countries.

The computers of a WAN are not connected directly to the communication channels but are connected to hardware devices called *packet-switching exchanges* (*PSEs*), which are special-purpose computers dedicated to the task of data communication. Therefore, the communication channels of the network interconnect the PSEs, which actually perform the task of data communication across the network (Fig. 2.6). A computer of a WAN only interacts with the PSE of the WAN to which it is connected for sending and receiving messages from other computers on the WAN.

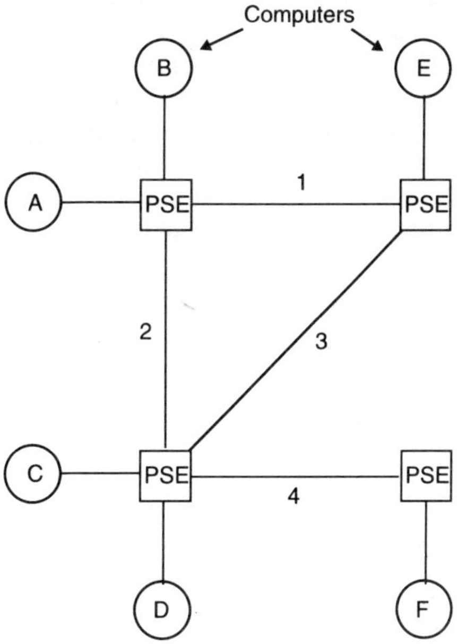


**Fig. 2.6** A WAN of computers.

To send a message packet to another computer on the network, a computer sends the packet to the PSE to which it is connected. The packet is transmitted from the sending computer's PSE to the receiving computer's PSE, possibly via other PSEs. The actual mode of packet transmission and the route used for forwarding a packet from its sending computer's PSE to its receiving computer's PSE depend on the switching and routing techniques used by the PSEs of the network. Various possible options for these techniques are described next. When the packet reaches its receiving computer's PSE, it is delivered to the receiving computer.

### 2.4.1 Switching Techniques

We saw that in a WAN communication is achieved by transmitting a packet from its source computer to its destination computer through two or more PSEs. The PSEs provide switching facility to move a packet from one PSE to another until the packet reaches its destination. That is, a PSE removes a packet from an input channel and places it on an output channel. Network latency is highly dependent on the switching technique used by the PSEs of the WAN. The two most commonly used schemes are circuit switching and packet switching. They are described next.

#### Circuit Switching

In this method, before data transmission starts, a physical circuit is constructed between the sender and receiver computers during the circuit establishment phase. During this phase, the channels constituting the circuit are reserved exclusively for the circuit; hence there is no need for buffers at the intermediate PSEs. Once the circuit is established, all packets of the data are transferred in the data transfer phase. Since all the packets of a message data are transmitted one after another through the dedicated circuit without being buffered at intermediate sites, the packets appear to form a continuous data stream. Finally, in the circuit termination phase, the circuit is torn down as the last packet of the data is transmitted. As soon as the circuit is torn down, the channels that were reserved for the circuit become available for use by others. If a circuit cannot be established because a desired channel is busy (being used), the circuit is said to be blocked. Depending on the way blocked circuits are handled, the partial circuit may be torn down, with establishment to be attempted later.

This scheme is similar to that used in the public telephone system. In this system, when a telephone call is made, a dedicated circuit is established by the telephone switching office from the caller's telephone to the callee's telephone. Once this circuit is established, the only delay involved in the communication is the time required for the propagation of the electromagnetic signal through all the wires and switches. While it might be hard to obtain a circuit sometimes (such as calling long distance on Christmas Day), once the circuit is established, exclusive access to it is guaranteed until the call is terminated.

The main advantage of a circuit-switching technique is that once the circuit is established, data is transmitted with no delay other than the propagation delay, which is negligible. Furthermore, since the full capacity of the circuit is available for exclusive use by the connected pair of computers, the transmission time required to send a message can be known and guaranteed after the circuit has been successfully established. However, the method requires additional overhead during circuit establishment and circuit disconnection phases, and channel bandwidths may be wasted if the channel capacities of the path forming the circuit are not utilized efficiently by the connected pair of computers.

Therefore, the method is considered suitable only for long continuous transmissions or for transmissions that require guaranteed maximum transmission delay. It is the preferred method for transmission of voice and real-time data in distributed applications.

Circuit switching is used in the Public Switched Telephone Network (PSTN).

### Packet Switching

In this method, instead of establishing a dedicated communication path between a sender and receiver pair (of computers), the channels are shared for transmitting packets of different sender-receiver pairs. That is, a channel is occupied by a sender-receiver pair only while transmitting a single packet of the message of that pair; the channel may then be used for transmitting either another packet of the same sender-receiver pair or a packet of some other sender-receiver pair.

In this method, each packet of a message contains the address of the destination computer, so that it can be sent to its destination independently of all other packets. Notice that different packets of the same message may take a different path through the network and, at the destination computer, the receiver may get the packets in an order different from the order in which they were sent. Therefore, at the destination computer, the packets have to be properly reassembled into a message. When a packet reaches a PSE, the packet is temporarily stored there in a packet buffer. The packet is then forwarded to a selected neighboring PSE when the next channel becomes available and the neighboring PSE has an available packet buffer. Hence the actual path taken by a packet to its destination is dynamic because the path is established as the packet travels along. Packet-switching technique is also known as *store-and-forward* communication because every packet is temporarily stored by each PSE along its route before it is forwarded to another PSE.

As compared to circuit switching, packet switching is suitable for transmitting small amounts of data that are bursty in nature. The method allows efficient usage of channels because the communication bandwidth of a channel is shared for transmitting several messages. Furthermore, the dynamic selection of the actual path to be taken by a packet gives the network considerable reliability because failed PSEs or channels can be ignored and alternate paths may be used. For example, in the WAN of Figure 2.6, if channel 2 fails, a message from computer A to D can still be sent by using the path 1–3. However, due to the need to buffer each packet at every PSE and to reassemble the packets at the destination computer, the overhead incurred per packet is large. Therefore, the method is inefficient for transmitting large messages. Another drawback of the method is that there is no guarantee of how long it takes a message to go from its source computer to its destination computer because the time taken for each packet depends on the route chosen for that packet, along with the volume of data being transferred along that route.

Packet switching is used in the X.25 public packet network and the Internet.

## 2.4.2 Routing Techniques

In a WAN, when multiple paths exist between the source and destination computers of a packet, any one of the paths may be used to transfer the packet. For example, in the WAN of Figure 2.6, there are two paths between computers E and F: 3–4 and

1–2–4—and any one of the two may be used to transmit a packet from computer E to F. The selection of the actual path to be used for transmitting a packet is determined by the routing technique used. An efficient routing technique is crucial to the overall performance of the network. This requires that the routing decision process must be as fast as possible to reduce the network latency. A good routing algorithm should be easily implementable in hardware. Furthermore, the decision process usually should not require global state information of the network because such information gathering is a difficult task and creates additional traffic in the network. Routing algorithms are usually classified based on the following three attributes:

- Place where routing decisions are made
- Time constant of the information upon which the routing decisions are based
- Control mechanism used for dynamic routing

Note that routing techniques are not needed in LANs because the sender of a message simply puts the message on the communication channel and the receiver takes it off from the channel. There is no need to decide the path to be used for transmitting the message from the sender to the receiver.

### Place Where Routing Decisions Are Made

Based on this attribute, routing algorithms may be classified into the following three types:

1. *Source routing*. In this method, the source computer's PSE selects the entire path before sending the packet. That is, all intermediate PSEs via which the packet will be transferred to its destination are decided at the source computer's PSE of the packet, and this routing information is included along with the packet. The method requires that the source computer's PSE must have fairly comprehensive information about the network environment. However, the routing decision process is efficient because the intermediate PSEs need not make any routing decision. A drawback of the method is that the path cannot be changed after the packet has left the source computer's PSE, rendering the method susceptible to component failures.

2. *Hop-by-hop routing*. In this method, each PSE along the path decides only the next PSE for the path. That is, each PSE maintains information about the status of all its outgoing channels and the adjacent PSEs and then selects a suitable adjacent PSE for the packet and transmits it to that PSE. The routing decisions are typically based on the channel availability and the readiness of the adjacent PSEs to receive and relay the packet. The method requires that each PSE must maintain a routing table of some sort. However, as compared to the static routing method, this method makes more efficient use of network bandwidth and provides resilience to failures because alternative paths can be used for packet transmissions.

3. *Hybrid routing*. This method combines the first two methods in the sense that the source computer's PSE specifies only certain major intermediate PSEs of the complete path, and the subpaths between any two of the specified PSEs are decided by the method of hop-by-hop routing.

### Static and Dynamic Routing

Depending on when the information used for making routing decisions is specified and how frequently it is modified, routing algorithms are classified into the following two types:

1. *Static routing*. In this method, routing tables (stored at PSEs) are set once and do not change for very long periods of time. They are changed only when the network undergoes major modifications. Static routing is also known as *fixed* or *deterministic routing*. Static routing is simple and easy to implement. However, it makes poor use of network bandwidth and causes blocking of a packet even when alternative paths are available for its transmission. Hence, static routing schemes are susceptible to component failures.

2. *Dynamic routing*. In this method, routing tables are updated relatively frequently, reflecting shorter term changes in the network environment. Dynamic routing strategy is also known as *adaptive routing* because it has a tendency to adapt to the dynamically changing state of the network, such as the presence of faulty or congested channels. Dynamic routing schemes can use alternative paths for packet transmissions, making more efficient use of network bandwidth and providing resilience to failures. The latter property is particularly important for large-scale architectures, since expanding network size can increase the probability of encountering a faulty network component. In dynamic routing, however, packets of a message may arrive out of order at the destination computer. This problem can be solved by appending a sequence number to each packet and properly reassembling the packets at the destination computer.

The path selection policy for dynamic routing may either be *minimal* or *nonminimal*. In the minimal policy, the selected path is one of the shortest paths between the source and destination pair of computers. Therefore, every channel visited will bring the packet closer to the destination. On the other hand, in the nonminimal policy, a packet may follow a longer path, usually in response to current network conditions. If the nonminimal policy is used, care must be taken to avoid a situation in which the packet will continue to be routed through the network but never reach the destination.

### Control Mechanisms for Dynamic Routing

In the dynamic routing strategy, routing tables are constantly updated. One of the following three approaches may be used for controlling the update action:

1. *Isolated manner*. In this approach, individual PSEs update the information in their local routing table in an isolated manner, perhaps by periodically trying various routes and observing performance.

2. *Centralized manner.* In this method, changes in the network environment, connectivity, or performance are constantly reported to one centralized PSE. Based on the information received, the global routing table maintained at the centralized PSE is constantly updated. The updated routing table information is periodically sent from the centralized PSE to the source PSEs (in the source-routing strategy) or to all PSEs (in the hop-by-hop routing strategy).

The main advantages of the centralized approach are that the routes are globally optimal and other PSEs are not involved in the information gathering of the global network status. However, the centralized approach suffers from poor performance in situations where the system is large or where traffic changes are frequent. Also, it has poor reliability since the table construction is performed at a single PSE.

3. *Decentralized manner.* To overcome the shortcomings of the centralized approach, several systems use the distributed control mechanism. In this method, each PSE maintains a routing table and the routing table updates are performed by mutual interaction among the PSEs. Often a PSE piggybacks the routing table update information along with some other message being sent to another PSE.

## 2.5 COMMUNICATION PROTOCOLS

In the last several sections of this chapter we saw that several types of agreements are needed between the communicating parties in a computer network. For example, it is important that the sender and receiver of a packet agree upon the positions and sizes of the various fields in the packet header, the position and size of actual data in the packet, the position and size of the checksum field, the method to calculate the checksum for error detection and so on. For transmission of message data comprised of multiple packets, the sender and receiver must also agree upon the method used for identifying the first packet and the last packet of the message, and since the last packet may only be partially filled, a method is needed to identify the last bit of the message in this packet. Moreover, agreement is also needed for handling duplicate messages, avoiding buffer overflows, and assuring proper message sequencing. All such agreements, needed for communication between the communicating parties, are defined in terms of rules and conventions by network designers. The term *protocol* is used to refer to a set of such rules and conventions.

Computer networks are implemented using the concept of *layered protocols*. According to this concept, the protocols of a network are organized into a series of layers in such a way that each layer contains protocols for exchanging data and providing functions in a logical sense with peer entities at other sites in the network. Entities in adjacent layers interact in a physical sense through the common interface defined between the two layers by passing parameters such as headers, trailers, and data parameters. The main reasons for using the concept of layered protocols in network design are as follows:

- The protocols of a network are fairly complex. Designing them in layers makes their implementation more manageable.

- Layering of protocols provides well-defined interfaces between the layers, so that a change in one layer does not affect an adjacent layer. That is, the various functionalities can be partitioned and implemented independently so that each one can be changed as technology improves without the other ones being affected. For example, a change to a routing algorithm in a network control program should not affect the functions of message sequencing, which is located in another layer of the network architecture.
- Layering of protocols also allows interaction between functionally paired layers in different locations. This concept aids in permitting the distribution of functions to remote sites.

The terms *protocol suite*, *protocol family*, or *protocol stack* are used to refer to the collection of protocols (of all layers) of a particular network system.

### 2.5.1 Protocols for Network Systems

In Chapter 1 we saw that distributed systems are basically different from network systems. Therefore, the requirements of communication protocols of these two types of systems are also different. The basic goal of communication protocols for network systems is to allow remote computers to communicate with each other and to allow users to access remote resources. On the other hand, the basic goal of communication protocols for distributed systems is not only to allow users to access remote resources but to do so in a transparent manner.

Several standards and protocols for network systems are already available. However, protocols for distributed systems are still in their infancy and no standards are yet available. Some standard network protocol models are described next. The protocols for distributed systems are presented in the next section.

#### The ISO/OSI Reference Model

The number of layers, the name of each layer, and the functions of each layer may be different for different networks. However, to make the job of the network communication protocol designers easier, the International Standardization Organization (ISO) has developed a reference model that identifies seven standard layers and defines the jobs to be performed at each layer. This model is called the *Open System International Reference Model* (abbreviated *OSI model*) [DePrycker et al. 1993, Larmouth 1993, Stallings 1993c]. It is a guide, not a specification. It provides a framework in which standards can be developed for the services and protocols at each layer. Note that adherence to standard protocols is important for designing open distributed systems. This is because if standard protocols are used, separate software components of distributed systems can be developed independently on computers having different architectures (different code ordering and data representations). To provide an understanding of the structure and functioning of layered network protocols, a brief description of the OSI model is presented next. There are many sources for more detail on this model [Tanenbaum 1988, Stallings 1993c, Larmouth 1993].

The architecture of the OSI model is shown in Figure 2.7. It is a seven-layer architecture in which a separate set of protocols is defined for each layer. Thus each layer has an independent function and deals with one or more specific aspects of the communication. The roles of the seven layers are briefly described below.

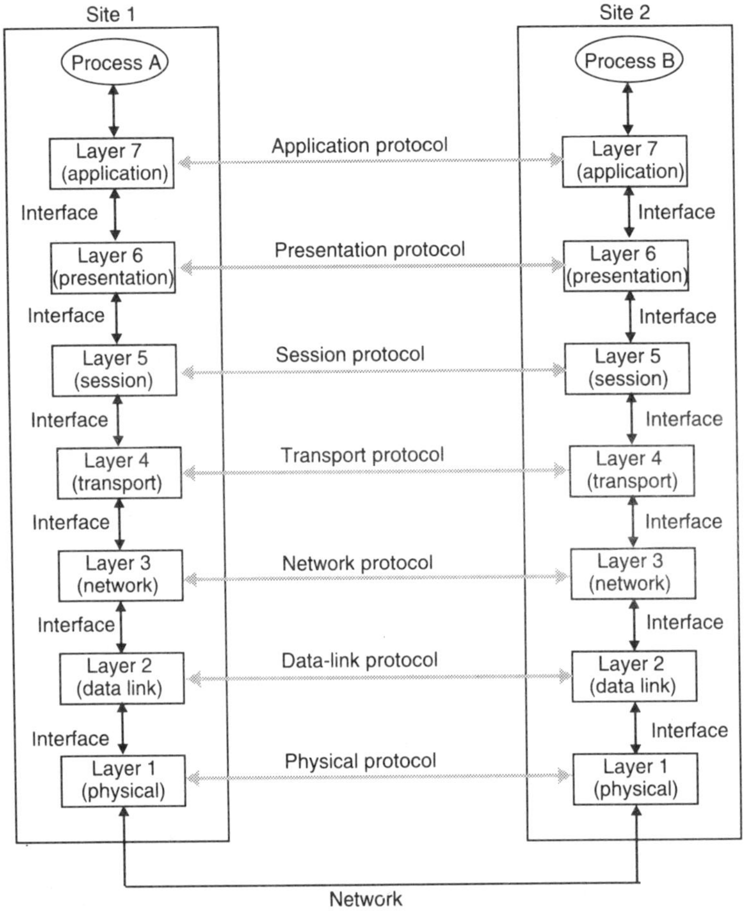


**Fig. 2.7** Layers, interfaces, and protocols in the OSI model.

***Physical Layer.*** The physical layer is responsible for transmitting raw bit streams between two sites. That is, it may convert the sequence of binary digits into electric signals, light signals, or electromagnetic signals depending on whether the two sites are on a cable circuit, fiber-optic circuit, or microwave/radio circuit, respectively. Electrical details such as how many volts to use for 0 and 1, how many bits can be sent per second, and whether transmission can take place only in one direction or in both directions simultaneously are also decided by the physical layer protocols. In addition, the physical layer protocols also deal with the mechanical details such as the size and shape of the connecting plugs, the number of pins in the plugs, and the function of each pin. In short, the physical layer protocols deal with the mechanical, electrical, procedural, and functional characteristics of transmission of raw bit streams between two sites. RS232–C is a popular physical layer standard for serial communication lines.

***Data-Link Layer.*** The physical layer simply transmits the data from the sender's site to the receiver's site as raw bits. It is the responsibility of the data-link layer to detect and correct any errors in the transmitted data. Since the physical layer is only concerned with a raw bit stream, the data-link layer partitions it into frames so that error detection and correction can be performed independently for each frame. The data-link layer also performs flow control of frames between two sites to ensure that a sender does not overwhelm a receiver by sending frames at a rate faster than the receiver can process. Therefore, the error control and flow control mechanisms of a network form the data-link layer protocols in the OSI model. Notice that the data-link layer and physical layer protocols establish an error-free communication of raw bits between two sites.

***Network Layer.*** The network layer is responsible for setting up a logical path between two sites for communication to take place. It encapsulates frames into packets that can be transmitted from one site to another using a high-level addressing and routing scheme. That is, routing is the primary job of the network layer and the routing algorithm forms the main part of the network layer protocols of the network.

Two popular network layer protocols are the *X.25 Protocol* and the *Internet Protocol* (called *IP*). The X.25 is a *connection-oriented protocol* that is based on the concept of establishing a virtual circuit between the sender and receiver before the actual communication starts between them. In this protocol, a request for connection is first sent to the destination, which can either be accepted or rejected. If the connection is accepted, the requesting party is given a connection identifier to use in subsequent requests. During the connection establishment phase, a route between the two parties is also decided that is used for the transmission of subsequent traffic.

On the other hand, IP is a *connectionless protocol* in which no connection is established between the sender and receiver before sending a message. Therefore, each packet of the message is transmitted independently and may take a different route. IP is part of the DoD (U.S. Department of Defense) protocol suite.

Notice that the functions performed at the network layer are primarily required in WANs. In a single LAN, the network layer is largely redundant because packets can be transmitted directly from any site on the network to any other site. Therefore the network layer, if present, has little work to do.

***Transport Layer.*** The job of the transport layer is to provide site-to-site communication and to hide all the details of the communication subnet from the session layer by providing a network-independent transport service. Using this service, all the details of the communication subnet are sealed and one subnet can be replaced with another without disturbing the layers above the transport layer.

In particular, the transport layer accepts messages of arbitrary length from the session layer, segments them into packets, submits them to the network layer for transmission, and finally reassembles the packets at the destination. Some packets may be lost on the way from the sender to the receiver, and depending on the routing algorithms used in the network layer, packets may arrive at the destination in a sequence that is different from the order in which they are sent. The transport layer protocols include mechanisms for handling lost and out-of-sequence packets. For this, the transport layer records a sequence number in each packet and uses the sequence numbers for detecting lost packets and for ensuring that messages are reconstructed in the correct sequence.

The ISO model provides five classes of transport protocols (known as *TP0* through *TP4*) which basically differ in their ability to handle errors. TP0 is the least powerful one and TP4 is the most powerful one. The choice of which one to use depends on the properties of the underlying network layer.

The two most popular transport layer protocols are the *Transport Control Protocol* (TCP) and the *User Datagram Protocol* (UDP). Both are implemented in the DARPA protocol suite of DARPA Internet. TCP is a connection-oriented transport protocol that provides the same services as TP4 of the ISO model. It uses end-to-end mechanisms to ensure reliable, ordered delivery of data over a logical connection. These goals are basically achieved by using packet sequence numbers and positive acknowledgments with timeout and retransmission.

The UDP is a connectionless transport protocol. It is an unreliable protocol because, when it is used, message packets can be lost, duplicated, or arrive out of order. Therefore, only those applications that do not need reliable communication should use UDP.

***Session Layer.*** The purpose of the session layer is to provide the means by which presentation entities can organize and synchronize their dialog and manage their data exchange. It allows the two parties to authenticate each other before establishing a dialog session between them. It also specifies dialog type—one way, two way alternate, or two way simultaneous–and initiates a dialog session if the message is a connection request message. The other services of the session layer include quarantine service, dialog control, and priority management. The quarantine service buffers a group of messages on the receiving side until the session layer on the sending side explicitly releases them. This is useful in database applications where a transaction (consisting of a group of messages) needs to be an atomic unit. The dialog control is useful for dialog sessions in which the user primitives used for sending and receiving messages are of the nonblocking type. In this case, the user may have multiple requests outstanding on the same session, and replies may come back in an order different from that in which the requests were sent. The dialog control reorders replies according to the order of requests. The priority management service is useful for giving priority to important and time-bound messages over normal, less-important messages. The session layer is not required for connectionless communication.

***Presentation Layer.*** The purpose of this layer is to represent message information to communicating application layer entities in a way that preserves meaning while resolving syntax differences. For this, the presentation layer may perform one or more of the following types of transformations on message data:

- A message usually contains structured information that may include any of the data types used in programming languages—integers, characters, arrays, records, and so on, including user-defined data types. Translation is therefore required where language systems or application programs in the source and destination computers use different representations for these data types.
- Data format conversions are also needed to transfer data between computers when the hardware of the sending and receiving computers uses different data representations. In this case, the presentation layer software in the sending computer transforms message data from the formats used in its own computer to a set of standard network representations called *eXternal Data Representation* (*XDR*) before transmission. The presentation layer software in the receiving computer transforms the message data from the network representations to the formats used in its own computer.
- For applications dealing with confidential or secret data, the presentation layer software in the sending computer encrypts message data before passing it to the session layer. On the receiver side, the encrypted message data is decrypted by the presentation layer before being passed on to the application layer.
- In a similar manner, when message data is large in volume (such as multimedia data) or with networks that are slow or heavily loaded, message data may be compressed and decompressed by the presentation layer software in the sending and receiving computers, respectively.

***Application Layer.*** The application layer provides services that directly support the end users of the network. Obviously, the functionality implemented at this layer of the architecture is application-specific. Since each application has different communication needs, no fixed or standard set of application layer protocols can meet the needs of all applications. Therefore, the application layer is basically a collection of miscellaneous protocols for various commonly used applications such as electronic mail, file transfer, remote login, remote job entry, and schemas for distributed databases. Some popular application layer protocols are X.400 (Electronic Mail Protocol), X.500 (Directory Server Protocol), FTP (File Transfer Protocol), and rlogin (Remote Login Protocol).

---

In actual implementation, of the seven layers, the first three layers are likely to be in hardware, the next two layers in the operating system, the presentation layer in library subroutines in the user's address space, and the application layer in the user's program.

***Example of Message Transfer in the OSI Model.*** To illustrate the functions of the various layers of the OSI model, let us consider a simple example of message transmission. With reference to Figure 2.8, let us assume that a process at the sending site wants to send a message $M$ to a process at the receiving site. The sending site's process builds the message $M$ and passes it to the application layer (layer 7) on its machine. The application layer software adds a header ($H_7$) to $M$ and passes the resulting message to the presentation layer (6) via the interface between layers 7 and 6. The presentation layer software performs text compression, code conversion, security encryption, and so on, on the received message, and after adding a header ($H_6$) to it,

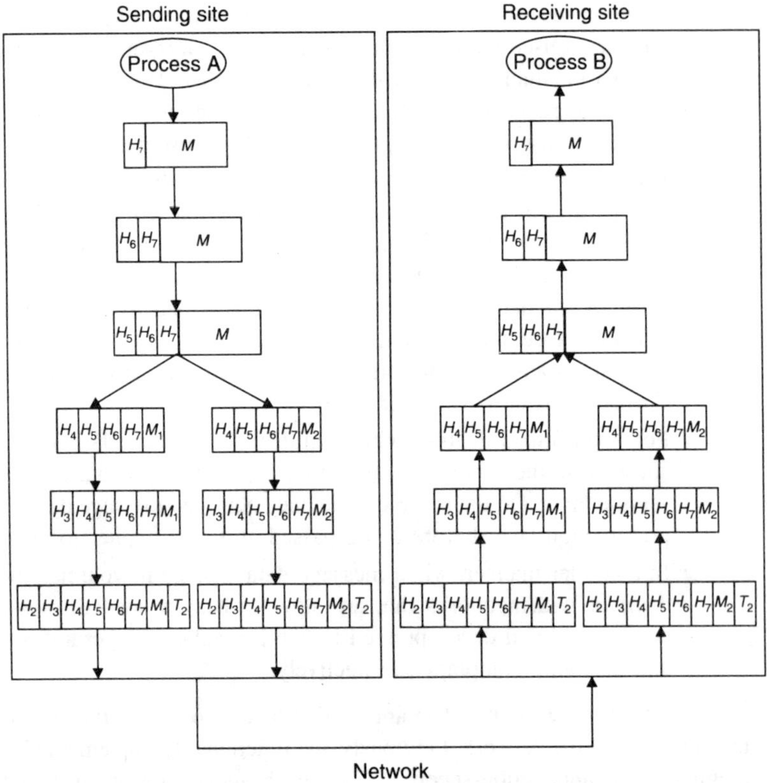


**Fig. 2.8** An example illustrating transfer of message M from sending site to receiving site in the OSI model: $H_n$, header added by layer $n$; $T_n$, trailer added by layer $n$.

it passes the resulting message on to the session layer (5). Depending on the type of dialog, the session layer software establishes a dialog between the sender and the receiver processes. It also regulates the direction of message flow. A header ($H_5$) is added to the message at this layer, and the resulting message is passed on to the transport layer (4). The transport layer software now splits the message into smaller units ($M_1$ and $M_2$) called packets and adds a header ($H_4$) to each packet. These headers contain the sequence numbers of the message packets. The packets are then passed on to the network layer (3). The network layer software makes routing decisions for the received packets and sets up a logical path between the sending and receiving sites for transmission of the packets. It then adds a header ($H_3$) to each packet and passes them on to the data-link layer (2). The data-link layer software adds a header ($H_2$) and a trailer ($T_2$) to each of these packets. The trailers contain the checksum of the data in the corresponding packets. The resulting message units are called frames, which are passed on to the physical layer (1). The physical layer software simply transmits the raw bits from the sender's machine to the receiver's machine using the physical connection between the two machines.

On the receiver's machine, the message data traverses up from the physical layer to the application layer. As the message data traverses to higher level layers, each layer performs the functions assigned to it and strips off the headers or trailers added by its peer layer at the sending site. For example, the data-link layer at the receiving machine performs error detection by recalculating the checksum for each frame and comparing it with the checksum in the trailer of the frame. It strips off the header ($H_2$) and the trailer ($T_2$) from the frames before passing them on to the network layer. The application layer of the receiver's machine finally passes on the message in its original form to the communicating process on the receiver's site. Notice that the software of a particular layer on the sending machine conceptually communicates only with its peer layer on the receiving machine, although physically it communicates only with the adjacent layers on the sending machine. This abstraction is crucial to network design.

### The IEEE 802 LAN Reference Model

The ISO model is oriented toward WANs rather than LANs because it was conceived as a model for computer networking primarily in the point-to-point packet-switching environment. In a LAN, the host computers are connected directly to a network circuit by relatively simple interface hardware. The interface hardware and network driver software in each site can send and receive data at high speeds with low error rates and without switching delays. These important characteristics of LANs give considerable advantages in cost, speed, and reliability in comparison to WANs. Due to these differences in characteristics between LANs and WANs, and also because of the following differences between the OSI model and LAN concepts, the OSI model is generally considered to be unsuitable for LAN environments:

- In the OSI model, information is exchanged between two communicating entities only after they have entered into an agreement about exchanging information. But in a LAN, no such prior agreement is needed for communication to take place, and information may be delivered to a destination from a number of different sources within a short time interval.
- In the OSI model, the model of communication is generally one to one and/or one to many. But in a LAN, the model of communication is generally many to many.
- The OSI model is often said to be connection oriented. But communications in a LAN is mostly connectionless.

This implies that a modified reference model particularly suited to LANs is needed. This problem was realized long ago, and a reference model suitable for LANs was built by IEEE in 1983, the *IEEE 802 LAN Reference Model* (abbreviated IEEE 802 LAN) [IEEE 1990]. The IEEE 802 LAN model was built with an aim to use as much as possible of the OSI model while providing compatibility between LAN equipments made by different manufacturers such that data communication can take place between these equipments with the minimum effort on the part of the users or builders of LANs. Therefore, the IEEE 802 LAN model modifies only the lowest two layers of the OSI model and does not include specifications for higher layers, suggesting the use of the OSI model protocols at higher layers. The modifications of the lowest two layers are mainly concerned with the most important features of LANs that result from the fact that the physical medium is a resource shared by all sites connected to it. The relationship between the IEEE 802 LAN model and the OSI model is shown in Figure 2.9.

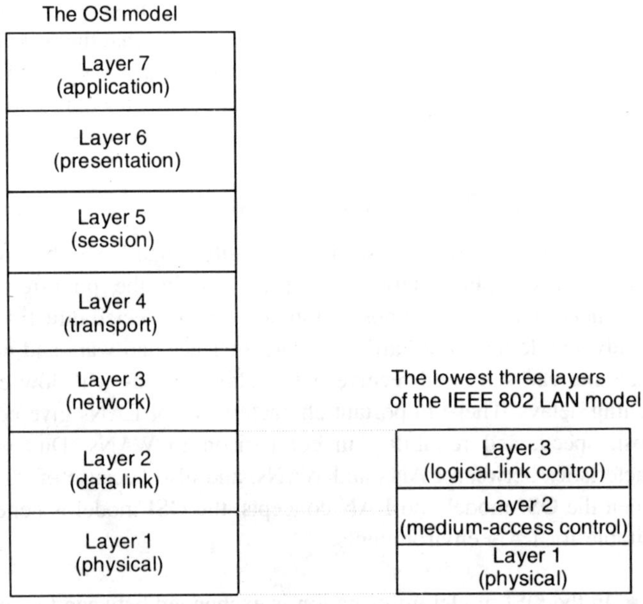


**Fig. 2.9** Relationship between the IEEE 802 LAN model and the OSI model.

As shown in the figure, the lowest three layers of the IEEE 802 LAN model are the physical layer, the medium-access-control layer, and the logical-link-control layer. The physical layer defines interface protocols for the following four types of media that are commonly used in LANs: baseband, broadband, fiber optics, and twisted pair. As the name implies, the medium-access-control layer deals with the medium-access-control protocols for LANs. This layer includes functions associated with both the physical and data-link layers of the OSI model. It includes the following four standards:

1. The IEEE 802.3 standard, which defines protocols for a LAN having bus topology that uses the CSMA/CD method for medium-access control.
2. The IEEE 802.4 standard, which defines protocols for a LAN having bus topology that uses the token-passing method for medium-access control. The sites connected to the bus are arranged in a logical ring to use the token-passing method.

3. The IEEE 802.5 standard, which defines protocols for a LAN having ring topology that uses the token-passing method for medium-access control.
4. The IEEE 802.6 standard, which defines protocols for a MAN.

The third layer, that is, the logical-link-control layer, contains the IEEE 802.2 standard. This standard basically defines a common logical-link-control protocol that can be used in conjunction with each of the four standards defined at the media-access-control layer.

Finally, the relationship between the protocols defined in the OSI model and the standards defined in the IEEE 802 LAN model is described in the IEEE 802.1 standard. Further details on the IEEE 802 LAN model can be found in [IEEE 1990, 1985a,b,c].

### Network Communication Protocol Case Study: The Internet Protocol Suite

Several protocol suites for network systems, such as the IP suite of the U.S. Department of Defense, Xerox Networking System (XNS) of Xerox, System Network Architecture (SNA) of IBM, Advanced Peer-to-Peer Networking (APPN) of IBM, and NetBIOS of IBM, are available today. Of the available protocol suites for network systems, IP is the most popular and widely used one because it has several attractive features. For instance, it is suitable for both LANs and WANs; it can be implemented on all types of computers, from personal computers to the larger supercomputers; and it is not vendor specific. It is an open standard governed by the nonaligned (vendor-independent) Internet Engineering Task Force (IETF). Every major vendor supports IP, making it the lingua franca on networking. Moreover, IP is such a dominant networking standard that companies in a position to use it as their backbone protocol will be able to move quickly to high-speed internetworking technologies like ATM, FDDI, switched Ethernet and Token Ring, or 100-Mbps Ethernet. Owing to its importance and wide popularity, IP is described below as a case study of protocol suites for network systems.

Figure 2.10 shows the structure of the IP suite. It consists of five layers and several protocols at each layer. The existence of multiple protocols in one layer allows greater flexibility to the users due to different protocols for different applications having different communication requirements. The protocols of each layer are briefly described next.

| Layers | Protocols at each layer |
|---|---|
| Application | FTP, TFTP, TELNET, SMTP, DNS, others |
| Transport | TCP, UDP |
| Network | IP, ICMP |
| Data link | ARP, RARP, others |
| Physical | SLIP, Ethernet, Token Ring, others |

**Fig. 2.10** The Internet Protocol suite structure.

***Physical Layer Protocols.*** Most systems using the IP suite for a LAN use the Ethernet protocol at the physical layer. However, LAN products using the IP suite with the Token Ring protocol used at the physical layer are also available. Moreover, implementations using the *SLIP* (*Serial Line Internet Protocol*), which uses an RS-232 serial line protocol (having speeds from 1200 bits per second to 19.2 Kbps), also exist. Networks using the IP suite with physical layer protocols for satellite and microwave links also exist.

***Data-link Layer Protocols.*** Every protocol suite defines some type of addressing for uniquely identifying each computer on a network. In the IP suite, a computer's address (called *Internet address* or *IP address*) consists of the following information:

1. *Net number.* Each network using the Internet protocol suite has a unique net number that is assigned by a central authority—the Network Information Center (NIC) located at SRI International.
2. *Subnet number.* This is an optional number representing the subnet to which the computer being addressed is attached. This number is assigned by a user to the subnet when the subnet is being set up. The subnet number is stated in the IP address of a computer only when the computer is on a subnet.
3. *Host number.* This number uniquely identifies the computer being addressed on the network identified by a net number.

All this information is represented by a 32-bit address divided into four 8-bit fields. Each field is called an *octet.* Each octet is separated from the next octet by a period. The decimal number represents 1 byte of the IP address, which can have a value of 0–255. Therefore, a typical IP address is 190.40.232.12.

There are three classes of Internet address—A, B, and C—plus a provision for Internet multicast communication that is useful for applications that need multicast facility. The format and the permissible values for each octet for each class of Internet address are shown in Figure 2.11. Due to the increasing importance of multicast-based applications, a group of user organizations has established a multicast network called *MBone* (*Multicast Backbone*) that is a virtual network in the Internet that multicasts audio, video, white-board, and other streams that need to be distributed to large groups simultaneously [Macedonia and Brutzman 1994]. MBone addresses such network issues as bandwidth constraints, routing protocols, data compression, and network topology. Many application tools are available free of cost for a wide variety of host platforms. Today, hundreds of researchers use MBone to develop protocols and applications for group communication.

The three classes of Internet addresses are designed to meet the requirements of different types of organizations. Thus class A addresses are used for those networks that need to accommodate a large number of computers (hosts) on a single network, while class C addresses allow for more networks but fewer hosts per network, and class B addresses provide a median distribution between number of networks and number of hosts per network. Notice from Figure 2.11 that there can be only 127 class A networks, and the

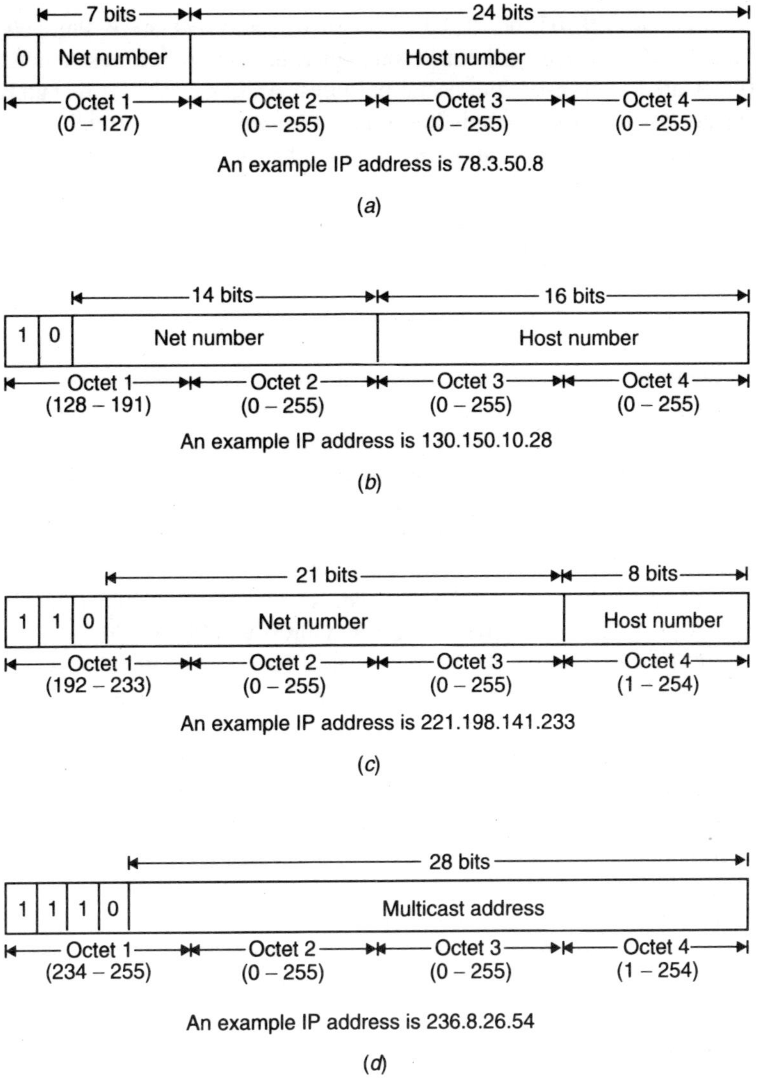


**Fig. 2.11** Internet address formats: Internet address for (*a*) class A, (*b*) class B, and (*c*) class C networks.

highest host address in a class A network can be 255.255.254, thus accommodating a possible 16,777,214 hosts. On the other hand, a class C network can accommodate only 254 hosts.

Values from 0 to 255 can be assigned to each octet for the host number part of an address, with the restriction that the host number part cannot be all 0's or all 1's. That is, for example, on a network having a net address of 78, a host could have the address 78.15.0.105 or 78.1.1.255 but it could not have the address 78.0.0.0 or 78.255.255.255. This is because Internet addresses with a host number part that is all 0's or all 1's are used for special purposes. Addresses with host number part set to all 0's are used to refer to "this host," and a host number set to all 1's is used to address a broadcast message to all of the hosts connected to the network specified in the net number part of the address.

A *multihomed host* is one that is connected to two or more networks. This implies that it must have two or more Internet addresses, one for each network to which it is connected. This means that every Internet address specifies a unique host but each host does not have a unique address.

Each packet received by the data-link layer from the network layer contains the IP addresses of the sender and receiver hosts. These IP addresses must be converted to physical network addresses for transmission across the network. Similarly, physical network addresses embedded in packets received from other networks must be converted to IP addresses before being passed on to the network layer. The job of translating IP addresses to physical network addresses and physical network addresses to IP addresses is performed by the data-link layer. Two important protocols that belong to this layer are ARP and RARP. *ARP* (*Address Resolution Protocol*) [Plummer 1982] is the Ethernet address resolution protocol that maps known IP addresses (32 bits long) to Ethernet addresses (48 bits long). On the other hand, *RARP* (*Reverse ARP*) [Finlayson et al. 1984] is the IP address resolution protocol that maps known Ethernet addresses (48 bits) to IP addresses (32 bits), the reverse of ARP.

***Network Layer Protocols.*** The two network layer protocols are IP [Postel 1981a] and *ICMP* (*Internet Control Message Protocol*) [Postel 1981b]. IP performs the transmission of datagrams from one host to another. A *datagram* is a group of information transmitted as a unit to and from the upper layer protocols on sending and receiving hosts. It contains the IP addresses of sending and receiving hosts. For datagram transmission, the two main jobs of IP are fragmentation and reassembly of datagrams into IP packets and routing of IP packets by determining the actual path to be taken by each packet from its source to the destination. For packet routing, a dynamic routing algorithm that uses a minimal path selection policy is used.

On the sending host, when a datagram is received at the network layer from the transport layer, the IP attaches a 20-byte header. This header contains a number of parameters, most significantly the IP addresses of the sending and receiving hosts. Other parameters include datagram length and identify information if the datagram exceeds the allowable byte size for network packets [called *MTU* (*maximum transfer unit*) of the network] and must be fragmented. If a datagram is found to be larger than the allowable byte size for network packets, the IP breaks up the datagram into fragments and sends each fragment as an IP packet. When fragmentation does occur, the IP duplicates the source address and destination address into each IP packet, so that the resulting IP packets can be delivered independently of each other. The fragments are reassembled into the original datagram by the IP on the receiving host and then passed on to the higher protocol layers.

The data transmission service of the IP has *best-effort delivery* semantics. That is, a best effort is made to deliver the packets but delivery is not guaranteed. The IP computes and verifies a checksum that covers its own header, which is inexpensive to calculate. There is no data checksum, which avoids overheads when crossing routers, but leaves the higher level protocols to provide their own checksums. On the receiving host, if the checksum of the header is found to be in error, the packet is discarded, with the assumption that a higher layer protocol will retransmit the packet. Hence, the data transmission service of the IP is unreliable.

The ICMP of the network layer provides an elementary form of flow control. When IP packets arrive at a host or router so fast that they are discarded, the ICMP sends a message to the original source informing it that the data is arriving too fast, which then decreases the amount of data being sent on that connection link.

***Transport Layer Protocols.*** Transport layer protocols enable communications between processes running on separate computers of a network. The two main protocols of this layer are *TCP* (*Transport Control Protocol*) [Postel 1981c] and *UDP* (*User Datagram Protocol*) [Postel 1980]. These two protocols are sometimes referred to as *TCP/IP* and *UDP/IP*, respectively, to indicate that they use the IP at the network layer.

The TCP provides a connection-oriented, reliable, byte-stream service to an application program. It is a reliable protocol because any data written to a TCP connection will be received by its peer or an error indication will be given. Since the IP of the network layer provides an unreliable, connectionless delivery service, it is the TCP that contains the logic necessary to provide a reliable, virtual circuit for a user process. Therefore, TCP handles the establishment and termination of connections between processes, the sequencing of data that might be received out of order, the end-to-end reliability (checksum, positive acknowledgments, timeouts), and the end-to-end flow control. Note that the ICMP of the network layer does not provide end-to-end flow control service between two communicating processes. TCP is used in most of the well-known Internet services that are defined at the application layer.

On the other hand, UDP provides a connectionless, unreliable datagram service. It is an unreliable protocol because no attempt is made to recover from failure or loss; packets may be lost, with no error indication given. Therefore, UDP is very similar to IP with two additional features that are not provided by IP: process addressing and an optional checksum to verify the contents of the UDP datagram. These two additional features are enough reason for a user process to use UDP instead of trying to use IP directly when a connectionless datagram protocol is required. UDP is often used for experimental or small-scale distributed applications in which either reliability of communication is not important or reliability of communication is taken care of at the application level. For example, *rwho* service, network monitoring, time service, Trivial File Transfer Protocol (TFTP), and so on, use UDP.

The IP layer provides host-to-host communication service, but the transport layer provides process-to-process communication service. For process addressing, both TCP and UDP use 16-bit integer *port numbers*. That is, both TCP and UDP attach a header to the data to be transmitted. Among other parameters, this header contains port numbers to specify sending and receiving processes. A port number uniquely identifies a process within a particular computer and is valid only within that computer. Once an IP packet has been delivered to the destination computer, the transport layer protocols dispatch it to the specified port number at that computer. The process identified by the port number picks up the packet from the port. Further details of the port-based process-addressing mechanism is given in Chapter 3.

***Application Layer Protocols.*** A variety of protocols exist at the application layer in the IP suite. These standard application protocols are available at almost all implementations of the IP suite. Some of the most widely used ones are briefly described next. Additional details of these protocols can be found in [Stallings 1992b]:

1. *File Transfer Protocol* (*FTP*). This protocol is used to transfer files to and from a remote host in a network. A file transfer takes place in the following manner:

- A user executes the *ftp* command on its local host, specifying the remote host as a parameter.
- The FTP client process of the user's machine establishes a connection with an FTP server process on the remote host using TCP.
- The user is then prompted for login name and password to ensure that the user is allowed to access the remote host.
- After successful login, the desired file(s) may be transferred in either direction by using *get* (for transfer from remote to local machine) and *put* (for transfer from local to remote machine) commands. Both binary and text files can be transferred. The user can also list directories or move between directories of the remote machine.

2. *Trivial File Transfer Protocol* (*TFTP*). This protocol also enables users to transfer files to and from a remote host in a network. However, unlike FTP, it uses UDP (not TCP), it cannot check the authenticity of the user, and it does not provide the facilities of listing directories and moving between directories.

3. *TELNET*. This protocol enables terminals and terminal-oriented processes to communicate with another host on the network. That is, a user can execute the *telnet* command on its local host to start a login session on a remote host. Once a login session is established, telnet enters the input mode. In this mode, anything typed on the keyboard by the user is sent to the remote host. The input mode entered will be either character or line mode depending on what the remote system supports. In the character mode, every character typed on the keyboard is immediately sent to the remote host for processing. On the other hand, in the line mode, all typed material is echoed locally, and (normally) only completed lines are sent to the remote host for processing. Like FTP, TELNET uses TCP.

4. *Simple Mail Transfer Protocol* (*SMTP*). This protocol enables two user processes on a network to exchange electronic mail using a TCP connection between them.

5. *Domain Name Service* (*DNS*). The client processes of application protocols, such as FTP, TFTP, TELNET, SMTP, can be designed to accept Internet addresses (in their

decimal form) from a user to identify the remote host with which the user wants to interact. However, as compared to numeric identifiers, symbolic names are easier for human beings to remember and use. Therefore, the Internet supports a scheme for the allocation and use of symbolic names for hosts and networks, such as *asuvax.eas.asu.edu* or *eas.asu.edu*. The named entities are called *domains* and the symbolic names are called *domain names*. The domain name space has a hierarchical structure that is entirely independent of the physical structure of the networks that constitute the Internet. A hierarchical naming scheme provides greater flexibility of name space management (described in detail in Chapter 10).

When domain names are accepted as parameters by application protocols such as FTP, TFTP, TELNET, SMTP, and so on, they must be translated to Internet addresses before making communication operation requests to lower level protocols. This job of mapping domain names to Internet addresses is performed by DNS. Further details of DNS are given in Chapter 10.

### 2.5.2 Protocols for Distributed Systems

Although the protocols mentioned previously provide adequate support for traditional network applications such as file transfer and remote login, they are not suitable for distributed systems and applications. This is mainly because of the following special requirements of distributed systems as compared to network systems [Kaashoek et al. 1993]:

- *Transparency.* Communication protocols for network systems use location-dependent process identifiers (such as port addresses that are unique only within a node). However, for efficient utilization of resources, distributed systems normally support process migration facility. With communication protocols for network systems, supporting process migration facility is difficult because when a process migrates, its identifier changes. Therefore, communication protocols for distributed systems must use location-independent process identifiers that do not change even when a process migrates from one node to another.
- *Client-server-based communication.* The communication protocols for network systems treat communication as an input/output device that is used to transport data between two nodes of a network. However, most communications in distributed systems are based on the client-server model in which a client requests a server to perform some work for it by sending the server a message and then waiting until the server sends back a reply. Therefore, communication protocols for distributed systems must have a simple, connectionless protocol having features to support request/response behavior.
- *Group communication.* Several distributed applications benefit from group communication facility that allows a message to be sent reliably from one sender to $n$ receivers. Although many network systems provide mechanisms to do broadcast or multicast at the data-link layer, their communication protocols often hide these useful capabilities from the applications. Furthermore, although broadcast can be done by sending $n$ point-to-point messages and waiting for $n$ acknowledgments, this algorithm is inefficient and wastes bandwidth. Therefore,

communication protocols for distributed systems must support more flexible and efficient group communication facility in which a group address can be mapped on one or more data-link addresses and the routing protocol can use a data-link multicast address to send a message to all the receivers belonging to the group defined by the multicast address.

- *Security*. Security is a critical issue in networks, and encryption is the commonly used method to ensure security of message data transmitted across a network. However, encryption is expensive to use, and all nodes and all communication channels of a network are not untrustworthy for a particular user. Therefore, encryption should be used only when there is a possibility of a critical message to travel via an untrustworthy node/channel from its source node to the destination node. Hence a communication protocol is needed that can support a flexible and efficient encryption mechanism in which a message is encrypted only if the path it takes across the network cannot be trusted. Existing communication protocols for network systems do not provide such flexibility.
- *Network management*. Network management activities, such as adding/removing a node from a network, usually require manual intervention by a system administrator to update the configuration files that reflect the current configuration of the network. For example, the allocation of new addresses is often done manually. Ideally, network protocols should automatically handle network management activities to reflect dynamic changes in network configuration.
- *Scalability*. A communication protocol for distributed systems must scale well and allow efficient communication to take place in both LAN and WAN environments. A single communication protocol must be usable on both types of networks.

Two communication protocols that have been designed to achieve higher throughput and/or fast response in distributed systems and to address one or more of the issues stated above are *VMTP* (*Versatile Message Transport Protocol*) and *FLIP* (*Fast Local Internet Protocol*). VMPT provides group communication facility and implements a secure and efficient client-server-based communication protocol [Cheriton and Williamson 1989]. On the other hand, FLIP is designed to support transparency, efficient client-server-based communication, group communication, secure communication, and easy network management [Kaashoek et al. 1993]. These protocols are briefly described next.

### The Versatile Message Transport Protocol

This is a transport protocol that has been especially designed for distributed operating systems and has been used in the V-System [Cheriton 1988]. It is a connectionless protocol that has special features to support request/response behavior between a client and one or more server processes. It is based on the concept of a message transaction that consists of a request message sent by a client to one or more servers followed by zero or more response messages sent back to the client by the servers, at most one per server. Most message transactions involve a single request message and a single response message.

For better performance, a response is used to serve as an acknowledgment for the corresponding request, and a response is usually acknowledged by the next request from the same client. Using special facilities, a client can request for an immediate acknowledgment for its request or a server can explicitly request an acknowledgment for its response.

To support transparency and to provide group communication facility, entities in VMTP are identified by 64-bit identifiers that are unique, stable, and independent of the host address. The latter property allows entities to be migrated and handled independent of network layer addressing. A portion of the entity identifier space is reserved for entity group identifiers that identify a group of zero or more entities. For example, each file server, as a separate entity, may belong to the group of file servers, identified by a single entity group identifier. To find out the location of a particular file directory, a client can send a request for this information to the entity group of file servers and receive a response from the server containing the directory. A group management protocol has been provided for creating new groups, adding new members or deleting members from an existing group, and querying information about existing groups.

Again for better performance, VMPT provides a *selective retransmission* mechanism. The packets of a message are divided into packet groups that contain up to a maximum of 16 kilobytes of segment data. The data segment is viewed as a sequence of segment blocks, each of 512 bytes (except for the last, which may be only partly full), allowing the portions of the segment in a packet group to be specified by a 32-bit mask. Each packet contains a delivery mask field that indicates the portions of the data segment the packet contains. The maximum number of blocks per packet is determined by the network maximum packet size. When a packet group is received, the delivery masks for the individual packets are ORed together to obtain a bitmap indicating which segment blocks are still outstanding. An acknowledgment packet contains this bitmap, and the sender selectively retransmits only the missing segment blocks.

The VMTP uses a rate-based flow control mechanism. In this mechanism, packets in a packet group are spaced out with interpacket gaps to reduce the arrival rate at the receiver. The mechanism allows clients and servers to explicitly communicate their desired interpacket gap times and to make adjustments based on selective retransmission requests described previously. For example, if the bitmap returned by the receiver indicates that every other packet needs to be retransmitted, the sender reasonably increases the interpacket gap. If the next acknowledgment bitmap indicates that every fourth packet is missing, the sender again increases the interpacket gap. When no packet loss occurs, the sender periodically reduces the interpacket gap to ensure that it is transmitting at the maximum rate the receiver can handle. Thus, selective retransmission provides feedback to indicate that the rate of transmission is too high and also minimizes the performance penalty arising from overflooding of packets from a fast sender to a slow receiver.

An optimization used in VMTP is to differentiate between idempotent and nonidempotent operations. An idempotent operation is one whose execution can be repeated any number of times without there being any side effects. For example, requesting the time of day is a typical idempotent operation, but transferring money from one bank account to another is a nonidempotent operation. In VMTP, a server can label a response to indicate that a message transaction was idempotent. By doing so, arrangements need not be made for retransmitting the response when it is lost because the server can reproduce the response when the request is retransmitted. However, when a response is nonidempotent, VMPT prevents the server from executing a request more than once.

In addition to the aforementioned features, VMTP provides a rich collection of optional facilities that expand its functionality and efficiency in various situations. One such facility that is particularly useful for real-time communication is the facility of conditional message delivery. With this facility, a client can specify that its message should only be delivered if the server is able to process it immediately. The optional facilities are carefully designed to provide critical extensions to the basic facilities without imposing a significant performance penalty, especially on common-case processing.

Further details of the VMTP protocol can be found in [Cheriton 1986, Cheriton and Williamson 1989].

### The Fast Local Internet Protocol

This is a connectionless protocol for distributed operating systems. It has been used in the Amoeba distributed system [Mullender et al. 1990]. Its main features include transparency, security, easy network management, group communication facility, and efficient client-server-based communication facility. The following description is based on the material presented in [Kaashoek et al. 1993].

For transparency, FLIP identifies entities, called *network service access points* (*NSAPs*), with location-independent 64-bit identifiers. Sites on an internetwork can have more than one NSAP, typically one or more for each entity (e.g., process). Each site is connected to the internetwork by a *FLIP box* that either can be a software layer in the operating system of the corresponding site or can be run on a separate communications processor. Each FLIP box maintains a routing table that is basically a dynamic hint cache mapping NSAP addresses on data-link addresses. Special primitives are provided to dynamically register and unregister NSAP addresses into the routing table of a FLIP box. An entity can register more than one address in a FLIP box (e.g., its own address to receive messages directed to the entity itself and the null address to receive broadcast messages). FLIP uses a one-way mapping between the private address used to register an entity and the public address used to advertise the entity. A one-way encryption function is used to ensure that one cannot deduce the private address from the public address. Therefore, entities that know the (public) address of an NSAP (because they have communicated with it) are not able to receive messages on that address, because they do not know the corresponding private address.

The FLIP messages are transmitted unreliably between NSAPs. A FLIP message may be of any size less than $2^{32} - 1$ bytes. If a message is too large for a particular network, it is fragmented into smaller chunks, called *fragments*. A fragment typically fits in a single network packet. The basic function of FLIP is to route an arbitrary-length message from the source NSAP to the destination NSAP. The path selection policy is based on the information stored in the routing tables of each FLIP box about the networks to which it is connected. The two main parameters used for this purpose are the *network weight* and a *security bit*. A low network weight means that the network is desirable on which to forward a message. The network weight can be based, for example, on physical properties of the network, such as bandwidth and delay. On the other hand, the secure bit indicates whether sensitive data can be sent unencrypted over the network or not.

The three types of calls provided in FLIP for sending a message to a public address are *flip_unicast*, *flip_multicast*, and *flip_broadcast*. These calls provide both point-to-point and group communication facilities. The group communication protocols make heavy use of *flip_multicast*. This has the advantage that a group of *n* processes can be addressed using one FLIP address, even if they are located on multiple networks.

Although FLIP does not encrypt messages itself, it provides the following two mechanisms for secure delivery of messages. In the first mechanism, a sender can mark its message sensitive by using the *security* bit. Such messages are routed only over trusted networks. In the second mechanism, messages routed over an untrusted network by a FLIP are marked unsafe by setting the *unsafe* bit. When the receiver receives the message, by checking the unsafe bit, it can tell the sender whether or not there is a safe route between them. If a safe route exists, the sender tries to send sensitive messages in unencrypted form but with the *security* bit set. If at some stage during routing no further trusted path is found for the message (which can only happen due to network configuration changes), it is returned to the sender with the *unreachable* bit set. If this happens, the sender encrypts the message and retransmits it with the *security* bit cleared. Therefore, message encryption is done only when required.

The FLIP supports easy network management because dynamic changes in network configuration are automatically handled. The only network management job that requires human intervention is the specification of trusted and untrusted networks. That is, FLIP relies on the system administrator to mark a network interface as trusted or untrusted, because FLIP itself cannot determine if a network can be considered trusted.

One requirement for which FLIP does not provide full support is wide-area networking. Although FLIP has been used successfully in small WANs, it does not scale well enough to be used as the WAN communication protocol in a large WAN. FLIP designers traded scalability for functionality because they felt that wide-area communication should not be done at the network layer, but in higher layers.

Further details of the FLIP protocol can be found in [Kaashoek et al. 1993].

## 2.6 INTERNETWORKING

We saw in Chapter 1 that two desirable features of distributed systems are extensibility and openness. Both these features call for a need to integrate two or more networks (possibly supplied by different vendors and based on different networking standards) to form a single network so that computers that could not communicate because they were on different networks before interconnection can now communicate with each other. Interconnecting of two or more networks to form a single network is called *internetworking*, and the resulting network is called an *internetwork*. Therefore, a WAN of multiple LANs is an internetwork.

Internetworks are often heterogeneous networks composed of several network segments that may differ in topology and protocol. For example, an internetwork may have multiple LANs, some of which may have multiaccess bus topology while others may have ring topology; some of these LANs may be using Ethernet technology while others may be using Token Ring technology; and some segments of the network may be using the IP suite while others may be using IBM's SNA (System Network Architecture) protocol suite. Internetworking allows these relatively unrelated networks to evolve into a single working system. That is, the goal of internetworking is to hide the details of different physical networks, so that the resulting internetwork functions as a single coordinated unit.

The three important internetworking issues are how to interconnect multiple (possibly heterogeneous) networks into a single network, which communication medium to use for connecting two networks, and how to manage the resulting internetwork. Some commonly used technologies to handle these issues are described below. An important point to remember here is that handling of internetworking issues becomes much easier if the network segments of the resulting internetwork were designed using widely accepted standards instead of proprietary topologies and protocols. If an organization has designed its networks using nonstandard technologies, interconnection to global networks may require tearing of the existing networks and starting over again. Therefore, adherence to standards is very important from an internetworking point of view.

### 2.6.1 Interconnection Technologies

Interconnection technologies enable interconnection of networks that may possibly have different topologies and protocols. Interconnecting two networks having the same topology and protocol is simple because the two networks can easily communicate with each other. However, interconnecting two dissimilar networks that have different topologies and protocols requires an internetworking scheme that provides some common point of reference for the two networks to communicate with each other. That point of reference might be a high-level protocol common to the two networks, a device that allows interconnection of different topologies with different physical and electrical characteristics, or a protocol that allows operating environment differences to be ignored. The most commonly used approach is to make use of common high-level protocols for moving data between common layers on a communications model such as the OSI or the IP suites. Internetworking tools, such as bridges, routers, brouters, and gateways, make extensive use of this approach. As described next, each of these tools has strengths, weaknesses, and specific applications in internetworking. These tools are "blackbox" internetworking technologies that enable interconnection of similar or dissimilar networks to form a single network system.

#### Bridges

Bridges operate at the bottom two layers of the OSI model (physical and data link). Therefore, they are used to connect networks that use the same communication protocols above the data-link layer but may or may not use the same protocols at the physical and data-link layers. For example, bridges may be used to connect two networks, one of which uses fiber-optic communication medium and the other uses coaxial cable; or one of which uses Ethernet technology and the other uses Token Ring technology. But both networks must use the same high-level protocols (e.g., TCP/IP or XNS) to communicate.

The similarity of higher level protocols implies that bridges do not modify either the format or the contents of the frames when they transfer them from one network segment to another (they simply copy the frames). Hence bridges feature high-level protocol transparency. They can transfer data between two network segments over a third segment in the middle that cannot understand the data passing through it. As far as the bridge is concerned, the intermediate segment exists for routing purposes only.

Bridges are intelligent devices in the sense that they use a process of learning and filtering in data forwarding to keep network traffic within the segment of the network to which it belongs. Therefore, bridges are also useful in network partitioning. When the performance of a network segment degrades due to excessive network traffic, it can be broken into two network segments with a bridge interconnecting the two segments.

### Routers

Routers operate at the network layer of the OSI model. Therefore, routers do not care what topologies or access-level protocols the interconnected network segments use. Since routers use the bottom three layers of the OSI model, they are usually used to interconnect those networks that use the same high-level protocols above the network layer. Note that the protocols of data-link and physical layers are transparent to routers. Therefore, if two network segments use different protocols at these two layers, a bridge must be used to connect them.

Unlike bridges, routers do not view an internetwork from end to end. That is, bridges know the ultimate destination of a data, but routers only know which is the next router for the data being transferred across the network. However, routers are smarter than bridges in the sense that they not only copy a data from one network segment to another, but they also choose the best route for the data by using information in a routing table to make this decision. That is, managing traffic congestion is a big plus of routers; they employ a flow control mechanism to direct traffic on to alternative, less congested paths.

Routers are commonly used to interconnect those network segments of large internetworks that use the same communication protocol. They are particularly useful in controlling traffic flow by making intelligent routing decisions.

An internetwork often uses both bridges and routers to handle both routing and multiprotocol issues. This requirement has resulted in the design of devices called *brouters*, which are a kind of hybrid of bridges and routers. They provide many of the advantages of both bridges and routers. They are complex, expensive, and difficult to install, but for very complex heterogeneous internetworks in which the network segments use the same high-level communication protocols, they often provide the best internetworking solution.

### Gateways

Gateways operate at the top three layers of the OSI model (session, presentation, and application). They are the most sophisticated internetworking tools and are used for interconnecting dissimilar networks that use different communication protocols. That is, gateways are used to interconnect networks that are built on totally different communications architectures. For instance, a gateway may be used to interconnect two networks, one of which uses the IP suite and the other uses the SNA protocol suite.

Since networks interconnected by a gateway use dissimilar protocols, protocol conversion is the major job performed by gateways. Additionally, gateways sometimes also perform routing functions.

## 2.6.2 Which Communication Medium to Use?

Another important issue in internetworking is to decide the communication medium that should be used to connect two networks. This largely depends on the locations of the two networks and the throughput desired. For example, *FDDI* (*Fiber Distributed Data Interface*), specified by the American National Standards Institute (ANSI), operates at a speed of 100 Mbps and is an ideal high-bandwidth backbone for interconnecting LANs that are located within a multistory building or housed in several buildings in a campuslike environment.

If the two networks are located a little far from each other (such as on opposite sides of a town or in nearby cities), then they may be connected by leased telephone lines if the data traffic between the two networks is not heavy. If the data traffic between the two networks is heavy, dedicated lines may be used to interconnect the two networks. Use of dedicated lines is also suggested for security reasons when the data exchanged between the two networks often contains sensitive information.

Finally, if the two networks are located very far from each other (such as in different countries or in two distantly located cities of a country), then communication channels of public data networks, such as telephone lines or communication satellites, may be used to interconnect them. Long-haul communication channels are expensive. Moreover, if communication channels of a public data network are used to interconnect the two networks, inconsistencies of traffic and system reliability influence the data throughput between the two networks. Security is also a problem in this case. The data throughput problem may be solved to some extent by using one's own method of traffic routing. For example, if the two networks are located in New York and Los Angeles, the total traffic between the two networks may be routed through both Denver and Dallas for better throughput. Methods to handle the security problem are described in Chapter 11.

## 2.6.3 Network Management Technologies

Network management deals with the monitoring and analysis of network status and activities. Network monitoring tools watch network segments and provide information on data throughput, node and link failures, and other global occurrences on the network that may be useful in some manner to network managers. Simple network monitoring tools report the existence, if not the cause, of a problem in any part of the network. On the other hand, network analysis tools analyze network activities from a wide variety of angles at a depth that includes packet-level protocol analysis. They add quantitative information to the monitor's qualitative data by providing a wide array of complete information about the operation of a network.

Management of an internetwork is more complex than management of a simple independent LAN because local problems become global problems when several LANs are interconnected to form an internetwork. Pinpointing the location of a problem in an internetwork is tricky because the problem may be on a local or remote LAN. Therefore, the tools available for managing a single independent LAN either work poorly or do not work at all when applied to internetworks. The heterogeneous nature of internetworks is also a major obstacle in the design of widely acceptable management tools for internetworks. Every manager of an internetwork dreams of a single tool that has the following features:

1. It can enfold all the protocols and devices found on a typical heterogeneous internetwork.
2. It should be easy to use. Highly graphical user interface that allows rapid user interaction and reduces the need for highly skilled network analysts at most levels is desirable.
3. It should be intelligent in the sense that it can learn and reason as it isolates network faults.
4. It should have no preferences regarding a device's vendor or protocol.

Unfortunately, no such tool exists at present. However, the future looks encouraging, as several network management frameworks and network management profiles are on the way. To provide for management of future interoperable multivendor networks, the ISO, the IETF, the OSF, and other organizations are currently developing management standards for communications networks based on several reference models and network management frameworks. Of the various emerging standards, three standards seem to be promising for future network management tools. These are *Simple Network Management Protocol* (*SNMP*), *Common Management Information Protocol* (*CMIP*), and *Distributed Management Environment* (*DME*).

The SNMP is a client-server protocol suitable for applications that operate in the client-server mode and do not require real-time notification of faults. It was introduced in the late 1980s to control and monitor networks that use the IP suite. Because of its simplicity for implementation and lower costs, SNMP-based tools are being implemented by most of the network management element vendors. To address speed, security, and manager-to-manager communication capability, IETF is working on version 2 of SNMP protocols. Further details of SNMP may be found in [Datapro 1990, Shevenell 1994, Janet 1993].

The CMIP is a network management standard developed by OSI (ISO/CCITT). It is designed to facilitate interoperability and true integration between large numbers of separate, isolated network management products and services in a multivendor environment. It is based on a manager-agent model. The managing system invokes the management operations, and the managed system forwards the notifications to the manager. Communications between managing systems is also facilitated by the agent-manager role. Further details of CMIP may be found in [IT 1990, Janet 1993].

There are a lot more SNMP-based products available as network management tools as compared to CMIP-based products. In spite of providing richer functionality and more sophisticated features than SNMP-based products, CMIP-based products are not enjoying rapid growth because they are more expensive, more complex, and require more processing power to implement.

The OSF's DME is a set of specifications for distributed network management products. Its goal is to provide a framework to enable a consistent system and network management scheme across a global, multivendor distributed environment. To achieve this goal, the design of DME has been based on SNMP, CMIP, and other de facto standards. DME-based products are not yet available in the market. Further details of DME may be found in [Datapro 1993].

### 2.6.4 Internetwork Case Study: The Internet

The Internet is the best example of an internetwork. It is a single worldwide collection of interconnected heterogeneous networks that share a uniform scheme for addressing host computers and a suite of agreed protocols. Hosts and other resources on the Internet are named by using the DNS (Domain Name System) naming scheme described in Chapter 10.

The Internet has its roots in the ARPANET system of the Advanced Research Projects Agency of the U.S. Department of Defense. ARPANET was the first WAN and had only four sites in 1969. The Internet evolved from the basic ideas of ARPANET and was initially used by research organizations and universities to share and exchange information. Since restrictions for commercial use were lifted in 1989, the Internet has rapidly grown into an internetwork that now interconnects more than 10,000 networks, allowing more than 3 million computers and more than 40 million computer users in more than 150 countries around the world to communicate with each other. The Internet continues to grow at a rapid pace.

The Internet is a vast ocean of information that is of interest to a wide variety of users. Several user-friendly tools are available that allow users to successfully navigate the Internet and find useful information for one's own purposes. A few of the most popular of these tools are Gopher, Archie, WAIS (Wide-Area Information Servers), WWW (World-Wide Web), and Mosaic.

*Gopher* [Martin 1993] is a text-based tool that provides hierarchical collections of information of all sorts across the Internet. It is a seemingly endless maze of directory menus. Developed at the University of Minnesota in 1991, Gopher is currently the most commonly used tool to locate information on the Internet. For further details, ftp to *boombox.micro.umn.edu* and look in the directory */pub/gopher/docs*.

*Archie* is a collection of tools that allows searching of indexes of files available on public servers by anonymous *ftp* on the Internet. For further details, gopher to *gopher.gmu.edu*.

*Wide-Area Information Servers* (*WAIS*) is a group of freeware, shareware, and commercial software programs that help users locate information on the Internet. For further details, gopher to *gopher.gmu.edu*.

*The World-Wide Web* (*WWW*) is a hypermedia distribution system that uses hypertext links to other textual documents or files. With this facility, users can click on a highlighted word or words in a document to provide additional information about the selected word(s). With WWW, users can also access graphic pictures, images, audio clips, or even full-motion video that is set up at sites all over the world to provide a wealth of useful information. WWW was invented by the European Centre for Nuclear Research (CERN) in 1992 in an attempt to build a distributed hypermedia system. WWW traffic is the fastest growing part of the Internet and it is today's preferred vehicle for the Internet commerce. For further details, refer to [Vetter et al. 1994] or gopher to *info.cern.ch*.

*Mosaic* is a hypermedia-based browsing tool for finding and retrieving information from the Internet. Mosaic browsers are currently available for UNIX workstations running X Windows, PCs running Microsoft Windows, and the Apple Macintosh computers. Mosaic can access data in WWW servers, WAIS, Gopher servers, Archie servers, and several others. Its popularity is rapidly increasing because of its many useful features and capabilities. For further details, refer to [Vetter et al. 1994] or anonymous ftp to *ftp.NCSA.uiuc.edu* and look in the directory */PC/Mosaic*.

The worldwide scope of the Internet makes it perhaps the single most valuable tool for use in many significant ways by both non-profit and commercial organizations. Some of the important current strategic uses of the Internet are listed here. The following description is based on the material presented in [Nejmeh 1994]:

1. *On-line communication*. The electronic mail service (known as *e-mail*) on the Internet is extensively used today by computer users around the world to communicate with each other. With this facility, the Internet has proved to be a rapid and productive communication tool for millions of users. As compared to paper mail, telephone, and fax, e-mail is preferred by many because (a) it is faster than paper mail; (b) unlike the telephone, the persons communicating with each other need not be available at the same time; and (c) unlike fax documents, e-mail documents can be stored in a computer and be easily manipulated using editing programs.

2. *Software sharing*. The Internet provides access to a large number of shareware software development tools and utilities. A few examples of such available shareware tools are C++ compilers, code libraries, mail servers, and operating systems (all available via *ftp* from *sunsite.unc.edu*). The Free Software Foundation also provides a wealth of GNU software (for details anonymous ftp to *prep.ai.mit.edu* and look in the directory */pub/GNU*).

3. *Exchange of views on topics of common interest*. The Internet has a number of news groups. Each news group allows a group of users to exchange their views on some topic of common interest. For example, the news group *comp.os.os2.advocacy* contains candid dialog about the OS/2 operating system.

4. *Posting of information of general interest.* The Internet is also being extensively used as a large electronic bulletin board on which information of general interest can be posted to bring it to the attention of interested users around the world. Some commonly posted information include career opportunities, conference and event announcements, and calls for papers for conferences and journals.

5. *Product promotion.* Several commercial organizations are effectively using the Internet services for promoting their products. These organizations make use of corporate *ftp*, Gopher, or WWW server sites focused on disseminating timely information about corporate happenings, product announcements, recent strategic alliances, press releases, and other information of potential interest to existing and prospective customers. For example, *comp.sys.sun.announce* news group contains information about Sun Microsystem's latest product announcements.

6. *Feedback about products.* In addition to product promotion, commercial organizations are also using the Internet to gather information about user satisfaction of existing products, market opportunities of new products, and ideas for potential new products. This is usually accomplished by putting up an interactive survey application by the organization on a WWW or Gopher site on the Internet.

7. *Customer support service.* Many software organizations are also using the Internet to provide unprecedented levels of timely customer support. The combined electronic mail, *ftp*, and other services on the Internet provide all of the enabling tools necessary to provide such first-rate customer support. For example, bugs in fielded software products can be reported to an organization via electronic mail, and bug fixes, minor releases, workarounds, known problems and limitations, and general advice about a product can be made available by an organization to its customers via an *ftp* server.

8. *On-line journals and magazines.* The Internet now has literally hundreds of electronic subscriptions that can be found both for free and low cost. There are many Gopher and WWW sites on the Internet that deal with electronic versions of many journals and magazines. For example, Dow Jones News/Retrieval provides fee-based access to the electronic version of the *Wall Street Journal* on the Internet. Researchers are working in the direction to extend this idea to support full-fledged electronic libraries on the Internet.

9. *On-line shopping.* The Internet has also facilitated the introduction of a new market concept that consists of virtual shops. These shops remain open 24 hours all the year round and are accessible to purchasers all around the world. They provide information about products or services for sale through *ftp*, Gopher, or WWW servers. Using the Internet services, customers submit specific product queries and request specific sales quotes. Through a well-defined authorization and authentication scheme, the Internet services are then used to accept orders placed by the customers, to handle order payments, and to track orders to fulfillment. For example, the Internet Mall is a collection of shops, each providing several products or services for sale. For a list of the available products or services at the Internet Mall, ftp to *ftp.netcom.com* and look in the directory */pubs/Guides*.

10. *Worldwide video conferencing*. Worldwide video conferencing is an emerging service on the Internet that allows a group of users located around the globe to talk and interact with each other as if they were sitting and discussing in a single room. The CU-SeeMe system developed at Cornell University is an example of an Internet-based video-conferencing system. For information on CU-SeeMe, ftp to *gated.cornell.edu* and look in the directory */pub/video/CU-SeeMe.FAQ.7-6.txt.*

## 2.7 ATM TECHNOLOGY

*Asynchronous Transfer Mode* (*ATM*) is often described as the future computer networking paradigm. It is a high-speed, connection-oriented switching and multiplexing technology that uses short, fixed-length packets (called *cells*) to transmit different types of traffic simultaneously, including voice, video, and data. It is asynchronous in that information streams can be sent independently without a common clock. This emerging technology is briefly described next. For a more complete treatment of the state of the art in ATM technology, see [DePrycker 1993, Newman 1994, Fischer et al. 1994, Haendel et al. 1994, Vetter 1995, Kim and Wang 1995].

### 2.7.1 Main Features of ATM Technology

ATM technology is expected to have an enormous impact on future distributed systems because of its following attractive features:

1. It enables high-bandwidth distributed applications by providing data transmission speeds of 155 Mbps, 622 Mbps, and potentially 2.5 Gbps. This feature will make possible several new distributed applications, such as applications based on video-on-demand technique, video-conferencing applications, and applications that need to access remote databases of multimedia data.

2. It provides high transmission speeds for both local and wide-area networks and services, enabling high-powered distributed applications that previously had little hope of extending beyond LAN environments to be used in WAN environments as well.

3. It supports both the fundamental approaches to switching (circuit switching and packet switching) within a single integrated switching mechanism (called *cell switching*). This feature makes it suitable both for distributed applications that generate *constant-bit-rate* (*CBR*) traffic and distributed applications that generate *variable-bit-rate* (*VBR*) traffic. For instance, applications dealing with video and digitized voice generate CBR traffic. Constant-bit-rate traffic requires guaranteed throughput rates and service levels. On the other hand, most data applications generate VBR traffic. Variable-bit-rate traffic can tolerate delays and fluctuating throughput rates.

4. It uses the concept of virtual networking to pass traffic between two locations. This concept allows the available bandwidth of a physical channel to be shared by multiple applications, enabling multiple applications to simultaneously communicate at

different rates over the same path between two end points. That is, it allows the total bandwidth available to be dynamically distributed among a variety of user applications.

5. In addition to point-to-point communication in which there is a single sender and a single receiver, it can easily support multicasting facility in which there is a single sender but multiple receivers. Such a facility is needed for transmitting broadcast television to many houses at the same time. Many collaborative distributed applications also require frequent use of this kind of facility.

6. It enables the use of a single network to efficiently transport a wide range of multimedia data such as text, voice, video, broadcast television, and so on. Therefore, the use of separate networks such as a telephone network for voice, an X.25 network for data, and a cable television network for video can now be replaced by a single ATM network that provides a means for integrating voice, video, data, and other information. This integration will in turn lead to substantial cost savings and simplification in the design of communication networks.

7. It is flexible in the way it grants access to bandwidth. That is, it enables supply of bandwidth on demand and allows billing network users on a per-cell basis (more probably on a giga-cell basis, given the speed and transfer capabilities of ATM). A user can grab as big or as small a chunk of network bandwidth as he or she needs and pay only for as much as he or she uses.

8. It is a scalable technology. It enables increase or decrease of such things as bandwidths and data rates and still maintains the architecture of the signaling process. Moreover, the same switching technology (cell switching) and the same cell format is used for the transport of all types of information (voice, video, and data) in both LAN and WAN environments.

9. It has a fairly solid base of standards. It has been adopted by the International Telecommunications Union (ITU) (formerly CCITT) and internationally standardized as the basis for the Broadband Integrated Services Digital Network (B-ISDN).

### 2.7.2 Basic Concepts of ATM Technology

There are two fundamental types of network traffic—CBR and VBR. The CBR traffic (comprising of video and digitized voice information) is smooth, whereas VBR traffic (comprising of data information) is bursty. The CBR traffic requires a low but constant bandwidth and guaranteed throughput rates and service levels. On the other hand, VBR traffic requires large bandwidth for very short periods of time at random intervals and can tolerate delays and fluctuating throughput rates. Due to this basic difference in characteristics of the two types of traffic, circuit switching is the most suitable networking technology for handling CBR traffic, whereas packet switching is the most suitable networking technology for handling VBR traffic. However, neither circuit switching nor packet switching is suitable for handling both classes of network traffic. Therefore, when the standards bodies of the ITU were working on a universal multiplexing and switching mechanism that could support integrated transport of multiple-bit-rate traffic in an efficient and cost-effective way, they came up with the idea of a hybrid form of switching technique called *cell switching*. ATM technology is based on this cell-switching technique.

Cell-switching technology is based on the digital packet-switching technology, which relays and routes traffic over virtual paths by means of an address contained within the packet (this is different from circuit-switching technology, which routes traffic not by address but over dedicated physical paths established before communication starts). However, unlike more familiar packet-switching technologies, such as X.25 or frame relay, cell-switching technology uses very short, fixed-length packets, called *cells*. In ATM, cells are 53 bytes long. They consist of a 5-byte header (containing the address) and a 48-byte information field.

The cell size of 53 bytes was chosen to make ATM useful for data as well as voice, video, and other real-time traffic that cannot tolerate randomly varying transmission intervals and delays. Pure data sources can produce very long messages—up to 64 kilobytes in many cases. By segmenting such messages into short cells, ATM ensures that CBR traffic such as voice and video can be given priority and need never wait more than one 53-byte cell transmission time (3 μs at a 155-Mbps transmission rate) before it can gain access to a communication channel. With frame-based packet-switching technology, the waiting time would be random, possibly several milliseconds in length. The use of short, fixed-size cells also eliminates the danger of a small packet being delayed because a big one is hogging a needed line. In case of cell switching, after each cell is transmitted, a new one (even one belonging to a different message) can be sent.

The proper size of a cell in ATM was the subject of much debate with the standards committees. This is because telephony people were in favor of a small cell to reduce delay for voice packets, whereas data communications people were in favor of a large cell to minimize the overhead involved in the segmentation and reassembly of message data. After much discussion, the cell size debate was narrowed into two choices—32-byte cells or 64-byte cells. As a compromise, the ITU set the cell size at 48 bytes plus the header.

Notice that with a fixed cell size of 53 bytes, ATM technology is not an ideal choice either for applications dealing with CBR traffic such as voice and video or for applications dealing with VBR traffic such as file transfers. It is, however, the best technology on the horizon for handling both types of traffic on a single integrated network. Because of its fast, hardware-based switching, it can emulate the dedicated circuits usually required for handling CBR traffic. And because it is packet based, it can efficiently handle VBR traffic as well.

The ATM is a connection-oriented technology because a sender first establishes a connection with the receiver. However, unlike circuit switching, in which a physical circuit is established between the sender and the receiver and reserved for them for the entire duration of their communication session, in ATM technology, a virtual circuit is established between the sender and the receiver. That is, ATM does not reserve the path for one user exclusively. Any time a given user is not occupying a channel, another user is free to use it. Connection establishment in ATM means that a route is determined from the sender to the receiver and routing information is stored in the switches along the route during connection establishment. All cells of messages from the sender to the receiver follow this virtual path stored in the switches. When the connection is no longer needed, it is released and the routing information for this connection is purged from the switches.

The address information in the header of each cell is used by the routing protocol to determine the virtual path that the cell will traverse. Addresses in ATM are only of local significance, in that they matter only between two adjacent pieces of ATM equipment. When a virtual path is established, each switch is provided with a set of lookup tables that identify an incoming cell by header address, route it through the switch to the proper output port, and overwrite the incoming address with a new one that the next switch along the route will recognize as an entry in its routing table. A message is thus passed from switch to switch over a prescribed route, but the route is virtual since the facility carrying the message is dedicated to it only while a cell of the message traverses it.

In ATM, a virtual path is essentially a bundle of virtual channels that can be multiplexed together. Therefore, over a single virtual path, two hosts may multiplex cells of many individual applications. Cells are statistically multiplexed, allowing the total available bandwidth to be dynamically distributed among a variety of distributed applications. This is achieved by selecting virtual channel paths according to the anticipated traffic and allocating the network resources needed. For guaranteed bandwidth applications, users are required to specify the amount of bandwidth required. It is the virtual nature of ATM services that provides greater network efficiencies.

### 2.7.3 ATM Protocol Reference Model

The protocol reference model in ATM is divided into three layers—physical layer, ATM layer, and ATM adaptation layer (AAL) (Fig. 2.12). Applications involving data, voice, and video are built on top of these three layers. The functionalities of the three layers are described next.

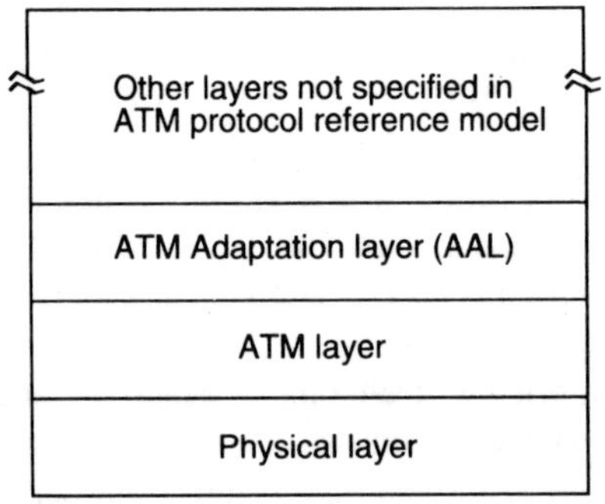


**Fig. 2.12** ATM protocol reference model.

#### Physical Layer

The physical layer is the bottom-most layer of the ATM protocol suite. It is concerned with putting bits on the wire and taking them off again. It has two sublayers: the physical medium dependent (PMD) sublayer and the transmission convergence (TC) sublayer. The

PMD sublayer defines the actual speed for traffic transmission on the physical communication medium (electrical/optical) used. On the other hand, the TC sublayer defines a protocol for the encoding and decoding of cell data into suitable electrical/optical waveforms for transmission and reception on the physical communication medium defined by the PMD sublayer. The protocol of the TC sublayer differs according to the physical communication medium used.

The physical layer can transfer cells from one user to another in one of the following two ways:

1. *By carrying cells as a synchronous data stream.* In this case, the user-network interface (UNI), which takes the form of an ATM adaptor board plugged into a computer, puts out a stream of cells on to a wire or fiber. The transmission stream must be continuous, and when there is no data to be sent, empty cells are transmitted.

2. *By carrying cells in the payload portion of an externally framed transmission structure.* In this case, the UNI uses some standard transmission structure for framing and synchronization at the physical layer. *SONET* (*Synchronous Optical NETwork*) [Omidyar and Aldridge 1993], the most commonly used standard for this purpose, is briefly described next. The SONET format is currently supported by single-mode fiber, multimode fiber, and twisted pair.

SONET is an international suite of standards for transmitting digital information over optical interfaces. In SONET, the basic unit of data transmission is a frame whose structure is shown in Figure 2.13. As shown in the figure, a SONET frame consists of a total of 810 bytes ($9 \times 90$), out of which 27 bytes ($9 \times 3$) are overhead and the remaining 783 bytes ($9 \times 87$) are payload. The overhead bytes are used for error monitoring, system maintenance functions, synchronization, and identification of payload type. The payload area can carry a variety of signals, such as several T1 signals, or a T3 signal, or several ATM virtual circuits. *T1* is a digital transmission service with a basic data rate of 1.544 Mbps, and *T3* is a digital transmission service with a basic data rate of 44.736 Mbps for transport of 28 T1 circuits.

The order of transmission of bytes is row by row, from left to right, with one entire frame transmitted every 125 $\mu$s. The basic time unit of one frame every 125 $\mu$s matches with the telephone system's standard sampling rate of 800 samples per second. Therefore, for the SONET frame format, the gross data rate is 51.840 Mbps (with the overhead bytes included), and the net data rate is 49.920 Mbps (with the overhead bytes excluded).

The basic unit of SONET with a bit rate of 51.840 Mbps is called *STS-1* (*Synchronous Transport Signal Level 1*). Higher rate SONET signals are obtained by byte-interleaving *n* frame-aligned STS-1's to form an STS-*n* signal [Vetter 1995].

STS uses an electrical rather than an optical signal. *Optical Carrier* (*OC*) levels are obtained from STS levels after scrambling (to avoid long strings of 1's and 0's and allow clock recovery at the receivers) and performing electrical-to-optical conversion [Vetter 1995]. Thus, OC-*n* level signals are obtained by scrambling and converting STS-*n* level signals. The most commonly used values of *n* are 1, 3, and 12, giving OC-1,

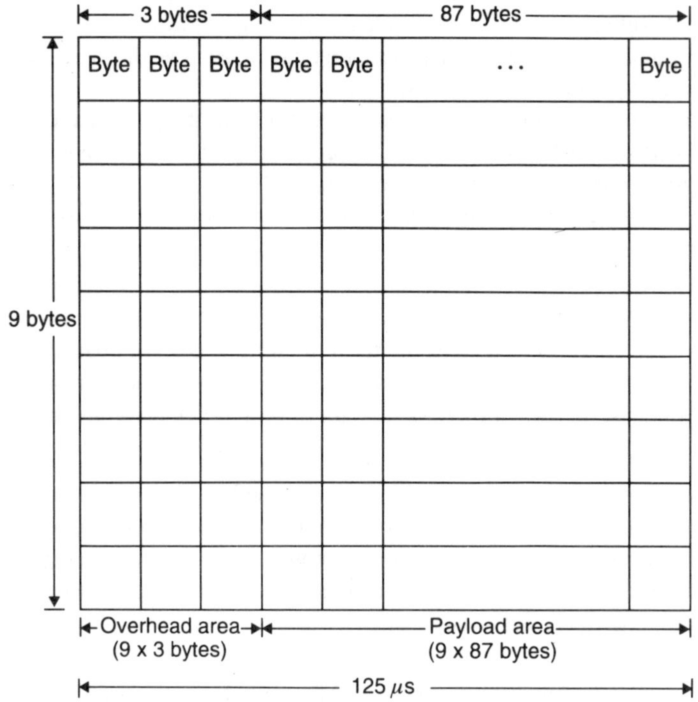


**Fig. 2.13** SONET frame format.

OC-3, and OC-12 signal levels having data rates of 51.84, 155.52, and 622.08 Mbps, respectively.

In Europe, another standard for frame formatting called *SDH* (*Synchronous Digital Hierarchy*) [Omidyar and Aldridge 1993] is also available. For the SDH frame format, the gross data rate for the basic unit is 155.52 Mbps, instead of the 51.84 Mbps for SONET.

### ATM Layer

The ATM layer handles most of the cell processing and routing activities. These include building the cell header, cell multiplexing of individual connections into composite flows of cells, cell demultiplexing of composite flows into individual connections, cell routing, cell payload type marking and differentiation, cell loss priority marking and reduction, cell reception and header validation, and generic flow control of cells. These functions are designed to be carried out in hardware at very high data rates. The ATM layer is independent of the physical medium used to transport the cells.

The functionality of the ATM layer is defined by the fields present in the ATM cell header (Fig. 2.14). These fields and their functions are as follows:

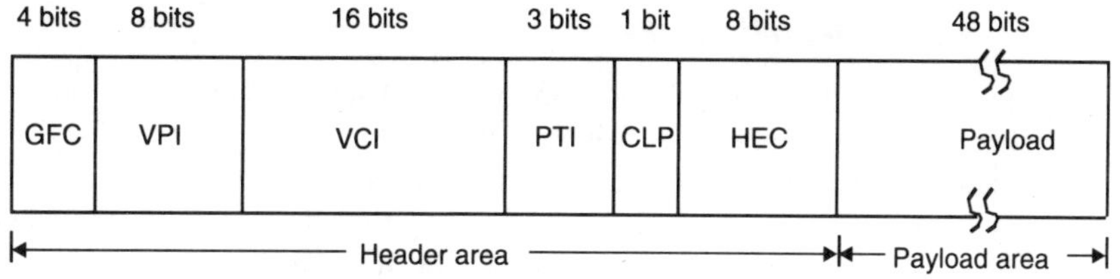


**Fig. 2.14** ATM cell format: GFC, Generic Flow Control; VPI, Virtual Path Identifier; VCI, Virtual Channel Identifier; PTI, Payload Type Identifier; CLP, Cell Loss Priority; HEC, Header Error Control.

- *Generic flow control (GFC) field.* This field occupies 4 bits in an ATM cell header. The default setting of four 0's indicates that the cell is uncontrolled. An uncontrolled cell does not take precedence over another cell when contending for a virtual circuit. The bits in the GFC field can be suitably set to implement some form of prioritized congestion control. For example, the bits in the GFC field could be used to prioritize voice over video or to indicate that both voice and video take precedence over other types of data. The GFC field is also used by the UNI to control the amount of traffic entering the network, allowing the UNI to limit the amount of data entering the network during periods of congestion [Vetter 1995].
- *Virtual path identifier (VPI) and virtual channel identifier (VCI) fields.* The VPI field occupies 8 bits and the VCI field occupies 16 bits in an ATM cell header. These two fields are used by the routing protocol to determine the path(s) and channel(s) the cell will traverse. These fields are modified at each hop along the path. That is, when a cell arrives at an ATM switch, its VPI and VCI values are used to determine the new virtual identifier to be placed in the cell header and the outgoing link over which to transmit the cell. As implied by its name, the VPI field is used to establish virtual paths between network end-points. Recall that in ATM two hosts may multiplex cells of many individual applications over a single virtual path connection. This is achieved by the VCI fields of the cells that distinguish among cells of different applications and thus establish virtual links over a given virtual path.
- *Payload-type identifier (PTI) field.* This field occupies 3 bits in an ATM cell header. It is used to distinguish data cells from control cells so that user data and control data can be transmitted on different subchannels.
- *Cell loss priority (CLP) field.* This field occupies 1 bit in an ATM cell header. When set, it indicates that the cell can be discarded, if necessary, during periods of network congestion. For example, voice data may be able to suffer lost cells without the need for retransmission, whereas text data cannot. In this case, an application may set the CLP field of the cells for voice traffic.
- *Header error control (HEC) field.* This field occupies 8 bits in an ATM cell header. It is used to protect the header field from transmission errors. It contains a checksum of only the header (not the payload).

### ATM Adaptation Layer

The functionality of the physical and the ATM layers of the ATM protocol suite is not tailored to any application. We saw that ATM can support various types of traffic, including voice, video, and data. The AAL is responsible for providing different types of services to different types of traffic according to their specific requirements. It packages various kinds of user traffic into 48-byte cells, together with the overhead needed to meet specific quality-of-service requirements of different types of traffic. To reflect the spectrum of applications, four service classes were defined by the ITU (Fig. 2.15):

1. *Class A*. Applications having delay-sensitive CBR traffic that require connection-oriented service belong to this class. Video and voice applications normally belong to this class.
2. *Class B*. Applications having delay-sensitive VBR traffic that require connection-oriented service belong to this class. Some video and audio applications belong to this class.
3. *Class C*. Applications having VBR traffic that are not delay-sensitive but that require connection-oriented service belong to this class. Connection-oriented file transfer is a typical example of an application that belongs to this class.
4. *Class D*. Applications having VBR traffic that are not delay-sensitive and does not require connection-oriented service belong to this class. LAN interconnection and electronic mail are typical examples of applications that belong to this class.

| Service class | Class A | Class B | Class C | Class D |
|---|---|---|---|---|
| Bit rate type | CBR | VBR | VBR | VBR |
| Delay sensitive? | Yes | Yes | No | No |
| Connection oriented? | Yes | Yes | Yes | No |
| AAL protocol to be used | AAL1 | AAL2 | AAL3/4 or AAL5 | AAL3/4 or AAL5 |

**Fig. 2.15** Service classes for the ATM Adaptation Layer (AAL).

To support the four service classes, initially the ITU recommended four types of AAL protocols, called AAL1, AAL2, AAL3, and AAL4. It was soon discovered that the differences between AAL3 and AAL4 protocols are minor. Therefore, they were later merged into a single protocol, called AAL3/4.

It was later discovered that the mechanisms of the AAL3/4 protocol were fairly complex for computer data traffic. Therefore, a new protocol called AAL5 was later added to the AAL layer for handling computer data traffic [Suzuki 1994]. The AAL5 protocol is also called *SEAL* (*Simple and Efficient Adaptation Layer*).

As shown in Figure 2.15, class A traffic will use the AAL1 protocol, class B traffic the AAL2 protocol, and class C and D traffic either AAL3/4 or AAL5. Since both AAL3/4 and AAL5 protocols are meant for use by class C and D traffic, it is important to know the basic differences between the two protocols. AAL3/4 performs error detection on each cell and uses a sophisticated error-checking mechanism that consumes 4 bytes of each 48-byte payload. AAL3/4 allows ATM cells to be multiplexed. On the other hand, AAL5 uses a conventional 5-byte header (no extra byte from the payload of a cell) and it does not support cell multiplexing.

### 2.7.4 ATM Networks

In its simplest form, an ATM network has a mesh-star architecture with two or more ATM switches interconnected with copper or optical cables and the host computers connected to the ATM switches. Figure 2.16 shows such an ATM network with three ATM switches and nine host computers. Cells originating at any of the nine host computers can be switched to any of the other host computers attached to the system by traversing through one or more ATM switches. This simple form is normally suitable for local area ATM networks. In addition to ATM switches and host computers, a wide-area ATM network also contains internetworking devices, such as routers, gateways, and interfaces, to the public network.

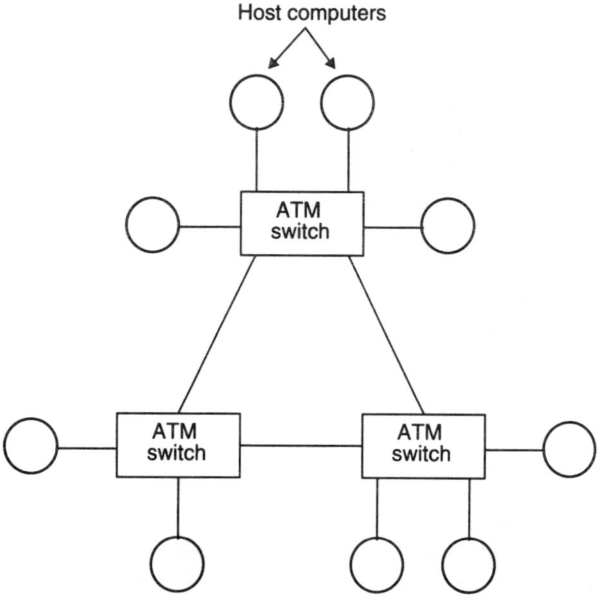


**Fig. 2.16** An ATM network.

An ATM switch has several input and output ports. Each input port has an input port controller, and each output port has an output port controller. Each input port controller consists of a table, referred to as the VCI table, which maps the VPI and VCI of an incoming cell to an output VCI and an output port address. Before an incoming cell is released by an input port controller to the switching fabric of the switch, the VCI of the cell is replaced by the output VCI, and the output port address is appended for self-routing. Each ATM switch also has a switch controller that performs different switch management functions, including updating the tables of the input port controllers. Moreover, each ATM switch usually also has buffers to temporarily store data when cells arriving at different input ports contend for the same output port. Separate buffers may be associated either with the input ports or with the output ports, or the switch may have a pool of buffers that can be used for both input and output buffering.

The ATM switches that contain only a few ports are cheaper and easier to build than switches containing many ports. Local area ATM networks normally contain a small number of ATM switches with only a few ports per switch, whereas wide-area ATM networks normally contain a large number of ATM switches with many ports per switch.

Each host computer in an ATM network is assigned an ATM address that could be based either on a hierarchical 8-byte-long ISDN telephone number scheme E.164 or a 20-byte address proposed by the ATM Forum [ATM Forum 1993]. The latter is modeled after the address format of an OSI network service access point.

The ATM networks having protocol support for a mixture of high-level communication services (e.g., TCP/IP, UDP/IP, Berkeley Software Distributor [BSD] sockets, and RPC) may also be used as backbone networks to interconnect existing networks.

### 2.7.5 Problems and Challenges

As a networking technology, ATM possesses many attractive features, including enormously high bandwidth, scalability, traffic integration, statistical multiplexing, and network simplicity. With these features, ATM technology is certainly going to have a significant impact on the design of future distributed systems. However, for the success of ATM as a networking technology for future distributed systems, several problems have yet to be solved. These problems offer a new set of challenges to network designers and users. Some of the most important of these problems that are currently under investigation by researchers working in the area of ATM technology are briefly described next.

#### Interoperability

If ATM is to succeed as a networking technology, it must interwork with existing installed bases. This property is important to the acceptance of ATM since it will allow a huge number of existing distributed applications to be run over ATM networks. Two remarkable efforts being made in this direction are *LAN emulation over ATM* by the ATM Forum (the primary organization developing and defining ATM standards) [ATM Forum 1994] and *IP over ATM* by the IETF (Internet Engineering Task Force) [Chao et al. 1994, Laubach 1994, Brazdziunas 1994]. They are described next.

***LAN Emulation over ATM.*** The LAN emulation over ATM (called *LAN emulation*) deals with enabling existing LAN-based distributed applications to be run over ATM networks. It also enables interconnection of ATM networks with traditional LANs.

Most existing LANs are based on shared-media interconnects and employ the IEEE 802 family of LAN protocols, which includes the Ethernet (802.3), the Token Bus (802.4), and the Token Ring (802.5) (see Section 2.5.1). Recall from Figure 2.9 that in the IEEE 802 model the data-link layer protocol of the ISO reference model is divided into two layers—the medium-access-control (MAC) layer, which defines the mechanisms that are used to access, share, and manage the communication medium, and the logical-link-control (LLC) layer, which defines a common interface for different network layer protocols to interwork with different MAC protocols. Each host attached to a LAN has a globally unique MAC address. MAC addresses are 48 bits long and form a flat address space. A host can send data to another host only if it knows the MAC address of the receiving host (if both the hosts are in the same LAN) or the MAC address of the next hop router (if both the hosts are in different LANs).

The key idea behind LAN emulation is to design a separate protocol layer, referred to as the ATM-MAC layer, above the AAL and below the LLC layer. Two key functions that must be supported by the ATM-MAC layer are as follows:

1. Emulation of the physical, broadcast, shared medium of LANs for supporting broadcast communication facility
2. Resolution of MAC addresses to ATM addresses for supporting point-to-point communication facility

The ATM emulates the physical, broadcast, shared medium of a conventional LAN by establishing an ATM multicast virtual connection between all of the hosts that are directly connected to the ATM network, referred to as the LAN emulation clients (LECs). This multicast connection is the broadcast channel of the ATM LAN segment. Any LEC may broadcast to all others on the ATM LAN segment by transmitting on the multicast virtual connection.

For point-to-point communication, an address resolution protocol is required to translate the 48-bit MAC address to an ATM address. Translating MAC addresses to ATM addresses can be done using either a broadcast-based approach or a server-based approach. The broadcast-based approach relies on the switch broadcast capability. On the other hand, in the server-based approach, a LAN emulation server (LES) is placed on a globally known virtual channel, and a set of query/response messages is implemented for interaction between the LES and the LECs. All MAC-to-ATM address resolution requests are sent to the LES, which responds to the requester using a predetermined virtual channel.

Once the ATM address of the receiving host has been obtained, a point-to-point ATM virtual connection may be established between the sending and receiving hosts by using the ATM signaling protocol. The result of the address resolution and the VCI of the established connection are cached in a table in the sending host on the assumption that further communication with the receiving host is likely. This mechanism operates entirely within the ATM-MAC layer and is totally transparent to the LLC and higher layer protocols in the hosts. Further details of LAN emulation can be found in [Newman 1994].

***IP over ATM.*** The IP over ATM deals with enabling existing distributed applications that have been designed for the IP suite to be run over ATM networks. Two cases that need to be considered for supporting IP over ATM are as follows:

1. Supporting IP over an ATM network that has LAN emulation functionality implemented over it
2. Supporting IP over a pure ATM network that consists of only ATM switches

Since LAN emulation defines the ATM-MAC layer above the AAL and below the LLC, supporting IP over an emulated LAN is the same as supporting IP over any IEEE 802 LAN. However, when IP is to be supported over a pure ATM network, it is possible to simplify the protocol stack and run IP directly over ATM. For implementing IP directly over ATM, an address resolution protocol is required to translate an IP address to an ATM address. Once again the server-based approach (as described for LAN emulation) can be used for this purpose. With IP over ATM, the address resolution server, referred to as the IP-ATM-ARP server, maintains tables that contain mapping information to map IP addresses to ATM addresses.

When a new host is added to the ATM network, it first goes through a registration process and obtains an ATM address for itself. It then sends a message to the IP-ATM-ARP server, requesting it to add its address resolution information in the mapping table. The message contains the IP and ATM addresses of the newly added host. The server updates the mapping table, allocates a new reserved VCI to the host, and returns the VCI to the host. The host uses this VCI to discriminate between messages received from the server and other hosts. The above process can also be adopted to allow port mobility of hosts. Further details of IP over ATM can be found in [Chao et al. 1994].

### Bandwidth Management

The ATM networks are meant for carrying a mix of synchronous, asynchronous, and isochronous traffic. To achieve the desired quality of service, users are often required to specify the bandwidth requirement for their applications. Two important issues that need to be resolved in this connection are how users estimate and indicate the bandwidth requirements of their applications to the network and how the network allocates the bandwidth to the applications to make best use of the available bandwidth while satisfying the requests of the applications. Some proposals made by researchers working in this area are as follows [Turner 1992, Vetter 1995]:

1. *Peak-rate allocation method.* In this method, users only specify the maximum traffic rate for their applications. Based on user's requests, the network assigns virtual channels to the applications in such a manner that on every link of the network the sum of the rates on the virtual channels is no more than the link's maximum cell rate. If an application's traffic exceeds its specified peak rate, its cells are simply discarded.

2. *Minimum-throughput allocation method.* In this method, users specify the desired minimum throughputs for their applications, and the network guarantees the specified throughputs to the applications on a best-effort basis.

3. *Bursty-traffic specification method.* In this method, users specify the maximum and average traffic rates plus the maximum burst size for their applications. These parameters are used to properly configure the network to allocate the available bandwidth to the applications to meet their specified requirements.

None of these methods has been found to be satisfactory. For instance, Vetter [1995] points out that the first method offers a strong performance guarantee and is easy to implement, but it may make poor use of the available network bandwidth in case of bursty traffic; the second method can provide high efficiency, but its performance guarantee is weak; and the third method involves large computation overhead in computing when a new virtual channel can be safely multiplexed with other virtual channels. Moreover, all three methods suffer from two additional drawbacks. First, since end-to-end protocols normally operate on data units comprising several cells, for an application needing reliable transport service, the loss or discard of a single cell forces retransmission of the entire data, resulting in lower protocol throughput [Vetter 1995]. The problem becomes more acute in a wide-area ATM network because the retransmission may also result in discarding a large amount of data already in the connection pipe. This can have a serious performance implication. The second drawback is that none of the three methods adequately handles multicast virtual circuits [Vetter 1995]. Therefore, new bandwidth management mechanisms that can overcome the problems mentioned previously are needed.

### Latency/Bandwidth Trade-off

Kleinrock [1992] pointed out that the latency/bandwidth trade-off in high-speed wide-area ATM networks will pose new challenges to the designers of these networks. This is primarily due to the fact that the propagation delay or speed of light over a wide area is several magnitudes greater than the time it takes to transmit an ATM cell. For instance, it takes roughly 15 ms for a bit to travel across the United States one way. At 1 Gbps, this time is more than 35,000 times greater than the time required to transmit a single ATM cell into the link [Vetter 1995]. This latency/bandwidth trade-off poses the following two main problems. These are the same problems described in [Tanenbaum 1995]:

1. Consider a WAN spanning across the United States. The round-trip propagation delay between two end sites of the WAN may be approximately 30 ms. Suppose the two sites are on a 622-Mbps ATM network. At 622 Mbps, it takes only about 1.6 ms (1/622 second) to pump all bits of a file of size 1 megabits on to the network. Since the round-trip propagation delay between the two sites is 30 ms, the receiver's reply can be received by the sender only after 31.6 ms. Therefore in this example, out of total 31.6 ms, the link was idle for 30 ms, or 95% of the total. The situation will be worse with higher speed networks and shorter messages. At higher speeds, the fraction of the available virtual circuit

bandwidth that can be effectively used will tend to zero. Hence, new protocols and system architectures are needed to deal with the latency problem in high-speed wide-area ATM networks.

2. Since the propagation delay is several magnitudes greater than the time it takes to transmit an ATM cell, a sender can send thousands of cells over the network before the first bit even arrives at the receiver's site. If the receiver does not possess a large amount of buffering capacity, most of the cells will be lost due to inadequate buffer space, and they will have to be retransmitted. This can have a serious performance implication. The use of the conventional sliding-window protocol for flow control to solve this problem does not work well in this case. This is because if it is decided that the sender must wait for an acknowledgment after sending every megabit of data, due to the latency problem already described above, the virtual circuit will be 95% idle. To solve this problem, areas that require particular attention include flow control, buffering, and congestion control. Some work performed in these areas may be found in [Hong and Suda 1991, Trajkovic and Golestani 1992, Eckberg 1992, Yazid and Mouftah 1992].

## 2.8 SUMMARY

A distributed system relies entirely on the underlying computer network for the communication of data and control information between the nodes of which they are composed. A computer network is a communication system that links the nodes by communication lines and software protocols to exchange data between two processes running on different nodes of the network.

Based on characteristics such as geographic distribution of nodes, data rate, error rate, and communication cost, networks are broadly classified into two types: LAN and WAN. Networks that share some of the characteristics of both LANs and WANs are sometimes referred to as MANs.

The two commonly used network topologies for constructing LANs are the multiaccess bus and ring. For both multiaccess bus and ring networks, a single channel is shared by all the sites of a network. Therefore, medium-access control protocols are needed to provide controlled access to the shared channel by all sites. Of many medium access control protocols, the CSMA/CD protocol is most commonly used for multiaccess bus networks, and the token ring and slotted ring protocols are used for ring networks.

A wide-area network of computers is constructed by interconnecting computers that are separated by large distances. Special hardware devices called packet-switching exchanges (PSEs) are used to connect the computers to the communication channels. The PSEs perform switching and routing activities to transmit data across the network. The two commonly used switching techniques are circuit switching and packet switching.

The selection of the actual path to be used to transmit a packet in a WAN is determined by the routing strategy used. The path used to transmit a packet from one site to another either may be fixed or may dynamically change based on network conditions. This depends on whether a static or a dynamic routing strategy is being used. Moreover, either the whole path may be decided at the source site or the subpath for each hop of the path may be decided by each site along the path. Furthermore, with a dynamic routing strategy, routing tables may be updated in an isolated, centralized, or decentralized manner.

Computer networks are implemented using the concept of layered protocols. The OSI model provides a standard for layered protocols for WANs, and the IEEE 802 LAN model defines a standard for LANs. The seven layers of the OSI model are physical, data link, network, transport, session, presentation, and application. On the other hand, the lowest three layers of the IEEE 802 LAN model are physical, medium-access control, and logical-link control. The IEEE 802 LAN model does not include specifications for higher layers. Of the available protocol suites for network systems, the Internet Protocol (IP) suite is the most popular and widely used.

The communication protocols designed for network systems are usually unsuitable for distributed systems because of the special requirements of distributed systems as compared to network systems. Several communication protocols have been designed to achieve higher throughput and/or fast response in distributed systems and to address one or more of the special requirements of distributed systems. Two such protocols whose characteristic features were described in this chapter are VMTP and FLIP.

Interconnecting two or more networks to form a single network is called internetworking, and the resulting network is called an internetwork. The goal of internetworking is to hide the details of different physical networks so that the resulting internetwork functions as a single coordinated unit. Tools such as bridges, routers, brouters, and gateways are used for internetworking. The Internet is the best example of an internetwork.

The ATM is a high-speed, connection-oriented switching and multiplexing technology that uses short, fixed-length packets (called cells) to transmit different types of traffic simultaneously, including voice, video, and data. Due to its many attractive features, ATM technology is often described as the future computer networking paradigm.

## EXERCISES

**2.1.** What are the main differences between a LAN and a WAN?

**2.2.** Why are medium-access control protocols needed? What properties must a good medium-access-control protocol have?

**2.3.** The CSMA/CD scheme for medium-access control allows random access to the shared medium, detects collisions, and takes necessary steps to retransmit if a collision is detected. Is it possible to devise a random-access scheme for medium-access control in which collisions never occur (collisions are totally avoided)? If no, explain why. If yes, describe a possible scheme of this type along with its advantages and disadvantages.

**2.4.** Answer the following questions for Ethernet:

(a) How does a site acquire the shared channel for transmitting its packets?

(b) How is a collision detected?

(c) How is a collision resolved after detection?

(d) How is the possibility of repeated collisions minimized?

**2.5.** In Ethernet, *collision interval* is the time required for a signal to propagate from one end of the medium to the other and back again, and *retransmission slot time* is set to be a little longer than the collision interval. Prove that no collisions will occur if every site transmits its packet only after it listens to the shared medium and finds it free for a time period that is at least equal to the retransmission slot time.

**2.6.** The token ring and the slotted-ring protocols for medium-access control organize the sites of a network in a logical ring structure. Present an algorithm for detecting the failure of a site in the ring and reconstructing the logical ring when the failure of a site is detected.

**2.7.** Present an algorithm to detect the loss of a token in the token ring scheme for medium-access control.

**2.8.** Suggest a priority-based token ring scheme for medium-access control that does not lead to the starvation of a low-priority site when higher priority sites always have something to transmit.

**2.9.** In a high-speed LAN, suppose the term *high speed* means a data transfer rate that is high enough to make the mean packet transmission time become less than the medium propagation delay. Consider a bus LAN that spans 6000 meters, uses a mean packet length of 1400 bits, and has a data transmission rate of $50 \times 10^6$ bits per second. If the communication medium used for this LAN has a propagation speed of $2 \times 10^8$ m/s, would the LAN be considered a high-speed LAN?

**2.10.** It has been shown that the performance of the CSMA/CD scheme degrades significantly as the ratio $a = (\tau W)/B$ increases, where $\tau$ is the end-to-end propagation delay of the signal across the network, $W$ is the channel bandwidth, and $B$ is the number of bits per packet. One finds that a good estimate of $\tau$ is 10 $\mu$s for each kilometer of cable (assuming one repeater for each 500 meters of cable). Experimental results have shown that, for $a = 0.1$, CSMA/CD provides adequate channel capacity, 0.65 or higher. For the definition of high-speed LAN given in Exercise 2.9, show that CSMA/CD scheme is unsuitable for high-speed LANs.

**2.11.** What is meant by *internetworking*? What are the main issues in internetworking? Explain the difference among the following terms:
(a) Bridge
(b) Router
(c) Gateway

**2.12.** Suppose that the following sequence of message exchanges are involved in transmitting a piece of data when circuit-switching technique is used:
(a) *connect_request* (from sender to receiver)
(b) *connection_acknowledgment* (from receiver to sender)
(c) *send_data* (data transfer from sender to receiver)
(d) *data_acknowledgment* (from receiver to sender)
(e) *disconnect_request* (from sender to receiver)
(f) *disconnection_acknowledgment* (from receiver to sender)
Suppose that the time to transfer each of the above message is $t$, except for the *send_data* message, for which the time taken is $t + ds$, where $d$ is a constant and $s$ is the size of the data in bytes. Now suppose that on the same network $t$ is also the time to transfer a packet of 100 bytes and a packet-switching technique used returns an acknowledgment from receiver to sender for every $n$ packets received. Compute the threshold value of $s$ at which both the circuit-switching and packet-switching techniques perform at the same data transmission rate.

**2.13.** Suggest three different routing strategies for use in computer networks. List the relative advantages and disadvantages of the strategies suggested by you.

**2.14.** A network system uses the dynamic routing strategy and the non-minimal-path selection policy. In this system, a packet may continue to be routed through the network but never reach its destination. Devise a mechanism that avoids the occurrence of this situation in the system.

**2.15.** Why are communication protocols needed in a network system? What are the main reasons for using the layered approach to communication protocol specification and design?

**2.16.** Draw a diagram showing the architecture of the OSI model. Briefly describe the functions of each layer of this architecture.

**2.17.** In Figure 2.8, we see that each layer adds its own header to the message being transmitted across the network. Instead of adding a separate header at each layer, it would have been more efficient to add a single header containing the control information in all these headers to the message before its transmission across the network. Explain why this is not done.

**2.18.** Most computer networks use fewer layers than those specified in the OSI model. Explain what might be the reason for this. What problems, if any, could this lead to?

**2.19.** What are the main differences between connection-oriented and connectionless communication protocols? Indicate which of the two protocols is preferable for the transmission of the following types of information:
(a) Voice
(b) Video
(c) Bursty data

**2.20.** The packets of a message may arrive at their destination in an order different from the order in which they were sent. Indicate for which of the following types of networks is this statement true:
(a) Ethernet LAN
(b) WAN
(c) ATM LAN
(d) ATM WAN
Give reasons for your answers.

**2.21.** Why is the OSI model considered to be unsuitable for use in a LAN environment? Give the architecture of a communication protocol model suitable for LANs. Briefly describe the functions of each layer of this architecture.

**2.22.** Why are conventional communication protocols for network systems generally considered to be unsuitable for distributed systems?

**2.23.** Explain the mechanism used in the VMTP protocol for each of the following:
(a) Handling of lost messages
(b) Group communication
(c) Flow control
(d) Transparent communication.

**2.24.** Explain the mechanism used in the FLIP protocol for each of the following:
(a) Transparent communication
(b) Group communication
(c) Secure communication
(d) Easy network management.

**2.25.** What are the main attractive features of ATM technology? What type of impact will each of these features have on future distributed systems?

**2.26.** Describe the functionalities of the different layers of the ATM protocol reference model.

**2.27.** Explain how the following can be achieved:
(a) LAN emulation over ATM
(b) IP over ATM

**2.28.** Give three different methods that may be used in ATM networks to allocate bandwidth to applications to make best use of the available bandwidth while satisfying the requests of the applications. Also give the relative advantages and limitations of the three methods.

**2.29.** Give examples to illustrate the problems that occur due to the latency/bandwidth trade-off in high-speed, wide-area ATM networks.

## BIBLIOGRAPHY

**[Abeysundara and Kamal 1991]** Abeysundara, B. W., and Kamal, A. E., "High-Speed Local Area Networks and Their Performance: A Survey," *ACM Computing Surveys*, Vol. 23, No. 2, pp. 221–264 (1991).

**[ATM Forum 1993]** *ATM User-Network Interface Specification Version 3.0*, Prentice-Hall, Englewood Cliffs, NJ (1993).

**[ATM Forum 1994]** "LAN Emulation Over ATM," Draft Specification—Revision 5 (ATM FORUM 94-0035R5), LAN Emulation Sub-Working Group of the ATM Forum Technical Committee (August 1994).

**[Black 1993]** Black, U., *Computer Networks: Protocols, Standards, and Interface*, 2nd ed., Prentice-Hall, Englewood Cliffs, NJ (1993).

**[Black 1995a]** Black, U., *ATM: Foundation for Broadband Networks*, Prentice-Hall, Englewood Cliffs, NJ (1995).

**[Black 1995b]** Black, U., *TCP/IP and Related Protocols*, 2nd ed., IEEE Computer Society Press, Los Alamitos, CA (1995).

**[Brazdziunas 1994]** Brazdziunas, C., "IPing Support for ATM Services," Internet RFC No. 1680 (1994).

**[Chao et al. 1994]** Chao, H. J., Ghosal, D., Saha, D., and Tripathi, S. K., "IP on ATM Local Area Networks," *IEEE Communications Magazine*, pp. 52–59, New York, NY (August 1994).

**[Cheriton 1986]** Cheriton, D. R., "VMTP: A Transport Protocol for the Next Generation of Communication Systems," In: *Proceedings of the SIGCOMM'86*, pp. 406–415 (August 1986).

**[Cheriton 1988]** Cheriton, D. R., "The V Distributed System," *Communications of the ACM*, Vol. 31, No. 3, pp. 314–333, ACM, New York, NY (1988).

**[Cheriton and Williamson 1989]** Cheriton, D. R., and Williamson, C. L., "VMTP As the Transport Layer for High-Performance Distributed Systems," *IEEE Communications Magazine*, Vol. 27, No. 6, pp. 37–44, New York, NY (1989).

**[Comer 1995]** Comer, D. E., *Internetworking with TCP/IP: Volume I—Principles, Protocols, and Architectures*, 3rd ed., Prentice-Hall, Englewood Cliffs, NJ (1995).

**[Comer and Stevens 1993]** Comer, D. E., and Stevens, D. L., *Internetworking with TCP/IP: Volume III—Client-Server Programming and Applications: BSD Socket Version*, Prentice-Hall, Englewood Cliffs, NJ (1993).

**[Comer and Stevens 1994]** Comer, D. E., and Stevens, D. L., *Internetworking with TCP/IP: Volume II—Design, Implementation, and Internals*, 2nd ed., Prentice-Hall, Englewood Cliffs, NJ (1994).

**[Datapro 1990]** Datapro, "An Overview of Simple Network Management Protocol," Datapro Network Management, NM40-300-201 (February 1990).

**[Datapro 1993]** Open Software Foundation (OSF) Distributed Management Environment (DME), A Datapro Report, Datapro Network Management, NM40-684-07 (April 1993).

**[DePrycker 1993]** DePrycker, M., *Asynchronous Transfer Mode: Solution for Broadband ISDN*, 2nd ed., Ellis Horwood (1993).

**[DePrycker et al. 1993]** DePrycker, M., Peschi, R., and Landegem, T., "B-ISDN and the OSI Protocol Reference Model," *IEEE Network*, Vol. 7, No. 2, pp. 10–18, New York, NY (March 1993).

**[Dutton and Lenhard 1995]** Dutton, Jr., H., and Lenhard, P., *High-Speed Networking Technology: An Introductory Survey*, Prentice-Hall, Englewood Cliffs, NJ (1995).

**[Eckberg 1992]** Eckberg, A., "B-ISDN/ATM Traffic and Congestion Control," *IEEE Network*, Vol. 6, No. 5, pp. 28–37, New York, NY (1992).

**[Finlayson et al. 1984]** Finlayson, R., Mann, T., Mogul, J., and Theimer, M., "A Reverse Address Resolution Protocol," RFC No. 903 (June 1984).

**[Fischer et al. 1994]** Fischer, W., Wallmeier, E., Worster, T., Davis, S. P., and Hayter, A., "Data Communications Using ATM: Architectures, Protocols, and Resource Management," *IEEE Communications Magazine*, pp. 24–33, New York, NY (August 1994).

**[Furht and Milenkovic 1995]** Furht, B., and Milenkovic, M., *Guided Tour of Multimedia Systems and Applications*, IEEE Computer Society Press, Los Alamitos, CA (1995).

**[Haendel et al. 1994]** Haendel, R., Huber, M. N., and Schroeder, S., *ATM Networks: Concepts, Protocols, Applications*, Addison-Wesley, Reading, MA (1994).

**[Helgert 1991]** Helgert, H. J., *Integrated Services Digital Networks: Architectures, Protocols, Standards*, Addison-Wesley, Reading, MA (1991).

**[Hong and Suda 1991]** Hong, D., and Suda, T., "Congestion Control and Prevention in ATM Networks," *IEEE Network*, Vol. 5, No. 4, pp. 10–16, New York, NY (1991).

**[Hughes 1994]** Hughes, K., "Entering the World-Wide Web: A Guide to Cyberspace," ftp:/taurus.cs.nps.navy.mil:/pub/mbmy/world-wide-web-guide.ps.Z (1994).

**[IEEE 1985a]** *Carrier Sense Multiple Access with Collision Detect (CSMA/CD) Access Method and Physical Layer Specifications*, ANSI/IEEE 802.3 (ISO/DIS 8802/3), IEEE, New York (1985).

**[IEEE 1985b]** *Token-Passing Bus Access Method and Physical Layer Specifications*, ANSI/IEEE 802.4 (ISO/DIS 8802/4), IEEE, New York (1985).

**[IEEE 1985c]** *Token Ring Access Method and Physical Layer Specifications*, ANSI/IEEE 802.5 (ISO/DIS 8802/5), IEEE, New York (1985).

**[IEEE 1990]** *IEEE Standard 802: Overview and Architecture*, American National Standard ANSI/IEEE 802, IEEE Computer Society Press, Los Alamitos, CA (1990).

**[IT 1990]** Information Technology—Open Systems Interconnection—Management Information Protocol Specification—Common Management Information Protocol, ISO/IEC 9596-1, ISO/IEC JTC1/SC21 N5303 (November 1990).

**[Janet 1993]** Janet, E. L., "Selecting a Network Management Protocol, Functional Superiority vs. Popular Appeal," *Telephony* (November 1993).

**[Kaashoek et al. 1993]** Kaashoek, M. F., Van Renesse, R., Staveren, H., and Tanenbaum, A. S., "FLIP: An Internetwork Protocol for Supporting Distributed Systems," *ACM Transactions on Computer Systems*, Vol. 11, No. 1, pp. 73–106 (1993). © ACM, Inc., 1993.

**[Kawarasaki and Jabbari 1991]** Kawarasaki, M., and Jabbari, B., "B-ISDN Architecture and Protocol," *IEEE Journal of Selected Areas on Communications*, Vol. SAC-9, No. 9, pp. 1405–1415, New York, NY (1991).

**[Kim and Wang 1995]** Kim, B. G., and Wang, P., "ATM Network: Goals and Challenges," *Communications of the ACM*, Vol. 38, No. 2, pp. 39–44 (1995).

**[King and Mitrani 1987]** King, P. J. B., and Mitrani, I., "Modeling a Slotted Ring Local Area Network," *IEEE Transactions on Computers*, Vol. C-36, No. 5, pp. 554–561, Piscataway, NJ (1987).

**[Kleinrock 1992]** Kleinrock, L., "The Latency/Bandwidth Tradeoff in Gigabit Networks," IEEE Communications Magazine, Vol. 30, No. 4, pp. 36–40, New York, NY (1992).

**[Krol 1994]** Krol, E., *The Whole Internet: User's Guide and Catalog*, 2nd ed., O'Reilly, Sebastopol, CA (1994).

**[Kung 1992]** Kung, H. T., "Gigabit Local Area Networks: A Systems Perspective," *IEEE Communications Magazine*, Vol. 30, No. 4, pp. 79–89, New York, NY (1992).

**[Larmouth 1993]** Larmouth, J., *Understanding OSI*, Prentice-Hall, London, UK (1993).

**[Laubach 1994]** Laubach, M., "Classical IP and ARP over ATM," RFC No. 1577 (January 1994).

**[Leinwand and Conroy 1996]** Leinwand, A., and Conroy, K. F., *Network Management: A Practical Perspective*, 2nd ed., Addison-Wesley, Reading, MA (1996).

**[Macedonia and Brutzman 1994]** Macedonia, M. R., and Brutzman, D. P., "MBone Provides Audio and Video Across the Internet," *IEEE Computer*, pp. 30–36 (April 1994).

**[Malamud 1992]** Malamud, C., *STACKS: Interoperability in Today's Computer Networks*, Prentice-Hall, Englewood Cliffs, NJ (1992).

**[Malamud 1993]** Malamud, C., *Exploring the Internet: A Technical Travelogue*, Prentice-Hall, Englewood Cliffs, NJ (1993).

**[Martin 1993]** Martin, J. L., "Travels with Gopher," *IEEE Computer*, Vol 26., No. 5, pp. 84–87 (1993).

**[Miller 1995]** Miller, M. A., *Inter Networking: A Guide to Network Communications LAN to LAN; LAN to WAN*, 2nd ed., M&T Books, New York, NY (1995).

**[Mosaic 1994]** "What's New with NCSA Mosaic," http:www.ncsa.uiuc.edu/SDG/Software/Mosaic/Docs/whatsnew.html (June 1994).

**[Mullender et al. 1990]** Mullender, S. J., Van Rossum, G., Tanenbaum, A. S., Van Renesse, R., and Van Staverene, H., "Amoeba: A Distributed Operating System for the 1990s," *IEEE Computer*, Vol. 23., No. 5, pp. 44–53 (1990).

**[Nejmeh 1994]** Nejmeh, B. A., "Internet: A Strategic Tool for the Software Enterprise," Communications of the ACM, Vol. 37, No. 11, pp. 23–27 (1994). © ACM, Inc., 1994.

**[Newman 1994]** Newman, P., "ATM Local Area Networks," *IEEE Communications Magazine*, Vol. 32, No. 3, pp. 86–98 (1994).

**[Omidyar and Aldridge 1993]** Omidyar, C., and Aldridge, A., "Introduction to SDH/SONET," *IEEE Communications Magazine*, Vol. 31, No. 9, pp. 30–33 (1993).

**[Partridge 1994]** Partridge, C., *Gigabit Networking*, Addison-Wesley, Reading, MA (1994).

**[Perlman 1992]** Perlman, R., *Interconnections: Bridges and Routers*, Addison-Wesley, Reading, MA (1992).

**[Plummer 1982]** Plummer, D. C., "An Ethernet Address Resolution Protocol," RFC No. 826 (November 1982).

**[Postel 1980]** Postel, J., "User Datagram Protocol," RFC No. 768, USC Information Sciences Institute (August 1980).

**[Postel 1981a]** Postel, J., "Internet Protocol: DARPA Internet Program Protocol Specification," RFC No. 791 (September 1981).

**[Postel 1981b]** Postel, J., "Internet Control Message Protocol," RFC No. 792 (September 1981).

**[Postel 1981c]** Postel, J., "Transmission Control Protocol: DARPA Internet Program Protocol Specification," RFC No. 793 (September 1981).

**[Press 1994]** Press, L., "Commercialization of the Internet," *Communications of the ACM*, Vol. 37, No. 11, pp. 17–21 (1994).

**[Ramos et al. 1996]** Ramos, E., Schroeder, A., and Beheler, A., *Computer Networking Concepts*, Prentice-Hall, Englewood Cliffs, NJ (1996).

**[Rooholamini 1995]** Rooholamini, R., "ATM-Based Multimedia Servers," *IEEE Multimedia*, pp. 39–52 (Spring 1995).

**[Santifaller 1994]** Santifaller, M., *TCP/IP and ONC/NFS, Internetworking in a UNIX Environment*, 2nd ed., Addison-Wesley, Reading, MA (1994).

**[Shevenell 1994]** Shevenell, M., "NMPv2 Needs Reworking to Emerge as a Viable Net Management Platform," *Network World* (March 7, 1994).

**[Smythe 1995]** Smythe, C., *Internetworking: Designing the Right Architectures*, Addison-Wesley, Reading, MA (1995).

**[Stallings 1992a]** Stallings, W. (Ed.), *Advances in ISDN and Broadband ISDN*, IEEE Computer Society Press, Los Alamitos, CA (1992).

**[Stallings 1992b]** Stallings, W., *Computer Communications: Architectures, Protocols and Standards*, 3rd ed., IEEE Computer Society Press, Los Alamitos, CA (1992).

**[Stallings 1993a]** Stallings, W. (Ed.), *Advances in Local and Metropolitan Area Networks*, IEEE Computer Society Press, Los Alamitos, CA (1993).

**[Stallings 1993b]** Stallings, W. (Ed.), *Network Management*, IEEE Computer Society Press, Los Alamitos, CA (1993).

**[Stallings 1993c]** Stallings, W., *Networking Standards: A Guide to OSI, ISDN, LAN, and MAN Standards*, Addison-Wesley, Reading, MA (1993).

**[Stallings 1995]** Stallings, W., *ISDN and Broadband ISDN with Frame Relay and ATM*, 3rd ed., Prentice-Hall, Englewood Cliffs, NJ (1995).

**[Suzuki 1994]** Suzuki, T., "ATM Adaptation Layer Protocol," *IEEE Communications Magazine*, Vol. 32, No. 4, pp. 80–83 (1994).

**[Tanenbaum 1988]** Tanenbaum, A. S., *Computer Networks*, 2nd ed., Prentice-Hall, Englewood Cliffs, NJ (1988).

**[Tanenbaum 1995]** Tanenbaum, A. S., *Distributed Operating Systems*, Prentice-Hall, Englewood Cliffs, NJ (1995).

**[Tittel and James 1996]** Tittel, E., and James, S., *ISDN Networking Essentials*, Academic Press, San Diego, CA (1996).

**[Trajkovic and Golestani 1992]** Trajkovic, L., and Golestani, S. J., "Congestion Control for Multimedia Services," *IEEE Network*, Vol. 6, No. 5, pp. 20–26 (1992).

**[Turner 1992]** Turner, J., "Managing Bandwidth in ATM Networks with Bursty Traffic," *IEEE Network*, Vol. 6, No. 5, pp. 50–58 (1992).

**[Umar 1993]** Umar, A., *Distributed Computing: A Practical Approach*, Prentice-Hall, Englewood Cliffs, NJ (1993).

**[Verma 1990]** Verma, P. K., *ISDN Systems: Architecture, Technology & Applications*, Prentice-Hall, Englewood Cliffs, NJ (1990).

**[Vetter 1995]** Vetter, R. J., "ATM Concepts: Architectures, and Protocols," *Communications of the ACM*, Vol. 38, No. 2, pp. 31–38 (1995).

**[Vetter and Du 1993]** Vetter, R. J., and Du, D. H. C., "Distributed Computing with High-Speed Optical Networks," *IEEE Computer*, Vol. 26, No. 2, pp. 8–18 (1993).

**[Vetter et al. 1994]** Vetter, R. J., Spell, C., and Ward, C., "Mosaic and the World-Wide Web," *IEEE Computer*, pp. 49–56 (October 1994).

**[Vickers and Suda 1994]** Vickers, B. J., and Suda, T., "Connectionless Service for Public ATM Networks," *IEEE Communications Magazine*, pp. 34–42 (August 1994).

**[Voruganti 1994]** Voruganti, R. R., "A Global Network Management Framework for the '90s," *IEEE Communications Magazine*, pp. 74–83 (August 1994).

**[Wilkes and Wheeler 1979]** Wilkes, M. V., and Wheeler, D. J., "The Cambridge Digital Communication Ring," In: *Proceedings of the Local Area Communications Network Symposium*, Boston, pp. 47–61 (May 1979).

**[Wittie 1991]** Wittie, L. D., "Computer Networks and Distributed Systems," *IEEE Computer*, Vol. 24, No. 9, pp. 67–75 (1991).

**[WWW 1994a]** "World-Wide Web Growth," *ftp*:nic.merit.edu (1994).

**[WWW 1994b]** "The WWW Virtual Library," http:info.cern.ch/hypertext/DataSources/bySubject/Overview.html (June 1994).

**[Yazid and Mouftah 1992]** Yazid, S., and Mouftah, H. T., "Congestion Control Methods for B-ISDN," *IEEE Communications Magazine*, Vol. 30, No. 7, pp. 42–47 (1992).

## POINTERS TO BIBLIOGRAPHIES ON THE INTERNET

Bibliographies containing references on *Computer Networking* can be found at:

ftp:ftp.cs.umanitoba.ca/pub/bibliographies/Distributed/network.html

ftp:ftp.cs.umanitoba.ca/pub/bibliographies/Distributed/CCR.html

Bibliography containing references on *Communication and Routing in Interconnection Networks* can be found at:

ftp:ftp.cs.umanitoba.ca/pub/bibliographies/Parallel/par.comm.html

Bibliography containing references on the *Internet* can be found at:

ftp:ftp.cs.umanitoba.ca/pub/bibliographies/Misc/internet.html

Bibliography containing references on *Gigabit or High-Speed Networks* can be found at:

ftp:ftp.cs.umanitoba.ca/pub/bibliographies/Distributed/gigabit.html

Bibliography containing references on *ATM Networks* can be found at:

ftp:ftp.cs.umanitoba.ca/pub/bibliographies/Distributed/ATM.html

# CHAPTER 3

# Message Passing

## 3.1 INTRODUCTION

A *process* is a program in execution. When we say that two computers of a distributed system are communicating with each other, we mean that two processes, one running on each computer, are in communication with each other. In a distributed system, processes executing on different computers often need to communicate with each other to achieve some common goal. For example, each computer of a distributed system may have a *resource manager* process to monitor the current status of usage of its local resources, and the resource managers of all the computers might communicate with each other from time to time to dynamically balance the system load among all the computers. Therefore, a distributed operating system needs to provide interprocess communication (IPC) mechanisms to facilitate such communication activities.

Interprocess communication basically requires information sharing among two or more processes. The two basic methods for information sharing are as follows:

1. Original sharing, or shared-data approach
2. Copy sharing, or message-passing approach

In the shared-data approach, the information to be shared is placed in a common memory area that is accessible to all the processes involved in an IPC. The shared-data paradigm gives the conceptual communication pattern illustrated in Figure 3.1(*a*). On the other hand, in the message-passing approach, the information to be shared is physically copied from the sender process's address space to the address spaces of all the receiver processes, and this is done by transmitting the data to be copied in the form of messages (a *message* is a block of information). The message-passing paradigm gives the conceptual communication pattern illustrated in Figure 3.1(*b*). That is, the communicating processes interact directly with each other.

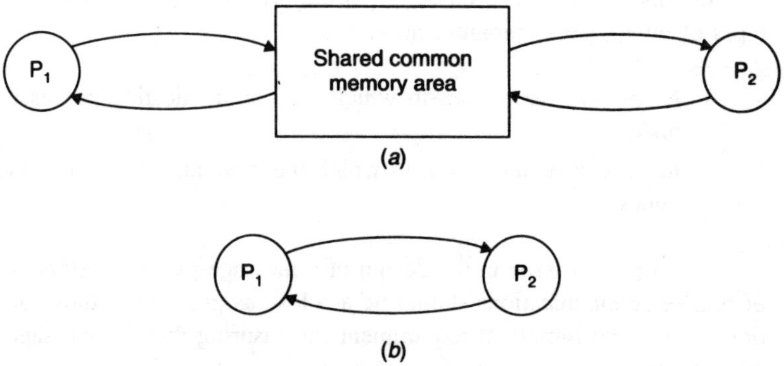


**Fig. 3.1** The two basic interprocess communication paradigms: (*a*) The shared-data approach. (*b*) The message-passing approach.

Since computers in a network do not share memory, processes in a distributed system normally communicate by exchanging messages rather than through shared data. Therefore, message passing is the basic IPC mechanism in distributed systems.

A *message-passing system* is a subsystem of a distributed operating system that provides a set of message-based IPC protocols and does so by shielding the details of complex network protocols and multiple heterogeneous platforms from programmers. It enables processes to communicate by exchanging messages and allows programs to be written by using simple communication primitives, such as *send* and *receive*. It serves as a suitable infrastructure for building other higher level IPC systems, such as remote procedure call (RPC; see Chapter 4) and distributed shared memory (DSM; see Chapter 5).

## 3.2 DESIRABLE FEATURES OF A GOOD MESSAGE-PASSING SYSTEM

### 3.2.1 Simplicity

A message-passing system should be simple and easy to use. It must be straightforward to construct new applications and to communicate with existing ones by using the primitives provided by the message-passing system. It should also be possible for a programmer to designate the different modules of a distributed application and to send and receive messages between them in a way as simple as possible without the need to worry about the system and/or network aspects that are not relevant for the application level. Clean and simple semantics of the IPC protocols of a message-passing system make it easier to build distributed applications and to get them right.

### 3.2.2 Uniform Semantics

In a distributed system, a message-passing system may be used for the following two types of interprocess communication:

1. *Local communication*, in which the communicating processes are on the same node
2. *Remote communication*, in which the communicating processes are on different nodes

An important issue in the design of a message-passing system is that the semantics of remote communications should be as close as possible to those of local communications. This is an important requirement for ensuring that the message-passing system is easy to use.

### 3.2.3 Efficiency

Efficiency is normally a critical issue for a message-passing system to be acceptable by the users. If the message-passing system is not efficient, interprocess communication may become so expensive that application designers will strenuously try to avoid its use in their applications. As a result, the developed application programs would be distorted. An IPC protocol of a message-passing system can be made efficient by reducing the number of message exchanges, as far as practicable, during the communication process. Some optimizations normally adopted for efficiency include the following:

- Avoiding the costs of establishing and terminating connections between the same pair of processes for each and every message exchange between them
- Minimizing the costs of maintaining the connections
- Piggybacking of acknowledgment of previous messages with the next message during a connection between a sender and a receiver that involves several message exchanges

### 3.2.4 Reliability

Distributed systems are prone to different catastrophic events such as node crashes or communication link failures. Such events may interrupt a communication that was in progress between two processes, resulting in the loss of a message. A reliable IPC protocol can cope with failure problems and guarantees the delivery of a message. Handling of lost messages usually involves acknowledgments and retransmissions on the basis of timeouts.

Another issue related to reliability is that of duplicate messages. Duplicate messages may be sent in the event of failures or because of timeouts. A reliable IPC protocol is also capable of detecting and handling duplicates. Duplicate handling usually involves generating and assigning appropriate sequence numbers to messages.

A good message-passing system must have IPC protocols to support these reliability features.

### 3.2.5 Correctness

A message-passing system often has IPC protocols for group communication that allow a sender to send a message to a group of receivers and a receiver to receive messages from several senders. Correctness is a feature related to IPC protocols for group communication. Although not always required, correctness may be useful for some applications. Issues related to correctness are as follows [Navratnam et al. 1988]:

- Atomicity
- Ordered delivery
- Survivability

Atomicity ensures that every message sent to a group of receivers will be delivered to either all of them or none of them. Ordered delivery ensures that messages arrive at all receivers in an order acceptable to the application. Survivability guarantees that messages will be delivered correctly despite partial failures of processes, machines, or communication links. Survivability is a difficult property to achieve.

### 3.2.6 Flexibility

Not all applications require the same degree of reliability and correctness of the IPC protocols. For example, in adaptive routing, it may be necessary to distribute the information regarding queuing delays in different parts of the network. A broadcast protocol could be used for this purpose. However, if a broadcast message is late in coming, due to communication failures, it might just as well not arrive at all as it will soon be outdated by a more recent one anyway. Similarly, many applications do not require atomicity or ordered delivery of messages. For example, a client may multicast a request message to a group of servers and offer the job to the first server that replies. Obviously, atomicity of message delivery is not required in this case. Thus the IPC protocols of a message-passing system must be flexible enough to cater to the various needs of different applications. That is, the IPC primitives should be such that the users have the flexibility to choose and specify the types and levels of reliability and correctness requirements of their applications. Moreover, IPC primitives must also have the flexibility to permit any kind of control flow between the cooperating processes, including synchronous and asynchronous *send/receive*.

### 3.2.7 Security

A good message-passing system must also be capable of providing a secure end-to-end communication. That is, a message in transit on the network should not be accessible to any user other than those to whom it is addressed and the sender. Steps necessary for secure communication include the following:

- Authentication of the receiver(s) of a message by the sender
- Authentication of the sender of a message by its receiver(s)
- Encryption of a message before sending it over the network

These issues will be described in detail in Chapter 11.

### 3.2.8 Portability

There are two different aspects of portability in a message-passing system:

1. The message-passing system should itself be portable. That is, it should be possible to easily construct a new IPC facility on another system by reusing the basic design of the existing message-passing system.

2. The applications written by using the primitives of the IPC protocols of the message-passing system should be portable. This requires that heterogeneity must be considered while designing a message-passing system. This may require the use of an external data representation format for the communications taking place between two or more processes running on computers of different architectures. The design of high-level primitives for the IPC protocols of a message-passing system should be done so as to hide the heterogeneous nature of the network.

## 3.3 ISSUES IN IPC BY MESSAGE PASSING

A message is a block of information formatted by a sending process in such a manner that it is meaningful to the receiving process. It consists of a fixed-length header and a variable-size collection of typed data objects. As shown in Figure 3.2, the header usually consists of the following elements:

- *Address.* It contains characters that uniquely identify the sending and receiving processes in the network. Thus, this element has two parts—one part is the sending process address and the other part is the receiving process address.
- *Sequence number.* This is the message identifier (ID), which is very useful for identifying lost messages and duplicate messages in case of system failures.

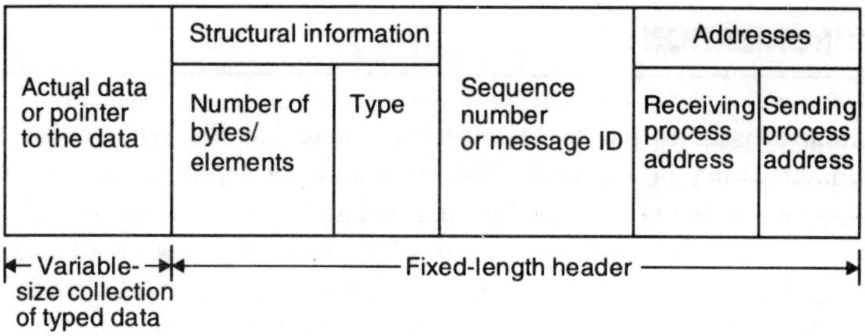


**Fig. 3.2** A typical message structure.

- *Structural information.* This element also has two parts. The *type* part specifies whether the data to be passed on to the receiver is included within the message or the message only contains a pointer to the data, which is stored somewhere outside the contiguous portion of the message. The second part of this element specifies the length of the variable-size message data.

In a message-oriented IPC protocol, the sending process determines the actual contents of a message and the receiving process is aware of how to interpret the contents. Special primitives are explicitly used for sending and receiving the messages. Therefore, in this method, the users are fully aware of the message formats used in the communication process and the mechanisms used to send and receive messages.

In the design of an IPC protocol for a message-passing system, the following important issues need to be considered:

- Who is the sender?
- Who is the receiver?
- Is there one receiver or many receivers?
- Is the message guaranteed to have been accepted by its receiver(s)?
- Does the sender need to wait for a reply?
- What should be done if a catastrophic event such as a node crash or a communication link failure occurs during the course of communication?
- What should be done if the receiver is not ready to accept the message: Will the message be discarded or stored in a buffer? In the case of buffering, what should be done if the buffer is full?
- If there are several outstanding messages for a receiver, can it choose the order in which to service the outstanding messages?

These issues are addressed by the semantics of the set of communication primitives provided by the IPC protocol. A general description of the various ways in which these issues are addressed by message-oriented IPC protocols is presented below.

## 3.4 SYNCHRONIZATION

A central issue in the communication structure is the synchronization imposed on the communicating processes by the communication primitives. The semantics used for synchronization may be broadly classified as *blocking* and *nonblocking* types. A primitive is said to have nonblocking semantics if its invocation does not block the execution of its invoker (the control returns almost immediately to the invoker); otherwise a primitive is said to be of the blocking type. The synchronization imposed on the communicating processes basically depends on one of the two types of semantics used for the *send* and *receive* primitives.

In case of a blocking *send* primitive, after execution of the *send* statement, the sending process is blocked until it receives an acknowledgment from the receiver that the message has been received. On the other hand, for nonblocking *send* primitive, after execution of the *send* statement, the sending process is allowed to proceed with its execution as soon as the message has been copied to a buffer.

In the case of a blocking *receive* primitive, after execution of the *receive* statement, the receiving process is blocked until it receives a message. On the other hand, for a nonblocking *receive* primitive, the receiving process proceeds with its execution after execution of the *receive* statement, which returns control almost immediately just after telling the kernel where the message buffer is.

An important issue in a nonblocking *receive* primitive is how the receiving process knows that the message has arrived in the message buffer. One of the following two methods is commonly used for this purpose:

1. *Polling*. In this method, a *test* primitive is provided to allow the receiver to check the buffer status. The receiver uses this primitive to periodically poll the kernel to check if the message is already available in the buffer.

2. *Interrupt*. In this method, when the message has been filled in the buffer and is ready for use by the receiver, a software interrupt is used to notify the receiving process. This method permits the receiving process to continue with its execution without having to issue unsuccessful *test* requests. Although this method is highly efficient and allows maximum parallelism, its main drawback is that user-level interrupts make programming difficult [Tanenbaum 1995].

A variant of the nonblocking *receive* primitive is the conditional *receive* primitive, which also returns control to the invoking process almost immediately, either with a message or with an indicator that no message is available.

In a blocking *send* primitive, the sending process could get blocked forever in situations where the potential receiving process has crashed or the sent message has been lost on the network due to communication failure. To prevent this situation, blocking *send* primitives often use a timeout value that specifies an interval of time after which the *send* operation is terminated with an error status. Either the timeout value may be a default value or the users may be provided with the flexibility to specify it as a parameter of the *send* primitive.

A timeout value may also be associated with a blocking *receive* primitive to prevent the receiving process from getting blocked indefinitely in situations where the potential sending process has crashed or the expected message has been lost on the network due to communication failure.

When both the *send* and *receive* primitives of a communication between two processes use blocking semantics, the communication is said to be *synchronous;* otherwise it is *asynchronous*. That is, for synchronous communication, the sender and the receiver must be synchronized to exchange a message. This is illustrated in Figure 3.3. Conceptually, the sending process sends a message to the receiving process, then waits for an acknowledgment. After executing the *receive* statement, the receiver remains blocked until it receives the message sent by the sender. On receiving the message, the receiver sends an acknowledgment message to the sender. The sender resumes execution only after receiving this acknowledgment message.

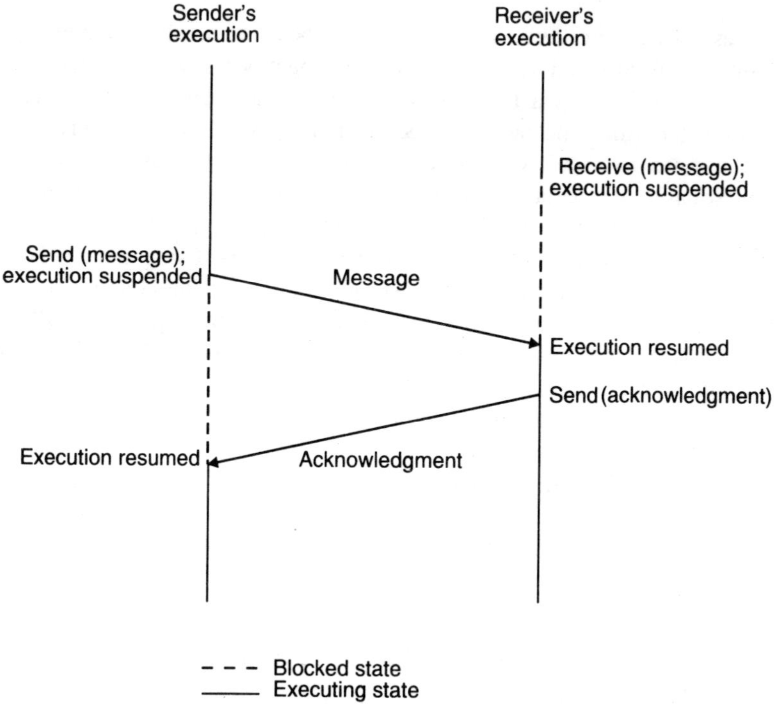


**Fig. 3.3** Synchronous mode of communication with both *send* and *receive* primitives having blocking-type semantics.

As compared to asynchronous communication, synchronous communication is simple and easy to implement. It also contributes to reliability because it assures the sending process that its message has been accepted before the sending process resumes execution. As a result, if the message gets lost or is undelivered, no backward error recovery is necessary for the sending process to establish a consistent state and resume execution [Shatz 1984]. However, the main drawback of synchronous communication is that it limits concurrency and is subject to communication deadlocks (communication deadlock is described in Chapter 6). It is less flexible than asynchronous communication because the sending process always has to wait for an acknowledgment from the receiving process even when this is not necessary. In a system that supports multiple threads in a single process (see Chapter 8), the blocking primitives can be used without the disadvantage of limited concurrency. How this is made possible is explained in Chapter 8.

A flexible message-passing system usually provides both blocking and nonblocking primitives for *send* and *receive* so that users can choose the most suitable one to match the specific needs of their applications.

## 3.5 BUFFERING

Messages can be transmitted from one process to another by copying the body of the message from the address space of the sending process to the address space of the receiving process (possibly via the address spaces of the kernels of the sending and receiving computers). In some cases, the receiving process may not be ready to receive a message transmitted to it but it wants the operating system to save that message for later reception. In these cases, the operating system will rely on the receiver having a buffer in which messages can be stored prior to the receiving process executing specific code to receive the message.

In interprocess communication, the message-buffering strategy is strongly related to synchronization strategy. The synchronous and asynchronous modes of communication correspond respectively to the two extremes of buffering: a *null buffer*, or *no buffering*, and a *buffer with unbounded capacity.* Other two commonly used buffering strategies are *single-message* and *finite-bound*, or *multiple-message*, buffers. These four types of buffering strategies are described below.

### 3.5.1 Null Buffer (or No Buffering)

In case of no buffering, there is no place to temporarily store the message. Hence one of the following implementation strategies may be used:

1. The message remains in the sender process's address space and the execution of the *send* is delayed until the receiver executes the corresponding *receive*. To do this, the sender process is backed up and suspended in such a way that when it is unblocked, it starts by reexecuting the *send* statement. When the receiver executes *receive*, an acknowledgment is sent to the sender's kernel saying that the sender can now send the message. On receiving the acknowledgment message, the sender is unblocked, causing the *send* to be executed once again. This time, the message is successfully transferred from the sender's address space to the receiver's address space because the receiver is waiting to receive the message.

2. The message is simply discarded and the timeout mechanism is used to resend the message after a timeout period. That is, after executing *send*, the sender process waits for

an acknowledgment from the receiver process. If no acknowledgment is received within the timeout period, it assumes that its message was discarded and tries again hoping that this time the receiver has already executed *receive*. The sender may have to try several times before succeeding. The sender gives up after retrying for a predecided number of times.

As shown in Figure 3.4(*a*), in the case of no buffering, the logical path of message transfer is directly from the sender's address space to the receiver's address space, involving a single copy operation.

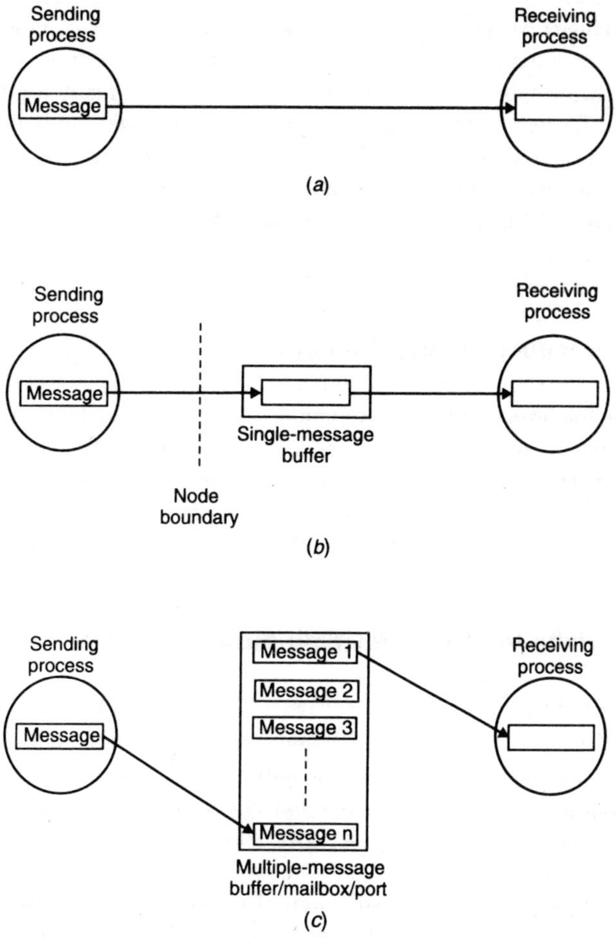


**Fig. 3.4** The three types of buffering strategies used in interprocess comunication mechanisms: (*a*) Message transfer in synchronous send with no buffering strategy (only one copy operation is needed). (*b*) Message transfer in synchronous send with single-message buffering strategy (two copy operations are needed). (*c*) Message transfer in asynchronous send with multiple-message buffering strategy (two copy operations are needed).

### 3.5.2 Single-Message Buffer

The null buffer strategy is generally not suitable for synchronous communication between two processes in a distributed system because if the receiver is not ready, a message has to be transferred two or more times, and the receiver of the message has to wait for the entire time taken to transfer the message across the network. In a distributed system, message transfer across the network may require significant time in some cases. Therefore, instead of using the null buffer strategy, synchronous communication mechanisms in network/distributed systems use a single-message buffer strategy. In this strategy, a buffer having a capacity to store a single message is used on the receiver's node. This is because in systems based on synchronous communication, an application module may have at most one message outstanding at a time. The main idea behind the single-message buffer strategy is to keep the message ready for use at the location of the receiver. Therefore, in this method, the request message is buffered on the receiver's node if the receiver is not ready to receive the message. The message buffer may either be located in the kernel's address space or in the receiver process's address space. As shown in Figure 3.4(*b*), in this case the logical path of message transfer involves two copy operations.

### 3.5.3 Unbounded-Capacity Buffer

In the asynchronous mode of communication, since a sender does not wait for the receiver to be ready, there may be several pending messages that have not yet been accepted by the receiver. Therefore, an unbounded-capacity message buffer that can store all unreceived messages is needed to support asynchronous communication with the assurance that all the messages sent to the receiver will be delivered.

### 3.5.4 Finite-Bound (or Multiple-Message) Buffer

Unbounded capacity of a buffer is practically impossible. Therefore, in practice, systems using asynchronous mode of communication use finite-bound buffers, also known as multiple-message buffers. When the buffer has finite bounds, a strategy is also needed for handling the problem of a possible buffer overflow. The buffer overflow problem can be dealt with in one of the following two ways:

1. *Unsuccessful communication.* In this method, message transfers simply fail whenever there is no more buffer space. The *send* normally returns an error message to the sending process, indicating that the message could not be delivered to the receiver because the buffer is full. Unfortunately, the use of this method makes message passing less reliable.

2. *Flow-controlled communication.* The second method is to use flow control, which means that the sender is blocked until the receiver accepts some messages, thus creating

space in the buffer for new messages. This method introduces a synchronization between the sender and the receiver and may result in unexpected deadlocks. Moreover, due to the synchronization imposed, the asynchronous send does not operate in the truly asynchronous mode for all *send* commands.

The amount of buffer space to be allocated in the bounded-buffer strategy is a matter of implementation. In the most often used approach, a *create_buffer* system call is provided to the users. This system call, when executed by a receiver process, creates a buffer (sometimes called a *mailbox* or *port*) of a size specified by the receiver. The receiver's mailbox may be located either in the kernel's address space or in the receiver process's address space. If it is located in the kernel's address space, mailboxes are a system resource that must be allocated to processes as and when required. This will tend to limit the number of messages that an individual process may keep in its mailbox. On the other hand, if the mailbox is located in the receiver process's address space, the operating system will have to rely on the process allocating an appropriate amount of memory, protecting the mailbox from mishaps, and so on.

As shown in Figure 3.4(*c*), in the case of asynchronous *send* with bounded-buffer strategy, the message is first copied from the sending process's memory into the receiving process's mailbox and then copied from the mailbox to the receiver's memory when the receiver calls for the message. Therefore, in this case also, the logical path of message transfer involves two copy operations.

Although message communication based on multiple-message-buffering capability provides better concurrency and flexibility as compared to no buffering or single-message buffering, it is more complex to design and use. This is because of the extra work and overhead involved in the mechanisms needed for the creation, deletion, protection, and other issues involved in buffer management.

## 3.6 MULTIDATAGRAM MESSAGES

Almost all networks have an upper bound on the size of data that can be transmitted at a time. This size is known as the *maximum transfer unit* (*MTU*) of a network. A message whose size is greater than the MTU has to be fragmented into multiples of the MTU, and then each fragment has to be sent separately. Each fragment is sent in a packet that has some control information in addition to the message data. Each packet is known as a *datagram*. Messages smaller than the MTU of the network can be sent in a single packet and are known as *single-datagram messages*. On the other hand, messages larger than the MTU of the network have to be fragmented and sent in multiple packets. Such messages are known as *multidatagram messages*. Obviously, different packets of a multidatagram message bear a sequential relationship to one another. The disassembling of a multidatagram message into multiple packets on the sender side and the reassembling of the packets on the receiver side is usually the responsibility of the message-passing system.

## 3.7 ENCODING AND DECODING OF MESSAGE DATA

A message data should be meaningful to the receiving process. This implies that, ideally, the structure of program objects should be preserved while they are being transmitted from the address space of the sending process to the address space of the receiving process. This obviously is not possible in a heterogeneous system in which the sending and receiving processes are on computers of different architectures. However, even in homogeneous systems, it is very difficult to achieve this goal mainly because of two reasons:

1. An absolute pointer value loses its meaning when transferred from one process address space to another. Therefore, such program objects that use absolute pointer values cannot be transferred in their original form, and some other form of representation must be used to transfer them. For example, to transmit a tree object, each element of the tree must be copied in a leaf record and properly aligned in some fixed order in a buffer before it can be sent to another process. The leaf records themselves have no meaning in the address space of the receiving process, but the tree can be regenerated easily from them. To facilitate such regeneration, object-type information must be passed between the sender and receiver, indicating not only that a tree object is being passed but also the order in which the leaf records are aligned. This process of flattening and shaping of tree objects also extends to other structured program objects, such as linked lists.

2. Different program objects occupy varying amount of storage space. To be meaningful, a message must normally contain several types of program objects, such as long integers, short integers, variable-length character strings, and so on. In this case, to make the message meaningful to the receiver, there must be some way for the receiver to identify which program object is stored where in the message buffer and how much space each program object occupies.

Due to the problems mentioned above in transferring program objects in their original form, they are first converted to a stream form that is suitable for transmission and placed into a message buffer. This conversion process takes place on the sender side and is known as *encoding* of a message data. The encoded message, when received by the receiver, must be converted back from the stream form to the original program objects before it can be used. The process of reconstruction of program objects from message data on the receiver side is known as *decoding* of the message data.

One of the following two representations may be used for the encoding and decoding of a message data:

1. *In tagged representation* the type of each program object along with its value is encoded in the message. In this method, it is a simple matter for the receiving process to check the type of each program object in the message because of the self-describing nature of the coded data format.

2. *In untagged representation* the message data only contains program objects. No information is included in the message data to specify the type of each program object. In

this method, the receiving process must have a prior knowledge of how to decode the received data because the coded data format is not self-describing.

The untagged representation is used in Sun XDR (eXternal Data Representation) [Sun 1990] and Courier [Xerox 1981], whereas the tagged representation is used in the ASN.1 (Abstract Syntax Notation) standard [CCITT 1985] and the Mach distributed operating system [Fitzgerald and Rashid 1986].

In general, tagged representation is more expensive than untagged representation, both in terms of the quantity of data transferred and the processing time needed at each side to encode and decode the message data. No matter which representation is used, both the sender and the receiver must be fully aware of the format of data coded in the message. The sender possesses the encoding routine for the coded data format and the receiver possesses the corresponding decoding routine. The encoding and decoding operations are perfectly symmetrical in the sense that decoding exactly reproduces the data that was encoded, allowing for differences in local representations. Sometimes, a receiver may receive a badly encoded data, such as encoded data that exceeds a maximum-length argument. In such a situation, the receiver cannot successfully decode the received data and normally returns an error message to the sender indicating that the data is not intelligible.

## 3.8 PROCESS ADDRESSING

Another important issue in message-based communication is addressing (or naming) of the parties involved in an interaction: To whom does the sender wish to send its message and, conversely, from whom does the receiver wish to accept a message? For greater flexibility, a message-passing system usually supports two types of process addressing:

1. *Explicit addressing.* The process with which communication is desired is explicitly named as a parameter in the communication primitive used. Primitives (*a*) and (*b*) of Figure 3.5 require explicit process addressing.

2. *Implicit addressing.* A process willing to communicate does not explicitly name a process for communication. Primitives (*c*) and (*d*) of Figure 3.5 support implicit process addressing. In primitive (*c*), the sender names a service instead of a process. This type of primitive is useful in client-server communications when the client is not concerned with which particular server out of a set of servers providing the service desired by the client actually services its request. This type of process addressing is also known as *functional addressing* because the address used in the communication primitive identifies a service rather than a process.

On the other hand, in primitive (*d*), the receiver is willing to accept a message from any sender. This type of primitive is again useful in client-server communications when the server is meant to service requests of all clients that are authorized to use its service.

(a) **send** (process_id, message)
Send a message to the process identified by "process_id".

(b) **receive** (process_id, message)
Receive a message from the process identified by "process_id".

(c) **send_any** (service_id, message)
Send a message to any process that provides the service of type "service_id".

(d) **receive_any** (process_id, message)
Receive a message from any process and return the process identifier ("process_id") of the process from which the message was received.

**Fig. 3.5** Primitives for explicit and implicit addressing of processes.

With the two basic types of process addressing used in communication primitives, we now look at the commonly used methods for process addressing.

A simple method to identify a process is by a combination of *machine_id* and *local_id*, such as *machine_id@local_id*. The *local_id* part is a process identifier, or a port identifier of a receiving process, or something else that can be used to uniquely identify a process on a machine. A process willing to send a message to another process specifies the receiving process's address in the form *machine_id@local_id*. The *machine_id* part of the address is used by the sending machine's kernel to send the message to the receiving process's machine, and the *local_id* part of the address is then used by the kernel of the receiving process's machine to forward the message to the process for which it is intended. This method of process addressing is used in Berkeley UNIX with 32-bit Internet addresses for *machine_id* and 16-bit numbers for *local_id*.

An attractive feature of this method is that no global coordination is needed to generate systemwide unique process identifiers because *local_ids* need to be unique only for one machine and can be generated locally without consultation with other machines. However, a drawback of this method is that it does not allow a process to migrate from one machine to another if such a need arises. For instance, one or more processes of a heavily loaded machine may be migrated to a lightly loaded machine to balance the overall system load.

To overcome the limitation of the above method, processes can be identified by a combination of the following three fields: *machine_id, local_id, and machine_id.*

1. The first field identifies the node on which the process is created
2. The second field is a local indentifier generated by the node on which the process is created
3. The third field identifies the last known location (node) of the process.

During the lifetime of a process, the values of the first two fields of its identifier never change; the third field, however, may. This method of process addressing is known as *link-based process addressing*. For this method to work properly, when a process is migrated from its current node to a new node, a link information (process identifier with the value of its third field equal to the *machine_id* of the process's new node) is left on its previous node, and on the new node, a new *local_id* is assigned to the process, and its process identifier and the new *local_id* is entered in a mapping table maintained by the kernel of the new node for all processes created on another node but running on this node. Note that the value of the third field of a process identifier is set equal to its first field when the process is created.

A process willing to send a message to another process specifies the receiving process's address in the form, say, *machine_id@local_id@machine_id*. The kernel of the sending machine delivers the message to the machine whose *machine_id* is specified in the third field of the receiving process's address. If the value of the third field is equal to the first field, the message will be sent to the node on which the process was created. If the receiving process was not migrated, the message is delivered to it by using the *local_id* information in the process identifier. On the other hand, if the receiving process was migrated, the link information left for it on that node is used to forward the message to the node to which the receiving process was migrated from this node. In this manner, the message may get forwarded from one node to another several times before it reaches the current node of the receiving process. When the message reaches the current node of the receiving process, the kernel of that node extracts the process identifiers of the sending and receiving processes from the message. The first two fields of the process identifier of the receiving process are used as its unique identifier to extract its *local_id* from the mapping table and then to deliver the message to the proper process. On the other hand, the process identifier of the sending process is used to return to it the current location of the receiving process. The sending process uses this information to update the value of the third field of the receiving process's identifier, which it caches in a local cache, so that from the next time the sending process can directly send a message for the receiving process to this location of the receiving process instead of sending it via the node on which the receiving process was created. A variant of this method of process addressing is used in DEMOS/MP [Miller et al. 1987] and Charlotte [Artsy et al. 1987]. Although this method of process addressing supports the process migration facility, it suffers from two main drawbacks:

1. The overload of locating a process may be large if the process has migrated several times during its lifetime.
2. It may not be possible to locate a process if an intermediate node on which the process once resided during its lifetime is down.

Both process-addressing methods previously described are nontransparent due to the need to specify the machine identifier. The user is well aware of the location of the process (or at least the location on which the process was created). However, we saw in Chapter 1 that location transparency is one of the main goals of a distributed operating system. Hence a location-transparent process-addressing mechanism is more desirable for a message-passing system. A simple method to achieve this goal is to ensure that the systemwide unique identifier of a process does not contain an embedded machine identifier. A centralized process identifier allocator that maintains a counter can be used for this purpose. When it receives a request for an identifier, it simply returns the current value of the counter and then increments it by 1. This scheme, however, suffers from the problems of poor reliability and poor scalability.

Another method to achieve the goal of location transparency in process addressing is to use a two-level naming scheme for processes. In this method, each process has two identifiers: a high-level name that is machine independent (an ASCII string) and a low-level name that is machine dependent (such as *machine_id@local_id*). A *name server* is used to maintain a mapping table that maps high-level names of processes to their low-level names. When this method of process addressing is used, a process that wants to send a message to another process specifies the high-level name of the receiving process in the communication primitive. The kernel of the sending machine first contacts the name server (whose address is well known to all machines) to get the low-level name of the receiving process from its high-level name. Using the low-level name, the kernel sends the message to the proper machine, where the receiving kernel delivers the message to the receiving process. The sending kernel also caches the high-level name to low-level name-mapping information of the receiving process in a local cache for future use, so that the name server need not be contacted when a message has to be sent again to the receiving process.

Notice that the name server approach allows a process to be migrated from one node to another without the need to change the code in the program of any process that wants to communicate with it. This is because when a process migrates its low-level identifier changes, and this change is incorporated in the name server's mapping table. However, the high-level name of the process remains unchanged.

The name server approach is also suitable for functional addressing. In this case, a high-level name identifies a service instead of a process, and the name server maps a service identifier to one or more processes that provide that service.

The name server approach also suffers from the problems of poor reliability and poor scalability because the name server is a centralized component of the system. One way to overcome these problems is to replicate the name server. However, this leads to extra overhead needed in keeping the replicas consistent.

## 3.9 FAILURE HANDLING

While a distributed system may offer potential for parallelism, it is also prone to partial failures such as a node crash or a communication link failure. As shown in Figure 3.6, during interprocess communication, such failures may lead to the following problems:

1. *Loss of request message*. This may happen either due to the failure of communication link between the sender and receiver or because the receiver's node is down at the time the request message reaches there.

2. *Loss of response message*. This may happen either due to the failure of communication link between the sender and receiver or because the sender's node is down at the time the response message reaches there.

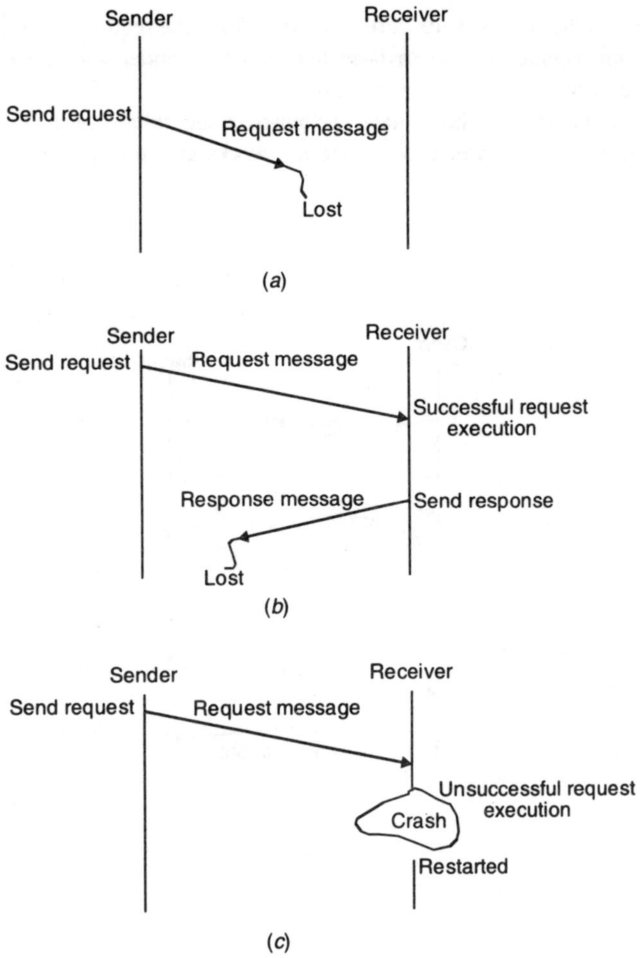


**Fig. 3.6** Possible problems in IPC due to different types of system failures. (*a*) Request message is lost. (*b*) Response message is lost. (*c*) Receiver's computer crashed.

3. *Unsuccessful execution of the request.* This happens due to the receiver's node crashing while the request is being processed.

To cope with these problems, a reliable IPC protocol of a message-passing system is normally designed based on the idea of internal retransmissions of messages after timeouts and the return of an acknowledgment message to the sending machine's kernel by the receiving machine's kernel. That is, the kernel of the sending machine is responsible for retransmitting the message after waiting for a timeout period if no acknowledgment is received from the receiver's machine within this time. The kernel of the sending machine frees the sending process only when the acknowledgment is received. The time duration for which the sender waits before retransmitting the request is normally slightly more than the approximate round-trip time between the sender and the receiver nodes plus the average time required for executing the request.

Based on the above idea, a four-message reliable IPC protocol for client-server communication between two processes works as follows (see Fig. 3.7):

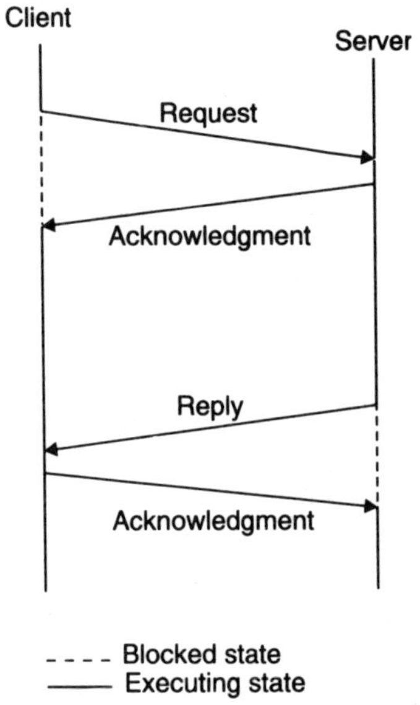


**Fig. 3.7** The four-message reliable IPC protocol for client-server communication between two processes.

1. The client sends a request message to the server.

2. When the request message is received at the server's machine, the kernel of that machine returns an acknowledgment message to the kernel of the client machine. If the acknowledgment is not received within the timeout period, the kernel of the client machine retransmits the request message.

3. When the server finishes processing the client's request, it returns a reply message (containing the result of processing) to the client.

4. When the reply message is received at the client's machine, the kernel of that machine returns an acknowledgment message to the kernel of the server machine. If the acknowledgment message is not received within the timeout period, the kernel of the server machine retransmits the reply message.

In client-server communication, the result of the processed request is sufficient acknowledgment that the request message was received by the server. Based on this idea, a three-message reliable IPC protocol for client-server communication between two processes works as follows (see Fig. 3.8):

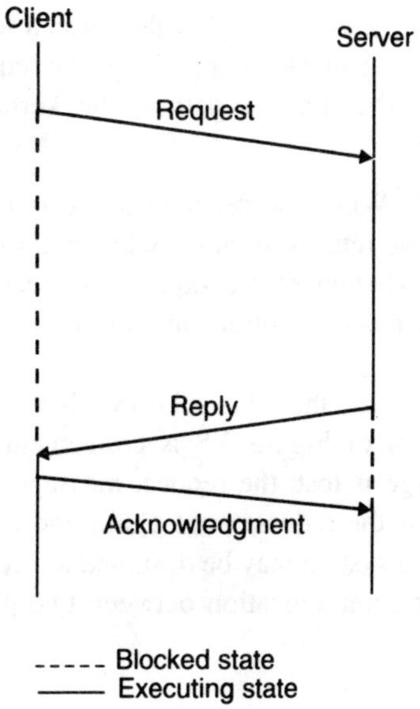


**Fig. 3.8** The three-message reliable IPC protocol for client-server communication between two processes.

1. The client sends a request message to the server.

2. When the server finishes processing the client's request, it returns a reply message (containing the result of processing) to the client. The client remains blocked until the reply is received. If the reply is not received within the timeout period, the kernel of the client machine retransmits the request message.

3. When the reply message is received at the client's machine, the kernel of that machine returns an acknowledgment message to the kernel of the server machine. If the acknowledgment message is not received within the timeout period, the kernel of the server machine retransmits the reply message.

In the protocol of Figure 3.8, a problem occurs if a request processing takes a long time. If the request message is lost, it will be retransmitted only after the timeout period, which has been set to a large value to avoid unnecessary retransmissions of the request message. On the other hand, if the timeout value is not set properly taking into consideration the long time needed for request processing, unnecessary retransmissions of the request message will take place. The following protocol may be used to handle this problem:

1. The client sends a request message to the server.

2. When the request message is received at the server's machine, the kernel of that machine starts a timer. If the server finishes processing the client's request and returns the reply message to the client before the timer expires, the reply serves as the acknowledgment of the request message. Otherwise, a separate acknowledgment is sent by the kernel of the server machine to acknowledge the request message. If an acknowledgment is not received within the timeout period, the kernel of the client machine retransmits the request message.

3. When the reply message is received at the client's machine, the kernel of that machine returns an acknowledgment message to the kernel of the server machine. If the acknowledgment message is not received within the timeout period, the kernel of the server machine retransmits the reply message.

Notice that the acknowledgment message from client to server machine in the protocol of Figure 3.8 is convenient but not a necessity. This is because if the reply message is lost, the request message will be retransmitted after timeout. The server can process the request once again and return the reply to the client. Therefore, a message-passing system may be designed to use the following two-message IPC protocol for client-server communication between two processes (see Fig. 3.9):

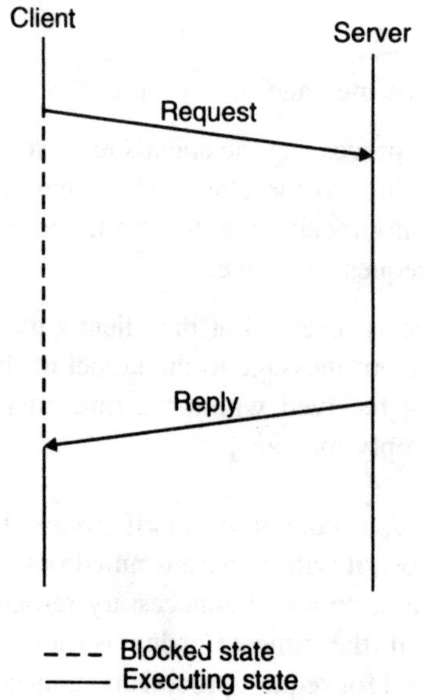


**Fig. 3.9** The two-message IPC protocol used in many systems for client-server communication between two processes.

1. The client sends a request message to the server and remains blocked until a reply is received from the server.
2. When the server finishes processing the client's request, it returns a reply message (containing the result of processing) to the client. If the reply is not received within the timeout period, the kernel of the client machine retransmits the request message.

Based on the protocol of Figure 3.9, an example of failure handling during communication between two processes is shown in Figure 3.10. The protocol of Figure 3.9 is said to obey *at-least-once* semantics, which ensures that at least one execution of the receiver's operation has been performed (but possibly more). It is more appropriate to call

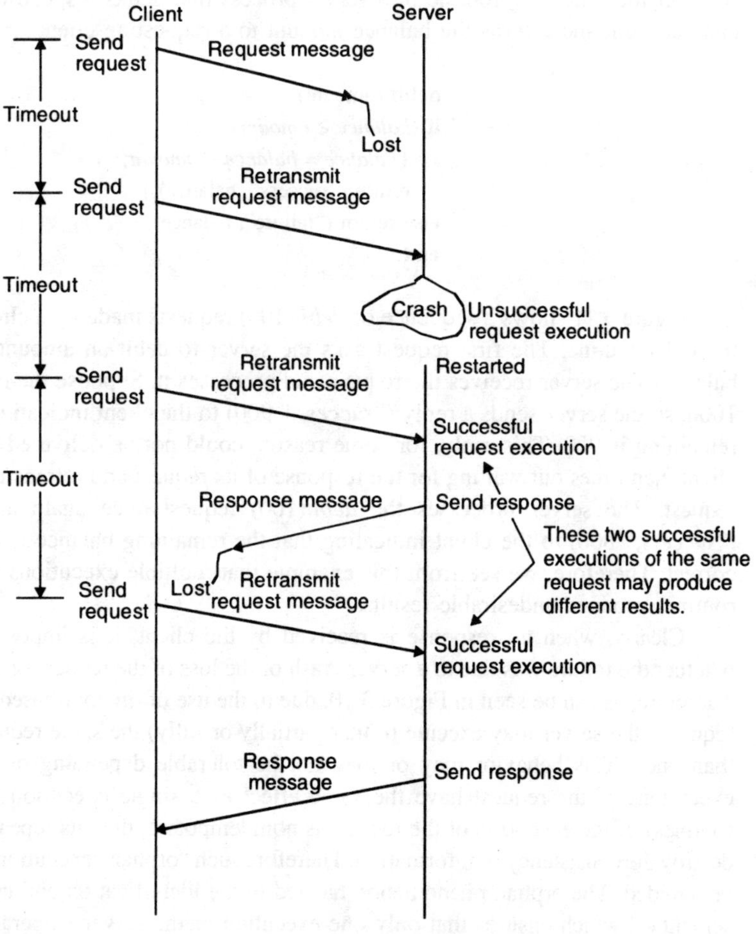


**Fig. 3.10** An example of fault-tolerant communication between a client and a server.

this semantics the *last-one* semantics because the results of the last execution of the request are used by the sender, although earlier (abandoned) executions of the request may have had side effects that survived the failure. As explained later, this semantics may not be acceptable to several applications.

### 3.9.1 Idempotency and Handling of Duplicate Request Messages

Idempotency basically means "repeatability." That is, an idempotent operation produces the same results without any side effects no matter how many times it is performed with the same arguments. An example of an idempotent routine is a simple *GetSqrt* procedure for calculating the square root of a given number. For example, *GetSqrt*(64) always returns 8.

On the other hand, operations that do not necessarily produce the same results when executed repeatedly with the same arguments are said to be nonidempotent. For example, consider the following routine of a server process that debits a specified amount from a bank account and returns the balance amount to a requesting client:

```
debit (amount)
if (balance ≥ amount)
    {balance = balance – amount;
    return ("success", balance);}
else return ("failure", balance);
end;
```

Figure 3.11 shows a sequence of *debit*(100) requests made by a client for processing the *debit* routine. The first request asks the server to debit an amount of 100 from the balance. The server receives the request and processes it. Suppose the initial balance was 1000, so the server sends a reply ("*success*," 900) to the client indicating that the balance remaining is 900. This reply, for some reason, could not be delivered to the client. The client then times out waiting for the response of its request and retransmits the *debit*(100) request. The server processes the *debit*(100) request once again and sends a reply ("*success*," 800) to the client indicating that the remaining balance is 800, which is not correct. Therefore, we see from this example that multiple executions of nonidempotent routines produce undesirable results.

Clearly, when no response is received by the client, it is impossible to determine whether the failure was due to a server crash or the loss of the request or response message. Therefore, as can be seen in Figure 3.10, due to the use of timeout-based retransmission of requests, the server may execute (either partially or fully) the same request message more than once. This behavior may or may not be tolerable depending on whether multiple executions of the request have the same effect as a single execution (as in idempotent routines). If the execution of the request is nonidempotent, then its repeated execution will destroy the consistency of information. Therefore such "orphan" executions must, in general, be avoided. The orphan phenomenon has led to the identification and use of *exactly-once* semantics, which ensures that only one execution of the server's operation is performed. Primitives based on exactly-once semantics are most desired but difficult to implement.

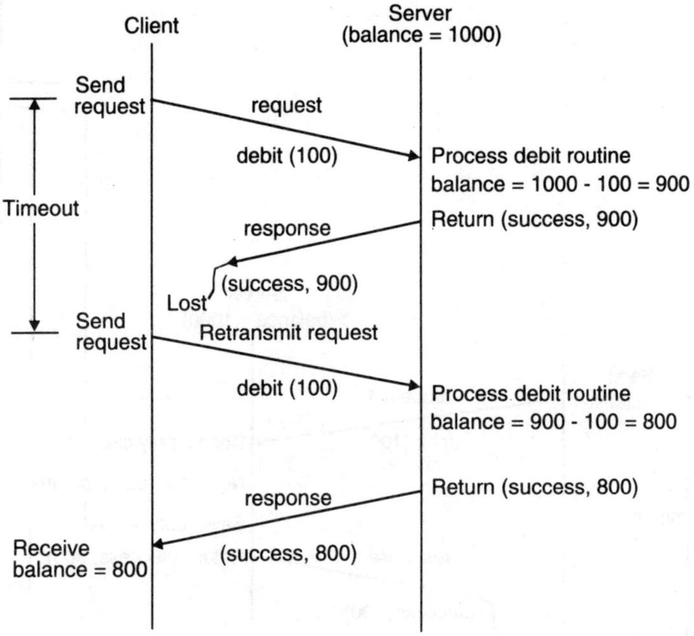

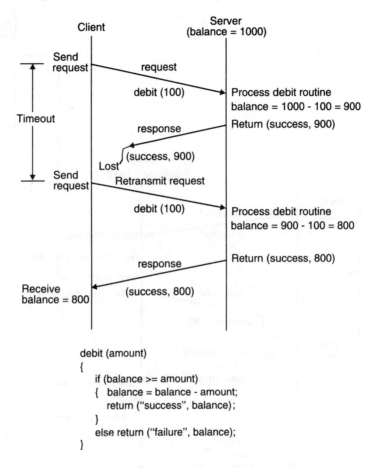

```
debit (amount)
{
   if (balance >= amount)
   {  balance = balance - amount;
      return ("success", balance);
   }
   else return ("failure", balance);
}
```

**Fig. 3.11** A nonidempotent routine.

One way to implement exactly-once semantics is to use a unique identifier for every request that the client makes and to set up a reply cache in the kernel's address space on the server machine to cache replies. In this case, before forwarding a request to a server for processing, the kernel of the server machine checks to see if a reply already exists in the reply cache for the request. If yes, this means that this is a duplicate request that has already been processed. Therefore, the previously computed result is extracted from the reply cache and a new response message is sent to the client. Otherwise, the request is a new one. In this case, the kernel forwards the request to the appropriate server for processing, and when the processing is over, it caches the request identifier along with the result of processing in the reply cache before sending a response message to the client.

An example of implementing exactly-once semantics is shown in Figure 3.12. This figure is similar to Figure 3.11 except that requests are now numbered, and a reply cache has been added to the server machine. The client makes *request-1;* the server machine's kernel receives *request-1* and then checks the reply cache to see if there is a cached reply

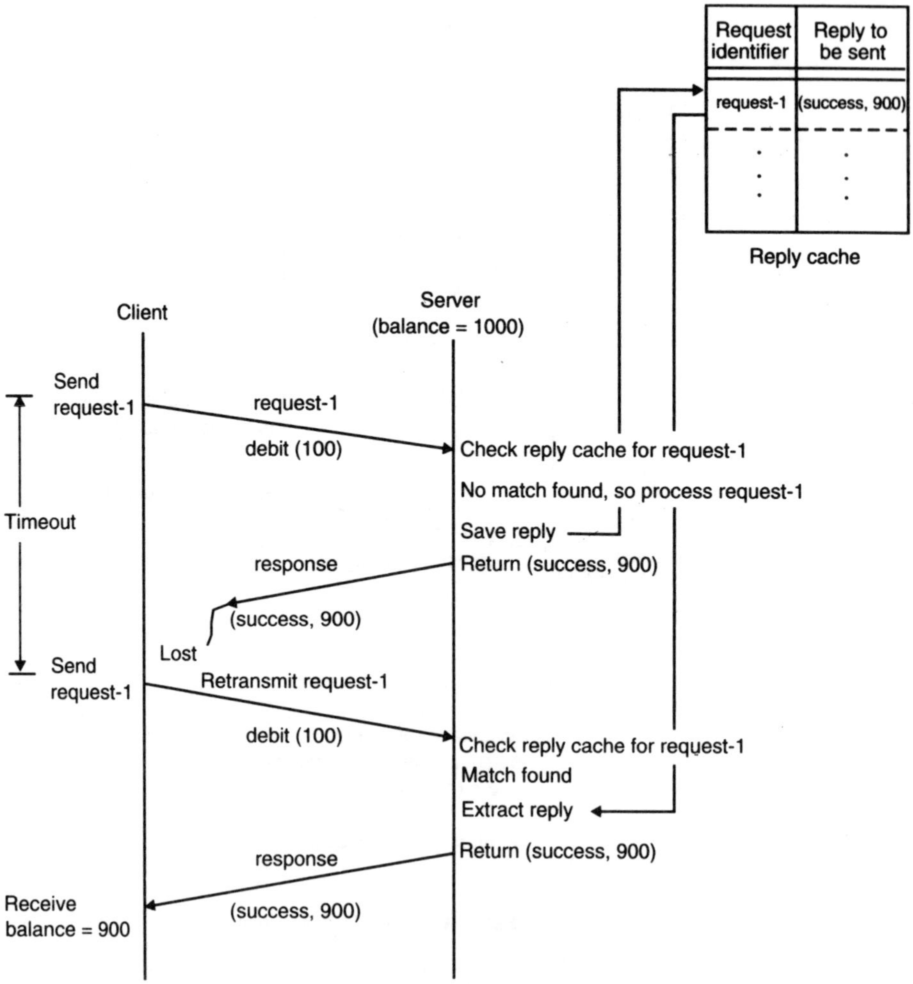


**Fig. 3.12** An example of exactly-once semantics using request identifiers and reply cache.

for *request-1*. There is no match, so it forwards the request to the appropriate server. The server processes the request and returns the result to the kernel. The kernel copies the request identifier and the result of execution to the reply cache and then sends the result in the form of a response message to the client. This reply is lost, and the client times out on *request-1* and retransmits *request-1*. The server machine's kernel receives *request-1* once again and checks the reply cache to see if there is a cached reply for *request-1*. This time a match is found so it extracts the result corresponding to *request-1* from the reply cache and once again sends it to the client as a response message. Thus the reprocessing of a duplicate request is avoided. Note that the range of the request identifiers should be much larger than the number of entries in the cache.

It is important to remember that the use of a reply cache does not make a nonidempotent routine idempotent. The cache is simply one possible way to implement nonidempotent routines with exactly-once semantics.

### 3.9.2 Keeping Track of Lost and Out-of-Sequence Packets in Multidatagram Messages

In the case of multidatagram messages, the logical transfer of a message consists of physical transfer of several packets. Therefore, a message transmission can be considered to be complete only when all the packets of the message have been received by the process to which it is sent. For successful completion of a multidatagram message transfer, reliable delivery of every packet is important. A simple way to ensure this is to acknowledge each packet separately (called *stop-and-wait protocol*). But a separate acknowledgment packet for each request packet leads to a communication overhead. Therefore, to improve communication performance, a better approach is to use a single acknowledgment packet for all the packets of a multidatagram message (called *blast protocol*). However, when this approach is used, a node crash or a communication link failure may lead to the following problems:

- One or more packets of the multidatagram message are lost in communication.
- The packets are received out of sequence by the receiver.

An efficient mechanism to cope with these problems is to use a bitmap to identify the packets of a message. In this mechanism, the header part of each packet consists of two extra fields, one of which specifies the total number of packets in the multidatagram message and the other is the bitmap field that specifies the position of this packet in the complete message. The first field helps the receiving process to set aside a suitably sized buffer area for the message and the second field helps in deciding the position of this packet in that buffer. Since all packets have information about the total number of packets in the message, so even in the case of out-of-sequence receipt of the packets, that is, even when the first packet is not received first, a suitably sized buffer area can be set aside by the receiver for the entire message and the received packet can be placed in its proper position inside the buffer area. After timeout, if all packets have not yet been received, a bitmap indicating the unreceived packets is sent to the sender. Using the bitmap information, the sender retransmits only those packets that have not been received by the receiver. This technique is called *selective repeat*. When all the packets of a multidatagram message are received, the message transfer is complete, and the receiver sends an acknowledgment message to the sending process. This method of multidatagram message communication is illustrated with an example in Figure 3.13 in which the multidatagram message consists of five packets.

## 3.10 GROUP COMMUNICATION

The most elementary form of message-based interaction is *one-to-one communication* (also known as *point-to-point*, or *unicast*, *communication*) in which a single-sender process sends a message to a single-receiver process. However, for performance and ease

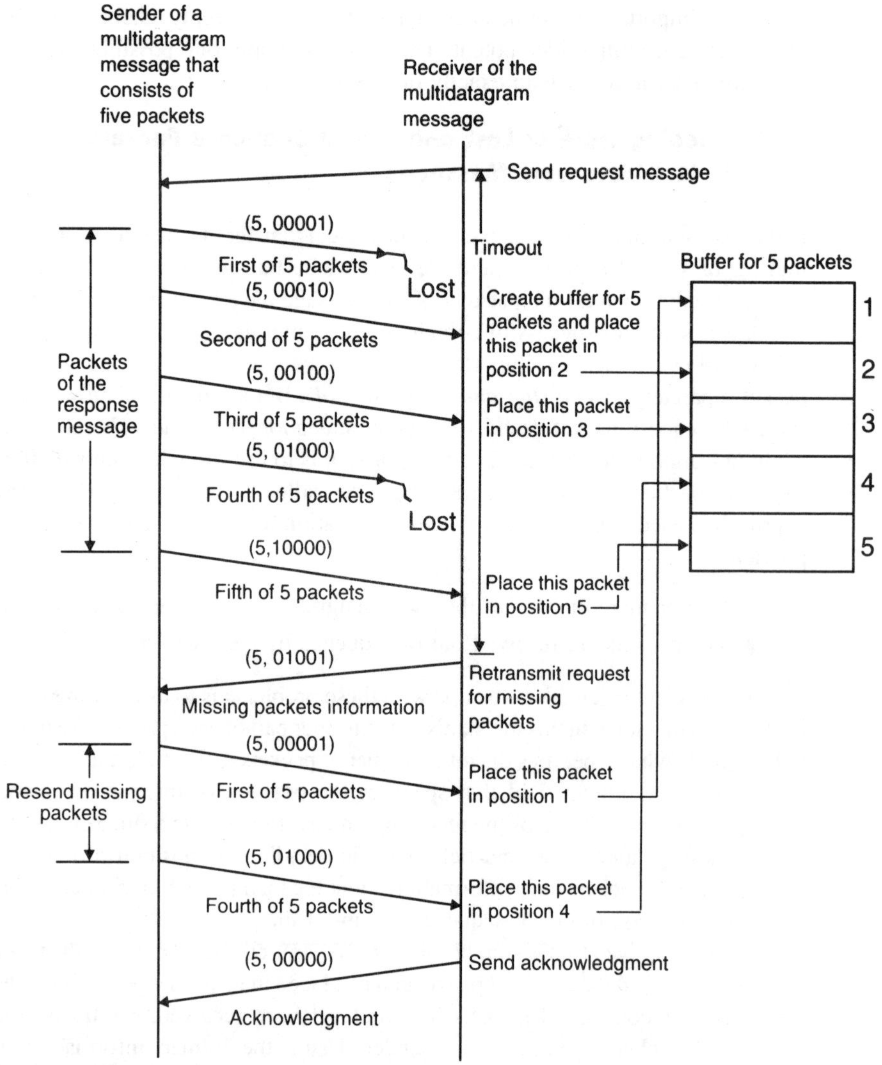


**Fig. 3.13** An example of the use of a bitmap to keep track of lost and out of sequence packets in a multidatagram message transmission.

of programming, several highly parallel distributed applications require that a message-passing system should also provide group communication facility. Depending on single or multiple senders and receivers, the following three types of group communication are possible:

1. One to many (single sender and multiple receivers)
2. Many to one (multiple senders and single receiver)

3. Many to many (multiple senders and multiple receivers)

The issues related to these communication schemes are described below.

### 3.10.1 One-to-Many Communication

In this scheme, there are multiple receivers for a message sent by a single sender. One-to-many scheme is also known as *multicast communication.* A special case of multicast communication is *broadcast communication,* in which the message is sent to all processors connected to a network.

Multicast/broadcast communication is very useful for several practical applications. For example, consider a server manager managing a group of server processes all providing the same type of service. The server manager can multicast a message to all the server processes, requesting that a free server volunteer to serve the current request. It then selects the first server that responds. The server manager does not have to keep track of the free servers. Similarly, to locate a processor providing a specific service, an inquiry message may be broadcast. In this case, it is not necessary to receive an answer from every processor; just finding one instance of the desired service is sufficient.

#### Group Management

In case of one-to-many communication, receiver processes of a message form a group. Such groups are of two types—closed and open. A *closed group* is one in which only the members of the group can send a message to the group. An outside process cannot send a message to the group as a whole, although it may send a message to an individual member of the group. On the other hand, an *open group* is one in which any process in the system can send a message to the group as a whole.

Whether to use a closed group or an open group is application dependent. For example, a group of processes working on a common problem need not communicate with outside processes and can form a closed group. On the other hand, a group of replicated servers meant for distributed processing of client requests must form an open group so that client processes can send their requests to them. Therefore, a flexible message-passing system with group communication facility should support both types of groups.

A message-passing system with group communication facility provides the flexibility to create and delete groups dynamically and to allow a process to join or leave a group at any time. Obviously, the message-passing system must have a mechanism to manage the groups and their membership information. A simple mechanism for this is to use a centralized *group server* process. All requests to create a group, to delete a group, to add a member to a group, or to remove a member from a group are sent to this process. Therefore, it is easy for the group server to maintain up-to-date information of all existing groups and their exact membership. This approach, however, suffers from the problems of poor reliability and poor scalability common to all centralized techniques. Replication of the group server may be done to solve these problems to some extent. However, replication leads to the extra overhead involved in keeping the group information of all group servers consistent.

### Group Addressing

A two-level naming scheme is normally used for group addressing. The high-level group name is an ASCII string that is independent of the location information of the processes in the group. On the other hand, the low-level group name depends to a large extent on the underlying hardware. For example, on some networks it is possible to create a special network address to which multiple machines can listen. Such a network address is called a *multicast address*. A packet sent to a multicast address is automatically delivered to all machines listening to the address. Therefore, in such systems a multicast address is used as a low-level name for a group.

Some networks that do not have the facility to create multicast addresses may have broadcasting facility. Networks with broadcasting facility declare a certain address, such as zero, as a *broadcast address*. A packet sent to a broadcast address is automatically delivered to all machines on the network. Therefore, the broadcast address of a network may be used as a low-level name for a group. In this case, the software of each machine must check to see if the packet is intended for it. If not, the packet is simply discarded. Since all machines receive every broadcast packet and must check if the packet is intended for it, the use of a broadcast address is less efficient than the use of a multicast address for group addressing. Also notice that in a system that uses a broadcast address for group addressing, all groups have the same low-level name, the broadcast address.

If a network does not support either the facility to create multicast addresses or the broadcasting facility, a one-to-one communication mechanism has to be used to implement the group communication facility. That is, the kernel of the sending machine sends the message packet separately to each machine that has a process belonging to the group. Therefore, in this case, the low-level name of a group contains a list of machine identifiers of all machines that have a process belonging to the group.

Notice that in the first two methods a single message packet is sent over the network, whereas in the third method the number of packets sent over the network depends on the number of machines that have one or more processes belonging to the group. Therefore the third method generates more network traffic than the other two methods and is in general less efficient. However, it is better than the broadcasting method in systems in which most groups involve only a few out of many machines on the network. Moreover the first two methods are suitable for use only on a single LAN. If the network contains multiple LANs interconnected by gateways and the processes of a group are spread over multiple LANs, the third method is simpler and easier to implement than the other two methods.

### Message Delivery to Receiver Processes

User applications use high-level group names in programs. The centralized group server maintains a mapping of high-level group names to their low-level names. The group server also maintains a list of the process identifiers of all the processes for each group.

When a sender sends a message to a group specifying its high-level name, the kernel of the sending machine contacts the group server to obtain the low-level name of the group and the list of process identifiers of the processes belonging to the group. The list of process identifiers is inserted in the message packet. If the low-level group name is either a multicast address or a broadcast address, the kernel simply sends the packet to the multicast/broadcast address. On the other hand, if the low-level group name is a list of machine identifiers, the kernel sends a copy of the packet separately to each machine in the list.

When the packet reaches a machine, the kernel of that machine extracts the list of process identifiers from the packet and forwards the message in the packet to those processes in the list that belong to its own machine. Note that when the broadcast address is used as a low-level group name, the kernel of a machine may find that none of the processes in the list belongs to its own machine. In this case, the kernel simply discards the packet.

Notice that a sender is not at all aware of either the size of the group or the actual mechanism used for group addressing. The sender simply sends a message to a group specifying its high-level name, and the operating system takes the responsibility to deliver the message to all the group members.

### Buffered and Unbuffered Multicast

Multicasting is an asynchronous communication mechanism. This is because multicast *send* cannot be synchronous due to the following reasons [Gehani 1984]:

1. It is unrealistic to expect a sending process to wait until all the receiving processes that belong to the multicast group are ready to receive the multicast message.
2. The sending process may not be aware of all the receiving processes that belong to the multicast group.

How a multicast message is treated on a receiving process side depends on whether the multicast mechanism is buffered or unbuffered. For an *unbuffered multicast*, the message is not buffered for the receiving process and is lost if the receiving process is not in a state ready to receive it. Therefore, the message is received only by those processes of the multicast group that are ready to receive it. On the other hand, for a *buffered multicast*, the message is buffered for the receiving processes, so each process of the multicast group will eventually receive the message.

### Send-to-All and Bulletin-Board Semantics

Ahamad and Bernstein [1985] described the following two types of semantics for one-to-many communications:

1. *Send-to-all semantics*. A copy of the message is sent to each process of the multicast group and the message is buffered until it is accepted by the process.

2. *Bulletin-board semantics*. A message to be multicast is addressed to a channel instead of being sent to every individual process of the multicast group. From a logical

point of view, the channel plays the role of a bulletin board. A receiving process copies the message from the channel instead of removing it when it makes a *receive* request on the channel. Thus a multicast message remains available to other processes as if it has been posted on the bulletin board. The processes that have *receive* access right on the channel constitute the multicast group.

Bulletin-board semantics is more flexible than send-to-all semantics because it takes care of the following two factors that are ignored by send-to-all semantics [Ahamad and Bernstein 1985]:

1. The relevance of a message to a particular receiver may depend on the receiver's state.
2. Messages not accepted within a certain time after transmission may no longer be useful; their value may depend on the sender's state.

To illustrate this, let us once again consider the example of a server manager multicasting a message to all the server processes to volunteer to serve the current request. Using send-to-all semantics, it would be necessary to multicast to all the servers, causing many contractors to process extraneous messages. Using bulletin-board semantics, only those contractors that are idle and in a state suitable for serving requests will make a *receive* request on the concerned channel, and thus only contractors in the correct state will process such messages [Ahamad and Bernstein 1985]. Furthermore, the message is withdrawn from the channel by the server manager as soon as the bid period is over; that is, the first bidder is selected (in this case). Therefore, the message remains available for being received only as long as the server manager is in a state in which bids are acceptable. While this does not completely eliminate extraneous messages (contractors may still reply after the bid period is over), it does help in reducing them.

### Flexible Reliability in Multicast Communication

Different applications require different degrees of reliability. Therefore multicast primitives normally provide the flexibility for user-definable reliability. Thus, the sender of a multicast message can specify the number of receivers from which a response message is expected. In one-to-many communication, the degree of reliability is normally expressed in the following forms:

1. The *0-reliable*. No response is expected by the sender from any of the receivers. This is useful for applications using asynchronous multicast in which the sender does not wait for any response after multicasting the message. An example of this type of application is a time signal generator.

2. The *1-reliable*. The sender expects a response from any of the receivers. The already described application in which a server manager multicasts a message to all the servers to volunteer to serve the current request and selects the first server that responds is an example of 1-reliable multicast communication.

3. The *m-out-of-n-reliable*. The multicast group consists of $n$ receivers and the sender expects a response from $m$ ($1 < m < n$) of the $n$ receivers. Majority consensus algorithms (described in Chapter 9) used for the consistency control of replicated information use this form of reliability, with the value $m = n/2$.

4. *All-reliable*. The sender expects a response message from all the receivers of the multicast group. For example, suppose a message for updating the replicas of a file is multicast to all the file servers having a replica of the file. Naturally, such a sender process will expect a response from all the concerned file servers.

### Atomic Multicast

Atomic multicast has an all-or-nothing property. That is, when a message is sent to a group by atomic multicast, it is either received by all the processes that are members of the group or else it is not received by any of them. An implicit assumption usually made in atomic multicast is that when a process fails, it is no longer a member of the multicast group. When the process comes up after failure, it must join the group afresh.

Atomic multicast is not always necessary. For example, applications for which the degree of reliability requirement is 0-reliable, 1-reliable, or $m$-out-of-$n$-reliable do not need atomic multicast facility. On the other hand, applications for which the degree of reliability requirement is all-reliable need atomic multicast facility. Therefore, a flexible message-passing system should support both atomic and nonatomic multicast facilities and should provide the flexibility to the sender of a multicast message to specify in the *send* primitive whether atomicity property is required or not for the message being multicast.

A simple method to implement atomic multicast is to multicast a message, with the degree of reliability requirement being all-reliable. In this case, the kernel of the sending machine sends the message to all members of the group and waits for an acknowledgment from each member (we assume that a one-to-one communication mechanism is used to implement the multicast facility). After a timeout period, the kernel retransmits the message to all those members from whom an acknowledgment message has not yet been received. The timeout-based retransmission of the message is repeated until an acknowledgment is received from all members of the group. When all acknowledgments have been received, the kernel confirms to the sender that the atomic multicast process is complete.

The above method works fine only as long as the machines of the sender process and the receiver processes do not fail during an atomic multicast operation. This is because if the machine of the sender process fails, the message cannot be retransmitted if one or more members did not receive the message due to packet loss or some other reason. Similarly, if the machine of a receiver process fails and remains down for some time, the message cannot be delivered to that process because retransmissions of the message cannot be continued indefinitely and have to be aborted after some predetermined time. Therefore, a fault-tolerant atomic multicast protocol must ensure that a multicast will be delivered to all members of the multicast group even in the event of failure of the sender's machine or a receiver's machine. One method to implement such a protocol is described next [Tanenbaum 1995].

In this method, each message has a message identifier field to distinguish it from all other messages and a field to indicate that it is an atomic multicast message. The sender sends the message to a multicast group. The kernel of the sending machine sends the message to all members of the group and uses timeout-based retransmissions as in the previous method. A process that receives the message checks its message identifier field to see if it is a new message. If not, it is simply discarded. Otherwise, the receiver checks to see if it is an atomic multicast message. If so, the receiver also performs an atomic multicast of the same message, sending it to the same multicast group. The kernel of this machine treats this message as an ordinary atomic multicast message and uses timeout-based retransmissions when needed. In this way, each receiver of an atomic multicast message will perform an atomic multicast of the message to the same multicast group. The method ensures that eventually all the surviving processes of the multicast group will receive the message even if the sender machine fails after sending the message or a receiver machine fails after receiving the message.

Notice that an atomic multicast is in general very expensive as compared to a normal multicast due to the large number of messages involved in its implementation. Therefore, a message-passing system should not use the atomicity property as a default property of multicast messages but should provide this facility as an option.

### Group Communication Primitives

In both one-to-one communication and one-to-many communication, the sender of a process basically has to specify two parameters: destination address and a pointer to the message data. Therefore ideally the same *send* primitive can be used for both one-to-one communication and one-to-many communication. If the destination address specified in the *send* primitive is that of a single process, the message is sent to that one process. On the other hand, if the destination address is a group address, the message is sent to all processes that belong to that group.

However, most systems having a group communication facility provide a different primitive (such as *send_group*) for sending a message to a group. There are two main reasons for this. First, it simplifies the design and implementation of a group communication facility. For example, suppose the two-level naming mechanism is used for both process addressing and group addressing. The high-level to low-level name mapping for processes is done by the name server, and for groups it is done by the group server. With this design, if a single *send* primitive is used for both one-to-one communication and one-to-many communication, the kernel of the sending machine cannot know whether the destination address specified by a user is a single process address or a group address. Consequently, it does not know whether the name server or the group server should be contacted for obtaining the low-level name of the specified destination address. Implementation methods to solve this problem are possible theoretically, but the design will become complicated. On the other hand, if separate primitives such as *send* and *send_group* are used, the kernel can easily make out whether the specified destination address is a single process address or a group address and can contact the appropriate server to obtain the corresponding low-level name.

Second, it helps in providing greater flexibility to the users. For instance, a separate parameter may be used in the *send_group* primitive to allow users to specify the degree of reliability desired (number of receivers from which a response message is expected), and another parameter may be used to specify whether the atomicity property is required or not.

### 3.10.2 Many-to-One Communication

In this scheme, multiple senders send messages to a single receiver. The single receiver may be selective or nonselective. A *selective receiver* specifies a unique sender; a message exchange takes place only if that sender sends a message. On the other hand, a *nonselective receiver* specifies a set of senders, and if any one sender in the set sends a message to this receiver, a message exchange takes place.

Thus we see that an important issue related to the many-to-one communication scheme is nondeterminism. The receiver may want to wait for information from any of a group of senders, rather than from one specific sender. As it is not known in advance which member (or members) of the group will have its information available first, such behavior is nondeterministic. In some cases it is useful to dynamically control the group of senders from whom to accept message. For example, a buffer process may accept a request from a producer process to store an item in the buffer whenever the buffer is not full; it may accept a request from a consumer process to get an item from the buffer whenever the buffer is not empty. To program such behavior, a notation is needed to express and control nondeterminism. One such construct is the "guarded command" statement introduced by Dijkstra [1975]. Since this issue is related to programming languages rather than operating systems, we will not discuss it any further.

### 3.10.3 Many-to-Many Communication

In this scheme, multiple senders send messages to multiple receivers. The one-to-many and many-to-one schemes are implicit in this scheme. Hence the issues related to one-to-many and many-to-one schemes, which have already been described above, also apply to the many-to-many communication scheme. In addition, an important issue related to many-to-many communication scheme is that of *ordered message delivery.*

Ordered message delivery ensures that all messages are delivered to all receivers in an order acceptable to the application. This property is needed by many applications for their correct functioning. For example, suppose two senders send messages to update the same record of a database to two server processes having a replica of the database. If the messages of the two senders are received by the two servers in different orders, then the final values of the updated record of the database may be different in its two replicas. Therefore, this application requires that all messages be delivered in the same order to all receivers.

Ordered message delivery requires message sequencing. In a system with a single sender and multiple receivers (one-to-many communication), sequencing messages to all the receivers is trivial. If the sender initiates the next multicast transmission only after confirming that the previous multicast message has been received by all the members, the messages will be delivered in the same order. On the other hand, in a system with multiple senders and a single receiver (many-to-one communication), the messages will be delivered to the receiver in the order in which they arrive at the receiver's machine. Ordering in this case is simply handled by the receiver. Thus we see that it is not difficult to ensure ordered delivery of messages in many-to-one or one-to-many communication schemes.

However, in many-to-many communication, a message sent from a sender may arrive at a receiver's destination before the arrival of a message from another sender; but this order may be reversed at another receiver's destination (see Fig. 3.14). The reason why messages of different senders may arrive at the machines of different receivers in different orders is that when two processes are contending for access to a LAN, the order in which messages of the two processes are sent over the LAN is nondeterministic. Moreover, in a WAN environment, the messages of different senders may be routed to the same destination using different routes that take different amounts of time (which cannot be correctly predicted) to the destination. Therefore, ensuring ordered message delivery requires a special message-handling mechanism in many-to-many communication scheme.

The commonly used semantics for ordered delivery of multicast messages are absolute ordering, consistent ordering, and causal ordering. These are described below.

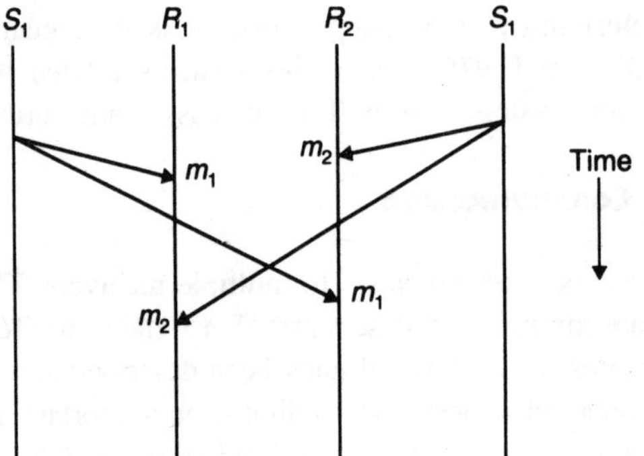


**Fig. 3.14** No ordering constraint for message delivery.

## Absolute Ordering

This semantics ensures that all messages are delivered to all receiver processes in the exact order in which they were sent (see Fig. 3.15). One method to implement this semantics is to use global timestamps as message identifiers. That is, the system is assumed to have a clock at each machine and all clocks are synchronized with each other, and when a sender sends a message, the clock value (timestamp) is taken as the identifier of that message and embedded in the message.

The kernel of each receiver's machine saves all incoming messages meant for a receiver in a separate queue. A sliding-window mechanism is used to periodically

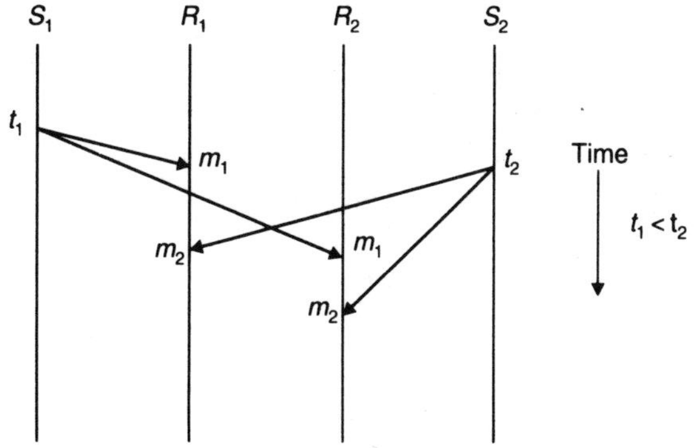


**Fig. 3.15** Absolute ordering of messages.

deliver the message from the queue to the receiver. That is, a fixed time interval is selected as the window size, and periodically all messages whose timestamp values fall within the current window are delivered to the receiver. Messages whose timestamp values fall outside the window are left in the queue because of the possibility that a tardy message having a timestamp value lower than that of any of the messages in the queue might still arrive. The window size is properly chosen taking into consideration the maximum possible time that may be required by a message to go from one machine to any other machine in the network.

### Consistent Ordering

Absolute-ordering semantics requires globally synchronized clocks, which are not easy to implement. Moreover, absolute ordering is not really what many applications need to function correctly. For instance, in the replicated database updation example, it is sufficient to ensure that both servers receive the update messages of the two senders in the same order even if this order is not the real order in which the two messages were sent. Therefore, instead of supporting absolute-ordering semantics, most systems support consistent-ordering semantics. This semantics ensures that all messages are delivered to all receiver processes in the same order. However, this order may be different from the order in which messages were sent (see Fig. 3.16).

One method to implement consistent-ordering semantics is to make the many-to-many scheme appear as a combination of many-to-one and one-to-many schemes [Chang and Maxemchuk 1985]. That is, the kernels of the sending machines send messages to a single receiver (known as a *sequencer*) that assigns a sequence number to each message and then multicasts it. The kernel of each receiver's machine saves all incoming messages meant for a receiver in a separate queue. Messages in a queue are delivered immediately to the receiver unless there is a gap in the message identifiers, in which case messages after the gap are not delivered until the ones in the gap have arrived.

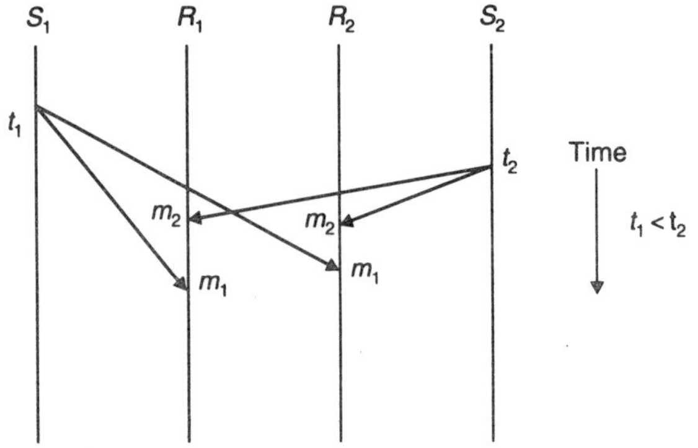


**Fig. 3.16** Consistent ordering of messages.

The sequencer-based method for implementing consistent-ordering semantics is subject to single point of failure and hence has poor reliability. A distributed algorithm for implementing consistent-ordering semantics that does not suffer from this problem is the *ABCAST protocol* of the ISIS system [Birman and Van Renesse 1994, Birman 1993, Birman et al. 1991, Birman and Joseph 1987]. It assigns a sequence number to a message by distributed agreement among the group members and the sender and works as follows:

1. The sender assigns a temporary sequence number to the message and sends it to all the members of the multicast group. The sequence number assigned by the sender must be larger than any previous sequence number used by the sender. Therefore, a simple counter can be used by the sender to assign sequence numbers to its messages.

2. On receiving the message, each member of the group returns a proposed sequence number to the sender. A member ($i$) calculates its proposed sequence number by using the function

$$\max(F_{max}, P_{max}) + 1 + i/N$$

where $F_{max}$ is the largest final sequence number agreed upon so far for a message received by the group (each member makes a record of this when a final sequence number is agreed upon), $P_{max}$ is the largest proposed sequence number by this member, and $N$ is the total number of members in the multicast group.

3. When the sender has received the proposed sequence numbers from all the members, it selects the largest one as the final sequence number for the message and sends it to all members in a *commit* message. The chosen final sequence number is guaranteed to be unique because of the term $i/N$ in the function used for the calculation of a proposed sequence number.

4. On receiving the *commit* message, each member attaches the final sequence number to the message.

5. Committed messages with final sequence numbers are delivered to the application programs in order of their final sequence numbers. Note that the algorithm for sequence number assignment to a message is a part of the runtime system, not the user processes.

It can be shown that this protocol ensures consistent ordering semantics.

### Causal Ordering

For some applications consistent-ordering semantics is not necessary and even weaker semantics is acceptable. Therefore, an application can have better performance if the message-passing system used supports a weaker ordering semantics that is acceptable to the application. One such weaker ordering semantics that is acceptable to many applications is the causal-ordering semantics. This semantics ensures that if the event of sending one message is causally related to the event of sending another message, the two messages are delivered to all receivers in the correct order. However, if two message-sending events are not causally related, the two messages may be delivered to the receivers in any order. Two message-sending events are said to be causally related if they are corelated by the *happened-before* relation (for a definition of *happened-before* relation see Chapter 6). That is, two message-sending events are causally related if there is any possibility of the second one being influenced in any way by the first one. The basic idea behind causal-ordering semantics is that when it matters, messages are always delivered in the proper order, but when it does not matter, they may be delivered in any arbitrary order.

An example of causal ordering of messages is given in Figure 3.17. In this example, sender $S_1$ sends message $m_1$ to receivers $R_1$, $R_2$, and $R_3$ and sender $S_2$ sends message $m_2$ to receivers $R_2$, and $R_3$. On receiving $m_1$, receiver $R_1$ inspects it, creates a new message $m_3$, and sends $m_3$ to $R_2$ and $R_3$. Note that the event of sending $m_3$ is causally related to the event of sending $m_1$ because the contents of $m_3$ might have been derived in part from $m_1$; hence the two messages must be delivered to both $R_2$ and $R_3$ in the proper order, $m_1$

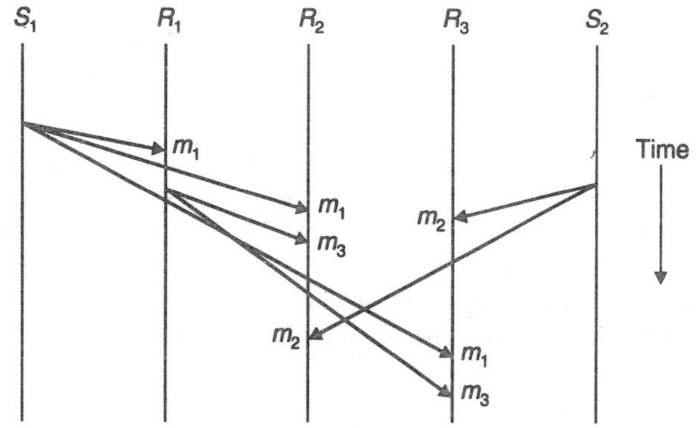


**Fig. 3.17** Causal ordering of messages.

before $m_3$. Also note that since $m_2$ is not causally related to either $m_1$ or $m_3$, $m_2$ can be delivered at any time to $R_2$ and $R_3$ irrespective of $m_1$ or $m_3$. This is exactly what the example of Figure 3.17 shows.

One method for implementing causal-ordering semantics is the *CBCAST protocol* of the ISIS system [Birman et al. 1991]. It works as follows:

1. Each member process of a group maintains a vector of $n$ components, where $n$ is the total number of members in the group. Each member is assigned a sequence number from 0 to $n$, and the $i$th component of the vectors corresponds to the member with sequence number $i$. In particular, the value of the $i$th component of a member's vector is equal to the number of the last message received in sequence by this member from member $i$.

2. To send a message, a process increments the value of its own component in its own vector and sends the vector as part of the message.

3. When the message arrives at a receiver process's site, it is buffered by the runtime system. The runtime system tests the two conditions given below to decide whether the message can be delivered to the user process or its delivery must be delayed to ensure causal-ordering semantics. Let $S$ be the vector of the sender process that is attached to the message and $R$ be the vector of the receiver process. Also let $i$ be the sequence number of the sender process. Then the two conditions to be tested are

$$S[i] = R[i] + 1 \quad \text{and} \quad S[j] \le R[j] \quad \text{for all } j \ne i$$

The first condition ensures that the receiver has not missed any message from the sender. This test is needed because two messages from the same sender are always causally related. The second condition ensures that the sender has not received any message that the receiver has not yet received. This test is needed to make sure that the sender's message is not causally related to a message missed by the receiver.

If the message passes these two tests, the runtime system delivers it to the user process. Otherwise, the message is left in the buffer and the test is carried out again for it when a new message arrives.

A simple example to illustrate the algorithm is given in Figure 3.18. In this example, there are four processes $A$, $B$, $C$, and $D$. The status of their vectors at some instance of time is (3, 2, 5, 1), (3, 2, 5, 1), (2, 2, 5, 1), and (3, 2, 4, 1), respectively. This means that, until now, $A$ has sent three messages, $B$ has sent two messages, $C$ has sent five messages, and $D$ has sent one message to other processes. Now $A$ sends a new message to other processes. Therefore, the vector attached to the message will be (4, 2, 5, 1). The message can be delivered to $B$ because it passes both tests. However, the message has to be delayed by the runtime systems of sites of processes $C$ and $D$ because the first test fails at the site of process $C$ and the second test fails at the site of process $D$.

A good message-passing system should support at least consistent- and causal-ordering semantics and should provide the flexibility to the users to choose one of these in their applications.

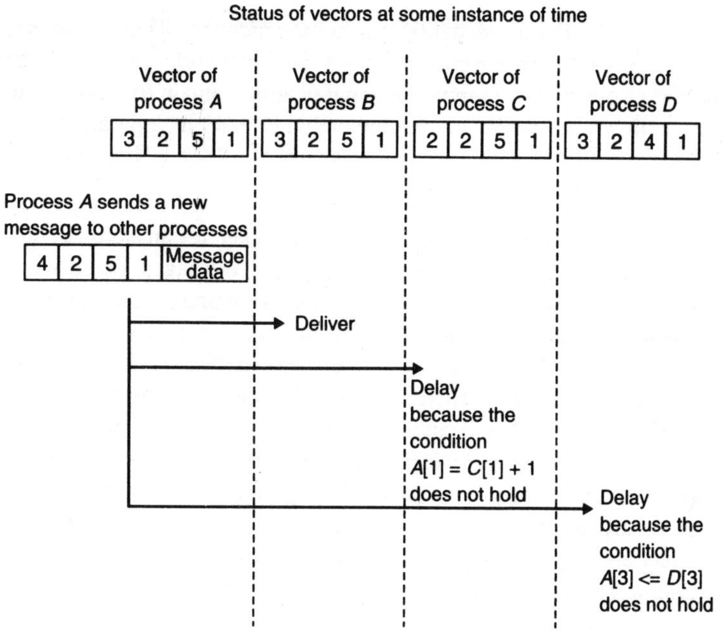


**Fig. 3.18** An example to illustrate the CBCAST protocol for implementing causal ordering semantics.

## 3.11 CASE STUDY: 4.3BSD UNIX IPC MECHANISM

The socket-based IPC of the 4.3BSD UNIX system illustrates how a message-passing system can be designed using the concepts and mechanisms presented in this chapter. The system was produced by the Computer Systems Research Group (CSRG) of the University of California at Berkeley and is the most widely used and well documented message-passing system.

### 3.11.1 Basic Concepts and Main Features

The IPC mechanism of the 4.3BSD UNIX provides a general interface for constructing network-based applications. Its basic concepts and main features are as follows:

1. It is network independent in the sense that it can support communication networks that use different sets of protocols, different naming conventions, different hardware, and so on. For this, it uses the notion of *communication domain*, which refers to a standard set of communication properties. In this chapter we have seen that there are different methods of naming a communication endpoint. We also have seen that there are different semantics of communication related to synchronization, reliability, ordering, and so on. Different networks often use different naming conventions for naming communication endpoints

and possess different semantics of communication. These properties of a network are known as its *communication properties*. Networks with the same communication properties belong to a common communication domain (or protocol family). By providing the flexibility to specify a communication domain as a parameter of the communication primitive used, the IPC mechanism of the 4.3BSD UNIX allows the users to select a domain appropriate to their applications.

2. It uses a unified abstraction, called *socket*, for an endpoint of communication. That is, a socket is an abstract object from which messages are sent and received. The IPC operations are based on socket pairs, one belonging to each of a pair of communicating processes that may be on the same or different computers. A pair of sockets may be used for unidirectional or bidirectional communication between two processes. A message sent by a sending process is queued in its socket until it has been transmitted across the network by the networking protocol and an acknowledgment has been received (only if the protocol requires one). On the receiver side, the message is queued in the receiving process's socket until the receiving process makes an appropriate system call to receive it.

Any process can create a socket for use in communication with another process. Sockets are created within a communication domain. A created socket exists until it is explicitly closed or until every process having a reference to it exits.

3. For location transparency, it uses a two-level naming scheme for naming communication endpoints. That is, a socket can be assigned a high-level name that is a human-readable string. The low-level name of a socket is communication-domain dependent. For example, it may consist of a local port number and an Internet address. For translation of high-level socket names to their low-level names, 4.3BSD provides functions for application programs rather than placing the translation functions in the kernel. Note that a socket's high-level name is meaningful only within the context of the communication domain in which the socket is created.

4. It is highly flexible in the sense that it uses a typing mechanism for sockets to provide the semantic aspects of communication to applications in a controlled and uniform manner. That is, all sockets are typed according to their communication semantics, such as ordered delivery, unduplicated delivery, reliable delivery, connectionless communication, connection-oriented communication, and so on. The system defines some standard socket types and provides the flexibility to the users to define and use their own socket types when needed. For example, a socket of type *datagram* models potentially unreliable, connectionless packet communication, and a socket of type *stream* models a reliable connection-based byte stream.

5. Messages can be broadcast if the underlying network provides broadcast facility.

### 3.11.2 The IPC Primitives

The primitives of the 4.3BSD UNIX IPC mechanism are provided as system calls implemented as a layer on top of network communication protocols such as TCP, UDP, and so on. Layering the IPC mechanism directly on top of network communication protocols helps in making it efficient. The most important available IPC primitives are briefly described below.

### s = socket (domain, type, protocol)

When a process wants to communicate with another process, it must first create a socket by using the *socket* system call. The first parameter of this call specifies the communication domain. The most commonly used domain is the Internet communication domain because a large number of hosts in the world support the Internet communication protocols. The second parameter specifies the socket type that is selected according to the communication semantics requirements of the application. The third parameter specifies the communication protocol (e.g., TCP/IP or UDP/IP) to be used for the socket's operation. If the value of this parameter is specified as zero, the system chooses an appropriate protocol. The *socket* call returns a descriptor by which the socket may be referenced in subsequent system calls. A created socket is discarded with the normal *close* system call.

### bind (s, addr, addrlen)

After creating a socket, the receiver must bind it to a socket address. Note that if two-way communication is desired between two processes, both processes have to receive messages, and hence both must separately bind their sockets to a socket address. The *bind* system call is used for this purpose. The three parameters of this call are the descriptor of the created socket, a reference to a structure containing the socket address to which the socket is to be bound, and the number of bytes in the socket address. Once a socket has been bound, its address cannot be changed.

It might seem more reasonable to combine the system calls for socket creation and binding a socket to a socket address (name) in a single system call. There are two main reasons for separating these two operations in different system calls. First, with this approach a socket can be useful without names. Forcing users to name every socket that is created causes extra burden on users and may lead to the assignment of meaningless names. Second, some communication domains might require additional, nonstandard information (such as type of service) for binding of a name to a socket. The need to supply this information at socket creation time will further complicate the interface.

### connect (s, server_addr, server_addrlen)

The two most commonly used communication types in the 4.3BSD UNIX IPC mechanism are connection-based (stream) communication and connectionless (datagram) communication. In connection-based communication, two processes first establish a connection between their pairs of sockets. The connection establishment process is asymmetric because one of the processes keeps waiting for a request for a connection and the other makes a request for a connection. Once connection has been established, data can be transmitted between the two processes in either direction. This type of communication is useful for implementing client-server applications. A server creates a socket, binds a name to it, and makes the name publicly known. It then waits for a connection request from client processes. Clients send connection requests to the server. Once the connection is established, they can exchange request and reply messages. Connection-based communication supports reliable exchange of messages.

In connectionless communication, a socket pair is identified each time a communication is made. For this, the sending process specifies its local socket descriptor and the socket address of the receiving process's socket each time it sends a message. Connectionless communication is potentially unreliable.

The *connect* system call is used in connection-based communication by a client process to request a connection establishment between its own socket and the socket of the server process with which it wants to communicate. The three parameters of this call are the descriptor of the client's socket, a reference to a structure containing the socket address of the server's socket, and the number of bytes in the socket address. The *connect* call automatically binds a socket address (name) to the client's socket. Hence prior binding is not needed.

**listen (s, backlog)**

The *listen* system call is used in case of connection-based communication by a server process to listen on its socket for client requests for connections. The two parameters of this call are the descriptor of the server's socket and the maximum number of pending connections that should be queued for acceptance.

**snew = accept (s, client_addr, client_addrlen)**

The *accept* system call is used in a connection-based communication by a server process to accept a request for a connection establishment made by a client and to obtain a new socket for communication with that client. The three parameters of this call are the descriptor of the server's socket, a reference to a structure containing the socket address of the client's socket, and the number of bytes in the socket address. Note that the call returns a descriptor (*snew*) that is the descriptor of a new socket that is automatically created upon execution of the *accept* call. This new socket is paired with the client's socket so that the server can continue to use the original socket with descriptor *s* for accepting further connection requests from other clients.

### Primitives for Sending and Receiving Data

A variety of system calls are available for sending and receiving data. The four most commonly used are:

*nbytes = read (snew, buffer, amount)*
*write (s, "message," msg_length)*
*amount = recvfrom (s, buffer, sender_address)*
*sendto (s, "message," receiver_address)*

The *read* and *write* system calls are most suitable for use in connection-based communication. The *write* operation is used by a client to send a message to a server. The socket to be used for sending the message, the message, and the length of the message are specified as parameters to the call. The *read* operation is used by the server process to receive the message sent by the client. The socket of the server to which the client's socket is connected and the buffer for storing the received message are specified as parameters to the call. The call returns the actual number of characters received. The socket connection establishment between the client and the server behaves like a channel of stream data that does not contain any message boundary indications. That is, the sender pumps data into the channel and the receiver reads them in the same sequence as written by the corresponding write operations. The channel size is limited by a bounded queue at the receiving socket. The sender blocks if the queue is full and the receiver blocks if the queue is empty.

On the other hand, the *recvfrom* and *sendto* system calls are most suitable for use in case of connectionless communication. The *sendto* operation is used by a sender to send a message to a particular receiver. The socket through which the message is to be sent, the message, and a reference to a structure containing the socket address of the receiver to which the message is to be sent are specified as parameters to this call. The *recvfrom* operation is used by a receiver to receive a message from a particular sender. The socket through which the message is to be received, the buffer where the message is to be stored, and a reference to a structure containing the socket address of the sender from which the message is to be received are specified as parameters to this call. The *recvfrom* call collects the first message in the queue at the socket. However, if the queue is empty, it blocks until a message arrives.

Figure 3.19 illustrates the use of sockets for connectionless communication between two processes. In the *socket* call, the specification of *AF_INET* as the first parameter indicates that the communication domain is the Internet communication domain, and the specification of *SOCK_DGRAM* as the second parameter indicates that the socket is of the datagram type (used for unreliable, connectionless communication).

Alternatively, Figure 3.20 illustrates the use of sockets for connection-based communication between a client process and a server process. The specification of *SOCK_STREAM* as the second parameter of the *socket* call indicates that the socket is of the stream type (used for reliable, connection-based communication).

## 3.12 SUMMARY

Interprocess communication (IPC) requires information sharing among two or more processes. The two basic methods for information sharing are original sharing (shared-data approach) and copy sharing (message-passing approach). Since computers in a network do not share memory, the message-passing approach is most commonly used in distributed systems.

A message-passing system is a subsystem of a distributed operating system that provides a set of message-based protocols, and it does so by shielding the details of complex network protocols and multiple heterogeneous platforms from programmers.

```
.
.
s = socket (AF_INET, SOCK_DGRAM, 0);
.
.
bind (s, sender_address, server_address_length);
.
.
sendto (s, "message", receiver_address);
.
.
close (s);
```

(*a*)

```
.
.
s = socket (AF_INET, SOCK_DGRAM, 0);
.
.
bind (s, receiver_address, receiver_address_length)
.
.
amount = recvfrom (s, buffer, sender_address);
.
.
close (s);
```

(*b*)

**Fig. 3.19** Use of sockets for connectionless communication between two processes. (*a*) Socket-related system calls in sender's program. (*b*) Socket-related system calls in receiver's program.

Some of the desirable features of a good message-passing system are simplicity, uniform semantics, efficiency, reliability, correctness, flexibility, security, and portability.

The sender and receiver of a message may communicate either in the synchronous or asynchronous mode. As compared to the synchronous mode of communication, the asynchronous mode provides better concurrency, reduced message traffic, and better flexibility. However, the asynchronous communication mode is more complicated to implement, needs message buffering, and requires programmers to deviate from the traditional centralized programming paradigm.

The four types of buffering strategies that may be used in the design of IPC mechanisms are a null buffer, or no buffering; a simple-message buffer; an unbounded-capacity buffer; and a finite-bound, or multiple-message, buffer.

Messages are transmitted over a transmission channel in the form of packets. Therefore, for transmitting a message that is greater than the maximum size of a packet, the logical message has to be separated (disassembled) and transmitted in multiple packets. Such a message is called a multipacket or a multidatagram message.

Encoding is the process of converting the program objects of a message to a stream form that is suitable for transmission over a transmission channel. This process takes place on the sender side of the message. The reverse process of reconstructing program objects from message data on the receiver side is known as decoding of the message data.

```
.
.
s = socket (AF_INET, SOCK_STREAM, 0);
.
.
connect (s, server_address, server_address_length);
.
.
write (s, "message", msg_length);
.
.
close (s);
```

(*a*)

```
.
.
s = socket (AF_INET, SOCK_STREAM, 0);
.
.
bind (s, server_address, server_address_length);
listen (s, backlog);
.
.
snew = accept (s, client_address, client_address_length
.
.
nbytes = read (snew, buffer, amount);
.
.
close (snew);
close(s);
```

(*b*)

**Fig. 3.20** Use of sockets for connection-based communication between a client and a server. (*a*) Socket-related system calls in client's program. (*b*) Socket-related system calls in server's program.

Another major issue in message passing is addressing (or naming) of the parties involved in an interaction. A process may or may not explicitly name a process with which it wants to communicate depending upon whether it wants to communicate only with a specific process or with any process of a particular type. An important goal in process addressing is to provide location transparency. The most commonly used method to achieve this goal is to use a two-level naming scheme for processes and a name server to map high-level, machine-independent process names to their low-level, machine-dependent names.

Failure handling is another important issue in the design of an IPC mechanism. The two commonly used methods in the design of a reliable IPC protocol are the use of internal retransmissions based on timeouts and the use of explicit acknowledgment packets. Two important issues related to failure handling in IPC mechanisms are idempotency and handling of duplicate request messages and keeping track of lost and out-of-sequence packets in multidatagram messages.

The most elementary form of message-based interaction is one-to-one communication in which a single sending process sends a message to a single receiving process. However, for better performance and flexibility, several distributed systems provide group communication facilities that may allow one-to-many, many-to-one, and many-to-many types of interactions between the senders and receivers. Some issues related to group communication are group management, group addressing, atomicity, and ordered message delivery.

## EXERCISES

**3.1.** What are the main reliability issues in designing a message-passing system? Describe a suitable mechanism for handling each of these issues.

**3.2.** What are the main issues related to the correctness of the IPC protocols of a message-passing system? Describe a suitable mechanism for handling each of these issues.

**3.3.** Describe some flexibility features that a message-passing system should provide to its users. Write suitable IPC primitives that will allow the users to take advantage of these flexibility features.

**3.4.** Describe blocking and nonblocking types of IPC. Which is easier to implement and why? Discuss their relative advantages and disadvantages.

**3.5.** Write the code for implementing a producer-consumer pair of processes for the following two cases:

(a) They use a single-message buffer.

(b) They use a buffer that can accommodate up to $n$ messages.

The producer produces messages and puts them in the message buffer, and the consumer consumes messages from the message buffer. Assume that all messages are of fixed size.

**3.6.** What is a datagram? Why are multidatagram messages used in IPC? What are the main issues in IPC of multidatagram messages? Describe a mechanism for handling each of these issues.

**3.7.** In a multidatagram communication, explain how the recipient can properly recognize and arrange the datagrams of the same message and how can it recognize the last datagram of a message.

**3.8.** A linked list of characters is to be sent across a network in the form of a stream of bytes. Write the code in any suitable programming language for encoding the data structure on the sender side and decoding it on the receiver side.

**3.9.** Write the code for implementing the bulletin-board semantics for one-to-many communication for the following cases:

(a) A message posted on the bulletin board is automatically removed after $n$ receivers have read it.

(b) A message posted on the bulletin board is automatically removed after the lapse of time $t$. Time $t$ is a parameter specified by the sender of a message.

Assume that only one message can be posted on the bulletin board at a time. If the bulletin board is not empty at the time a sender wants to post a message, a "not empty, try again" message is returned to the sender. You may make any other assumptions that you feel necessary, but clearly state your assumptions.

**3.10.** Give two examples of applications for which each of the following types of multicast communication is most suitable:

(a) The 0-reliable

(b) The 1-reliable

(c) The $m$-out-of-$n$ reliable ($1 < m < n$)

(d) All-reliable

**3.11.** What is meant by "ordered message delivery"? Do all applications need the same semantics for this property? If yes, explain why. If no, give examples of two applications that need different semantics for this property.

**3.12.** Explain what is meant by absolute ordering, consistent ordering, and causal ordering of messages. Give a mechanism to implement each one.

**3.13.** Describe a mechanism for implementing consistent ordering of messages in each of the following cases:
(a) One-to-many communication
(b) Many-to-one communication
(c) Many-to-many communication

**3.14.** Describe three different process-addressing mechanisms. Discuss their relative advantages and disadvantages. Which of the mechanisms described by you is most suitable for each of the following cases (give reasons for your answer):
(a) For communication between a server process and several client processes. The client processes send request messages to the server process and the server process returns a reply for each client request.
(b) For allowing a sender process to send messages to a group of processes.
(c) For allowing a sender process to send messages to a receiver process that is allowed to migrate from one node to another.
(d) For allowing a sender process to send messages to a receiver process that is allowed to migrate from one node to another and to allow the receiver process to return a reply to the sender process.
(e) For allowing a client process to receive service from any one of the several server processes providing that service.

**3.15.** What is an idempotent operation? Which of the following operations are idempotent:
(a) *read_next_record* (filename)
(b) *read_record* (filename, record_number)
(c) *append_record* (filename, record)
(d) *write_record* (filename, after_record_n, record)
(e) *seek* (filename, position)
(f) *add* (integer_1, integer_2)
(g) *increment* (variable_name)

**3.16.** Suggest a suitable mechanism for implementing each of the following types of IPC semantics:
(a) Last one
(b) At least once
(c) Exactly once

**3.17.** The operations performed by a server are nonidempotent. Describe a mechanism for implementing exactly-once IPC semantics in this case.

**3.18.** Suggest whether at-least-once or exactly-once semantics should be used for each of the following applications (give reasons for your answer):
(a) For making a request to a file server to read a file
(b) For making a request to a file server to append some data to an existing file
(c) For making a request to a compilation server to compile a file
(d) For making a request to a database server to update a bank account
(e) For making a request to a database server to get the current balance of a bank account
(f) For making a request to a booking server to cancel an already booked seat

**3.19.** Suggest a suitable mechanism for implementing reliable IPC with exactly-once semantics in each of the following cases:
(a) The computers of the sender and receiver processes are reliable but the communication links connecting them are unreliable.
(b) The computers of the sender and receiver processes are unreliable but the communication links connecting them are reliable.
(c) The computer of the sender process and the communication links connecting the computers of the sender and receiver processes are reliable but the computer of the receiver process is unreliable.
(d) The computer of the receiver process and the communication links connecting the computers of the sender and receiver processes are reliable but the computer of the sender process is unreliable.

**3.20.** Is it always necessary for the sender of a message to know that the message arrived safely at its destination? If yes, explain why. If no, give two examples in support of your answer.

**3.21.** What is the main purpose of using an acknowledgment message in an IPC protocol? Are acknowledgment messages always needed for reliable communication? Give reasons for your answer.

**3.22.** What is "piggybacking" of a message? How does it help in reducing network traffic? Give some examples of where the piggybacking scheme may be used to improve performance in distributed systems.

**3.23.** In many client-server systems, the timeout mechanism is used to guard against the hanging of a client forever if the server crashes. That is, in these systems, if after sending a request message to a server a client does not receive a reply from the server within a fixed timeout interval, the client assumes that the server has crashed and can take necessary corrective actions. What should be the ideal length of the timeout period in these systems? If the server computer is fully reliable, is it still useful to use the timeout mechanism? Give reasons for your answer.

**3.24.** A file server services file read/write requests of multiple clients. Clients can directly communicate with the file server by sending messages to it and receiving messages from it.
(a) Describe the contents of the message that a client must send to the file server for reading a portion of a file.
(b) Describe the contents of the message that the server must return to the client in reply to part (a).
(c) Describe the contents of the message that a client must send to the file server for writing some data to an existing file.
(d) Describe the contents of the message that the server must return to the client in reply to part (c).
(e) Describe a mechanism by which the file server can cope with multiple client requests arriving almost simultaneously.

**3.25.** In a client-server IPC, a client sends a request message to a server, and the server processes the request and returns the result of the request processing to the client. Is it useful for a process to behave both as a client and a server? If no, explain why. If yes, give an example in support of your answer.

**3.26.** A file storage and retrieval system consists of the following types of processes: several client processes, a file manager process, a cache manager process, and several disk manager processes. These processes perform the following jobs:

(a) A client process sends file access requests to the file manager process.
(b) The file manager process, on receiving a client request, sends the request to the cache manager.
(c) If the data is available in the cache, the cache manager extracts the data from the cache and sends it in a reply message to the file manager. Otherwise, the cache manager sends a request for the data to all the disk managers.
(d) On receiving a request from the cache manager, a disk manager searches for the data in its own disk and returns a suitable reply to the cache manager. That is, if the data is not found, a "not found" message is returned; otherwise the requested data is returned in a message.
(e) Upon receipt of the data, the cache manager caches the data in the cache and also sends it to the file manager.
(f) The file manager performs the requested operation on the data and finally returns a suitable reply to the client process.

What form of IPC do the different types of processes of this application use for interaction among them? Write proper IPC primitives to define the interface between these processes.

**3.27.** Write the skeleton of the processes of the file storage and retrieval system of Exercise 3.26 using the primitives of the 4.3BSD UNIX IPC mechanism to show how they will communicate with each other. Use connection-based communication.

## BIBLIOGRAPHY


**[Ahamad and Bernstein 1985]** Ahamad, M., and Bernstein, A. J., "An Application of Name Based Addressing to Low Level Distributed Algorithms," *IEEE Transactions on Software Engineering*, Vol. SE-11, No. 1, pp. 59–67 (1985).

**[Andrews 1991]** Andrews, G., "Paradigms for Process Interaction in Distributed Programs," *ACM Computing Surveys*, Vol. 23, No. 1, pp. 49–90 (1991).

**[Artsy et al. 1987]** Artsy, Y., Chang, H., and Finkel, R., "Interprocess Communication in Charlotte," *IEEE Software*, pp. 22–28 (1987).

**[Bal and Tanenbaum 1989]** Bal, H. E., and Tanenbaum, A. S., "Programming Languages for Distributed Computing Systems," *ACM Computing Surveys*, Vol. 21, No. 3, pp. 261–322 (1989).

**[Birman 1993]** Birman, K. P., "The Process Group Approach to Reliable Distributed Computing," *Communications of the ACM*, Vol. 36, pp. 36–53 (1993).

**[Birman and Joseph 1987]** Birman, K. P., and Joseph, T. A., "Reliable Communication in the Presence of Failures," *ACM Transactions on Computer Systems*, Vol. 5, No. 1, pp. 47–76 (1987).

**[Birman and Van Renesse 1994]** Birman, K. P., and Van Renesse, R., *Reliable Distributed Computing with the ISIS Toolkit*, IEEE Computer Society Press, Los Alamitos, CA (1994).

**[Birman et al. 1991]** Birman, K. P., Schiper, A., and Stephenson, P., "Lightweight Causal and Atomic Group Multicast," *ACM Transactions on Computer Systems*, Vol. 9, No. 3, pp. 272–314 (1991).

**[CCITT 1985]** *Recommendation X.409*: Presentation Transfer Syntax and Notation. Red Book, Vol. VIII, International Telecommunications Union, Geneva, Switzerland (1985).

**[Chang and Maxemchuk 1984]** Chang, J. M., and Maxemchuk, N. F., "Reliable Broadcast Protocols," *ACM Transactions on Computer Systems*, Vol. 2, pp. 39–59 (1984).

**[Chang and Maxemchuk 1985]** Chang, J. M., and Maxemchuk, N. F., "A Broadcast Protocol for Broadcast Networks," *ACM Transactions on Computer Systems*, Vol. 3, No. 1 (1985).

**[Dijkstra 1975]** Dijkstra, E. W., "Guarded Commands, Nondeterminacy, and Formal Derivation of Programs," *Communications of the ACM*, Vol. 18, No. 8, pp. 453–457 (1975).

**[Draves 1990]** Draves, R. P., "The Revised IPC Interface," In: *Proceedings of the First USENIX Mach Symposium*, USENIX, Berkeley, CA, pp. 101–121, (1990).

**[Ezhilchelvan et al. 1995]** Ezhilchelvan, P. D., Macedo, R. A., and Shrivastava, S. K., "Newtop: A Fault-Tolerant Group Communication Protocol," In: *Proceedings of the 15th International Conference on Distributed Computing Systems*, IEEE (1995).

**[Fitzgerald and Rashid 1986]** Fitzgerald, R., and Rashid, R. F., "The Integration of Virtual Memory Management and Interprocess Communication in Accent," *ACM Transactions on Computer Systems*, Vol. 4, No. 2, pp. 147–177 (1986).

**[Frank et al. 1985]** Frank, A. J., Wittie, L. D., and Bernstein, A. J., "Multicast Communication on Network Computers," *IEEE Software*, Vol. 2, No. 3, pp. 49–61 (1985).

**[Gammage and Casey 1985]** Gammage, N., and Casey, L., "XMS: A Rendezvous Based Distributed System Software Architecture," *IEEE Software*, Vol. 2, No. 3, pp. 9–19 (1985).

**[Gammage et al. 1987]** Gammage, N. D., Kamel, R. F., and Casey, L., "Remote Rendezvous," *Software—Practice and Experience*, Vol. 17, No. 10, pp. 741–755 (1987).

**[Garcia-Molina and Spauster 1991]** Garcia-Molina, H., and Spauster, A., "Ordered and Reliable Multicast Communication," *ACM Transactions on Computer Systems*, Vol. 9, No. 3, pp. 242–271 (1991).

**[Garg 1996]** Garg, V. K., *Principles of Distributed Systems*, Kluwer Academic, Norwell, MA (1996).

**[Gehani 1984]** Gehani, N. H., "Broadcast Sequential Processes (BSP)," *IEEE Transactions on Software Engineering*, Vol. SE-10, No. 4, pp. 343–351 (1984).

**[Gehani 1987]** Gehani, N. H., "Message Passing: Synchronous versus Asynchronous," AT&T Bell Laboratories, Murray Hill, NJ (1987).

**[Islam and Roy 1995]** Islam, N., and Roy, H., "Techniques for Global Optimization of Message Passing Communication on Unreliable Networks," In: *Proceedings of the 15th International Conference on Distributed Computing Systems*, IEEE, Piscataway, NJ (1995).

**[Jalote 1994]** Jalote, P., *Fault Tolerance in Distributed Systems*, Prentice-Hall, Englewood Cliffs, NJ (1994).

**[Jia 1995]** Jia, X., "A Total Ordering Multicast Protocol Using Propagation Trees," *IEEE Transactions on Parallel and Distributed Systems*, Vol. 6, No. 6, pp. 617–627 (1995).

**[Kaashoek and Tanenbaum 1991]** Kaashoek, M. F., and Tanenbaum, A. S., "Group Communication in the Amoeba Distributed Operating System," In: *Proceedings of the 11th International Conference on Distributed Computing Systems*, IEEE Press, Piscataway, NJ, pp. 222–230 (1991).

**[Kaashoek et al. 1989]** Kaashoek, M. F., Tanenbaum, A. S., Hummel, S., and Bal, H. E., "An Efficient Reliable Broadcast Protocol," *Operating Systems Review*, Vol. 23, pp. 5–19 (1989).

**[Kranz et al. 1993]** Kranz, D., Johnson, K., Agarwal, A., Kubiatowicz, J. J., and Lim, B., "Integrating Message Passing and Shared Memory: Early Experiences," In: *Proceedings of the 4th Symposium on Principles and Practice of Parallel Programming*, Association for Computing Machinery, New York, NY, pp. 54–63 (1993).

**[Liang et al. 1990]** Liang, L., Chanson, S. T., and Neufeld, W., "Process Groups and Group Communications: Classifications and Requirements," *IEEE Computer*, Vol. 23, pp. 56–66 (1990).

**[Luan and Gligor 1990]** Luan, S. W., and Gligor, V. D., "A Fault-Tolerant Protocol for Atomic Broadcast," *IEEE Transactions on Parallel and Distributed Systems*, Vol. 1, pp. 271–285 (1990).

**[Meliar-Smith et al. 1990]** Meliar-Smith, P. M., Moser, L. E., and Agrawala, V., "Broadcast Protocols for Distributed Systems," *IEEE Transactions on Parallel and Distributed Systems*, Vol. 1, pp. 17–25 (1990).

**[Milenkovic 1992]** Milenkovic, M., *Operating Systems: Concepts and Design*, 2nd ed., McGraw-Hill, New York, NY (1992).

**[Miller et al. 1987]** Miller, B. P., Presotto, D. L., and Powell, M. L., "DEMOS/MP: The Development of a Distributed Operating System," *Software—Practice and Experience*, Vol. 17, No. 4, pp. 277–290 (1987).

**[Mullender 1993]** "Interprocess Communication," In: S. Mullender (Eds.), *Distributed Systems*, 2nd ed., Association for Computing Machinery, New York, NY, pp. 217–250 (1993).

**[Natrajan 1985]** Natrajan, N., "Communication and Synchronization Primitives for Distributed Programs," *IEEE Transactions on Software Engineering*, Vol. SE-11, No. 4, pp. 396–416 (1985).

**[Navratnam et al. 1988]** Navratnam, S., Chanson, S., and Neufeld, G., "Reliable Group Communication in Distributed Systems," In: *Proceedings of the 8th International Conference on Distributed Computing Systems*, IEEE Press, Piscataway, NJ, pp. 439–446 (1988).

**[Ramanathan and Shin 1992]** Ramanathan, P., and Shin, K. G., "Delivery of Time-Critical Messages Using a Multiple Copy Approach," *ACM Transactions on Computer Systems*, Vol. 10, pp. 144–166 (1992).

**[Shatz 1984]** Shatz, S. M., "Communication Mechanisms for Programming Distributed Systems," *IEEE Computer*, pp. 21–28 (June 1984).

**[Stemple et al. 1986]** Stemple, D. W., Vinter S. T., and Ramamritham, K., "Functional Addressing in Gutenberg: Interprocess Communication without Process Identifiers," *IEEE Transactions on Software Engineering*, Vol. SE-12, No. 11, pp. 1056–1066 (1986).

**[Sun 1990]** Sun Microsystems Inc., *Network Programming*, Sun Microsystems, Mountain View, CA (March 1990).

**[Tanenbaum 1995]** Tanenbaum, A. S., *Distributed Operating Systems*, Prentice-Hall, Englewood Cliffs, NJ (1995).

**[Tanenbaum et al. 1992]** Tanenbaum, A. S., Kaashoek, M. F., and Bal, H. E., "Parallel Programming Using Shared Objects and Broadcasting," *IEEE Computer*, pp. 10–19 (August 1992).

**[Xerox 1981]** Xerox Corporation, *Courier: The Remote Procedure Call Protocol. Xerox Systems Integration Standards*, Xerox Corporation, Standard, CT (1981).

**[Yeung and Yum 1995]** Yeung, K. H., and Yum, T. S., "Selective Broadcast Data Distribution Systems," In: *Proceedings of the 15th International Conference on Distributed Computing Systems*, IEEE Press, Piscataway, NJ (1995).

## POINTERS TO BIBLIOGRAPHIES ON THE INTERNET

I could not find a bibliography dedicated only to message passing. However, the following bibliographies contain references on the topics covered in this chapter:

ftp:ftp.cs.umanitoba.ca/pub/bibliographies/Os/IMMD_IV.html

ftp:ftp.cs.umanitoba.ca/pub/bibliographies/Os/os.html

ftp:ftp.cs.umanitoba.ca/pub/bibliographies/Parallel/JPDC.html

ftp:ftp.cs.umanitoba.ca/pub/bibliographies/Parallel/pvm.html

CHAPTER 4

# Remote Procedure Calls

## 4.1 INTRODUCTION

The general message-passing model of interprocess communication (IPC) was presented in the previous chapter. The IPC part of a distributed application can often be adequately and efficiently handled by using an IPC protocol based on the message-passing model. However, an independently developed IPC protocol is tailored specifically to one application and does not provide a foundation on which to build a variety of distributed applications. Therefore, a need was felt for a general IPC protocol that can be used for designing several distributed applications. The Remote Procedure Call (RPC) facility emerged out of this need. It is a special case of the general message-passing model of IPC. Providing the programmers with a familiar mechanism for building distributed systems is one of the primary motivations for developing the RPC facility. While the RPC facility is not a universal panacea for all types of distributed applications, it does provide a valuable communication mechanism that is suitable for building a fairly large number of distributed applications.

The RPC has become a widely accepted IPC mechanism in distributed systems. The popularity of RPC as the primary communication mechanism for distributed applications is due to its following features:

1. Simple call syntax.
2. Familiar semantics (because of its similarity to local procedure calls).
3. Its specification of a well-defined interface. This property is used to support compile-time type checking and automated interface generation.
4. Its ease of use. The clean and simple semantics of a procedure call makes it easier to build distributed computations and to get them right.
5. Its generality. This feature is owing to the fact that in single-machine computations procedure calls are often the most important mechanism for communication between parts of the algorithm [Birrell and Nelson 1984].
6. Its efficiency. Procedure calls are simple enough for communication to be quite rapid.
7. It can be used as an IPC mechanism to communicate between processes on different machines as well as between different processes on the same machine.

## 4.2 THE RPC MODEL

The RPC model is similar to the well-known and well-understood procedure call model used for the transfer of control and data within a program in the following manner:

1. For making a procedure call, the caller places arguments to the procedure in some well-specified location.
2. Control is then transferred to the sequence of instructions that constitutes the body of the procedure.
3. The procedure body is executed in a newly created execution environment that includes copies of the arguments given in the calling instruction.
4. After the procedure's execution is over, control returns to the calling point, possibly returning a result.

The RPC mechanism is an extension of the procedure call mechanism in the sense that it enables a call to be made to a procedure that does not reside in the address space of the calling process. The called procedure (commonly called *remote procedure*) may be on the same computer as the calling process or on a different computer.

In case of RPC, since the caller and the callee processes have disjoint address spaces (possibly on different computers), the remote procedure has no access to data and variables of the caller's environment. Therefore the RPC facility uses a message-passing scheme for information exchange between the caller and the callee processes. As shown in Figure 4.1, when a remote procedure call is made, the caller and the callee processes interact in the following manner:

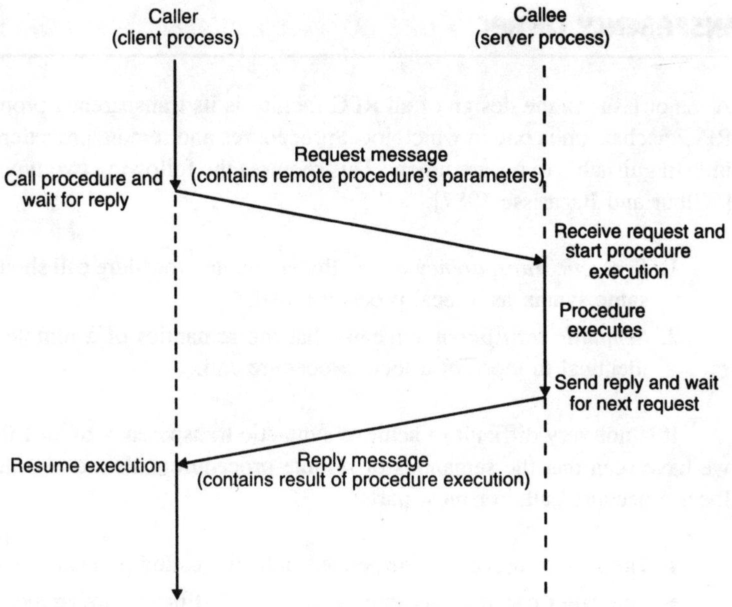


**Fig. 4.1** A typical model of Remote Procedure Call.

1. The caller (commonly known as *client process*) sends a call (request) message to the callee (commonly known as *server process*) and waits (blocks) for a reply message. The request message contains the remote procedure's parameters, among other things.
2. The server process executes the procedure and then returns the result of procedure execution in a reply message to the client process.
3. Once the reply message is received, the result of procedure execution is extracted, and the caller's execution is resumed.

The server process is normally dormant, awaiting the arrival of a request message. When one arrives, the server process extracts the procedure's parameters, computes the result, sends a reply message, and then awaits the next call message.

Note that in this model of RPC, only one of the two processes is active at any given time. However, in general, the RPC protocol makes no restrictions on the concurrency model implemented, and other models of RPC are possible depending on the details of the parallelism of the caller's and callee's environments and the RPC implementation. For example, an implementation may choose to have RPC calls to be asynchronous, so that the client may do useful work while waiting for the reply from the server. Another possibility is to have the server create a thread (threads are described in Chapter 8) to process an incoming request, so that the server can be free to receive other requests.

## 4.3 TRANSPARENCY OF RPC

A major issue in the design of an RPC facility is its transparency property. A transparent RPC mechanism is one in which local procedures and remote procedures are (effectively) indistinguishable to programmers. This requires the following two types of transparencies [Wilbur and Bacarisse 1987]:

1. *Syntactic transparency* means that a remote procedure call should have exactly the same syntax as a local procedure call.
2. *Semantic transparency* means that the semantics of a remote procedure call are identical to those of a local procedure call.

It is not very difficult to achieve syntactic transparency of an RPC mechanism, and we have seen that the semantics of remote procedure calls are also analogous to that of local procedure calls for most parts:

- The calling process is suspended until the called procedure returns.
- The caller can pass arguments to the called procedure (remote procedure).
- The called procedure (remote procedure) can return results to the caller.

Unfortunately, achieving exactly the same semantics for remote procedure calls as for local procedure calls is close to impossible [Tanenbaum and Van Renesse 1988]. This is mainly because of the following differences between remote procedure calls and local procedure calls:

1. Unlike local procedure calls, with remote procedure calls, the called procedure is executed in an address space that is disjoint from the calling program's address space. Due to this reason, the called (remote) procedure cannot have access to any variables or data values in the calling program's environment. Thus in the absence of shared memory, it is meaningless to pass addresses in arguments, making call-by-reference pointers highly unattractive. Similarly, it is meaningless to pass argument values containing pointer structures (e.g., linked lists), since pointers are normally represented by memory addresses. According to Bal et al. [1989], dereferencing a pointer passed by the caller has to be done at the caller's side, which implies extra communication. An alternative implementation is to send a copy of the value pointed at the receiver, but this has subtly different semantics and may be difficult to implement if the pointer points into the middle of a complex data structure, such as a directed graph. Similarly, call by reference can be replaced by copy in/copy out, but at the cost of slightly different semantics.

2. Remote procedure calls are more vulnerable to failure than local procedure calls, since they involve two different processes and possibly a network and two different computers. Therefore programs that make use of remote procedure calls must have the capability of handling even those errors that cannot occur in local procedure calls. The need for the ability to take care of the possibility of processor crashes and communication

problems of a network makes it even more difficult to obtain the same semantics for remote procedure calls as for local procedure calls.

3. Remote procedure calls consume much more time (100–1000 times more) than local procedure calls. This is mainly due to the involvement of a communication network in RPCs. Therefore applications using RPCs must also have the capability to handle the long delays that may possibly occur due to network congestion.

Because of these difficulties in achieving normal call semantics for remote procedure calls, some researchers feel that the RPC facility should be nontransparent. For example, Hamilton [1984] argues that remote procedures should be treated differently from local procedures from the start, resulting in a nontransparent RPC mechanism. Similarly, the designers of RPC in Argus [Liskov and Scheifler 1983] were of the opinion that although the RPC system should hide low-level details of message passing from the users, failures and long delays should not be hidden from the caller. That is, the caller should have the flexibility of handling failures and long delays in an application-dependent manner. In conclusion, although in most environments total semantic transparency is impossible, enough can be done to ensure that distributed application programmers feel comfortable.

## 4.4 IMPLEMENTING RPC MECHANISM

To achieve the goal of semantic transparency, the implementation of an RPC mechanism is based on the concept of *stubs*, which provide a perfectly normal (local) procedure call abstraction by concealing from programs the interface to the underlying RPC system. We saw that an RPC involves a client process and a server process. Therefore, to conceal the interface of the underlying RPC system from both the client and server processes, a separate stub procedure is associated with each of the two processes. Moreover, to hide the existence and functional details of the underlying network, an RPC communication package (known as *RPCRuntime*) is used on both the client and server sides. Thus, implementation of an RPC mechanism usually involves the following five elements of program [Birrell and Nelson 1984]:

1. The client
2. The client stub
3. The RPCRuntime
4. The server stub
5. The server

The interaction between them is shown in Figure 4.2. The client, the client stub, and one instance of RPCRuntime execute on the client machine, while the server, the server stub, and another instance of RPCRuntime execute on the server machine. The job of each of these elements is described below.

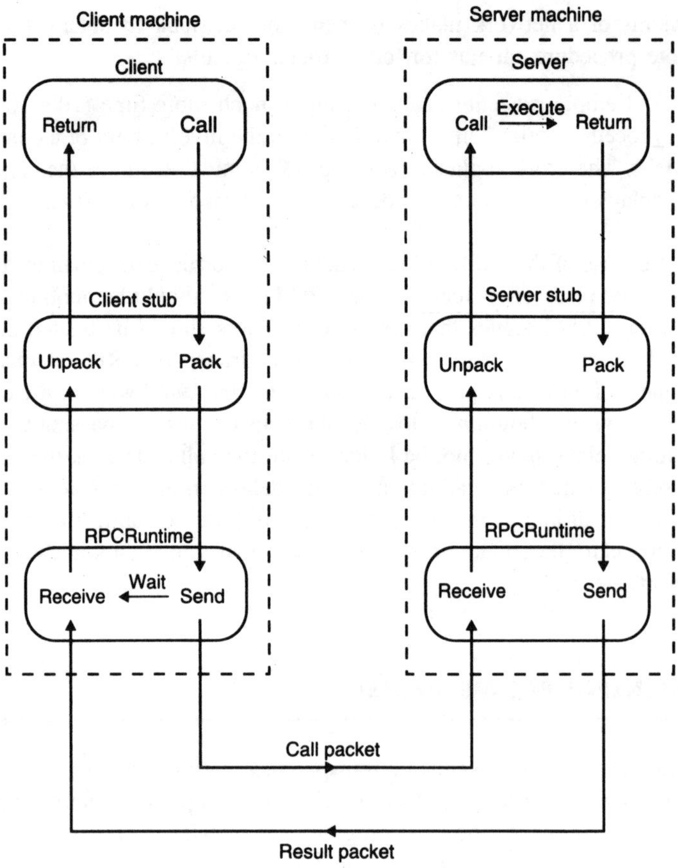


**Fig. 4.2** Implementation of RPC mechanism.

### 4.4.1 Client

The client is a user process that initiates a remote procedure call. To make a remote procedure call, the client makes a perfectly normal local call that invokes a corresponding procedure in the client stub.

### 4.4.2 Client Stub

The client stub is responsible for carrying out the following two tasks:

- On receipt of a call request from the client, it packs a specification of the target procedure and the arguments into a message and then asks the local RPCRuntime to send it to the server stub.

- On receipt of the result of procedure execution, it unpacks the result and passes it to the client.

### 4.4.3 RPCRuntime

The RPCRuntime handles transmission of messages across the network between client and server machines. It is responsible for retransmissions, acknowledgments, packet routing, and encryption. The RPCRuntime on the client machine receives the call request message from the client stub and sends it to the server machine. It also receives the message containing the result of procedure execution from the server machine and passes it to the client stub.

On the other hand, the RPCRuntime on the server machine receives the message containing the result of procedure execution from the server stub and sends it to the client machine. It also receives the call request message from the client machine and passes it to the server stub.

### 4.4.4 Server Stub

The job of the server stub is very similar to that of the client stub. It performs the following two tasks:

- On receipt of the call request message from the local RPCRuntime, the server stub unpacks it and makes a perfectly normal call to invoke the appropriate procedure in the server.
- On receipt of the result of procedure execution from the server, the server stub packs the result into a message and then asks the local RPCRuntime to send it to the client stub.

### 4.4.5 Server

On receiving a call request from the server stub, the server executes the appropriate procedure and returns the result of procedure execution to the server stub.

---

Note here that the beauty of the whole scheme is the total ignorance on the part of the client that the work was done remotely instead of by the local kernel. When the client gets control following the procedure call that it made, all it knows is that the results of the procedure execution are available to it. Therefore, as far as the client is concerned, remote services are accessed by making ordinary (local) procedure calls, not by using the *send* and *receive* primitives of Chapter 3. All the details of the message passing are hidden in the client and server stubs, making the steps involved in message passing invisible to both the client and the server.

## 4.5 STUB GENERATION

Stubs can be generated in one of the following two ways:

1. *Manually.* In this method, the RPC implementor provides a set of translation functions from which a user can construct his or her own stubs. This method is simple to implement and can handle very complex parameter types.

2. *Automatically.* This is the more commonly used method for stub generation. It uses *Interface Definition Language* (*IDL*) that is used to define the interface between a client and a server. An interface definition is mainly a list of procedure names supported by the interface, together with the types of their arguments and results. This is sufficient information for the client and server to independently perform compile-time type-checking and to generate appropriate calling sequences. However, an interface definition also contains other information that helps RPC reduce data storage and the amount of data transferred over the network. For example, an interface definition has information to indicate whether each argument is input, output, or both—only input arguments need be copied from client to server and only output arguments need be copied from server to client. Similarly, an interface definition also has information about type definitions, enumerated types, and defined constants that each side uses to manipulate data from RPC calls, making it unnecessary for both the client and the server to store this information separately. (See Figure 4.21 for an example of an interface definition.)

A server program that implements procedures in an interface is said to *export* the interface, and a client program that calls procedures from an interface is said to *import* the interface. When writing a distributed application, a programmer first writes an interface definition using the IDL. He or she can then write the client program that imports the interface and the server program that exports the interface. The interface definition is processed using an IDL compiler to generate components that can be combined with client and server programs, without making any changes to the existing compilers. In particular, from an interface definition, an IDL compiler generates a client stub procedure and a server stub procedure for each procedure in the interface, the appropriate marshaling and unmarshaling operations (described later in this chapter) in each stub procedure, and a header file that supports the data types in the interface definition. The header file is included in the source files of both the client and server programs, the client stub procedures are compiled and linked with the client program, and the server stub procedures are compiled and linked with the server program. An IDL compiler can be designed to process interface definitions for use with different languages, enabling clients and servers written in different languages, to communicate by using remote procedure calls.

## 4.6 RPC MESSAGES

Any remote procedure call involves a client process and a server process that are possibly located on different computers. The mode of interaction between the client and server is that the client asks the server to execute a remote procedure and the server returns the result of execution of the concerned procedure to the client. Based on this mode of interaction, the two types of messages involved in the implementation of an RPC system are as follows:

1. *Call messages* that are sent by the client to the server for requesting execution of a particular remote procedure
2. *Reply messages* that are sent by the server to the client for returning the result of remote procedure execution

The protocol of the concerned RPC system defines the format of these two types of messages. Normally, an RPC protocol is independent of transport protocols. That is, RPC does not care how a message is passed from one process to another. Therefore an RPC protocol deals only with the specification and interpretation of these two types of messages.

### 4.6.1 Call Messages

Since a call message is used to request execution of a particular remote procedure, the two basic components necessary in a call message are as follows:

1. The identification information of the remote procedure to be executed
2. The arguments necessary for the execution of the procedure

In addition to these two fields, a call message normally has the following fields:

3. A message identification field that consists of a sequence number. This field is useful in two ways—for identifying lost messages and duplicate messages in case of system failures and for properly matching reply messages to outstanding call messages, especially in those cases where the replies of several outstanding call messages arrive out of order.
4. A message type field that is used to distinguish call messages from reply messages. For example, in an RPC system, this field may be set to 0 for all call messages and set to 1 for all reply messages.
5. A client identification field that may be used for two purposes—to allow the server of the RPC to identify the client to whom the reply message has to be returned and to allow the server to check the authentication of the client process for executing the concerned procedure.

Thus, a typical RPC call message format may be of the form shown in Figure 4.3.

### 4.6.2 Reply Messages

When the server of an RPC receives a call message from a client, it could be faced with one of the following conditions. In the list below, it is assumed for a particular condition that no problem was detected by the server for any of the previously listed conditions:

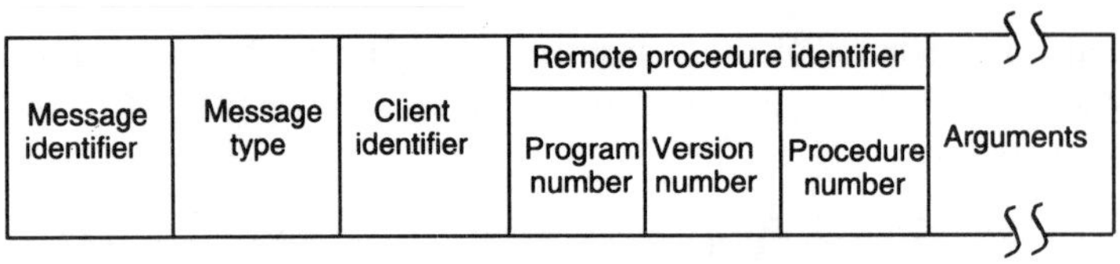


**Fig. 4.3** A typical RPC call message format.

1. The server finds that the call message is not intelligible to it. This may happen when a call message violates the RPC protocol. Obviously the server will reject such calls.
2. The server detects by scanning the client's identifier field that the client is not authorized to use the service. The server will return an unsuccessful reply without bothering to make an attempt to execute the procedure.
3. The server finds that the remote program, version, or procedure number specified in the remote procedure identifier field of the call message is not available with it. Again the server will return an unsuccessful reply without bothering to make an attempt to execute the procedure.
4. If this stage is reached, an attempt will be made to execute the remote procedure specified in the call message. Therefore it may happen that the remote procedure is not able to decode the supplied arguments. This may happen due to an incompatible RPC interface being used by the client and server.
5. An exception condition (such as division by zero) occurs while executing the specified remote procedure.
6. The specified remote procedure is executed successfully.

Obviously, in the first five cases, an unsuccessful reply has to be sent to the client with the reason for failure in processing the request and a successful reply has to be sent in the sixth case with the result of procedure execution. Therefore the format of a successful reply message and an unsuccessful reply message is normally slightly different. A typical RPC reply message format for successful and unsuccessful replies may be of the form shown in Figure 4.4.

The message identifier field of a reply message is the same as that of its corresponding call message so that a reply message can be properly matched with its call message. The message type field is properly set to indicate that it is a reply message. For a successful reply, the reply status field is normally set to zero and is followed by the field containing the result of procedure execution. For an unsuccessful reply, the reply status field is either set to 1 or to a nonzero value to indicate failure. In the latter case, the value of the reply status field indicates the type of error. However, in either case, normally a short statement describing the reason for failure is placed in a separate field following the reply status field.

Since RPC protocols are generally independent of transport protocols, it is not possible for an RPC protocol designer to fix the maximum length of call and reply

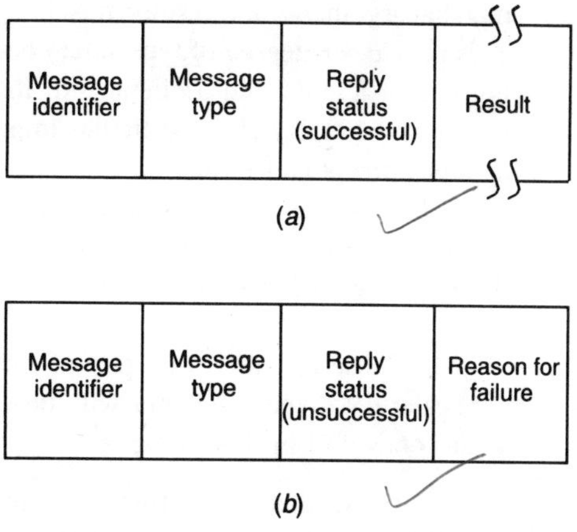


**Fig. 4.4** A typical RPC reply message format: (*a*) a successful reply message format; (*b*) an unsuccessful reply message format.

messages. Therefore, for a distributed application to work for a group of transports, it is important for the distributed application developers to ensure that their RPC call and reply messages do not exceed the maximum length specified by any of the transports of the concerned group.

## 4.7 MARSHALING ARGUMENTS AND RESULTS

Implementation of remote procedure calls involves the transfer of arguments from the client process to the server process and the transfer of results from the server process to the client process. These arguments and results are basically language-level data structures (program objects), which are transferred in the form of message data between the two computers involved in the call. We have seen in the previous chapter that transfer of message data between two computers requires encoding and decoding of the message data. For RPCs this operation is known as *marshaling* and basically involves the following actions:

1. Taking the arguments (of a client process) or the result (of a server process) that will form the message data to be sent to the remote process.
2. Encoding the message data of step 1 above on the sender's computer. This encoding process involves the conversion of program objects into a stream form that is suitable for transmission and placing them into a message buffer.
3. Decoding of the message data on the receiver's computer. This decoding process involves the reconstruction of program objects from the message data that was received in stream form.

In order that encoding and decoding of an RPC message can be performed successfully, the order and the representation method (tagged or untagged) used to marshal arguments and results must be known to both the client and the server of the RPC. This provides a degree of type safety between a client and a server because the server will not accept a call from a client until the client uses the same interface definition as the server. Type safety is of particular importance to servers since it allows them to survive against corrupt call requests.

The marshaling process must reflect the structure of all types of program objects used in the concerned language. These include primitive types, structured types, and user-defined types. Marshaling procedures may be classified into two groups:

1. Those provided as a part of the RPC software. Normally marshaling procedures for scalar data types, together with procedures to marshal compound types built from the scalar ones, fall in this group.

2. Those that are defined by the users of the RPC system. This group contains marshaling procedures for user-defined data types and data types that include pointers. For example, in Concurrent CLU, developed for use in the Cambridge Distributed Computer System [Bacon and Hamilton 1987], for user-defined types, the type definition must contain procedures for marshaling.

A good RPC system should always generate in-line marshaling code for every remote call so that the users are relieved of the burden of writing their own marshaling procedures. However, practically it is difficult to achieve this goal because of the unacceptable large amounts of code that may have to be generated for handling all possible data types.

## 4.8 SERVER MANAGEMENT

In RPC-based applications, two important issues that need to be considered for server management are server implementation and server creation.

### 4.8.1 Server Implementation

Based on the style of implementation used, servers may be of two types: stateful and stateless.

#### Stateful Servers

A stateful server maintains clients' state information from one remote procedure call to the next. That is, in case of two subsequent calls by a client to a stateful server, some state information pertaining to the service performed for the client as a result of the first call execution is stored by the server process. These clients' state information is subsequently used at the time of executing the second call.

For example, let us consider a server for byte-stream files that allows the following operations on files:

**Open** (*filename, mode*): This operation is used to open a file identified by *filename* in the specified *mode*. When the server executes this operation, it creates an entry for this file in a *file-table* that it uses for maintaining the file state information of all the open files. The file state information normally consists of the identifier of the file, the open mode, and the current position of a nonnegative integer pointer, called the *read-write pointer*. When a file is opened, its *read-write pointer* is set to zero and the server returns to the client a file identifier (*fid*), which is used by the client for subsequent accesses to that file.

**Read** (*fid, n, buffer*): This operation is used to get *n* bytes of data from the file identified by *fid* into the buffer named *buffer*. When the server executes this operation, it returns to the client *n* bytes of file data starting from the byte currently addressed by the *read-write pointer* and then increments the *read-write pointer* by *n*.

**Write** (*fid, n, buffer*): On execution of this operation, the server takes *n* bytes of data from the specified *buffer*, writes it into the file identified by *fid* at the byte position currently addressed by the *read-write pointer*, and then increments the *read-write pointer* by *n*.

**Seek** (*fid, position*): This operation causes the server to change the value of the *read-write pointer* of the file identified by *fid* to the new value specified as *position*.

**Close** (*fid*): This statement causes the server to delete from its *file-table* the file state information of the file identified by *fid*.

The file server mentioned above is stateful because it maintains the current state information for a file that has been opened for use by a client. Therefore, as shown in Figure 4.5, after opening a file, if a client makes two subsequent **Read** (*fid, 100, buf*) calls, the first call will return the first 100 bytes (bytes 0–99) and the second call will return the next 100 bytes (bytes 100–199).

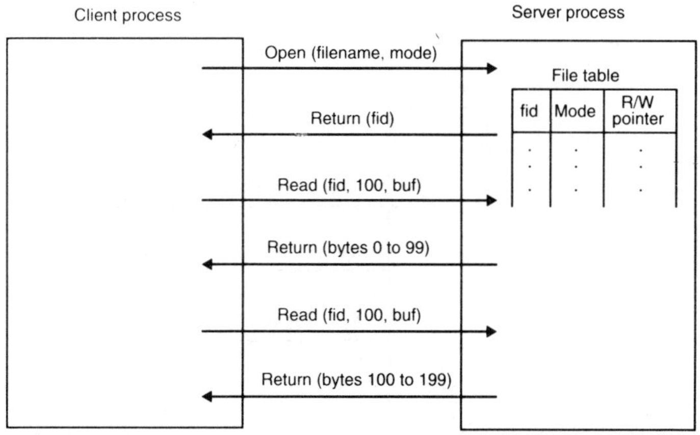


**Fig. 4.5** An example of a stateful file server.

### Stateless Servers

A stateless server does not maintain any client state information. Therefore every request from a client must be accompanied with all the necessary parameters to successfully carry out the desired operation. For example, a server for byte stream files that allows the following operations on files is stateless.

**Read** (*filename, position, n, buffer*): On execution of this operation, the server returns to the client *n* bytes of data of the file identified by *filename*. The returned data is placed in the buffer named *buffer*. The value of actual number of bytes read is also returned to the client. The position within the file from where to begin reading is specified as the *position* parameter.

**Write** (*filename, position, n, buffer*): When the server executes this operation, it takes *n* bytes of data from the specified *buffer* and writes it into the file identified by *filename*. The *position* parameter specifies the byte position within the file from where to start writing. The server returns to the client the actual number of bytes written.

As shown in Figure 4.6, this file server does not keep track of any file state information resulting from a previous operation. Therefore if a client wishes to have similar effect as that in Figure 4.5, the following two *Read* operations must be carried out:

**Read** (*filename, 0, 100, buf*)
**Read** (*filename, 100, 100, buf*)

Notice that in this case the client has to keep track of the file state information.

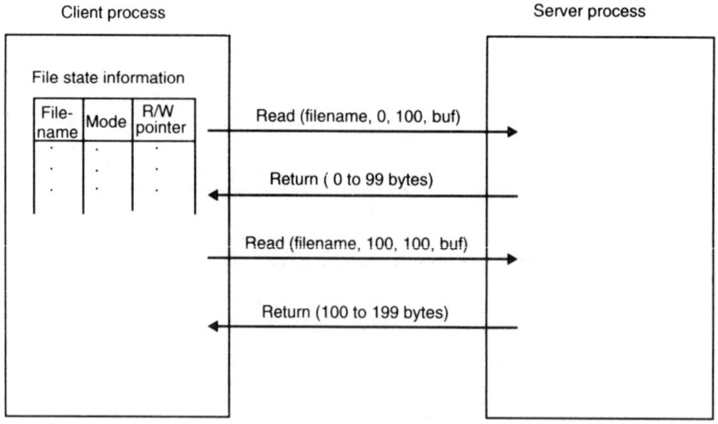


**Fig. 4.6** An example of a stateless file server.

### Why Stateless Servers?

From the description of stateful and stateless servers, readers might have observed that stateful servers provide an easier programming paradigm because they relieve the clients from the task of keeping track of state information. In addition, stateful servers are typically more efficient than stateless servers. Therefore, the obvious question that arises is why should stateless servers be used at all.

The use of stateless servers in many distributed applications is justified by the fact that stateless servers have a distinct advantage over stateful servers in the event of a failure. For example, with stateful servers, if a server crashes and then restarts, the state information that it was holding may be lost and the client process might continue its task unaware of the crash, producing inconsistent results. Similarly, when a client process crashes and then restarts its task, the server is left holding state information that is no longer valid but cannot easily be withdrawn. Therefore, the client of a stateful server must be properly designed to detect server crashes so that it can perform necessary error-handling activities. On the other hand, with stateless servers, a client has to only retry a request until the server responds; it does not need to know that the server has crashed or that the network temporarily went down. Therefore, stateless servers, which can be constructed around repeatable operations, make crash recovery very easy.

Both stateless and stateful servers have their own advantages and disadvantages. The choice of using a stateless or a stateful server is purely application dependent. Therefore, distributed application system designers must carefully examine the positive and negative aspects of both approaches for their applications before making a choice.

## 4.8.2 Server Creation Semantics

In RPC, the remote procedure to be executed as a result of a remote procedure call made by a client process lies in a server process that is totally independent of the client process. Independence here means that the client and server processes have separate lifetimes, they normally run on separate machines, and they have their own address spaces. Since a server process is independent of a client process that makes a remote procedure call to it, server processes may either be created and installed before their client processes or be created on a demand basis. Based on the time duration for which RPC servers survive, they may be classified as instance-per-call servers, instance-per-transaction/session servers, or persistent servers.

### Instance-per-Call Servers

Servers belonging to this category exist only for the duration of a single call. A server of this type is created by RPCRuntime on the server machine only when a call message arrives. The server is deleted after the call has been executed.

This approach for server creation is not commonly used because of the following problems associated with it:

- The servers of this type are stateless because they are killed as soon as they have serviced the call for which they were created. Therefore, any state that has to be preserved across server calls must be taken care of by either the client process or the supporting operating system. The involvement of the operating system in maintaining intercall state information will make the remote procedure calls expensive. On the other hand, if the intercall state information is maintained by the client process, the state information must be passed to and from the server with each call. This will lead to the loss of data abstraction across the client-server interface, which will ultimately result in loss of attractiveness of the RPC mechanism to the programmers.

- When a distributed application needs to successively invoke the same type of server several times, this approach appears more expensive, since resource (memory space to provide buffer space and control structures) allocation and deallocation has to be done many times. Therefore, the overhead involved in server creation and destruction dominates the cost of remote procedure calls.

### Instance-per-Session Servers

Servers belonging to this category exist for the entire session for which a client and a server interact. Since a server of this type exists for the entire session, it can maintain intercall state information, and the overhead involved in server creation and destruction for a client-server session that involves a large number of calls is also minimized.

In this method, normally there is a server manager for each type of service. All these server managers are registered with the binding agent (binding agent mechanism for binding a client and a server is described later in this chapter). When a client contacts the binding agent, it specifies the type of service needed and the binding agent returns the address of the server manager of the desired type to the client. The client then contacts the concerned server manager, requesting it to create a server for it. The server manager then spawns a new server and passes back its address to the client. The client now directly interacts with this server for the entire session. This server is exclusively used by the client for which it was created and is destroyed when the client informs back to the server manager of the corresponding type that it no longer needs that server.

A server of this type can retain useful state information between calls and so can present a cleaner, more abstract interface to its clients. Note that a server of this type only services a single client and hence only has to manage a single set of state information.

### Persistent Servers

A persistent server generally remains in existence indefinitely. Moreover, we saw that the servers of the previous two types cannot be shared by two or more clients because they are exclusively created for a particular client on demand. Unlike them, a persistent server is usually shared by many clients.

Servers of this type are usually created and installed before the clients that use them. Each server independently exports its service by registering itself with the binding agent. When a client contacts the binding agent for a particular type of service, the binding agent selects a server of that type either arbitrarily or based on some in-built policy (such as the minimum number of clients currently bound to it) and returns the address of the selected server to the client. The client then directly interacts with that server.

Note that a persistent server may be simultaneously bound to several clients. In this case, the server interleaves requests from a number of clients and thus has to concurrently manage several sets of state information. If a persistent server is shared by multiple clients, the remote procedure that it offers must be designed so that interleaved or concurrent requests from different clients do not interfere with each other.

Persistent servers may also be used for improving the overall performance and reliability of the system. For this, several persistent servers that provide the same type of service may be installed on different machines to provide either load balancing or some measure of resilience to failure.

## 4.9 PARAMETER-PASSING SEMANTICS

The choice of parameter-passing semantics is crucial to the design of an RPC mechanism. The two choices are call-by-value and call-by-reference.

### 4.9.1 Call-by-Value

In the *call-by-value* method, all parameters are copied into a message that is transmitted from the client to the server through the intervening network. This poses no problems for simple compact types such as integers, counters, small arrays, and so on. However, passing larger data types such as multidimensional arrays, trees, and so on, can consume much time for transmission of data that may not be used. Therefore this method is not suitable for passing parameters involving voluminous data.

An argument in favor of the high cost incurred in passing large parameters by value is that it forces the users to be aware of the expense of remote procedure calls for large-parameter lists. In turn, the users are forced to carefully consider their design of the interface needed between client and server to minimize the passing of unnecessary data. Therefore, before choosing RPC parameter-passing semantics, it is important to carefully review and properly design the client-server interfaces so that parameters become more specific with minimal data being transmitted.

### 4.9.2 Call-by-Reference

Most RPC mechanisms use the call-by-value semantics for parameter passing because the client and the server exist in different address spaces, possibly even on different types of machines, so that passing pointers or passing parameters *by reference* is meaningless. However, a few RPC mechanisms do allow passing of parameters by reference in which pointers to the parameters are passed from the client to the server. These are usually closed systems, where a single address space is shared by all processes in the system. For example, distributed systems having distributed shared-memory mechanisms (described in Chapter 5) can allow passing of parameters by reference.

In an object-based system that uses the RPC mechanism for object invocation, the call-by-reference semantics is known as *call-by-object-reference*. This is because in an object-based system, the value of a variable is a reference to an object, so it is this reference (the object name) that is passed in an invocation.

Emerald [Black et al. 1986, 1987] designers observed that the use of a call-by-object-reference mechanism in distributed systems presents a potentially serious performance problem because on a remote invocation access by the remote operation to an argument is likely to cause an additional remote invocation. Therefore to avoid many remote references, Emerald supports a new parameter-passing mode that is known as *call-by-move*. In call-by-move, a parameter is passed by reference, as in the method of call-by-object-reference, but at the time of the call, the parameter object is moved to the destination node (site of the callee). Following the call, the argument object may either return to the caller's node or remain at the callee's node (these two modes are known as *call-by-visit* and *call-by-move*, respectively).

Obviously, the use of the call-by-move mode for parameter passing requires that the underlying system supports mobile objects that can be moved from one node to another. Emerald objects are mobile.

Notice that call-by-move does not change the parameter-passing semantics, which is still call-by-object-reference. Therefore call-by-move is basically convenient and optimizes performance. This is because call-by-move could be emulated as a two-step operation:

- First move each call-by-move parameter object to the invokee's node.
- Then invoke the object.

However, performing the moves separately would cause multiple messages to be sent across the network. Thus, providing call-by-move as a parameter-passing mode allows packaging of the argument objects in the same network packet as the invocation message, thereby reducing the network traffic and message count.

Although call-by-move reduces the cost of references made by the invokee, it increases the cost of the invocation itself. If the parameter object is mutable and shared, it also increases the cost of references by the invoker [Black et al. 1987].

## 4.10 CALL SEMANTICS

In RPC, the caller and the callee processes are possibly located on different nodes. Thus it is possible for either the caller or the callee node to fail independently and later to be restarted. In addition, failure of communication links between the caller and the callee nodes is also possible. Therefore, the normal functioning of an RPC may get disrupted due to one or more of the following reasons:

- The call message gets lost.
- The response message gets lost.

- The callee node crashes and is restarted.
- The caller node crashes and is restarted.

Some element of a caller's node that is involved in the RPC must contain necessary code to handle these failures. Obviously, the code for the caller's procedure should not be forced to deal with these failures. Therefore, the failure-handling code is generally a part of RPCRuntime. The call semantics of an RPC system that determines how often the remote procedure may be executed under fault conditions depends on this part of the RPCRuntime code. This part of the code may be designed to provide the flexibility to the application programmers to select from different possible call semantics supported by an RPC system. The different types of call semantics used in RPC systems are described below.

### 4.10.1 Possibly or May-Be Call Semantics

This is the weakest semantics and is not really appropriate to RPC but is mentioned here for completeness. In this method, to prevent the caller from waiting indefinitely for a response from the callee, a timeout mechanism is used. That is, the caller waits until a predetermined timeout period and then continues with its execution. Therefore the semantics does not guarantee anything about the receipt of the call message or the procedure execution by the caller. This semantics may be adequate for some applications in which the response message is not important for the caller and where the application operates within a local area network having a high probability of successful transmission of messages.

### 4.10.2 Last-One Call Semantics

This call semantics is similar to the one described in Section 3.9 and illustrated with an example in Figure 3.10. It uses the idea of retransmitting the call message based on timeouts until a response is received by the caller. That is, the calling of the remote procedure by the caller, the execution of the procedure by the callee, and the return of the result to the caller will eventually be repeated until the result of procedure execution is received by the caller. Clearly, the results of the last executed call are used by the caller, although earlier (abandoned) calls may have had side effects that survived the crash. Hence this semantics is called last-one semantics.

Last-one semantics can be easily achieved in the way described above when only two processors (nodes) are involved in the RPC. However, achieving last-one semantics in the presence of crashes turns out to be tricky for nested RPCs that involve more than two processors (nodes) [Bal et al. 1989]. For example, suppose process *P*1 of node *N*1 calls procedure *F*1 on node *N*2, which in turn calls procedure *F*2 on node *N*3. While the process on *N*3 is working on *F*2, node *N*1 crashes. Node *N*1's processes will be restarted, and *P*1's call to *F*1 will be repeated. The second invocation of *F*1 will again call procedure *F*2 on node *N*3. Unfortunately, node *N*3 is totally unaware of node *N*1's crash. Therefore procedure *F*2 will be executed twice on node *N*3 and *N*3 may return the results of the two executions of *F*2 in any order, possibly violating last-one semantics.

The basic difficulty in achieving last-one semantics in such cases is caused by orphan calls. An *orphan call* is one whose parent (caller) has expired due to a node crash. To achieve last-one semantics, these orphan calls must be terminated before restarting the crashed processes. This is normally done either by waiting for them to finish or by tracking them down and killing them ("*orphan extermination*"). As this is not an easy job, other weaker semantics have been proposed for RPC.

### 4.10.3 Last-of-Many Call Semantics

This is similar to the last-one semantics except that the orphan calls are neglected [Bal et al. 1989]. A simple way to neglect orphan calls is to use call identifiers to uniquely identify each call. When a call is repeated, it is assigned a new call identifier. Each response message has the corresponding call identifier associated with it. A caller accepts a response only if the call identifier associated with it matches with the identifier of the most recently repeated call; otherwise it ignores the response message.

### 4.10.4 At-Least-Once Call Semantics

This is an even weaker call semantics than the last-of-many call semantics. It just guarantees that the call is executed one or more times but does not specify which results are returned to the caller. It can be implemented simply by using timeout-based retransmissions without caring for the orphan calls. That is, for nested calls, if there are any orphan calls, it takes the result of the first response message and ignores the others, whether or not the accepted response is from an orphan.

### 4.10.5 Exactly-Once Call Semantics

This is the strongest and the most desirable call semantics because it eliminates the possibility of a procedure being executed more than once no matter how many times a call is retransmitted. The last-one, last-of-many, and at-least-once call semantics cannot guarantee this. The main disadvantage of these cheap semantics is that they force the application programmer to design idempotent interfaces that guarantee that if a procedure is executed more than once with the same parameters, the same results and side effects will be produced. For example, let us consider the example given in [Wilbur and Bacarisse 1987] for reading and writing a record in a sequential file of fixed-length records. For reading successive records from such a file, a suitable procedure is

ReadNextRecord(Filename)

Ignoring initialization and end-of-file effects, each execution of this procedure will return the next record from the specified file. Obviously, this procedure is not idempotent because multiple execution of this procedure will return the successive records, which is not desirable for duplicate calls that are retransmitted due to the loss of response messages. This happens because in the implementation of this procedure, the server needs to keep track of the current record position for each client that has opened the file for accessing. Therefore to design an idempotent interface for reading the next record from the file, it is important that each client keeps track of its own current record position and the server is made stateless, that is, no client state should be maintained on the server side. Based on this idea, an idempotent procedure for reading the next record from a sequential file is

ReadRecordN(Filename, N)

which returns the *N*th record from the specified file. In this case, the client has to correctly specify the value of *N* to get the desired record from the file.

However, not all nonidempotent interfaces can be so easily transformed to an idempotent form. For example, consider the following procedure for appending a new record to the same sequential file:

AppendRecord(Filename, Record)

It is clearly not idempotent since repeated execution will add further copies of the same record to the file. This interface may be converted into an idempotent interface by using the following two procedures instead of the one defined above:

GetLastRecordNo(Filename)
WriteRecordN(Filename, Record, N)

The first procedure returns the record number of the last record currently in the file, and the second procedure writes a record at a specified position in the file. Now, for appending a record, the client will have to use the following two procedures:

Last = GetLastRecordNo(Filename)
WriteRecordN(Filename, Record, Last)

For exactly-once semantics, the programmer is relieved of the burden of implementing the server procedure in an idempotent manner because the call semantics itself takes care of executing the procedure only once. As already described in Section 3.9 and illustrated with an example in Figure 3.12, the implementation of exactly-once call semantics is based on the use of timeouts, retransmissions, call identifiers with the same identifier for repeated calls, and a reply cache associated with the callee.

## 4.11 COMMUNICATION PROTOCOLS FOR RPCs

Different systems, developed on the basis of remote procedure calls, have different IPC requirements. Based on the needs of different systems, several communication protocols have been proposed for use in RPCs. A brief description of these protocols is given below.

### 4.11.1 The Request Protocol

This protocol is also known as the *R* (request) protocol [Spector 1982]. It is used in RPCs in which the called procedure has nothing to return as the result of procedure execution and the client requires no confirmation that the procedure has been executed. Since no acknowledgment or reply message is involved in this protocol, only one message per call is transmitted (from client to server) (Fig. 4.7). The client normally proceeds immediately after sending the request message as there is no need to wait for a reply message. The protocol provides may-be call semantics and requires no retransmission of request messages.

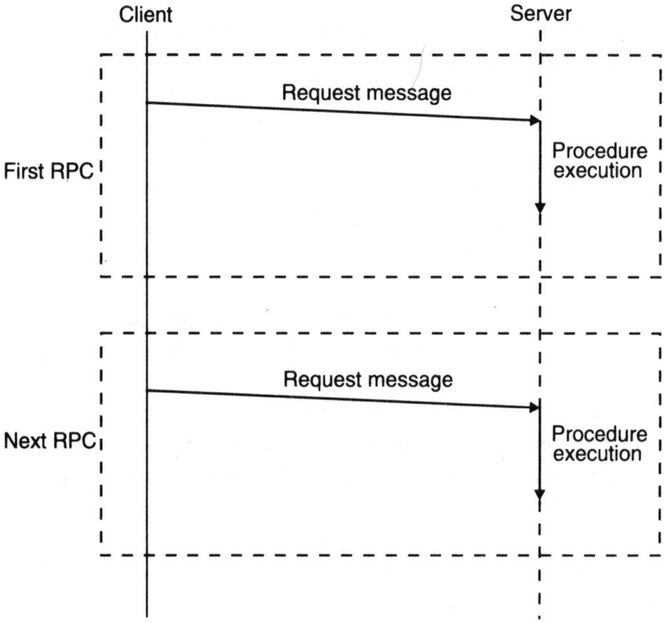


**Fig. 4.7** The request (R) protocol.

An RPC that uses the R protocol is called *asynchronous RPC*. An asynchronous RPC helps in improving the combined performance of both the client and the server in those distributed applications in which the client does not need a reply to each request. Client performance is improved because the client is not blocked and can immediately continue to do other work after making the call. On the other hand, server performance is improved because the server need not generate and send any reply for the request. One such application is a distributed window system. A distributed window system, such as X-11 [Davison et al. 1992], is programmed as a server, and application programs wishing to display items in windows on a display screen are its clients. To display items in a window, a client normally sends many requests (each request containing a relatively small amount of information for a small change in the displayed information) to the server one after another without waiting for a reply for each of these requests because it does not need replies for the requests.

Notice that for an asynchronous RPC, the RPCRuntime does not take responsibility for retrying a request in case of communication failure. This means that if an unreliable datagram transport protocol such as UDP is used for the RPC, the request message could be lost without the client's knowledge. Applications using asynchronous RPC with unreliable transport protocol must be prepared to handle this situation. However, if a reliable, connection-oriented transport protocol such as TCP is used for the RPC, there is no need to worry about retransmitting the request message because it is delivered reliably in this case.

Asynchronous RPCs with unreliable transport protocol are generally useful for implementing periodic update services. For example, a time server node in a distributed system may send time synchronization messages every *T* seconds to other nodes using the asynchronous RPC facility. In this case, even if a message is lost, the correct time is transmitted in the next message. Each node can keep track of the last time it received an update message to prevent it from missing too many update messages. A node that misses too many update messages can send a special request message to the time server node to get a reliable update after some maximum amount of time.

### 4.11.2 The Request/Reply Protocol

This protocol is also known as the *RR* (request/reply) protocol [Spector 1982]. It is useful for the design of systems involving simple RPCs. A *simple RPC* is one in which all the arguments as well as all the results fit in a single packet buffer and the duration of a call and the interval between calls are both short (less than the transmission time for a packet between the client and server) [Birrell and Nelson 1984]. The protocol is based on the idea of using implicit acknowledgment to eliminate explicit acknowledgment messages. Therefore in this protocol:

- A server's reply message is regarded as an acknowledgment of the client's request message.
- A subsequent call packet from a client is regarded as an acknowledgment of the server's reply message of the previous call made by that client.

The exchange of messages between a client and a server in the RR protocol is shown in Figure 4.8. Notice from the figure that the protocol involves the transmission of only two packets per call (one in each direction).

The RR protocol in its basic form does not possess failure-handling capabilities. Therefore to take care of lost messages, the timeouts-and-retries technique is normally used along with the RR protocol. In this technique, a client retransmits its request message if it does not receive the response message before a predetermined timeout period elapses. Obviously, if duplicate request messages are not filtered out, the RR protocol, compounded with this technique, provides at-least-once call semantics.

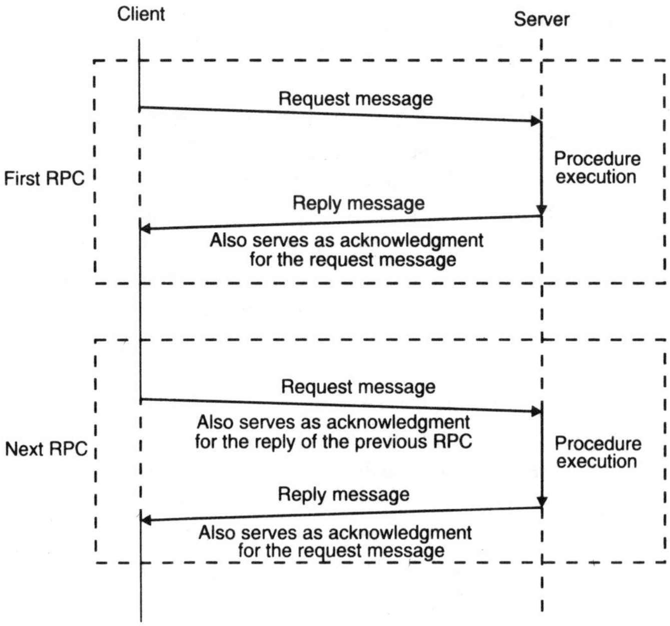


**Fig. 4.8** The request/reply (RR) protocol.

However, servers can support exactly-once call semantics by keeping records of the replies in a reply cache that enables them to filter out duplicate request messages and to retransmit reply messages without the need to reprocess a request. The details of this technique were given in Section 3.9.

### 4.11.3 The Request/Reply/Acknowledge-Reply Protocol

This protocol is also known as the *RRA* (request/reply/acknowledge-reply) protocol [Spector 1982]. The implementation of exactly-once call semantics with RR protocol requires the server to maintain a record of the replies in its reply cache. In situations where a server has a large number of clients, this may result in servers needing to store large quantities of information. In some implementations, servers restrict the quantity of such data by discarding it after a limited period of time. However, this approach is not fully reliable because sometimes it may lead to the loss of those replies that have not yet been successfully delivered to their clients. To overcome this limitation of the RR protocol, the RRA protocol is used, which requires clients to acknowledge the receipt of reply messages. The server deletes an information from its reply cache only after receiving an acknowledgment for it from the client. As shown in Figure 4.9, the RRA protocol involves the transmission of three messages per call (two from the client to the server and one from the server to the client).

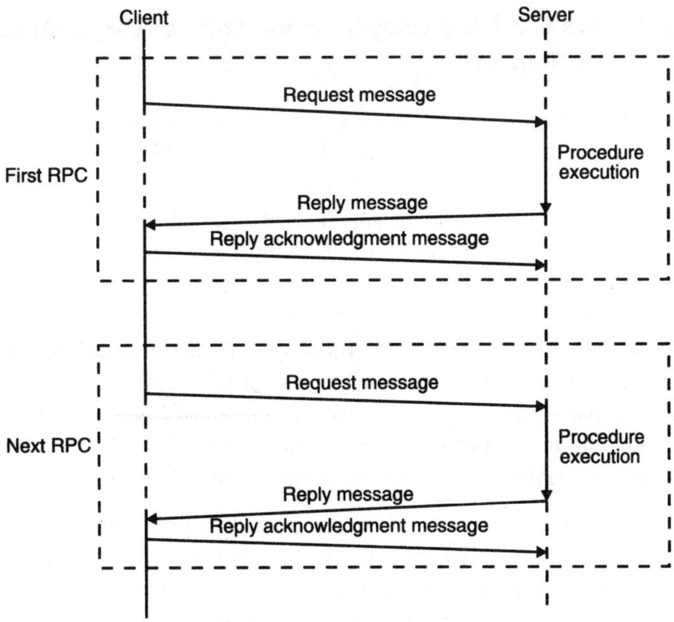


**Fig. 4.9** The request/reply/acknowledge-reply (RRA) protocol.

In the RRA protocol, there is a possibility that the acknowledgment message may itself get lost. Therefore implementation of the RRA protocol requires that the unique message identifiers associated with request messages must be ordered. Each reply message contains the message identifier of the corresponding request message, and each acknowledgment message also contains the same message identifier. This helps in matching a reply with its corresponding request and an acknowledgment with its corresponding reply. A client acknowledges a reply message only if it has received the replies to all the requests previous to the request corresponding to this reply. Thus an acknowledgment message is interpreted as acknowledging the receipt of all reply messages corresponding to the request messages with lower message identifiers. Therefore the loss of an acknowledgment message is harmless.

## 4.12 COMPLICATED RPCs

Birrell and Nelson [1984] categorized the following two types of RPCs as complicated:

1. RPCs involving long-duration calls or large gaps between calls
2. RPCs involving arguments and/or results that are too large to fit in a single-datagram packet

Different protocols are used for handling these two types of complicated RPCs.

### 4.12.1 RPCs Involving Long-Duration Calls or Large Gaps between Calls

One of the following two methods may be used to handle complicated RPCs that belong to this category [Birrell and Nelson 1984]:

1. *Periodic probing of the server by the client.* In this method, after a client sends a request message to a server, it periodically sends a probe packet to the server, which the server is expected to acknowledge. This allows the client to detect a server's crash or communication link failures and to notify the corresponding user of an exception condition. The message identifier of the original request message is included in each probe packet. Therefore, if the original request is lost, in reply to a probe packet corresponding to that request message, the server intimates the client that the request message corresponding to the probe packet has not been received. Upon receipt of such a reply from the server, the client retransmits the original request.

2. *Periodic generation of an acknowledgment by the server.* In this method, if a server is not able to generate the next packet significantly sooner than the expected retransmission interval, it spontaneously generates an acknowledgment. Therefore for a long-duration call, the server may have to generate several acknowledgments, the number of acknowledgments being directly proportional to the duration of the call. If the client does not receive either the reply for its request or an acknowledgment from the server within a predetermined timeout period, it assumes that either the server has crashed or communication link failure has occurred. In this case, it notifies the concerned user of an exception condition.

### 4.12.2 RPCs Involving Long Messages

In some RPCs, the arguments and/or results are too large to fit in a single-datagram packet. For example, in a file server, quite large quantities of data may be transferred as input arguments to the *write* operation or as results to the *read* operation. A simple way to handle such an RPC is to use several physical RPCs for one logical RPC. Each physical RPC transfers an amount of data that fits in a single-datagram packet. This solution is inefficient due to a fixed amount of overhead involved with each RPC independent of the amount of data sent.

Another method of handling complicated RPCs of this category is to use multidatagram messages. In this method, a long RPC argument or result is fragmented and transmitted in multiple packets. To improve communication performance, a single acknowledgment packet is used for all the packets of a multidatagram message. In this case, the same approach that was described in Section 3.9 is used to keep track of lost and out-of-sequence packets of a multidatagram RPC message.

Some RPC systems are limited to small sizes. For example, the Sun Microsystem's RPC is limited to 8 kilobytes. Therefore, in these systems, an RPC involving messages larger than the allowed limit must be handled by breaking it up into several physical RPCs.

## 4.13 CLIENT-SERVER BINDING

It is necessary for a client (actually a client stub) to know the location of a server before a remote procedure call can take place between them. The process by which a client becomes associated with a server so that calls can take place is known as *binding*. From the application level's point of view, the model of binding is that servers "export" operations to register their willingness to provide service and clients' "import" operations, asking the RPCRuntime system to locate a server and establish any state that may be needed at each end [Bershad et al. 1987]. The client-server binding process involves proper handling of several issues:

1. How does a client specify a server to which it wants to get bound?
2. How does the binding process locate the specified server?
3. When is it proper to bind a client to a server?
4. Is it possible for a client to change a binding during execution?
5. Can a client be simultaneously bound to multiple servers that provide the same service?

These binding issues are described below.

### 4.13.1 Server Naming

The specification by a client of a server with which it wants to communicate is primarily a naming issue. For RPC, Birrell and Nelson [1984] proposed the use of interface names for this purpose. An *interface name* has two parts—a *type* and an *instance*. Type specifies the interface itself and instance specifies a server providing the services within that interface. For example, there may be an interface of type *file_server*, and there may be several instances of servers providing file service. When a client is not concerned with which particular server of an interface services its request, it need not specify the instance part of the interface name.

The type part of an interface usually also has a version number field to distinguish between old and new versions of the interface that may have different sets of procedures or the same set of procedures with different parameters. It is inevitable in the course of distributed application programming that an application needs to be updated after a given version has been released. The use of a version number field allows old and new versions of a distributed application to coexist. One would hope that the new version of an interface would eventually replace all the old versions of the interface. However, experience has shown that it is always better to maintain backward compatibility with old versions of the software because someone might still be using one of the old versions.

According to Birrell and Nelson [1984], the interface name semantics are based on an arrangement between the exporter and the importer. Therefore, interface names are created by the users. They are not dictated by the RPC package. The RPC package only dictates the means by which an importer uses the interface name to locate an exporter.

### 4.13.2 Server Locating

The interface name of a server is its unique identifier. Thus when a client specifies the interface name of a server for making a remote procedure call, the server must be located before the client's request message can be sent to it. This is primarily a locating issue and any locating mechanism (locating mechanisms are described in Chapter 10) can be used for this purpose. The two most commonly used methods are as follows:

1. *Broadcasting*. In this method, a message to locate the desired server is broadcast to all the nodes from the client node. The nodes on which the desired server is located return a response message. Note that the desired server may be replicated on several nodes so the client node will receive a response from all these nodes. Normally, the first response that is received at the client's node is given to the client process and all subsequent responses are discarded.

This method is easy to implement and is suitable for use for small networks. However, the method is expensive for large networks because of the increase in message traffic due to the involvement of all the nodes in broadcast processing. Therefore the second method, which is based on the idea of using a name server, is generally used for large networks.

2. *Binding agent*. A binding agent is basically a name server used to bind a client to a server by providing the client with the location information of the desired server. In this method, a binding agent maintains a binding table, which is a mapping of a server's interface name to its locations. All servers register themselves with the binding agent as a part of their initialization process. To register with the binding agent, a server gives the binder its identification information and a handle used to locate it. The handle is system dependent and might be an Ethernet address, an IP address, an X.500 address, a process identifier containing a node number and port number, or something else. A server can also deregister with the binding agent when it is no longer prepared to offer service. The binding agent can also poll the servers periodically, automatically deregistering any server that fails to respond.

To locate a server, a client contacts the binding agent. If the server is registered with the binding agent, it returns the handle (location information) of the server to the client. The method is illustrated in Figure 4.10.

The binding agent's location is known to all nodes. This is accomplished by using either a fixed address for the binding agent that is known to all nodes or a broadcast message to locate the binding agent when a node is booted. In either case, when the binding agent is relocated, a message is sent to all nodes informing the new location of the binding agent.

A binding agent interface usually has three primitives: (a) *register* is used by a server to register itself with the binding agent, (b) *deregister* is used by a server to deregister itself with the binding agent, and (c) *lookup* is used by a client to locate a server.

The binding agent mechanism for locating servers has several advantages. First, the method can support multiple servers having the same interface type so that any of the available servers may be used to service a client's request. This helps to achieve a degree of fault tolerance. Second, since all bindings are done by the binding agent, when multiple

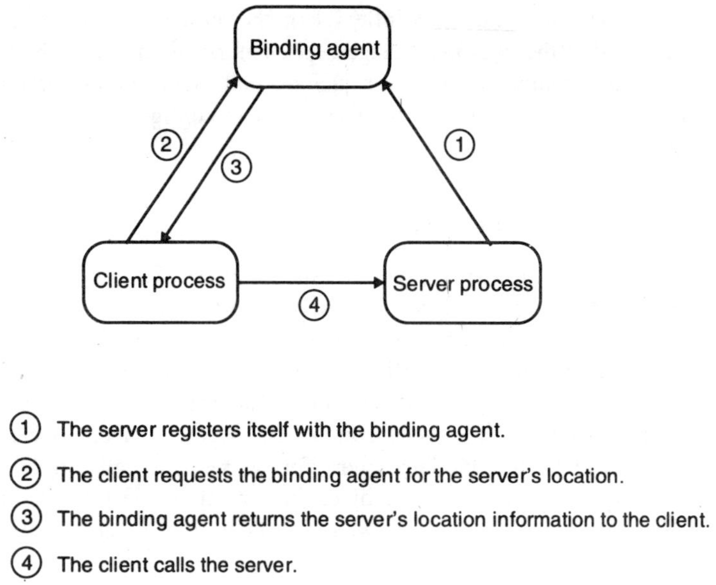

Binding agent
Client process
Server process
1
2
3
4
1 The server registers itself with the binding agent.
2 The client requests the binding agent for the server's location.
3 The binding agent returns the server's location information to the client.
4 The client calls the server.


**Fig. 4.10** The binding agent mechanism for locating a server in case of RPC.

servers provide the same service, the clients can be spread evenly over the servers to balance the load. Third, the binding mechanism can be extended to allow servers to specify a list of users who may use its service, in which case the binding agent would refuse to bind those clients to the servers who are not authorized to use its service.

However, the binding agent mechanism has drawbacks. The overhead involved in binding clients to servers is large and becomes significant when many client processes are short lived. Moreover, in addition to any functional requirements, a binding agent must be robust against failures and should not become a performance bottleneck. Distributing the binding function among several binding agents and replicating information among them can satisfy both these criteria. Unfortunately, replication often involves extra overhead of keeping the multiple replicas consistent. Therefore, the functionality offered by many binding agents is lower than might be hoped for.

### 4.13.3 Binding Time

A client may be bound to a server at compile time, at link time, or at call time [Goscinski 1991].

#### Binding at Compile Time

In this method, the client and server modules are programmed as if they were intended to be linked together. For example, the server's network address can be compiled into the client code by the programmer and then it can be found by looking up the server's name in a file.

The method is extremely inflexible in the sense that if the server moves or the server is replicated or the interface changes, all client programs using the server will have to be found and recompiled. However, the method is useful in certain limited cases. For example, it may be used in an application whose configuration is expected to remain static for a fairly long time.

#### Binding at Link Time

In this method, a server process exports its service by registering itself with the binding agent as part of its initialization process. A client then makes an import request to the binding agent for the service before making a call. The binding agent binds the client and the server by returning to the client the server's handle (details that are necessary for making a call to the server). Calls can take place once the client has received the server's handle. The server's handle is cached by the client to avoid contacting the binding agent for subsequent calls to be made to the same server. Due to the overhead involved in contacting the binding agent, this method is suitable for those situations in which a client calls a server several times once it is bound to it.

#### Binding at Call Time

In this method, a client is bound to a server at the time when it calls the server for the first time during its execution. A commonly used approach for binding at call time is the *indirect call* method. As shown in Figure 4.11, in this method, when a client calls a server for the first time, it passes the server's interface name and the arguments of the RPC call to the binding agent. The binding agent looks up the location of the target server in its binding table, and on behalf of the client it sends an RPC call message to the target server, including in it the arguments received from the client. When the target server returns the results to the binding agent, the binding agent returns this result to the client along with the target server's handle so that the client can subsequently call the target server directly.

### 4.13.4 Changing Bindings

The flexibility provided by a system to change bindings dynamically is very useful from a reliability point of view. Binding is a connection establishment between a client and a server. The client or server of a connection may wish to change the binding at some instance of time due to some change in the system state. For example, a client willing to get a request serviced by any one of the multiple servers for that service may be programmed to change a binding to another server of the same type when a call to the already connected server fails. Similarly, the server of a binding may want to alter the binding and connect the client to another server in situations such as when the service needs to move to another node or a new version of the server is installed. When a binding is altered by the concerned server, it is

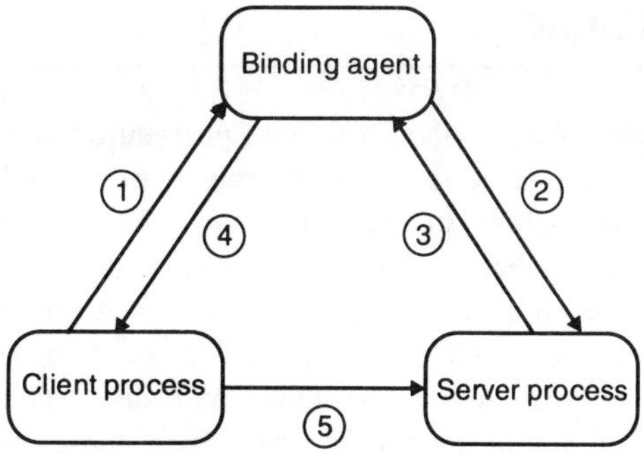


① The client process passes the server's interface name and the arguments of the RPC call to the binding agent.

② The binding agent sends an RPC call message to the server, including in it the arguments received from the client.

③ The server returns the result of request processing to the binding agent.

④ The binding agent returns this result to the client along with the server's handle.

⑤ Subsequent calls are sent directly from the client process to the server process.

**Fig. 4.11** Illustrating binding at call time by the method of indirect call.

important to ensure that any state data held by the server is no longer needed or can be duplicated in the replacement server. For example, when a file server has to be replaced with a new one, either it must be replaced when no files are open or the state of all the open files must be transferred from the old server to the new one as a part of the replacement process.

### 4.13.5 Multiple Simultaneous Bindings

In a system, a service may be provided by multiple servers. We have seen that, in general, a client is bound to a single server of the several servers of the same type. However, there may be situations when it is advantageous for a client to be bound simultaneously to all or multiple servers of the same type. Logically, a binding of this sort gives rise to multicast communication because when a call is made, all the servers bound to the client for that service will receive and process the call. For example, a client may wish to update multiple copies of a file that is replicated at several nodes. For this, the client can be bound simultaneously to file servers of all those nodes where a replica of the file is located.

## 4.14 EXCEPTION HANDLING

We saw in Figure 4.4 that when a remote procedure cannot be executed successfully, the server reports an error in the reply message. An RPC also fails when a client cannot contact the server of the RPC. An RPC system must have an effective exception-handling mechanism for reporting such failures to clients. One approach to do this is to define an exception condition for each possible error type and have the corresponding exception raised when an error of that type occurs, causing the exception-handling procedure to be called and automatically executed in the client's environment. This approach can be used with those programming languages that provide language constructs for exception handling. Some such programming languages are ADA, CLU [Liskov et al. 1981], and Modula-3 [Nelson 1991, Harbinson 1992]. In C language, signal handlers can be used for the purpose of exception handling.

However, not every language has an exception-handling mechanism. For example, Pascal does not have such a mechanism. RPC systems designed for use with such languages generally use the method provided in conventional operating systems for exception handling. One such method is to return a well-known value to the process, making a system call to indicate failure and to report the type of error by storing a suitable value in a variable in the environment of the calling program. For example, in UNIX the value –1 is used to indicate failure, and the type of error is reported in the global variable *errno*. In an RPC, a return value indicating an error is used both for errors due to failure to communicate with the server and errors reported in the reply message from the server. The details of the type of error is reported by storing a suitable value in a global variable in the client program. This approach suffers from two main drawbacks. First, it requires the client to test every return value. Second, it is not general enough because a return value used to indicate failure may be a perfectly legal value to be returned by a procedure. For example, if the value –1 is used to indicate failure, this value is also the return value of a procedure call with arguments –5 and 4 to a procedure for getting the sum of two numbers.

## 4.15 SECURITY

Some implementations of RPC include facilities for client and server authentication as well as for providing encryption-based security for calls. For example, in [Birrell and Nelson 1984], callers are given a guarantee of the identity of the callee, and vice versa, by using the authentication service of Grapevine [Birrell et al. 1982]. For full end-to-end encryption of calls and results, the federal data encryption standard [DES 1977] is used in [Birrell and Nelson 1984]. The encryption techniques provide protection from eavesdropping (and conceal patterns of data) and detect attempts at modification, replay, or creation of calls.

In other implementations of RPC that do not include security facilities, the arguments and results of RPC are readable by anyone monitoring communications between the caller and the callee. Therefore in this case, if security is desired, the user must implement his or her own authentication and data encryption mechanisms. When designing an application, the user should consider the following security issues related with the communication of messages:

- Is the authentication of the server by the client required?
- Is the authentication of the client by the server required when the result is returned?
- Is it all right if the arguments and results of the RPC are accessible to users other than the caller and the callee?

These and other security issues are described in detail in Chapter 11.

## 4.16 SOME SPECIAL TYPES OF RPCs

### 4.16.1 Callback RPC

In the usual RPC protocol, the caller and callee processes have a client-server relationship. Unlike this, the callback RPC facilitates a peer-to-peer paradigm among the participating processes. It allows a process to be both a client and a server.

Callback RPC facility is very useful in certain distributed applications. For example, remotely processed interactive applications that need user input from time to time or under special conditions for further processing require this type of facility. As shown in Figure 4.12, in such applications, the client process makes an RPC to the concerned server process, and during procedure execution for the client, the server process makes a callback RPC to the client process. The client process takes necessary action based on the server's request and returns a reply for the callback RPC to the server process. On receiving this reply, the server resumes the execution of the procedure and finally returns the result of the initial call to the client. Note that the server may make several callbacks to the client before returning the result of the initial call to the client process.

The ability for a server to call its client back is very important, and care is needed in the design of RPC protocols to ensure that it is possible. In particular, to provide callback RPC facility, the following are necessary:

- Providing the server with the client's handle
- Making the client process wait for the callback RPC
- Handling callback deadlocks

Commonly used methods to handle these issues are described below.

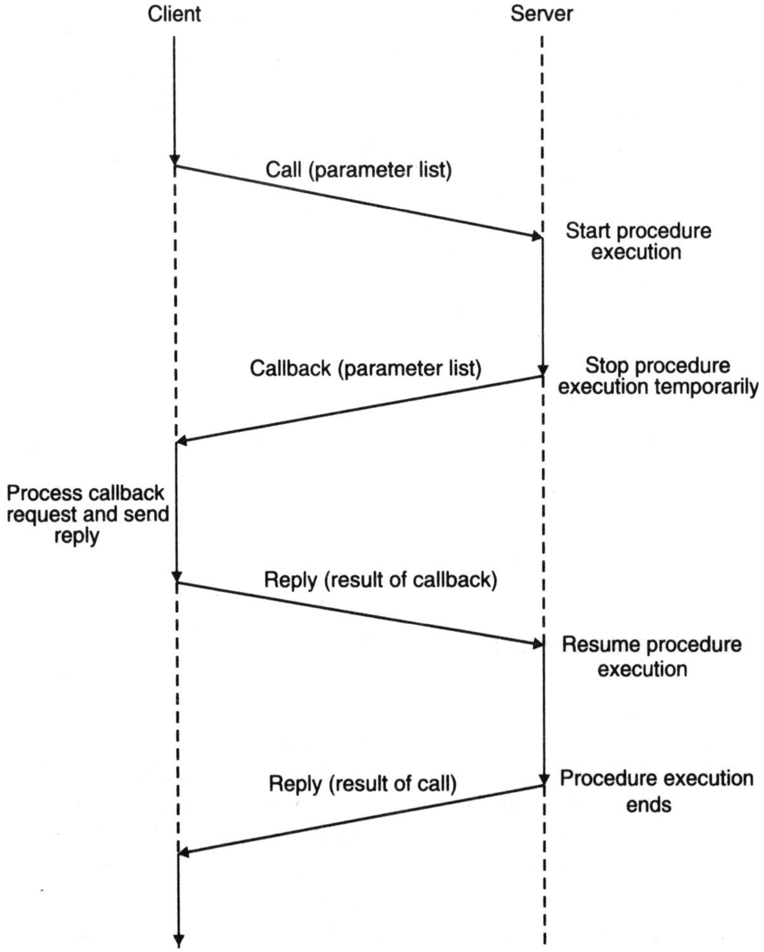


**Fig. 4.12** The callback RPC.

### Providing the Server with the Client's Handle

The server must have the client's handle to call the client back. The client's handle uniquely identifies the client process and provides enough information to the server for making a call to it. Typically, the client process uses a transient program number for the callback service and exports the callback service by registering its program number with the binding agent. The program number is then sent as a part of the RPC request to the server. To make a callback RPC, the server initiates a normal RPC request to the client using the given program number. Instead of having the client just send the server the program number, it could also send its handle, such as the port number. The client's handle could then be used by the server to directly communicate with the client and would save an RPC to the binding agent to get the client's handle.

### Making the Client Process Wait for the Callback RPC

The client process must be waiting for the callback so that it can process the incoming RPC request from the server and also to ensure that a callback RPC from the server is not mistaken to be the reply of the RPC call made by the client process. To wait for the callback, a client process normally makes a call to a *svc-routine*. The *svc-routine* waits until it receives a request and then dispatches the request to the appropriate procedure.

### Handling Callback Deadlocks

In callback RPC, since a process may play the role of either a client or a server, callback deadlocks can occur. For example, consider the most simple case in which a process $P_1$ makes an RPC call to a process $P_2$ and waits for a reply from $P_2$. In the meantime, process $P_2$ makes an RPC call to another process $P_3$ and waits for a reply from $P_3$. In the meantime, process $P_3$ makes an RPC call to process $P_1$ and waits for a reply from $P_1$. But $P_1$ cannot process $P_3$'s request until its request to $P_2$ has been satisfied, and $P_2$ cannot process $P_1$'s request until its request to $P_3$ has been satisfied, and $P_3$ cannot process $P_2$'s request until its request to $P_1$ has been satisfied. As shown in Figure 4.13, a situation now exists where $P_1$ is waiting for a reply from $P_2$, which is waiting for a reply from $P_3$, which is waiting for a reply from $P_1$. The result is that none of the three processes can have their request satisfied, and hence all three will continue to wait indefinitely. In effect, a callback deadlock has occurred due to the interdependencies of the three processes.

While using a callback RPC, care must be taken to handle callback deadlock situations. Various methods for handling deadlocks are described in Chapter 6.

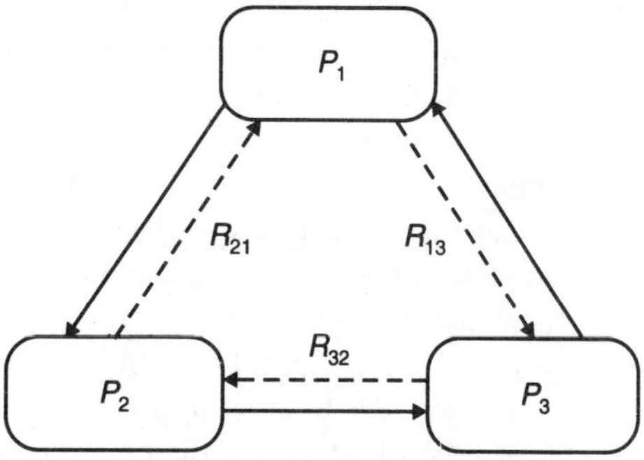


**Fig. 4.13** An example of a callback deadlock in case of callback RPC mechanism.

$P_1$ is waiting for $R_{21}$ (reply from $P_2$ to $P_1$)
$P_2$ is waiting for $R_{32}$ (reply from $P_3$ to $P_2$)
$P_3$ is waiting for $R_{13}$ (reply from $P_1$ to $P_3$)

### 4.16.2 Broadcast RPC

The RPC-based IPC is normally of the one-to-one type, involving a single client process and a single server process. However, we have seen in the previous chapter that for performance reasons several highly parallel distributed applications require the communication system to provide the facility of broadcast and multicast communication. The RPC-based IPC mechanisms normally support broadcast RPC facility for such applications. In broadcast RPC, a client's request is broadcast on the network and is processed by all the servers that have the concerned procedure for processing that request. The client waits for and receives numerous replies.

A broadcast RPC mechanism may use one of the following two methods for broadcasting a client's request:

1. The client has to use a special broadcast primitive to indicate that the request message has to be broadcasted. The request is sent to the binding agent, which forwards the request to all the servers registered with it. Note that in this method, since all broadcast RPC messages are sent to the binding agent, only services that register themselves with their binding agent are accessible via the broadcast RPC mechanism.

2. The second method is to declare broadcast ports. A network port of each node is connected to a broadcast port. A network port of a node is a queuing point on that node for broadcast messages. The client of the broadcast RPC first obtains a binding for a broadcast port and then broadcasts the RPC message by sending the message to this port. Note that the same primitive may be used for both unicast and broadcast RPCs. Moreover, unlike the first method, this method also has the flexibility of being used for multicast RPC in which the RPC message is sent only to a subset of the available servers. For this, the port declaration mechanism should have the flexibility to associate only a subset of the available servers to a newly declared multicast port.

Since a broadcast RPC message is sent to all the nodes of a network, a reply is expected from each node. As already described in the previous chapter, depending on the degree of reliability desired, the client process may wait for zero, one, *m*-out-of-*n*, or all the replies. In some implementations, servers that support broadcast RPC typically respond only when the request is successfully processed and are silent in the face of errors. Such systems normally use some type of timeout-based retransmission mechanism for improving the reliability of the broadcast RPC protocol. For example, in SunOS, the broadcast RPC protocol transmits the broadcast and waits for 4 seconds before retransmitting the request. It then waits for 6 seconds before retransmitting the request and continues to increment the amount of time to wait by 2 seconds until the timeout period becomes greater than 14 seconds. Therefore, in the worst case, the request is broadcast six times and the total wait time is 54 seconds ($4+6+8+10+12+14$). In SunOS, the broadcast RPC uses unreliable, packet-based protocol for broadcasting the request, and so the routine retransmits the broadcast requests by default. Increasing the amount of time between retransmissions is known as a *back-off algorithm*. The use of a back-off algorithm for timeout-based retransmissions helps in reducing the load on the physical network and computers involved.

### 4.16.3 Batch-Mode RPC

Batch-mode RPC is used to queue separate RPC requests in a transmission buffer on the client side and then send them over the network in one batch to the server. This helps in the following two ways:

1. It reduces the overhead involved in sending each RPC request independently to the server and waiting for a response for each request.
2. Applications requiring higher call rates (50–100 remote calls per second) may not be feasible with most RPC implementations. Such applications can be accommodated with the use of batch-mode RPC.

However, batch-mode RPC can be used only with those applications in which a client has many RPC requests to send to a server and the client does not need any reply for a sequence of requests. Therefore, the requests are queued on the client side, and the entire queue of requests is flushed to the server when one of the following conditions becomes true:

1. A predetermined interval elapses.
2. A predetermined number of requests have been queued.
3. The amount of batched data exceeds the buffer size.
4. A call is made to one of the server's procedures for which a result is expected. From a programming standpoint, the semantics of such a call (nonqueueing RPC request) should be such that the server can distinguish it from the queued requests and send a reply for it to the client.

The flushing out of queued requests in cases 1, 2, and 3 happens independent of a nonqueuing RPC request and is not noticeable by the client.

Obviously, the queued messages should be sent reliably. Hence, a batch-mode RPC mechanism requires reliable transports such as TCP. Moreover, although the batch-mode optimization retains syntactic transparency, it may produce obscure timing-related effects where other clients are accessing the server simultaneously.

## 4.17 RPC IN HETEROGENEOUS ENVIRONMENTS

Heterogeneity is an important issue in the design of any distributed application because typically the more portable an application, the better. When designing an RPC system for a heterogeneous environment, the three common types of heterogeneity that need to be considered are as follows:

1. *Data representation.* Machines having different architectures may use different data representations. For example, integers may be represented with the most significant byte at the low-byte address in one machine architecture and at the high-byte address in another machine architecture. Similarly, integers may be represented in 1's complement

notation in one machine architecture and in 2's complement notation in another machine architecture. Floating-point representations may also vary between two different machine architectures. Therefore, an RPC system for a heterogeneous environment must be designed to take care of such differences in data representations between the architectures of client and server machines of a procedure call.

2. *Transport protocol.* For better portability of applications, an RPC system must be independent of the underlying network transport protocol. This will allow distributed applications using the RPC system to be run on different networks that use different transport protocols.

3. *Control protocol.* For better portability of applications, an RPC system must also be independent of the underlying network control protocol that defines control information in each transport packet to track the state of a call.

The most commonly used approach to deal with these types of heterogeneity while designing an RPC system for a heterogeneous environment is to delay the choices of data representation, transport protocol, and control protocol until bind time. In conventional RPC systems, all these decisions are made when the RPC system is designed. That is, the binding mechanism of an RPC system for a heterogeneous environment is considerably richer in information than the binding mechanism used by a conventional RPC system. It includes mechanisms for determining which data conversion software (if any conversion is needed), which transport protocol, and which control protocol should be used between a specific client and server and returns the correct procedures to the stubs as result parameters of the binding call. These binding mechanism details are transparent to the users. That is, application programs never directly access the component structures of the binding mechanism; they deal with bindings only as atomic types and acquire and discard them via the calls of the RPC system.

Some RPC systems designed for heterogeneous environments are the HCS (Heterogeneous Computer Systems) RPC (called HRPC) [Bershad et al. 1987], the DCE SRC (System Research Center) Firefly RPC [Schroeder and Burrows 1990], Matchmaker [Jones et al. 1985], and Horus [Gibbons 1987].

## 4.18 LIGHTWEIGHT RPC

The *Lightweight Remote Procedure Call* (*LRPC*) was introduced by Bershad et al. [1990] and integrated into the Taos operating system of the DEC SRC Firefly microprocessor workstation. The description below is based on the material in their paper [Bershad et al. 1990].

As mentioned in Chapter 1, based on the size of the kernel, operating systems may be broadly classified into two categories—monolithic-kernel operating systems and microkernel operating systems. Monolithic-kernel operating systems have a large, monolithic kernel that is insulated from user programs by simple hardware boundaries. On the other hand, in microkernel operating systems, a small kernel provides only primitive operations and most of the services are provided by user-level servers. The servers are usually implemented as processes and can be programmed separately. Each server forms a component of the operating system and usually has its own address space. As compared to the monolithic-kernel approach, in this approach services are provided less efficiently because the various components of the operating system have to use some form of IPC to communicate with each other. The advantages of this approach include simplicity and flexibility. Due to modular structure, microkernel operating systems are simple and easy to design, implement, and maintain.

In the microkernel approach, when different components of the operating system have their own address spaces, the address space of each component is said to form a *domain*, and messages are used for all interdomain communication. In this case, the communication traffic in operating systems are of two types [Bershad et al. 1990]:

1. *Cross-domain*, which involves communication between domains on the same machine
2. *Cross-machine*, which involves communication between domains located on separate machines

The LRPC is a communication facility designed and optimized for cross-domain communications.

Although conventional RPC systems can be used for both cross-domain and cross-machine communications, Bershad et al. observed that the use of conventional RPC systems for cross-domain communications, which dominate cross-machine communications, incurs an unnecessarily high cost. This cost leads system designers to coalesce weakly related components of microkernel operating systems into a single domain, trading safety and performance. Therefore, the basic advantages of using the microkernel approach are not fully exploited. Based on these observations, Bershad et al. designed the LRPC facility for cross-domain communications, which has better performance than conventional RPC systems. Nonetheless, LRPC is safe and transparent and represents a viable communication alternative for microkernel operating systems.

To achieve better performance than conventional RPC systems, the four techniques described below are used by LRPC.

### 4.18.1 Simple Control Transfer

Whenever possible, LRPC uses a control transfer mechanism that is simpler than that used in conventional RPC systems. For example, it uses a special threads scheduling mechanism, called handoff scheduling (details of the threads and handoff scheduling mechanism are given in Chapter 8), for direct context switch from the client thread to the server thread of an LRPC. In this mechanism, when a client calls a server's procedure, it provides the server with an argument stack and its own thread of execution. The call causes a trap to the kernel. The kernel validates the caller, creates a call linkage, and dispatches the client's thread directly to the server domain, causing the server to start executing immediately. When the called procedure completes, control and results return through the kernel back to the point of the client's call. In contrast to this, in conventional RPC implementations, context switching between the client and server threads of an RPC is slow because the client thread and the server thread are fixed in their own domains, signaling one another at a rendezvous, and the scheduler must manipulate system data structures to block the client's thread and then select one of the server's threads for execution.

### 4.18.2 Simple Data Transfer

In an RPC, arguments and results need to be passed between the client and server domains in the form of messages. As compared to traditional RPC systems, LRPC reduces the cost of data transfer by performing fewer copies of the data during its transfer from one domain to another. For example, let us consider the path taken by a procedure's argument during a traditional cross-domain RPC. As shown in Figure 4.14($a$), an argument in this case normally has to be copied four times:

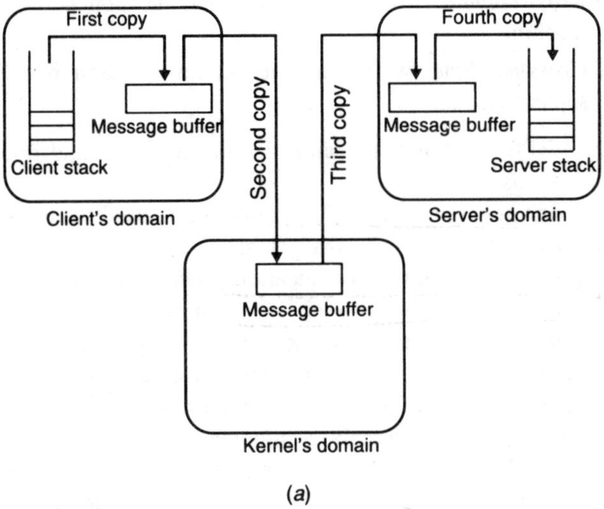


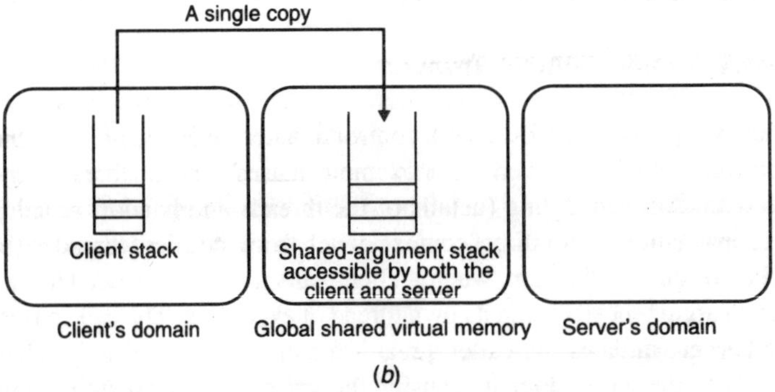


**Fig. 4.14** Data transfer mechanisms in traditional cross-domain RPC and LRPC. ($a$) The path taken by a procedure's argument during a traditional cross-domain RPC involves four copy operations. ($b$) The path taken by a procedure's argument during LRPC involves a single-copy operation.

1. From the client's stack to the RPC message
2. From the message in the client domain to the message in the kernel domain
3. From the message in the kernel domain to the message in the server domain
4. From the message in the server domain to the server's stack

To simplify this data transfer operation, LRPC uses a shared-argument stack that is accessible to both the client and the server. Therefore, as shown in Figure 4.14(*b*), the same argument in an LRPC can be copied only once—from the client's stack to the shared-argument stack. The server uses the argument from the argument stack. Pairwise allocation of argument stacks enables LRPC to provide a private channel between the client and server and also allows the copying of parameters and results as many times as are necessary to ensure correct and safe operation.

### 4.18.3 Simple Stubs

The distinction between cross-domain and cross-machine calls is usually made transparent to the stubs by lower levels of the RPC system. This results in an interface and execution path that are general but infrequently needed.

The use of a simple model of control and data transfer in LRPC facilitates the generation of highly optimized stubs. Every procedure has a call stub in the client's domain and an entry stub in the server's domain. A three-layered communication protocol is defined for each procedure in an LRPC interface:

1. End to end, described by the calling conventions of the programming language and architecture
2. Stub to stub, implemented by the stubs themselves
3. Domain to domain, implemented by the kernel

To reduce the cost of interlayer crossings, LRPC stubs blur the boundaries between the protocol layers. For example, at the time of transfer of control, the kernel associates execution stacks with the initial call frame expected by the called server's procedure and directly invokes the corresponding procedure's entry in the server's domain. No intermediate message examination or dispatching is done, and the server stub starts executing the procedure by directly branching to the procedure's first instruction. Notice that with this arrangement a simple LRPC needs only one formal procedure call (into the client stub) and two returns (one out of the server procedure and one out of the client stub).

### 4.18.4 Design for Concurrency

When the node of the client and server processes of an LRPC has multiple processors with a shared memory, special mechanisms are used to achieve higher call throughput and lower call latency than is possible on a single-processor node. Throughput is increased by avoiding needless lock contention by minimizing the use of shared-data structures on the critical domain transfer path. On the other hand, latency is reduced by reducing context-switching overhead by caching domains on idle processors. This is basically a generalization of the idea of decreasing operating system latency by caching recently blocked threads on idle processors to reduce wake-up latency. Instead of threads, LRPC caches domains so that any thread that needs to run in the context of an idle domain can do so quickly, not just the thread that ran there most recently.

Based on the performance evaluation made by Bershad et al. [1990], it was found that LRPC achieves a factor-of-three performance improvement over more traditional approaches. Thus LRPC reduces the cost of cross-domain communication to nearly the lower bound imposed by conventional hardware.

## 4.19 OPTIMIZATIONS FOR BETTER PERFORMANCE

As with any software design, performance is an issue in the design of a distributed application. The description of LRPC shows some optimizations that may be adopted for better performance of distributed applications using RPC. Some other optimizations that may also have significant payoff when adopted for designing RPC-based distributed applications are described below.

### 4.19.1 Concurrent Access to Multiple Servers

Although one of the benefits of RPC is its synchronization property, many distributed applications can benefit from concurrent access to multiple servers. One of the following three approaches may be used for providing this facility:

1. The use of threads (described in Chapter 8) in the implementation of a client process where each thread can independently make remote procedure calls to different servers. This method requires that the addressing in the underlying protocol is rich enough to provide correct routing of responses.

2. Another method is the use of the early reply approach [Wilbur and Bacarisse 1987]. As shown in Figure 4.15, in this method a call is split into two separate RPC calls, one passing the parameters to the server and the other requesting the result. In reply to the first call, the server returns a tag that is sent back with the second call to match the call with the correct result. The client decides the time delay between the two calls and carries out other activities during this period, possibly making several other RPC calls. A drawback of this method is that the server must hold the result of a call until the client makes a request for it. Therefore, if the request for results is delayed, it may cause congestion or unnecessary overhead at the server.

3. The third approach, known as the call buffering approach, was proposed by Gimson [1985]. In this method, clients and servers do not interact directly with each other. They interact indirectly via a call buffer server. To make an RPC call, a client sends its call request to the call buffer server, where the request parameters together with the name of the server and the client are buffered. The client can then perform other activities until it

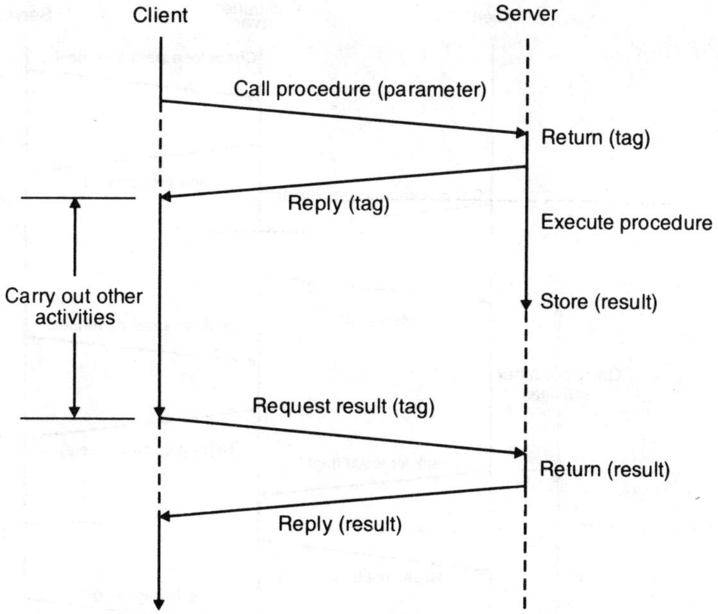


**Fig. 4.15** The early reply approach for providing the facility of concurrent access to multiple servers.

needs the result of the RPC call. When the client reaches a state in which it needs the result, it periodically polls the call buffer server to see if the result of the call is available, and if so, it recovers the result. On the server side, when a server is free, it periodically polls the call buffer server to see if there is any call for it. If so, it recovers the call request, executes it, and makes a call back to the call buffer server to return the result of execution to the call buffer server. The method is illustrated in Figure 4.16.

A variant of this approach is used in the Mercury communication system developed at MIT [Liskov and Shrira 1988] for supporting asynchronous RPCs. The Mercury communication system has a new data type called *promise* that is created during an RPC call and is given a type corresponding to those of the results and exceptions of the remote procedure. When the results arrive, they are stored in the appropriate promise, from where the caller claims the results at a time suitable to it. Therefore, after making a call, a caller can continue with other work and subsequently pick up the results of the call from the appropriate promise.

A promise is in one of two states—blocked or ready. It is in a blocked state from the time of creation to the time the results of the call arrive, whereupon it enters the ready state. A promise in the ready state is immutable.

Two operations (*ready* and *claim*) are provided to allow a caller to check the status of the promise for the call and to claim the results of the call from it. The *ready* operation is used to test the status (blocked/ready) of the promise. It returns true or false according to whether the promise is ready or blocked. The *claim* operation is

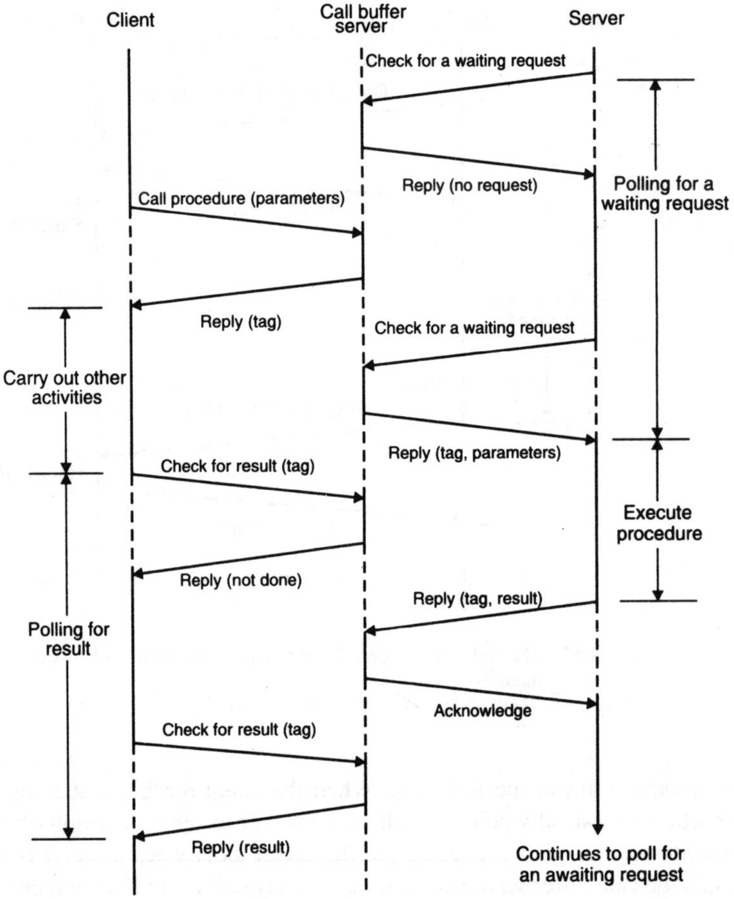


**Fig. 4.16** The call buffering approach for providing the facility of concurrent access to multiple servers.

used to obtain the results of the call from the promise. The *claim* operation blocks the caller until the promise is ready, whereupon it returns the results of the call. Therefore, if the caller wants to continue with other work until the promise becomes ready, it can periodically check the status of the promise by using the *ready* operation.

### 4.19.2 Serving Multiple Requests Simultaneously

The following types of delays are commonly encountered in RPC systems:

1. Delay caused while a server waits for a resource that is temporarily unavailable. For example, during the course of a call execution, a server might have to wait for accessing a shared file that is currently locked elsewhere.

2. A delay can occur when a server calls a remote function that involves a considerable amount of computation to complete or involves a considerable transmission delay.

For better performance, good RPC implementations must have mechanisms to allow the server to accept and process other requests, instead of being idle while waiting for the completion of some operation. This requires that a server be designed in such a manner that it can service multiple requests simultaneously. One method to achieve this is to use the approach of a multiple-threaded server with dynamic threads creation facility for server implementation (details of this approach are given in Chapter 8).

### 4.19.3 Reducing Per-Call Workload of Servers

Numerous client requests can quickly affect a server's performance when the server has to do a lot of processing for each request. Thus, to improve the overall performance of an RPC system, it is important to keep the requests short and the amount of work required by a server for each request low. One way of accomplishing this improvement is to use stateless servers and let the clients keep track of the progression of their requests sent to the servers. This approach sounds reasonable because, in most cases, the client portion of an application is really in charge of the flow of information between a client and a server.

### 4.19.4 Reply Caching of Idempotent Remote Procedures

The use of a reply cache to achieve exactly-once semantics in nonidempotent remote procedures has already been described. However, a reply cache can also be associated with idempotent remote procedures for improving a server's performance when it is heavily loaded. When client requests to a server arrive at a rate faster than the server can process the requests, a backlog develops, and eventually client requests start timing out and the clients resend the requests, making the problem worse. In such a situation, the reply cache helps because the server has to process a request only once. If a client resends its request, the server just sends the cached reply.

### 4.19.5 Proper Selection of Timeout Values

To deal with failure problems, timeout-based retransmissions are necessary in distributed applications. An important issue here is how to choose the timeout value. A "too small" timeout value will cause timers to expire too often, resulting in unnecessary retransmissions. On the other hand, a "too large" timeout value will cause a needlessly long delay in the event that a message is actually lost. In RPC systems, servers are likely to take varying amounts of time to service individual requests, depending on factors such as server load, network routing, and network congestion. If clients continue to retry sending those requests for which replies have not yet been received, the server loading and network congestion problem will become worse. To prevent this situation, proper selection of timeout values is important. One method to handle this issue is to use some sort of back-off strategy of exponentially increasing timeout values.

### 4.19.6 Proper Design of RPC Protocol Specification

For better performance, the protocol specification of an RPC system must be properly designed so as to minimize the amount of data that has to be sent over the network and the frequency at which it is sent. Reducing the amount of data to be transferred helps in two ways: It requires less time to encode and decode the data and it requires less time to transmit the data over the network. Several existing RPC systems use TCP/IP or UDP/IP as the basic protocol because they are easy to use and fit in well with existing UNIX systems and networks such as the Internet. This makes it straightforward to write clients and servers that run on UNIX systems and standard networks. However, the use of a standard general-purpose protocol for RPC generally leads to poor performance because general-purpose protocols have many features to deal with different problems in different situations. For example, packets in the IP suite (to which TCP/IP and UDP/IP belong) have in total 13 header fields, of which only 3 are useful for an RPC—the source and destination addresses and the packet length. However, several of these header fields, such as those dealing with fragmentation and checksum, have to be filled in by the sender and verified by the receiver to make them legal IP packets. Some of these fields, such as the checksum field, are time consuming to compute. Therefore, for better performance, an RPC system should use a specialized RPC protocol. Of course, a new protocol for this purpose has to be designed from scratch, implemented, tested, and embedded in existing systems, so it requires considerably more work.

## 4.20 CASE STUDIES: SUN RPC, DCE RPC

Many RPC systems have been built and are in use today. Notable ones include the Cedar RPC system [Birrell and Nelson 1984], Courier in the Xerox NS family of protocols [Xerox Corporation 1981], the Eden system [Almes et al. 1985], the CMU Spice system [Jones et al. 1985], Sun RPC [Sun Microsystems 1985], Argus [Liskov and Scheifler 1983], Arjuna [Shrivastava et al. 1991], the research system built at HP Laboratories [Gibbons 1987], NobelNet's EZ RPC [Smith 1994], Open Software Foundation's (OSF's) DCE RPC [Rosenberry et al. 1992], which is a descendent of Apollo's Network Computing Architecture (NCA), and the HRPC system developed at the University of Washington [Bershad et al. 1987]. Of these, the best known UNIX RPC system is the Sun RPC. Therefore, the Sun RPC will be described in this section as a case study. In addition, due to the policy used in this book to describe DCE components as case studies, the DCE RPC will also be briefly described.

### 4.20.1 Sun RPC

#### Stub Generation

Sun RPC uses the automatic stub generation approach, although users have the flexibility of writing the stubs manually. An application's interface definition is written in an IDL called RPC Language (RPCL). RPCL is an extension of the Sun XDR language that was originally designed for specifying external data representations. As an example, the interface definition of the stateless file service, described in Section 4.8.1, is given in Figure 4.17. As shown in the figure, an interface definition contains a program number (which is 0 x 20000000 in our example) and a version number of the service (which is 1 in our example), the procedures supported by the service (in our example READ and WRITE), the input and output parameters along with their types for each procedure, and the supporting type definitions. The three values program number (STATELESS_FS_PROG), version number (STATELESS_FS_VERS), and a procedure number (READ or WRITE) uniquely identify a remote procedure. The READ and WRITE procedures are given numbers 1 and 2, respectively. The number 0 is reserved for a null procedure that is automatically generated and is intended to be used to test whether a server is available. Interface definition file names have an extension *.x.* (for example, *StatelessFS.x*).

```
/* Interface definition for a stateless file service (StatelessFS)
   in file StatelessFS.x */
const FILE_NAME_SIZE = 16
const BUFFER_SIZE = 1024

typedef string FileName<FILE_NAME_SIZE>;
typedef long Position;
typedef long Nbytes;

struct Data {
        long n;
        char buffer[BUFFER_SIZE];
};

struct readargs {
        FileName        filename;
        Position        position;
        Nbytes          n;
};

struct writeargs {
        FileName        filename;
        Position        position;
        Data            data;
};

program STATELESS_FS_PROG {
        version STATELESS_FS_VERS {
                        Data        READ (readargs) = 1;
                        Nbytes      WRITE (writeargs) = 2;
        } = 1;
} = 0x20000000;
```

**Fig. 4.17** Interface definition for a stateless file service written in RPCL of Sun RPC.

The IDL compiler is called *rpcgen* in Sun RPC. From an interface definition file, *rpcgen* generates the following:

1. A header file that contains definitions of common constants and types defined in the interface definition file. It also contains external declarations for all XDR marshaling and unmarshaling procedures that are automatically generated. The name of the header file is formed by taking the base name of the input file to *rpcgen* and adding a *.h* suffix (for example, *StatelessFS.h*). This file is manually included in client and server program files and automatically included in client stub, server stub, and XDR filters files using *#include*.

2. An XDR filters file that contains XDR marshaling and unmarshaling procedures. These procedures are used by the client and server stub procedures. The name of this file is formed by taking the base name of the input file to *rpcgen* and adding a *_xdr.c* suffix (for example, *StatelessFS_xdr.c*).

3. A client stub file that contains one stub procedure for each procedure defined in the interface definition file. A client stub procedure name is the name of the procedure given in the interface definition, converted to lowercase and with an underscore and the version number appended. For instance, in our example, the client stub procedure names for *READ* and *WRITE* procedures will be *read_1* and *write_1*, respectively. The name of the client stub file is formed by taking the base name of the input file to *rpcgen* and adding a *_clnt.c* suffix (for example, *StatelessFS_clnt.c*).

4. A server stub file that contains the *main* routine, the *dispatch* routine, and one stub procedure for each procedure defined in the interface definition file plus a null procedure.

   The *main* routine creates the transport handles and registers the service. The default is to register the program on both the UDP and TCP transports. However, a user can select which transport to use with a command-line option to *rpcgen*.

   The *dispatch* routine dispatches incoming remote procedure calls to the appropriate procedure. The name used for the dispatch routine is formed by mapping the program name to lowercase characters and appending an underscore followed by the version number (for example, *stateless_fs_prog_1*).

   The name of the server stub file is formed by taking the base name of the input file to *rpcgen* and adding a *_svc.c* suffix (for example, *StatelessFS_svc.c*).

Now using the files generated by *rpcgen*, an RPC application is created in the following manner:

1. The application programmer manually writes the client program and server program for the application. The skeletons of these two programs for our example application of stateless file service are given Figures 4.18 and 4.19, respectively. Notice that the remote procedure names used in these two programs are those of the stub procedures (*read_1* and *write_1*).

```
/* A skeleton of client source program for the stateless file service in file client.c */
#include <stdio.h>
#include <rpc/rpc.h>
#include "StatelessFS.h"

main (argc, argv)
        int argc;
        char **argv;
{
        CLIENT          *client_handle;
        char            *server_host_name = "paris";
        readargs        read_args;
        writeargs       write_args;
        Data            *read_result;
        Nbytes          *write_result;

        client_handle = clnt_create (server_host_name, STATELESS_FS_PROG,
                        STATELESS_FS_VERS, "udp");
                        /* Get a client handle. Creates socket */
        if (client_handle == NULL) {
                        clnt_pcreateerror (server_host_name);
                        return (1); /* Cannot contact server */
        };

        /* Prepare parameters and make an RPC to read procedure */
        read_args.filename = "example";
        read_args.position = 0;
        read_args.n = 500;
        read_result = read_1 (&read_args, client_handle);
        . . .
        . . .
        . . .

        /* Prepare parameters and make an RPC to write procedure */
        write_args.filename = "example";
        write_args.position = 501;
        write_args.data.n = 100;
        /* Statements for putting 100 bytes of data in &write_args.data.buffer */
        write_result = write_1 (&write_args, client_handle);
        . . .
        . . .
        . . .
        clnt_destroy (client_handle);
        /* Destroy the client handle when done. Closes socket */
}
```

**Fig. 4.18** A skeleton of client source program for the stateless file service of Figure 4.17.

```
/* A skeleton of server source program for the stateless file service in file server.c */
#include <stdio.h>
#include <rpc/rpc.h>
#include "StatelessFS.h"


/* READ PROCEDURE */
Data     *read_1 (args) /* Input parameters as a single argument */
         readargs              *args;
{
         static Data result; /* Must be declared as static */

         /* Statements for reading args.n bytes from the file args.filename starting
         from position args.position, and for putting the data read in &result.buffer
         and the actual number of bytes read in result.n */

         return (&result); /* Return the result as a single argument */
}

/* WRITE PROCEDURE */
Nbytes    *write_1 (args) /* Input parameters as a single argument */
          writeargs             *args;
{
          static Nbytes result; /* Must be declared as static */

          /* Statements for writing args.data.n bytes of data from the buffer
          &args.data.buffer into the file args.filename starting at position
          args.position */

          /* Statement for putting the actual number of bytes written in result */

          return (&result);
}
```

**Fig. 4.19** A skeleton of server source program for the stateless file service of Figure 4.17.

2. The client program file is compiled to get a client object file.
3. The server program file is compiled to get a server object file.
4. The client stub file and the XDR filters file are compiled to get a client stub object file.
5. The server stub file and the XDR filters file are compiled to get a server stub object file.
6. The client object file, the client stub object file, and the client-side RPCRuntime library are linked together to get the client executable file.
7. The server object file, the server stub object file, and the server-side RPCRuntime library are linked together to get the server executable file.

The entire process is summarized in Figure 4.20.

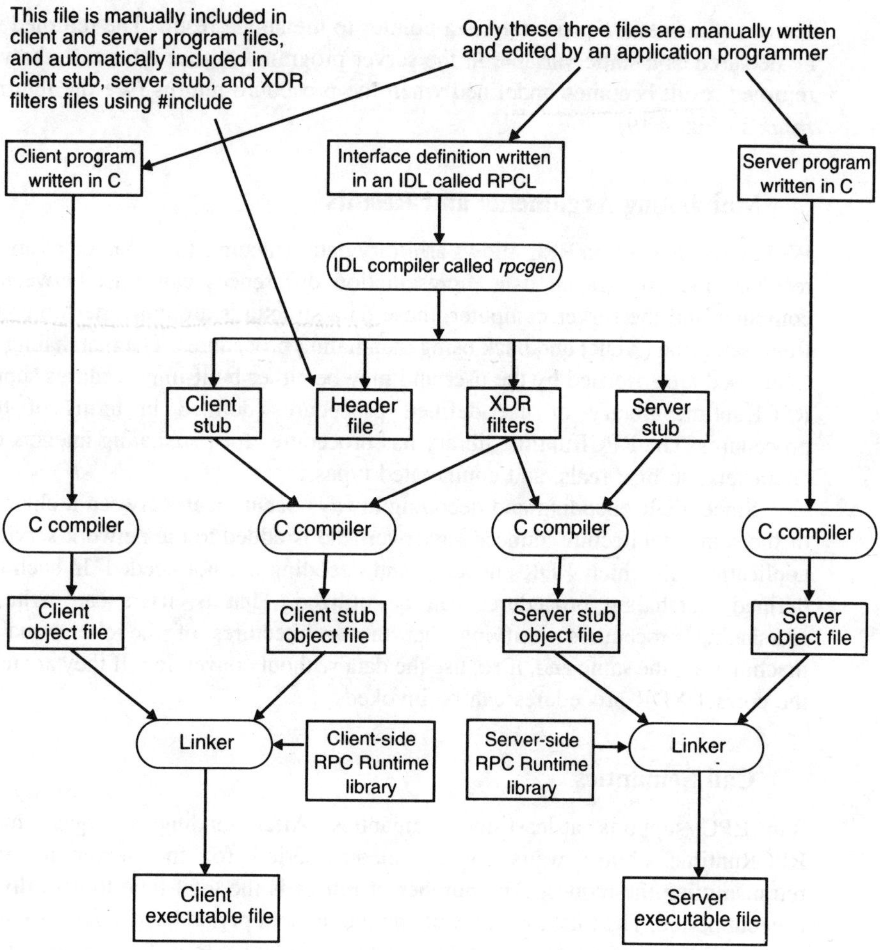


**Fig. 4.20** The steps in creating an RPC application in Sun RPC.

## Procedure Arguments

In Sun RPC, a remote procedure can accept only one argument and return only one result. Therefore, procedures requiring multiple parameters as input or as output must include them as components of a single structure. This is the reason why the structures *Data* (used as a single output argument to the *READ* procedure), *readargs* (used as a single input argument to the *READ* procedure), and *writeargs* (used as a single input argument to the *WRITE* procedure) have been defined in our example of Figures 4.17–4.19. If a remote procedure does not take an argument, a NULL pointer must still be passed as an argument to the remote procedure. Therefore, a Sun RPC call always has two arguments—the first is a pointer to the single argument of the remote procedure and the second is a pointer to a client handle (see the calls for *read_1* and *write_1* in Fig. 4.18). On the other hand, a return argument of a procedure is a pointer to the single result. The returned result must be declared as a static variable in the server program because otherwise the value of the returned result becomes undefined when the procedure returns (see the return argument *result* in Fig. 4.19).

### Marshaling Arguments and Results

We have seen that Sun RPC allows arbitrary data structures to be passed as arguments and results. Since significant data representation differences can exist between the client computer and the server computer, these data structures are converted to eXternal Data Representation (XDR) and back using marshaling procedures. The marshaling procedures to be used are specified by the user and may be either built-in procedures supplied in the RPCRuntime library or user-defined procedures defined in terms of the built-in procedures. The RPCRuntime library has procedures for marshaling integers of all sizes, characters, strings, reals, and enumerated types.

Since XDR encoding and decoding always occur, even between a client and server of the same architecture, unnecessary overhead is added to the network service for those applications in which XDR encoding and decoding are not needed. In such cases, user-defined marshaling procedures can be utilized. That is, users can write their own marshaling procedures verifying that the architectures of the client and the server machines are the same and, if so, use the data without conversion. If they are not the same, the correct XDR procedures can be invoked.

### Call Semantics

Sun RPC supports at-least-once semantics. After sending a request message, the RPCRuntime library waits for a timeout period for the server to reply before retransmitting the request. The number of retries is the total time to wait divided by the timeout period. The total time to wait and the timeout period have default values of 25 and 5 seconds, respectively. These default values can be set to different values by the users. Eventually, if no reply is received from the server within the total time to wait, the RPCRuntime library returns a timeout error.

### Client-Server Binding

Sun RPC does not have a networkwide binding service for client-server binding. Instead, each node has a local binding agent called *portmapper* that maintains a database of mapping of all local services (as already mentioned, each service is identified by its program number and version number) and their port numbers. The portmapper runs at a well-known port number on every node.

When a server starts up, it registers its program number, version number, and port number with the local portmapper. When a client wants to do an RPC, it must first find out the port number of the server that supports the remote procedure. For this, the client makes a remote request to the portmapper at the server's host, specifying the program number and version number (see *clnt_create* part of Fig. 4.18). This means that a client must specify the host name of the server when it imports a service interface. In effect, this means that Sun RPC has no location transparency.

The procedure *clnt_create* is used by a client to import a service interface. It returns a client handle that contains the necessary information for communicating with the corresponding server port, such as the socket descriptor and socket address. The client handle is used by the client to directly communicate with the server when making subsequent RPCs to procedures of the service interface (see RPCs made to *read_1* and *write_1* procedures in Fig. 4.18).

### Exception Handling

The RPCRuntime library of Sun RPC has several procedures for processing detected errors. The server-side error-handling procedures typically send a reply message back to the client side, indicating the detected error. However, the client-side error-handling procedures provide the flexibility to choose the error-reporting mechanism. That is, errors may be reported to users either by printing error messages to *stderr* or by returning strings containing error messages to clients.

### Security

Sun RPC supports the following three types of authentication (often referred to as *flavors*):

1. *No authentication*. This is the default type. In this case, no attempt is made by the server to check a client's authenticity before executing the requested procedure. Consequently, clients do not pass any authentication parameters in request messages.

2. *UNIX-style authentication*. This style is used to restrict access to a service to a certain set of users. In this case, the *uid* and *gid* of the user running the client program are passed in every request message, and based on this authentication information, the server decides whether to execute the requested procedure or not.

3. *DES-style authentication*. Data Encryption Standard (DES) is an encryption technique described in Chapter 11. In DES-style authentication, each user has a globally unique name called *netname*. The *netname* of the user running the client program is passed in encrypted form in every request message. On the server side, the encrypted *netname* is first decrypted and then the server uses the information in *netname* to decide whether to execute the requested procedure or not.

The DES-style authentication is recommended for users who need more security than UNIX-style authentication. RPCs using DES-style authentication are also referred to as *secure RPC*.

Clients have the flexibility to select any of the above three authentication flavors for an RPC. The type of authentication can be specified when a client handle is created. It is possible to use a different authentication mechanism for different remote procedures within a distributed application by setting the authentication type to the flavor desired before doing the RPC.

The authentication mechanism of Sun RPC is open ended in the sense that in addition to the three authentication types mentioned above users are free to invent and use new authentication types.

### Special Types of RPCs

Sun RPC provides support for asynchronous RPC, callback RPC, broadcast RPC, and batch-mode RPC.

Asynchronous RPC is accomplished by setting the timeout value of an RPC to zero and writing the server such that no reply is generated for the request.

To facilitate callback RPC, the client registers the callback service using a transient program number with the local portmapper. The program number is then sent as part of the RPC request to the server. The server initiates a normal RPC request to the client using the given program number when it is ready to do the callback RPC.

A broadcast RPC is directed to the portmapper of all nodes. Each node's portmapper then passes it on to the local service with the given program name. The client picks up any replies one by one.

Batch-mode RPC is accomplished by batching of client calls that require no reply and then sending them in a pipeline to the server over TCP/IP.

### Critiques of Sun RPC

In spite of its popularity, some of the criticisms normally made against Sun RPC are as follows:

1. Sun RPC lacks location transparency because a client has to specify the host name of the server when it imports a service interface.
2. The interface definition language of Sun RPC does not allow a general specification of procedure arguments and results. It allows only a single argument and a single result. This requirement forces multiple arguments or return values to be packaged as a single structure.
3. Sun RPC is not transport independent and the transport protocol is limited to either UDP or TCP. However, a transport-independent version of Sun RPC, known as TI-RPC (transport-independent RPC), has been developed by Sun-Soft, Inc. TI-RPC provides a simple and consistent way in which transports can be dynamically selected depending upon user preference and the availability of the transport. Details of TI-RPC can be found in [Khanna 1994].
4. In UDP, Sun RPC messages are limited to 8 kilobytes in length.
5. Sun RPC supports only at-least-once call semantics, which may not be acceptable for some applications.
6. Sun RPC does not have a networkwide client-server binding service.
7. We saw in Section 4.18 that threads can be used in the implementation of a client or a server process for better performance of an RPC-based application. Sun RPC does not include any integrated facility for threads in the client or server, although Sun OS has a separate threads package.

### 4.20.2 DCE RPC

The DCE RPC is one of the most fundamental components of DCE because it is the basis for all communication in DCE. It is derived from the Network Computing System (NCS) developed by Apollo (now part of Hewlett-Packard).

The DCE RPC also uses the automatic stub generation approach. An application's interface definition is written in IDL. As an example, the interface definition of the stateless file service of Figure 4.17 is rewritten in Figure 4.21 in IDL. Notice that, unlike Sun RPC, DCE RPC IDL allows a completely general specification of procedure arguments and results. As shown in the figure, each interface is uniquely identified by a universally unique identifier (UUID) that is a 128-bit binary number represented in the IDL file as an ASCII string in hexadecimal. The uniqueness of each UUID is ensured by incorporating in it the timestamp and the location of creation. A UUID as well as a template for the interface definition is produced by using the *uuidgen* utility. Therefore, to create the interface definition file for a service, the first step is to call the *uuidgen* program. The automatically generated template file is then manually edited to define the constants and the procedure interfaces of the service.

When the IDL file is complete, it is compiled using the IDL compiler to generate the client and server stubs and a header file. The client and server programs are then manually written for an application. Finally, the same steps as that of Figure 4.20 are used to get the client and server executable files.

```
[uuid (b20a1705-3c26-12d8-8ea3-04163a0dcefz)
 version (1.0)]

interface stateless_fs
{
        const long FILE_NAME_SIZE = 16
        const long BUFFER_SIZE = 1024
        typedef char FileName[FILE_NAME_SIZE];
        typedef char Buffer[BUFFER_SIZE];

        void read (
                [in] FileName               filename;
                [in] long                   position;
                [in, out] long              nbytes;
                [out] Buffer                buffer;
        );

        void write (
                [in] FileName               filename;
                [in] long                   position;
                [in, out] long              nbytes;
                [in] Buffer                 buffer;
        );
}
```

**Fig. 4.21** Interface definition of the stateless file service of Figure 4.17 written in the IDL of DCE RPC.

The default call semantics of a remote procedure in DCE RPC is at-most-once semantics. However, for procedures that are of idempotent nature, this rather strict call semantics is not necessary. Therefore, DCE RPC provides the flexibility to application programmers to indicate as part of a procedure's IDL definition that it is idempotent. In this case, error recovery is done via a simple retransmission strategy rather than the more complex protocol used to implement at-most-once semantics.

The DCE RPC has a networkwide binding service for client-server binding that is based on its directory service (the details of the DCE directory service are given in Chapter 10). For the description here, it is sufficient to know that every cell in a DCE system has a component called Cell Directory Service (CDS), which controls the naming environment used within a cell. Moreover, on each DCE server node runs a daemon process called *rpcd* (RPC daemon) that maintains a database of (server, endpoint) entries. An *endpoint* is a process address (such as the TCP/IP port number) of a server on its machine.

When an application server initializes, it asks the operating system for an endpoint. It then registers this endpoint with its local rpcd. At the time of initialization, the server also registers its host address with the CDS of its cell.

When a client makes its first RPC involving the server, the client stub first gets the server's host address by interacting with the server(s) of the CDS, making a request to find it a host running an instance of the server. It then interacts with the rpcd (an rpcd has a well-known endpoint on every host) of the server's host to get the endpoint of the server. The RPC can take place once the server's endpoint is known. Note that this lookup is not needed on subsequent RPCs made to the same server.

The steps described above are used for client-server binding when the client and the server belong to the same cell. A client can also do an RPC with a server that belongs to another cell. In this case, the process of getting the server's host address also involves Global Directory Service (GDS), which controls the global naming environment outside (between) cells (for details see Chapter 10).

The DCE RPC also provides broadcast facility. To use this facility, a remote procedure has to be given the broadcast attribute in its defining IDL file. When a procedure with this attribute is called, the request is sent to all servers of the requested interface. All the servers receiving the request respond, but only the first response is returned to the caller; the others are discarded by the RPCRuntime library.

## 4.21 SUMMARY

Remote Procedure Call (RPC) is a special case of the general message-passing model of IPC that has become a widely accepted IPC mechanism in distributed computing systems. Its popularity is due to its simple call syntax, familiar procedure call semantics, ease of use, generality, efficiency, and specification of a well-defined interface. Ideal transparency of RPC means that remote procedure calls are indistinguishable from local procedure calls. However, this is usually only partially achievable.

In the implementation of an RPC mechanism, five pieces of programs are involved: the client, the client stub, the RPCRuntime, the server stub, and the server. The purpose of the client and server stubs is to manipulate the data contained in a call or reply message so that it is suitable for transmission over the network or for use by the receiving process. On the other hand, the RPCRuntime provides network services in a transparent manner.

The two types of messages involved in the implementation of an RPC system are call messages and reply messages. Call messages are sent by the client to the server for requesting the execution of a remote procedure, and reply messages are sent by the server to the client for returning the result of remote procedure execution. The process of encoding and decoding of the data of these RPC messages is known as marshaling.

Servers of an RPC-based application may either be stateful or stateless. Moreover, depending on the time duration for which an RPC server survives, servers may be of three types—instance-per-call servers, instance-per-transaction/session servers, and persistent servers. The choice of a particular type of server depends on the needs of the application being designed.

The two choices of parameter-passing semantics in the design of an RPC mechanism are call-by-value and call-by-reference. Most RPC mechanisms use the call-by-value semantics because the client and server processes exist in different address spaces.

The call semantics of an RPC mechanism determines how often the remote procedure may be executed under fault conditions. The different types of call semantics used in RPC mechanisms are possibly or may be, last one, last of many, at least once, and exactly once. Of these, the exactly-once call semantics is the strongest and most desirable.

Based on their IPC needs, different systems use one of the following communication protocols for RPC: the request (R) protocol, the request/reply (RR) protocol, and the request/reply/acknowledge-reply (RRA) protocol. In addition to these, special communication protocols are used for handling complicated RPCs that involve long-duration calls or large gaps between calls or whose arguments and/or results are too large to fit in a single-datagram packet.

Client-server binding is necessary for a remote procedure call to take place. The general model used for binding is that servers export operations to register their willingness to provide service and clients import operations when they need some service. A client may be bound to a server at compile time, at link time, or at call time.

Some special types of RPCs operate in a manner different from the usual RPC protocol. For example, asynchronous RPC provides a one-way message facility from client to server, callback RPC facilitates a peer-to-peer paradigm instead of a client-server relationship among the participating processes, broadcast RPC provides the facility of broadcast and multicast communication instead of one-to-one communication, and batch-mode RPC allows the batching of client requests, which is a type of asynchronous mode of communication, instead of the usual synchronous mode of communication.

Unlike the conventional RPC systems, in which most of the implementation decisions are made when the RPC system is designed, the choices of transport protocol, data representation, and control protocol are delayed until bind time in an RPC system designed for a heterogeneous environment. For this, the binding facility used by such an RPC system is made considerably richer in information than the binding used by conventional RPC systems.

Bershad et al. [1990] proposed the use of Lightweight Remote Procedure Call (LRPC), which is a communication facility designed and optimized for cross-domain communications in microkernel operating systems. For achieving better performance than conventional RPC systems, LRPC uses the following four techniques: simple control transfer, simple data transfer, simple stubs, and design for concurrency.

Some optimizations that may be used to improve the performance of distributed applications that use an RPC facility are concurrent access to multiple servers, serving multiple requests simultaneously, reducing per call workload of servers, reply caching of idempotent remote procedures, proper selection of timeout values, and proper design of RPC protocol specification.

## EXERCISES

**4.1.** What was the primary motivation behind the development of the RPC facility? How does an RPC facility make the job of distributed applications programmers simpler?

**4.2.** What are the main similarities and differences between the RPC model and the ordinary procedure call model?

**4.3.** In the conventional procedure call model, the caller and the callee procedures often use global variables to communicate with each other. Explain why such global variables are not used in the RPC model.

**4.4.** In RPC, the called procedure may be on the same computer as the calling procedure or it may be on a different computer. Explain why the term *remote procedure call* is used even when the called procedure is on the same computer as the calling procedure.

**4.5.** What are the main issues in designing a transparent RPC mechanism? Is it possible to achieve complete transparency of an RPC mechanism? If no, explain why. If yes, explain how.

**4.6.** Achieving complete transparency of an RPC mechanism that allows the caller and callee processes to be on different computers is nearly impossible due to the involvement of the network in message communication between the two processes. Suppose an RPC mechanism is to be designed in which the caller and callee processes are always on the same computer. Is it possible to achieve complete transparency of this RPC mechanism? Give reasons for your answer.

**4.7.** What is a "stub"? How are stubs generated? Explain how the use of stubs helps in making an RPC mechanism transparent.

**4.8.** A server is designed to perform simple integer arithmetic operations (addition, substraction, multiplication, and division). Clients interact with this server by using an RPC mechanism. Describe the contents of the call and reply messages of this RPC application, explaining the purpose of each component. In case of an error, such as division by zero or arithmetic overflow, the server must suitably inform the client about the type of error.

**4.9.** Write marshaling procedures for both tagged and untagged representations for marshaling the message contents of the RPC application of Exercise 4.8.

**4.10.** A user-defined program object is a structure consisting of the following basic data types in that order: a Boolean, an integer, a long integer, and a fixed-length character string of eight characters. Write marshaling procedures for both tagged and untagged representations for this program object. Assume that the RPC software provides marshaling of the basic data types.

**4.11.** The caller process of an RPC must wait for a reply from the callee process after making a call. Explain how this can actually be done.

**4.12.** Differentiate between stateful and stateless servers. Why do some distributed applications use stateless servers in spite of the fact that stateful servers provide an easier programming paradigm and are typically more efficient than stateless servers?

**4.13.** Suggest a suitable server creation semantics for each of the following types of applications:

(a) A service is needed only once in a while, and the session for which a client interacts with the server of this service involves the exchange of a single call and a single reply message between the client and server processes.

(b) A service is needed only once in a while, and the session for which a client interacts with the server of this service normally involves the exchange of several call and reply messages between the client and server processes.

(c) A server can service the requests of multiple clients.

**4.14.** A server is to be shared by multiple clients. Describe a scheme for designing the remote procedures offered by the server so that interleaved or concurrent requests from different clients do not interfere with each other.

**4.15.** Why do most RPC systems support call-by-value semantics for parameter passing?

**4.16.** Discuss the similarities and differences between the following parameter-passing semantics that may be used in an object-based system:

(a) Call-by-object-reference

(b) Call-by-move

(c) Call-by-visit

**4.17.** Explain why RPC semantics is normally different from the conventional procedure call semantics. Clarify the differences among may-be, last-one, last-of-many, at-least-once, and exactly-once call semantics. Explain how each of these may be implemented.

**4.18.** What is an *orphan call*? How are orphan calls handled in the implementation of the following types of call semantics:

(a) Last-one call semantics

(b) Last-of-many call semantics

(c) At-least-once call semantics

**4.19.** Suggest whether may-be, last-one, last-of-many, at-least-once, or exactly-once call semantics should be used for each of the following applications (give reasons for your answer):

(a) For making a request to a time server to get the current time.

(b) For making a request to a node's resource manager to get the current status of resource availability of its node.

(c) For periodically broadcasting the total number of current jobs at its node by a process manager in a system in which the process managers of all nodes mutually cooperate to share the overall system load.

(d) For making a request to a computation server to compute the value of an equation.

(e) For making a request to a booking server to get the current status of availability of seats.

(f) For making a request to a booking server to reserve a seat.

(g) For making a request to a file server to position the *read-write pointer* of a file to a specified position.

(h) For making a request to a file server to append a record to an existing file.

(i) For making a request to a name server to get the location of a named object in a system that does not support object mobility.

(j) For making a request to a name server to get the location of a named object in a system that supports object mobility.

**4.20.** Explain why most RPC systems do not use acknowledgment messages. Differentiate among R, RR, and RRA protocols for RPCs. Give an example of an application in which each type of protocol may be the most suitable one to use.

**4.21.** Suppose it takes time $T$ ($T$ is very large) for a server to process an RPC request. Even though a client making the RPC request knows that it will receive the reply for its request from the server only after time $T$, it will unnecessarily keep waiting for the reply from the server for this entire duration in situations where the request message does not reach the server due to failure of the communication link between the client and the server or the server crashes while processing the client's request. Devise a mechanism to avoid this situation. That is, it should be possible for a client to detect an exception condition and to take corrective action as early as possible.

**4.22.** Suppose you have to design an RPC mechanism for interaction between clients and a file server, frequently requiring transfer of large volume of data in between them. However, the underlying network has a limitation of maximum packet size of 4 kilobytes. Suppose the time to transfer a 4-kilobyte packet is 4 ms, and the time to do a null RPC (i.e., 0 data bytes) is 0.5 ms. If the average amount of data transferred for each RPC request is 16 kilobytes, which of the following two methods will you prefer to use in your design:

(a) Using several physical RPCs for one logical RPC, each physical RPC transferring a single packet of data

(b) Using a single RPC with the data transferred as multidatagram messages

**4.23.** What are the main advantages of an RPC system that allows the binding between a client and a server to change dynamically? What are the main issues involved in providing this flexibility? Describe a mechanism to handle each of the issues mentioned by you.

**4.24.** A server is normally designed to service multiple clients and is often bound simultaneously to multiple clients. Does a situation ever arise when a client should be simultaneously bound to multiple servers? If no, explain why. If yes, give two examples of such a situation.

**4.25.** Discuss the relative advantages and disadvantages of binding a client and a server at compile time, at link time, and at call time.

**4.26.** Given the interface name of a server, discuss the relative advantages and disadvantages of using the broadcast method and the method of using a name server for locating the server.

**4.27.** What is *callback RPC* facility? Give an example of an application where this facility may be useful. What are the main issues involved in supporting this facility in an RPC system? Describe a mechanism to handle each of these issues.

**4.28.** Give an example of an application where each of the following facilities may be useful:

(a) Broadcast RPC facility

(b) Multicast RPC facility

Describe a mechanism to implement each of these facilities.

**4.29.** Give the characteristics of applications for which the batch-mode RPC facility may be useful. What are the main problems in using this facility?

**4.30.** Find out the details of the client-server binding mechanism of the HRPC system [Bershad et al. 1987], and explain how the choices of transport protocol, data representation, and control protocol are delayed until bind time in this system.

**4.31.** What was the primary motivation behind the development of the Lightweight RPC (LRPC) system [Bershad et al. 1990]? Describe some of the techniques used in the LRPC system that makes it more efficient than conventional RPC systems.

**4.32.** In a client-server model that is implemented by using a simple RPC mechanism, after making an RPC request, a client keeps waiting until a reply is received from the server for its request. It would be more efficient to allow the client to perform other jobs while the server is processing its request (especially when the request processing time is long). Describe three mechanisms that may be used in this case to allow a client to perform other jobs while the server is processing its request.

**4.33.** A client-server model is to be implemented by using an RPC mechanism. It has been realized that a shared server is an expensive resource of an RPC mechanism because it has to service requests from many clients. Suggest some guidelines that may be used for designing a shared server for improving the overall performance of the corresponding RPC mechanism.

## BIBLIOGRAPHY

**[Almes 1986]** Almes, G. T., "The Impact of Language and System on Remote Procedure Call Design," In: *Proceedings of the 6th International Conference on Distributed Computing Systems*, IEEE Press, Piscataway, NJ, pp. 414–421 (May 1986).

**[Almes et al. 1985]** Almes, G. T., Black, A. P., Lazowska, E. D., and Noe, J. D., "The Eden System: A Technical Review," *IEEE Transactions on Software Engineering*, Vol. SE-11, No. 1, pp. 43–59 (1985).

**[Bacon and Hamilton 1987]** Bacon, J. M., and Hamilton, K. G., "Distributed Computing with RPC: The Cambridge Approach," Technical Report No. 117, Computer Laboratory, University of Cambridge, England (1987).

**[Bal et al. 1987]** Bal, H. E., Renesse, R., and Tanenbaum, A. S., "Implementing Distributed Algorithms Using Remote Procedure Calls," In: *Proceedings of the AFIPS National Computer Conference*, Chicago, IL, pp. 499–506 (June 1987).

**[Bal et al. 1989]** Bal, H. E., Steiner, J. G., and Tanenbaum, A. S., "Programming Languages for Distributed Computing Systems," *ACM Computing Surveys*, Vol. 21, No. 3, pp. 261–322 (1989).

**[Bershad et al. 1987]** Bershad, B. N., Ching, D. T., Lazowska, E. D., Sanislo, J., and Schwartz, M., "A Remote Procedure Call Facility for Interconnecting Heterogeneous Computer Systems," *IEEE Transactions on Software Engineering*, Vol. SE-13, No. 8, pp. 880–894 (1987).

**[Bershad et al. 1990]** Bershad, B. N., Anderson, T. E., Lazowska, E. D., and Levy, H. M., "Lightweight Remote Procedure Call," *ACM Transactions on Computer Systems*, Vol. 8, No. 1, pp. 37–55 (1990). © ACM, Inc., 1990.

**[Birrell 1985]** Birrell, A. D., "Secure Communication Using Remote Procedure Calls," *ACM Transactions on Computer Systems*, Vol. 3, No. 1, pp. 1–14 (1985).

**[Birrell and Nelson 1984]** Birrell, A. D., and Nelson, B., "Implementing Remote Procedure Calls," *ACM Transactions on Computer Systems*, Vol. 2, No. 1, pp. 39–59 (1984).

**[Birrell et al. 1982]** Birrell, A. D., Levin, R., Needham, R. M., and Schroeder, M. D., "Grapevine: An Exercise in Distributed Computing," *Communications of the ACM*, Vol. 25, No. 4, pp. 260–274 (1982).

**[Black et al. 1986]** Black, A., Hutchinson, N., Jul, E., and Levy, H., "Object Structure in the Emerald System," In: *Proceedings of the 1st ACM Conference on Object-Oriented Programming Systems, Languages, and Applications* (*OOPSLA-1986*), pp. 78–86 (1986).

**[Black et al. 1987]** Black, A., Hutchinson, N., Jul, E., Levy, H., and Carter, L., "Distribution and Abstract Types in Emerald," *IEEE Transactions on Software Engineering*, Vol. SE-13, No. 1, pp. 65–76 (1987).

**[Corbin 1991]** Corbin, J. R., *The Art of Distributed Applications*, Springer-Verlag, New York, NY (1991).

**[Davison et al. 1992]** Davison, A., Drake, K., Roberts, W., and Slater, M., *Distributed Window Systems, A Practical Guide to X11 and OpenWindows*, Addison-Wesley, Reading, MA (1992).

**[DES 1977]** DATA ENCRYPTION STANDARD, *FIPS Publication 46*, National Bureau of Standards, U.S. Department of Commerce, Washington DC (January 1977).

**[Gibbons 1987]** Gibbons, P. B., "A Stub Generator for Multi-language RPC in Heterogeneous Environment," *IEEE Transactions on Software Engineering*, Vol. SE-13, No. 1, pp. 77–87 (1987).

**[Gifford and Glasser 1988]** Gifford, D., and Glasser, N., "Remote Pipes and Procedures for Efficient Distributed Communication," *ACM Transactions on Computer Systems*, Vol. 6, No. 3, pp. 258–283 (1988).

**[Gimson 1985]** Gimson, R., "Call Buffering Service," Technical Report No. 19, Programming Research Group, Oxford University, Oxford, England (1985).

**[Goscinski 1991]** Goscinski, A., "Distributed Operating Systems, The Logical Design," Addison-Wesley, Reading, MA (1991).

**[Hamilton 1984]** Hamilton, K. G., "A Remote Procedure Call System," Ph.D. Dissertation, Technical Report No. 70, Computer Laboratory, University of Cambridge, England (December 1984).

**[Harbinson 1992]** Harbinson, S. P., *Modula-3*, Prentice-Hall, Englewood Cliffs, NJ (1992).

**[Hiltunen and Schlichting 1995]** Hiltunen, M. A., and Schlichting, R. D., "Constructing a Configurable Group RPC Service," In: *Proceedings of the 15th International Conference on Distributed Computing Systems*, IEEE Press, Piscataway, NJ (May 1995).

**[Hutchinson et al. 1989]** Hutchinson, N. C., Peterson, L. L., Abbott, M. B., and O'Malley, S., "RPC in the *x*-Kernel: Evaluating New Design Techniques," In: *Proceedings of the 12th ACM Symposium on Operating Systems Principles*, pp. 91–101 (1989).

**[Jones et al. 1985]** Jones, M. B., Rashid, R. F., and Thompson, M. R.,"Matchmaker: An Interface Specification Language for Distributed Processing," In: *Proceedings of the 12th ACM Symposium on Principles of Programming Languages*, pp. 225–235 (1985).

**[Karger 1989]** Karger, P. A., "Using Registers to Optimize Cross-Domain Call Performance," In: *Proceedings of the 3rd Conference on Architectural Support for Programming Languages and Operating Systems*, pp. 194–204 (April 1989).

**[Khanna 1994]** Khanna, R. (Ed.), *Distributed Computing: Implementation and Management Strategies*, Prentice-Hall, Englewood Cliffs, NJ (1994).

**[Kim and Purtilo 1995]** Kim, T. H., and Purtilo, J. M.,"Configuration-Level Optimization of RPC-Based Distributed Programs," In: *Proceedings of the 15th International Conference on Distributed Computing Systems*, IEEE Press, Piscataway, NJ (May 1995).

**[Lin and Gannon 1985]** Lin, K. J., and Gannon, J. D., "Atomic Remote Procedure Call," *IEEE Transactions on Software Engineering*, Vol. SE-11, No. 10, pp. 1126–1135 (1985).

**[Liskov et al. 1981]** Liskov, B., Moss, E., Schaffert, C., Sheifler, R., and Snyder, A., "CLU Reference Manual," In: *Lecture Notes in Computer Science 114*, Springer-Verlag, Berlin (1981).

**[Liskov and Scheifler 1983]** Liskov, B., and Scheifler, R., "Guardians and Actions: Linguistic Support for Robust, Distributed Programs," *ACM Transactions on Programming Languages and Systems*, Vol. 5, No. 3, pp. 381–404 (1983).

**[Liskov and Shrira 1988]** Liskov, B., and Shrira, L., "Promises: Linguistic Support for Efficient Asynchronous Procedure Calls in Distributed Systems," In: *Proceedings of the ACM SIGPLAN'88 Conference on Programming Language Design and Implementation*, Association for Computing Machinery, New York, NY, pp. 260–267 (June 1988).

**[Lockhart Jr. 1994]** Lockhart, Jr., H. W., *OSF DCE: Guide to Developing Distributed Applications*, IEEE Computer Society Press, Los Alamitos, CA (1994).

**[Nelson 1991]** Nelson, G. (Ed.), *Systems Programming with Modula-3*, Prentice-Hall, Englewood Cliffs, NJ (1991).

**[Panzieri and Srivastava 1988]** Panzieri, F., and Srivastava, S. K., "Rajdoot: A Remote Procedure Call Mechanism with Orphan Detection and Killing," *IEEE Transactions on Software Engineering*, Vol. SE-14, pp. 30–37 (1988).

**[Rosenberry et al. 1992]** Rosenberry, W., Kenney, D., and Fisher, G., *OSF DISTRIBUTED COMPUTING ENVIRONMENT, Understanding DCE*, O'Reilly & Associates, Sebastopol, CA (1992).

**[Schroeder and Burrows 1990]** Schroeder, M. D., and Burrows, M., "Performance of Firefly RPC," *ACM Transactions on Computer Systems*, Vol. 8, No. 1, pp. 1–17 (1990).

**[Shirley et al. 1994]** Shirley, J., Hu, W., and Magid, D., *Guide to Writing DCE Applications*, 2nd ed., O'Reilly & Associates, Sebastopol, CA (1994).

**[Shrivastava et al. 1991]** Shrivastava, S., Dixon, G. N., and Parrington, G. D., "An Overview of the Arjuna Programming System," *IEEE Software* (January 1991).

**[Smith 1994]** Smith, B., "Client/Server Made Easy," *BYTE* (March 1994).

**[Spector 1982]** Spector, A. Z.,"Performing Remote Operations Efficiently on a Local Computer Network," *Communications of the ACM*, Vol. 25, No. 4, pp. 246–259 (1982).

**[Srivastava and Panzieri 1982]** Srivastava, S. K., and Panzieri, F., "The Design of Reliable Remote Procedure Call Mechanism," *IEEE Transactions on Computers*, Vol. C-31, No. 7 (1982).

**[Sun Microsystems 1985]** "Remote Procedure Call Protocol Specification," *Networking on the Sun Workstation*, Sun Microsystems, Mountain View, CA (1985).

**[Sun Microsystems 1990]** *Network Programming*, Sun Microsystems, Mountain View, CA (1990).

**[Tanenbaum and Van Renesse 1988]** Tanenbaum, A. S., and Van Renesse, R., "A Critique of the Remote Procedure Call Paradigm," In: *Proceedings of the EUTECO'88 Conference*, Vienna, Austria, North-Holland, Amsterdam, pp. 775–783 (April 1988).

**[Tay and Ananda 1990]** Tay, B. H., and Ananda, A. L., "A Survey of Remote Procedure Calls," *Operating Systems Review*, Vol. 24, pp. 68–79 (1990).

**[Walker et al. 1990]** Walker, E. F., Floyd, R., and Neves, P., "Asynchronous Remote Operation Execution in Distributed Systems," In: *Proceedings of the 10th International Conference on Distributed Computing Systems*, IEEE Press, Piscataway, NJ, pp. 253–259 (1990).

**[Wilbur and Bacarisse 1987]** Wilbur, S., and Bacarisse, B., "Building Distributed Systems with Remote Procedure Call," *Software Engineering Journal*, pp. 148–159 (September 1987).

**[Xerox Corporation 1981]** "Courier: The Remote Procedure Call Protocol," Xerox System Integration Standard XSIS-038112, Stamford, CT (1981).

## POINTERS TO BIBLIOGRAPHIES ON THE INTERNET

I could not find a bibliography dedicated only to Remote Procedure Calls. However, the following bibliographies contain references on this topic:

ftp:ftp.cs.umanitoba.ca/pub/bibliographies/Os/IMMD_IV.html

ftp:ftp.cs.umanitoba.ca/pub/bibliographies/Os/os.html

ftp:ftp.cs.umanitoba.ca/pub/bibliographies/Misc/misc.1.html

ftp:ftp.cs.umanitoba.ca/pub/bibliographies/Parallel/JPDC.html

CHAPTER 5

# Distributed Shared Memory

## 5.1 INTRODUCTION

In Chapter 3, it was mentioned that the two basic paradigms for interprocess communication are as follows:

- Shared-memory paradigm
- Message-passing paradigm

Message-passing systems (described in Chapter 3), or systems supporting Remote Procedure Calls (RPCs) (described in Chapter 4), adhere to the message-passing paradigm. This paradigm consists of two basic primitives for interprocess communication:

**Send** (*recipient, data*)
**Receive** (*data*)

The sending process generates the *data* to be shared and sends it to the recipient(s) with which it wants to communicate. The recipient(s) receive the *data*.

This functionality is sometimes hidden in language-level constructs. For example, RPC provides automatic message generation and reception according to a procedural specification. However, the basic communication paradigm remains the same because the communicating processes directly interact with each other for exchanging the shared data.

In contrast to the message-passing paradigm, the shared-memory paradigm provides to processes in a system with a shared address space. Processes use this address space in the same way they use normal local memory. That is, processes access data in the shared address space through the following two basic primitives, of course, with some variations in the syntax and semantics in different implementations:

*data* = **Read** (*address*)
**Write** (*address*, *data*)

*Read* returns the *data* item referenced by *address*, and *write* sets the contents referenced by *address* to the value of *data*.

We saw in Chapter 1 that the two major kinds of multiple-instruction, multiple-data-stream (MIMD) multiprocessors that have become popular and gained commercial acceptance are tightly coupled shared-memory multiprocessors and loosely coupled distributed-memory multiprocessors. The use of a shared-memory paradigm for interprocess communication is natural for distributed processes running on tightly coupled shared-memory multiprocessors. However, for loosely coupled distributed-memory systems, no physically shared memory is available to support the shared-memory paradigm for interprocess communication. Therefore, until recently, the interprocess communication mechanism in loosely coupled distributed-memory multiprocessors was limited only to the message-passing paradigm. But some recent loosely coupled distributed-memory systems have implemented a software layer on top of the message-passing communication system to provide a shared-memory abstraction to the programmers. The shared-memory abstraction gives these systems the illusion of physically shared memory and allows programmers to use the shared-memory paradigm. The software layer, which is used for providing the shared-memory abstraction, can be implemented either in an operating system kernel or in runtime library routines with proper system kernel support. The term Distributed Shared Memory (DSM) refers to the shared-memory paradigm applied to loosely coupled distributed-memory systems [Stumm and Zhou 1990].

As shown in Figure 5.1, DSM provides a virtual address space shared among processes on loosely coupled processors. That is, DSM is basically an abstraction that integrates the local memory of different machines in a network environment into a single logical entity shared by cooperating processes executing on multiple sites. The shared memory itself exists only virtually. Application programs can use it in the same way as a traditional virtual memory, except, of course, that processes using it can run on different machines in parallel. Due to the virtual existence of the shared memory, DSM is sometimes also referred to as *Distributed Shared Virtual Memory* (*DSVM*).

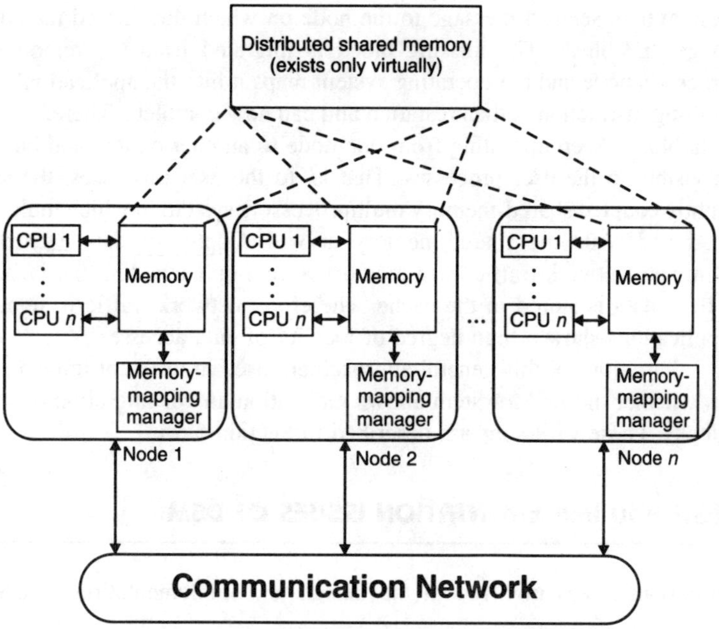


**Fig. 5.1** Distributed shared memory (DSM).

## 5.2 GENERAL ARCHITECTURE OF DSM SYSTEMS

The DSM systems normally have an architecture of the form shown in Figure 5.1. Each node of the system consists of one or more CPUs and a memory unit. The nodes are connected by a high-speed communication network. A simple message-passing system allows processes on different nodes to exchange messages with each other.

The DSM abstraction presents a large shared-memory space to the processors of all nodes. In contrast to the shared physical memory in tightly coupled parallel architectures, the shared memory of DSM exists only virtually. A software memory-mapping manager routine in each node maps the local memory onto the shared virtual memory. To facilitate the mapping operation, the shared-memory space is partitioned into *blocks*.

Data caching is a well-known solution to address memory access latency. The idea of data caching is used in DSM systems to reduce network latency. That is, the main memory of individual nodes is used to cache pieces of the shared-memory space. The memory-mapping manager of each node views its local memory as a big cache of the shared-memory space for its associated processors. The basic unit of caching is a memory block.

When a process on a node accesses some data from a memory block of the shared-memory space, the local memory-mapping manager takes charge of its request. If the memory block containing the accessed data is resident in the local memory, the request is satisfied by supplying the accessed data from the local memory. Otherwise, a network block fault is generated and the control is passed to the operating system. The operating system then sends a message to the node on which the desired memory block is located to get the block. The missing block is migrated from the remote node to the client process's node and the operating system maps it into the application's address space. The faulting instruction is then restarted and can now complete. Therefore, the scenario is that data blocks keep migrating from one node to another on demand but no communication is visible to the user processes. That is, to the user processes, the system looks like a tightly coupled shared-memory multiprocessors system in which multiple processes freely read and write the shared-memory at will. Copies of data cached in local memory eliminate network traffic for a memory access on cache hit, that is, access to an address whose data is stored in the cache. Therefore, network traffic is significantly reduced if applications show a high degree of locality of data accesses.

Variations of this general approach are used in different implementations depending on whether the DSM system allows replication and/or migration of shared-memory data blocks. These variations are described in Section 5.6.1.

## 5.3 DESIGN AND IMPLEMENTATION ISSUES OF DSM

Important issues involved in the design and implementation of DSM systems are as follows:

1. *Granularity.* Granularity refers to the block size of a DSM system, that is, to the unit of sharing and the unit of data transfer across the network when a network block fault occurs. Possible units are a few words, a page, or a few pages. Selecting proper block size is an important part of the design of a DSM system because block size is usually a measure of the granularity of parallelism explored and the amount of network traffic generated by network block faults.

2. *Structure of shared-memory space.* Structure refers to the layout of the shared data in memory. The structure of the shared-memory space of a DSM system is normally dependent on the type of applications that the DSM system is intended to support.

3. *Memory coherence and access synchronization.* In a DSM system that allows replication of shared data items, copies of shared data items may simultaneously be available in the main memories of a number of nodes. In this case, the main problem is to solve the memory coherence problem that deals with the consistency of a piece of shared data lying in the main memories of two or more nodes. This problem is similar to that which arises with conventional caches [Smith 1982], in particular with multicache schemes for shared-memory multiprocessors [Frank 1984, Goodman 1983, Katz et al. 1985, Yen et al. 1985]. Since different memory coherence protocols make different assumptions and trade-offs, the choice is usually dependent on the pattern of memory access. The terms *coherence* and *consistency* are used interchangeably in the literature.

In a DSM system, concurrent accesses to shared data may be generated. Therefore, a memory coherence protocol alone is not sufficient to maintain the consistency of shared data. In addition, synchronization primitives, such as semaphores, event count, and lock, are needed to synchronize concurrent accesses to shared data.

4. *Data location and access.* To share data in a DSM system, it should be possible to locate and retrieve the data accessed by a user process. Therefore, a DSM system must implement some form of data block locating mechanism in order to service network data block faults to meet the requirement of the memory coherence semantics being used.

5. *Replacement strategy.* If the local memory of a node is full, a cache miss at that node implies not only a fetch of the accessed data block from a remote node but also a replacement. That is, a data block of the local memory must be replaced by the new data block. Therefore, a cache replacement strategy is also necessary in the design of a DSM system.

6. *Thrashing.* In a DSM system, data blocks migrate between nodes on demand. Therefore, if two nodes compete for write access to a single data item, the corresponding data block may be transferred back and forth at such a high rate that no real work can get done. A DSM system must use a policy to avoid this situation (usually known as thrashing).

7. *Heterogeneity.* The DSM systems built for homogeneous systems need not address the heterogeneity issue. However, if the underlying system environment is heterogeneous, the DSM system must be designed to take care of heterogeneity so that it functions properly with machines having different architectures.

These design and implementation issues of DSM systems are described in subsequent sections.

## 5.4 GRANULARITY

One of the most visible parameters to be chosen in the design of a DSM system is the block size. Several criteria for choosing this granularity parameter are described below. Just as with paged main memory, there are a number of trade-offs and no single criterion dominates.

### 5.4.1 Factors Influencing Block Size Selection

In a typical loosely coupled multiprocessor system, sending large packets of data (for example, 4 kilobytes) is not much more expensive than sending small ones (for example, 256 bytes) [Li and Hudak 1989]. This is usually due to the typical software protocols and overhead of the virtual memory layer of the operating system. This fact favors relatively large block sizes. However, other factors that influence the choice of block size are described below [Nitzberg and Virginia Lo 1991].

1. *Paging overhead.* Because shared-memory programs provide locality of reference, a process is likely to access a large region of its shared address space in a small amount of time. Therefore, paging overhead is less for large block sizes as compared to the paging overhead for small block sizes.

2. *Directory size.* Another factor affecting the choice of block size is the need to keep directory information about the blocks in the system. Obviously, the larger the block size, the smaller the directory. This ultimately results in reduced directory management overhead for larger block sizes.

3. *Thrashing.* The problem of thrashing may occur when data items in the same data block are being updated by multiple nodes at the same time, causing large numbers of data block transfers among the nodes without much progress in the execution of the application. While a thrashing problem may occur with any block size, it is more likely with larger block sizes, as different regions in the same block may be updated by processes on different nodes, causing data block transfers that are not necessary with smaller block sizes.

4. *False sharing.* False sharing occurs when two different processes access two unrelated variables that reside in the same data block (Fig. 5.2). In such a situation, even though the original variables are not shared, the data block appears to be shared by the two processes. The larger is the block size, the higher is the probability of false sharing, due to the fact that the same data block may contain different data structures that are used independently. Notice that false sharing of a block may lead to a thrashing problem.

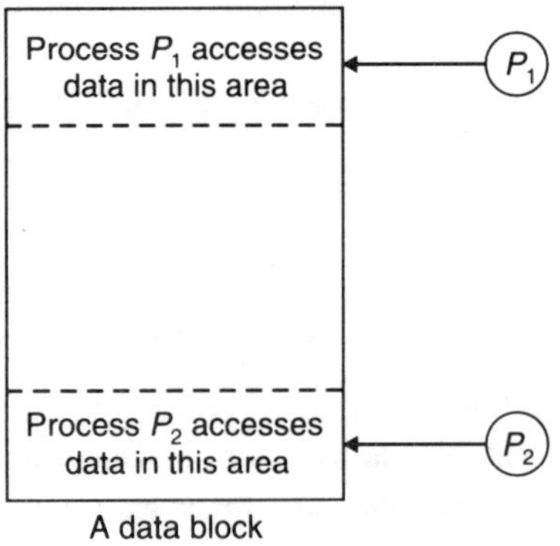


**Fig. 5.2** False sharing.

### 5.4.2 Using Page Size as Block Size

The relative advantages and disadvantages of small and large block sizes make it difficult for a DSM designer to decide on a proper block size. Therefore, a suitable compromise in granularity, adopted by several existing DSM systems, is to use the typical page size of a conventional virtual memory implementation as the block size of a DSM system. Using page size as the block size of a DSM system has the following advantages [Li and Hudak 1989]:

1. It allows the use of existing page-fault schemes (i.e., hardware mechanisms) to trigger a DSM page fault. Thus memory coherence problems can be resolved in page-fault handlers.

2. It allows the access right control (needed for each shared entity) to be readily integrated into the functionality of the memory management unit of the system.
3. As long as a page can fit into a packet, page sizes do not impose undue communication overhead at the time of network page fault.
4. Experience has shown that a page size is a suitable data entity unit with respect to memory contention.

## 5.5 STRUCTURE OF SHARED-MEMORY SPACE

Structure defines the abstract view of the shared-memory space to be presented to the application programmers of a DSM system. For example, the shared-memory space of one DSM system may appear to its programmers as a storage for words, while the programmers of another DSM system may view its shared-memory space as a storage for data objects. The structure and granularity of a DSM system are closely related [Nitzberg and Virginia Lo 1991]. The three commonly used approaches for structuring the shared-memory space of a DSM system are [Nitzberg and Virginia Lo 1991] as follows:

1. *No structuring*. Most DSM systems do not structure their shared-memory space. In these systems, the shared-memory space is simply a linear array of words. An advantage of the use of unstructured shared-memory space is that it is convenient to choose any suitable page size as the unit of sharing and a fixed grain size may be used for all applications. Therefore, it is simple and easy to design such a DSM system. It also allows applications to impose whatever data structures they want on the shared memory. IVY [Li and Hudak 1989] and Mether [Minnich and Farber 1989] use this approach.

2. *Structuring by data type*. In this method, the shared-memory space is structured either as a collection of objects (as in Clouds [Dasgupta et al. 1991] and Orca [Bal et al. 1992]) or as a collection of variables in the source language (as in Munin [Bennett et al. 1990] and Midway [Bershad et al. 1993]). The granularity in such DSM systems is an object or a variable. But since the sizes of the objects and data types vary greatly, these DSM systems use variable grain size to match the size of the object/variable being accessed by the application. The use of variable grain size complicates the design and implementation of these DSM systems.

3. *Structuring as a database*. Another method is to structure the shared memory like a database. For example, Linda [Carriero and Gelernter 1989] takes this approach. Its shared-memory space is ordered as an associative memory (a memory addressed by content rather than by name or address) called a *tuple space*, which is a collection of immutable tuples with typed data items in their fields. A set of primitives that can be added to any base language (such as C and FORTRAN) are provided to place tuples in the tuple space and to read or extract them from tuple space. To perform updates, old data items in the DSM are replaced by new data items. Processes select tuples by specifying the number of their fields and their values or types. Although this structure allows the location of data to be separated from its value, it requires programmers to use special

access functions to interact with the shared-memory space. Therefore, access to shared data is nontransparent. In most other systems, access to shared data is transparent.

## 5.6 CONSISTENCY MODELS

Consistency requirements vary from application to application [Bennett et al. 1990, Cheriton 1986, Garcia-Molina and Wiederhold 1982]. A *consistency model* basically refers to the degree of consistency that has to be maintained for the shared-memory data for the memory to work correctly for a certain set of applications. It is defined as a set of rules that applications must obey if they want the DSM system to provide the degree of consistency guaranteed by the consistency model. Several consistency models have been proposed in the literature. Of these, the main ones are described below.

It may be noted here that the investigation of new consistency models is currently an active area of research. The basic idea is to invent a consistency model that can allow consistency requirements to be relaxed to a greater degree than existing consistency models, with the relaxation done in such a way that a set of applications can function correctly. This helps in improving the performance of these applications because better concurrency can be achieved by relaxing the consistency requirement. However, applications that depend on a stronger consistency model may not perform correctly if executed in a system that supports only a weaker consistency model. This is because if a system supports the stronger consistency model, then the weaker consistency model is automatically supported but the converse is not true.

### Strict Consistency Model

The *strict consistency model* is the strongest form of memory coherence, having the most stringent consistency requirement. A shared-memory system is said to support the strict consistency model if the value returned by a read operation on a memory address is always the same as the value written by the most recent write operation to that address, irrespective of the locations of the processes performing the read and write operations. That is, all writes instantaneously become visible to all processes.

Implementation of the strict consistency model requires the existence of an absolute global time so that memory read/write operations can be correctly ordered to make the meaning of "most recent" clear. However, as explained in Chapter 6, absolute synchronization of clocks of all the nodes of a distributed system is not possible. Therefore, the existence of an absolute global time in a distributed system is also not possible. Consequently, implementation of the strict consistency model for a DSM system is practically impossible.

### Sequential Consistency Model

The *sequential consistency model* was proposed by Lamport [1979]. A shared-memory system is said to support the sequential consistency model if all processes see the same order of all memory access operations on the shared memory. The exact order in which the memory access operations are interleaved does not matter. That is, if the three operations read ($r_1$), write ($w_1$), read ($r_2$) are performed on a memory address in that order, any of the orderings ($r_1$, $w_1$, $r_2$), ($r_1$, $r_2$, $w_1$), ($w_1$, $r_1$, $r_2$), ($w_1$, $r_2$, $r_1$), ($r_2$, $r_1$, $w_1$), ($r_2$, $w_1$, $r_1$) of the three operations is acceptable provided all processes see the same ordering. If one process sees one of the orderings of the three operations and another process sees a different one, the memory is not a sequentially consistent memory. Note here that the only acceptable ordering for a strictly consistent memory is ($r_1$, $w_1$, $r_2$).

The consistency requirement of the sequential consistency model is weaker than that of the strict consistency model because the sequential consistency model does not guarantee that a read operation on a particular memory address always returns the same value as written by the most recent write operation to that address. As a consequence, with a sequentially consistent memory, running a program twice may not give the same result in the absence of explicit synchronization operations. This problem does not exist in a strictly consistent memory.

A DSM system supporting the sequential consistency model can be implemented by ensuring that no memory operation is started until all the previous ones have been completed. A sequentially consistent memory provides *one-copy/single-copy* semantics because all the processes sharing a memory location always see exactly the same contents stored in it. This is the most intuitively expected semantics for memory coherence. Therefore, sequential consistency is acceptable by most applications.

### Causal Consistency Model

The *causal consistency model*, proposed by Hutto and Ahamad [1990], relaxes the requirement of the sequential consistency model for better concurrency. Unlike the sequential consistency model, in the causal consistency model, all processes see only those memory reference operations in the same (correct) order that are potentially causally related. Memory reference operations that are not potentially causally related may be seen by different processes in different orders. A memory reference operation (read/write) is said to be potentially causally related to another memory reference operation if the first one might have been influenced in any way by the second one. For example, if a process performs a read operation followed by a write operation, the write operation is potentially causally related to the read operation because the computation of the value written may have depended in some way on the value obtained by the read operation. On the other hand, a write operation performed by one process is not causally related to a write operation performed by another process if the first process has not read either the value written by the second process or any memory variable that was directly or indirectly derived from the value written by the second process.

A shared memory system is said to support the causal consistency model if all write operations that are potentially causally related are seen by all processes in the same (correct) order. Write operations that are not potentially causally related may be seen by different processes in different orders. Note that "correct order" means that if a write operation ($w_2$) is causally related to another write operation ($w_1$), the acceptable order is ($w_1$, $w_2$) because the value written by $w_2$ might have been influenced in some way by the value written by $w_1$. Therefore, ($w_2$, $w_1$) is not an acceptable order.

Obviously, in the implementation of a shared-memory system supporting the causal consistency model, there is a need to keep track of which memory reference operation is dependent on which other memory reference operations. This can be done by constructing and maintaining a dependency graph for the memory access operations.

### Pipelined Random-Access Memory Consistency Model

The *pipelined random-access memory* (*PRAM*) *consistency model*, proposed by Lipton and Sandberg [1988], provides a weaker consistency semantics than the consistency models described so far. It only ensures that all write operations performed by a single process are seen by all other processes in the order in which they were performed as if all the write operations performed by a single process are in a pipeline. Write operations performed by different processes may be seen by different processes in different orders. For example, if $w_{11}$ and $w_{12}$ are two write operations performed by a process $P_1$ in that order, and $w_{21}$ and $w_{22}$ are two write operations performed by a process $P_2$ in that order, a process $P_3$ may see them in the order $[(w_{11}, w_{12}), (w_{21}, w_{22})]$ and another process $P_4$ may see them in the order $[(w_{21}, w_{22}), (w_{11}, w_{12})]$.

The PRAM consistency model is simple and easy to implement and also has good performance. It can be implemented by simply sequencing the write operations performed at each node independently of the write operations performed on other nodes. It leads to better performance than the previous models because a process need not wait for a write operation performed by it to complete before starting the next one since all write operations of a single process are pipelined. Notice that in sequential consistency all processes agree on the same order of memory reference operations, but in PRAM consistency all processes do not agree on the same order of memory reference operations. Therefore, for the example given above, either $[(w_{11}, w_{12}), (w_{21}, w_{22})]$ or $[(w_{21}, w_{22}), (w_{11}, w_{12})]$ is an acceptable ordering for sequential consistency but not both. That is, unlike PRAM consistency, both processes $P_3$ and $P_4$ must agree on the same order.

### Processor Consistency Model

The *processor consistency model*, proposed by Goodman [1989], is very similar to the PRAM consistency model with an additional restriction of memory coherence. That is, a processor consistent memory is both coherent and adheres to the PRAM consistency model. Memory coherence means that for any memory location all processes agree on the same order of all write operations to that location. In effect, processor consistency ensures that all write operations performed on the same memory location (no matter by which process they are performed) are seen by all processes in the same order. This requirement is in addition to the requirement imposed by the PRAM consistency model. Therefore, in the example given for PRAM consistency, if $w_{12}$ and $w_{22}$ are write operations for writing to the same memory location $x$, all processes must see them in the same order—$w_{12}$ before $w_{22}$ or $w_{22}$ before $w_{12}$. This means that for processor consistency both processes $P_3$ and $P_4$ must see the write operations in the same order, which may be either $[(w_{11}, w_{12}), (w_{21}, w_{22})]$ or $[(w_{21}, w_{22}), (w_{11}, w_{12})]$. Notice that, for this example, processor consistency and sequential consistency lead to the same final result, but this may not be true for other cases.

### Weak Consistency Model

The *weak consistency model*, proposed by Dubois et al. [1988], is designed to take advantage of the following two characteristics common to many applications:

1. It is not necessary to show the change in memory done by every write operation to other processes. The results of several write operations can be combined and sent to other processes only when they need it. For example, when a process executes in a critical section, other processes are not supposed to see the changes made by the process to the memory until the process exits from the critical section. In this case, all changes made to the memory by the process while it is in its critical section need be made visible to other processes only at the time when the process exits from the critical section.

2. Isolated accesses to shared variables are rare. That is, in many applications, a process makes several accesses to a set of shared variables and then no access at all to the variables in this set for a long time.

Both characteristics imply that better performance can be achieved if consistency is enforced on a group of memory reference operations rather than on individual memory reference operations. This is exactly the basic idea behind the weak consistency model.

The main problem in implementing this idea is determining how the system can know that it is time to show the changes performed by a process to other processes since this time is different for different applications. Since there is no way for the system to know this on its own, the programmers are asked to tell this to the system for their applications. For this, a DSM system that supports the weak consistency model uses a special variable called a *synchronization variable*. The operations on it are used to synchronize memory. That is, when a synchronization variable is accessed by a process, the entire (shared) memory is synchronized by making all the changes to the memory made by all processes visible to all other processes. Note that memory synchronization in a DSM system will involve propagating memory updates done at a node to all other nodes having a copy of the same memory addresses.

For supporting weak consistency, the following requirements must be met:

1. All accesses to synchronization variables must obey sequential consistency semantics.
2. All previous write operations must be completed everywhere before an access to a synchronization variable is allowed.
3. All previous accesses to synchronization variables must be completed before access to a nonsynchronization variable is allowed.

Note that the weak consistency model provides better performance at the cost of putting extra burden on the programmers.

### Release Consistency Model

We saw that in the weak consistency model the entire (shared) memory is synchronized when a synchronization variable is accessed by a process, and memory synchronization basically involves the following operations:

1. All changes made to the memory by the process are propagated to other nodes.
2. All changes made to the memory by other processes are propagated from other nodes to the process's node.

A closer observation shows that this is not really necessary because the first operation need only be performed when the process exits from a critical section and the second operation need only be performed when the process enters a critical section. Since a single synchronization variable is used in the weak consistency model, the system cannot know whether a process accessing a synchronization variable is entering a critical section or exiting from a critical section. Therefore, both the first and second operations are performed on every access to a synchronization variable by a process. For better performance, the *release consistency model* [Gharachorloo et al. 1990] provides a mechanism to clearly tell the system whether a process is entering a critical section or exiting from a critical section so that the system can decide and perform only either the first or the second operation when a synchronization variable is accessed by a process. This is achieved by using two synchronization variables (called *acquire* and *release*) instead of a single synchronization variable. *Acquire* is used by a process to tell the system that it is about to enter a critical section, so that the system performs only the second operation when this variable is accessed. On the other hand, *release* is used by a process to tell the system that it has just exited a critical section, so that the system performs only the first operation when this variable is accessed. Programmers are responsible for putting *acquire* and *release* at suitable places in their programs.

Release consistency may also be realized by using the synchronization mechanism based on barriers instead of critical sections. A *barrier* defines the end of a phase of execution of a group of concurrently executing processes. All processes in the group must complete their execution up to a barrier before any process is allowed to proceed with its execution following the barrier. That is, when a process of a group encounters a barrier during its execution, it blocks until all other processes in the group complete their executions up to the barrier. When the last process completes its execution up to the barrier, all shared variables are synchronized and then all processes resume with their executions. Therefore, *acquire* is departure from a barrier, and *release* is completion of the execution of the last process up to a barrier.

A barrier can be implemented by using a centralized barrier server. When a barrier is created, it is given a count of the number of processes that must be waiting on it before they can all be released. Each process of a group of concurrently executing processes sends a message to the barrier server when it arrives at a barrier and then blocks until a reply is received from the barrier server. The barrier server does not send any replies until all processes in the group have arrived at the barrier.

For supporting release consistency, the following requirements must be met:

1. All accesses to *acquire* and *release* synchronization variables obey processor consistency semantics.
2. All previous *acquires* performed by a process must be completed successfully before the process is allowed to perform a data access operation on the memory.
3. All previous data access operations performed by a process must be completed successfully before a *release* access done by the process is allowed.

Note that *acquires* and *releases* of locks of different critical regions (or barriers) can occur independently of each other. Gharachorloo et al. [1990] showed that if processes use appropriate synchronization accesses properly, a release consistent DSM system will produce the same results for an application as that if the application was executed on a sequentially consistent DSM system.

A variation of release consistency is *lazy release consistency*, proposed by Keleher et al. [1992], and is more efficient than the conventional release consistency. In the conventional approach, when a process does a *release* access, the contents of all the modified memory locations at the process's node are sent to all other nodes that have a copy of the same memory locations in their local cache. However, in the lazy approach, the modifications are not sent to other nodes at the time of release. Rather, these modifications are sent to other nodes only on demand. That is, when a process does an *acquire* access, all modifications of other nodes are acquired by the process's node. Therefore, the modifications that were to be sent to this node at the time of *release* access will be received by the node now (exactly when it is needed there). Lazy release consistency has better performance because in this method no network traffic is generated at all until an *acquire* access is done by a process at some other node.

### Discussion of Consistency Models

In the description above, we saw some of the main consistency models. Several others have been proposed in the literature. A nice overview of the consistency models can be found in [Mosberger 1993]. It is difficult to grade the consistency models based on performance because quite different results are usually obtained for different applications. That is, one application may have good performance for one model, but another application may have good performance for some other model. Therefore, in the design of a DSM system, the choice of a consistency model usually depends on several other factors, such as how easy is it to implement, how close is its semantics to intuition, how much concurrency does it allow, and how easy is it to use (does it impose extra burden on the programmers).

Among the consistency models described above, strict consistency is never used in the design of a DSM system because its implementation is practically impossible. The most commonly used model in DSM systems is the sequential consistency model because it can be implemented, it supports the most intuitively expected semantics for memory coherence, and it does not impose any extra burden on the programmers. Another important reason for its popularity is that a sequentially consistent DSM system allows existing multiprocessor programs to be run on multicomputer architectures without modification. This is because programs written for multiprocessors normally assume that memory is sequentially consistent. However, it is very restrictive and hence suffers from the drawback of low concurrency. Therefore, several DSM systems are designed to use other consistency models that are weaker than sequential consistency.

Causal consistency, PRAM consistency, processor consistency, weak consistency, and release consistency are the main choices in the weaker category. The main problem with the use of causal consistency, PRAM consistency, and processor consistency models in the design of a DSM system is that they do not support the intuitively expected semantics for memory coherence because different processes may see different sequences of operations. Therefore, with these three models it becomes the responsibility of the programmers to avoid doing things that work only if the memory is sequentially consistent. In this respect, these models impose extra burden on the programmers.

Weak consistency and release consistency models, which use explicit synchronization variables, seem more promising for use in DSM design because they provide better concurrency and also support the intuitively expected semantics. The only problem with these consistency models is that they require the programmers to use the synchronization variables properly. This imposes some burden on the programmers.

Note that one of the main reasons for taking all the trouble to implement a DSM system is to support the shared-memory paradigm to make programming of distributed applications simpler than in the message-passing paradigm. Therefore, some DSM system designers are of the opinion that no extra burden should be imposed on the programmers. Designers having this view prefer to use the sequential consistency model.

### 5.6.1 Implementing Sequential Consistency Model

We saw above that the most commonly used consistency model in DSM systems is the sequential consistency model. Hence, a description of the commonly used protocols for implementing sequentially consistent DSM systems is presented below. A protocol for implementing a release-consistent DSM system will be presented in the next section.

Protocols for implementing the sequential consistency model in a DSM system depend to a great extent on whether the DSM system allows replication and/or migration of shared-memory data blocks. The designer of a DSM system may choose from among the following replication and migration strategies [Stumm and Zhou 1990]:

1. Nonreplicated, nonmigrating blocks (NRNMBs)
2. Nonreplicated, migrating blocks (NRMBs)
3. Replicated, migrating blocks (RMBs)
4. Replicated, nonmigrating blocks (RNMBs)

The protocols that may be used for each of these categories are described below. The data-locating mechanisms suitable for each category have also been described. Several of the ideas presented below were first proposed and used in the IVY system [Li 1988].

### Nonreplicated, Nonmigrating Blocks

This is the simplest strategy for implementing a sequentially consistent DSM system. In this strategy, each block of the shared memory has a single copy whose location is always fixed. All access requests to a block from any node are sent to the *owner node* of the block, which has the only copy of the block. On receiving a request from a client node, the memory management unit (MMU) and operating system software of the owner node perform the access request on the block and return a response to the client (Fig. 5.3).

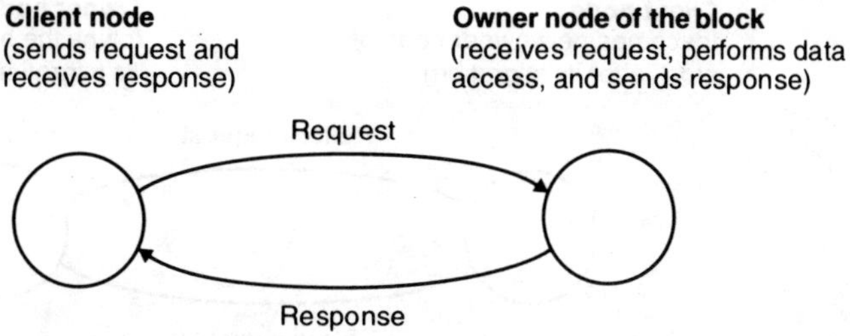


**Fig. 5.3** Nonreplicated, nonmigrating blocks (NRNMB) strategy.

Enforcing sequential consistency is trivial in this case because a node having a shared block can merely perform all the access requests (on the block) in the order it receives them.

Although the method is simple and easy to implement, it suffers from the following drawbacks:

- Serializing data access creates a bottleneck.
- Parallelism, which is a major advantage of DSM, is not possible with this method.

***Data Locating in the NRNMB Strategy.*** The NRNMB strategy has the following characteristics:

1. There is a single copy of each block in the entire system.
2. The location of a block never changes.

Based on these characteristics, the best approach for locating a block in this case is to use a simple mapping function to map a block to a node. When a fault occurs, the fault handler of the faulting node uses the mapping function to get the location of the accessed block and forwards the access request to that node.

### Nonreplicated, Migrating Blocks

In this strategy each block of the shared memory has a single copy in the entire system. However, each access to a block causes the block to migrate from its current node to the node from where it is accessed. Therefore, unlike the previous strategy in which the owner node of a block always remains fixed, in this strategy the owner node of a block changes as soon as the block is migrated to a new node (Fig. 5.4). When a block is migrated away, it is removed from any local address space it has been mapped into. Notice that in this strategy only the processes executing on one node can read or write a given data item at any one time. Therefore the method ensures sequential consistency.

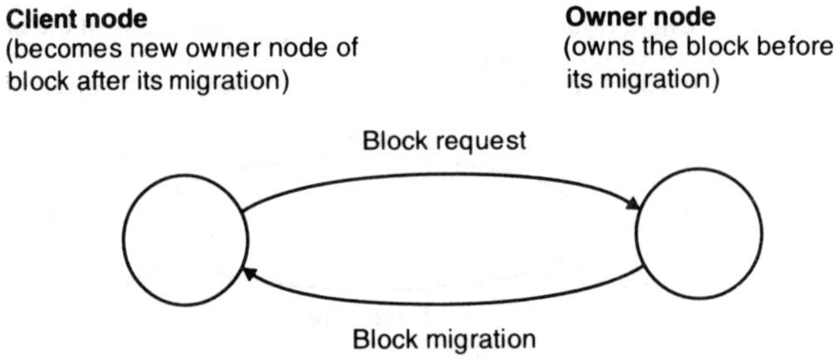


**Fig. 5.4** Nonreplicated, migrating blocks (NRMB) strategy.

The method has the following advantages [Stumm and Zhou 1990]:

1. No communication costs are incurred when a process accesses data currently held locally.
2. It allows the applications to take advantage of data access locality. If an application exhibits high locality of reference, the cost of data migration is amortized over multiple accesses.

However, the method suffers from the following drawbacks:

1. It is prone to thrashing problem. That is, a block may keep migrating frequently from one node to another, resulting in few memory accesses between migrations and thereby poor performance.
2. The advantage of parallelism cannot be availed in this method also.

***Data Locating in the NRMB Strategy.*** In the NRMB strategy, although there is a single copy of each block, the location of a block keeps changing dynamically. Therefore, one of the following methods may be used in this strategy to locate a block:

1. *Broadcasting*. In this method, each node maintains an *owned blocks table* that contains an entry for each block for which the node is the current owner (Fig. 5.5). When

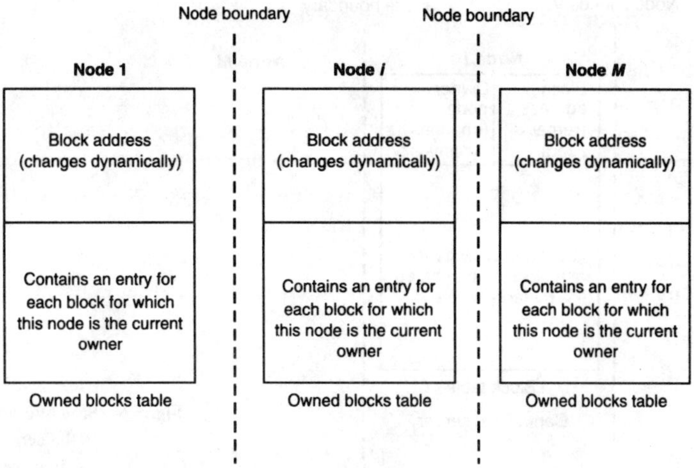


**Fig. 5.5** Structure and locations of owned blocks table in the broadcasting data-locating mechanism for NRMB strategy.

a fault occurs, the fault handler of the faulting node broadcasts a read/write request on the network. The node currently having the requested block then responds to the broadcast request by sending the block to the requesting node.

A major disadvantage of the broadcasting algorithm is that it does not scale well. When a request is broadcast, not just the node that has the requested block but all nodes must process the broadcast request. This makes the communication subsystem a potential bottleneck. The network latency of a broadcast may also require accesses to take a long time to complete.

2. *Centralized-server algorithm.* In this method, a centralized server maintains a block table that contains the location information for all blocks in the shared-memory space (Fig. 5.6). The location and identity of the centralized server is well known to all nodes.

When a fault occurs, the fault handler of the faulting node ($N$) sends a request for the accessed block to the centralized server. The centralized server extracts the location information of the requested block from the block table, forwards the request to that node, and changes the location information in the corresponding entry of the block table to node $N$. On receiving the request, the current owner transfers the block to node $N$, which becomes the new owner of the block.

The centralized-server method suffers from two drawbacks: (a) the centralized server serializes location queries, reducing parallelism, and (b) the failure of the centralized server will cause the DSM system to stop functioning.

3. *Fixed distributed-server algorithm.* The fixed distributed-server scheme is a direct extension of the centralized-server scheme. It overcomes the problems of the centralized-server scheme by distributing the role of the centralized server. Therefore, in this scheme, there is a block manager on several nodes, and each block manager is given a

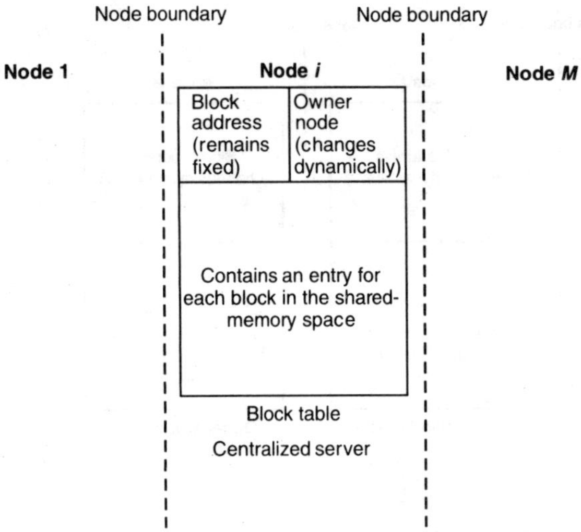


**Fig. 5.6** Structure and location of block table in the centralized-server data-locating mechanism for NRMB strategy.

predetermined subset of data blocks to manage (Fig. 5.7). The mapping from data blocks to block managers and their corresponding nodes is described by a mapping function. Whenever a fault occurs, the mapping function is used by the fault handler of the faulting node to find out the node whose block manager is managing the currently accessed block. Then a request for the block is sent to the block manager of that node. The block manager handles the request exactly in the same manner as that described for the centralized-server algorithm.

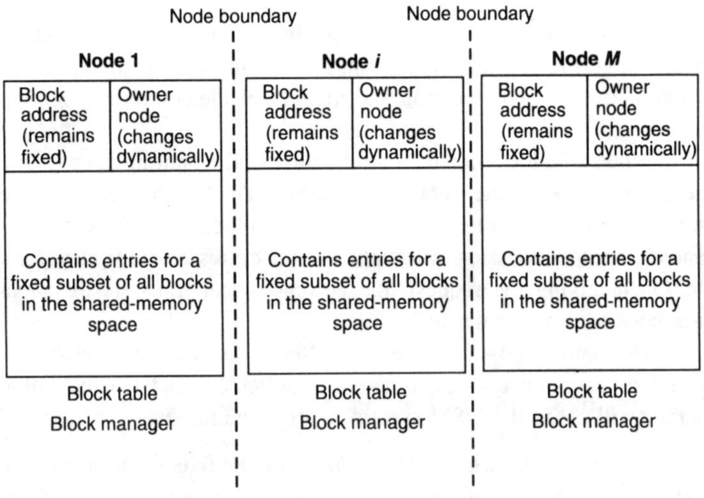


**Fig. 5.7** Structure and locations of block table in the fixed distributed-server data-locating mechanism for NRMB strategy.

4. *Dynamic distributed-server algorithm.* This scheme does not use any block manager and attempts to keep track of the ownership information of all blocks in each node. For this, each node has a block table that contains the ownership information for all blocks in the shared-memory space (Fig. 5.8). However, the information contained in the ownership field is not necessarily correct at all times, but if incorrect, it at least provides the beginning of a sequence of nodes to be traversed to reach the true owner node of a block. Therefore, this field gives the node a hint on the location of the owner of a block and hence is called the *probable owner.*

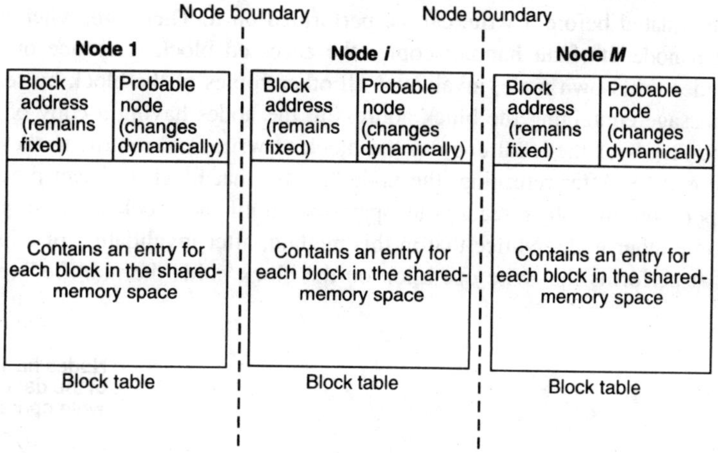


**Fig. 5.8** Structure and locations of block table in the dynamic distributed-server data-locating mechanism for NRMB strategy.

When a fault occurs, the faulting node (*N*) extracts from its local block table the node information stored in the probable owner field of the entry for the accessed block. It then sends a request for the block to that node. If that node is the true owner of the block, it transfers the block to node *N* and updates the location information of the block in its local block table to node *N*. Otherwise, it looks up its local block table, forwards the request to the node indicated in the probable-owner field of the entry for the block, and updates the value of this field to node *N*. When node *N* receives the block, it becomes the new owner of the block.

## Replicated, Migrating Blocks

A major disadvantage of the nonreplication strategies is lack of parallelism because only the processes on one node can access data contained in a block at any given time. To increase parallelism, virtually all DSM systems replicate blocks. With replicated blocks, read operations can be carried out in parallel at multiple nodes by accessing the local copy of the data. Therefore, the average cost of read operations is reduced because no communication overhead is involved if a replica of the data exists at the local node. However, replication tends to increase the cost of write operations because for a write to a block all its replicas must be invalidated or updated to maintain consistency. Nevertheless, if the read/write ratio is large, the extra expense for the write operations may be more than offset by the lower average cost of the read operations.

Replication complicates the memory coherence protocol due to the requirement of keeping multiple copies of a block consistent. The two basic protocols that may be used for ensuring sequential consistency in this case are as follows:

1. *Write-invalidate*. In this scheme, all copies of a piece of data except one are invalidated before a write can be performed on it. Therefore, when a write fault occurs at a node, its fault handler copies the accessed block from one of the block's current nodes to its own node, invalidates all other copies of the block by sending an invalidate message containing the block address to the nodes having a copy of the block, changes the access of the local copy of the block to write, and returns to the faulting instruction (Fig. 5.9). After returning, the node "owns" that block and can proceed with the write operation and other read/write operations until the block ownership is relinquished to some other node. Notice that in this method, after invalidation of a block, only the node that performs the write operation on the block holds the modified version of the block.

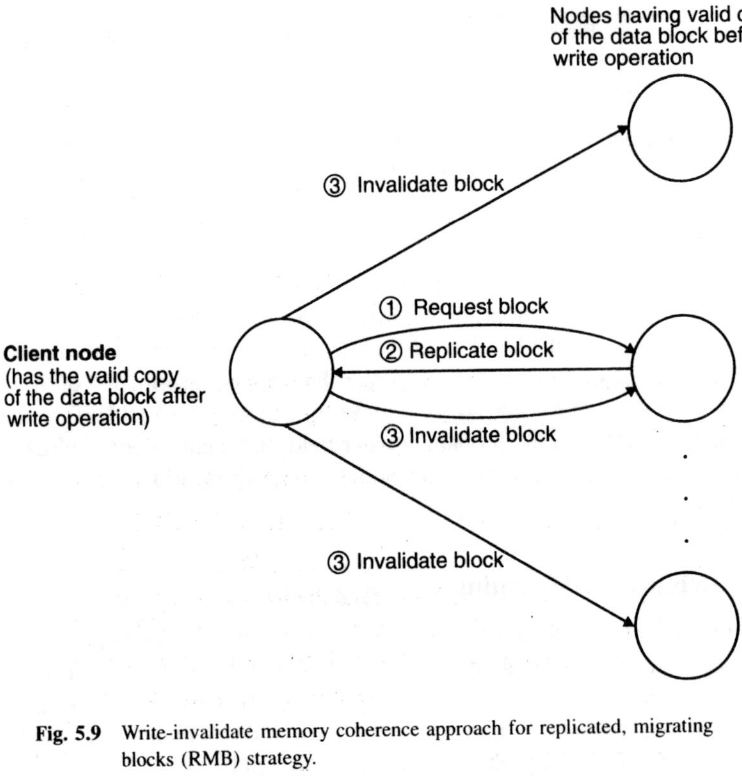


**Fig. 5.9** Write-invalidate memory coherence approach for replicated, migrating blocks (RMB) strategy.

If one of the nodes that had a copy of the block before invalidation tries to perform a memory access operation (read/write) on the block after invalidation, a cache miss will occur and the fault handler of that node will have to fetch the block again from a node having a valid copy of the block. Therefore the scheme achieves sequential consistency.

2. *Write-update*. In this scheme, a write operation is carried out by updating all copies of the data on which the write is performed. Therefore, when a write fault occurs at a node, the fault handler copies the accessed block from one of the block's current nodes to its own node, updates all copies of the block by performing the write operation on the local copy of the block and sending the address of the modified memory location and its new value to the nodes having a copy of the block, and then returns to the faulting instruction (Fig. 5.10). The write operation completes only after all the copies of the block have been successfully updated. Notice that in this method, after a write operation completes, all the nodes that had a copy of the block before the write also have a valid copy of the block after the write. In this method, sequential consistency can be achieved by using a mechanism to totally order the write operations of all the nodes so that all processes agree on the order of writes. One method to do this is to use a global sequencer to sequence the write operations of all nodes. In this method, the intended modification of each write operation is first sent to the global sequencer. The sequencer assigns the next

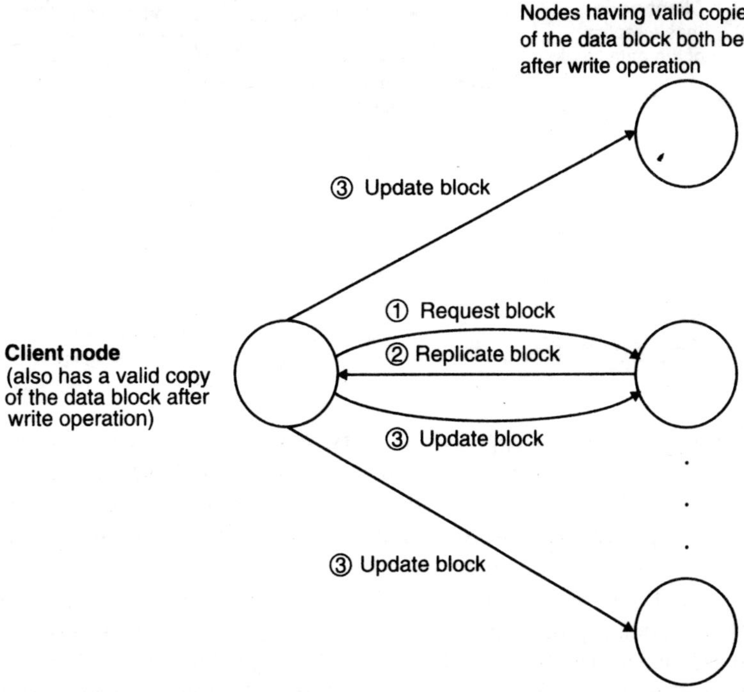


**Fig. 5.10** Write-update memory coherence approach for replicated, migrating blocks (RMB) strategy.

sequence number to the modification and multicasts the modification with this sequence number to all the nodes where a replica of the data block to be modified is located (Fig. 5.11). The write operations are processed at each node in sequence number order. That is, when a new modification arrives at a node, its sequence number is verified as the next expected one. If the verification fails, either a modification was missed or a modification was received out of order, in which case the node requests the sequencer for a retransmission of the missing modification. Obviously, a log of recent write requests must be maintained somewhere in this method. Note that the set of reads that take place between any two consecutive writes is well defined, and their ordering is immaterial to sequential consistency.

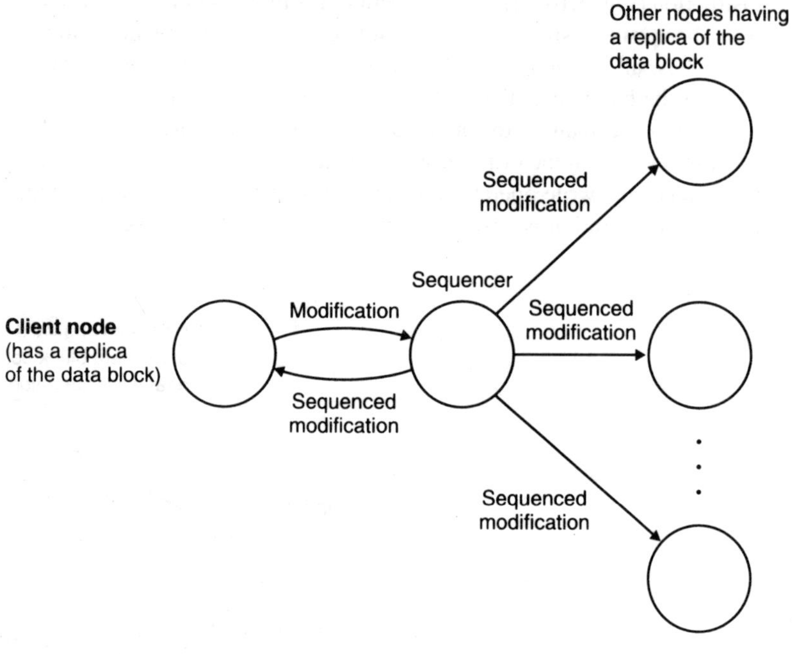


**Fig. 5.11** Global sequencing mechanism to sequence the write operations of all nodes.

The write-update approach is very expensive for use with loosely coupled distributed-memory systems because it requires a network access on every write operation and updates all copies of the modified block. On the other hand, in the write-invalidate approach, updates are only propagated when data are read, and several updates can take place (because many programs exhibit locality of reference) before communication is necessary. Therefore, most DSM systems use the write-invalidate protocol. In the basic implementation approach of the write-invalidate protocol, there is a status tag associated with each block. The status tag indicates whether the block is valid, whether it is shared, and whether it is read-only or writable. With this status information, read and write requests are carried out in the following manner [Nitzberg and Virginia Lo 1991]:

### Read Request

1. If there is a local block containing the data and if it is valid, the request is satisfied by accessing the local copy of the data.
2. Otherwise, the fault handler of the requesting node generates a read fault and obtains a copy of the block from a node having a valid copy of the block. If the block was writable on another node, this read request will cause it to become read-only. The read request is now satisfied by accessing the data from the local block, which remains valid until an invalidate request is received.

### Write Request

1. If there is a local block containing the data and if it is valid and writable, the request is immediately satisfied by accessing the local copy of the data.
2. Otherwise, the fault handler of the requesting node generates a write fault and obtains a valid copy of the block and changes its status to writable. A write fault for a block causes the invalidation of all other copies of the block. When the invalidation of all other copies of the block completes, the block is valid locally and writable, and the original write request may now be performed.

***Data Locating in the RMB Strategy.*** The following data-locating issues are involved in the write-invalidate protocol used with the RMB strategy:

1. Locating the owner of a block. An *owner* of a block is the node that owns the block, namely, the most recent node to have write access to it.
2. Keeping track of the nodes that currently have a valid copy of the block.

One of the following algorithms may be used to address these two issues:

1. *Broadcasting*. In this method, each node has an owned blocks table (Fig. 5.12). This table of a node has an entry for each block for which the node is the owner. Each entry of this table has a *copy-set* field that contains a list of nodes that currently have a valid copy of the corresponding block.

When a read fault occurs, the faulting node ($N$) sends a broadcast read request on the network to find the owner of the required block. The owner of the block responds by adding node $N$ to the block's copy-set field in its owned blocks table and sending a copy of the block to node $N$. Similarly, when a write fault occurs, the faulting node sends a broadcast write request on the network for the required block. On receiving this request, the owner of the block relinquishes its ownership to node $N$ and sends the block and its copy set to node $N$. When node $N$ receives the block and the copy set, it sends an invalidation message to all nodes in the copy set. Node $N$ now becomes the new owner of the block, and therefore an entry is made for the block in its local-owned blocks table. The copy-set field of the entry is initialized to indicate that there are no other copies of the block since all the copies were invalidated.

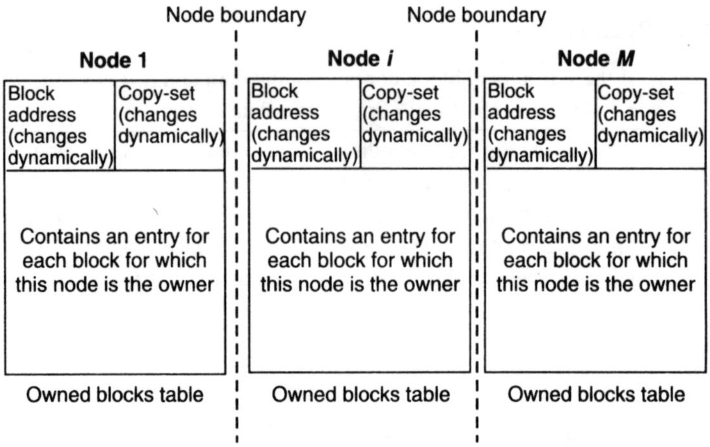


**Fig. 5.12** Structure and locations of owned blocks table in the broadcasting data-locating mechanism for RMB strategy.

The method of broadcasting suffers from the disadvantages mentioned during the description of the data-locating mechanisms for the NRMB strategy.

2. *Centralized-server algorithm.* This method is similar to the centralized-server algorithm of the NRMB strategy. However, in this case, each entry of the block table, managed by the centralized server, has an *owner-node* field that indicates the current owner node of the block and a *copy-set* field that contains a list of nodes having a valid copy of the block (Fig. 5.13).

When a read/write fault occurs, the faulting node ($N$) sends a read/write fault request for the accessed block to the centralized server. For a read fault, the centralized server adds node $N$ to the block's copy set and returns the owner node information to node $N$. On the other hand, for a write fault, it returns both the copy set and owner node information to node $N$ and then initializes the copy-set field to contain only node $N$. Node $N$ then sends a request for the block to the owner node. On receiving this request, the owner node returns a copy of the block to node $N$. In a write fault, node $N$ also sends an invalidate message to all nodes in the copy set. Node $N$ can then perform the read/write operation.

The disadvantages of the centralized-server algorithm have already been mentioned during description of the data-locating mechanisms for the NRMB strategy.

3. *Fixed distributed-server algorithm.* This scheme is a direct extension of the centralized-server scheme. In this scheme, the role of the centralized server is distributed to several distributed servers. Therefore, in this scheme, there is a block manager on several nodes (Fig. 5.14). Each block manager manages a predetermined subset of blocks, and a mapping function is used to map a block to a particular block manager and its corresponding node. When a fault occurs, the mapping function is used to find the location of the block manager that is managing the currently requested block. Then a request for

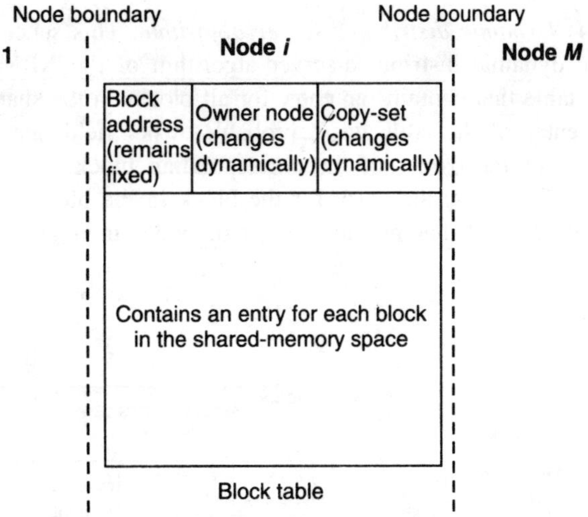


**Fig. 5.13** Structure and location of block table in the centralized-server data-locating mechanism for RMB strategy.

the accessed block is sent to the block manager of that node. A request is handled in exactly the same manner as that described for the centralized-server algorithm.

The advantages and limitations of the fixed distributed-server algorithm have already been mentioned during the description of the data-locating mechanisms for the NRMB strategy.

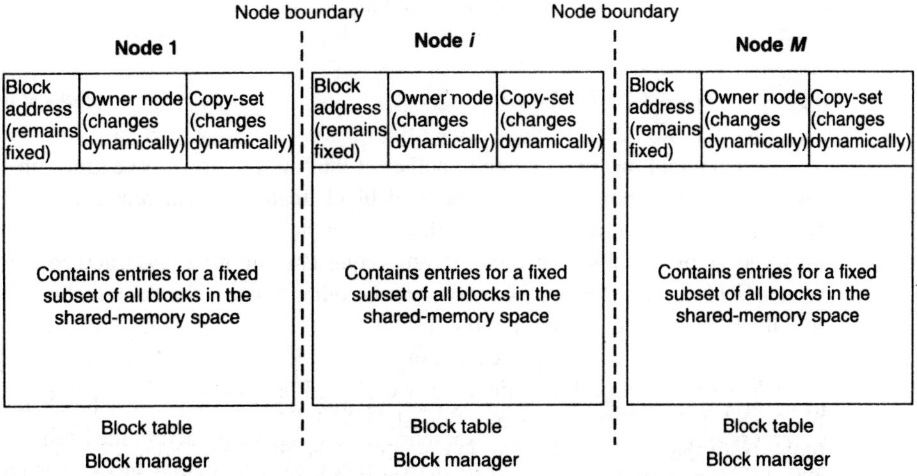


**Fig. 5.14** Structure and locations of block table in the fixed distributed-server data-locating mechanism for RMB strategy.

4. *Dynamic distributed-server algorithm.* This scheme works in a similar manner as the dynamic distributed-server algorithm of the NRMB strategy. Each node has a block table that contains an entry for all blocks in the shared-memory space (Fig. 5.15). Each entry of the table has a probable-owner field that gives the node a hint on the location of the owner of the corresponding block. In addition, if a node is the true owner of a block, the entry for the block in the block table of the node also contains a copy-set field that provides a list of nodes having a valid copy of the block.

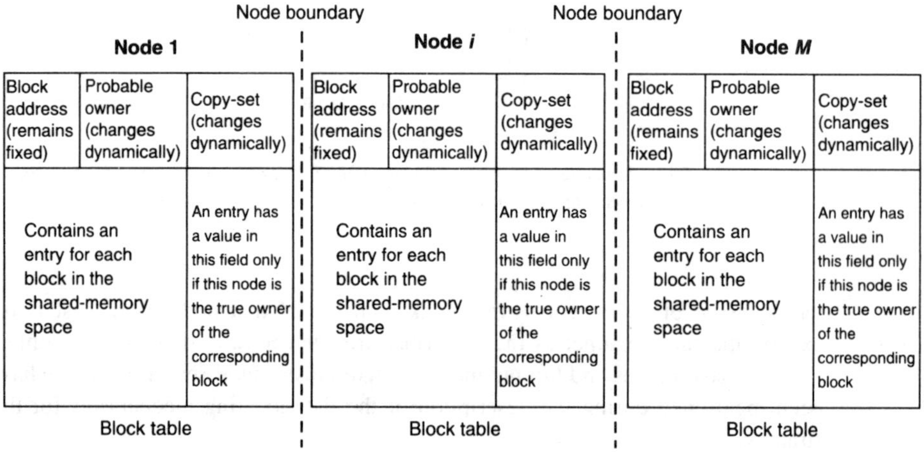


**Fig. 5.15** Structure and locations of block table in the dynamic distributed-server data-locating mechanism for RMB strategy.

When a fault occurs, the fault handler of the faulting node ($N$) extracts the probable-owner node information for the accessed block from its local block table and sends a request for the block to that node. If that node is not the true owner of the block, it looks up its local block table and forwards the request to the node indicated in the probable-owner field of the entry for the block. On the other hand, if the node is the true owner of the block, it proceeds with the request as follows. For a read fault, it adds node $N$ in the copy-set field of the entry corresponding to the block and sends a copy of the block to node $N$, which then performs the read operation. For a write fault, it sends a copy of the block and its copy-set information to node $N$ and deletes the copy-set information of that block from the local block table. On receiving the block and copy-set information, node $N$ sends an invalidation request to all nodes in the copy set. After this, it becomes the new owner of the block, updates its local block table, and proceeds with performing the write operation.

To reduce the length of the chain of nodes to be traversed to reach the true owner of a block, the probable-owner field of a block in a node's block table is updated as follows [Li and Hudak 1989]:

(a) Whenever the node receives an invalidation request

(b) Whenever the node relinquishes ownership, that is, on a write fault

(c) Whenever the node forwards a fault request

In the first two cases, the probable-owner field is changed to the new owner of the block. In the third case, the probable-owner field is changed to the original faulting node ($N$). This is because, if the request is for write, the faulting node ($N$) is going to be the new owner. If the request is for read, we know that after the request is satisfied, the faulting node ($N$) will have the correct ownership information. In either case, it is a good idea to change the probable-owner field of the block to node $N$.

It has been proved in [Li and Hudak 1989] that a fault on any node for a block eventually reaches the true owner of the block, and if there are altogether $M$ nodes, it will take at most $M - 1$ messages to locate the true owner of a block.

Some refinements of the data-locating algorithms described above may be found in [Li and Hudak 1989].

### Replicated, Nonmigrating Blocks

In this strategy, a shared-memory block may be replicated at multiple nodes of the system, but the location of each replica is fixed. A read or write access to a memory address is carried out by sending the access request to one of the nodes having a replica of the block containing the memory address. All replicas of a block are kept consistent by updating them all in case of a write access. A protocol similar to the write-update protocol is used for this purpose. Sequential consistency is ensured by using a global sequencer to sequence the write operations of all nodes (Fig. 5.11).

***Data Locating in the RNMB Strategy.*** The RNMB strategy has the following characteristics:

1. The replica locations of a block never change.
2. All replicas of a data block are kept consistent.
3. Only a read request can be directly sent to one of the nodes having a replica of the block containing the memory address on which the read request is performed and all write requests have to be first sent to the sequencer.

Based on these characteristics, the best approach of data locating for handling read/write operations in this case is to have a block table at each node and a sequence table with the sequencer (Fig. 5.16). The block table of a node has an entry for each block in the shared memory. Each entry maps a block to one of its replica locations. The sequence table also has an entry for each block in the shared-memory space. Each entry of the sequence table has three fields—a field containing the block address, a replica-

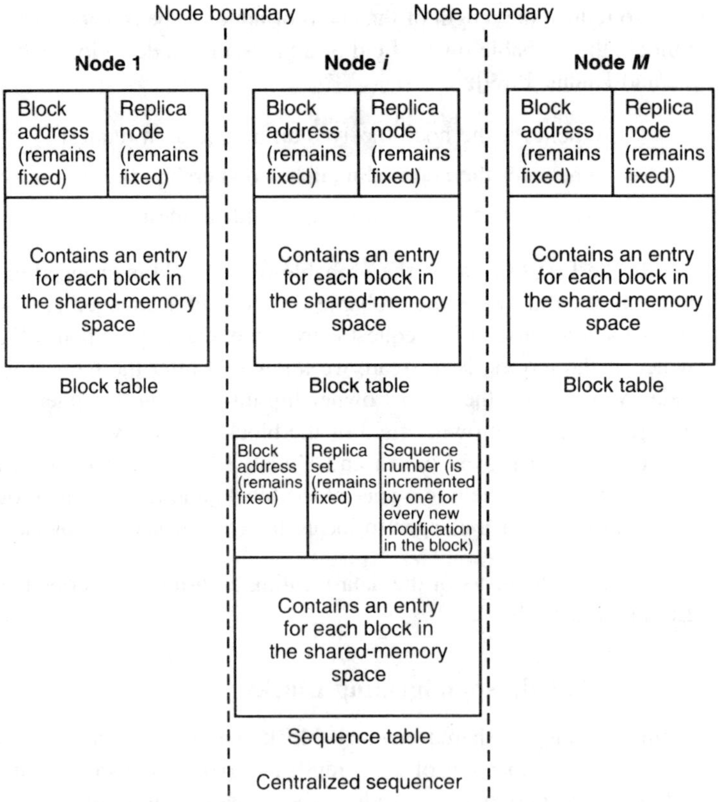


**Fig. 5.16** Structure and locations of block table and sequence table in the centralized sequencer data-locating mechanism for RNMB strategy.

set field containing a list of nodes having a replica of the block, and a sequence number field that is incremented by 1 for every new modification performed on the block.

For performing a read operation on a block, the replica location of the block is extracted from the local block table and the read request is directly sent to that node. A write operation on a block is sent to the sequencer. The sequencer assigns the next sequence number to the requested modification. It then multicasts the modification with this sequence number to all the nodes listed in the replica-set field of the entry for the block. The write operations are performed at each node in sequence number order.

Note that, to prevent all read operations on a block getting serviced at the same replica node, as far as practicable, the block table of different nodes should have different replica locations entered in the entry corresponding to the block. This will help in evenly distributing the read operations on the same block emerging from different nodes.

### 5.6.2 Munin: A Release Consistent DSM System

We saw in the discussion of consistency models that in addition to sequential consistency, release consistency is also promising and attractive for use in DSM systems. Therefore, as a case study of a release consistent DSM system, a description of the Munin system is presented below [Bennett et al. 1990, Carter et al. 1991, Carter et al. 1994].

#### Structure of Shared-Memory Space

The shared-memory space of Munin is structured as a collection of *shared variables* (includes program data structures). The shared variables are declared with the keyword *shared* so the compiler can recognize them. A programmer can annotate a shared variable with one of the standard annotation types (annotation types for shared variables are described later). Each shared variable, by default, is placed by the compiler on a separate page that is the unit of data transfer across the network by the MMU hardware. However, programmers can specify that multiple shared variables having the same annotation type be placed in the same page. Placing of variables of different annotation types in the same page is not allowed because the consistency protocol used for a page depends on the annotation type of variables contained in the page. Obviously, variables of size larger than the size of a page occupy multiple pages. The shared variables are declared with the keyword *shared* so the compiler can recognize them.

#### Implementation of Release Consistency

In the description of release consistency, we saw that for release consistency applications must be modeled around critical sections. Therefore a DSM system that supports release consistency must have mechanisms and programming language constructs for critical sections. Munin provides two such synchronization mechanisms—a locking mechanism and a barrier mechanism.

The locking mechanism uses *lock* synchronization variables with *acquireLock* and *releaseLock* primitives for accessing these variables. The *acquireLock* primitive with a lock variable as its parameter is executed by a process to enter a critical section, and the *releaseLock* primitive with the same lock variable as its parameter is executed by the process to exit from the critical section. To ensure release consistency, write operations on shared variables must be performed only within critical sections, but read operations on shared variables may be performed either within or outside a critical section. Modifications made to a shared variable within a critical section are sent to other nodes having a replica of the shared variable only when the process making the update exits from the critical section. If programs of an application are properly structured as described above, the DSM system will appear to be sequentially consistent.

When a process makes an *acquireLock* request for acquiring a lock variable, the system first checks if the lock variable is available on the local node. If not, the probable-owner mechanism is used to find the location of the current owner of the lock variable, and the request is sent to that node. Whether the lock is on the local or remote node, if it is free, it is granted to the requesting process. Otherwise, the requesting process is added to the end of the queue of processes waiting to acquire the lock variable. When the lock variable is released by its current owner, it is given to the next process in the waiting queue.

The barrier mechanism uses *barrier* synchronization variables with a *waitAtBarrier* primitive for accessing these variables. Barriers are implemented by using the centralized barrier server mechanism.

In a network page fault, the probable-owner-based dynamic distributed-server algorithm (already described during the description of RMB strategy) is used in Munin to locate a page containing the accessed shared variable. A mechanism similar to the copy-set mechanism (also described during the description of RMB strategy) is used to keep track of all the replica locations of a page.

### Annotations for Shared Variables

The release consistency of Munin allows applications to have better performance than in a sequentially consistent DSM system. For further performance improvement, Munin defines several standard annotations for shared variables and uses a different consistency protocol for each type that is most suitable for that type. That is, consistency protocols in this approach are applied at the granularity of individual data items. The standard annotations and the consistency protocol for variables of each type are as follows [Bennett et al. 1990]:

1. *Read-only.* Shared-data variables annotated as read-only are immutable data items. These variables are read but never written after initialization. Therefore, the question of consistency control does not arise. As these variables are never modified, their average read cost can be reduced drastically by freely replicating them on all nodes from where they are accessed. Therefore, when a reference to such a variable causes a network page fault, the page having the variable is copied to the faulting node from one of the nodes already having a copy of the page. Read-only variables are protected by the MMU hardware, and an attempt to write to such a variable causes a fatal error.

2. *Migratory.* Shared variables that are accessed in phases, where each phase corresponds to a series of accesses by a single process, may be annotated as migratory variables. The locking mechanism is used to keep migratory variables consistent. That is, migratory variables are protected by lock synchronization variables and are used within critical sections.

To access a migratory variable, a process first acquires a lock for the variable, uses the variable for some time, and then releases the lock when it has finished using it. At a time, the system allows only a single process to acquire a lock for a migratory variable. If a network page fault occurs when a process attempts to acquire a lock for a migratory variable, the page is migrated to the faulting node from the node that is its current owner. The NRMB strategy is used in this case. That is, pages migrate from one node to another on a demand basis, but pages are not replicated. Therefore, only one copy of a page containing a migratory variable exists in the system.

Migratory variables are handled efficiently by integrating their movement with that of the lock associated with them. That is, the lock and the variable are sent together in a single message to the location of the next process that is given the lock for accessing it.

3. *Write-shared.* A programmer may use this annotation with a shared variable to indicate to the system that the variable is updated concurrently by multiple processes, but the processes do not update the same parts of the variable. For example, in a matrix, different processes can concurrently update different row/column elements, with each process updating only the elements of one row/column. Munin avoids the false sharing problem of write-shared variables by allowing them to be concurrently updated by multiple processes.

A write-shared variable is replicated on all nodes where a process sharing is located. That is, when access to such a variable causes a network page fault to occur, the page having the variable is copied to the faulting node from one of its current nodes. If the access is a write access, the system first makes a copy of the page (called *twin page*) and then updates the original page. The process may perform several writes to the page before releasing it. When the page is released, the system performs a word-by-word comparison of the original page and the twin page and sends the differences to all nodes having a replica of the page.

When a node receives the differences of a modified page, the system checks if the local copy of the page was also modified. If not, the local copy of the page is updated by incorporating the received differences in it. On the other hand, if the local copy of the page was also modified, the local copy, its twin, and the received differences are compared word by word. If the same word has not been modified in both the local and remote copies of the page, the words of the original local page are updated by using the differences received from the remote node. On the other hand, if the comparison indicates that the same word was updated in both the local and remote copies of the page, a conflict occurs, resulting in a runtime error.

4. *Producer-consumer.* Shared variables that are written (produced) by only one process and read (consumed) by a fixed set of other processes may be annotated to be of producer-consumer type. Munin uses an "eager object movement" mechanism for this type of variable. In this mechanism, a variable is moved from the producer's node to the nodes of the consumers in advance of when they are required so that no network page fault occurs when a consumer accesses the variable. Moreover, the write-update protocol is used to update existing replicas of the variable whenever the producer updates the variable. If desired, the producer may send several updates together by using the locking mechanism. In this case, the procedure acquires a synchronization lock, makes several updates on the variable, and then releases the lock when the variable or the updates are sent to the nodes of consumer processes.

5. *Result.* Result variables are just the opposite of producer-consumer variables in the sense that they are written by multiple processes but read by only one process. Different processes write to different parts of the variable that do not conflict. The variable is read only when all its parts have been written. For example, in an application there may be different "worker" processes to generate and fill the elements of each row/column of a matrix, and once the matrix is complete, it may be used by a "master" process for further processing.

Munin uses a special write-update protocol for result variables in which updates are sent only to the node having the master process and not to all replica locations of the variable (each worker process node has a replica of the variable). Since writes to the variable by different processes do not conflict, all worker processes are allowed to perform write operations concurrently. Moreover, since result variables are not read until all parts have been written, a worker process releases the variable only when it has finished writing all parts that it is supposed to write, when all updates are sent together in a single message to the master process node.

6. *Reduction*. Shared variables that must be atomically modified may be annotated to be of reduction type. For example, in a parallel computation application, a global minimum must be atomically fetched and modified if it is greater than the local minimum. In Munin, a reduction variable is always modified by being locked (acquire lock), read, updated, and unlocked (release lock). For better performance, a reduction variable is stored at a fixed owner that receives updates to the variable from other processes, synchronizes the updates received from different processes, performs the updates on the variable, and propagates the updated variable to its replica locations.

7. *Conventional*. Shared variables that are not annotated as one of the above types are conventional variables. The already described release consistency protocol of Munin is used to maintain the consistency of replicated conventional variables. The write invalidation protocol is used in this case to ensure that no process ever reads a stale version of a conventional variable. The page containing a conventional variable is dynamically moved to the location of a process that wants to perform a write operation on the variable.

Experience with Munin has shown that read-only, migratory, and write-shared annotation types are very useful because variables of these types are frequently used, but producer-consumer, result, and reduction annotation types are of little use because variables of these types are less frequently used.

## 5.7 REPLACEMENT STRATEGY

In DSM systems that allow shared-memory blocks to be dynamically migrated/replicated, the following issues must be addressed when the available space for caching shared data fills up at a node:

1. Which block should be replaced to make space for a newly required block?
2. Where should the replaced block be placed?

### 5.7.1 Which Block to Replace

The problem of replacement has been studied extensively for paged main memories and shared-memory multiprocessor systems. The usual classification of replacement algorithms group them into the following categories [Smith 1982]:

1. *Usage based versus non-usage based.* Usage-based algorithms keep track of the history of usage of a cache line (or page) and use this information to make replacement decisions. That is, the reuse of a cache line normally improves the replacement status of that line. Least recently used (LRU) is an example of this type of algorithm. Conversely, non-usage-based algorithms do not take the record of use of cache lines into account when doing replacement. First in, first out (FIFO) and Rand (random or pseudorandom) belong to this class.

2. *Fixed space versus variable space.* Fixed-space algorithms assume that the cache size is fixed while variable-space algorithms are based on the assumption that the cache size can be changed dynamically depending on the need. Therefore, replacement in fixed-space algorithms simply involves the selection of a specific cache line. On the other hand, in a variable-space algorithm, a fetch does not imply a replacement, and a swap-out can take place without a corresponding fetch.

Variable-space algorithms are not suitable for a DSM system because each node's memory that acts as cache for the virtually shared memory is fixed in size. Moreover, as compared to non-usage-based algorithms, usage-based algorithms are more suitable for DSM systems because they allow to take advantage of the data access locality feature. However, unlike most caching systems, which use a simple LRU policy for replacement, most DSM systems differentiate the status of data items and use a priority mechanism. As an example, the replacement policy used by the DSM system of IVY [Li 1986, 1988] is presented here. In the DSM system of IVY, each memory block of a node is classified into one of the following five types:

1. *Unused.* A free memory block that is not currently being used.
2. *Nil.* A block that has been invalidated.
3. *Read-only.* A block for which the node has only read access right.
4. *Read-owned.* A block for which the node has only read access right but is also the owner of the block.
5. *Writable.* A block for which the node has write access permission. Obviously, the node is the owner of the block because IVY uses the write-invalidate protocol.

Based on this classification of blocks, the following replacement priority is used:

1. Both unused and nil blocks have the highest replacement priority. That is, they will be replaced first if a block is needed. It is obvious for an unused block to have the highest replacement priority. A nil block also has the same replacement priority because it is no longer useful and future access to the block would cause a network fault to occur. Notice that a nil block may be a recently referenced block, and this is exactly why a simple LRU policy is not adequate.

2. The read-only blocks have the next replacement priority. This is because a copy of a read-only block is available with its owner, and therefore it is possible to simply discard that block. When the node again requires that block in the future, the block has to be brought from its owner node at that time.

3. Read-owned and writable blocks for which replica(s) exist on some other node(s) have the next replacement priority because it is sufficient to pass ownership to one of the replica nodes. The block itself need not be sent, resulting in a smaller message.

4. Read-owned and writable blocks for which only this node has a copy have the lowest replacement priority because replacement of such a block involves transfer of the block's ownership as well as the block from the current node to some other node. An LRU policy is used to select a block for replacement when all the blocks in the local cache have the same priority.

### 5.7.2 Where to Place a Replaced Block

Once a memory block has been selected for replacement, it should be ensured that if there is some useful information in the block, it should not be lost. For example, simply discarding a block having unused, nil, or read-only status does not lead to any loss of data. Similarly, discarding a read-owned or a writable block for which replica(s) exist on some other node(s) is also harmless. However, discarding a read-owned or a writable block for which there is no replica on any other node may lead to loss of useful data. Therefore, care must be taken to store them somewhere before discarding. The two commonly used approaches for storing a useful block at the time of its replacement are as follows:

1. *Using secondary store.* In this method, the block is simply transferred on to a local disk. The advantage of this method is that it does not waste any memory space, and if the node wants to access the same block again, it can get the block locally without a need for network access.

2. *Using the memory space of other nodes.* Sometimes it may be faster to transfer a block over the network than to transfer it to a local disk. Therefore, another method for storing a useful block is to keep track of free memory space at all nodes in the system and to simply transfer the replaced block to the memory of a node with available space. This method requires each node to maintain a table of free memory space in all other nodes. This table may be updated by having each node piggyback its memory status information during normal traffic.

## 5.8 THRASHING

*Thrashing* is said to occur when the system spends a large amount of time transferring shared data blocks from one node to another, compared to the time spent doing the useful work of executing application processes. It is a serious performance problem with DSM systems that allow data blocks to migrate from one node to another. Thrashing may occur in the following situations:

1. When interleaved data accesses made by processes on two or more nodes causes a data block to move back and forth from one node to another in quick succession (a ping-pong effect)

2. When blocks with read-only permissions are repeatedly invalidated soon after they are replicated

Such situations indicate poor (node) locality in references. If not properly handled, thrashing degrades system performance considerably. Therefore, steps must be taken to solve this problem. The following methods may be used to solve the thrashing problem in DSM systems:

1. *Providing application-controlled locks.* Locking data to prevent other nodes from accessing that data for a short period of time can reduce thrashing. An application-controlled lock can be associated with each data block to implement this method.

2. *Nailing a block to a node for a minimum amount of time.* Another method to reduce thrashing is to disallow a block to be taken away from a node until a minimum amount of time *t* elapses after its allocation to that node. The time *t* can either be fixed statically or be tuned dynamically on the basis of access patterns. For example, Mirage [Fleisch and Popek 1989] employs this method to reduce thrashing and dynamically determines the minimum amount of time for which a block will be available at a node on the basis of access patterns.

The main drawback of this scheme is that it is very difficult to choose the appropriate value for the time *t*. If the value is fixed statically, it is liable to be inappropriate in many cases. For example, if a process accesses a block for writing to it only once, other processes will be prevented from accessing the block until time *t* elapses. On the other hand, if a process accesses a block for performing several write operations on it, time *t* may elapse before the process has finished using the block and the system may grant permission to another process for accessing the block. Therefore, tuning the value of *t* dynamically is the preferred approach. In this case, the value of *t* for a block can be decided based on past access patterns of the block. The MMU's reference bits may be used for this purpose. Another factor that may be used for deciding the value of *t* for a block is the length of the queue of processes waiting for their turn to access the block.

3. *Tailoring the coherence algorithm to the shared-data usage patterns.* Thrashing can also be minimized by using different coherence protocols for shared data having different characteristics. For example, the coherence protocol used in Munin for write-shared variables avoids the false sharing problem, which ultimately results in the avoidance of thrashing.

Notice from the description above that complete transparency of distributed shared memory is compromised somewhat while trying to minimize thrashing. This is because most of the approaches described above require the programmer's assistance. For example, in the method of application-controlled locks, the use of locks needs to be directed toward a particular shared-memory algorithm and hence the shared-memory abstraction can no longer be transparent. Moreover, the application must be aware of the shared data it is accessing and its shared access patterns. Similarly, Munin requires programmers to annotate shared variables with standard annotation types, which makes the shared-memory abstraction nontransparent.

## 5.9 OTHER APPROACHES TO DSM

Depending on the manner in which data caching (placement and migration of data) is managed, there are three main approaches for designing a DSM system:

1. Data caching managed by the operating system
2. Data caching managed by the MMU hardware
3. Data caching managed by the language runtime system

This being a book on operating systems, in this chapter we mainly concentrate on the first approach. Systems such as IVY [Li 1986] and Mirage [Fleish and Popek 1989] fall in this category. In these systems, each node has its own memory and access to a word in another node's memory, causes a trap to the operating system. The operating system then fetches and acquires the page containing the accessed word from the remote node's memory by exchanging messages with that machine. Therefore, in these systems, the placement and migration of data are handled by the operating system. For completion, the other two approaches of designing a DSM system are briefly described below.

The second approach is to manage caching by the MMU. This approach is used in multiprocessors having hardware caches. In these systems, the DSM implementation is done either entirely or mostly in hardware. For example, if the multiprocessors are interconnected by a single bus, their caches are kept consistent by snooping on the bus. In this case, the DSM is implemented entirely in hardware. The DEC Firefly workstation belongs to this category. On the other hand, if the multiprocessors are interconnected by switches, directories are normally used in addition to hardware caching to keep track of which CPUs have which cache blocks. Algorithms used to keep cached data consistent are stored mainly in MMU microcode. Therefore, in this case, the DSM is implemented mostly in hardware. Stanford's Dash [Lenoski et al. 1992] and MIT's Alewife [Agarwal et al. 1991, Kranz et al. 1993] systems belong to this category. Notice that in these systems, when a remote access is detected, a message is sent to the remote memory by the cache controller or MMU (not by the operating system software).

The third approach is to manage caching by the language runtime system. In these systems, the DSM is structured not as a raw linear memory of bytes from 0 to total size of the combined memory of all machines, but as a collection of programming language constructs, which may be shared variables and data structures (in conventional programming languages) or shared objects (in object-oriented programming languages). In these systems, the placement and migration of shared variables/objects are handled by the language runtime system in cooperation with the operating system. That is, when a variable/object is accessed by a process, it is the responsibility of the runtime system and the operating system to successfully perform the requested access operation on the variable/object independently of its current location. An advantage of this approach is that programming languages may be provided with features to allow programmers to specify the usage pattern of shared variables/objects for their applications, and the system can support several consistency protocols and use the one most suitable for a shared variable/object. Therefore, these systems can allow consistency protocols to be applied at the granularity of individual data items and can rely on weaker consistency models than sequential consistency model for better concurrency. However, a drawback of this approach is that it imposes extra burden on programmers. Munin [Bennett et al. 1990] and Midway [Bershad et al. 1993] are examples of systems that structure their DSM as a collection of shared variables and data structures. On the other hand, Orca [Bal et al. 1992] and Linda [Carriero and Gelernter 1989] are examples of systems that structure their DSM as a collection of shared objects.

## 5.10 HETEROGENEOUS DSM

Computers of different architectures normally have different characteristic features. For example, supercomputers and multiprocessors are good at compute-intensive applications while personal computers and workstations usually have good user interfaces. A heterogeneous computing environment allows the applications to exploit the best of all the characteristic features of several different types of computers. Therefore, heterogeneity is often desirable in distributed systems.

Heterogeneous DSM is a mechanism that provides the shared-memory paradigm in a heterogeneous environment and allows memory sharing among machines of different architectures. At first glance, sharing memory among machines of different architectures seems almost impossible. However, based on the measurements made on their experimental prototype heterogeneous DSM, called Mermaid, Zhou et al. [1990, 1992] have concluded that heterogeneous DSM is not only feasible but can also be comparable in performance to its homogeneous counterpart (at least for some applications). The two main issues in building a DSM system on a network of heterogeneous machines are data conversion and selection of block size. These issues are described below. The following description is based on the material presented in [Zhou et al. 1990, 1992].

### 5.10.1 Data Conversion

Machines of different architectures may use different byte orderings and floating-point representations. When data is transferred from a node of one type to a node of another type, it must be converted before it is accessed on the destination node. However, the unit of data transfer in a DSM system is normally a block. Therefore, when a block is migrated between two nodes of different types, the contents of the block must be converted. But the conversion itself has to be based on the types of data stored in the block. It is not possible for the DSM system to convert a block without knowing the type of application-level data contained in the block and the actual block layout. Therefore, it becomes necessary to take assistance from application programmers, who know the layout of the memory being used by their application programs. Two approaches proposed in the literature for data conversion in a heterogeneous DSM are described below.

### Structuring the DSM System as a Collection of Source Language Objects

In this method, the DSM system is structured as a collection of variables or objects in the source language so that the unit of data migration is an object instead of a block. A DSM compiler is used that adds conversion routines for translating variables/objects in the source language among various machine architectures. For each access to a shared-memory object from a remote node, a check is made by the DSM system if the machine of the node that holds the object and the requesting node are compatible. If not, a suitable conversion routine is used to translate the object before migrating it to the requesting node.

This method of data conversion is used in the Agora shared-memory system [Bisiani et al. 1987]. In Agora, each machine marks messages with a machine tag. A message contains an object being migrated from one node to another. Messages between identical or compatible machines do not require translation. When translation is necessary, the type of information associated with the destination context is used to do a one-pass translation of the object. Depending on the field tag and the machine requirements for data alignment, the translation process may involve such operations as field-by-field swapping of bytes, inserting/removing gaps where necessary, and shuffling of bits.

Structuring a DSM system as a collection of source language objects may be useful from the data conversion point of view but is generally not recommended due to performance reasons. This is because objects in conventional programming languages typically are scalars (single-memory words), arrays, and structures. None of these types is suitable as a shared entity of a DSM system. For each shared entity, access rights must be issued for every entity and the migration of an entity involves communication overhead. Therefore, the choice of scalar data types as a unit of sharing would make a system very inefficient. On the other hand, arrays may easily be too large to be treated as units of sharing and data migration. Large data objects lead to false sharing and thrashing, and their migration often requires fragmentation and reassembly operations to be carried out on them due to the limited packet size of transport protocols.

### Allowing Only One Type of Data in a Block

This mechanism is used in Mermaid [Zhou et al. 1990, 1992], which uses a page size as its block size. Therefore, a page can contain only one type of data. In Mermaid, the DSM page (block) table entry keeps additional information identifying the type of data maintained in that page and the amount of data allocated to the page. Whenever a page is moved between two machines of different architectures, a routine converts the data in the page to the appropriate format. Mermaid requires the application programmers to provide the conversion routine for each user-defined data type in the application. Mermaid designers pointed out that the cost of converting a page is small compared to the overall cost of page migration.

Zhou et al. [1990] identified the following limitations of this approach:

1. Allowing a page to contain data of only one type may lead to wastage of memory due to fragmentation, resulting in increased paging activity.

2. The mechanism requires that the compilers used on different types of machines must be compatible in the sense that in the compiler-generated code the size of each data type and the order of the fields within compound structures must be the same on each machine. If incompatible compilers are used for an application to generate code for two different machines such that the size of the application-level data structures differs for the two machines, the mapping between pages on the two machines would not be one to one. That is, it may not be possible for a structure to fit on a page in its entirety after the conversion or, conversely, some data from the following page may be needed in order to complete the conversion of the current page [Zhou et al. 1990]. This complicates the conversion process.

3. Another problem associated with this method is that entire pages are converted even though only a small portion may be accessed before it is transferred away. Sometimes this problem may be more severe in the first method, which converts an entire object. For example, a large array may occupy several pages of memory, and migration of this object would convert the data in all the occupied pages even when only the first few array elements may be accessed before the object is transferred away.

4. The mechanism is not fully transparent because it requires the users to provide the conversion routines for user-defined data types and a table specifying the mapping of data types to conversion routines. The transparency problem may be solved by automatically generating the conversion routines and the mapping table by using a preprocessor on the user program [Zhou et al. 1990].

Another serious problem associated with the data conversion issue in heterogeneous DSM systems is that of the accuracy of floating-point values in numerical applications. Since an application has no control over how often a data is migrated or converted, numerical accuracy of floating-point data may be lost if the data is converted several times and the results may become numerically questionable.

### 5.10.2 Block Size Selection

Recall that in a homogeneous DSM system the block size is usually the same size as a native virtual memory (VM) page, so that the MMU hardware can be used to trigger a DSM block fault. However, in a heterogeneous environment, the virtual memory page size may be different for machines of different types. Therefore, block size selection becomes a complicated task in such a situation. Zhou et al. [1990, 1992] proposed the use of one of the following algorithms for block size selection in a heterogeneous DSM system:

1. *Largest page size algorithm.* In this method, the DSM block size is taken as the largest VM page size of all machines. Since VM page sizes are normally powers of 2, multiple smaller VM pages fit exactly in one DSM block. If a page fault occurs on a node with a smaller page size, it will receive a block of multiple pages that includes the desired page. This algorithm suffers from the same false sharing and thrashing problems associated with large-sized blocks.

2. *Smallest page size algorithm.* In this method, the DSM block size is taken as the smallest VM page size of all machines. If a page fault occurs on a node with a larger page size, multiple blocks (whose total size is equal to the page size of the faulting node) are moved to satisfy the page fault. Although this algorithm reduces data contention, it suffers from the increased communication and block table management overheads associated with small-sized blocks.

3. *Intermediate page size algorithm.* To balance between the problems of large- and small-sized blocks, a heterogeneous DSM system may select to choose a block size somewhere in between the largest VM page size and the smallest VM page size of all machines.

## 5.11 ADVANTAGES OF DSM

Distributed Shared Memory is a high-level mechanism for interprocess communication in loosely coupled distributed systems. It is receiving increased attention because of the advantages it has over the message-passing mechanisms. These advantages are discussed below.

### 5.11.1 Simpler Abstraction

By now it is widely recognized that directly programming loosely coupled distributed-memory machines using message-passing models is tedious and error prone. The main reason is that the message-passing models force programmers to be conscious of data movement between processes at all times, since processes must explicitly use communication primitives and channels or ports. To alleviate this burden, RPC was introduced to provide a procedure call interface. However, even in RPC, since the procedure call is performed in an address space different from that of the caller's address space, it is difficult for the caller to pass context-related data or complex data structures; that is, parameters must be passed by value. In the message-passing model, the programming task is further complicated by the fact that data structures passed between processes in the form of messages must be packed and unpacked. The shared-memory programming paradigm shields the application programmers from many such low-level concerns. Therefore, the primary advantage of DSM is the simpler abstraction it provides to the application programmers of loosely coupled distributed-memory machines.

### 5.11.2 Better Portability of Distributed Application Programs

The access protocol used in case of DSM is consistent with the way sequential applications access data. This allows for a more natural transition from sequential to distributed applications. In principle, distributed application programs written for a shared-memory multiprocessor system can be executed on a distributed shared-memory system without change. Therefore, it is easier to port an existing distributed application program to a distributed-memory system with DSM facility than to a distributed-memory system without this facility.

### 5.11.3 Better Performance of Some Applications

The layer of software that provides DSM abstraction is implemented on top of a message-passing system and uses the services of the underlying message-passing communication system. Therefore, in principle, the performance of applications that use DSM is expected to be worse than if they use message-passing directly. However, this is not always true, and it has been found that some applications using DSM can even outperform their message-passing counterparts. This is possible for three reasons [Stumm and Zhou 1990]:

1. *Locality of data.* The computation model of DSM is to make the data more accessible by moving it around. DSM algorithms normally move data between nodes in large blocks. Therefore, in those applications that exhibit a reasonable degree of locality in their data accesses, communication overhead is amortized over multiple memory accesses. This ultimately results in reduced overall communication cost for such applications.

2. *On-demand data movement.* The computation model of DSM also facilitates on-demand movement of data as they are being accessed. On the other hand, there are several distributed applications that execute in phases, where each computation phase is preceded by a data-exchange phase. The time needed for the data-exchange phase is often dictated by the throughput of existing communication bottlenecks. Therefore, in such applications, the on-demand data movement facility provided by DSM eliminates the data-exchange phase, spreads the communication load over a longer period of time, and allows for a greater degree of concurrency.

3. *Larger memory space.* With DSM facility, the total memory size is the sum of the memory sizes of all the nodes in the system. Thus, paging and swapping activities, which involve disk access, are greatly reduced.

### 5.11.4 Flexible Communication Environment

The message-passing paradigm requires recipient identification and coexistence of the sender and receiver processes. That is, the sender process of a piece of data must know the names of its receiver processes (except in multicast communication), and the receivers of the data must exist at the time the data is sent and in a state that they can (or eventually can) receive the data. Otherwise, the data is undeliverable. In contrast, the shared-memory paradigm of DSM provides a more flexible communication environment in which the sender process need not specify the identity of the receiver processes of the data. It simply places the data in the shared memory and the receivers access it directly from the shared memory. Therefore, the coexistence of the sender and receiver processes is also not necessary in the shared-memory paradigm. In fact, the lifetime of the shared data is independent of the lifetime of any of its receiver processes.

### 5.11.5 Ease of Process Migration

Migration of a process from one node to another in a distributed system (described in Chapter 8) has been shown to be tedious and time consuming due to the requirement of transferring the migrant process's address space from its old node to its new node. However, the computation model of DSM provides the facility of on-demand migration of data between processors. This facility allows the migrant process to leave its address space on its old node at the time of migration and fetch the required pages from its new node on demand at the time of accessing. Hence in a distributed system with DSM facility, process migration is as simple as detaching the process control block (PCB) of the migrant process from the processor of the old node and attaching it to the ready queue of the new node's processor. A PCB is a data block or a record associated with each process that contains useful information such as process state, CPU registers, scheduling information, memory management information, I/O status information, and so on. This approach provides a very natural and efficient form of process migration between processors in a distributed system.

## 5.12 SUMMARY

Programming of applications for loosely coupled distributed-memory machines with the message-passing paradigm is a difficult and error-prone task. The Distributed Shared Memory (DSM) facility simplifies this programming task by providing a higher level abstraction that allows programmers to write programs with the shared-memory paradigm, which is consistent with the way sequential applications access data.

Important issues involved in the design and implementation of a DSM system are granularity of data sharing, structure of the shared-memory space, memory coherence and access synchronization, data location and access, replacement strategy, handling of thrashing, and heterogeneity.

Granularity refers to block size, which is the unit of data sharing and data transfer across the network. Both large- and small-sized blocks have their own advantages and limitations. Several DSM systems choose the virtual memory page size as block size so that the MMU hardware can be used to trigger a DSM block fault.

The structure of the shared-memory space of a DSM system defines the abstract view to be presented to application programmers of that system. The three commonly used methods for structuring the shared-memory space of a DSM system are no structuring, structuring by data type, and structuring as a database. The structure and granularity of a DSM system are closely related.

Memory coherence is an important issue in the design of a DSM system. It deals with the consistency of a data block lying in the main memories of two or more nodes of the system. Several consistency models have been proposed in the literature to handle this issue. The main ones described in this chapter are strict consistency, sequential consistency, causal consistency, PRAM consistency, processor consistency, weak consistency, and release consistency. Of these, sequential consistency and release consistency are appropriate for a large number of applications.

Protocols for implementing the sequential consistency model in a DSM system depend on the following four replication and migration strategies used by the DSM system:

1. Nonreplicated, nonmigrating blocks (NRNMBs)
2. Nonreplicated, migrating blocks (NRMBs)
3. Replicated, migrating blocks (RMBs)
4. Replicated, nonmigrating blocks (RNMBs)

Protocols for implementing sequential consistency for each of these strategies have been described in this chapter. The data-locating mechanisms suitable for each case have also been described. In addition, the Munin system has been presented as an example of a release consistent DSM system.

Replacement strategy deals with the selection of a block to be replaced when the available space for caching shared data fills up and the placement of a replaced block. The usual classifications of replacement algorithms are usage-based versus non-usage-based and fixed-space versus variable-space. DSM systems use fixed-space, usage-based replacement algorithms. At the time of its replacement, a useful block may be placed in either the secondary storage of the local node or the memory space of some other node.

Thrashing is a serious performance problem with DSM systems that allow data blocks to migrate from one node to another. Methods that may be used to solve the thrashing problem in DSM systems are providing application-controlled locks, nailing a block to a node for a minimum amount of time, and tailoring the coherence algorithm to the shared-data usage patterns.

Depending on the manner in which data caching is managed, there are three main approaches to designing a DSM system: data caching managed by the operating system, data caching managed by the MMU hardware, and data caching managed by the language runtime system.

Heterogeneous DSM is a mechanism that provides the shared-memory paradigm in a heterogeneous environment and allows memory sharing among machines with different architectures. The two main issues in building this facility are data conversion and selection of block size. Two approaches proposed in the literature for data conversion in a heterogenous DSM are structuring the DSM system as a collection of source language objects and allowing only one type of data in a DSM block. Three algorithms that may be used for block size selection in a heterogeneous DSM system are largest page size algorithm, smallest page size algorithm, and intermediate page size algorithm.

Research has shown that DSM systems are viable, and they have several advantages over the message-passing systems. However, they are still far from mature. Most existing DSM systems are very small experimental or prototype systems consisting of only a few nodes. The performance results to date are also preliminary and based on a small group of applications or a synthetic workload. Nevertheless, research has proved that DSM effectively supports parallel processing and promises to be a fruitful and exciting area of research for the coming decade.

## EXERCISES

5.1. The distributed shared-memory abstraction is implemented by using the services of the underlying message-passing communication system. Therefore, in principle, the performance of applications that use DSM is expected to be worse than if they use message passing directly. In spite of this fact, why do some distributed operating system designers support the DSM abstraction in their systems? Are there any applications that can have better performance in a system with DSM facility than in a system that has only message-passing facility? If yes, give the types of such applications. If no, explain why.

5.2. Discuss the relative advantages and disadvantages of using large block size and small block size in the design of a block-based DSM system. Why do most DSM system designers prefer to use the typical page size used in a conventional virtual-memory implementation as the block size of the DSM system?

5.3. It is often said that the structure of the shared-memory space and the granularity of data sharing in a DSM system are closely related. Explain why.

5.4. What is false sharing? When is it likely to occur? Can this problem lead to any other problem in a DSM system? Give reasons for your answer.

5.5. What should be done to minimize the false sharing problem? Can this problem be completely eliminated? What other problems may occur if one tries to completely eliminate the false sharing problem?

5.6. Discuss the relative advantages and disadvantages of using the NRNMB, NRMB, RMB, and RNMB strategies in the design of a DSM system.

5.7. Discuss the relative advantages and disadvantages of the various data-locating mechanisms that may be used in a DSM system that uses the NRMB strategy.

5.8. A sequentially consistent DSM system uses the RMB strategy. It employs the write-invalidate approach for updating data blocks and the centralized-server algorithm for locating the owner of a block and keeping track of the nodes that currently have a valid copy of the block. Write pseudocode for the implementation of the memory coherence scheme of this DSM system.

5.9. Why is a global sequencer needed in a sequentially consistent DSM system that employs the write-update protocol?

5.10. Most DSM systems in which caching is managed by the operating system use the write-invalidate scheme for consistency instead of the write-update scheme. Explain why.

5.11. Differentiate between weak consistency and release consistency. Which of the two will you prefer to use in the design of a DSM system? Give reasons for your answer.

5.12. A programmer is writing an application for a release-consistent DSM system. However the application needs sequential consistency to produce correct results. What precautions must the programmer take?

5.13. Differentiate between PRAM consistency and processor consistency.

5.14. Give the relative advantages and disadvantages of sequential and release consistency models.

5.15. What is causal consistency? Give an example of an application for which causal consistency is the most suitable consistency model.

5.16. Propose a suitable replacement algorithm for a DSM system whose shared-memory space is structured as objects. One of the goals in this case may be to minimize memory fragmentation.

5.17. Why does the simple LRU policy often used for replacing cache lines in a buffer cache not work well as a replacement policy for replacing blocks in a DSM system?

**5.18.** To handle the issue of where to place a replaced block, the DSM system of Memnet [Delp 1988] uses the concept of "home memory," in which each block has a home memory. When replacement of a block requires that the block be transferred to some other node's memory, the block is transferred to the node whose memory is the home memory for the block. What are the advantages and disadvantages of this approach as compared to the one presented in this chapter?

**5.19.** What are the main causes of thrashing in a DSM system? What are the commonly used methods to solve the trashing problem in a DSM system?

**5.20.** Complete transparency of a DSM system is compromised somewhat when a method is used to minimize thrashing. Therefore, the designer of a DSM system is of the opinion that instead of using a method to minimize thrashing, a method should be used by which the system automatically detects and resolves this problem. Propose a method by which the system can detect thrashing and a method to resolve it once it has been detected.

**5.21.** A distributed system has DSM facility. The process-scheduling mechanism of this system selects another process to run when a fault occurs for the currently running process, and the CPU is utilized while the block is being fetched. Two system engineers arguing about how to better utilize the CPUs of this system have the following opinions:

(a) The first one says that if a large number of processes are scheduled for execution at a node, the available memory space of the node can be distributed among these processes so that almost always there will be a ready process to run when a page fault occurs. Thus, CPU utilization can be kept high.

(b) The second one says that if only a few processes are scheduled for execution at a node, the available memory space of the node can be allocated to each of the few processes, and each process will produce fewer page faults. Thus, CPU utilization can be kept high.

Whose argument is correct? Give reasons for your answer.

**5.22.** What are the three main approaches for designing a DSM system?

**5.23.** What are some of the issues involved in building a DSM system on a network of heterogeneous machines? Suggest suitable methods for handling these issues.

**5.24.** Are DSM systems suitable for both LAN and WAN environments? Give reasons for your answer.

**5.25.** Suggest some programming practices that will reduce network block faults in a DSM system.

**5.26.** Write pseudocode descriptions for handling a block fault in each of the following types of DSM systems:

(a) A DSM system that uses the NRNMB strategy
(b) A DSM system that uses the NRMB strategy
(c) A DSM system that uses the RMB strategy
(d) A DSM system that uses the RNMB strategy

You can make any assumptions that you feel necessary, but state the assumptions made.

## BIBLIOGRAPHY

**[Adve and Hill 1990]** Adve, S., and Hill, M., "Weak Ordering: A New Definition," In: *Proceedings of the 17th International Symposium on Computer Architecture*, Association for Computing Machinery, New York, NY, pp. 2–14 (1990).

**[Agarwal et al. 1991]** Agarwal, A., Chaiken, D., D'Souza, G., Johnson, K., Kranz, D., Kubiatowicz, J., Kurihara, K., Lim, B., Maa, G., Nussbaum, D., Parkin, M., and Yeung, D., "The MIT Alewife Machine: A Large-Scale Distributed Memory Multiprocessor," In: *Proceedings of the Workshop on Scalable Shared Memory Multiprocessors*, Kluwer Academic, Norwell, MA (1991).

**[Bal 1991]** Bal, H. E., *Programming Distributed Systems*, Prentice-Hall, London, England (1991).

**[Bal et al. 1992]** Bal, H. E., Kaashoek, M. F., and Tanenbaum, A. S., "Orca: A Language for Parallel Programming of Distributed Systems," *IEEE Transactions on Software Engineering*, Vol. SE-18, pp. 190–205 (1992).

**[Baldoni et al. 1995]** Baldoni, R., Mostefaoui, A., and Raynal, M., "Efficient Causally Ordered Communications for Multimedia Real Time Applications," In: *Proceedings of the 4th International Symposium on High Performance Distributed Computing*, IEEE, New York (1995).

**[Bennett et al. 1990]** Bennett, J., Carter, J., and Zwaenepoel, W., "Munin: Distributed Shared Memory Based on Type-Specific Memory Coherence," In: *Proceedings of the 1990 Conference on Principles and Practice of Parallel Programming*, Association for Computing Machinery, New York, pp. 168–176 (1990).

**[Bershad et al. 1993]** Bershad, B. N., Zekauskas, M. J., and Sawdon, W. A., "The Midway Distributed Shared Memory System," In: *Proceedings of the IEEE COMPCON Conference*, IEEE, New York, pp. 528–537 (1993).

**[Bisiani and Ravishankar 1990]** Bisiani, R., and Ravishankar, M., "Plus: A Distributed Shared-Memory System," In: *Proceedings of the 17th International Symposium on Computer Architecture*, Association for Computing Machinery, New York, NY, pp. 115–124 (1990).

**[Bisiani et al. 1987]** Bisiani, R., Alleva, F., Correrini, F., Forin, A., Lecouat, F., and Lerner, R., "Heterogeneous Parallel Processing: The Agora Shared Memory," Technical Report No. CMU-CS-87-112, Computer Science Department, Carnegie-Mellon University (March 1987).

**[Bisiani et al. 1989]** Bisiani, R., Nowatzyk, A., and Ravishankar, M., "Coherent Shared Memory on a Distributed Memory Machine," In: *Proceedings of the International Conference on Parallel Processing*, IEEE, New York, pp. 133–141 (August 1989).

**[Campine et al. 1990]** Campine, G. A., Geer, Jr., D. E, and Ruh, W. N., "Project Athena as a Distributed Computer System," *IEEE Computer*, Vol. 23, pp. 40–51 (1990).

**[Carriero and Gelernter 1989]** Carriero, N., and Gelernter, D., "Linda in Context," *Communications of the ACM*, Vol. 32, No. 4, pp. 444–458 (1989).

**[Carriero et al. 1986]** Carriero, N., Gelernter, D., and Leichter, J., "Distributed Data Structures in Linda," In: *Proceedings of the ACM Symposium on Principles of Programming Languages*, Association for Computing Machinery, New York (1986).

**[Carter et al. 1991]** Carter, J. B., Bennett, J. K., and Zwaenepoel, W., "Implementation and Performance of Munin," In: *Proceedings of the 13th Symposium on Operating Systems Principles*, Association for Computing Machinery, New York, NY, pp. 152–164 (1991).

**[Carter et al. 1994]** Carter, J. B., Bennett, J. K., and Zwaenepoel, W., "Techniques for Reducing Consistency-Related Communication in Distributed Shared Memory Systems," *ACM Transactions on Computer Systems*, Vol. 12 (1994).

**[Chase et al. 1989]** Chase, J. S., Amador, F. G., Lazowska, E. D., Levy, H. M., and Littlefield, R. J., "The Amber System: Parallel Programming on a Network of Multiprocessors," In: *Proceedings of the 12th Symposium on Operating Systems Principles*, Association for Computing Machinery, New York, NY, pp. 147–158 (1989).

**[Cheong and Veidenbaum 1988]** Cheong, H., and Veidenbaum, A. V., "A Cache Coherence Scheme with Fast Selective Invalidation," In: *Proceedings of the 15th International Symposium on Computer Architecture*, Association for Computing Machinery, New York, NY, pp. 299–307 (1988).

**[Cheriton 1986]** Cheriton, D. R., "Problem-Oriented Shared Memory: A Decentralized Approach to Distributed System Design," In: *Proceedings of the 6th International Conference on Distributed Computing Systems*, IEEE, New York, pp. 190–197 (May 1986).

**[Cheriton et al. 1991]** Cheriton, D. R., Goosen, H. A., and Boyle, P. D., "Paradigm: A Highly Scalable Shared-Memory Multicomputer Architecture," *IEEE Computer*, Vol. 24, No. 2, pp. 33–46 (1991).

**[Cox and Fowler 1989]** Cox, A. L., and Fowler, R. J., "The Implementation of a Coherent Memory Abstraction on a NUMA Multiprocessor: Experiences with PLATINUM," In: *Proceedings of the 12th Symposium on Operating Systems Principles*, Association for Computing Machinery, New York, NY, pp. 32–34 (December 1989).

**[Dasgupta et al. 1991]** Dasgupta, P., LeBlanc, R. J., Ahmad, Jr., M., and Ramachandran, U., "The Clouds Distributed Operating System," *IEEE Computer*, Vol. 24, No. 11, pp. 34–44 (1991).

**[Delp 1988]** Delp, G. S., "The Architecture and Implementation of MemNet: An Experiment on High-Speed Memory Mapped Network Interface," Ph.D. Dissertation, Department of Computer Science, University of Delaware (1988).

**[Delp et al. 1991]** Delp, G. S., Farber, D. J., Minnich, R. G., Smith, J. M., and Tam, M. C., "Memory as a Network Abstraction," *IEEE Network*, Vol. 5, pp. 34–41 (1991).

**[Dubois et al. 1986]** Dubois, M., Scheurich, C., and Briggs, F. A., "Memory Access Buffering in Multiprocessors," In: *Proceedings of the 13th Annual Symposium on Computer Architecture*, Association for Computing Machinery, New York, NY, pp. 343–442 (1986).

**[Dubois et al. 1988]** Dubois, M., Scheurich, C., and Briggs, F. A.,"Synchronization, Coherence, and Event Ordering in Multiprocessors," *IEEE Computer*, Vol. 21, No. 2, pp. 9–21 (1988).

**[Fekete et al. 1995]** Fekete, A, Kaashoek, F., and Lynch, N., "Providing Sequentially-Consistent Shared Objects Using Group and Point-to-Point Communication," In: *Proceedings of the 15th International Conference on Distributed Computing Systems*, IEEE, New York (May-June 1995).

**[Fleisch 1987]** Fleisch, B. D., "Distributed Shared Memory in a Loosely Coupled Distributed System," In: *Proceedings of the 1987 ACM SIGCOMM Workshop*, Association for Computing Machinery, New York, NY (1987).

**[Fleisch and Popek 1989]** Fleisch, B. D., and Popek, G. J., "Mirage: A Coherent Distributed Shared Memory Design," In: *Proceedings of the 12th ACM Symposium on Operating System Principles*, Association for Computing Machinery, New York, NY, pp. 211–223 (December 1989).

**[Forin et al. 1989]** Forin, A., Barrera, J., Young, M., and Rashid, R.,"Design, Implementation, and Performance Evaluation of a Distributed Shared Memory Server for Mach," In: *Proceedings of the 1989 Winter Usenix Conference* (January 1989).

**[Frank 1984]** Frank, S. J., "Tightly Coupled Multiprocessor System Speeds Memory-Access Times," *Electronics*, pp. 164–169 (January 1984).

**[Garcia Molina and Wiederhold 1982]** Garcia-Molina, H., and Wiederhold, G., "Read-Only Transactions in a Distributed Database," *ACM Transactions on Database Systems*, Vol. 7, No. 2, Association for Computing Machinery, New York, NY, pp. 209–234 (1982).

**[Gharachorloo et al. 1990]** Gharachorloo, K., Lenoski, D., Laudon, J., Gibbons, P., Gupta, A., and Hennessy, J., "Memory Consistency and Event Ordering in Scalable Shared-Memory Multiprocessors," In: *Proceedings of the 17th Annual Symposium on Computer Architecture*, Association for Computing Machinery, New York, NY, pp. 15–26 (1990).

**[Gharachorloo et al. 1991]** Gharachorloo, K., Gupta, A., and Hennessy, J., "Performance Evaluation of Memory Consistency Models for Shared-Memory Multiprocessors," In: *Proceedings of the 4th International Conference on Architectural Support for Programming Languages and Operating Systems*, IEEE Computer Society Press, Los Alamitos, CA, pp. 245–257 (1991).

**[Ghose 1995]** Ghose, K., "SNOW: Hardware Supported Distributed Shared Memory over a Network of Workstations," In: *Proceedings of the 24th Annual International Conference on Parallel Processing*, IEEE, New York (August 1995).

**[Goodman 1983]** Goodman, J. R., "Using Cache Memory to Reduce Processor-Memory Traffic," In: *Proceedings of the 10th Annual Symposium on Computer Architecture*, Association for Computing Machinery, New York, NY, pp. 124–131 (June 1983).

**[Goodman 1989]** Goodman, J. R., "Cache Consistency and Sequential Consistency," Technical Report No. 61, IEEE Scalable Coherent Interface Working Group, IEEE, New York (1989).

**[Goodman et al. 1989]** Goodman, J. R., Vernon, M. K., and Woest, P. J., "Efficient Synchronization Primitives for Large-Scale Cache-Coherent Multiprocessors," In: *Proceedings of the 3rd International Conference on Architectural Support for Programming Languages and Operating Systems*, IEEE Computer Society Press, Los Alamitos, CA, pp. 64–73 (1989).

**[Harty and Cheriton 1992]** Harty, K., and Cheriton, D., "Application-Controlled Physical Memory Using External Page-Cache Management," In: *Proceedings of the 5th International Conference on Architectural Support for Programming Languages and Operating Systems*, Association for Computing Machinery, New York, NY, pp. 187–199 (1992).

**[Hutto and Ahamad 1990]** Hutto, P. W., and Ahamad, M., "Slow Memory: Weakening Consistency to Enhance Concurrency in Distributed Shared Memories," In: *Proceedings of the 10th International Conference on Distributed Computing Systems*, IEEE, New York, pp. 302–311 (1990).

**[Johnson et al. 1995]** Johnson, D., Lilja, D., and Riedl, J., "A Circulating Active Barrier Synchronization Mechanism," In: *Proceedings of the 24th Annual International Conference on Parallel Processing*, IEEE, New York (August 1995).

**[Katz et al. 1985]** Katz, R. H., Eggers, S. J., Wood, D. A., Perkins, C. L., and Sheldon, R. G., "Implementing a Cache Consistency Protocol," In: *Proceedings of the 12th Annual Symposium on Computer Architecture*, Association for Computing Machinery, New York, NY, pp. 276–283 (June 1985).

**[Keleher et al. 1992]** Keleher, P., Cox, A. L., and Zwaenepoel, W., "Lazy Release Consistency," In: *Proceedings of the 19th International Symposium on Computer Architecture*, Association for Computing Machinery, New York, NY, pp. 13–21 (1992).

**[Kessler and Livny 1989]** Kessler, R. E., and Livny, M., "An Analysis of Distributed Shared Memory Algorithms," In: *Proceedings of the 9th International Conference on Distributed Computing Systems*, IEEE, New York, pp. 98–104 (June 1989).

**[Kranz et al. 1993]** Kranz, D., Johnson, K., Agarwal, A., Kubiatowicz, J. J., and Lim, B., "Integrating Message Passing and Shared Memory: Early Experiences," In: *Proceedings of the 4th Symposium on Principles and Practice of Parallel Programming*, Association for Computing Machinery, New York, NY, pp. 54–63 (May 1993).

**[Lamport 1979]** Lamport, L., "How to Make a Multiprocessor Computer That Correctly Executes Multiprocess Programs," *IEEE Transactions on Computers*, Vol. C-28, IEEE, New York, pp. 690–691 (1979).

**[Lenoski and Weber 1995]** Lenoski, D. E., and Weber, W. D., *Scalable Shared-Memory Multiprocessing*, Morgan Kaufmann, San Francisco, CA (1995).

**[Lenoski et al. 1992]** Lenoski, D., Laudon, J., Gharachorloo, K., Weber, W. D., Gupta, A., Hennessy, J., Horowitz, M., and Lam, M. S., "The Stanford Dash Multiprocessor," *IEEE Computer*, Vol. 25, No. 3, pp. 63–79 (1992).

**[Lenoski et al. 1993]** Lenoski, D., Laudon, J., Joe, T., Nakahira, D., Steves, L., Gupta, A., and Hennessy, J., "The DASH Prototype: Logic Overhead and Performance," *IEEE Transactions on Parallel and Distributed Systems*, Vol. 4, No. 1, pp. 41–61 (1993).

**[Li 1986]** Li, K., "Shared Virtual Memory on Loosely Coupled Multiprocessors," Ph.D. Dissertation, Technical Report No. YALE/DCS/RR-492, Department of Computer Science, Yale University (September 1986).

**[Li 1988]** Li, K., "IVY: A Shared Virtual Memory System for Parallel Computing," In: *Proceedings of the International Conference on Parallel Processing*, IEEE, New York, pp. 94–101 (August 1988).

**[Li and Hudak 1989]** Li, K., and Hudak, P., "Memory Coherence in Shared Virtual Memory Systems," *ACM Transactions on Computing Systems*, Vol. 7, No. 4, pp. 321–359 (1989).

**[Li and Schaefer 1989]** Li, K., and Schaefer, R.,"A Hypercube Shared Virtual Memory System," In: *Proceedings of the International Conference on Parallel Processing*, Pennsylvania State University Press, pp. 125–132 (1989).

**[Lilja 1993]** Lilja, D. J., "Cache Coherence in Large-Scale Shared-Memory Multiprocessors: Issues and Comparisons," *ACM Computing Surveys*, Vol. 25, pp. 303–338 (1993).

**[Lipton and Sandberg 1988]** Lipton, R. J., and Sandberg, J. S., "Pram: A Scalable Shared Memory," Technical Report No. CS-TR-180–88, Princeton University (1988).

**[Liskov 1988]** Liskov, B., "Distributed Programming in Argus," *Communications of the ACM*, Vol. 31, No. 3, pp. 300–313 (1988).

**[Minnich and Farber 1989]** Minnich, R. G., and Farber, D. J., "The Mether System: A Distributed Shared Memory for SunOS 4.0," In: *Proceedings of the 1989 Summer Usenix Conference*, pp. 51–60 (1989).

**[Minnich and Farber 1990]** Minnich, R. G., and Farber, D. J., "Reducing Host Load, Network Load, and Latency in a Distributed Shared Memory," In: *Proceedings of the 10th International Conference on Distributed Computing Systems*, IEEE, New York (June 1990).

**[Mosberger 1993]** Mosberger, D., "Memory Consistency Models," Technical Report No. TR 93/11, Department of Computer Science, University of Arizona (1993).

**[Nitzberg and Virginia Lo 1991]** Nitzberg, N., and Virginia Lo, "Distributed Shared Memory: A Survey of Issues and Algorithms," *IEEE Computer*, Vol. 24, No. 11, pp. 52–60 (1991).

**[Oguchi et al. 1995]** Oguchi, M., Aida, H., and Saito, T., "A Proposal for a DSM Architecture Suitable for a Widely Distributed Environment and Its Evaluation," In: *Proceedings of the 4th International Symposium on High Performance Distributed Computing*, IEEE, New York (August 1995).

**[Ramachandran and Khalidi 1989]** Ramachandran, U., and Khalidi, M.Y. A., "An Implementation of Distributed Shared Memory," *First Workshop on Experiences with Building Distributed and Multiprocessor Systems*, Usenix Association, Berkeley, CA, pp. 21–38 (1989).

**[Sane et al. 1990]** Sane, A., MacGregor, K., and Campbell, R., "Distributed Virtual Memory Consistency Protocols: Design and Performance," *Second IEEE Workshop on Experimental Distributed Systems*, IEEE, New York, pp. 91–96 (October 1990).

**[Scheurich and Dubois 1988]** Scheurich, C., and Dubois, M., "Dynamic Page Migration in Multiprocessors with Distributed Global Memory," In: *Proceedings of the 8th International Conference on Distributed Computing Systems*, IEEE Computer Society Press, Los Alamitos, CA, pp. 162–169 (June 1988).

**[Shrivastava et al. 1991]** Shrivastava, S., Dixon, G. N., and Parrington, G. D., "An Overview of the Arjuna Distributed Programming System," *IEEE Software*, pp. 66–73 (January 1991).

**[Singhal and Shivaratri 1994]** Singhal, M., and Shivaratri, N. G., *Advanced Concepts in Operating Systems*, McGraw Hill, New York (1994).

**[Sinha et al. 1991]** Sinha, P. K., Ashihara, H., Shimizu, K., and Maekawa, M., "Flexible User-Definable Memory Coherence Scheme in Distributed Shared Memory of GALAXY," In: *Proceedings of the 2nd European Distributed Memory Computing Conference (EDMCC2)*, Springer-Verlag, New York, pp. 52–61 (April 1991).

**[Smith 1982]** Smith, A. J., "Cache Memories," *ACM Computing Surveys*, Vol. 14, No. 3, pp. 437–530, New York, NY (1982).

**[Stumm and Zhou 1990]** Stumm, M., and Zhou, S., "Algorithms Implementing Distributed Shared Memory," *IEEE Computer*, Vol. 23, No. 5, New York, NY, pp. 54–64 (1990).

**[Tam and Hsu 1990]** Tam, V., and Hsu, M., "Fast Recovery in Distributed Shared Virtual Memory Systems," In: *Proceedings of the 10th International Conference on Distributed Computing Systems*, IEEE, New York, pp. 38–45 (May–June 1990).

**[Tam et al. 1990]** Tam, M. C., Smith, J. M., and Farber, D. J., "A Taxonomy-Based Comparison of Several Distributed Shared Memory Systems," *Operating Systems Review*, Vol. 24, pp. 40–67 (1990).

**[Tartalja and Milutinovic 1996]** Tartalja, I., and Milutinovic, V. (Eds.), *The Cache Coherence Problem in Shared-Memory Multiprocessors: Software Solutions*, IEEE Computer Society Press, Los Alamitos, CA (1996).

**[Theel and Fleisch 1995]** Theel, O. E., and Fleisch, B. D., "Design and Analysis of Highly Available and Scalable Coherence Protocols for Distributed Shared Memory Systems Using Stochastic Modeling," In: *Proceedings of the 24th Annual International Conference on Parallel Processing*, IEEE, New York (August 1995).

**[Wu and Fuchs 1989]** Wu, K. L., and Fuchs, W. K., "Recoverable Distributed Shared Virtual Memory: Memory Coherence and Storage Structures," In: *Proceedings of the 19th International Symposium on Fault-Tolerant Computing*, pp. 520–527 (June 1989).

**[Yen et al. 1985]** Yen, D. W. L., Yen, W. C., and Fu, K., "Data Coherence Problem in a Multicache System," *IEEE Transactions on Computers*, Vol. C-34, No. 1, pp. 56–65, New York, NY (1985).

**[Zhou et al. 1990]** Zhou, S., Stumm, M., and McInerney, T., "Extending Distributed Shared Memory to Heterogeneous Environments," In: *Proceedings of the 10th International Conference on Distributed Computing Systems*, IEEE, New York, pp. 30–37 (May–June 1990).

**[Zhou et al. 1992]** Zhou, S., Stumm, M., Li, K., and Wortman, D., "Heterogeneous Distributed Shared Memory," *IEEE Transactions on Parallel and Distributed Systems*, Vol. 13, No. 5, New York, NY, pp. 540–554 (1992).

## POINTERS TO BIBLIOGRAPHIES ON THE INTERNET

Bibliography containing references on *Distributed Shared Memory* can be found at:

ftp:ftp.cs.umanitoba.ca/pub/bibliographies/Parallel/dsm.html

Bibliography containing references on *Distributed Memory Systems* can be found at:

ftp:ftp.cs.umanitoba.ca/pub/bibliographies/Parallel/distmem.html

Bibliography containing references on *Cache Memories and Related Topics* can be found at:

ftp:ftp.cs.umanitoba.ca/pub/bibliographies/Misc/cache.html

Bibliography containing references on *Single Address Space Operating Systems (SASOS) and Related Topics* can be found at:

ftp:ftp.cs.umanitoba.ca/pub/bibliographies/Os/sasos.html

# CHAPTER 6

# Synchronization

## 6.1 INTRODUCTION

A distributed system consists of a collection of distinct processes that are spatially separated and run concurrently. In systems with multiple concurrent processes, it is economical to share the system resources (hardware or software) among the concurrently executing processes. In such a situation, sharing may be cooperative or competitive. That is, since the number of available resources in a computing system is restricted, one process must necessarily influence the action of other concurrently executing processes as it competes for resources. For example, for a resource (such as a tape drive) that cannot be used simultaneously by multiple processes, a process willing to use it must wait if another process is using it. At times, concurrent processes must cooperate either to achieve the desired performance of the computing system or due to the nature of the computation being performed. Typical examples of process cooperation involve two processes that bear a producer-consumer or client-server relationship to each other. For instance, a client process and a file server process must cooperate when performing file access operations. Both cooperative and competitive sharing require adherence to certain rules of behavior that guarantee that correct interaction occurs. The rules for enforcing correct interaction are implemented in the form of synchronization mechanisms. This chapter presents synchronization mechanisms that are suitable for distributed systems. In particular, the following synchronization-related issues are described:

- Clock synchronization
- Event ordering
- Mutual exclusion
- Deadlock
- Election algorithms

## 6.2 CLOCK SYNCHRONIZATION

Every computer needs a timer mechanism (called a computer clock) to keep track of current time and also for various accounting purposes such as calculating the time spent by a process in CPU utilization, disk I/O, and so on, so that the corresponding user can be charged properly. In a distributed system, an application may have processes that concurrently run on multiple nodes of the system. For correct results, several such distributed applications require that the clocks of the nodes are synchronized with each other. For example, for a distributed on-line reservation system to be fair, the only remaining seat booked almost simultaneously from two different nodes should be offered to the client who booked first, even if the time difference between the two bookings is very small. It may not be possible to guarantee this if the clocks of the nodes of the system are not synchronized. In a distributed system, synchronized clocks also enable one to measure the duration of distributed activities that start on one node and terminate on another node, for instance, calculating the time taken to transmit a message from one node to another at any arbitrary time. It is difficult to get the correct result in this case if the clocks of the sender and receiver nodes are not synchronized. There are several other applications of synchronized clocks in distributed systems. Some good examples of such applications may be found in [Liskov 1993].

The discussion above shows that it is the job of a distributed operating system designer to devise and use suitable algorithms for properly synchronizing the clocks of a distributed system. This section presents a description of such algorithms. However, for a better understanding of these algorithms, we will first discuss how computer clocks are implemented and what are the main issues in synchronizing the clocks of a distributed system.

### 6.2.1 How Computer Clocks Are Implemented

A computer clock usually consists of three components—a quartz crystal that oscillates at a well-defined frequency, a *counter* register, and a *constant* register. The constant register is used to store a constant value that is decided based on the frequency of oscillation of the quartz crystal. The counter register is used to keep track of the oscillations of the quartz crystal. That is, the value in the counter register is decremented by 1 for each oscillation of the quartz crystal. When the value of the counter register becomes zero, an interrupt is generated and its value is reinitialized to the value in the constant register. Each interrupt is called a *clock tick.*

To make the computer clock function as an ordinary clock used by us in our day-to-day life, the following things are done:

1. The value in the constant register is chosen so that 60 clock ticks occur in a second.
2. The computer clock is synchronized with real time (external clock). For this, two more values are stored in the system—a fixed starting date and time and the number of ticks. For example, in UNIX, time begins at 0000 on January 1, 1970. At the time of initial booting, the system asks the operator to enter the current date and time. The system converts the entered value to the number of ticks after the fixed starting date and time. At every clock tick, the interrupt service routine increments the value of the number of ticks to keep the clock running.

### 6.2.2 Drifting of Clocks

A clock always runs at a constant rate because its quartz crystal oscillates at a well-defined frequency. However, due to differences in the crystals, the rates at which two clocks run are normally different from each other. The difference in the oscillation period between two clocks might be extremely small, but the difference accumulated over many oscillations leads to an observable difference in the times of the two clocks, no matter how accurately they were initialized to the same value. Therefore, with the passage of time, a computer clock drifts from the real-time clock that was used for its initial setting. For clocks based on a quartz crystal, the drift rate is approximately $10^{-6}$, giving a difference of 1 second every 1,000,000 seconds, or 11.6 days [Coulouris et al. 1994]. Hence a computer clock must be periodically resynchronized with the real-time clock to keep it nonfaulty. Even nonfaulty clocks do not always maintain perfect time. A clock is considered nonfaulty if there is a bound on the amount of drift from real time for any given finite time interval.

More precisely, let us suppose that when the real time is $t$, the time value of a clock $p$ is $C_p(t)$. If all clocks in the world were perfectly synchronized, we would have $C_p(t) = t$ for all $p$ and all $t$. That is, if $C$ denotes the time value of a clock, in the ideal case $dC/dt$ should be 1. Therefore, if the *maximum drift rate* allowable is $\rho$, a clock is said to be nonfaulty if the following condition holds for it:

$$1 - \rho \leq \frac{dC}{dt} \leq 1 + \rho$$

As shown in Figure 6.1, after synchronization with a perfect clock, slow and fast clocks drift in opposite directions from the perfect clock. This is because for slow clocks $dC/dt < 1$ and for fast clocks $dC/dt > 1$.

A distributed system consists of several nodes, each with its own clock, running at its own speed. Because of the nonzero drift rates of all clocks, the set of clocks of a distributed system do not remain well synchronized without some periodic resynchroniza-

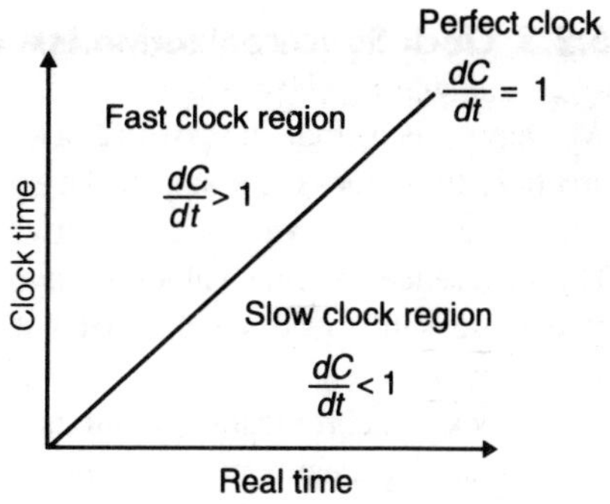


**Fig. 6.1** Slow, perfect, and fast clocks.

tion. This means that the nodes of a distributed system must periodically resynchronize their local clocks to maintain a global time base across the entire system. Recall from Figure 6.1 that slow and fast clocks drift in opposite directions from the perfect clock. Therefore, of two clocks, if one is slow and one is fast, at a time $\Delta t$ after they were synchronized, the maximum deviation between the time value of the two clocks will be $2\rho\Delta t$. Hence, to guarantee that no two clocks in a set of clocks ever differ by more than $\delta$, the clocks in the set must be resynchronized periodically, with the time interval between two synchronizations being less than or equal to $\delta/2\rho$. Therefore, unlike a centralized system in which only the computer clock has to be synchronized with the real-time clock, a distributed system requires the following types of clock synchronization:

1. *Synchronization of the computer clocks with real-time (or external) clocks*. This type of synchronization is mainly required for real-time applications. That is, external clock synchronization allows the system to exchange information about the timing of events with other systems and users.

   An external time source that is often used as a reference for synchronizing computer clocks with real time is the *Coordinated Universal Time (UTC)*. The UTC is an international standard. Many standard bodies disseminate UTC signals by radio, telephone, and satellite. For instance, the WWV radio station in the United States and the Geostationary Operational Environmental Satellites (GEOS) are two such standard bodies. Commercial devices (called *time providers*) are available to receive and interpret these signals. Computers equipped with time provider devices can synchronize their clocks with these timing signals.

2. *Mutual (or internal) synchronization of the clocks of different nodes of the system.* This type of synchronization is mainly required for those applications that require a consistent view of time across all nodes of a distributed system as well as for the measurement of the duration of distributed activities that terminate on a node different from the one on which they start.

Note that externally synchronized clocks are also internally synchronized. However, the converse is not true because with the passage of time internally synchronized clocks may drift arbitrarily far from external time.

### 6.2.3 Clock Synchronization Issues

We have seen that no two clocks can be perfectly synchronized. Therefore, in practice, two clocks are said to be synchronized at a particular instance of time if the difference in time values of the two clocks is less than some specified constant δ. The difference in time values of two clocks is called *clock skew*. Therefore, a set of clocks are said to be synchronized if the clock skew of any two clocks in this set is less than δ.

Clock synchronization requires each node to read the other nodes' clock values. The actual mechanism used by a node to read other clocks differs from one algorithm to another. However, regardless of the actual reading mechanism, a node can obtain only an approximate view of its clock skew with respect to other nodes' clocks in the system. Errors occur mainly because of unpredictable communication delays during message passing used to deliver a clock signal or a clock message from one node to another. A minimum value of the unpredictable communication delays between two nodes can be computed by counting the time needed to prepare, transmit, and receive an empty message in the absence of transmission errors and any other system load. However, in general, it is rather impossible to calculate the upper bound of this value because it depends on the amount of communication and computation going on in parallel in the system, on the possibility that transmission errors will cause messages to be transmitted several times, and on other random events, such as page faults, process switches, or the establishment of new communication routes.

An important issue in clock synchronization is that time must never run backward because this could cause serious problems, such as the repetition of certain operations that may be hazardous in certain cases. Notice that during synchronization a fast clock has to be slowed down. However, if the time of a fast clock is readjusted to the actual time all at once, it may lead to running the time backward for that clock. Therefore, clock synchronization algorithms are normally designed to gradually introduce such a change in the fast running clock instead of readjusting it to the correct time all at once. One way to do this is to make the interrupt routine more intelligent. When an intelligent interrupt routine is instructed by the clock synchronization algorithm to slow down its clock, it readjusts the amount of time to be added to the clock time for each interrupt. For example, suppose that if 8 msec is added to the clock time on each interrupt in the normal situation, when slowing down, the interrupt routine only adds 7 msec on each interrupt until the correction has been made. Although not necessary, for smooth readjustment, the intelligent interrupt routine may also advance its clock forward, if it is found to be slow, by adding 9 msec on each interrupt, instead of readjusting it to the correct time all at once.

### 6.2.4 Clock Synchronization Algorithms

Clock synchronization algorithms may be broadly classified as centralized and distributed.

### Centralized Algorithms

In centralized clock synchronization algorithms one node has a real-time receiver. This node is usually called the *time server node*, and the clock time of this node is regarded as correct and used as the reference time. The goal of the algorithm is to keep the clocks of all other nodes synchronized with the clock time of the time server node. Depending on the role of the time server node, centralized clock synchronization algorithms are again of two types—passive time server and active time server.

***Passive Time Server Centralized Algorithm.*** In this method, each node periodically (with the interval between two periods being less than or equal to $\delta/2\rho$) sends a message ("*time = ?*") to the time server. When the time server receives the message, it quickly responds with a message ("*time* = *T*"), where *T* is the current time in the clock of the time server node. Let us assume that when the client node sends the "*time = ?*" message, its clock time is $T_0$, and when it receives the "*time* = *T*" message, its clock time is $T_1$. Since $T_0$ and $T_1$ are measured using the same clock, in the absence of any other information, the best estimate of the time required for the propagation of the message "*time* = *T*" from the time server node to the client's node is $(T_1 - T_0)/2$. Therefore, when the reply is received at the client's node, its clock is readjusted to $T+(T_1 - T_0)/2$.

Since there may be unpredictable variation in the message propagation time between two nodes, $(T_1 - T_0)/2$ is not a very good estimate of the time to be added to $T$ for calculating the current time of the client's node clock. Several proposals have been made to improve this estimated value. Two such methods are described below. The first one assumes the availability of some additional information and the second one assumes that no additional information is available:

1. In this method, it is assumed that the approximate time taken by the time server to handle the interrupt and process a "*time = ?*" request message is known. Let this time be equal to $I$. Then a better estimate of the time taken for propagation of the message "*time* = *T*" from the time server node to the client's node would be $(T_1 - T_0 - I)/2$. Therefore, in this method, when the reply is received at the client's node, its clock is readjusted to $T + (T_1 - T_0 - I)/2$.

2. This method was proposed by Cristian [1989]. In this method, several measurements of $T_1 - T_0$ are made, and those measurements for which $T_1 - T_0$ exceeds some threshold value are considered to be unreliable and discarded. The average of the remaining measurements is then calculated, and half of the calculated value is used as the value to be added to $T$. Alternatively, the measurement for which the value of $T_1 - T_0$ is minimum is considered to be the most accurate one, and half of this value is used as the value to be added to $T$. One limitation of this approach is the need to restrict the number of measurements for estimating the value to be added to $T$, since these are directly related to the message traffic generated and the overhead imposed by the algorithm.

***Active Time Server Centralized Algorithm.*** In the passive time server approach, the time server only responds to requests for time from other nodes. On the other hand, in the active time server approach, the time server periodically broadcasts its clock time ("*time* = *T*"). The other nodes receive the broadcast message and use the clock time in the message for correcting their own clocks. Each node has a priori knowledge of the approximate time ($T_a$) required for the propagation of the message "*time* = *T*" from the time sever node to its own node. Therefore, when the broadcast message is received at a node, the node's clock is readjusted to the time $T + T_a$. A major drawback of this method is that it is not fault tolerant. If the broadcast message reaches too late at a node due to some communication fault, the clock of that node will be readjusted to an incorrect value. Another drawback of this approach is that it requires broadcast facility to be supported by the network.

Another active time server algorithm that overcomes the drawbacks of the above algorithm is the *Berkeley algorithm*. It was proposed by Gusella and Zatti [1989] for internal synchronization of clocks of a group of computers running the Berkeley UNIX. In this algorithm, the time server periodically sends a message ("*time* = ?") to all the computers in the group. On receiving this message, each computer sends back its clock value to the time server. The time server has a priori knowledge of the approximate time required for the propagation of a message from each node to its own node. Based on this knowledge, it first readjusts the clock values of the reply messages. It then takes a *fault-tolerant average* of the clock values of all the computers (including its own). To take the fault-tolerant average, the time server chooses a subset of all clock values that do not differ from one another by more than a specified amount, and the average is taken only for the clock values in this subset. This approach eliminates readings from unreliable clocks whose clock values could have a significant adverse effect if an ordinary average was taken.

The calculated average is the current time to which all the clocks should be readjusted. The time server readjusts its own clock to this value. However, instead of sending the calculated current time back to the other computers, the time server sends the amount by which each individual computer's clock requires adjustment. This can be a positive or a negative value and is calculated based on the knowledge the time server has about the approximate time required for the propagation of a message from each node to its own node.

Centralized clock synchronization algorithms suffer from two major drawbacks:

1. They are subject to single-point failure. If the time server node fails, the clock synchronization operation cannot be performed. This makes the system unreliable. Ideally, a distributed system should be more reliable than its individual nodes. If one goes down, the rest should continue to function correctly.
2. From a scalability point of view, it is generally not acceptable to get all the time requests serviced by a single time server. In a large system, such a solution puts a heavy burden on that one process.

Distributed algorithms overcome these drawbacks.

### Distributed Algorithms

Recall that externally synchronized clocks are also internally synchronized. That is, if each node's clock is independently synchronized with real time, all the clocks of the system remain mutually synchronized. Therefore, a simple method for clock synchronization may be to equip each node of the system with a real-time receiver so that each node's clock can be independently synchronized with real time. Multiple real-time clocks (one for each node) are normally used for this purpose.

Theoretically, internal synchronization of clocks is not required in this approach. However, in practice, due to the inherent inaccuracy of real-time clocks, different real-time clocks produce different time. Therefore, internal synchronization is normally performed for better accuracy. One of the following two approaches is usually used for internal synchronization in this case.

***Global Averaging Distributed Algorithms.*** In this approach, the clock process at each node broadcasts its local clock time in the form of a special "resync" message when its local time equals $T_0 + iR$ for some integer $i$, where $T_0$ is a fixed time in the past agreed upon by all nodes and $R$ is a system parameter that depends on such factors as the total number of nodes in the system, the maximum allowable drift rate, and so on. That is, a resync message is broadcast from each node at the beginning of every fixed-length resynchronization interval. However, since the clocks of different nodes run at slightly different rates, these broadcasts will not happen simultaneously from all nodes.

After broadcasting the clock value, the clock process of a node waits for time $T$, where $T$ is a parameter to be determined by the algorithm. During this waiting period, the clock process collects the resync messages broadcast by other nodes. For each resync message, the clock process records the time, according to its own clock, when the message was received. At the end of the waiting period, the clock process estimates the skew of its clock with respect to each of the other nodes on the basis of the times at which it received resync messages. It then computes a fault-tolerant average of the estimated skews and uses it to correct the local clock before the start of the next resynchronization interval.

The global averaging algorithms differ mainly in the manner in which the fault-tolerant average of the estimated skews is calculated. Two commonly used algorithms are described here:

1. The simplest algorithm is to take the average of the estimated skews and use it as the correction for the local clock. However, to limit the impact of faulty clocks on the average value, the estimated skew with respect to each node is compared against a threshold, and skews greater than the threshold are set to zero before computing the average of the estimated skews.

2. In another algorithm, each node limits the impact of faulty clocks by first discarding the $m$ highest and $m$ lowest estimated skews and then calculating the average of the remaining skews, which is then used as the correction for the local clock. The value of $m$ is usually decided based on the total number of clocks (nodes).

***Localized Averaging Distributed Algorithms.*** The global averaging algorithms do not scale well because they require the network to support broadcast facility and also because of the large amount of message traffic generated. Therefore, they are suitable for small networks, especially for those that have fully connected topology (in which each node has a direct communication link to every other node). The localized averaging algorithms attempt to overcome these drawbacks of the global averaging algorithms. In this approach, the nodes of a distributed system are logically arranged in some kind of pattern, such as a ring or a grid. Periodically, each node exchanges its clock time with its neighbors in the ring, grid, or other structure and then sets its clock time to the average of its own clock time and the clock times of its neighbors.

### 6.2.5 Case Study: Distributed Time Service

Two popular services for synchronizing clocks and for providing timing information over a wide variety of interconnected networks are the Distributed Time Service (DTS) and the Network Time Protocol (NTP). DTS is a component of DCE (Distributed Computing Environment) that is used to synchronize clocks of a network of computers running DCE, and NTP is used in the Internet for clock synchronization. DTS is briefly described below as a case study of clock synchronization. Details of NTP can be found in [Mills 1991].

In a DCE system, each node is configured as either a *DTS client* or a *DTS server*. On each DTS client node runs a daemon process called a *DTS clerk*. To synchronize its local clock, each DTS clerk makes requests to the DTS servers on the same LAN for timing information. The DTS servers provide timing information to DTS clerks or to other DTS servers upon request. To make them publicly known, each DTS server exports its name to a LAN profile.

DTS does not define time as a single value. Instead, time is expressed as an interval containing the correct time. By using intervals instead of values, DTS provides the users with a clear idea of how far off the clock might be from reference time.

A DTS clerk synchronizes its local clock in the following manner. It keeps track of the drift rate of its local clock, and when it discovers that the time error of the local clock has exceeded the allowable limit, it initiates resynchronization by doing an RPC with all the DTS servers on its LAN requesting for the time. Each DTS server that receives this message returns a reply containing a time interval based on the server's own clock. From the received replies, the DTS clerk computes its new value of time in the following manner (see Fig. 6.2 for an example). At first, time intervals that do not intersect with the majority of time intervals are considered to be faulty and discarded. For instance, in Figure 6.2, the value supplied by DTS server 3 is discarded. Then the largest intersection falling within the remaining intervals is computed. The DTS clerk then resets its clock value to the midpoint of this interval. However, instead of resetting the clock to the calculated value all at once, an intelligent interrupt routine is used to gradually introduce such a change in the clock time.

Note that due to the use of the method of intersection for computing new clock value, it is recommended that each LAN in a DCE system should have at least three DTS servers to provide time information.

In addition to DTS clerks synchronizing their clocks with DTS servers, the DTS servers of a LAN also communicate among themselves periodically to keep their clocks mutually synchronized. They also use the algorithm of Figure 6.2 to compute the new clock value.

So far we have seen how clocks of nodes belonging to the same LAN are synchronized. However, a DCE system may have several interconnected LANs. In this case, a need arises to synchronize the clocks of all nodes in the network. For this, one DTS

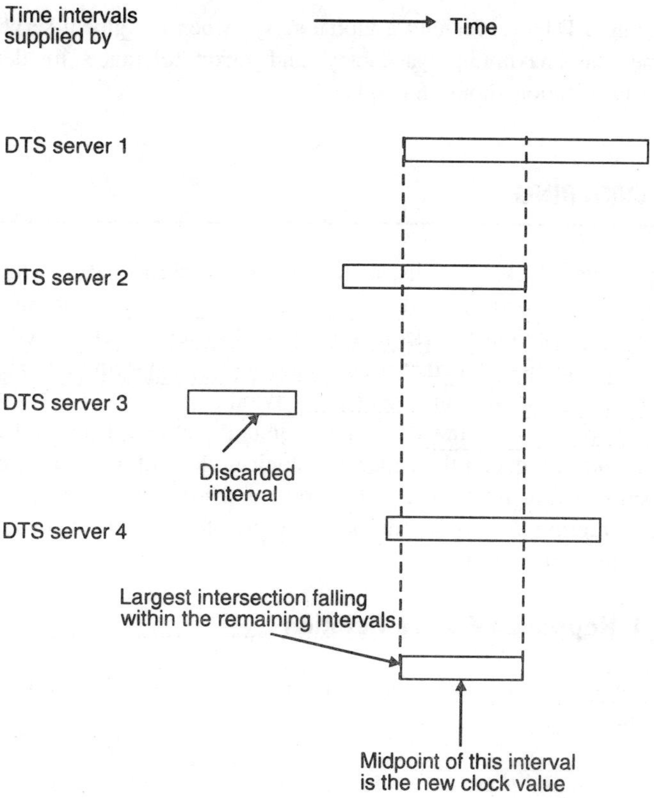


**Fig. 6.2** Computation of new clock value in DTS from obtained time intervals.

server of each LAN is designated a *global server*. Although not necessary for external synchronization, it is recommended that each global server be equipped with a time provider device to receive UTC signals. The global servers of all LANs communicate among themselves periodically to keep their clocks mutually synchronized. Since the global server of a LAN is also a DTS server, its clock value is automatically used to synchronize the clocks of other nodes in the LAN. In this manner, DTS synchronizes the clocks of all nodes in the network.

DTS is transparent to DCE users in the sense that users cannot access DTS directly. However, DTS application programming interface (API) provides a rich set of library procedures to allow DTS applications to perform time-related activities to control their executions. In particular, there are library procedures to get the current time, to convert between binary and ASCII representations of time, to manipulate binary time information, to compare two times, to perform arithmetic operations on times, to get time zone information, and so on. In addition, there is an administrative interface to DTS that allows a system administrator to perform administrative operations such as configuring and dynamically reconfiguring the number of DTS clients and DTS servers on a LAN, changing a DTS server into a global server when the global server of a LAN fails, and setting the maximum inaccuracy and error tolerance to decide how frequently resynchronization should take place.

## 6.3 EVENT ORDERING

Keeping the clocks in a distributed system synchronized to within 5 or 10 msec is an expensive and nontrivial task. Lamport [1978] observed that for most applications it is not necessary to keep the clocks in a distributed system synchronized. Rather, it is sufficient to ensure that all events that occur in a distributed system be totally ordered in a manner that is consistent with an observed behavior.

For partial ordering of events, Lamport defined a new relation called *happened-before* and introduced the concept of logical clocks for ordering of events based on the happened-before relation. He then gave a distributed algorithm extending his idea of partial ordering to a consistent total ordering of all the events in a distributed system. His idea is presented below.

### 6.3.1 Happened-Before Relation

The happened-before relation (denoted by $\rightarrow$) on a set of events satisfies the following conditions:

1. If $a$ and $b$ are events in the same process and $a$ occurs before $b$, then $a \rightarrow b$.
2. If $a$ is the event of sending a message by one process and $b$ is the event of the receipt of the same message by another process, then $a \rightarrow b$. This condition holds by the law of causality because a receiver cannot receive a message until the sender sends it, and the time taken to propagate a message from its sender to its receiver is always positive.
3. If $a \rightarrow b$ and $b \rightarrow c$, then $a \rightarrow c$. That is, happened-before is a transitive relation.

Notice that in a physically meaningful system, an event cannot happen before itself, that is, $a \rightarrow a$ is not true for any event $a$. This implies that happened-before is an irreflexive partial ordering on the set of all events in the system.

In terms of the happened-before relation, two events $a$ and $b$ are said to be *concurrent* if they are not related by the happened-before relation. That is, neither $a \rightarrow b$ nor $b \rightarrow a$ is true. This is possible if the two events occur in different processes that do not exchange messages either directly or indirectly via other processes. Notice that this definition of concurrency simply means that nothing can be said about when the two events happened or which one happened first. That is, two events are concurrent if neither can causally affect the other. Due to this reason, the happened-before relation is sometimes also known as the relation of *causal ordering*.

A space-time diagram (such as the one shown in Fig. 6.3) is often used to illustrate the concepts of the happened-before relation and concurrent events. In this diagram, each

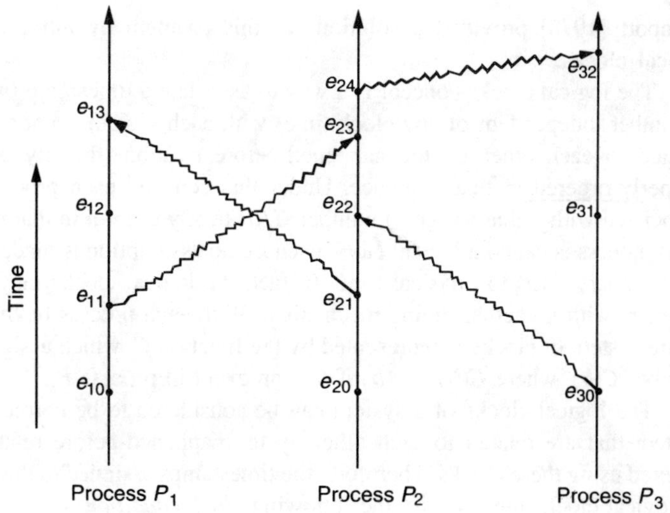


**Fig. 6.3** Space-time diagram for three processes.

vertical line denotes a process, each dot on a vertical line denotes an event in the corresponding process, and each wavy line denotes a message transfer from one process to another in the direction of the arrow.

From this space-time diagram it is easy to see that for two events $a$ and $b$, $a \rightarrow b$ is true if and only if there exists a path from $a$ to $b$ by moving forward in time along process and message lines in the direction of the arrows. For example, some of the events of Figure 6.3 that are related by the happened-before relation are

$$e_{10} \rightarrow e_{11} \qquad e_{20} \rightarrow e_{24} \qquad e_{11} \rightarrow e_{23} \qquad e_{21} \rightarrow e_{13}$$
$$e_{30} \rightarrow e_{24} \quad \text{(since } e_{30} \rightarrow e_{22} \text{ and } e_{22} \rightarrow e_{24}\text{)}$$
$$e_{11} \rightarrow e_{32} \quad \text{(since } e_{11} \rightarrow e_{23},\ e_{23} \rightarrow e_{24}, \text{ and } e_{24} \rightarrow e_{32}\text{)}$$

On the other hand, two events $a$ and $b$ are concurrent if and only if no path exists either from $a$ to $b$ or from $b$ to $a$. For example, some of the concurrent events of Figure 6.3 are

$e_{12}$ and $e_{20}$ $\quad$ $e_{21}$ and $e_{30}$ $\quad$ $e_{10}$ and $e_{30}$ $\quad$ $e_{11}$ and $e_{31}$ $\quad$ $e_{12}$ and $e_{32}$ $\quad$ $e_{13}$ and $e_{22}$

## 6.3.2 Logical Clocks Concept

To determine that an event $a$ happened before an event $b$, either a common clock or a set of perfectly synchronized clocks is needed. We have seen that neither of these is available in a distributed system. Therefore, in a distributed system the happened-before relation must be defined without the use of globally synchronized physical clocks.

Lamport [1978] provided a solution for this problem by introducing the concept of logical clocks.

The logical clocks concept is a way to associate a timestamp (which may be simply a number independent of any clock time) with each system event so that events that are related to each other by the happened-before relation (directly or indirectly) can be properly ordered in that sequence. Under this concept, each process $P_i$ has a clock $C_i$ associated with it that assigns a number $C_i(a)$ to any event $a$ in that process. The clock of each process is called a logical clock because no assumption is made about the relation of the numbers $C_i(a)$ to physical time. In fact, the logical clocks may be implemented by counters with no actual timing mechanism. With each process having its own clock, the entire system of clocks is represented by the function $C$, which assigns to any event $b$ the number $C(b)$, where $C(b) = C_j(b)$ if $b$ is an event in process $P_j$.

The logical clocks of a system can be considered to be correct if the events of the system that are related to each other by the happened-before relation can be properly ordered using these clocks. Therefore, the timestamps assigned to the events by the system of logical clocks must satisfy the following *clock condition:*

For any two events $a$ and $b$, if $a \rightarrow b$, then $C(a) < C(b)$.

Note that we cannot expect the converse condition to hold as well, since that would imply that any two concurrent events must occur at the same time, which is not necessarily true for all concurrent events.

### 6.3.3 Implementation of Logical Clocks

From the definition of the happened-before relation, it follows that the clock condition mentioned above is satisfied if the following conditions hold:

**C1:** If $a$ and $b$ are two events within the same process $P_i$ and $a$ occurs before $b$, then $C_i(a) < C_i(b)$.

**C2:** If $a$ is the sending of a message by process $P_i$ and $b$ is the receipt of that message by process $P_j$, then $C_i(a) < C_j(b)$.

In addition to these conditions, which are necessary to satisfy the clock condition, the following condition is necessary for the correct functioning of the system:

**C3:** A clock $C_i$ associated with a process $P_i$ must always go forward, never backward. That is, corrections to time of a logical clock must always be made by adding a positive value to the clock, never by subtracting value.

Obviously, any algorithm used for implementing a set of logical clocks must satisfy all these three conditions. The algorithm proposed by Lamport is given below.

To meet conditions C1, C2, and C3, Lamport's algorithm uses the following implementation rules:

**IR1:** Each process $P_i$ increments $C_i$ between any two successive events.

**IR2:** If event $a$ is the sending of a message $m$ by process $P_i$, the message $m$ contains a timestamp $T_m = C_i(a)$, and upon receiving the message $m$ a process $P_j$ sets $C_j$ greater than or equal to its present value but greater than $T_m$.

Rule IR1 ensures that condition C1 is satisfied and rule IR2 ensures that condition C2 is satisfied. Both IR1 and IR2 ensure that condition C3 is also satisfied. Hence the simple implementation rules IR1 and IR2 guarantee a correct system of logical clocks.

The implementation of logical clocks can best be illustrated with an example. How a system of logical clocks can be implemented either by using counters with no actual timing mechanism or by using physical clocks is shown below.

### Implementation of Logical Clocks by Using Counters

As shown in Figure 6.4, two processes $P_1$ and $P_2$ each have a counter $C_1$ and $C_2$, respectively. The counters act as logical clocks. At the beginning, the counters are initialized to zero and a process increments its counter by 1 whenever an event occurs in that process. If the event is sending of a message (e.g., events $e_{04}$ and $e_{14}$), the process includes the incremented value of the counter in the message. On the other hand, if the event is receiving of a message (e.g., events $e_{13}$ and $e_{08}$), instead of simply incrementing the counter by 1, a check is made to see if the incremented counter value is less than or equal to the timestamp in the received message. If so, the counter value is corrected and

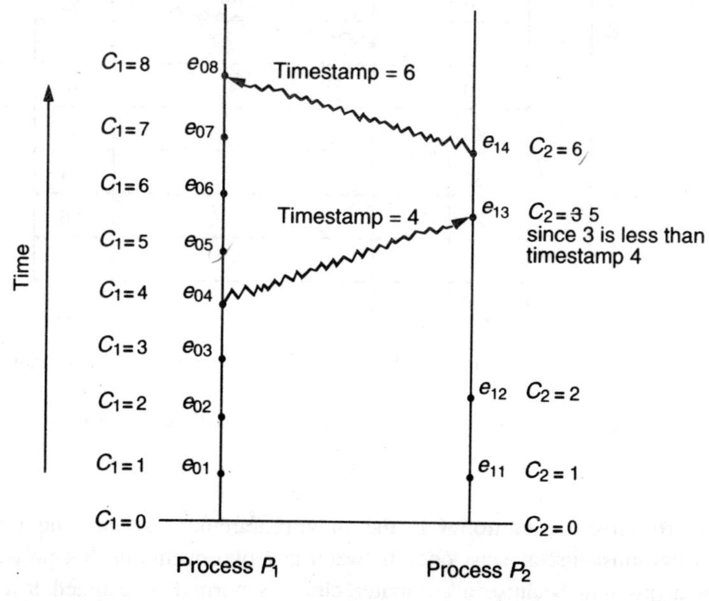


**Fig. 6.4** Example illustrating the implementation of logical clocks by using counters.

set to 1 plus the timestamp in the received message (e.g., in event $e_{13}$). If not, the counter value is left as it is (e.g., in event $e_{08}$).

### Implementation of Logical Clocks by Using Physical Clocks

The implementation of the example of Figure 6.4 by using physical clocks instead of counters is shown in Figure 6.5. In this case, each process has a physical clock associated with it. Each clock runs at a constant rate. However, the rates at which different clocks run are different. For instance, in the example of Figure 6.5, when the clock of process $P_1$ has ticked 10 times, the clock of process $P_2$ has ticked only 8 times.

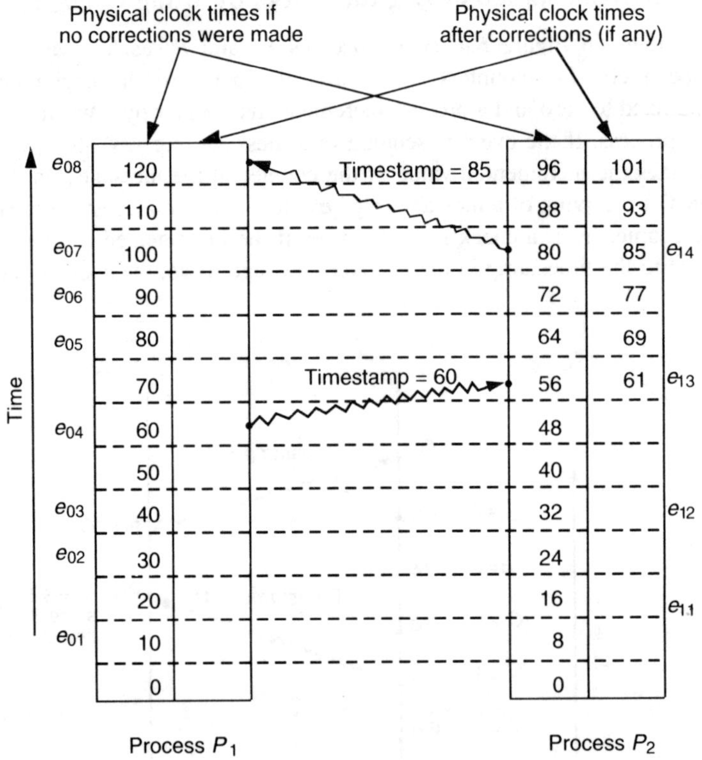


**Fig. 6.5** Example illustrating the implementation of logical clocks by using physical clocks.

To satisfy condition C1, the only requirement is that the physical clock of a process must tick at least once between any two events in that process. This is usually not a problem because a computer clock is normally designed to click several times between two events that happen in quick succession. To satisfy condition C2, for a message-sending event (e.g., events $e_{04}$ and $e_{14}$), the process sending the message includes its current physical time in the message. And for a message-receiving event (e.g., events $e_{13}$ and $e_{08}$), a check is made to see if the current time in the receiver's clock is less than or equal to the time included in the message. If so, the receiver's physical clock is corrected by fast forwarding its clock to be 1 more than the time included in the message (e.g., in event $e_{13}$). If not, the receiver's clock is left as it is (e.g., in event $e_{08}$).

### 6.3.4 Total Ordering of Events

We have seen how a system of clocks satisfying the clock condition can be used to order the events of a system based on the happened-before relationship among the events. We simply need to order the events by the times at which they occur. However, recall that the happened-before relation is only a partial ordering on the set of all events in the system. With this event-ordering scheme, it is possible that two events $a$ and $b$ that are not related by the happened-before relation (either directly or indirectly) may have the same timestamps associated with them. For instance, if events $a$ and $b$ happen respectively in processes $P_1$ and $P_2$, when the clocks of both processes show exactly the same time (say 100), both events will have a timestamp of 100. In this situation, nothing can be said about the order of the two events. Therefore, for total ordering on the set of all system events, an additional requirement is desirable: No two events ever occur at exactly the same time. To fulfill this requirement, Lamport proposed the use of any arbitrary total ordering of the processes. For example, process identity numbers may be used to break ties and to create a total ordering of events. For instance, in the situation described above, the timestamps associated with events $a$ and $b$ will be 100.001 and 100.002, respectively, where the process identity numbers of processes $P_1$ and $P_2$ are 001 and 002, respectively. Using this method, we now have a way to assign a unique timestamp to each event in a distributed system to provide a total ordering of all events in the system.

## 6.4 MUTUAL EXCLUSION

There are several resources in a system that must not be used simultaneously by multiple processes if program operation is to be correct. For example, a file must not be simultaneously updated by multiple processes. Similarly, use of unit record peripherals such as tape drives or printers must be restricted to a single process at a time. Therefore, exclusive access to such a shared resource by a process must be ensured. This exclusiveness of access is called *mutual exclusion* between processes. The sections of a program that need exclusive access to shared resources are referred to as *critical sections*. For mutual exclusion, means are introduced to prevent processes from executing concurrently within their associated critical sections.

An algorithm for implementing mutual exclusion must satisfy the following requirements:

1. *Mutual exclusion.* Given a shared resource accessed by multiple concurrent processes, at any time only one process should access the resource. That is, a process that has been granted the resource must release it before it can be granted to another process.
2. *No starvation.* If every process that is granted the resource eventually releases it, every request must be eventually granted.

In single-processor systems, mutual exclusion is implemented using semaphores, monitors, and similar constructs. The three basic approaches used by different algorithms for implementing mutual exclusion in distributed systems are described below. Interested readers who want to explore further on this topic may refer to [Agarwal and Abbadi 1991, Bulgannawar and Vaidya 1995, Raynal 1991, Sanders 1987, Suzuki and Kasami 1985]. To simplify our description, we assume that each process resides at a different node.

### 6.4.1 Centralized Approach

In this approach, one of the processes in the system is elected as the coordinator (algorithms for electing a coordinator are described later in this chapter) and coordinates the entry to the critical sections. Each process that wants to enter a critical section must first seek permission from the coordinator. If no other process is currently in that critical section, the coordinator can immediately grant permission to the requesting process. However, if two or more processes concurrently ask for permission to enter the same critical section, the coordinator grants permission to only one process at a time in accordance with some scheduling algorithm. After executing a critical section, when a process exits the critical section, it must notify the coordinator so that the coordinator can grant permission to another process (if any) that has also asked for permission to enter the same critical section.

An algorithm for mutual exclusion that uses the centralized approach is described here with the help of an example. As shown in Figure 6.6, let us suppose that there is a coordinator process ($P_c$) and three other processes $P_1$, $P_2$, and $P_3$ in the system. Also assume that the requests are granted in the first-come, first-served order for which the coordinator maintains a request queue. Suppose $P_1$ wants to enter a critical section for which it sends a *request* message to $P_c$. On receiving the request message, $P_c$ checks to see whether some other process is currently in that critical section. Since no other process is in the critical section, $P_c$ immediately sends back a *reply* message granting permission to $P_1$. When the reply arrives, $P_1$ enters the critical section.

Now suppose that while $P_1$ is in the critical section $P_2$ asks for permission to enter the same critical section by sending a request message to $P_c$. Since $P_1$ is already in the critical section, $P_2$ cannot be granted permission. The exact method used to deny permission varies from one algorithm to another. For our algorithm, let us assume that the coordinator does not return any reply and the process that made the request remains blocked until it receives the reply from the coordinator. Therefore, $P_c$ does not send a reply to $P_2$ immediately and enters its request in the request queue.

Again suppose that while $P_1$ is still in the critical section $P_3$ also sends a request message to $P_c$ asking for permission to enter the same critical section. Obviously, $P_3$

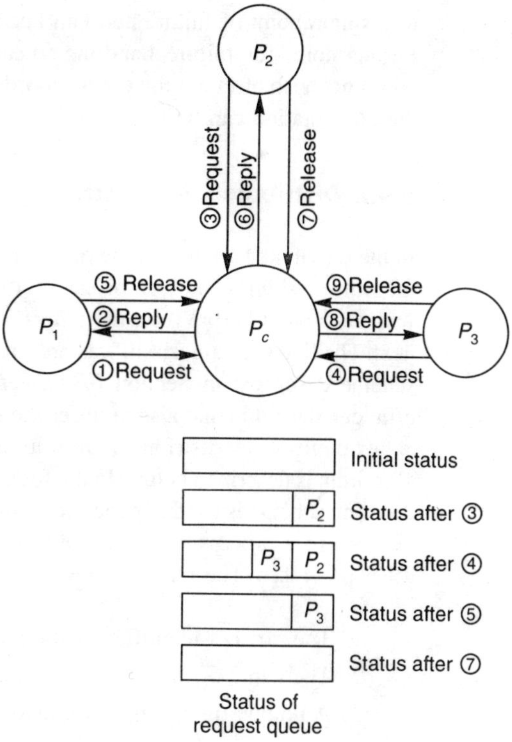


**Fig. 6.6** Example illustrating the centralized approach for mutual exclusion.

cannot be granted permission, so no reply is sent immediately to $P_3$ by $P_c$, and its request is queued in the request queue.

Now suppose $P_1$ exits the critical section and sends a *release* message to $P_c$ releasing its exclusive access to the critical section. On receiving the release message, $P_c$ takes the first request from the queue of deferred requests and sends a reply message to the corresponding process, granting it permission to enter the critical section. Therefore, in this case, $P_c$ sends a reply message to $P_2$.

On receiving the reply message, $P_2$ enters the critical section, and when it exits the critical section, it sends a release message to $P_c$. Again $P_c$ takes the first request from the request queue (in this case request of $P_3$) and sends a reply message to the corresponding process ($P_3$). On receiving the reply message, $P_3$ enters the critical section, and when it exits the critical section, it sends a release message to $P_c$. Now since there are no more requests, $P_c$ keeps waiting for the next request message.

This algorithm ensures mutual exclusion because, at a time, the coordinator allows only one process to enter a critical section. The algorithm also ensures that no starvation will occur because of the use of first-come, first-served scheduling policy. The main advantages of this algorithm is that it is simple to implement and requires only three messages per critical section entry: a request, a reply, and a release. However, it suffers from the usual drawbacks of centralized schemes. That is, a single coordinator is subject to a single point of failure and can become a performance bottleneck in a large system. Furthermore, for failure handling, means must be provided to detect a failure of the coordinator, to elect a unique new coordinator, and to reconstruct its request queue before the computation can be resumed.

### 6.4.2 Distributed Approach

In the distributed approach, the decision making for mutual exclusion is distributed across the entire system. That is, all processes that want to enter the same critical section cooperate with each other before reaching a decision on which process will enter the critical section next. The first such algorithm was presented by Lamport [1978] based on his event-ordering scheme described in Section 6.3. Later, Ricart and Agrawala [1981] proposed a more efficient algorithm that also requires there be a total ordering of all events in the system. As an example of a distributed algorithm for mutual exclusion, Ricart and Agrawala's algorithm is described below. In the following description we assume that Lamport's event-ordering scheme is used to generate a unique timestamp for each event in the system.

When a process wants to enter a critical section, it sends a request message to all other processes. The message contains the following information:

1. The process identifier of the process
2. The name of the critical section that the process wants to enter
3. A unique timestamp generated by the process for the request message

On receiving a request message, a process either immediately sends back a reply message to the sender or defers sending a reply based on the following rules:

1. If the receiver process is itself currently executing in the critical section, it simply queues the request message and defers sending a reply.
2. If the receiver process is currently not executing in the critical section but is waiting for its turn to enter the critical section, it compares the timestamp in the received request message with the timestamp in its own request message that it has sent to other processes. If the timestamp of the received request message is lower, it means that the sender process made a request before the receiver process to enter the critical section. Therefore, the receiver process immediately sends back a reply message to the sender. On the other hand, if the receiver process's own request message has a lower timestamp, the receiver queues the received request message and defers sending a reply message.
3. If the receiver process neither is in the critical section nor is waiting for its turn to enter the critical section, it immediately sends back a reply message.

A process that sends out a request message keeps waiting for reply messages from other processes. It enters the critical section as soon as it has received reply messages from all processes. After it finishes executing in the critical section, it sends reply messages to all processes in its queue and deletes them from its queue.

To illustrate how the algorithm works, let us consider the example of Figure 6.7. There are four processes $P_1$, $P_2$, $P_3$, and $P_4$. While process $P_4$ is in a critical section, processes $P_1$ and $P_2$ want to enter the same critical section. To get permission from other processes, processes $P_1$ and $P_2$ send request messages with timestamps 6 and 4 respectively to other processes (Fig. 6.7(*a*)).

Now let us consider the situation in Figure 6.7(*b*). Since process $P_4$ is already in the critical section, it defers sending a reply message to $P_1$ and $P_2$ and enters them in its queue. Process $P_3$ is currently not interested in the critical section, so it sends a reply

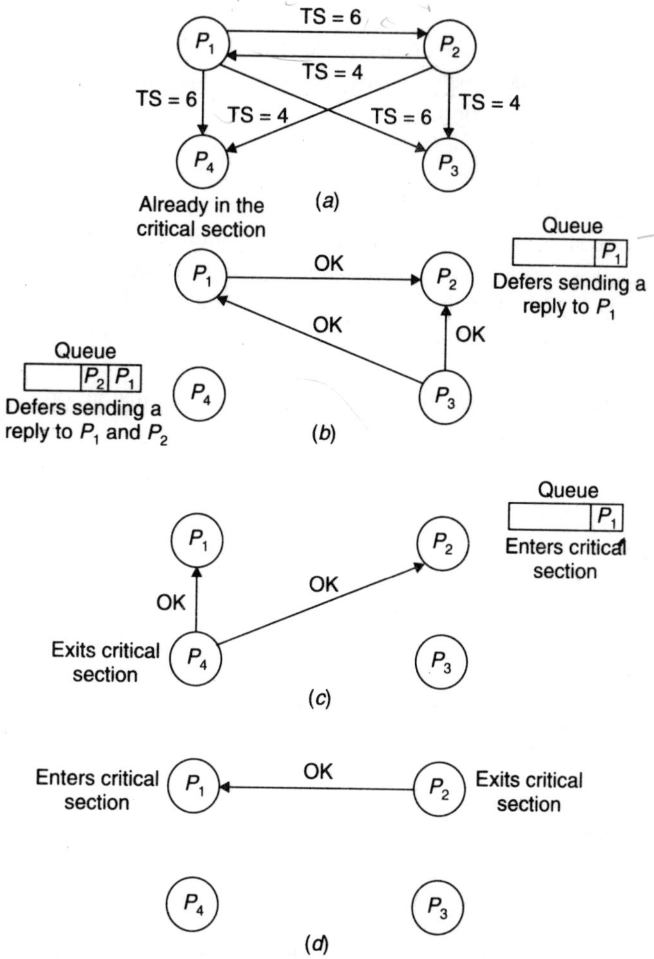


**Fig. 6.7** Example illustrating the distributed algorithm for mutual exclusion: (*a*) status when processes $P_1$ and $P_2$ send request messages to other processes while process $P_4$ is already in the critical section; (*b*) status while process $P_4$ is still in critical section; (*c*) status after process $P_4$ exits critical section; (*d*) status after process $P_2$ exits critical section.

message to both $P_1$ and $P_2$. Process $P_2$ defers sending a reply message to $P_1$ and enters $P_1$ in its queue because the timestamp (4) in its own request message is less than the timestamp (6) in $P_1$'s request message. On the other hand, $P_1$ immediately replies to $P_2$ because the timestamp (6) in its request message is found to be greater than the timestamp (4) of $P_2$'s request message.

Next consider the situation in Figure 6.7(*c*). When process $P_4$ exits the critical section, it sends a reply message to all processes in its queue (in this case to processes $P_1$ and $P_2$) and deletes them from its queue. Now since process $P_2$ has received a reply message from all other processes ($P_1$, $P_3$, and $P_4$), it enters the critical section. However, process $P_1$ continues to wait since it has not yet received a reply message from process $P_2$.

Finally, when process $P_2$ exits the critical section, it sends a reply message to $P_1$ (Fig. 6.7(*d*)). Now since process $P_1$ has received a reply message from all other processes, it enters the critical section.

The algorithm guarantees mutual exclusion because a process can enter its critical section only after getting permission from all other processes, and in the case of a conflict only one of the conflicting processes can get permission from all other processes. The algorithm also ensures freedom from starvation since entry to the critical section is scheduled according to the timestamp ordering. It has also been proved by Ricart and Agrawala [1981] that the algorithm is free from deadlock. Furthermore, if there are $n$ processes, the algorithm requires $n$–1 request messages and $n$–1 reply messages, giving a total of 2($n$–1) messages per critical section entry. However, this algorithm suffers from the following drawbacks because of the requirement that all processes must participate in a critical section entry request by any process:

1. In a system having $n$ processes, the algorithm is liable to $n$ points of failure because if one of the processes fails, the entire scheme collapses. This is because the failed process will not reply to request messages that will be falsely interpreted as denial of permission by the requesting processes, causing all the requesting processes to wait indefinitely.

Tanenbaum [1995] proposed a simple modification to the algorithm to solve this problem. In the modified algorithm, instead of remaining silent by deferring the sending of the reply message in cases when permission cannot be granted immediately, the receiver sends a "permission denied" reply message to the requesting process and then later sends an OK message when the permission can be granted. Therefore, a reply message (either "permission denied" or OK) is immediately sent to the requesting process in any case. If the requesting process does not receive a reply from a process within a fixed timeout period, it either keeps trying until the process replies or concludes that the process has crashed. When the requesting process receives a "permission denied" reply message from one or more of the processes, it blocks until an OK message is received from all of them.

2. The algorithm requires that each process know the identity of all the processes participating in the mutual-exclusion algorithm. This requirement makes implementation of the algorithm complex because each process of a group needs to dynamically keep track

of the processes entering or leaving the group. That is, when a process joins a group, it must receive the names of all the other processes in the group, and the name of the new process must be distributed to all the other processes in the group. Similarly, when a process leaves the group or crashes, all members of that group must be informed so that they can delete it from their membership list. Updating of the membership list is particularly difficult when request and reply messages are already being exchanged among the processes of the group. Therefore, the algorithm is suitable only for groups whose member processes are fixed and do not change dynamically.

3. In this algorithm, a process willing to enter a critical section can do so only after communicating with all other processes and getting permission from them. Therefore, assuming that the network can handle only one message at a time, the waiting time from the moment the process makes a request to enter a critical region until it actually enters the critical section is the time for exchanging $2(n-1)$ messages in a system having $n$ processes. This waiting time may be large if there are too many processes in the system. Therefore, the algorithm is suitable only for a small group of cooperating processes.

Some improvements to this algorithm have been proposed in the literature. For instance, a simple improvement is possible by using the idea of majority consensus rather than the consensus of all other processes for critical section entry [Tanenbaum 1995]. That is, in an algorithm that uses the idea of majority consensus, a process can enter a critical section as soon as it has collected permission from a majority of the other processes, rather than from all of them. Note that in this algorithm a process can grant permission for a critical section entry to only a single process at a time. Two other possible improvements to the algorithm can be found in [Carvalho and Roucairol 1983, Maekawa et al. 1987].

### 6.4.3 Token-Passing Approach

In this method, mutual exclusion is achieved by using a single token that is circulated among the processes in the system. A *token* is a special type of message that entitles its holder to enter a critical section. For fairness, the processes in the system are logically organized in a ring structure, and the token is circulated from one process to another around the ring always in the same direction (clockwise or anticlockwise).

The algorithm works as follows. When a process receives the token, it checks if it wants to enter a critical section and acts as follows:

- If it wants to enter a critical section, it keeps the token, enters the critical section, and exits from the critical section after finishing its work in the critical section. It then passes the token along the ring to its neighbor process. Note that the process can enter only one critical section when it receives the token. If it wants to enter another critical section, it must wait until it gets the token again.
- If it does not want to enter a critical section, it just passes the token along the ring to its neighbor process. Therefore, if none of the processes is interested in entering a critical section, the token simply keeps circulating around the ring.

Mutual exclusion is guaranteed by the algorithm because at any instance of time only one process can be in a critical section, since there is only a single token. Furthermore, since the ring is unidirectional and a process is permitted to enter only one critical section each time it gets the token, starvation cannot occur. In this algorithm the number of messages per critical section entry may vary from 1 (when every process always wants to enter a critical section) to an unbounded value (when no process wants to enter a critical section). Moreover, for a total of $n$ processes in the system, the waiting time from the moment a process wants to enter a critical section until its actual entry may vary from the time needed to exchange 0 to $n$–1 token-passing messages. Zero token-passing messages are needed when the process receives the token just when it wants to enter the critical section, whereas $n$–1 messages are needed when the process wants to enter the critical section just after it has passed the token to its neighbor process.

The algorithm, however, requires the handling of the following types of failures:

1. *Process failure*. A process failure in the system causes the logical ring to break. In such a situation, a new logical ring must be established to ensure the continued circulation of the token among other processes. This requires detection of a failed process and dynamic reconfiguration of the logical ring when a failed process is detected or when a failed process recovers after failure.

Detection of a failed process can be easily done by making it a rule that a process receiving the token from its neighbor always sends an acknowledgment message to its neighbor. With this rule, a process detects that its neighbor has failed when it sends the token to it but does not receive the acknowledgment message within a fixed timeout period. On the other hand, dynamic reconfiguration of the logical ring can be done by maintaining the current ring configuration with each process. When a process detects that its neighbor has failed, it removes the failed process from the group by skipping it and passing the token to the process after it (actually to the next alive process in the sequence). When a process becomes alive after recovery, it simply informs the neighbor previous to it in the ring so that it gets the token during the next round of circulation.

2. *Lost token*. If the token is lost, a new token must be generated. Therefore, the algorithm must also have mechanisms to detect and regenerate a lost token. One method to solve this problem is to designate one of the processes on the ring as a "monitor" process. The monitor process periodically circulates a "who has the token?" message on the ring. This message rotates around the ring from one process to another. All processes simply pass this message to their neighbor process, except the process that has the token when it receives this message. This process writes its identifier in a special field of the message before passing it to its neighbor. When the message returns to the monitor process after one complete round, it checks the special field of the message. If there is no entry in this field, it concludes that the token has been lost, generates a new token, and circulates it around the ring.

There are two problems associated with this method—the monitor process may itself fail and the "who has the token?" message may itself get lost. Both problems may be solved by using more than one monitor processes. Each monitor process independently checks the availability of the token on the ring. However, when a monitor process detects that the token is lost, it holds an election with other monitor processes to decide which monitor process will generate and circulate a new token (election algorithms are described later in this chapter). An election is needed to prevent the generation of multiple tokens that may happen when each monitor process independently detects that the token is lost, and each one generates a new token.

## 6.5 DEADLOCK

We saw in the previous section that there are several resources in a system for which the resource allocation policy must ensure exclusive access by a process. Since a system consists of a finite number of units of each resource type (for example, three printers, six tape drives, four disk drives, two CPUs, etc.), multiple concurrent processes normally have to compete to use a resource. In this situation, the sequence of events required to use a resource by a process is as follows:

1. *Request*. The process first makes a request for the resource. If the requested resource is not available, possibly because it is being used by another process, the requesting process must wait until the requested resource is allocated to it by the system. Note that if the system has multiple units of the requested resource type, the allocation of any unit of the type will satisfy the request. Also note that a process may request as many units of a resource as it requires with the restriction that the number of units requested may not exceed the total number of available units of the resource.

2. *Allocate*. The system allocates the resource to the requesting process as soon as possible. It maintains a table in which it records whether each resource is free or allocated and, if it is allocated, to which process. If the requested resource is currently allocated to another process, the requesting process is added to a queue of processes waiting for this resource. Once the system allocates the resource to the requesting process, that process can exclusively use the resource by operating on it.

3. *Release*. After the process has finished using the allocated resource, it releases the resource to the system. The system table records are updated at the time of allocation and release to reflect the current status of availability of resources.

The request and release of resources are system calls, such as *request* and *release* for devices, *open* and *close* for files, and *allocate* and *free* for memory space. Notice that of the three operations, *allocate* is the only operation that the system can control. The other two operations are initiated by a process.

With the above-mentioned pattern of request, allocation, and release of resources, if the total request made by multiple concurrent processes for resources of a certain type exceeds the amount available, some strategy is needed to order the assignment of resources in time. Care must be taken that the strategy applied cannot cause a deadlock, that is, a situation in which competing processes prevent their mutual progress even though no single one requests more resources than are available. It may happen that some of the processes that entered the waiting state (because the requested resources were not available at the time of request) will never again change state, because the resources they have requested are held by other waiting processes. This situation is called *deadlock*, and the processes involved are said to be *deadlocked*. Hence, deadlock is the state of permanent blocking of a set of processes each of which is waiting for an event that only another process in the set can cause. All the processes in the set block permanently because all the processes are waiting and hence none of them will ever cause any of the events that could wake up any of the other members of the set.

A deadlock situation can be best explained with the help of an example. Suppose that a system has two tape drives $T_1$ and $T_2$ and the resource allocation strategy is such that a requested resource is immediately allocated to the requester if the resource is free. Also suppose that two concurrent processes $P_1$ and $P_2$ make requests for the tape drives in the following order:

1. $P_1$ requests for one tape drive and the system allocates $T_1$ to it.
2. $P_2$ requests for one tape drive and the system allocates $T_2$ to it.
3. $P_1$ requests for one more tape drive and enters a waiting state because no tape drive is presently available.
4. $P_2$ requests for one more tape drive and it also enters a waiting state because no tape drive is presently available.

From now on, $P_1$ and $P_2$ will wait for each other indefinitely, since $P_1$ will not release $T_1$ until it gets $T_2$ to carry out its designated task, that is, not until $P_2$ has released $T_2$, whereas $P_2$ will not release $T_2$ until it gets $T_1$. Therefore, the two processes are in a state of deadlock. Note that the requests made by the two processes are totally legal because each is requesting for only two tape drives, which is the total number of tape drives available in the system. However, the deadlock problem occurs because the total requests of both processes exceed the total number of units for the tape drive and the resource allocation policy is such that it immediately allocates a resource on request if the resource is free.

In the context of deadlocks, the term "resource" applies not only to physical objects (such as tape and disk drives, printers, CPU cycles, and memory space) but also to logical objects (such as a locked record in a database, files, tables, semaphores, and monitors). However, these resources should permit only exclusive use by a single process at a time and should be nonpreemptable. A *nonpreemptable resource* is one that cannot be taken away from a process to which it was allocated until the process voluntarily releases it. If taken away, it has ill effects on the computation already performed by the process. For example, a printer is a nonpreemptable resource because taking the printer away from a process that has started printing but has not yet completed its printing job and giving it to another process may produce printed output that contains a mixture of the output of the two processes. This is certainly unacceptable.

### 6.5.1 Necessary Conditions for Deadlock

Coffman et al. [1971] stated that the following conditions are necessary for a deadlock situation to occur in a system:

1. *Mutual-exclusion condition.* If a resource is held by a process, any other process requesting for that resource must wait until the resource has been released.
2. *Hold-and-wait condition.* Processes are allowed to request for new resources without releasing the resources that they are currently holding.
3. *No-preemption condition.* A resource that has been allocated to a process becomes available for allocation to another process only after it has been voluntarily released by the process holding it.
4. *Circular-wait condition.* Two or more processes must form a circular chain in which each process is waiting for a resource that is held by the next member of the chain.

All four conditions must hold simultaneously in a system for a deadlock to occur. If any one of them is absent, no deadlock can occur. Notice that the four conditions are not completely independent because the circular-wait condition implies the hold-and-wait condition. Although these four conditions are somewhat interrelated, it is quite useful to consider them separately to devise methods for deadlock prevention.

### 6.5.2 Deadlock Modeling

Deadlocks can be modeled using directed graphs. Before presenting a graphical model for deadlocks, some terminology from graph theory is needed:

1. *Directed graph.* A directed graph is a pair $(N, E)$, where $N$ is a nonempty set of nodes and $E$ is a set of directed edges. A directed edge is an ordered pair $(a, b)$, where $a$ and $b$ are nodes in $N$.
2. *Path.* A path is a sequence of nodes $(a, b, c, \ldots, i, j)$ of a directed graph such that $(a, b), (b, c), \ldots, (i, j)$ are directed edges. Obviously, a path contains at least two nodes.
3. *Cycle.* A cycle is a path whose first and last nodes are the same.
4. *Reachable set.* The reachable set of a node $a$ is the set of all nodes $b$ such that a path exists from $a$ to $b$.
5. *Knot.* A knot is a nonempty set $K$ of nodes such that the reachable set of each node in $K$ is exactly the set $K$. A knot always contains one or more cycles.

An example of a directed graph is shown in Figure 6.8. The graph has a set of nodes $\{a, b, c, d, e, f\}$ and a set of directed edges $\{(a, b), (b, c), (c, d), (d, e), (e, f), (f, a), (e, b)\}$. It has two cycles $(a, b, c, d, e, f, a)$ and $(b, c, d, e, b)$. It also has a knot $\{a, b, c, d, e, f\}$ that contains the two cycles of the graph.

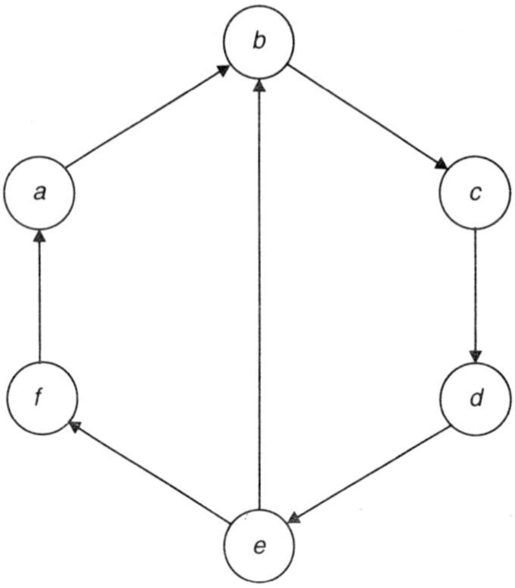


**Fig. 6.8** A directed graph.

For deadlock modeling, a directed graph, called a *resource allocation graph*, is used in which both the set of nodes and the set of edges are partitioned into two types, resulting in the following graph elements:

1. *Process nodes*. A process node represents a process of the system. In a resource allocation graph, it is normally shown as a circle, with the name of the process written inside the circle (nodes $P_1$, $P_2$, and $P_3$ of Fig. 6.9).

2. *Resource nodes*. A resource node represents a resource of the system. In a resource allocation graph, it is normally shown as a rectangle with the name of the resource written inside the rectangle. Since a resource type $R_j$ may have more than one unit in the system, each such unit is represented as a bullet within the rectangle. For instance, in the resource allocation graph of Figure 6.9, there are two units of resource $R_1$, one unit of $R_2$, and three units of $R_3$.

3. *Assignment edges*. An assignment edge is a directed edge from a resource node to a process node. It signifies that the resource is currently held by the process. In multiple units of a resource type, the tail of an assignment edge touches one of the bullets in the rectangle to indicate that only one unit of the resource is held by that process. Edges ($R_1$, $P_1$), ($R_1$, $P_3$), and ($R_2$, $P_2$) are the three assignment edges in the resource allocation graph of Figure 6.9.

4. *Request edges*. A request edge is a directed edge from a process node to a resource node. It signifies that the process made a request for a unit of the resource type and is currently waiting for that resource. Edges ($P_1$, $R_2$) and ($P_2$, $R_1$) are the two request edges in the resource allocation graph of Figure 6.9.

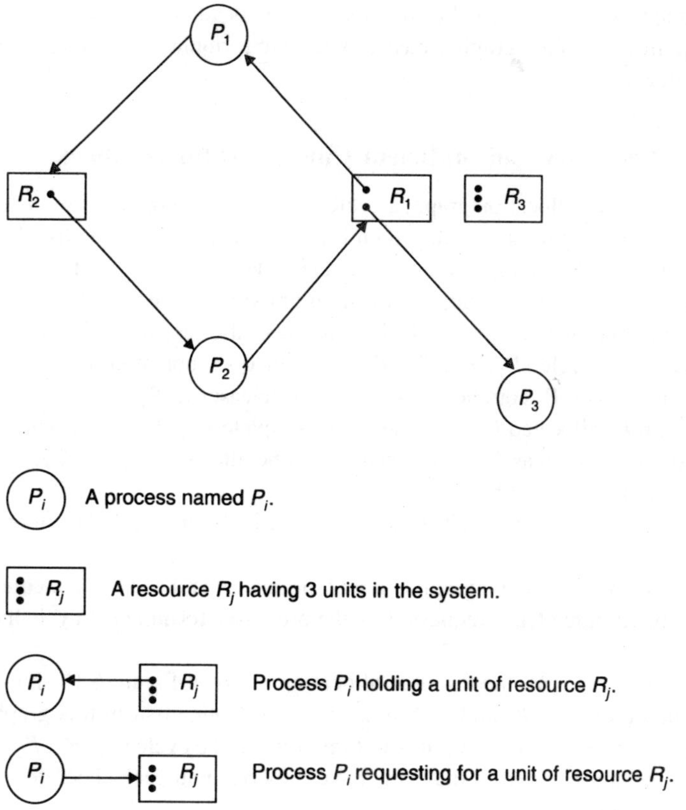


**Fig. 6.9** Resource allocation graph.

## Constructing a Resource Allocation Graph

A resource allocation graph provides an overall view of the processes holding or waiting for the various resources in the system. Therefore, the graph changes dynamically as the processes in the system request for or release resources or the system allocates a resource to a process. That is, when a process $P_i$ requests for a unit of resource type $R_j$, a request edge $(P_i, R_j)$ is inserted in the resource allocation graph. When this request can be fulfilled, a unit of resource $R_j$ is allocated to $P_i$ and the request edge $(P_i, R_j)$ is instantaneously transformed to an assignment edge $(R_j, P_i)$. Later, when $P_i$ releases $R_j$, the assignment edge $(R_j, P_i)$ is deleted from the graph.

Note that in many systems the resource allocation graph is not constructed in the above-mentioned manner. Rather it is used as a tool for making resource allocation decisions that do not lead to deadlock. In these systems, for the available resources, different request/release sequences are simulated step by step, and after every step, the graph is checked for deadlock. Later, in the resource allocation strategy, only those sequences are allowed that do not lead to deadlock. Therefore, in these systems, the resource allocation graph is basically used to formulate a deadlock free resource allocation strategy.

### Necessary and Sufficient Conditions for Deadlock

In a resource allocation graph, a cycle is a necessary condition for a deadlock to exist. That is, if the graph has no cycles, then it represents a state that is free from deadlock. On the other hand, if the graph contains a cycle, a deadlock may exist. Therefore, the presence of a cycle in a general resource allocation graph is a necessary but not a sufficient condition for the existence of deadlock. For instance, the resource allocation graph of Figure 6.9 contains a cycle ($P_1$, $R_2$, $P_2$, $R_1$, $P_1$) but does not represent a deadlock state. This is because when $P_3$ completes using $R_1$ and releases it, $R_1$ can be allocated to $P_2$. With both $R_1$ and $R_2$ allocated to it, $P_2$ can now complete its job after which it will release both $R_1$ and $R_2$. As soon as $R_2$ is released, it can be allocated to $P_1$. Therefore, all processes can finish their job one by one.

The sufficient condition for deadlock is different for the following different cases:

1. A cycle in the graph is both a necessary and a sufficient condition for deadlock if all the resource types requested by the processes forming the cycle have only a single unit each.

For example, the resource allocation graph of Figure 6.10 shows a deadlock state in which processes $P_1$ and $P_2$ are deadlocked. Notice that in this graph, although there are three units of resource $R_3$, it is not involved in the cycle ($P_1$, $R_2$, $P_2$, $R_1$, $P_1$). Both $R_1$ and $R_2$ that are involved in the cycle have only one unit each. Therefore, the cycle represents a deadlock state.

2. A cycle in the graph is a necessary but not a sufficient condition for deadlock if one or more of the resource types requested by the processes forming the cycle have more than one unit. In this case, a knot is a sufficient condition for deadlock.

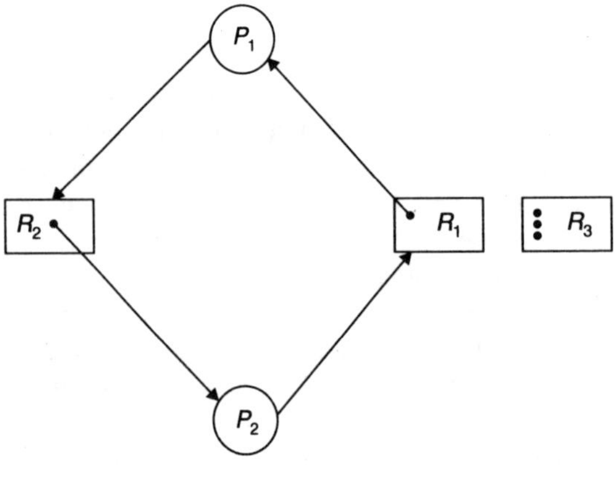


**Fig. 6.10** A cycle representing a deadlock.

We have already seen that the cycle ($P_1$, $R_2$, $P_2$, $R_1$, $P_1$) in the graph of Figure 6.9 does not represent a deadlock. This is because resource type $R_1$ has two units and there are no knots in the graph. Now suppose that in the same graph $P_3$ requests for $R_2$ and a request edge ($P_3$, $R_2$) is added to the graph. The modified graph is shown in Figure 6.11. This graph has two cycles ($P_1$, $R_2$, $P_2$, $R_1$, $P_1$) and ($P_3$, $R_2$, $P_2$, $R_1$, $P_3$) and a knot {$P_1$, $P_2$, $P_3$, $R_1$, $R_2$}. Since the graph contains a knot, it represents a deadlock state in which processes $P_1$, $P_2$, and $P_3$ are deadlocked.

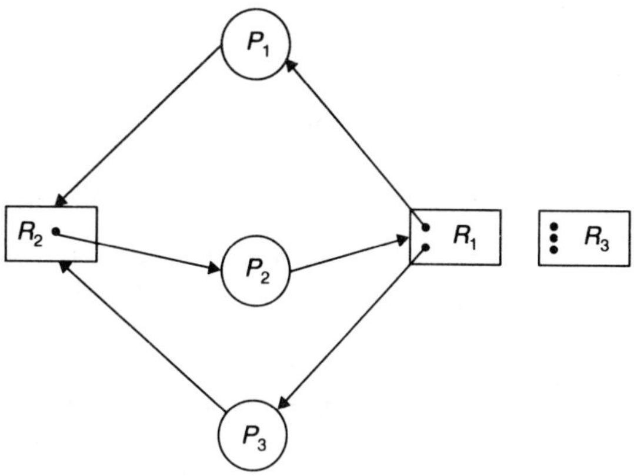


**Fig. 6.11** A knot representing a deadlock.

In terms of the resource allocation graph, the necessary and sufficient conditions for deadlock can be summarized as follows:

- A cycle is a necessary condition for deadlock.
- If there is only a single unit of each resource type involved in the cycle, a cycle is both a necessary and a sufficient condition for a deadlock to exist.
- If one or more of the resource types involved in the cycle have more than one unit, a knot is a sufficient condition for a deadlock to exist.

### Wait-for Graph

When all the resource types have only a single unit each, a simplified form of resource allocation graph is normally used. The simplified graph is obtained from the original resource allocation graph by removing the resource nodes and collapsing the appropriate edges. This simplification is based on the observation that a resource can always be identified by its current owner (process holding it). Figure 6.12 shows an example of a resource allocation graph and its simplified form.

The simplified graph is commonly known as a *wait-for graph* (*WFG*) because it clearly shows which processes are waiting for which other processes. For instance, in the WFG of Figure 6.12(*b*), processes $P_1$ and $P_3$ are waiting for $P_2$ and process $P_2$ is waiting for $P_1$. Since WFG is constructed only when each resource type has only a single unit, a cycle is both a necessary and sufficient condition for deadlock in a WFG.

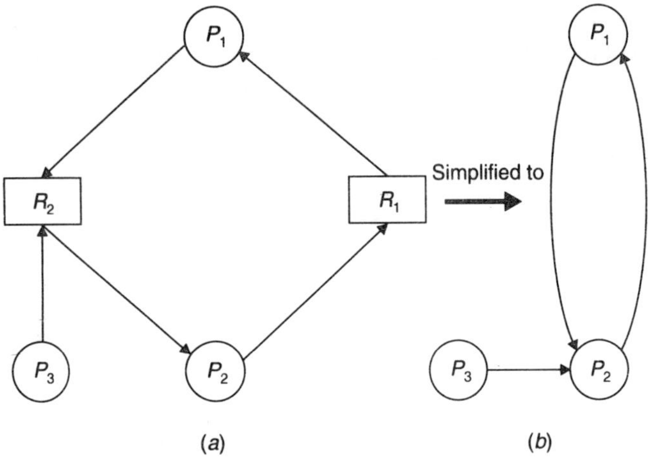


**Fig. 6.12** A conversion from a resource allocation graph to a WFG: (*a*) resource allocation graph; (*b*) corresponding WFG.

### 6.5.3 Handling Deadlocks in Distributed Systems

In principle, deadlocks in distributed systems are similar to deadlocks in centralized systems. Therefore, the description of deadlocks presented above holds good both for centralized and distributed systems. However, handling of deadlocks in distributed systems is more complex than in centralized systems because the resources, the processes, and other relevant information are scattered on different nodes of the system.

Three commonly used strategies to handle deadlocks are as follows:

1. *Avoidance*. Resources are carefully allocated to avoid deadlocks.
2. *Prevention*. Constraints are imposed on the ways in which processes request resources in order to prevent deadlocks.
3. *Detection and recovery*. Deadlocks are allowed to occur and a detection algorithm is used to detect them. After a deadlock is detected, it is resolved by certain means.

Although the third strategy is the most commonly used one in distributed systems, for completion, the other two strategies will also be briefly described.

At this point, it may also be noted that some people prefer to make a distinction between two kinds of distributed deadlocks—*resource deadlocks* and *communication deadlocks*. As already described, a resource deadlock occurs when two or more processes wait permanently for resources held by each other. On the other hand, a communication deadlock occurs among a set of processes when they are blocked waiting for messages from other processes in the set in order to start execution but there are no messages in transit between them. When there are no messages in transit between any pair of processes in the set, none of the processes will ever receive a message. This implies that all processes in the set are deadlocked. Communication deadlocks can be easily modeled by using WFGs to indicate which processes are waiting to receive messages from which other processes. Hence, the detection of communication deadlocks can be done in the same manner as that for systems having only one unit of each resource type.

### Deadlock Avoidance

Deadlock avoidance methods use some advance knowledge of the resource usage of processes to predict the future state of the system for avoiding allocations that can eventually lead to a deadlock. Deadlock avoidance algorithms are usually in the following steps:

1. When a process requests for a resource, even if the resource is available for allocation, it is not immediately allocated to the process. Rather, the system simply assumes that the request is granted.
2. With the assumption made in step 1 and advance knowledge of the resource usage of processes, the system performs some analysis to decide whether granting the process's request is safe or unsafe.
3. The resource is allocated to the process only when the analysis of step 2 shows that it is safe to do so; otherwise the request is deferred.

Since the algorithms for deadlock avoidance are based on the concept of safe and unsafe states, it is important to look at the notion of safety in resource allocation. A system is said to be in a *safe state* if it is not in a deadlock state and there exists some ordering of the processes in which the resource requests of the processes can be granted to run all of them to completion. For a particular safe state there may be many such process orderings. Any ordering of the processes that can guarantee the completion of all the processes is called a *safe sequence*. The formation of a safe sequence is based on the idea of satisfying the condition that, for any process $P_i$ in a safe sequence, the resources that $P_i$ can still request can be satisfied by the currently available resources plus the resources held by all the processes lying before $P_i$ in the safe sequence. This condition guarantees that process $P_i$ can be run to completion because if the resources that $P_i$ needs are not immediately available, $P_i$ can wait until all other processes in the sequence lying before $P_i$ have finished. When they have finished, $P_i$ can obtain all its needed resources and run to completion. A system state is said to be *unsafe* if no safe sequence exists for that state.

The concept of safe and unsafe states can be best illustrated with the help of an example. Let us assume that in a system there are a total of 8 units of a particular resource type for which three processes $P_1$, $P_2$, and $P_3$ are competing. Suppose the maximum units of the resource required by $P_1$, $P_2$, and $P_3$ are 4, 5, and 6, respectively. Also suppose that currently each of the three processes is holding 2 units of the resource. Therefore, in the current state of the system, 2 units of the resource are free. The current state of the system can be modeled as shown in Figure 6.13($a$).

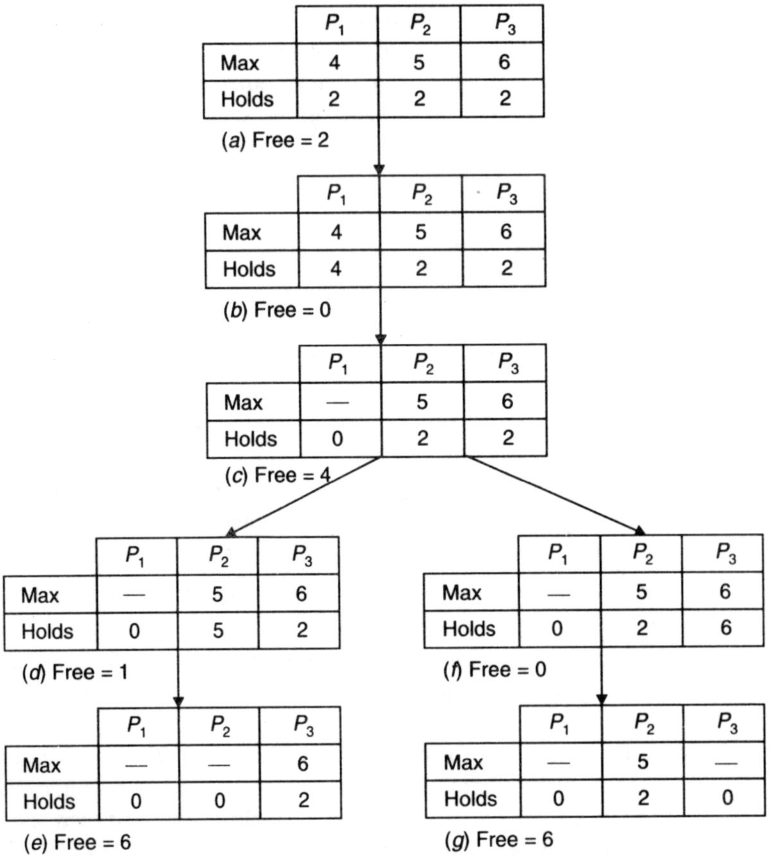


**Fig. 6.13** Demonstration that the state in (*a*) is a safe state and has two safe sequences.

Now let us try to find out whether the state of Figure 6.13(*a*) is safe or unsafe. The analysis performed in Figure 6.13 shows that this state is safe because there exists a sequence of allocations that allows all processes to complete. In fact, as shown in the figure, for this state there are two safe sequences, $(P_1, P_2, P_3)$ and $(P_1, P_3, P_2)$. Let us see the scheduling of the resource units for the first of these two safe sequences. Starting from the state of Figure 6.13(*a*), the scheduler could simply run $P_1$ exclusively, until it asked for and got two more units of the resource that are currently free, leading to the state of Figure 6.13(*b*). When $P_1$ completes and releases the resources held by it, we get the state of Figure 6.13(*c*). Then the scheduler chooses to run $P_2$, eventually leading to the state of Figure 6.13(*d*). When $P_2$ completes and releases the resources held by it, the system enters the state of Figure 6.13(*e*). Now with the available resources, $P_3$ can be run to completion. The initial state of Figure 6.13(*a*) is a safe state because the system, by careful scheduling, can avoid deadlock. This example also shows that for a particular state there may be more than one safe sequence.

If resource allocation is not done cautiously, the system may move from a safe state to an unsafe state. For instance, let us consider the example shown in Figure 6.14. Figure 6.14(*a*) is the same initial state as that of Figure 6.13(*a*). This time, suppose process $P_2$ requests for one additional unit of the resource and the same is allocated to it by the system. The resulting system state is shown in Figure 6.14(*b*). The system is no longer in a safe state because we only have one unit of the resource free, which is not sufficient to run any of the three processes to completion. Therefore, there is no safe sequence for the state of Figure 6.14(*b*). Thus the decision to allocate one unit of the resource to $P_2$ moved the system from a safe state to an unsafe state.

| | $P_1$ | $P_2$ | $P_3$ |
|---|---|---|---|
| Max | 4 | 5 | 6 |
| Holds | 2 | 2 | 2 |

(*a*) Free = 2

| | $P_1$ | $P_2$ | $P_3$ |
|---|---|---|---|
| Max | 4 | 5 | 6 |
| Holds | 2 | 3 | 2 |

(*b*) Free = 1

**Fig. 6.14** Demonstration that an allocation may move the system from a safe to an unsafe state.

It is important to note the following remarks about safe and unsafe states:

1. The initial state in which no resources are yet allocated and all are available (free) is always a safe state.
2. From a safe state, the system can guarantee that all processes can be run to completion.
3. An unsafe state is not a deadlock state, but it may lead to a deadlock state. That is, from an unsafe state, the system cannot guarantee that all processes can be run to completion.

Deadlock avoidance algorithms basically perform resource allocation in such a manner as to ensure that the system will always remain in a safe state. Since the initial state of a system is always a safe state, whenever a process requests a resource that is currently available, the system checks to find out if the allocation of the resource to the process will change the state of the system from safe to unsafe. If no, the request is immediately granted; otherwise it is deferred.

Although theoretically attractive, deadlock avoidance algorithms are rarely used in practice due to the following reasons:

1. The algorithms work on the assumption that advance knowledge of the resource requirements of the various processes is available. However, in practice, processes rarely know in advance what their maximum resource needs will be. Modern operating systems

are attempting to provide more and more user-friendly interfaces, and as a result, it is becoming common to have users who do not have the slightest idea about what their resource needs are.

2. The algorithms also assume that the number of processes that compete for a particular resource is fixed and known in advance. However, in practice, the number of processes is not fixed but dynamically varies as new users log in and log out.

3. The algorithms also assume that the number of units of a particular resource type is always fixed and known in advance. However, in practice, the actual number of units available may change dynamically due to the sudden breakdown and repair of one or more units.

4. The manner in which these algorithms work restricts resource allocation too severely and consequently degrades the system performance considerably. This is because the algorithms first consider the worst possible case and then guarantee that the system is deadlock free even in the worst situation. This worst situation may arise but would be very unlikely. Thus many safe requests could be turned down.

The practical limitations of deadlock avoidance algorithms become more severe in a distributed system because the collection of information needed for making resource allocation decisions at one point is difficult and inefficient. Therefore, the deadlock avoidance strategy is never used in distributed operating systems.

### Deadlock Prevention

This approach is based on the idea of designing the system in such a way that deadlocks become impossible. It differs from avoidance and detection in that no runtime testing of potential allocations need be performed.

We saw that mutual-exclusion, hold-and-wait, no-preemption, and circular-wait are the four necessary conditions for a deadlock to occur in a system. Therefore, if we can somehow ensure that at least one of these conditions is never satisfied, deadlocks will be impossible. Based on this idea, there are three important deadlock-prevention methods—collective requests, ordered requests, and preemption. The first one denies the hold-and-wait condition, the second one denies the circular-wait condition, and the third one denies the no-preemption condition.

The mutual-exclusion condition can also be denied for some nonsharable resources by devising an alternative way of using them. For instance, the following example, taken from [Tanenbaum 1992], illustrates how this can be done for a printer. A printer is a nonsharable resource. However, by spooling printer output, several processes can generate output at the same time. The spooled outputs are transferred one by one to the printer by the printer daemon. Therefore, the printer daemon is the only process that actually requests for the physical printer. Since the daemon never requests for any other resources, deadlock for the printer becomes structurally impossible. Unfortunately, in general, it is not possible to prevent deadlocks by denying the mutual-exclusion condition because some resources are intrinsically nonsharable and it is not possible to devise an alternative way of using them. Therefore, denial of the mutual-exclusion condition for deadlock prevention is rarely used. The other three methods that are more commonly used are described below.

***Collective Requests.*** This method denies the hold-and-wait condition by ensuring that whenever a process requests a resource, it does not hold any other resources. One of the following resource allocation policies may be used to ensure this:

1. A process must request all of its resources before it begins execution. If all the needed resources are available, they are allocated to the process so that the process can run to completion. If one or more of the requested resources are not available, none will be allocated and the process would just wait.

2. Instead of requesting all its resources before its execution starts, a process may request resources during its execution if it obeys the rule that it requests resources only when it holds no other resources. If the process is holding some resources, it can adhere to this rule by first releasing all of them and then re-requesting all the necessary resources.

The second policy has the following advantages over the first one:

1. In practice, many processes do not know how many resources they will need until they have started running. For such cases, the second approach is more useful.
2. A long process may require some resources only toward the end of its execution. In the first policy, the process will unnecessarily hold these resources for the entire duration of its execution. In the second policy, however, the process can request for these resources only when it needs them.

The collective requests method of deadlock prevention is simple and effective but has the following problems:

1. It generally has low resource utilization because a process may hold many resources but may not actually use several of them for fairly long periods.
2. It may cause starvation of a process that needs many resources, but whenever it makes a request for the needed resources, one or more of the resources is not available.
3. The method also raises an accounting question. When a process holds resources for extended periods during which they are not needed, it is not clear who should pay the charge for the idled resources.

***Ordered Requests.*** In this method, each resource type is assigned a unique global number to impose a total ordering of all resource types. Now a resource allocation policy is used according to which a process can request a resource at any time, but the process should not request a resource with a number lower than the number of any of the resources that it is already holding. That is, if a process holds a resource type whose number is $i$, it may request a resource type having the number $j$ only if $j > i$. If the process needs several units of the same resource type, it must issue a single request for all the units. It has been proven that with this rule the resource allocation graph can never have cycles (denying the circular-wait condition), and hence deadlock is impossible.

Note that this algorithm does not require that a process must acquire all its resources in strictly increasing sequence. For instance, a process holding two resources having numbers 3 and 7 may release the resource having number 7 before requesting a resource having number 5. This is allowed because when the process requests for the resource having number 5, it is not holding any resource having number larger than 5.

The ordering of resources is decided according to the natural usage pattern of the resources. For example, since the tape drive is usually needed before the printer, it would be reasonable to assign a lower number to the tape drive than to the printer. However, the natural ordering is not always the same for all jobs. Therefore, a job that matches the decided ordering can be expected to use resources efficiently but others would waste resources. Another difficulty is that once the ordering is decided, it will stay for a long time because the ordering is coded into programs. Reordering will require reprogramming of several jobs. However, reordering may become inevitable when new resources are added to the system. Despite these difficulties, the method of ordered requests is one of the most efficient methods for handling deadlocks.

***Preemption.*** A *preemptable* resource is one whose state can be easily saved and restored later. Such a resource can be temporarily taken away from the process to which it is currently allocated without causing any harm to the computation performed so far by the process. The CPU registers and main memory are examples of preemptable resources. If the resources are preemptable, deadlocks can be prevented by using either of the following resource allocation policies that deny the no-preemption condition:

1. When a process requests for a resource that is not currently available, all the resources held by the process are taken away (preempted) from it and the process is blocked. The process is unblocked when the resource requested by it and the resources preempted from it become available and can be allocated to it.

2. When a process requests a resource that is not currently available, the system checks if the requested resource is currently held by a process that is blocked, waiting for some other resource. If so, the requested resource is taken away (preempted) from the waiting process and given to the requesting process. Otherwise, the requesting process is blocked and waits for the requested resource to become available. Some of the resources that this process is already holding may be taken away (preempted) from it while it is blocked, waiting for the allocation of the requested resource. The process is unblocked when the resource requested by it and any other resource preempted from it become available and can be allocated to it.

In general, the applicability of this method for deadlock prevention is extremely limited because it works only for preemptable resources. However, the availability of atomic transactions and global timestamps makes this method an attractive approach for deadlock prevention in distributed and database transaction processing systems. The transaction mechanism allows a transaction (process) to be aborted (killed) without any ill effect (transactions are described in Chapter 9). This makes it possible to preempt resources from processes holding them without any harm.

In the transaction-based deadlock prevention method, each transaction is assigned a unique priority number by the system, and when two or more transactions compete for the same resource, their priority numbers are used to break the tie. For example, Lamport's algorithm may be used to generate systemwide globally unique timestamps, and each transaction may be assigned a unique timestamp when it is created. A transaction's timestamp may serve as its priority number; a transaction having lower value of timestamp may have higher priority because it is older.

Rosenkrantz et al. [1978] proposed the following deadlock prevention schemes based on this idea:

1. *Wait-die scheme*. In this scheme, if a transaction $T_i$ requests a resource that is currently held by another transaction $T_j$, $T_i$ is blocked (waits) if its timestamp is lower than that of $T_j$; otherwise it is aborted (dies). For example, suppose that of the three transactions $T_1$, $T_2$, and $T_3$, $T_1$ is the oldest (has the lowest timestamp value) and $T_3$ is the youngest (has the highest timestamp value). Now if $T_1$ requests a resource that is currently held by $T_2$, $T_1$ will be blocked and will wait until the resource is voluntarily released by $T_2$. On the other hand, if $T_3$ requests a resource held by $T_2$, $T_3$ will be aborted.

2. *Wait-wound scheme*. In this scheme, if a transaction $T_i$ requests a resource currently held by another transaction $T_j$, $T_i$ is blocked (waits) if its timestamp is larger than that of $T_j$; otherwise $T_j$ is aborted (wounded by $T_i$). Once again considering the same example of transactions $T_1$, $T_2$, and $T_3$, if $T_1$ requests a resource held by $T_2$, the resource will be preempted by aborting $T_2$ and will be given to $T_1$. On the other hand, if $T_3$ requests a resource held by $T_2$, $T_3$ will be blocked and will wait until the resource is voluntarily released by $T_2$.

Notice that both schemes favor older transactions, which is quite justified because, in general, an older transaction has run for a longer period and has used more system resources than a younger transaction. However, the manner in which the two schemes treat a younger transaction is worth noticing. In the wait-die scheme, a younger transaction is aborted when it requests for a resource held by an older transaction. The aborted transaction will be restarted after a predetermined time and will be aborted again if the older transaction is still holding the resource. This cycle may be repeated several times before the younger transaction actually gets the resource. This problem of the wait-die scheme can be solved by using an implementation mechanism that ensures that an aborted transaction is restarted only when its requested resource becomes available.

On the other hand, in the wait-wound scheme, when a younger transaction is aborted (wounded) by an older transaction, it will be restarted after a predetermined time, and this time it will be blocked (will wait) if its preempted resource is being held by the older transaction. Therefore, the implementation of the wait-wound scheme is simpler than the wait-die scheme. Furthermore, to avoid starvation, it is important that in the implementation of both schemes, a transaction should not be assigned a new timestamp when it is restarted after being aborted (a younger transaction will become older as time passes and will not be aborted again and again).

### Deadlock Detection

In this approach for deadlock handling, the system does not make any attempt to prevent deadlocks and allows processes to request resources and to wait for each other in an uncontrolled manner. Rather, it uses an algorithm that keeps examining the state of the system to determine whether a deadlock has occurred. When a deadlock is detected, the system takes some action to recover from the deadlock. Some methods for deadlock detection in distributed systems are presented below, and some of the ways to recover from a deadlock situation are presented in the next section.

In principle, deadlock detection algorithms are the same in both centralized and distributed systems. It is based on maintenance of information on resource allocation to various processes in the form of a resource allocation graph and searching for a cycle/knot in the graph depending on whether the system has single/multiple units of each resource type. However, for simplicity, in the following description we consider only the case of a single unit of each resource type. Therefore, the deadlock detection algorithms get simplified to maintaining WFG and searching for cycles in the WFG.

The following steps may be followed to construct the WFG for a distributed system:

1. Construct a separate WFG for each site of the system in the following manner. Using the convention of Figure 6.9, construct a resource allocation graph for all the resources located on this site. That is, in the resource allocation graph of a site, a resource node exists for all the local resources and a process node exists for all processes that are either holding or waiting for a resource of this site immaterial of whether the process is local or nonlocal.
2. Convert the resource allocation graph constructed in step 1 to a corresponding WFG by removing the resource nodes and collapsing the appropriate edges. It may be noted that step 1 and this step are mentioned here only for clarity of presentation. The actual algorithm may be designed to directly construct a WFG.
3. Take the union of the WFGs of all sites and construct a single global WFG.

Let us illustrate the procedure with the help of the simple example shown in Figure 6.15. Suppose that the system is comprised of only two sites ($S_1$ and $S_2$) with $S_1$ having two resources $R_1$ and $R_2$ and $S_2$ having one resource $R_3$. Also suppose that there are three processes ($P_1$, $P_2$, $P_3$) that are competing for the three resources in the following manner:

- $P_1$ is holding $R_1$ and requesting for $R_3$
- $P_2$ is holding $R_2$ and requesting for $R_1$
- $P_3$ is holding $R_3$ and requesting for $R_2$

The corresponding resource allocation graphs for the two sites are shown in Figure 6.15($a$). Notice that processes $P_1$ and $P_3$ appear in the graph of both the sites because they have requested for resources on both sites. On the other hand, process $P_2$ appears only in the graph of site $S_1$ because both resources requested by it are on $S_1$.

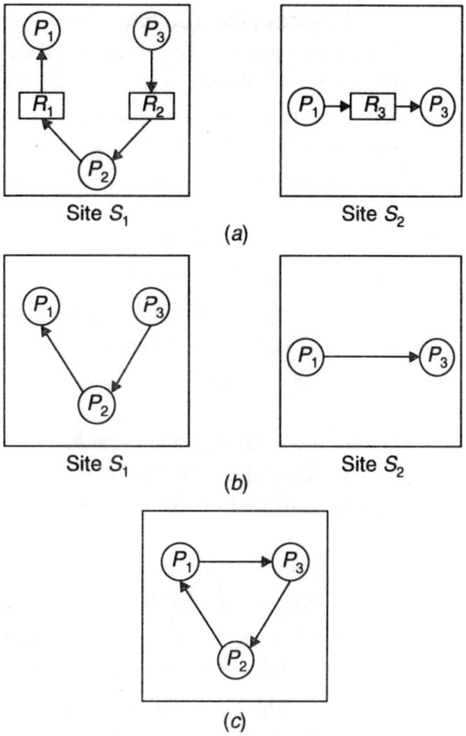


**Fig. 6.15** Illustration of the construction of a WFG in a distributed system: (*a*) resource allocation graphs of each site; (*b*) WFGs corresponding to graphs in (*a*); (*c*) global WFG by taking the union of the two local WFGs of (*b*).

Figure 6.15(*b*) shows the corresponding WFGs for the two sites and Figure 6.15(*c*) shows the global WFG obtained by taking the union of the local WFGs of the two sites. Notice that although the local WFGs of the two sites do not contain any cycle, the global WFG contains a cycle, implying that the system is in a deadlock state. Therefore, this example shows that the local WFGs are not sufficient to characterize all deadlocks in a distributed system and the construction of a global WFG by taking the union of all local WFGs is required to finally conclude whether the system is in a state of deadlock or not.

The main difficulty in implementing deadlock detection in a distributed system is how to maintain the WFG. Three commonly used techniques for organizing the WFG in a distributed system are centralized, hierarchical, and distributed. These techniques are described below. However, before we describe them, it may be noted that one of the most important features of deadlock detection algorithms is correctness, which depends on the following properties [Knapp 1987]:

1. *Progress property.* This property states that all deadlocks must be detected in a finite amount of time.
2. *Safety property.* If a deadlock is detected, it must indeed exist. Message delays and out-of-date WFGs sometimes cause false cycles to be detected, resulting in the detection of deadlocks that do not actually exist. Such deadlocks are called *phantom deadlocks*.

***Centralized Approach for Deadlock Detection.*** In the centralized deadlock detection approach, there is a local coordinator at each site that maintains a WFG for its local resources, and there is a central coordinator (also known as a centralized deadlock detector) that is responsible for constructing the union of all the individual WFGs. The central coordinator constructs the global WFG from information received from the local coordinators of all the sites. In this approach, deadlock detection is performed as follows:

1. If a cycle exists in the local WFG of any site, it represents a local deadlock. Such deadlocks are detected and resolved locally by the local coordinator of the site.
2. Deadlocks involving resources at two or more sites get reflected as cycles in the global WFG. Therefore, such deadlocks are detected and resolved by the central coordinator.

In the centralized approach, the local coordinators send local state information to the central coordinator in the form of messages. One of the following methods is used to transfer information from local coordinators to the central coordinator:

1. *Continuous transfer.* A local coordinator sends a message providing the update done in the local WFG whenever a new edge is added to or deleted from it.
2. *Periodic transfer.* To reduce the number of messages, a local coordinator periodically (when a number of changes have occurred in its local WFG) sends a list of edges added to or deleted from its WFG since the previous message was sent.
3. *Transfer-on-request.* A local coordinator sends a list of edges added to or deleted from its WFG since the previous message is sent only when the central coordinator makes a request for it. In this case, the central coordinator invokes the cycle detection algorithm periodically and requests information from each site just before invoking the algorithm.

Although the centralized deadlock detection approach is conceptually simple, it suffers from several drawbacks. First, it is vulnerable to failures of the central coordinator. Hence special provision for handling such faults have to be made. One approach is to provide a back-up central coordinator that duplicates the job of the central coordinator. Second, the centralized coordinator can constitute a performance bottleneck in large systems having too many sites. Third, the centralized coordinator may detect false deadlocks. Below we illustrate with a simple example how the algorithm may lead to the detection of false deadlocks and then we describe a method to overcome this third drawback.

Let us consider the same system configuration as that of Figure 6.15 and this time suppose that the three processes ($P_1$, $P_2$, $P_3$) compete for the three resources ($R_1$, $R_2$, $R_3$) in the following manner:

*Step 1:* $P_1$ requests for $R_1$ and $R_1$ is allocated to it.

*Step 2:* $P_2$ requests for $R_2$ and $R_2$ is allocated to it.

*Step 3:* $P_3$ requests for $R_3$ and $R_3$ is allocated to it.

*Step 4:* $P_2$ requests for $R_1$ and waits for it.

Step 5: $P_3$ requests for $R_2$ and waits for it.

*Step 6:* $P_1$ releases $R_1$ and $R_1$ is allocated to $P_2$.

*Step 7:* $P_1$ requests for $R_3$ and waits for it.

Assuming that the method of continuous transfer is employed by the algorithm, the following sequence of messages will be sent to the central coordinator:

$m_1$: from site $S_1$ to add the edge $(R_1, P_1)$
$m_2$: from site $S_1$ to add the edge $(R_2, P_2)$
$m_3$: from site $S_2$ to add the edge $(R_3, P_3)$
$m_4$: from site $S_1$ to add the edge $(P_2, R_1)$
$m_5$: from site $S_1$ to add the edge $(P_3, R_2)$
$m_6$: from site $S_1$ to delete edges $(R_1, P_1)$ and $(P_2, R_1)$, and add edge $(R_1, P_2)$
$m_7$: from site $S_2$ to add edge $(P_1, R_3)$

The resource allocation graphs maintained by the local coordinators of the two sites and the central coordinator are shown in Figure 6.16 (for clarity of presentation, the resource allocation graphs are shown instead of the WFGs). Figure 6.16(*a*) shows the graphs after step 5, that is, after message $m_5$ has been received by the central coordinator, and Figure 6.16(*b*) shows the graphs after message $m_7$ has been received by the central coordinator. The graph of the central coordinator in Figure 6.16(*b*) has no cycles, indicating that the system is free from deadlocks. However, suppose that message $m_7$ from site $S_2$ is received before message $m_6$ from site $S_1$ by the central coordinator. In this case, the central coordinator's view of the system will be as shown in the resource allocation graph of Figure 6.16(*c*). Therefore, the central coordinator will incorrectly conclude that a deadlock has occurred and may initiate deadlock recovery actions. Although the above example shows the possibility of detection of phantom deadlocks when the method of continuous transfer of information is used, phantom deadlocks may even get detected in the other two methods of information transfer due to incomplete or delayed information.

One method to avoid the detection of false deadlocks is to use Lamport's algorithm to append a unique global timestamp with each message. In our above example, since message $m_7$ from site $S_2$ to the central coordinator is caused by the request from site $S_1$ (see step 7), message $m_7$ will have a later timestamp than message $m_6$. Now if the central coordinator receives message $m_7$ before $m_6$ and detects a false deadlock, before taking any action to resolve the deadlock, it first confirms if the detected deadlock is a real one. For confirmation, it broadcasts a message asking all sites if any site has a message with timestamp earlier than $T$ for updation of the global WFG. On receiving this message, if a site has a message with timestamp earlier than $T$, it immediately sends it to the central coordinator; otherwise it simply sends a negative reply. After receiving replies from all the sites, the central coordinator updates the global WFG (if there are any update messages), and if the cycle detected before still exists, it concludes that the deadlock is a real one and

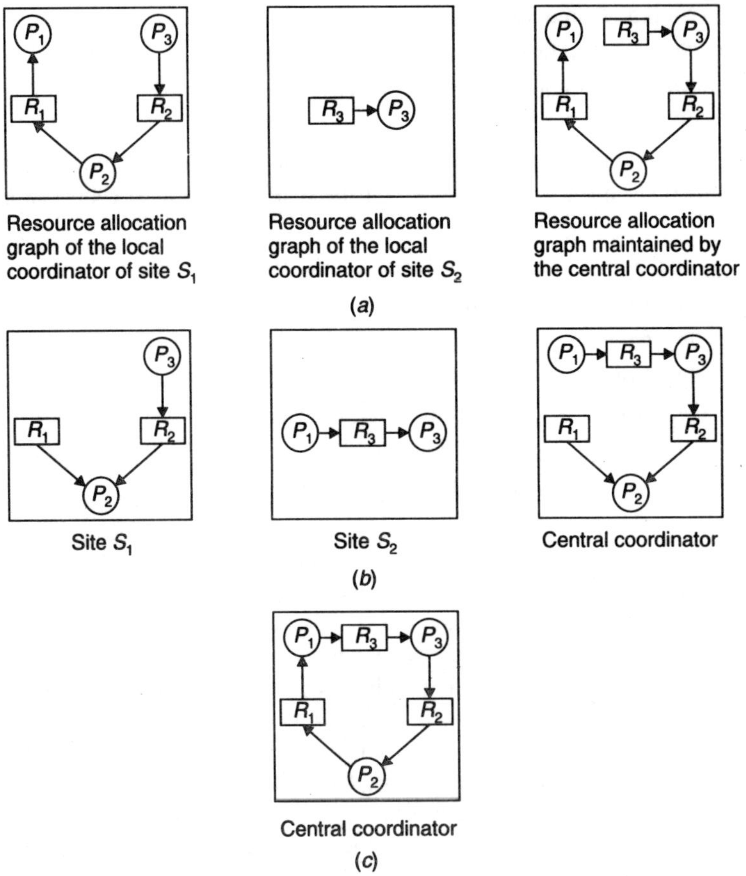


**Fig. 6.16** Local and global resource allocation graphs in the centralized deadlock detection approach: (*a*) resource allocation graphs after step 5; (*b*) resource allocation graphs after step 7; (*c*) resource allocation graph of the central coordinator showing false deadlock if message $m_7$ is received before $m_6$ by the central coordinator.

initiates recovery actions. Notice that in our above example, in reply to its broadcast message, the central coordinator will receive message $m_6$ from site $S_1$ and a negative reply from site $S_2$. Therefore, after final updation of the global graph, the central coordinator's view of the system will change from that of Figure 6.16(*c*) to that in Figure 6.16(*b*). Hence no deadlock resolution action will be initiated.

***Hierarchical Approach for Deadlock Detection.*** It has been observed that for typical applications most WFG cycles are very short. In particular, experimental measurements have shown that 90% of all deadlock cycles involve only two processes [Gray et al. 1981]. Therefore, the centralized approach seems to be less attractive for most real applications because of the significant time and message overhead involved in assembling all the local WFGs at the central coordinator. Furthermore, to minimize communications cost, in geographically distributed systems, deadlock should be detected by a site located as close as possible to the sites involved in the cycle. But this is not possible in the centralized approach. The hierarchical approach overcomes these and other drawbacks of the centralized approach.

The hierarchical deadlock detection approach uses a logical hierarchy (tree) of deadlock detectors. These deadlock detectors are called *controllers*. Each controller is responsible for detecting only those deadlocks that involve the sites falling within its range in the hierarchy. Therefore, unlike the centralized approach in which the entire global WFG is maintained at a single site, in the hierarchical approach it is distributed over a number of different controllers. Each site has its own local controller that maintains its own local graph.

In the tree representing the hierarchy of controllers, the WFG to be maintained by a particular controller is decided according to the following rules:

1. Each controller that forms a leaf of the hierarchy tree maintains the local WFG of a single site.
2. Each nonleaf controller maintains a WFG that is the union of the WFGs of its immediate children in the hierarchy tree.

The lowest level controller that finds a cycle in its WFG detects a deadlock and takes necessary action to resolve it. Therefore, a WFG that contains a cycle will never be passed as it is to a higher level controller.

Let us illustrate the method with the help of the example shown in Figure 6.17. There are four sites and seven controllers in the system. Controllers *A*, *B*, *C*, and *D* maintain the local WFGs of sites $S_1$, $S_2$, $S_3$, and $S_4$, respectively. They form the leaves of the controllers' hierarchy tree. Controller *E*, being the parent of controllers *A* and *B*, maintains the union of the WFGs of controllers *A* and *B*. Similarly, controller *F* maintains the union of the WFGs of controllers *C* and *D*. Finally, controller *G* maintains the union of the WFGs of controllers *E* and *F*.

Notice from the figure that the deadlock cycle ($P_1$, $P_3$, $P_2$, $P_1$) that involves sites $S_1$ and $S_2$ gets reflected in the WFG of controller *E*, but the deadlock cycle ($P_4$, $P_5$, $P_6$, $P_7$, $P_4$) that involves sites $S_2$, $S_3$, and $S_4$ gets reflected only in the WFG of controller *G*. This is because controller *G* is the first controller in the hierarchy in whose range all the three sites $S_2$, $S_3$, and $S_4$ are covered. Also notice that although we have shown the deadlock cycle ($P_1$, $P_3$, $P_2$, $P_1$) in the WFG of controller *G* to reflect the union of the WFGs of controllers *E* and *F*, this will never happen in practice. This is because, when controller *E* detects the deadlock, it will initiate a recovery action instead of passing its WFG as it is to controller *G*.

***Fully Distributed Approaches for Deadlock Detection.*** In the fully distributed deadlock detection approach, each site of the system shares equal responsibility for deadlock detection. Surveys of several algorithms based on this approach can be found in [Knapp 1987, Singhal 1989]. Below we describe two such algorithms. The first one is based on the construction of WFGs, and the second one is a probe-based algorithm.

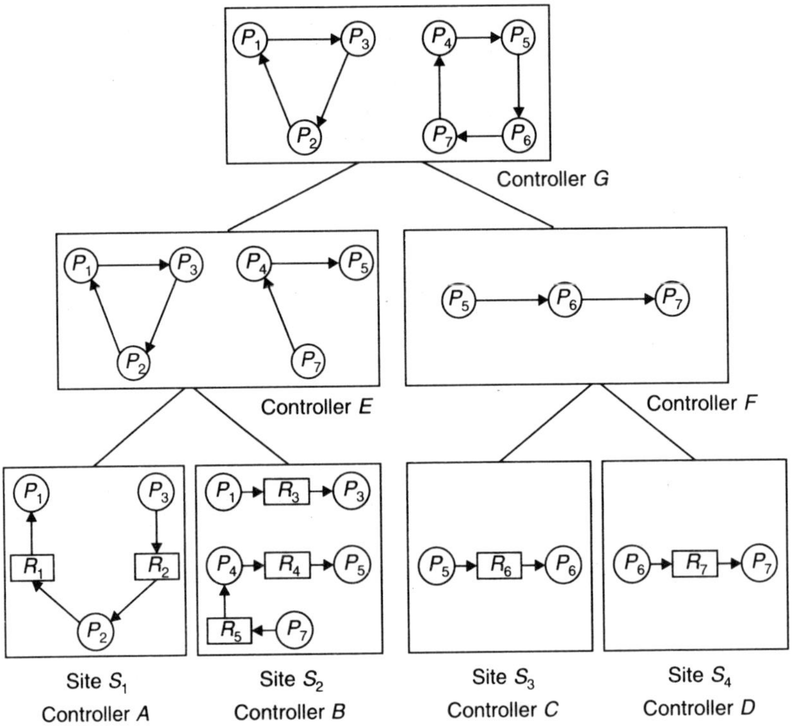


**Fig. 6.17** Hierarchical deadlock detection approach.

***WFG-Based Distributed Algorithm for Deadlock Detection.*** The description below follows from the description of the fully distributed deadlock detection algorithm presented in [Silberschatz and Galvin 1994]. As in the centralized and hierarchical approaches, in the WFG-based distributed algorithm, each site maintains its own local WFG. However, to model waiting situations that involve external (nonlocal) processes, a slightly modified form of WFG is used. In this modified WFG, an extra node $P_{ex}$ is added to the local WFG of each site, and this node is connected to the WFG of the corresponding site in the following manner:

1. An edge $(P_i, P_{ex})$ is added if process $P_i$ is waiting for a resource in another site being held by any process.
2. An edge $(P_{ex}, P_j)$ is added if $P_j$ is a process of another site that is waiting for a resource currently being held by a process of this site.

To illustrate the construction of this modified WFG, let us consider the example of Figure 6.18. In this example there are two sites, and the local WFGs of each site are shown in Figure 6.18($a$). The modified WFGs of the two sites after the addition of node $P_{ex}$ are shown in Figure 6.18($b$). The explanation for the edges involving node $P_{ex}$ are as follows:

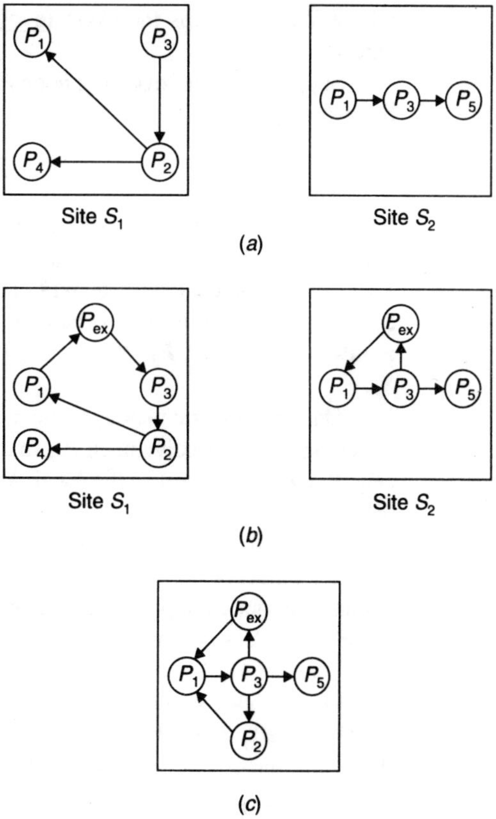


**Fig. 6.18** Example illustrating the WFG-based fully distributed deadlock detection algorithm: (*a*) local WFGs; (*b*) local WFGs after addition of node $P_{ex}$; (*c*) updated local WFG of site $S_2$ after receiving the deadlock detection message from site $S_1$.

1. In the WFG of site $S_1$, edge $(P_1, P_{ex})$ is added because process $P_1$ is waiting for a resource in site $S_2$ that is held by process $P_3$, and edge $(P_{ex}, P_3)$ is added because process $P_3$ is a process of site $S_2$ that is waiting to acquire a resource currently held by process $P_2$ of site $S_1$.
2. In the WFG of site $S_2$, edge $(P_3, P_{ex})$ is added because process $P_3$ is waiting for a resource in site $S_1$ that is held by process $P_2$, and edge $(P_{ex}, P_1)$ is added because process $P_1$ is a process of site $S_1$ that is waiting to acquire a resource currently held by process $P_3$ of site $S_2$.

Now these modified WFGs are used for deadlock detection in the following manner. If a local WFG contains a cycle that does not involve node $P_{ex}$, a deadlock that involves only local processes of that site has occurred. Such deadlocks can be locally resolved without the need to consult any other site.

On the other hand, if a local WFG contains a cycle that involves node $P_{ex}$, there is a possibility of a distributed deadlock that involves processes of multiple sites. To confirm a distributed deadlock, a distributed deadlock detection algorithm is invoked by the site whose WFG contains the cycle involving node $P_{ex}$. The algorithm works as described below.

Suppose a cycle involving node $P_{ex}$ is detected in the WFG of site $S_i$. This cycle must be of the form

$$(P_{ex}, P_i, P_j, \ldots, P_k, P_{ex})$$

which means that process $P_k$ is waiting for an external resource that belongs to some other site (say $S_j$). Therefore, site $S_i$ sends a deadlock detection message to site $S_j$. This message does not contain the complete WFG of site $S_i$ but only that part of the WFG that forms the cycle. For instance, in our example of Figure 6.18, if site $S_1$ detects its cycle first, it sends a message like $(P_{ex}, P_3, P_2, P_1, P_{ex})$ to site $S_2$ since $P_1$ is waiting for a resource in site $S_2$.

On receiving the message, site $S_j$ updates its local WFG by adding those edges of the cycle that do not involve node $P_{ex}$ to its WFG. That is, in our example, edges $(P_3, P_2)$ and $(P_2, P_1)$ will be added to the local WFG of site $S_2$, resulting in the new WFG of Figure 6.18(*c*).

Now if the newly constructed WFG of site $S_j$ contains a cycle that does not involve node $P_{ex}$, a deadlock exists and an appropriate recovery procedure must be initiated. For instance, in our example, the newly constructed WFG of site $S_2$ contains a cycle $(P_1, P_3, P_2, P_1)$ that does not involve node $P_{ex}$. Hence, in our example, the system is in a deadlock state.

On the other hand, if a cycle involving node $P_{ex}$ is found in the newly constructed WFG of site $S_j$, $S_j$ sends a deadlock detection message to the appropriate site (say $S_k$), and the whole procedure is repeated by site $S_k$. In this manner, after a finite number of deadlock detection message transfers from one site to another, either a deadlock is detected or the computation for deadlock detection halts.

A problem associated with the above algorithm is that two sites may initiate the deadlock detection algorithm independently for a deadlock that involves the same processes. For instance, in our example of Figure 6.18, sites $S_1$ and $S_2$ may almost simultaneously detect the cycles $(P_{ex}, P_3, P_2, P_1, P_{ex})$ and $(P_{ex}, P_1, P_3, P_{ex})$ respectively in their local WFGs, and both may send a deadlock detection message to the other site. The result will be that both sites will update their local WFGs and search for cycles. After detecting a deadlock, both may initiate a recovery procedure that may result in killing more processes than is actually required to resolve the deadlock. Furthermore, this problem also leads to extra overhead in unnecessary message transfers and duplication of deadlock detection jobs performed at the two sites.

One way to solve the above problem is to assign a unique identifier to each process $P_i$ [denoted as $\text{ID}(P_i)$]. Now when a cycle of the form $(P_{ex}, P_i, P_j, \ldots, P_k, P_{ex})$ is found in the local WFG of a site, this site initiates the deadlock detection algorithm by sending a deadlock detection message to the appropriate site only if

$$\text{ID}(P_k) < \text{ID}(P_i).$$

Otherwise, this site does not take any action and leaves the job of initiating the deadlock detection algorithm to some other site.

Let us apply the modified algorithm to our example of Figure 6.18. Let

$$\text{ID}(P_1) < \text{ID}(P_2) < \text{ID}(P_3) < \text{ID}(P_4) < \text{ID}(P_5)$$

Now suppose both sites $S_1$ and $S_2$ almost simultaneously detect the cycles ($P_{ex}$, $P_3$, $P_2$, $P_1$, $P_{ex}$) and ($P_{ex}$, $P_1$, $P_3$, $P_{ex}$), respectively, in their local WFGs. Since ID($P_1$) < ID($P_3$), so site $S_1$ will initiate the deadlock detection algorithm. On the other hand, since ID($P_3$) > ID($P_1$), site $S_2$ does not take any action on seeing the cycle in its local WFG. When site $S_2$ receives the deadlock detection message sent to it by site $S_1$, it updates its local WFG and searches for a cycle in the updated WFG. It detects the cycle ($P_1$, $P_3$, $P_2$, $P_1$) in the graph and then initiates a deadlock recovery procedure.

***Probe-Based Distributed Algorithm for Deadlock Detection.*** The probe-based distributed deadlock detection algorithm described below was proposed by Chandy et al. [1983] and is known as the Chandy-Misra-Hass (or CMH) algorithm. It is considered to be the best algorithm to date for detecting global deadlocks in distributed systems. The algorithm allows a process to request for multiple resources at a time.

The algorithm is conceptually simple and works in the following manner. When a process that requests for a resource (or resources) fails to get the requested resource (or resources) and times out, it generates a special *probe* message and sends it to the process (or processes) holding the requested resource (or resources). The probe message contains the following fields (assuming that each process in the system is assigned a unique identifier):

1. The identifier of the process just blocked
2. The identifier of the process sending this message
3. The identifier of the process to whom this message is being sent

On receiving a probe message, the recipient checks to see if it itself is waiting for any resource (or resources). If not, this means that the recipient is using the resource requested by the process that sent the probe message to it. In this case, the recipient simply ignores the probe message. On the other hand, if the recipient is waiting for any resource (or resources), it passes the probe message to the process (or processes) holding the resource (or resources) for which it is waiting. However, before the probe message is forwarded, the recipient modifies its fields in the following manner:

1. The first field is left unchanged.
2. The recipient changes the second field to its own process identifier.
3. The third field is changed to the identifier of the process that will be the new recipient of this message.

Every new recipient of the probe message repeats this procedure. If the probe message returns back to the original sender (the process whose identifier is in the first field of the message), a cycle exists and the system is deadlocked.

Let us illustrate the algorithm with the help of the simple example shown in Figure 6.19. Notice that this figure depicts the same situation as that of Figure 6.18(*a*) but in a slightly different style. Suppose that process $P_1$ gets blocked when it requests for the resource held by process $P_3$. Therefore $P_1$ generates a probe message $(P_1, P_1, P_3)$ and sends it to $P_3$. When $P_3$ receives this message, it discovers that it is itself blocked on processes $P_2$ and $P_5$. Therefore $P_3$ forwards the probes $(P_1, P_3, P_2)$ and $(P_1, P_3, P_5)$ to processes $P_2$ and $P_5$, respectively. When $P_5$ receives the probe message, it ignores it because it is not blocked on any other process. However, when $P_2$ receives the probe message, it discovers that it is itself blocked on processes $P_1$ and $P_4$. Therefore $P_2$ forwards the probes $(P_1, P_2, P_1)$ and $(P_1, P_2, P_4)$ to processes $P_1$ and $P_4$, respectively. Since the probe returns to its original sender $(P_1)$, a cycle exists and the system is deadlocked.

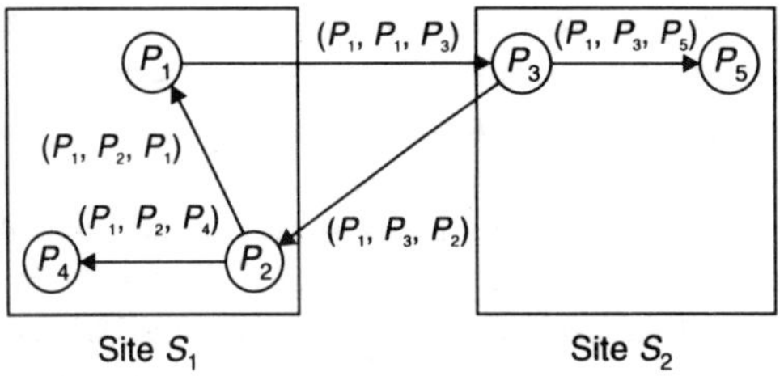


**Fig. 6.19** Example illustrating the CMH distributed deadlock detection algorithm.

The CMH algorithm is popular, and variants of this algorithm are used in most distributed locking schemes due to the following attractive features of the algorithm:

1. The algorithm is easy to implement, since each message is of fixed length and requires few computational steps.
2. The overhead of the algorithm is fairly low.
3. There is no graph constructing and information collecting involved.
4. False deadlocks are not detected by the algorithm.
5. It does not require any particular structure among the processes.

### Ways for Recovery from Deadlock

When a system chooses to use the detection and recovery strategy for handling deadlocks, it is not sufficient to simply detect deadlocks. The system must also have some way to recover from a detected deadlock. One of the following methods may be used in a system to recover from a deadlock:

- Asking for operator intervention
- Termination of process(es)
- Rollback of process(es)

***Asking for Operator Intervention.*** The simplest way is to inform the operator that a deadlock has occurred and to let the operator deal with it manually. The system may assist the operator in decision making for recovery by providing him or her with a list of the processes involved in the deadlock.

This method is not suitable for use in modern systems because the concept of an operator continuously monitoring the smooth running of the system from the console has gradually vanished. Furthermore, although this method may work for a centralized system, it does not work in a distributed environment because when a deadlock involving processes of multiple sites is detected, it is not clear which site should be informed. If all the sites whose processes are involved in the deadlock are informed, each site's operator may independently take some action for recovery. On the other hand, if the operator of only a single site is informed, the operator may favor the process (or processes) of its own site while taking a recovery action. Furthermore, the operator of one site may not have the right to interfere with a process of another site for taking recovery action. Therefore, distributed systems normally use other methods described below in which the system recovers automatically from a deadlock.

***Termination of Process(es).*** The simplest way to automatically recover from a deadlock is to terminate (kill) one or more processes and to reclaim the resources held by them, which can then be reallocated. Deadlock recovery algorithms based on this idea analyze the resource requirements and interdependencies of the processes involved in a deadlock cycle and then select a set of processes, which, if killed, can break the cycle.

***Rollback of Process(es).*** Killing a process requires its restart from the very beginning, which proves to be very expensive, particularly when the process has already run for a substantially long time. To break a deadlock, it is sufficient to reclaim the needed resources from the processes that were selected for being killed. Also notice that to reclaim a resource from a process, it is sufficient to roll back the process to a point where the resource was not allocated to the process. The method of rollback is based on this idea.

In this method, processes are checkpointed periodically. That is, a process's state (its memory image and the list of resources held by it) is written to a file at regular intervals. Therefore, the file maintains a history of the process's states so that, if required, the process can be restarted from any of its checkpoints. Now when a deadlock is detected, the method described in the process termination approach is used to select a set of processes to be killed. However, this time, instead of total rollback (killing) of the selected processes, the processes are rolled back only as far as necessary to break the deadlock. That is, each selected process is rolled back to a checkpoint at which the needed resources can be reclaimed from it.

Although the rollback approach may appear to be less expensive than the process termination approach, this is not always true because of the extra overhead involved in the periodic checkpointing of all the processes. If deadlocks are rare in a system, it may be cheaper to use the process termination approach.

### Issues in Recovery from Deadlock

Two important issues in the recovery action are selection of victims and use of transaction mechanism. These are described below.

***Selection of Victim(s).*** In any of the recovery approaches described above, deadlock is broken by killing or rolling back one or more processes. These processes are called victims. Notice that even in the operator intervention approach, recovery involves killing one or more victims. Therefore, an important issue in any recovery procedure is to select the victims. Selection of victim(s) is normally based on two major factors:

1. *Minimization of recovery cost.* This factor suggests that those processes should be selected as victims whose termination/rollback will incur the minimum recovery cost. Unfortunately, it is not possible to have a universal cost function, and therefore, each system should determine its own cost function to select victims. Some of the factors that may be considered for this purpose are (a) the priority of the processes; (b) the nature of the processes, such as interactive or batch and possibility of rerun with no ill effects; (c) the number and types of resources held by the processes; (d) the length of service already received and the expected length of service further needed by the processes; and (e) the total number of processes that will be affected.

2. *Prevention of starvation.* If a system only aims at minimization of recovery cost, it may happen that the same process (probably because its priority is very low) is repeatedly selected as a victim and may never complete. This situation, known as *starvation*, must be somehow prevented in any practical system. One approach to handle this problem is to raise the priority of the process every time it is victimized. Another approach is to include the number of times a process is victimized as a parameter in the cost function.

***Use of Transaction Mechanism.*** After a process is killed or rolled back for recovery from deadlock, it has to be rerun. However, rerunning a process may not always be safe, especially when the operations already performed by the process are nonidempotent. For example, if a process has updated the amount of a bank account by adding a certain amount to it, reexecution of the process will result in adding the same amount once again, leaving the balance in the account in an incorrect state. Therefore, the use of a transaction mechanism (which ensures all or no effect) becomes almost inevitable for most processes when the system chooses the method of detection and recovery for handling deadlocks. However, notice that the transaction mechanism need not be used for those processes that can be rerun with no ill effects. For example, rerun of a compilation process has no ill effects because all it does is read a source file and produce an object file.

## 6.6 ELECTION ALGORITHMS

Several distributed algorithms require that there be a *coordinator* process in the entire system that performs some type of coordination activity needed for the smooth running of other processes in the system. Two examples of such coordinator processes encountered in this chapter are the coordinator in the centralized algorithm for mutual exclusion and the central coordinator in the centralized deadlock detection algorithm. Since all other processes in the system have to interact with the coordinator, they all must unanimously agree on who the coordinator is. Furthermore, if the coordinator process fails due to the failure of the site on which it is located, a new coordinator process must be elected to take up the job of the failed coordinator. *Election algorithms* are meant for electing a coordinator process from among the currently running processes in such a manner that at any instance of time there is a single coordinator for all processes in the system.

Election algorithms are based on the following assumptions:

1. Each process in the system has a unique priority number.
2. Whenever an election is held, the process having the highest priority number among the currently active processes is elected as the coordinator.
3. On recovery, a failed process can take appropriate actions to rejoin the set of active processes.

Therefore, whenever initiated, an election algorithm basically finds out which of the currently active processes has the highest priority number and then informs this to all other active processes. Different election algorithms differ in the way they do this. Two such election algorithms are described below. Readers interested in other election algorithms may refer to [Tel 1994]. For simplicity, in the description of both algorithms we will assume that there is only one process on each node of the distributed system.

### 6.6.1 The Bully Algorithm

This algorithm was proposed by Garcia-Molina [1982]. In this algorithm it is assumed that every process knows the priority number of every other process in the system. The algorithm works as follows.

When a process (say $P_i$) sends a *request* message to the coordinator and does not receive a reply within a fixed timeout period, it assumes that the coordinator has failed. It then initiates an election by sending an *election* message to every process with a higher priority number than itself. If $P_i$ does not receive any response to its election message within a fixed timeout period, it assumes that among the currently active processes it has the highest priority number. Therefore it takes up the job of the coordinator and sends a message (let us call it a *coordinator* message) to all processes having lower priority numbers than itself, informing that from now on it is the new coordinator. On the other hand, if $P_i$ receives a response for its election message, this means that some other process having higher priority number is alive. Therefore $P_i$ does not take any further action and just waits to receive the final result (a coordinator message from the new coordinator) of the election it initiated.

When a process (say $P_j$) receives an election message (obviously from a process having a lower priority number than itself), it sends a response message (let us call it *alive* message) to the sender informing that it is alive and will take over the election activity. Now $P_j$ holds an election if it is not already holding one. In this way, the election activity gradually moves on to the process that has the highest priority number among the currently active processes and eventually wins the election and becomes the new coordinator.

As part of the recovery action, this method requires that a failed process (say $P_k$) must initiate an election on recovery. If the current coordinator's priority number is higher than that of $P_k$, then the current coordinator will win the election initiated by $P_k$ and will continue to be the coordinator. On the other hand, if $P_k$'s priority number is higher than that of the current coordinator, it will not receive any response for its election message. So it wins the election and takes over the coordinator's job from the currently active coordinator. Therefore, the active process having the highest priority number always wins the election. Hence the algorithm is called the "bully" algorithm. It may also be noted here that if the process having the highest priority number recovers after a failure, it does not initiate an election because it knows from its list of priority numbers that all other processes in the system have lower priority numbers than that of its own. Therefore, on recovery, it simply sends a coordinator message to all other processes and bullies the current coordinator into submission.

Let us now see the working of this algorithm with the help of an example. Suppose the system consists of five processes $P_1$, $P_2$, $P_3$, $P_4$, and $P_5$ and their priority numbers are 1, 2, 3, 4, and 5 respectively. Also suppose that at a particular instance of time the system is in a state in which $P_2$ is crashed, and $P_1$, $P_3$, $P_4$, and $P_5$ are active. Starting from this state, the functioning of the bully algorithm with the changing system states is illustrated below.

1. Obviously, $P_5$ is the coordinator in the starting state.
2. Suppose $P_5$ crashes.
3. Process $P_3$ sends a request message to $P_5$ and does not receive a reply within the fixed timeout period.
4. Process $P_3$ assumes that $P_5$ has crashed and initiates an election by sending an election message to $P_4$ and $P_5$ (recall that an election message is sent only to processes with higher priority numbers).
5. When $P_4$ receives $P_3$'s election message, it sends an alive message to $P_3$, informing that it is alive and will take over the election activity. Process $P_5$ cannot respond to $P_3$'s election message because it is down.
6. Now $P_4$ holds an election by sending an election message to $P_5$.
7. Process $P_5$ does not respond to $P_4$'s election message because it is down, and therefore, $P_4$ wins the election and sends a coordinator message to $P_1$, $P_2$, and $P_3$, informing them that from now on it is the new coordinator. Obviously, this message is not received by $P_2$ because it is currently down.
8. Now suppose $P_2$ recovers from failure and initiates an election by sending an election message to $P_3$, $P_4$, and $P_5$. Since $P_2$'s priority number is lower than that of $P_4$ (current coordinator), $P_4$ will win the election initiated by $P_2$ and will continue to be the coordinator.
9. Finally, suppose $P_5$ recovers from failure. Since $P_5$ is the process with the highest priority number, it simply sends a coordinator message to $P_1$, $P_2$, $P_3$, and $P_4$ and becomes the new coordinator.

### 6.6.2 A Ring Algorithm

The following algorithm is based on the ring-based election algorithms presented in [Tanenbaum 1995, Silberschatz and Galvin 1994]. In this algorithm it is assumed that all the processes in the system are organized in a logical ring. The ring is unidirectional in the sense that all messages related to the election algorithm are always passed only in one direction (clockwise/anticlockwise). Every process in the system knows the structure of the ring, so that while trying to circulate a message over the ring, if the successor of the sender process is down, the sender can skip over the successor, or the one after that, until an active member is located. The algorithm works as follows.

When a process (say $P_i$) sends a request message to the current coordinator and does not receive a reply within a fixed timeout period, it assumes that the coordinator has crashed. Therefore it initiates an election by sending an election message to its successor (actually to the first successor that is currently active). This message contains the priority number of process $P_i$. On receiving the election message, the successor appends its own priority number to the message and passes it on to the next active member in the ring. This member appends its own priority number to the message and forwards it to its own successor. In this manner, the election message circulates over the ring from one active process to another and eventually returns back to process $P_i$. Process $P_i$ recognizes the message as its own election message by seeing that in the list of priority numbers held within the message the first priority number is its own priority number.

Note that when process $P_i$ receives its own election message, the message contains the list of priority numbers of all processes that are currently active. Therefore of the processes in this list, it elects the process having the highest priority number as the new coordinator. It then circulates a coordinator message over the ring to inform all the other active processes who the new coordinator is. When the coordinator message comes back to process $P_i$ after completing its one round along the ring, it is removed by process $P_i$. At this point all the active processes know who the current coordinator is.

When a process (say $P_j$) recovers after failure, it creates an *inquiry* message and sends it to its successor. The message contains the identity of process $P_j$. If the successor is not the current coordinator, it simply forwards the enquiry message to its own successor. In this way, the inquiry message moves forward along the ring until it reaches the current coordinator. On receiving an inquiry message, the current coordinator sends a reply to process $P_j$ informing that it is the current coordinator.

Notice that in this algorithm two or more processes may almost simultaneously discover that the coordinator has crashed and then each one may circulate an election message over the ring. Although this results in a little waste of network bandwidth, it does not cause any problem because every process that initiated an election will receive the same list of active processes, and all of them will choose the same process as the new coordinator.

### 6.6.3 Discussion of the Two Election Algorithms

In the bully algorithm, when the process having the lowest priority number detects the coordinator's failure and initiates an election, in a system having total $n$ processes, altogether $n$–2 elections are performed one after another for the initiated one. That is, all the processes, except the active process with the highest priority number and the coordinator process that has just failed, perform elections by sending messages to all processes with higher priority numbers. Hence, in the worst case, the bully algorithm requires $O(n^2)$ messages. However, when the process having the priority number just below the failed coordinator detects that the coordinator has failed, it immediately elects itself as the coordinator and sends $n$–2 coordinator messages. Hence, in the best case, the bully algorithm requires only $n$–2 messages.

On the other hand, in the ring algorithm, irrespective of which process detects the failure of the coordinator and initiates an election, an election always requires 2($n$–1) messages (assuming that only the coordinator process has failed); $n$–1 messages are needed for one round rotation of the election message, and another $n$–1 messages are needed for one round rotation of the coordinator message.

Next let us consider the complexity involved in the recovery of a process. In the bully algorithm, a failed process must initiate an election on recovery. Therefore, once again depending on the priority number of the process that initiates the recovery action, the bully algorithm requires $O(n^2)$ messages in the worst case, and $n$–1 messages in the best case. On the other hand, in the ring algorithm, a failed process does not initiate an election on recovery but simply searches for the current coordinator. Hence, the ring algorithm requires only $n$/2 messages on an average for recovery action.

In conclusion, as compared to the bully algorithm, the ring algorithm is more efficient and easier to implement.

## 6.7 SUMMARY

Sharing system resources among multiple concurrent processes may be cooperative or competitive in nature. Both cooperative and competitive sharing require adherence to certain rules of behavior that guarantee that correct interaction occurs. The rules for enforcing correct interaction are implemented in the form of synchronization mechanisms. In this chapter we saw the synchronization issues in distributed systems and mechanisms to handle these issues.

For correct functioning of several distributed applications, the clocks of different nodes of a distributed system must be mutually synchronized as well as with the external world (physical clock). Clock synchronization algorithms used in distributed systems are broadly classified into two types—centralized and distributed. In the centralized approach, there is a time server node and the goal of the algorithm is to keep the clocks of all other nodes synchronized with the clock time of the time server node. In the distributed approach, clock synchronization is done either by global averaging or localized averaging of the clocks of various nodes of the system.

Lamport observed that for most applications clock synchronization is not required, and it is sufficient to ensure that all events that occur in a distributed system can be totally ordered in a manner that is consistent with an observed behavior. Therefore, he defined the happened-before relation and introduced the concept of logical clocks for ordering of events based on the happened-before relation. The happened-before relation, however, is only a partial ordering on the set of all events in the system. Therefore, for total ordering on the set of all system events, Lamport proposed the use of any arbitrary total ordering of the processes.

There are several resources in a system for which exclusive access by a process must be ensured. This exclusiveness of access is called mutual exclusion between processes, and the sections of a program that need exclusive access to shared resources are referred to as critical sections. The three basic approaches used by different algorithms for implementing mutual exclusion in distributed systems are centralized, distributed, and token passing. In the centralized approach, one of the processes in the system is elected as the coordinator, which coordinates the entry to the critical sections. In the distributed approach, all processes that want to enter the same critical section cooperate with each other before reaching a decision on which process will enter the critical section next. In the token-passing approach, mutual exclusion is achieved by using a single token that is circulated among the processes in the system.

Deadlock is the state of permanent blocking of a set of processes each of which is waiting for an event that only another process in the set can cause. In principle, deadlocks in distributed systems are similar to deadlocks in centralized systems. However, handling of deadlocks in distributed systems is more complex than in centralized systems because the resources, the processes, and other relevant information are scattered on different nodes of the system.

The three commonly used strategies to handle deadlocks are avoidance, prevention, and detection and recovery. Deadlock avoidance methods use some advance knowledge of the resource usage of processes to predict the future state of the system for avoiding allocations that can eventually lead to a deadlock. Deadlock prevention consists of carefully designing the system so that deadlocks become impossible. In the detection and recovery approach, deadlocks are allowed to occur, are detected by the system, and then are recovered. Of the three approaches, detection and recovery is the recommended approach for handling deadlocks in distributed systems. The three approaches used for deadlock detection in distributed systems are centralized, hierarchical, and fully distributed. For recovery from a detected deadlock, a system may use one of the following methods: asking for operator intervention, termination of process(es), or rollback of process(es).

Several distributed algorithms require that there be a coordinator process in the entire system. Election algorithms are meant for electing a coordinator process from among the currently running processes. Two election algorithms that were described in this chapter are the bully algorithm and the ring algorithm.

## EXERCISES

**6.1.** Write pseudocode for an algorithm that decides whether a given set of clocks are synchronized or not. What input parameters are needed in your algorithm?

**6.2.** How do clock synchronization issues differ in centralized and distributed computing systems?

**6.3.** Explain why one-time synchronization of the clocks of all the nodes of a distributed system is not sufficient and periodic resynchronization is necessary. How will you determine the interval for periodic resynchronization?

**6.4.** A distributed system has three nodes $N_1$, $N_2$, and $N_3$, each having its own clock. The clocks of nodes $N_1$, $N_2$, and $N_3$ tick 800, 810, and 795 times per millisecond. The system uses the external synchronization mechanism, in which all three nodes receive the real time every 30 seconds from an external time source and readjust their clocks. What is the maximum clock skew that will occur in this system?

**6.5.** Differentiate between internal synchronization and external synchronization of clocks in a distributed system. Externally synchronized clocks are also internally synchronized, but the converse is not true. Explain why.

**6.6.** An important issue in clock synchronization in computer systems is that time must never run backward. Give two examples to show why this issue is important. How can a fast clock be readjusted to take care of this issue?

**6.7.** In distributed systems, there may be unpredictable variation in the message propagation time between two nodes. Explain why. How does this problem make the task of synchronizing clocks in a distributed system difficult? Give two methods that can be used in a clock synchronization algorithm to handle this problem.

**6.8.** Give two examples to show that for most distributed applications, what usually matters is not that all processes agree on exactly what time it is, but rather that they agree on the order in which events occur.

**6.9.** Using the space-time diagram of Figure 6.20, list all pairs of concurrent events according to the happened-before relation.

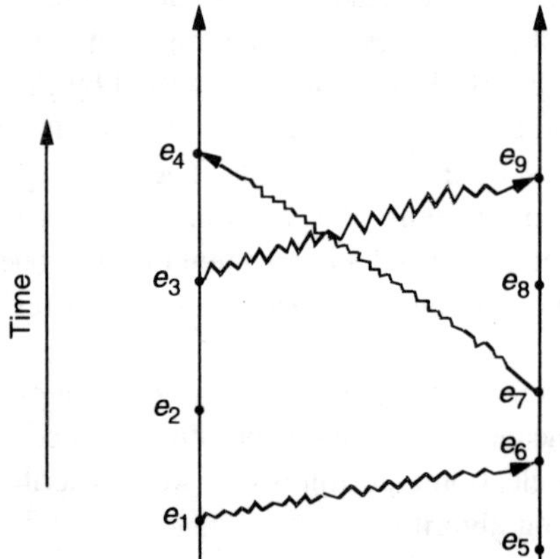


**Fig. 6.20** A space-time diagram.

**6.10.** Add a message-sending event to the space-time diagram of Figure 6.20 that is concurrent to events $e_5$, $e_6$, and $e_7$. Now add a non-message-sending event that is concurrent to events $e_1$, $e_2$, and $e_3$.

**6.11.** Explain the concept of logical clocks and their importance in distributed systems. A clock of a computer system must never run backward. Explain how this issue can be handled in an implementation of the logical clocks concept.

**6.12.** In the centralized approach to mutual exclusion described in this chapter, the coordinator grants permission for critical section entry to the first process in the queue. In some systems, it may be desirable to grant permission to some higher priority jobs before other lower priority jobs. Modify the algorithm to take care of this and show how your algorithm satisfies the no-starvation property.

**6.13.** The first general algorithm for implementing mutual exclusion in a distributed environment was developed by Lamport [1978]. Find the details of this algorithm and compare its performance and reliability with that of Ricart and Agrawala's [1981] algorithm.

**6.14.** Write pseudocode for the majority-consensus-based distributed algorithm for mutual exclusion in which a process willing to enter a critical region sends a request message to all other processes and enters the critical region as soon as it receives permission from a majority of the processes.

**6.15.** What is a "deadlock"? What are the four necessary conditions for a deadlock to occur? Give suitable examples to prove that if any one of the four conditions is absent, no deadlock is possible.

**6.16.** Prove that the presence of a cycle in a general resource allocation graph is a necessary but not a sufficient condition for the existence of deadlock.

**6.17.** Prove that for a system having only one unit of each resource type the presence of a cycle in a resource allocation graph is both a necessary and a sufficient condition for the existence of deadlock.

**6.18.** Write the pseudocode of an algorithm that determines whether a given resource allocation graph contains a deadlock.

**6.19.** A system has three types of resources, $R_1$, $R_2$, and $R_3$, and their numbers of units are 3, 2, and 2, respectively. Four processes $P_1$, $P_2$, $P_3$, and $P_4$ are currently competing for these resources in the following manner:
(a) $P_1$ is holding one unit of $R_1$ and is requesting for one unit of $R_2$.
(b) $P_2$ is holding two units of $R_2$ and is requesting for one unit each of $R_1$ and $R_3$.
(c) $P_3$ is holding one unit of $R_1$ and is requesting for one unit of $R_2$.
(d) $P_4$ is holding two units of $R_3$ and is requesting for one unit of $R_1$.
Determine which, if any, of the processes are deadlocked in this system state.

**6.20.** A distributed system uses the following IPC primitives:
(a) *send* (receiver_process_id, sender_process_id, message)
(b) *receive* (sender_process_id, message)
The primitives are synchronous in the sense that the sender blocks if the receiver is not ready to receive the message and the receiver blocks until a message is received from the sender. What is the minimum number of communicating processes for a communication deadlock to occur in this system? Give reasons for your answer and give an example of a communication deadlock that involves a minimum number of processes.

**6.21.** Assume that in the distributed system of Exercise 6.20 an IPC takes place only between two types of processes—clients and servers. That is, one is always a client and the other is a server. A client always executes the IPC primitives in (*send*, *receive*) sequence. That is, for all IPCs, a client first executes a *send* to send a request message to a server and then executes a *receive* to receive the reply for its request. On the other hand, a server always executes the IPC primitives in (*receive*, *send*) sequence. That is, for all IPCs, a server first executes a *receive* to receive a request from a client and then, after processing, it executes a *send* to send the result of processing to the client. Is a communication deadlock possible in this system? Give reasons for your answer.

**6.22.** Differentiate among safe, unsafe, and deadlock states. Assume that in a system there are total 10 units of a resource for which four processes $P_1, P_2, P_3$, and $P_4$ are competing. Suppose the maximum units of the resource required by $P_1, P_2, P_3$, and $P_4$ are 3, 6, 5, and 4, respectively, and they are currently holding 2, 1, 3, and 2 units of the resource, respectively. Find out whether the current state of the system is safe or unsafe. If it is safe, enumerate all the safe sequences.

**6.23.** There are four units of a resource in a system. Three processes compete to use this resource, each of which needs at most two units. Prove that a deadlock situation will never arise no matter in which order the processes acquire and release the resource units.

**6.24.** Prove that an unsafe state is not a deadlock state.

**6.25.** Give an example to show that if the resources are not cleverly scheduled to the competing processes, a system may enter an unsafe state from a safe state. Now use the same example to show the following:

(a) The system may enter a deadlock state from the unsafe state.

(b) All competing processes may successfully complete without the system entering into a deadlock state from the unsafe state.

**6.26.** Discuss why advance knowledge of the resource usage of processes is essential to avoid deadlocks. Why is the deadlock avoidance strategy never used in distributed systems for handling deadlocks?

**6.27.** Deadlocks may be prevented in a system by carefully designing the system so that at least one of the necessary conditions for deadlock is never satisfied. Based on this idea, suggest a deadlock prevention scheme for each of the following:

(a) That denies the mutual-exclusion condition

(b) That denies the hold-and-wait condition

(c) That denies the circular-wait condition

(d) That denies the no-preemption condition

Discuss the practical applicability of each of these schemes.

**6.28.** Prove that the following resource allocation policies prevent deadlocks:

(a) Ordered requests

(b) Collective requests

**6.29.** A system uses the preemption method for deadlock prevention. Suppose the system currently has five transactions $T_1, T_2, T_3, T_4$, and $T_5$, their timestamp values being $t_1, t_2, t_3, t_4$, and $t_5$, respectively ($t_1 > t_2 > t_3 > t_4 > t_5$). Explain what happens if:

(a) The system uses the wait-die scheme and $T_2$ requests for a resource held by $T_5$.

(b) The system uses the wait-die scheme and $T_4$ requests for a resource held by $T_1$.

(c) The system uses the wait-wound scheme and $T_3$ requests for a resource held by $T_4$.

(d) The system uses the wait-wound scheme and $T_5$ requests for a resource held by $T_2$.

**6.30.** What is a phantom deadlock? What might be the reason for phantom deadlocks in a distributed system? Suppose that in the centralized deadlock detection scheme described in this chapter the transfer-on-request method is used to transfer information from local coordinators to the central coordinator. Give an example to show that the algorithm may still detect a phantom deadlock.

**6.31.** A centralized deadlock detection algorithm that does not detect false deadlocks was developed by Stuart et al. [1984]. Find out how this algorithm prevents the detection of false deadlocks.

**6.32.** Write pseudocode for the probe-based distributed algorithm for deadlock detection in a distributed system. What are the main advantages of this algorithm over a WFG-based distributed algorithm?

**6.33.** What problems may arise when a process is killed/rolled back and then restarted as the result of a deadlock? Suggest suitable methods to handle these problems. What conclusions can be drawn from these problems in connection with the proper selection of victims for recovery from a deadlock state?

**6.34.** What are the main issues involved in the selection of victims for recovery from a detected deadlock? Suggest a suitable victim selection algorithm. How does your algorithm take care of a starvation problem?

**6.35.** Why are election algorithms normally needed in a distributed system? A LAN-based distributed system has broadcast facility. Suggest a simple election algorithm for use in this system.

**6.36.** Initiation of an election is actually needed only when the current coordinator process fails. However, this is not the case in the bully algorithm, in which an election is also initiated whenever a failed process recovers. Is this really necessary? If yes, explain why. If no, suggest a modification to the bully algorithm in which an election is initiated only when the current coordinator fails.

**6.37.** In the ring-based election algorithm described in this chapter, a unidirectional ring was used. Suppose the ring is bidirectional. Can the election algorithm be made more efficient? If no, explain why. If yes, suggest such an algorithm and compare the number of messages needed for electing a coordinator in the two algorithms, assuming that there are $n$ processes in the system.

**6.38.** In the ring-based election algorithm described in this chapter, two or more processes may almost simultaneously discover that the coordinator has crashed and then each one may circulate an election message over the ring. Although this does not cause any problem in the election, it results in waste of network bandwidth. Modify the algorithm so that only one election message circulates completely round the ring and others are detected and killed as soon as possible.

**6.39.** What will happen in a bully algorithm for electing a coordinator when two or more processes almost simultaneously discover that the coordinator has crashed?

## BIBLIOGRAPHY

**[Adelstein and Singhal 1995]** Adelstein, F., and Singhal, M., "Real-Time Causal Message Ordering in Multimedia Systems," In: *Proceedings of the 15th International Conference on Distributed Computing Systems*, IEEE, New York (May–June 1995).

**[Agarwal and Abbadi 1991]** Agarwal, D., and El Abbadi, A., "An Efficient and Fault-Tolerant Solution of Distributed Mutual Exclusion," *ACM Transactions on Computer Systems*, Vol. 9, Association for Computing Machinery, New York, pp. 1–20 (1991).

**[Badal 1986]** Badal, D. Z., "The Distributed Deadlock Detection Algorithm," *ACM Transactions on Computer Systems*, Vol. 4, No. 4, Association for Computing Machinery, New York, pp. 320–337 (1986).

**[Barborak et al. 1993]** Barborak, M., Malek, M., and Dahbura, A., "The Consensus Problem in Fault-Tolerant Computing," *ACM Computing Surveys*, Vol. 25, Association for Computing Machinery, New York, pp. 171–220 (1993).

**[Bernstein et al. 1987]** Bernstein, P. A., Hadzilacos, V., and Goodman, N., *Concurrency and Recovery in Database Systems*, Addison-Wesley, Reading, MA, pp. 289–307 (1987).

**[Bracha and Toueg 1984]** Bracha, G., and Toueg, S., "A Distributed Algorithm for Generalized Deadlock Detection," In: *Proceedings of the 3rd ACM Symposium on Principles of Distributed Computing*, Association for Computing Machinery, New York, pp. 285–301 (1984).

**[Bracha and Toueg 1987]** Bracha, G., and Toueg, S., "Distributed Deadlock Detection," *Distributed Computing*, Vol. 2, pp. 127–138 (1987).

**[Bulgannawar and Vaidya 1995]** Bulgannawar, S., and Vaidya, N. H., "Distributed K-Mutual Exclusion," In: *Proceedings of the 15th International Conference on Distributed Computing Systems*, IEEE, New York (May–June 1995).

**[Carvalho and Roucairol 1983]** Carvalho, O. S. F., and Roucairol, G., "On Mutual Exclusion in Computer Networks," *Communications of the ACM*, Vol. 26, No. 2, Association for Computing Machinery, New York, pp. 146–147 (1983).

**[Chandy and Lamport 1985]** Chandy, K. M., and Lamport, L., "Distributed Snapshots: Determining Global States of Distributed Systems," *ACM Transactions on Computer Systems*, Vol. 3, No. 1, Association for Computing Machinery, New York, pp. 63–75 (1985).

**[Chandy and Misra 1982]** Chandy, K. M., and Misra, J., "A Distributed Algorithm for Detecting Resource Deadlocks in Distributed Systems," In: *Proceedings of the ACM Symposium on Principles of Distributed Computing*, Association for Computing Machinery, New York, pp. 157–164 (August 1982).

**[Chandy et al. 1983]** Chandy, K. M., Misra, J., and Haas, L. M., "Distributed Deadlock Detection," *ACM Transactions on Computer Systems*, Vol. 1, No. 2, Association for Computing Machinery, New York, pp. 144–156 (1983).

**[Choudhary et al. 1989]** Choudhary, A. N., Kohler, W. H., Stankovic, J. A., and Towsley, D., "A Modified Priority Based Probe Algorithm for Distributed Deadlock Detection and Resolution," *IEEE Transactions on Software Engineering*, Vol. SE-15, No. 1, pp. 10–17 (1989).

**[Cidon et al. 1987]** Cidon, I., Jaffe, J. M., and Sidi, M., "Local Distributed Deadlock Detection by Cycle Detection and Clustering," *IEEE Transactions on Software Engineering*, Vol. SE-13, No. 1, pp. 3–14 (1987).

**[Coffman et al. 1971]** Coffman, Jr., E. G. Elphick, M. J., and Shoshani, A., "System Deadlocks," *ACM Computing Surveys*, Vol. 3, No. 2, Association for Computing Machinery, New York, pp. 67–78 (1971).

**[Coulouris et al. 1994]** Coulouris, G. F., Dollimore, J., and Kindberg, T., *Distributed Systems Concepts and Design*, 2nd ed., Addison-Wesley, Reading, MA (1994).

**[Cristian 1989]** Cristian, F., "Probabilistic Clock Synchronization," *Distributed Computing*, Vol. 3, pp. 146–158 (1989).

**[Cristian 1991]** Cristian, F., "Understanding Fault-Tolerant Distributed Systems," *Communications of the ACM*, Vol. 34, Association for Computing Machinery, New York, pp. 56–78 (1991).

**[Cristian and Fetzer 1995]** Cristian, F., and Fetzer, C., "Fault-Tolerant External Clock Synchronization," In: *Proceedings of the 15th International Conference on Distributed Computing Systems*, IEEE, New York (May–June 1995).

**[Drummond and Babaoglu 1993]** Drummond, R., and Babaoglu, O., "Low-Cost Clock Synchronization," *Distributed Computing*, Vol. 6, pp. 193–203 (1993).

**[Dubois et al. 1988]** Dubois, M., Scheurich, C., and Briggs, F. A., "Synchronization, Coherence, and Event Ordering in Multiprocessors," *IEEE Computer*, Vol. 21, pp. 9–21 (1988).

**[Elmagarmid 1986]** Elmagarmid, A. K., "A Survey of Distributed Deadlock Detection Algorithms," *ACM SIGMOD*, Vol. 15, No. 3, pp. 37–45 (1986).

**[Fidge 1991]** Fidge, C., "Logical Time in Distributed Computing Systems," *IEEE Computer*, Vol. 24, pp. 28–33 (1991).

**[Fredrickson and Lynch 1987]** Fredrickson, N., and Lynch, N., "Electing a Leader in a Synchronous Ring," *Journal of the ACM*, Vol. 34, pp. 98–115 (1987).

**[Garcia-Molina 1982]** Garcia-Molina, H., "Elections in a Distributed Computing System," *IEEE Transactions on Computers*, Vol. C-31, No. 1, pp. 48–59 (1982).

**[Garg 1996]** Garg, V. K., *Principles of Distributed Systems*, Kluwer Academic, Norwell, MA (1996).

**[Goscinski 1991]** Goscinski, A., *Distributed Operating Systems, The Logical Design*, Addison-Wesley, Reading, MA (1991).

**[Gray et al. 1981]** Gray, J. N., Homan, P., Korth, H. F., and Obermarck, R. L., "A Straw Man Analysis of the Probability of Waiting and Deadlock in Database Systems," Technical Report RJ 3066, IBM Research Laboratory, San Jose, CA (1981).

**[Gusella and Zatti 1989]** Gusella, R., and Zatti, S., "The Accuracy of the Clock Synchronization Achieved by TEMPO in Berkeley UNIX 4.3BSD," *IEEE Transactions on Software Engineering*, Vol. SE-15, No. 7, pp. 847–853 (1989).

**[Jefferson 1985]** Jefferson, D. R., "Virtual Time," *ACM Transactions on Programming Languages and Systems*, Vol. 7, No. 3, pp. 404–425 (1985).

**[Knapp 1987]** Knapp, E., "Deadlock Detection in Distributed Databases," *ACM Computing Surveys*, Vol. 19, No. 4, pp. 303–328 (1987).

**[Kopetz and Ochsenreiter 1987]** Kopetz, H., and Ochsenreiter, W., "Clock Synchronization in Distributed Real-Time Systems," *IEEE Transactions on Computers*, Vol. C-36, pp. 933–940 (1987).

**[Lamport 1978]** Lamport, L., "Time, Clocks, and the Ordering of Events in a Distributed System," *Communications of the ACM*, Vol. 21, No. 7, pp. 558–565 (1978).

**[Lamport 1990]** Lamport, L., "Concurrent Reading and Writing of Clocks," *ACM Transactions on Computer Systems*, Vol. 8, pp. 305–310 (1990).

**[Lamport and Smith 1984]** Lamport, L., and Smith, P. M., "Byzantine Clock Synchronization," In: *Proceedings of the 3rd ACM Symposium on Principles of Distributed Computing*, Association for Computing Machinery, New York, pp. 68–74 (1984).

**[Lamport and Smith 1985]** Lamport, L., and Smith, P. M., "Synchronizing Clocks in the Presence of Faults," *Journal of the ACM*, Vol. 32, No. 1, Association for Computing Machinery, New York, pp. 52–78 (1985).

**[Lee and Kim 1995]** Lee, S., and Kim, J. L., "An Efficient Distributed Deadlock Detection Algorithm," In: *Proceedings of the 15th International Conference on Distributed Computing Systems*, IEEE, New York (May–June 1995).

**[Liskov 1993]** Liskov, B., "Practical Uses of Synchronized Clocks in Distributed Systems," *Distributed Computing*, Vol. 6, pp. 211–219 (1993).

**[Lockhart 1994]** Lockhart, Jr., H. W., *OSF DCE: Guide to Developing Distributed Applications*, IEEE Computer Society Press, Los Alamitos, CA (1994).

**[Maekawa et al. 1987]** Maekawa, M., Oldehoeft, A. E., and Oldehoeft, R. R., *Operating Systems: Advanced Concepts*, Benjamin/Cummings, White Plains, NY (1987).

**[Mattern 1993]** Mattern, F., "Efficient Algorithms for Distributed Snapshots and Global Virtual Time Approximation," *Journal of Parallel and Distributed Computing*, Vol. 18, No. 4, pp. 423–434 (1993).

**[Mills 1991]** Mills, D. L., "Internet Time Synchronization: The Network Time Protocol," *IEEE Transactions on Communications*, Vol. 39, No. 10, pp. 1482–1493 (1991).

**[Misra and Chandy 1982]** Misra, J., and Chandy, K. M., "A Distributed Graph Algorithm: Knot Detection," *ACM Transactions on Programming Languages and Systems*, Vol. 4, No. 4, pp. 678–686 (1982).

**[Mitchell and Merritt 1984]** Mitchell, D. P., and Merritt, M. J., "A Distributed Algorithm for Deadlock Detection and Resolution," In: *Proceedings of the 3rd ACM Symposium on Principles of Distributed Computing*, Association for Computing Machinery, New York, pp. 282–284 (1984).

**[Natrajan 1986]** Natrajan, N., "A Distributed Scheme for Detecting Communication Deadlocks," *IEEE Transactions on Software Engineering*, Vol. SE-12, No. 4, pp. 531–537 (1986).

**[Pratt and Nguyen 1995]** Pratt, G. A., and Nguyen, J., "Distributed Synchronous Clocking," *IEEE Transactions on Parallel and Distributed Systems*, Vol. 6, No. 3, pp. 314–328 (1995).

**[Ramanathan et al. 1990a]** Ramanathan, P., Kandlur, D. D., and Shin, K. G., "Hardware-Assisted Software Clock Synchronization for Homogeneous Distributed Systems," *IEEE Transactions on Computers*, Vol. C-39, No. 4, pp. 514–524 (1990).

**[Ramanathan et al. 1990b]** Ramanathan, P., Shin, K. G., and Butler, R. W., "Fault-Tolerant Clock Synchronization in Distributed Systems," *IEEE Computer*, Vol. 23, No. 10, pp. 33–42 (1990).

**[Raynal 1991]** Raynal, M., "A Simple Taxonomy for Distributed Mutual Exclusion Algorithms," *ACM Operating Systems Review*, Vol. 25, pp. 47–50 (1991).

**[Raynal 1992]** Raynal, M., "About Logical Clocks for Distributed Systems," *ACM Operating Systems Review*, Vol. 26, No. 1, pp. 41–48 (1992).

**[Ricart and Agrawala 1981]** Ricart, G., and Agrawala, A. K., "An Optimal Algorithm for Mutual Exclusion in Computer Networks," *Communications of the ACM*, Vol. 24, No. 1, pp. 9–17 (1981).

**[Roesler and Burkhard 1989]** Roesler, M., and Burkhard, W. A., "Resolution of Deadlocks in Object-Oriented Distributed Systems," *IEEE Transactions on Computers*, Vol. 38, No. 8, pp. 1212–1224 (1989).

**[Rosenberry et al. 1992]** Rosenberry, W., Kenney, D., and Fisher, G., *OSF DISTRIBUTED COMPUTING ENVIRONMENT, Understanding DCE*, O'Reilly & Associates, Sebastopol, CA (1992).

**[Rosenkrantz et al. 1978]** Rosenkrantz, D. J., Stearns, R. E., and Lewis, P. M., "System Level Concurrency Control for Distributed Database Systems," *ACM Transactions on Database Systems*, Vol. 3, No. 2, pp. 178–198 (1978).

**[Sanders 1987]** Sanders, B. A., "The Information Structure of Distributed Mutual Exclusion," *ACM Transactions on Computer Systems*, Vol. 5, pp. 284–299 (1987).

**[Shin and Ramanathan 1987]** Shin, K. G., and Ramanathan, P., "Clock Synchronization of a Large Multiprocessor System in the Presence of Malicious Faults," *IEEE Transactions on Computers*, Vol. C-36, No. 1, pp. 2–12 (1987).

**[Shin and Ramanathan 1988]** Shin, K. G., and Ramanathan, P., "Transmission Delays in Hardware Clock Synchronization," *IEEE Transactions on Computers*, Vol. C-37, No. 11, pp. 1465–1467 (1988).

**[Silberschatz and Galvin 1994]** Silberschatz, A., and Galvin, P. B., *Operating Systems Concepts*, 4th ed., Addison-Wesley, Reading, MA (1994).

**[Singh and Kurose 1994]** Singh, S., and Kurose, J., "Electing 'Good' Leaders," *Journal of Parallel and Distributed Computing*, Vol. 21, pp. 184–201 (1994).

**[Singhal 1989]** Singhal, M., "Deadlock Detection in Distributed Systems," *IEEE Computer*, Vol. 22, No. 11, pp. 37–48 (1989).

**[Singhal and Shivaratri 1994]** Singhal, M., and Shivaratri, N. G., *Advanced Concepts in Operating Systems*, McGraw-Hill, New York (1994).

**[Sinha and Natrajan 1985]** Sinha, M. K., and Natrajan, N., "A Priority Based Distributed Deadlock Detection Algorithm," *IEEE Transactions on Software Engineering*, Vol. SE-11, No. 1, pp. 67–80 (1985).

**[Srikanth and Teueg 1987]** Srikanth, T. K., and Teueg, S., "Optimal Clock Synchronization," *Journal of ACM*, Vol. 34, No. 3, pp. 626–645 (1987).

**[Stalling 1995]** Stalling, W., *Operating Systems*, 2nd ed., Prentice-Hall, Englewood Cliffs, NJ (1995).

**[Steinman et al. 1995]** Steinman, J. S., Lee, C. A., Wilson, L. F., and Nicol, D. M., "Global Virtual Time and Distributed Synchronization," In: *Proceedings of the 9th Workshop on Parallel and Distributed Simulation*, pp. 139–148 (1995).

**[Stuart et al. 1984]** Stuart, D., Buckley, G., and Silberschatz, A., "A Centralized Deadlock Detection Algorithm," Technical Report, University of Texas at Austin (1984).

**[Suzuki and Kasami 1985]** Suzuki, I., and Kasami, T., "A Distributed Mutual Exclusion Algorithm," *ACM Transactions on Computer Systems*, Vol. 3, No. 4, pp. 344–349 (1985).

**[Tanenbaum 1992]** Tanenbaum, A. S., *Modern Operating Systems*, Prentice-Hall, Englewood Cliffs, NJ (1992).

**[Tanenbaum 1995]** Tanenbaum, A. S., *Distributed Operating Systems*, Prentice-Hall, Englewood Cliffs, NJ (1995).

Election **[Tel 1994]** Tel, G., *Introduction to Distributed Algorithms*, Cambridge University Press, New York, NY (1994).

**[Turek and Shasha 1992]** Turek, J., and Shasha, D., "The Many Faces of Consensus in Distributed Systems," *IEEE Computer*, Vol. 25, pp. 8–17 (1992).

**[Vasanthavada and Marinos 1988]** Vasanthavada, N., and Marinos, P. N., "Synchronization of Fault-Tolerant Clocks in the Presence of Malicious Failures," *IEEE Transactions on Computers*, Vol. C-37, No. 4, pp. 440–448 (1988).

**[Wuu and Bernstein 1985]** Wuu, G. T., and Bernstein, A. J., "False Deadlock Detection in Distributed Systems," *IEEE Transactions on Software Engineering*, Vol. SE-11, No. 8, pp. 820–821 (1985).

**[Yang and Marsland 1994]** Yang, Z., and Marsland, T. A. (Eds.), *Global States and Time in Distributed Systems*, IEEE Computer Society Press, Los Alamitos, CA (1994).

## POINTERS TO BIBLIOGRAPHIES ON THE INTERNET

Bibliography containing references on *Time in Distributed Systems* can be found at:

ftp:ftp.cs.umanitoba.ca/pub/bibliographies/Distributed/dist-time.html

Bibliography containing references on *Synchronization of Concurrent Processes* can be found at:

ftp:ftp.cs.umanitoba.ca/pub/bibliographies/Parallel/par.synch.html

Bibliographies containing references on other topics covered in this chapter can be found at:

ftp:ftp.cs.umanitoba.ca/pub/bibliographies/Os/IMMD_IV.html

ftp:ftp.cs.umanitoba.ca/pub/bibliographies/Misc/misc.1.html

## CHAPTER 7

# Resource Management

## 7.1 INTRODUCTION

Distributed systems are characterized by resource multiplicity and system transparency. Every distributed system consists of a number of resources interconnected by a network. Besides providing communication facilities, the network facilitates resource sharing by migrating a local process and executing it at a remote node of the network. A process may be migrated because the local node does not have the required resources or the local node has to be shut down. A process may also be executed remotely if the expected turnaround time will be better. From a user's point of view, the set of available resources in a distributed system acts like a single virtual system. Hence, when a user submits a process for execution, it becomes the responsibility of the resource manager of the distributed operating system to control the assignment of resources to processes and to route the processes to suitable nodes of the system according to these assignments. A resource can be logical, such as a shared file, or physical, such as a CPU. For our purpose, we will consider a resource to be a processor of the system and assume that each processor forms a node of the distributed system. Thus, in this chapter, we will be interchangeably using the terms *node* and *processor* to mean the same thing.

A resource manager schedules the processes in a distributed system to make use of the system resources in such a manner that resource usage, response time, network congestion, and scheduling overhead are optimized. A variety of widely differing techniques and methodologies for scheduling processes of a distributed system have been proposed. These techniques can be broadly classified into three types:

1. *Task assignment approach*, in which each process submitted by a user for processing is viewed as a collection of related tasks and these tasks are scheduled to suitable nodes so as to improve performance
2. *Load-balancing approach*, in which all the processes submitted by the users are distributed among the nodes of the system so as to equalize the workload among the nodes
3. *Load-sharing approach*, which simply attempts to conserve the ability of the system to perform work by assuring that no node is idle while processes wait for being processed

Of the three approaches, the task assignment approach has limited applicability in practical situations because it works on the assumption that the characteristics of all the processes to be scheduled are known in advance. Furthermore, the scheduling algorithms that fall in this category do not normally take care of the dynamically changing state of the system. Therefore, this approach will be covered very briefly just to give an idea of how it works. Before presenting a description of each of these techniques, the desirable features of a good global scheduling algorithm are presented.

## 7.2 DESIRABLE FEATURES OF A GOOD GLOBAL SCHEDULING ALGORITHM

### 7.2.1 No A Priori Knowledge about the Processes

A good process scheduling algorithm should operate with absolutely no a priori knowledge about the processes to be executed. Scheduling algorithms that operate based on the information about the characteristics and resource requirements of the processes normally pose an extra burden upon the users who must specify this information while submitting their processes for execution.

### 7.2.2 Dynamic in Nature

It is intended that a good process-scheduling algorithm should be able to take care of the dynamically changing load (or status) of the various nodes of the system. That is, process assignment decisions should be based on the current load of the system and not on some fixed static policy. For this, sometimes it is also recommended that the scheduling algorithm should possess the flexibility to migrate a process more than once because the initial decision of placing a process on a particular node may have to be changed after some time to adapt to the new system load. This feature may also require that the system support preemptive process migration facility in which a process can be migrated from one node to another during the course of its execution.

### 7.2.3 Quick Decision-Making Capability

A good process-scheduling algorithm must make quick decisions about the assignment of processes to processors. This is an extremely important aspect of the algorithms and makes many potential solutions unsuitable. For example, an algorithm that models the system by a mathematical program and solves it on-line is unsuitable because it does not meet this requirement. Heuristic methods requiring less computational effort while providing near-optimal results are therefore normally preferable to exhaustive (optimal) solution methods.

### 7.2.4 Balanced System Performance and Scheduling Overhead

Several global scheduling algorithms collect global state information and use this information in making process assignment decisions. A common intuition is that greater amounts of information describing global system state allow more intelligent process assignment decisions to be made that have a positive affect on the system as a whole. In a distributed environment, however, information regarding the state of the system is typically gathered at a higher cost than in a centralized system. The general observation is that, as overhead is increased in an attempt to obtain more information regarding the global state of the system, the usefulness of that information is decreased due to both the aging of the information being gathered and the low scheduling frequency as a result of the cost of gathering and processing that information. Hence algorithms that provide near-optimal system performance with a minimum of global state information gathering overhead are desirable.

### 7.2.5 Stability

A scheduling algorithm is said to be unstable if it can enter a state in which all the nodes of the system are spending all of their time migrating processes without accomplishing any useful work in an attempt to properly schedule the processes for better performance. This form of fruitless migration of processes is known as *processor thrashing*. Processor thrashing can occur in situations where each node of the system has the power of scheduling its own processes and scheduling decisions either are made independently of decisions made by other processors or are based on relatively old data due to transmission delay between nodes. For example, it may happen that nodes $n_1$ and $n_2$ both observe that node $n_3$ is idle and then both offload a portion of their work to node $n_3$ without being aware of the offloading decision made by the other. Now if node $n_3$ becomes overloaded due to the processes received from both nodes $n_1$ and $n_2$, then it may again start transferring its processes to other nodes. This entire cycle may be repeated again and again, resulting in an unstable state. This is certainly not desirable for a good scheduling algorithm.

Processor thrashing can also occur if processes in transit to a lightly loaded node are not taken into account. In this case, several processes may be migrated to the same node, possibly producing instabilities. For example, suppose at a particular instance of time node $n_1$ is very busy and node $n_2$ is the least busy node. Also suppose that node $n_1$ is activated every 2 seconds and on an average it takes 20 seconds for a process to reach node $n_2$ from node $n_1$. Then node $n_1$ could conceivably send at least 10 processes to node $n_2$ before the first one was received. This could result in an unstable situation. A simple method to overcome this problem is to keep track of which node has been sent processes recently and use this information in an effort to mitigate the problem and to minimize process movement. More sophisticated techniques to deal with stability are possible, but they require the retention of more past data and hence are expensive.

### 7.2.6 Scalability

A scheduling algorithm should be capable of handling small as well as large networks. An algorithm that makes scheduling decisions by first inquiring the workload from all the nodes and then selecting the most lightly loaded node as the candidate for receiving the process(es) has poor scalability factor. Such an algorithm may work fine for small networks but gets crippled when applied to large networks. This is because the inquirer receives a very large number of replies almost simultaneously, and the time required to process the reply messages for making a host selection is normally too long. Moreover, the $N^2$ ($N$ is the total number of nodes in the system) nature of the algorithm creates heavy network traffic and quickly consumes network bandwidth. A simple approach to make an algorithm scalable is to probe only $m$ of $N$ nodes for selecting a host. The value of $m$ can be dynamically adjusted depending upon the value of $N$.

### 7.2.7 Fault Tolerance

A good scheduling algorithm should not be disabled by the crash of one or more nodes of the system. At any instance of time, it should continue functioning for nodes that are up at that time. Moreover, if the nodes are partitioned into two or more groups due to link failures, the algorithm should be capable of functioning properly for the nodes within a group. Algorithms that have decentralized decision-making capability and consider only available nodes in their decision-making approach have better fault tolerance capability.

### 7.2.8 Fairness of Service

While the average quality of service provided is clearly an important performance index, how fairly service is allocated is also a common concern. For example, two users simultaneously initiating equivalent processes expect to receive about the same quality of service. Several researchers think that global scheduling policies that blindly attempt to balance the average load on all the nodes of the system are not good from the point of view of fairness of service. This is because in any load-balancing scheme, heavily loaded nodes will obtain all the benefits while lightly loaded nodes will suffer poorer response time than that in a stand-alone configuration. What is desirable is a fair strategy that will improve response time to the former without unduly affecting the latter. For this, the concept of load balancing has to be replaced by the concept of load sharing, that is, a node will share some of its resources as long as its users are not significantly affected.

## 7.3 TASK ASSIGNMENT APPROACH

### 7.3.1 The Basic Idea

In this approach, a process is considered to be composed of multiple tasks and the goal is to find an optimal assignment policy for the tasks of an individual process. Typical assumptions found in task assignment work are as follows:

- A process has already been split into pieces called tasks. This split occurs along natural boundaries, so that each task will have integrity in itself and data transfers among the tasks will be minimized.
- The amount of computation required by each task and the speed of each processor are known.
- The cost of processing each task on every node of the system is known. This cost is usually derived based on the information about the speed of each processor and the amount of computation required by each task.
- The interprocess communication (IPC) costs between every pair of tasks is known. The IPC cost is considered zero (negligible) for tasks assigned to the same node. They are usually estimated by an analysis of the static program of a process. For example, during the execution of the process, if two tasks communicate $n$ times and if the average time for each intertask communication is $t$, the intertask communication cost for the two tasks is $n \times t$.
- Other constraints, such as resource requirements of the tasks and the available resources at each node, precedence relationships among the tasks, and so on, are also known.
- Reassignment of the tasks is generally not possible.

With these assumptions, the task assignment algorithms seek to assign the tasks of a process to the nodes of the distributed system in such a manner so as to achieve goals such as the following:

- Minimization of IPC costs
- Quick turnaround time for the complete process
- A high degree of parallelism
- Efficient utilization of system resources in general

These goals often conflict with each other. For example, while minimizing IPC tends to assign all the tasks of a process to a single node, efficient utilization of system resources tries to distribute the tasks evenly among the nodes. Similarly, while quick turnaround time and a high degree of parallelism encourage parallel execution of the tasks, the precedence relationship among the tasks limits their parallel execution. Also notice that in case of $m$ tasks and $q$ nodes, there are $m^q$ possible assignments of tasks to nodes. In practice, however, the actual number of possible assignments of tasks to nodes may be less than $m^q$ due to the restriction that certain tasks cannot be assigned to certain nodes due to their specific resource requirements; the required resource(s) may not be available on all the nodes of the system.

To illustrate with an example, let us consider the assignment problem of Figure 7.1. This is the same problem discussed by Stone [1977]. It involves only two task assignment parameters—the task execution cost and the intertask communication cost. This system is made up of six tasks $\{t_1, t_2, t_3, t_4, t_5, t_6\}$ and two nodes $\{n_1, n_2\}$. The intertask communication costs ($c_{ij}$) and the execution costs ($x_{ab}$) of the tasks are given in tabular form in Figure 7.1($a$) and ($b$), respectively. An infinite cost for a particular task against a particular node in Figure 7.1($b$) indicates that the task cannot be executed on that node due to the task's requirement of specific resources that are not available on that node. Thus, task $t_2$ cannot be executed on node $n_2$ and task $t_6$ cannot be executed on node $n_1$. In this model of a distributed computing system, there is no parallelism or multitasking of task execution within a program. Thus the total cost of process execution consists of the total execution cost of the tasks on their assigned nodes plus the intertask communication costs between tasks assigned to different nodes.

Figure 7.1($c$) shows a serial assignment of the tasks to the two nodes in which the first three tasks are assigned to node $n_1$ and the remaining three are assigned to node $n_2$. Observe that this assignment is aimed at minimizing the total execution cost. But if both the execution costs and the communication costs are taken into account, the total cost for this assignment comes out to be 58. Figure 7.1($d$) shows an optimal assignment of the tasks to the two nodes that minimizes total execution and communication costs. In this case, although the execution cost is more than that of the previous assignment, the total assignment cost is only 38.

### 7.3.2 Finding an Optimal Assignment

The problem of finding an assignment of tasks to nodes that minimizes total execution and communication costs was elegantly analyzed using a network flow model and network flow algorithms by Stone [1977, 1978] and a number of other researchers [Lo 1988, Wu and Liu 1980, Bokhari 1979]. In this approach, an optimal assignment is found by creating a static assignment graph, as shown in Figure 7.2. In this graph, nodes $n_1$ and $n_2$ represent the two nodes (processors) of the distributed system and nodes $t_1$ through $t_6$ represent the tasks of the process. The weights of the edges joining pairs of task nodes represent intertask communication costs. The weight on the edge joining a task node to node $n_1$ represents the execution cost of that task on node $n_2$ and vice versa.

A *cutset* in this graph is defined to be a set of edges such that when these edges are removed, the nodes of the graph are partitioned into two disjoint subsets such that the nodes in one subset are reachable from $n_1$ and the nodes in the other are reachable from $n_2$. Each task node is reachable from either $n_1$ or $n_2$. No proper subset of a cutset is also

| Intertask communications cost | | | | | | |
|---|---|---|---|---|---|---|
| | $t_1$ | $t_2$ | $t_3$ | $t_4$ | $t_5$ | $t_6$ |
| $t_1$ | 0 | 6 | 4 | 0 | 0 | 12 |
| $t_2$ | 6 | 0 | 8 | 12 | 3 | 0 |
| $t_3$ | 4 | 8 | 0 | 0 | 11 | 0 |
| $t_4$ | 0 | 12 | 0 | 0 | 5 | 0 |
| $t_5$ | 0 | 3 | 11 | 5 | 0 | 0 |
| $t_6$ | 12 | 0 | 0 | 0 | 0 | 0 |

(*a*)

| Execution costs | | |
|---|---|---|
| Tasks | Nodes | |
| | $n_1$ | $n_2$ |
| $t_1$ | 5 | 10 |
| $t_2$ | 2 | $\infty$ |
| $t_3$ | 4 | 4 |
| $t_4$ | 6 | 3 |
| $t_5$ | 5 | 2 |
| $t_6$ | $\infty$ | 4 |

(*b*)

| Serial assignment | |
|---|---|
| Task | Node |
| $t_1$ | $n_1$ |
| $t_2$ | $n_1$ |
| $t_3$ | $n_1$ |
| $t_4$ | $n_2$ |
| $t_5$ | $n_2$ |
| $t_6$ | $n_2$ |

(*c*)

| Optimal assignment | |
|---|---|
| Task | Node |
| $t_1$ | $n_1$ |
| $t_2$ | $n_1$ |
| $t_3$ | $n_1$ |
| $t_4$ | $n_1$ |
| $t_5$ | $n_1$ |
| $t_6$ | $n_2$ |

(*d*)

Serial assignment execution cost $(x) = x_{11} + x_{21} + x_{31} + x_{42} + x_{52} + x_{62}$
$= 5 + 2 + 4 + 3 + 2 + 4 = 20$

Serial assignment communication cost $(c) = c_{14} + c_{15} + c_{16} + c_{24} + c_{25} + c_{26} + c_{34} + c_{35} + c_{36}$
$= 0 + 0 + 12 + 12 + 3 + 0 + 0 + 11 + 0 = 38$

Serial assignment total cost $= x + c = 20 + 38 = 58$

Optimal assignment execution cost $(x) = x_{11} + x_{21} + x_{31} + x_{41} + x_{51} + x_{62}$
$= 5 + 2 + 4 + 6 + 5 + 4 = 26$

Optimal assignment communication cost $(c) = c_{16} + c_{26} + c_{36} + c_{46} + c_{56}$
$= 12 + 0 + 0 + 0 + 0 = 12$

Optimal assignment total cost $= x + c = 26 + 12 = 38$

**Fig. 7.1** A task assignment problem example. (*a*) intertask communication costs; (*b*) execution costs of the tasks on the two nodes; (*c*) serial assignment; (*d*) optimal assignment.

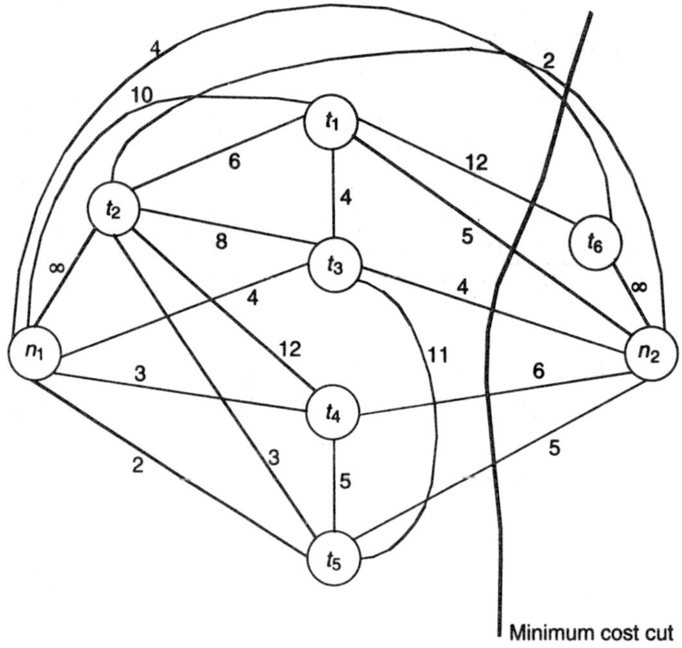


**Fig. 7.2** Assignment graph for the assignment problem of Figure 7.1 with minimum cost cut.

a cutset, that is, a cutset is a minimal set. Each cutset corresponds in a one-to-one manner to a task assignment.

The weight of a cutset is the sum of the weights of the edges in the cutset. It represents the cost of the corresponding task assignment since the weight of a cutset sums up the execution and communication costs for that assignment. An optimal assignment may be obtained by finding a minimum-weight cutset. This may be done by the use of network flow algorithms, which are among the class of algorithms with relatively low computational complexity. The bold line in Figure 7.2 indicates a minimum-weight cutset that corresponds to the optimal assignment of Figure 7.1(*d*). Note that if task $t_1$ is assigned to node $n_2$, then the edge to node $n_2$ is cut, but this edge carries the cost of executing task $t_1$ on node $n_1$. Similarly, other edges cut between task $t_1$ and other nodes of the graph represent actual communication costs incurred by this assignment for communication between task $t_1$ and the other corresponding nodes.

In a two-processor system, an optimal assignment can be found in polynomial time by utilizing Max Flow/Min Cut algorithms [Shen and Tsai 1985]. However, for an arbitrary number of processors, the problem is known to be Nonpolynomial (NP) hard. An NP hard problem is computationally intractable because it cannot be solved in polynomial time. Thus, for more general cases, several researchers have turned to heuristic algorithms that are computationally efficient but may yield suboptimal assignments. Readers interested in some of these heuristic algorithms may refer to [Arora and Rana 1980, Efe 1982, Lo 1988].

It may be noted that in the model described above, the tasks of a process were assigned to the various nodes of the system. This model may be generalized to the general task assignment problem in which several processes are to be assigned. In this case, each process is treated to be a task of the process force and the interprocess communication costs are assumed to be known.

Several extensions to the basic task assignment model described above have been proposed in the literature. In addition to the task assignment cost and the intertask communication cost parameters of the basic task assignment model, the extended models take into account other parameters such as memory size requirements of the task and memory size constraint of the processors, precedence relationship among the tasks, and so on. However, we will not discuss this topic any further because of the limited applicability of the task assignment approach in practical situations. Readers interested in some of these extended models may refer to [Lo 1988, Chu and Lan 1987, Rao et al. 1979].

## 7.4 LOAD-BALANCING APPROACH

The scheduling algorithms using this approach are known as *load-balancing algorithms* or *load-leveling algorithms*. These algorithms are based on the intuition that, for better resource utilization, it is desirable for the load in a distributed system to be balanced evenly. Thus, a load-balancing algorithm tries to balance the total system load by transparently transferring the workload from heavily loaded nodes to lightly loaded nodes in an attempt to ensure good overall performance relative to some specific metric of system performance. When considering performance from the user point of view, the metric involved is often the response time of the processes. However, when performance is considered from the resource point of view, the metric involved is the total system throughput. In contrast to response time, throughput is concerned with seeing that all users are treated fairly and that all are making progress. Notice that the resource view of maximizing resource utilization is compatible with the desire to maximize system throughput. Thus the basic goal of almost all the load-balancing algorithms is to maximize the total system throughput.

### 7.4.1 A Taxonomy of Load-Balancing Algorithms

The taxonomy presented here is a hierarchy of the features of load-balancing algorithms. The structure of the taxonomy is shown in Figure 7.3. To describe a specific load-balancing algorithm, a taxonomy user traces paths through the hierarchy. A description of this taxonomy is given below.

#### Static versus Dynamic

At the highest level, we may distinguish between *static* and *dynamic* load-balancing algorithms. Static algorithms use only information about the average behavior of the system, ignoring the current state of the system. On the other hand, dynamic algorithms react to the system state that changes dynamically.

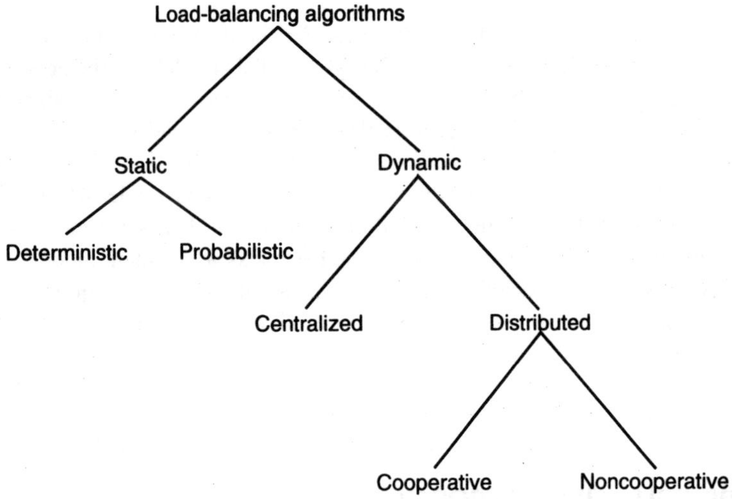


**Fig. 7.3** A taxonomy of load-balancing algorithms.

Static load-balancing algorithms are simpler because there is no need to maintain and process system state information. However, the potential of static algorithms is limited by the fact that they do not react to the current system state. The attraction of dynamic algorithms is that they do respond to system state and so are better able to avoid those states with unnecessarily poor performance. Owing to this reason, dynamic policies have significantly greater performance benefits than static policies. However, since dynamic algorithms must collect and react to system state information, they are necessarily more complex than static algorithms.

### Deterministic versus Probabilistic

Static load-balancing algorithms may be either *deterministic* or *probabilistic*. Deterministic algorithms use the information about the properties of the nodes and the characteristics of the processes to be scheduled to deterministically allocate processes to nodes. Notice that the task assignment algorithms basically belong to the category of deterministic static load-balancing algorithms.

A probabilistic load-balancing algorithm uses information regarding static attributes of the system such as number of nodes, the processing capability of each node, the network topology, and so on, to formulate simple process placement rules. For example, suppose a system has two processors $p_1$ and $p_2$ and four terminals $t_1$, $t_2$, $t_3$, and $t_4$. Then a simple process placement rule can be, assign all processes originating at terminals $t_1$ and $t_2$ to processor $p_1$ and processes originating at terminals $t_3$ and $t_4$ to processor $p_2$. Obviously, such static load-balancing algorithms have limited potential to avoid those states that have unnecessarily poor performance. For example, suppose at the time a particular process originates at terminal $t_1$ processor $p_1$ is very heavily loaded and processor $p_2$ is idle. Certainly, processor $p_2$ is a better choice for the process in such a situation.

In general, the deterministic approach is difficult to optimize and costs more to implement. The probabilistic approach is easier to implement but often suffers from having poor performance.

### Centralized versus Distributed

Dynamic scheduling algorithms may be *centralized* or *distributed*. In a centralized dynamic scheduling algorithm, the responsibility of scheduling physically resides on a single node. On the other hand, in a distributed dynamic scheduling algorithm, the work involved in making process assignment decisions is physically distributed among the various nodes of the system. In the centralized approach, the system state information is collected at a single node at which all scheduling decisions are made. This node is called the *centralized server node*. All requests for process scheduling are handled by the centralized server, which decides about the placement of a new process using the state information stored in it. The centralized approach can efficiently make process assignment decisions because the centralized server knows both the load at each node and the number of processes needing service. In the basic method, the other nodes periodically send status update messages to the central server node. These messages are used to keep the system state information up to date at the centralized server node. One might consider having the centralized server query the other nodes for state information. This would reduce message traffic if state information was used to answer several process assignment requests, but since nodes can change their load any time due to local activities, this would introduce problems of stale state information.

A problem associated with the centralized mechanism is that of reliability. If the centralized server fails, all scheduling in the system would cease. A typical approach to overcome this problem would be to replicate the server on $k+1$ nodes if it is to survive $k$ faults (node failures). In this approach, the overhead involved in keeping consistent all the $k+1$ replicas of the server may be considerably high. A typical solution to reduce this overhead is to forgo strong consistency and use a cheaper mechanism to update the multiple copies of the server. This solution is based on the idea that strict consistency is not necessary in this case for the system to function properly.

Theimer and Lantz [1989] proposed that if occasional delays in service of several seconds are acceptable, one can use the simpler approach of *reinstantiation* to improve the reliability of the centralized scheduling mechanism. In this approach, rather than maintaining $k+1$ server replicas, a single server is maintained and there are $k$ entities monitoring the server to detect its failure. When failure is detected, a new instance of the server is brought up, which reconstructs its state information by sending a multicast message requesting immediate state update. The time during which the scheduling service is unavailable will be the sum of the time to detect failure of the previous server, the time to load the server program on the new server, the time to resolve the possibility of multiple concurrent instantiations among the $k$ entities, and the time to reconstruct the global state information on the new server [Theimer and Lantz 1989].

In contrast to the centralized scheme, a distributed scheme does not limit the scheduling intelligence to one node. It avoids the bottleneck of collecting state information at a single node and allows the scheduler to react quickly to dynamic changes in the system state. A distributed dynamic scheduling algorithm is composed of $k$ physically distributed entities $e_1, e_2, \ldots, e_k$. Each entity is considered a local controller. Each local controller runs asynchronously and concurrently with the others, and each is responsible for making scheduling decisions for the processes of a predetermined set of nodes. Each entity $e_i$ makes decisions based on a systemwide objective function, rather than on a local one. Each $e_i$ makes decisions on an equal basis with the other entities; that is, there is no master entity, even for a short period of time. In a fully distributed algorithm, each node has its own entity and hence $k=N$ for a system having $N$ nodes. In this case, each entity is responsible for making scheduling decisions for the processes of its own node, which includes both transfer of local processes and acceptance of remote processes.

### Cooperative versus Noncooperative

Distributed dynamic scheduling algorithms may be categorized as *cooperative* and *noncooperative*. In noncooperative algorithms, individual entities act as autonomous entities and make scheduling decisions independently of the actions of other entities. On the other hand, in cooperative algorithms, the distributed entities cooperate with each other to make scheduling decisions. Hence, cooperative algorithms are more complex and involve larger overhead than noncooperative ones. However, the stability of a cooperative algorithm is better than that of a noncooperative algorithm.

## 7.4.2 Issues in Designing Load-Balancing Algorithms

Designing a good load-balancing algorithm is a difficult task because of the following issues:

- Load estimation policy, which determines how to estimate the workload of a particular node of the system
- Process transfer policy, which determines whether to execute a process locally or remotely
- State information exchange policy, which determines how to exchange the system load information among the nodes
- Location policy, which determines to which node a process selected for transfer should be sent
- Priority assignment policy, which determines the priority of execution of local and remote processes at a particular node
- Migration limiting policy, which determines the total number of times a process can migrate from one node to another

These issues are discussed below. For this discussion, we divide the processes within the system into two classes: local processes and remote processes. A *local process* is one that is processed at its originating node and a *remote process* is one that is processed at a node different from the one on which it originated. A new process, arriving from the external world at a node, becomes a local process if it is admitted to that node for processing. Otherwise, it is transferred across the network and becomes a remote process at the destination node.

### Load Estimation Policies

The main goal of load-balancing algorithms is to balance the workload on all the nodes of the system. However, before an algorithm can attempt to balance the workload, it is necessary to decide how to measure the workload of a particular node. Hence the first issue in any load-balancing algorithm is to decide on the method to be used to estimate the workload of a particular node. Estimation of the workload of a particular node is a difficult problem for which no completely satisfactory solution exists. A node's workload can be estimated based on some measurable parameters. These parameters could include time-dependent and node-dependent factors such as the following:

- Total number of processes on the node at the time of load estimation
- Resource demands of these processes
- Instruction mixes of these processes
- Architecture and speed of the node's processor

Since the measurement of load would occur quite often and the load would reflect the current state of the node, its calculation must be very efficient. This rules out an exhaustive use of all parameters even if their relative importance is known. Thus several load-balancing algorithms use the total number of processes present on the node as a measure of the node's workload. However, several designers believe that this is an unsuitable measure for such an estimate since the true load could vary widely depending on the remaining service times for those processes. Therefore another measure used for estimating a node's workload is the sum of the remaining service times of all the processes on that node. However, in this case another issue that must be resolved is how to estimate the remaining service time of the processes. Bryant and Finkel [1981] have proposed the use of one of the following methods for this purpose:

1. *Memoryless method.* This method assumes that all processes have the same expected remaining service time, independent of the time used so far. The use of this method for remaining service time estimation of a process basically reduces the load estimation method to that of total number of processes.
2. *Pastrepeats.* This method assumes that the remaining service time of a process is equal to the time used so far by it.
3. *Distribution method.* If the distribution of service times is known, the associated process's remaining service time is the expected remaining time conditioned by the time already used.

Neither the method of counting the total number of processes nor the method of taking the sum of the remaining service times of all processes is suitable for use as load estimation policies in modern distributed systems. This is because in modern distributed systems, even on an idle node, several processes such as mail and news daemons, window managers, and so on, exist permanently. Moreover, many of these daemon processes wake up periodically, check to see if there is anything that they have to do, and if not, go back to sleep. Therefore, an acceptable method for use as the load estimation policy in these systems would be to measure the CPU utilization of the nodes [Tanenbaum 1995]. *Central processing unit (CPU) utilization* is defined as the number of CPU cycles actually executed per unit of real time. Obviously, the CPU utilization of a heavily loaded node will be greater than the CPU utilization of a lightly loaded node. The CPU utilization of a node can be measured by setting up a timer to periodically observe the CPU state (idle/busy).

### Process Transfer Policies

The strategy of load-balancing algorithms is based on the idea of transferring some processes from the heavily loaded nodes to the lightly loaded nodes for processing. However, to facilitate this, it is necessary to devise a policy to decide whether a node is lightly or heavily loaded. Most of the load-balancing algorithms use the *threshold policy* to make this decision. The threshold value of a node is the limiting value of its workload and is used to decide whether a node is lightly or heavily loaded. Thus a new process at a node is accepted locally for processing if the workload of the node is below its threshold value at that time. Otherwise, an attempt is made to transfer the process to a lightly loaded node. The threshold value of a node may be determined by any of the following methods:

1. *Static policy.* In this method, each node has a predefined threshold value depending on its processing capability. This threshold value does not vary with the dynamic changes in workload at local or remote nodes. The main advantage of this method is that no exchange of state information among the nodes is required in deciding the threshold value.

2. *Dynamic policy.* In this method, the threshold value of a node ($n_i$) is calculated as a product of the average workload of all the nodes and a predefined constant ($c_i$). For each node $n_i$, the value of $c_i$ depends on the processing capability of node $n_i$ relative to the processing capability of all other nodes. In this method, the nodes exchange state information by using one of the state information exchange policies (described later). Although the dynamic policy gives a more realistic value of threshold for each node, the overhead involved in exchange of state information makes its applicability questionable.

Most load-balancing algorithms use a single threshold and thus only have overloaded and underloaded regions [Fig. 7.4(*a*)]. In this single-threshold policy, a node accepts new processes (either local or remote) if its load is below the threshold value and attempts to transfer local processes and rejects remote execution requests if its load is above the threshold value. Therefore the decision regarding both the transfer of local processes and the acceptance of remote processes is done based on a single-threshold value. The use of

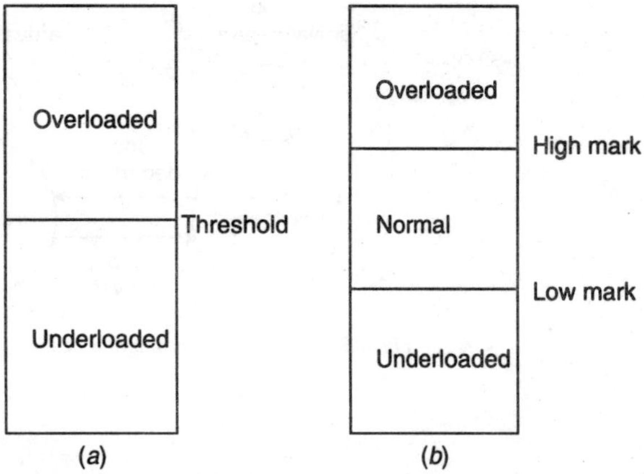


**Fig. 7.4** The load regions of (*a*) single-threshold policy and (*b*) double-threshold policy.

a single-threshold value may lead to fruitless process transfers, making the scheduling algorithm unstable because a node's load may be below the threshold when it decides to accept a remote process, but its load may become larger than the threshold as soon as the remote process arrives. Therefore, immediately after receiving the remote process, the node will again try to transfer one or more of its processes to some other node. Moreover, Alonso and Cova [1988] observed:

- A node should only transfer one or more of its processes to another node if such a transfer greatly improves the performance of the rest of its local processes.
- A node should accept remote processes only if its load is such that the added workload of processing these incoming processes does not significantly affect the service to the local ones.

To reduce the instability of the single-threshold policy and to take care of these two notions, Alonso and Cova [1988] proposed a double-threshold policy called the *high-low policy*. As shown in Figure 7.4(*b*), the high-low policy uses two threshold values called *high mark* and *low mark*, which divide the space of possible load states of a node into the following three regions:

- Overloaded—above the high-mark and low-mark values
- Normal—above the low-mark value and below the high-mark value
- Underloaded—below both values

A node's load state switches dynamically from one region to another, as shown in Figure 7.5.

Now depending on the current load status of a node, the decision to transfer a local process or to accept a remote process is based on the following policies [Alonso and Cova 1988]:

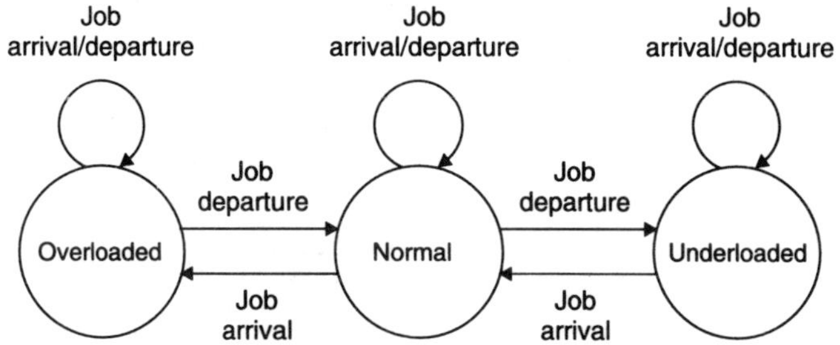


**Fig. 7.5** State transition diagram of the load of a node in case of double-threshold policy.

- When the load of the node is in the overloaded region, new local processes are sent to be run remotely and requests to accept remote processes are rejected.
- When the load of the node is in the normal region, new local processes run locally and requests to accept remote processes are rejected.
- When the load of the node is in the underloaded region, new local processes run locally and requests to accept remote processes are accepted.

Notice that the high-low policy guarantees a predefined level of performance to the node owners. It accounts for the overhead that the load-balancing algorithm may incur in transferring and receiving a remote process. A process will not be transferred to another node unless it is worthwhile, and a remote process will not be accepted unless there is enough excess capacity to handle it [Alonso and Cova 1988].

### Location Policies

Once a decision has been made through the transfer policy to transfer a process from a node, the next step is to select the destination node for that process's execution. This selection is made by the location policy of a scheduling algorithm. The main location policies proposed in the literature are described below.

***Threshold.*** In this method, a destination node is selected at random and a check is made to determine whether the transfer of the process to that node would place it in a state that prohibits the node to accept remote processes. If not, the process is transferred to the selected node, which must execute the process regardless of its state when the process actually arrives. On the other hand, if the check indicates that the selected node is in a state that prohibits it to accept remote processes, another node is selected at random and probed in the same manner. This continues until either a suitable destination node is found or the number of probes exceeds a static probe limit $L_p$. In the latter case, the node on which the process originated must execute the process. Eager et al. [1986b] performed simulations by using the single static threshold transfer policy and this threshold location policy. Their simulation results showed that the performance of this policy is surprisingly insensitive to the choice of probe limit; the performance with a small (and economical) probe limit (e.g., 3 or 5) is almost as good as the performance with a large probe limit (e.g., 20). The simulation results also showed that the threshold policy provides substantial performance improvement relative to no load balancing. This indicates that very simple schemes can yield significant benefits.

***Shortest.*** In this method, $L_p$ distinct nodes are chosen at random, and each is polled in turn to determine its load. The process is transferred to the node having the minimum load value, unless that node's load is such that it prohibits the node to accept remote processes. If none of the polled nodes can accept the process, it is executed at its originating node. If a destination node is found and the process is transferred there, the destination node must execute the process regardless of its state at the time the process actually arrives. A simple improvement to the basic shortest policy is to discontinue probing whenever a node with zero load is encountered, since that node is guaranteed to be an acceptable destination.

The shortest policy uses more state information, in a more complex manner, than does the threshold policy. But Eager et al. [1986b] found, through their simulation results, that the performance of the shortest policy is not significantly better than that of the simpler threshold policy. This suggests that state information beyond that used by the threshold policy or a more complex usage of state information is of little benefit.

***Bidding.*** In this method, the system is turned into a distributed computational economy with buyers and sellers of services [Waldspurger et al. 1992, Malone et al. 1988]. Each node in the network is responsible for two roles with respect to the bidding process: manager and contractor. The *manager* represents a node having a process in need of a location to execute, and the *contractor* represents a node that is able to accept remote processes. Note that a single node takes on both these roles and no nodes are strictly managers or contractors alone. To select a node for its process, the manager broadcasts a request-for-bids message to all other nodes in the system. Upon receiving this message, the contractor nodes return bids to the manager node. The bids contain the quoted prices, which vary based on the processing capability, memory size, resource availability, and so on, of the contractor nodes. Of the bids received from the contractor nodes, the manager node chooses the best bid. The best bid for a manager's request may mean the cheapest, fastest, or best price-performance, depending on the application for which the request was made. Once the best bid is determined, the process is transferred from the manager node to the winning contractor node. But it is possible that a contractor node may simultaneously win many bids from many other manager nodes and thus become overloaded. To prevent this situation, when the best bid is selected, a message is sent to the owner of that bid. At that point the bidder may choose to accept or reject that process. A message is sent back to the concerned manager node informing it as to whether the process has been accepted or rejected. A contractor node may reject a winning bid because of changes in its state between the time the bid was made and the time it was notified that it won the bid. If the bid is rejected, the bidding procedure is started all over again.

Bidding algorithms are interesting because they provide full autonomy to the nodes to decide whether to participate in the global scheduling process. For example, a manager node has the power to decide whether to send a process to a contractor node, which responds with bids, and a contractor node has the power to decide whether it wants to accept remote processes. A contractor node is never forced to accept remote processes if it does not choose to do so. On the other hand, the two main drawbacks of bidding algorithms are that they create a great deal of communication overhead and it is very difficult to decide a good pricing policy. Both factors call for a proper choice of the amount and type of information exchanged during bidding. For a bidding algorithm, the amount and type of information exchanged are generally decided in such a manner so as to balance the effectiveness and performance of the algorithm. A variety of possibilities exist concerning the type and amount of information exchanged in order to make decisions [Stankovic and Sidhu 1984, Smith 1980, Hwang et al. 1982, Stankovic 1984].

***Pairing.*** The method of accomplishing load balancing employed by the policies described until now is to balance or reduce the variance between the loads experienced by all the nodes of the system. Contrary to this approach, the method of accomplishing load balancing by the pairing policy is to reduce the variance of loads only between pairs of nodes of the system. This location policy was proposed by Bryant and Finkel [1981]. In this method, two nodes that differ greatly in load are temporarily paired with each other, and the load-balancing operation is carried out between the nodes belonging to the same pair by migrating one or more processes from the more heavily loaded node to the other node. Several node pairs may exist simultaneously in the system. A node only tries to find a partner if it has at least two processes; otherwise migration from this node is never reasonable. However, every node is willing to respond favorably to a pairing request.

In the basic pairing method, each node asks some randomly chosen node if it will pair with it. While awaiting an answer, the querier rejects any queries from other nodes. If it receives a rejection, it randomly selects another node and tries to pair again. If it receives a query from its own intended partner, a pair is formed. After the formation of a pair, one or more processes are migrated from the more heavily loaded node of the two nodes to the other node in order to balance the loads on these two nodes. The processes to be migrated are selected by comparing their expected time to complete on their current node with the expected time to complete on its partner. Migration delay is included in this estimate. The process with the best ratio of service time on the partner node to service time on the current node is selected to be sent first. Decisions for migrating other processes are based on the assumption that the first process has been received by the partner node and the load of the partner node has been updated to reflect the presence of this process on it. The pair is broken as soon as the process migration is over. During the time that a pair is in force, both members of the pair reject other pairing queries. Some other variations of the pairing mechanism can be found in [Bryant and Finkel 1981].

### State Information Exchange Policies

We have seen that the dynamic policies require frequent exchange of state information among the nodes of the system. In fact, a dynamic load-balancing algorithm faces a transmission dilemma because of the two opposing impacts the transmission of a message has on the overall performance of the system. On the one hand, the transmission improves the ability of the algorithm to balance the load. On the other hand, it raises the expected queuing time of messages because of the increase in the utilization of the communication channel. Thus proper selection of the state information exchange policy is essential. The proposed load-balancing algorithms use one of the following policies for this purpose.

***Periodic Broadcast.*** In this method each node broadcasts its state information after the elapse of every *t* units of time. Obviously this method is not good because it generates heavy network traffic and also because there is a possibility of fruitless messages (messages from those nodes whose state has not changed during the last *t* units of time) being broadcast. Furthermore, the scalability of this method is poor because the number of messages generated for state information exchanges will be too large for networks having many nodes.

***Broadcast When State Changes.*** This method avoids the problem of fruitless message exchanges of the periodic broadcast method by ensuring that a node broadcasts its state information only when the state of the node changes. A node's state changes when a process arrives at that node or when a process departs from that node. A process may arrive at a node either from the external world or from some other node in the system. A process departs from a node when either its execution is over or it is transferred to some other node.

A further improvement in this method can be obtained by observing that it is not necessary to report every small change in the state of a node to all other nodes because a node can participate in the load-balancing process only when it is either underloaded or overloaded. Therefore in the refined method, a node broadcasts its state information only when its state switches from the normal load region to either the underloaded region or the overloaded region. Obviously this refined method works only with the two-threshold transfer policy.

***On-Demand Exchange.*** A node needs to know about the state of other nodes only when it is either underloaded or overloaded. The method of on-demand exchange of state information is based on this observation. In this method a node broadcasts a *StateInformationRequest* message when its state switches from the normal load region to either the underloaded region or the overloaded region. On receiving this message, other nodes send their current state to the requesting node. Notice that this method also works only with the two-threshold transfer policy.

Further reduction in the number of messages is possible in this method by observing that the requesting node does not need the state information of all other nodes. Rather, the state information of only those nodes is useful for the requesting node, which can cooperate with it in the load-balancing process. That is, if the requesting node is underloaded, only overloaded nodes can cooperate with it in the load-balancing process and vice versa. Therefore, in the improved on-demand exchange policy, the status of the requesting node is included in the *StateInformationRequest* message. On receiving the *StateInformationRequest* message, only those nodes reply that can cooperate with the requesting node in the load-balancing process. Other nodes do not send any reply.

***Exchange by Polling.*** All the methods described above use the method of broadcasting due to which their scalability is poor. The polling mechanism overcomes this limitation by avoiding the use of broadcast protocol. This method is based on the idea that there is no need for a node to exchange its state information with all other nodes in the system. Rather, when a node needs the cooperation of some other node for load balancing, it can search for a suitable partner by randomly polling the other nodes one by one. Therefore state information is exchanged only between the polling node and the polled nodes. The polling process stops either when a suitable partner is found or a predefined poll limit is reached.

### Priority Assignment Policies

When process migration is supported by a distributed operating system, it becomes necessary to devise a priority assignment rule for scheduling both local and remote processes at a particular node. One of the following priority assignment rules may be used for this purpose:

1. *Selfish*. Local processes are given higher priority than remote processes.
2. *Altruistic*. Remote processes are given higher priority than local processes.
3. *Intermediate*. The priority of processes depends on the number of local processes and the number of remote processes at the concerned node. If the number of local processes is greater than or equal to the number of remote processes, local processes are given higher priority than remote processes. Otherwise, remote processes are given higher priority than local processes.

Lee and Towsley [1986] studied the effect of these three priority assignment policies on the overall response time performance. The results of their study show the following:

- The selfish priority assignment rule yields the worst response time performance of the three policies. This is due to the extremely poor performance of remote processes under this policy. However, it yields the best response time performance for local processes. Consequently, this policy imposes a severe penalty for processes that arrive at a busy node and is beneficial for processes arriving at a lightly loaded node.
- The altruistic priority assignment rule achieves the best response time performance of the three policies. However, under this policy remote processes incur lower delays than local processes, which is somewhat unrealistic in the sense that local processes are the principal workload at each node while remote processes are secondary workload.
- The performance of the intermediate priority assignment rule falls between the other two policies. Interestingly enough, the overall response time performance of this policy is much closer to that of the altruistic policy. Under this policy, local processes are treated better than remote processes for a wide range of system utilizations.

### Migration-Limiting Policies

Another important policy to be used by a distributed operating system that supports process migration is to decide about the total number of times a process should be allowed to migrate. One of the following two policies may be used for this purpose.

***Uncontrolled.*** In this case, a remote process arriving at a node is treated just as a process originating at the node. Therefore, under this policy, a process may be migrated any number of times. This policy has the unfortunate property of causing instability.

***Controlled.*** To overcome the instability problem of the uncontrolled policy, most systems treat remote processes different from local processes and use a *migration count* parameter to fix a limit on the number of times that a process may migrate. Several system designers feel that process migration is an expensive operation and hence a process should not be allowed to migrate too frequently. Hence this group of designers normally favors an irrevocable migration policy. That is, the upper limit of the value of migration count is fixed to 1, and hence a process cannot be migrated more than once under this policy. However, some system designers feel that multiple process migrations, especially for long processes, may be very useful for adapting to the dynamically changing states of the nodes. Thus this group of designers sets the upper limit of the value of migration count to some value $k > 1$. The value of $k$ may be decided either statically or dynamically. Its value may also be different for processes having different characteristics. For example, a long process (a process whose execution time is large) may be allowed to migrate more times as compared to a short process.

## 7.5 LOAD-SHARING APPROACH

Several researchers believe that load balancing, with its implication of attempting to equalize workload on all the nodes of the system, is not an appropriate objective. This is because the overhead involved in gathering state information to achieve this objective is normally very large, especially in distributed systems having a large number of nodes. Moreover, load balancing in the strictest sense is not achievable because the number of processes in a node is always fluctuating and the temporal unbalance among the nodes exists at every moment, even if the static (average) load is perfectly balanced [Livny and Melman 1982]. In fact, for the proper utilization of the resources of a distributed system, it is not required to balance the load on all the nodes. Rather, it is necessary and sufficient to prevent the nodes from being idle while some other nodes have more than two processes. Therefore this rectification is often called *dynamic load sharing* instead of *dynamic load balancing*.

### 7.5.1 Issues in Designing Load-Sharing Algorithms

Similar to the load-balancing algorithms, the design of a load-sharing algorithm also requires that proper decisions be made regarding load estimation policy, process transfer policy, state information exchange policy, location policy, priority assignment policy, and migration limiting policy. However, as compared to load balancing, it is simpler to decide about most of these policies in the case of load sharing. This is because, unlike load-balancing algorithms, load-sharing algorithms do not attempt to balance the average workload on all the nodes of the system. Rather, they only attempt to ensure that no node is idle when a node is heavily loaded. The priority assignment policies and the migration limiting policies for load-sharing algorithms are the same as that for the load-balancing algorithms. Hence their description will not be repeated again. Other policies for load sharing are described below.

### Load Estimation Policies

Since load-sharing algorithms simply attempt to ensure that no node is idle while processes wait for service at some other node, it is sufficient to know whether a node is busy or idle. Thus load-sharing algorithms normally employ the simplest load estimation policy of counting the total number of processes on a node.

Once again the simple load estimation policy of counting the total number of processes on a node is not suitable for use in modern distributed systems because of the permanent existence of several processes on an idle node. Therefore, measuring CPU utilization should be used as a method of load estimation in these systems.

### Process Transfer Policies

Since load-sharing algorithms are normally interested only in the busy or idle states of a node, most of them employ the *all-or-nothing strategy*. This strategy uses the single-threshold policy with the threshold value of all the nodes fixed at 1. That is, a node becomes a candidate for accepting a remote process only when it has no process, and a node becomes a candidate for transferring a process as soon as it has more than one process. Krueger and Livny [1987] pointed out that the *all-or-nothing* strategy is not good in the sense that a node that becomes idle is unable to immediately acquire new processes to execute even though processes wait for service at other nodes, resulting in a loss of available processing power in the system. They suggested that, to avoid this loss, anticipatory transfers to nodes that are not idle but are expected to soon become idle are necessary. Thus to take care of this loss, some load-sharing algorithms use a threshold value of 2 instead of 1.

Notice here that if the measure of CPU utilization is used as the load estimation policy, the high-low policy (as discussed for load balancing) should be used as the process transfer policy.

### Location Policies

In load-sharing algorithms, the location policy decides the sender node or the receiver node of a process that is to be moved within the system for load sharing. Depending on the type of node that takes the initiative to globally search for a suitable node for the process, the location policies are of the following types:

- *Sender-initiated policy*, in which the sender node of the process decides where to send the process
- *Receiver-initiated policy*, in which the receiver node of the process decides from where to get the process

Each of these policies are described below along with their relative merits and demerits.

***Sender-Initiated Location Policy.*** In the sender-initiated location policy, heavily loaded nodes search for lightly loaded nodes to which work may be transferred. That is, in this method, when a node's load becomes more than the threshold value, it either broadcasts a message or randomly probes the other nodes one by one to find a lightly loaded node that can accept one or more of its processes. A node is a viable candidate for receiving a process from the sender node only if the transfer of the process to that node would not increase the receiver node's load above its threshold value. In the broadcast method, the presence or absence of a suitable receiver node is known as soon as the sender node receives reply messages from the other nodes. On the other hand, in the random probing method, the probing continues until either a suitable receiver node is found or the number of probes reaches a static probe limit, as $L_p$. If a suitable receiver node is not found, the node on which the process originated must execute that process. The method of probing with a fixed limit has better scalability than the broadcast method because it ensures that the cost of executing the load-sharing policy will not be prohibitive even in large networks. Eager et al. [1986a] found through their analysis that the performance of this policy is insensitive to the choice of probe limit: the performance with a small probe limit (e.g., 3 or 5) is nearly as good as the performance with a large probe limit (e.g., 20).

***Receiver-Initiated Location Policy.*** In the receiver-initiated location policy, lightly loaded nodes search for heavily loaded nodes from which work may be transferred. That is, in this method, when a node's load falls below the threshold value, it either broadcasts a message indicating its willingness to receive processes for executing or randomly probes the other nodes one by one to find a heavily loaded node that can send one or more of its processes. A node is a viable candidate for sending one of its processes only if the transfer of the process from that node would not reduce its load below the threshold value. In the broadcast method, a suitable node is found as soon as the receiver node receives reply messages from the other nodes. On the other hand, in the random probing method, the probing continues until either a node is found from which a process can be obtained or the number of probes reaches a static probe limit, $L_p$. In the latter case, the node waits for a fixed timeout period before attempting again to initiate a transfer.

---

It may be noted here that, in sender-initiated algorithms, scheduling decisions are usually made at process arrival epochs (or a subset thereof), whereas in receiver-initiated algorithms, scheduling decisions are usually made at process departure epochs (or a subset thereof). Owing to this, receiver-initiated policies typically require the preemptive transfer of processes while sender-initiated policies can work even with those systems that do not support preemptive process migration facility. A *preemptive process migration* facility allows the transfer of an executing process from one node to another. On the other hand, in systems supporting only *non-preemptive process migration* facility, a process can only be transferred prior to beginning its execution. Preemptive process migration is costlier than non-preemptive process migration since the process state, which must accompany the process to its new node, becomes much more complex after execution begins. Receiver-initiated process transfers are mostly preemptive since it is unlikely that a receiver node would open negotiation with a potential sender at the moment that a new process arrived at the sender node. Process transfers that are sender initiated, however, may be either non-preemptive or preemptive, depending on which process the sender chooses to transfer.

Eager et al. [1986a] used simple analytical models for comparing the performance of the two policies relative to each other and to that of a system in which there is no load sharing. Their results, which are valid over a wide range of system parameters, show the following [Eager et al. 1986a]:

- Both sender-initiated and receiver-initiated policies offer substantial performance advantages over the situation in which no load sharing is attempted.
- Sender-initiated policies are preferable to receiver-initiated policies at light to moderate system loads. This is because in a lightly loaded system the receiver-initiated policy generates a large number of probe messages because all the free nodes desperately hunt for work.
- Receiver-initiated policies are preferable at high system loads, but only if the costs of process transfer under the two strategies are comparable. This is because the receiver-initiated policy does not put extra load on the system at critical times (when the system is heavily loaded), but the sender-initiated policy generates a large number of probe messages precisely when the system is heavily loaded and can least tolerate extra load generated by probe messages.
- If the cost of process transfer under receiver-initiated policies is significantly greater than under the sender-initiated policies due to the preemptive transfer of processes, sender-initiated policies provide uniformly better performance.

### State Information Exchange Policies

Since load-sharing algorithms do not aim at equalizing the average load on all the nodes, it is not necessary for the nodes to periodically exchange the state information with each other. Rather, a node needs to know the state of other nodes only when it is either underloaded or overloaded. Therefore, in load-sharing algorithms, a node normally exchanges state information with other nodes only when its state changes. The two commonly used policies for this purpose are described below.

***Broadcast When State Changes.*** In this method, a node broadcasts a *StateInformationRequest* message when it becomes either underloaded or overloaded. Obviously, in the sender-initiated policy, a node broadcasts this message only when it becomes overloaded, and in the receiver-initiated policy, this message is broadcast by a node when it becomes underloaded. In receiver-initiated policies that use a fixed threshold value of 1, this method of state information exchange is called *broadcast-when-idle* policy.

***Poll When State Changes.*** Since a mechanism that uses broadcast protocol is unsuitable for large networks, the polling mechanism is normally used in such systems. In this method, when a node's state changes, it does not exchange state information with all other nodes but randomly polls the other nodes one by one and exchanges state information with the polled nodes. The state exchange process stops either when a suitable node for sharing load with the probing node has been found or the number of probes has reached the probe limit. Obviously, in sender-initiated policy, polling is done by a node when it becomes overloaded, and in receiver-initiated policy, polling is done by a node when it becomes underloaded. In receiver-initiated policies that use a fixed threshold value of 1, this method of state information exchange is called *poll-when-idle* policy.

## 7.6 SUMMARY

A resource manager of a distributed operating system schedules the processes in a distributed system to any one or more or a pool of free resources that can optimize a combination of resource usage, response time, network congestion, and scheduling overhead. The process scheduling decisions are based on such factors as the resource requirements of the processes, the availability of the various resources on different nodes of the system, and the static and/or dynamic state information of the various nodes of the system. A good global scheduling algorithm should possess features such as having no a priori knowledge about the processes, being dynamic in nature, and having quick decision-making capability, balanced system performance and scheduling efficiency, stability, scalability, fault tolerance, and fairness of service. The three different approaches used for the design of global scheduling algorithms are the task assignment approach, the load-balancing approach, and the load-sharing approach.

In the task assignment approach, the process assignment decisions are basically based on a priori knowledge of the characteristics of both the processes to be executed and the system. The basic task assignment model deals with the assignment of tasks to the various nodes of the system in such a manner so as to minimize interprocess communication costs and improve the turnaround time for the complete task force. Some extensions to the basic task assignment model also consider factors such as interference costs, precedence relationships, or memory size constraints. The task assignment approach has limited applicability because it works on the assumption that the characteristics of all the processes to be scheduled are known in advance and also because task assignment algorithms are generally not dynamic in nature.

In the load-balancing approach, the process assignment decisions attempt to equalize the average workload on all the nodes of the system. The basic problem associated with the dynamic load-balancing algorithms is to decide about the amount of global state information to be used. Although only limited success has been achieved in this direction, the results of the efforts made have shown that attempting to gather a large amount of information to describe the current global state of the system more accurately is not always beneficial. Hence, the degree of global knowledge in an algorithm must be, in some way, normalized to the complexity of the performance objective of the algorithm. This relationship and normalization are the subject of current research.

Finally, in the load-sharing approach, the process assignment decisions attempt to keep all the nodes busy if there are sufficient processes in the system for all the nodes. This is achieved by ensuring that no node is idle while processes wait to be processed at other nodes. Since load-sharing algorithms do not attempt to balance the load on all the nodes, they are simpler and easier to implement as compared to load-balancing algorithms. However, for the various global scheduling algorithms, there is no absolute answer to the question, "Is algorithm *A* better than *B*?" Therefore, getting a better understanding of the processes involved in global scheduling has to be the aim of study of this type of algorithms.

## EXERCISES

**7.1.** For global scheduling algorithms, why are heuristic methods providing near-optimal results normally preferable to optimal solution methods?

**7.2.** What is "processor thrashing"? Give examples of two global scheduling algorithms that may lead to processor thrashing. Suggest necessary measures to be taken to handle this problem.

**7.3.** Suppose you have to design a scheduling algorithm based on the task assignment approach for scheduling the tasks of processes to be processed in a distributed system. What types of cost information would you like to have for the tasks of a process? Suggest methods that may be used to make a rough estimate of these costs.

**7.4.** A system consists of three processors $p_1$, $p_2$, and $p_3$, and a process having four tasks $t_1$, $t_2$, $t_3$, and $t_4$ is to be executed on this system. Suppose $E_{ij}$ is the cost of executing task $t_i$ on processor $p_j$ and $C_{ij}$ is the communication cost between tasks $t_i$ and $t_j$ when the two tasks are assigned to different processors. Let $E_{11}=31$, $E_{12}=4$, $E_{13}=14$, $E_{21}=1$, $E_{22}=5$, $E_{23}=6$, $E_{31}=2$, $E_{32}=4$, $E_{33}=24$, $E_{41}=3$, $E_{42}=28$, $E_{43}=10$, $C_{12}=35$, $C_{13}=3$, $C_{14}=8$, $C_{23}=6$, $C_{24}=4$, and $C_{34}=23$. Find an optimal assignment of the tasks to the processors and calculate the cost of optimal assignment. Now compare this cost with the assignment cost of the case in which $t_1$ and $t_2$ are assigned to $p_1$, $t_3$ is assigned to $p_2$, and $t_4$ is assigned to $p_3$.

**7.5.** A system consists of two processors $p_1$ and $p_2$, and a process having six tasks $t_1$, $t_2$, $t_3$, $t_4$, $t_5$, and $t_6$ is to be executed on this system. Suppose $E_{ij}$ is the cost of executing task $t_i$ on processor $p_j$, $C_{ij}$ is the communication cost between tasks $t_i$ and $t_j$ when the two tasks are assigned to different processors, and $I_{ij}$ is the interference cost between tasks $t_i$ and $t_j$ when the two tasks are assigned to the same processor. *Interference costs* reflect the degree of incompatibility between two tasks and are incurred when the two tasks are assigned to the same node [Lo 1988]. Let $E_{11}=20$, $E_{12}=50$, $E_{21}=25$, $E_{22}=10$, $E_{31}=5$, $E_{32}=20$, $E_{41}=10$, $E_{42}=20$, $E_{51}=10$, $E_{52}=20$, $E_{61}=50$, $E_{62}=10$, $C_{12}=15$, $C_{23}=50$, $C_{34}=15$, $C_{45}=50$, and $C_{56}=15$. The values of all other $C_{ij}$ are zero. Furthermore, the interference cost between any pair of tasks is 10 (i.e., $I_{ij}=10$ if $i$ is not equal to $j$). Find the assignment costs for the following cases:

(a) Task $t_1$ is assigned to $p_1$ and all other tasks are assigned to $p_2$, and interference cost is not taken into account.

(b) Task sets $\{t_1, t_2, t_3\}$ and $\{t_4, t_5, t_6\}$ are assigned to $p_1$ and $p_2$, respectively, and interference cost is not taken into account.

(c) Task $t_1$ is assigned to $p_1$ and all other tasks are assigned to $p_2$, and interference cost is taken into account.

(d) Task sets $\{t_1, t_2, t_3\}$ and $\{t_4, t_5, t_6\}$ are assigned to $p_1$ and $p_2$, respectively, and interference cost is taken into account.

What conclusion can be drawn from the assignment costs of these four cases?

**7.6.** A computer system has three processors $p_1$, $p_2$, and $p_3$. It is to be used to process the same type of processes, all of which have six tasks $t_1$, $t_2$, $t_3$, $t_4$, $t_5$, and $t_6$. Assume that the arrival rate of processes is a deterministic process. Also assume that every task's execution time is exponentially distributed with the mean execution time of tasks $t_1$, $t_2$, $t_3$, $t_4$, $t_5$, and $t_6$ being 1, 10, 1, 10, 1, and 10, respectively. There is a strong precedence relationship among the tasks of a process, and task $t_j$ of a process can be executed only when the execution of task $t_i$ $(i < j)$ of the same process has been completed. Which one of the following assignments will yield the best response times and which one will yield the worst response times for the processes executed on this system:

(a) Task pairs $(t_1, t_2)$, $(t_3, t_4)$, and $(t_5, t_6)$ are assigned to processors $p_1$, $p_2$, and $p_3$, respectively.

(b) Task pairs $(t_1, t_6)$, $(t_2, t_3)$, and $(t_4, t_5)$ are assigned to processors $p_1$, $p_2$, and $p_3$, respectively.

(c) Task pairs $(t_1, t_4)$, $(t_2, t_5)$, and $(t_3, t_6)$ are assigned to processors $p_1$, $p_2$, and $p_3$, respectively.

Give reasons for your answer.

**7.7.** A system has two processors $p_1$ and $p_2$ with $p_1$ having limited memory capacity and $p_2$ having unlimited memory. A process having multiple tasks is to be executed on this system. The execution costs for each task on each processor, the intertask communication costs, the memory requirement of each task, and the total memory capacity of processor $p_1$ is given. Suppose $a_1$ is the assignment that minimizes the total execution and communication costs without the memory size constraint, and $a_2$ is the assignment that minimizes the total execution and communication costs with the memory size constraint. Prove that the tasks assigned to $p_1$ for assignment $a_2$ is a subset of the tasks assigned to $p_1$ for assignment $a_1$.

**7.8.** Comment on the practical applicability of the task assignment approach as a scheduling scheme for distributed systems.

**7.9.** Comment on the practical applicability of the load-balancing approach as a scheduling scheme for the following types of distributed systems:

(a) A LAN-based distributed system

(b) A WAN-based distributed system

(c) A distributed system based on the processor-pool model

(d) A distributed system based on the workstation-server model

**7.10.** A distributed operating system designer is of the opinion that state information in a distributed system is typically gathered at a high cost. Therefore, for a distributed system based on the processor-pool model, he or she decides to use a load-balancing policy that uses the following simple process placement rule: *Execute all processes originating from terminal* i *on processor* j (j << i). *The value of* j *is defined for all values of* i, *and for several values of* i, *the value of* j *may be the same.*

In your opinion, is the designer's choice of the scheduling algorithm appropriate for this system? Give reasons for your answer. What drawbacks, if any, does this scheduling algorithm have? If you feel that this algorithm is not appropriate for this system, suggest a suitable global scheduling algorithm for this system.

**7.11.** Suppose you have to design a centralized load-balancing algorithm for global scheduling of processes in a distributed system. What issues must you handle? Suggest a suitable method for handling each of the issues mentioned by you.

**7.12.** Suppose you have to design a load-balancing algorithm for a distributed system. Which of the selfish, altruistic, and intermediate priority assignment policies will you use in your algorithm if the distributed system is based on the following:
(a) Workstation-server model
(b) Processor-pool model
Give reasons for your answer.

**7.13.** Suppose you have decided to use the high-low policy as the process transfer policy of a load-balancing algorithm for a distributed system. Suggest a suitable method that you will use in your implementation for choosing the high-mark and low-mark values. Do these threshold values have to be the same for all processors in the system? Give reasons for your answer.

**7.14.** Load balancing in the strictest sense is not achievable in distributed systems. Discuss.

**7.15.** What are the main differences between the load-balancing and load-sharing approaches for process scheduling in distributed systems? Which of the various policies to be used in the implementation of the two approaches are different and which of them are same?

**7.16.** Suppose you have to design a load-sharing algorithm for a distributed system. Will you prefer to use a sender-initiated or a receiver-initiated location policy in your algorithm? Give reasons for your answer.

**7.17.** Suggest some policies that may be used for load estimation in load-balancing algorithms. Discuss the relative advantages and disadvantages of the policies suggested by you. Which one of the policies suggested by you can also be used for load-sharing algorithms? If none, suggest a suitable load estimation policy for a load-sharing algorithm.

**7.18.** A system has two processors $p_1$ and $p_2$. Suppose at a particular instance of time, $p_1$ has one process with remaining service time of 200 seconds and $p_2$ has 100 processes each with a remaining service time of 1 second. Now suppose a new process enters the system. Calculate the response time of the new process if:
(a) The new process is a 1-second process and it is allocated to $p_1$ for execution.
(b) The new process is a 1-second process and it is allocated to $p_2$ for execution.
(c) The new process is a 200-second process and it is allocated to $p_1$ for execution.
(d) The new process is a 200-second process and it is allocated to $p_2$ for execution
Assume that there are no other new arrivals in the system. From the obtained results, what can you conclude about load estimation policies to be used in load-balancing algorithms?

**7.19.** A distributed system does not support preemptive process migration facility. You are to design a load-sharing algorithm for scheduling of processes in this system. Will you use a sender-initiated or a receiver-initiated location policy for your algorithm? Give reasons for your answer.

**7.20.** A distributed system uses the all-or-nothing strategy as the process transfer policy for its load-sharing algorithm. Explain why the processing capabilities of the processors of this system may not be properly utilized. Suggest a suitable method to overcome this problem.

**7.21.** What research issues do you think need further attention in the area of global scheduling of processes in distributed systems?

## BIBLIOGRAPHY

**[Ahrens and Hansen 1995]** Ahrens, J. P., and Hansen, C. D., "Cost-Effective Data-Parallel Load Balancing," In: *Proceedings of the 24th Annual International Conference on Parallel Processing*, CRC Press, Boca Raton, FL (August 1995).

**[Alonso and Cova 1988]** Alonso, R., and Cova, L. L., "Sharing Jobs Among Independently Owned Processors," In: *Proceedings of the 8th International Conference on Distributed Computing Systems*, IEEE, New York, pp. 282–288 (June 1988).

**[Arora and Rana 1980]** Arora, R. K., and Rana, S. P., "Heuristic Algorithms for Process Assignment in Distributed Computing Systems," *Information Processing Letters*, Vol. 11, No. 4/5, pp. 199–203 (1980).

**[Atallah et al. 1992]** Atallah, M. J., Black, D. C., Marinescu, D. C., Seigel, H. J., and Casavant, T. L., "Models and Algorithms for Co-scheduling Compute-Intensive Tasks on a Network of Workstations," *Journal of Parallel and Distributed Computing*, Vol. 16, pp. 319–327 (1992).

**[Barak and Shiloh 1985]** Barak, A., and Shiloh, A., "A Distributed Load Balancing Policy for a Multicomputer," *Software—Practice and Experience*, Vol. 15, No. 9, pp. 901–913 (1985).

**[Bokhari 1979]** Bokhari, S. H., "Dual Processor Scheduling with Dynamic Reassignment," *IEEE Transactions on Software Engineering*, Vol. SE-5, No. 4, pp. 341–349 (1979).

**[Bokhari 1981a]** Bokhari, S. H., "On the Mapping Problem," *IEEE Transactions on Computers*, Vol. C-30, No. 3, pp. 207–214 (1981).

**[Bokhari 1981b]** Bokhari, S. H., "A Shortest Tree Algorithm for Optimal Assignments Across Space and Time in a Distributed Processor System," *IEEE Transactions on Software Engineering*, Vol. SE-7, No. 6, pp. 583–589 (1981).

**[Bonomi and Kumar 1990]** Bonomi, F., and Kumar, A., "Adaptive Optimal Load Balancing in a Heterogeneous Multiserver System with a Central Job Scheduler," *IEEE Transactions on Computers*, Vol. C-39, pp. 1232–1250 (1990).

**[Bryant and Finkel 1981]** Bryant, R. M., and Finkel, R. A., "A Stable Distributed Scheduling Algorithm," In: *Proceedings of the 2nd International Conference on Distributed Computing Systems*, IEEE, New York, pp. 314–323 (April 1981).

**[Casavant and Kuhl 1986]** Casavant, T. L., and Kuhl, J. G., "A Formal Model of Distributed Decision Making and Its Application to Distributed Load Balancing," In: *Proceedings of the 6th International Conference on Distributed Computing Systems*, IEEE, New York, pp. 232–239 (May 1986).

**[Casavant and Kuhl 1988a]** Casavant, T. L., and Kuhl, J. G., "A Taxonomy of Scheduling in General Purpose Distributed Computing System," *IEEE Transactions on Software Engineering*, Vol. SE-14, No. 2, pp. 141–154 (1988).

**[Casavant and Kuhl 1988b]** Casavant, T. L., and Kuhl, J. G., "Effects of Response and Stability on Scheduling in Distributed Computing Systems," *IEEE Transactions on Software Engineering*, Vol. SE-14, No. 11, pp. 1578–1587 (1988).

**[Chang and Oldham 1995]** Chang, H. W. D., and Oldham, W. J. B., "Dynamic Task Allocation Models for Large Distributed Computing Systems," *IEEE Transactions on Parallel and Distributed Systems*, Vol. 6, No. 12, pp. 1301–1315 (1995).

**[Chou and Abraham 1982]** Chou, T. C. K., and Abraham, J. A., "Load Balancing in Distributed Systems," *IEEE Transactions on Software Engineering*, Vol. SE-8, No. 4, pp. 401–412 (1982).

**[Chou and Abraham 1983]** Chou, T. C. K., and Abraham, J. A., "Load Distribution Under Failure in Distributed Systems," *IEEE Transactions on Computers*, Vol. C-32, No. 9, pp. 799–808 (1983).

**[Chu et al. 1980]** Chu, W., Holloway, L. J., Lan, M. T., and Efe, K., "Task Allocation in Distributed Data Processing," *IEEE Computer*, Vol. 13, pp. 57–69 (1980).

**[Chu and Lan 1987]** Chu, W. W., and Lan, L. M-T., "Task Allocation and Precedence Relations for Distributed Real-Time Systems," *IEEE Transactions on Computers*, Vol. C-36, No. 6, pp. 667–679 (1987).

**[Clark and McMillin 1992]** Clark, H., and McMillin, B., "DAWGS—A Distributed Compute Server Utilizing Idle Workstations," *Journal of Parallel and Distributed Computing*, pp. 175–186 (February 1992).

**[Dandamudi 1995]** Dandamudi, S., "Performance Impact of Scheduling Discipline on Adaptive Load Sharing in Homogeneous Distributed Systems," In: *Proceedings of the 15th International Conference on Distributed Computing Systems* IEEE, New York (1995).

**[Eager et al. 1986a]** Eager, D. L., Lazowska, E. D., and Zahorjan, J., "A Comparison of Receiver-Initiated and Sender-Initiated Adaptive Load Sharing," *Performance Evaluation*, Vol. 6, pp. 53–68 (1986).

**[Eager et al. 1986b]** Eager, D. L., Lazowska, E. D., and Zahorjan, J., "Adaptive Load Sharing in Homogeneous Distributed Systems," *IEEE Transactions on Software Engineering*, Vol. SE-12, No. 5, pp. 662–675 (1986).

**[Efe 1982]** Efe, K., "Heuristic Models of Task Assignment Scheduling in Distributed Systems," *IEEE Computer*, Vol. 15., pp. 50–56 (1982).

**[Efe and Groselj 1989]** Efe, K., and Groselj, B., "Minimizing Control Overheads in Adaptive Load Sharing," In: *Proceedings of the 9th International Conference on Distributed Computing Systems*, IEEE, New York, pp. 307–315 (June 1989).

**[Efe and Krishnamoorthy 1995]** Efe, K., and Krishnamoorthy, V., "Optimal Scheduling of Compute-Intensive Tasks on a Network of Workstations," *IEEE Transactions on Parallel and Distributed Systems*, Vol. 6, No. 6, pp. 668–673 (1995).

**[Efe and Schaar 1993]** Efe, K., and Schaar, M., "Performance of Co-scheduling on a Network of Workstations," In: *Proceedings of the 13th International Conference on Distributed Computing Systems*, IEEE, New York, pp. 525–531 (1993).

**[El-Rewini et al. 1994]** El-Rewini, H., Lewis, T., and Ali, H., *Task Scheduling in Parallel and Distributed Systems*, Prentice-Hall, Englewood Cliffs, NJ (1994).

**[El-Rewini et al. 1995]** El-Rewini, H., Lewis, T., and Ali, H., "Task Scheduling in Multiprocessing Systems," *IEEE Computer*, Vol. 28, No. 12, pp. 27–37 (December 1995).

**[Ferguson et al. 1988]** Ferguson, D., Yemini, Y., and Nikolaou, C., "Microeconomic Algorithms for Load Balancing in Distributed Computer Systems," In: *Proceedings of the 8th International Conference on Distributed Computing Systems*, IEEE, New York, pp. 491–499 (1988).

**[Gao et al. 1984]** Gao, C., Liu, J. W. S., and Railey, M., "Load Balancing Algorithms in Homogeneous Distributed Systems," In: *Proceedings of the 1984 International Conference on Parallel Processing*, CRC Press, Boca Raton, FL, pp. 302–306 (August 1984).

**[Hagman 1986]** Hagman, R., "Process Server: Sharing Processing Power in a Workstation Environment," In: *Proceedings of the 6th International Conference on Distributed Computing Systems*, IEEE, New York, pp. 260–267 (1986).

**[Heirich and Taylor 1995]** Heirich, A., and Taylor, S., "A Parabolic Load Balancing Method," In: *Proceedings of the 24th Annual International Conference on Parallel Processing*, CRC Press, Boca Raton, FL (August 1995).

**[Hsu and Liu 1986]** Hsu, C. H., and Liu, J. W. S., "Dynamic Load Balancing Algorithm in Homogeneous Distributed Systems," In: *Proceedings of the 6th International Conference on Distributed Computing Systems*, IEEE, New York, pp. 216–222 (May 1986).

**[Hwang et al. 1982]** Hwang, K., Croft, W. J., Goble, G. H., Wah, B. W., Briggs, F. A., Simmons, W. R., and Coates, C. L., "A UNIX-Based Local Computer Network with Load Balancing," *IEEE Computer*, Vol. 15, pp. 55–66 (April 1982).

**[Kleinrock and Korfhage 1989]** Kleinrock, L., and Korfhage, W., "Collecting Unused Processing Capacity: An Analysis of Transient Distributed System," In: *Proceedings of the 9th International Conference on Distributed Computing Systems*, IEEE, New York, pp. 482–489 (June 1989).

**[Krueger and Chawla 1991]** Krueger, P., and Chawla, R., "The Stealth Distributed Scheduler," In: *Proceedings of the 11th International Conference on Distributed Computing Systems*, IEEE, New York, pp. 336–343 (1991).

**[Krueger and Livny 1987]** Krueger, P., and Livny, M., "The Diverse Objectives of Distributed Scheduling Policies," In: *Proceedings of the 7th International Conference on Distributed Computing Systems*, IEEE, New York, pp. 242–249 (September 1987).

**[Kunz 1991]** Kunz, T., "The Influence of Different Workload Descriptions on a Heuristic Load Balancing Scheme," *IEEE Transactions on Software Engineering*, Vol. SE-17, No. 7, pp. 725–730 (1991).

**[Lee and Towsley 1986]** Lee, K. J., and Towsley, D., "A Comparison of Priority-Based Decentralized Load Balancing Policies," In: *Proceedings of the 10th Symposium on Operating System Principles*, Association for Computing Machinery, New York, NY, pp. 70–77 (November 1986).

**[Lin and Raghavendra 1992]** Lin, H. C., and Raghavendra, C. S., "A Dynamic Load-Balancing Policy with a Central Job Dispatcher (LBC)," *IEEE Transactions on Software Engineering*, Vol. 18, No. 2, pp. 148–158 (1992).

**[Litzkow et al. 1988]** Litzkow, M. J., Livny, M., and Mukta, M. W., "Condor—A Hunter of Idle Workstations," In: *Proceedings of the 8th International Conference on Distributed Computing Systems*, IEEE, New York, pp. 104–111 (June 1988).

**[Livny and Melman 1982]** Livny, M., and Melman, M., "Load Balancing in Homogeneous Broadcast Distributed Systems," In: *Proceedings of the ACM Computer Network Performance Symposium*, pp. 47–55 (April 1982).

**[Lo 1988]** Lo, V. M., "Heuristic Algorithms for Task Assignment in Distributed Systems," *IEEE Transactions on Computers*, Vol. 37, No. 11, pp. 1384–1397 (1988).

**[Malone et al. 1988]** Malone, T. W., Fikes, R. E., Grant, K. R., and Howard, M. T., "Enterprise: A Market-like Task Scheduler for Distributed Computing Environments," *The Ecology of Computation*, Huberman, B. A., Ed., North-Holland, Amsterdam, pp. 177–205 (1988).

**[Mehra and Wah 1995a]** Mehra, P., and Wah, B., "Synthetic Workload Generation for Load-Balancing Experiments," *IEEE Parallel and Distributed Technology, Systems and Applications*, pp. 4–19 (Fall 1995).

**[Mehra and Wah 1995b]** Mehra, P., and Wah, B., *Load Balancing: An Automated Learning Approach*, World Scientific, River Edge, NJ (1995).

**[Milojcic 1994]** Milojcic, D. S., *Load Distribution, Implementation for the Mach Microkernel*, Verlag Vieweg, Wiesbaden (1994).

**[Mirchandaney et al. 1989a]** Mirchandaney, R., Towsley, D., and Stankovic, J. A., "Adaptive Load Sharing in Heterogeneous Systems," In: *Proceedings of the 9th International Conference on Distributed Computing Systems*, IEEE, New York, NY, pp. 298–306 (June 1989).

**[Mirchandaney et al. 1989b]** Mirchandaney, R., Towsley, D., and Stankovic, J. A., "Analysis of the Effects of Delays on Load Sharing," *IEEE Transactions on Computers*, Vol. 38, pp. 1513–1525 (1989).

**[Mukta and Livny 1987]** Mukta, M. W., and Livny, M., "Scheduling Remote Processing Capacity in a Workstation-Processor Bank Computing Systems," In: *Proceedings of the 7th International Conference on Distributed Computing Systems*, IEEE, New York, NY, pp. 2–9 (September 1987).

**[Ni and Hwang 1985]** Ni, L. M., and Hwang, K., "Optimal Load Balancing in a Multiple Processor System with Many Job Classes," *IEEE Transactions on Software Engineering*, Vol. SE-11, No. 5, pp. 491–496 (1985).

**[Ni et al. 1985]** Ni, L. M., Xu, C. W., and Gendreau, T. B., "A Distributed Drafting Algorithm for Load Balancing," *IEEE Transactions on Software Engineering*, Vol. SE-11, No. 10, pp. 1153–1161 (1985).

**[Nichols 1987]** Nichols, D. A., "Using Idle Workstations in a Shared Computing Environment," In: *Proceedings of the 11th Symposium on Operating System Principles*, Association for Computing Machinery, New York, NY, pp. 5–12, (November 1987).

**[Pulidas et al. 1988]** Pulidas, S., Towsley, D., and Stankovic, J. A., "Imbedding Gradient Estimators in Load Balancing Algorithms," In: *Proceedings of the 8th International Conference on Distributed Computing Systems*, IEEE, New York, NY, pp. 482–490 (1988).

**[Rao et al. 1979]** Rao, G. S., Stone, H. S., and Hu, T. C., "Assignment of Tasks in a Distributed Processor System with Limited Memory," *IEEE Transactions on Computers*, Vol. C-28, No. 4, pp. 291–299 (1979).

**[Shen and Tsai 1985]** Shen, C. C., and Tsai, W. H., "A Graph Matching Approach to Optimal Task Assignment in Distributed Computing Systems with Minimax Criterion," *IEEE Transactions on Computers*, Vol. C-34, pp. 197–203 (1985).

**[Shirazi et al. 1995]** Shirazi, B. A., Hurson, A. R., and Kavi, K. M. (Eds.), *Scheduling and Load Balancing in Parallel and Distributed Systems*, IEEE Computer Society Press, Los Alamitos, CA (1995).

**[Shivaratri and Krueger 1990]** Shivaratri, N. G., and Krueger, P., "Two Adaptive Location Policies for Global Scheduling Algorithms," In: *Proceedings of the 10th International Conference on Distributed Computing Systems*, IEEE, New York, NY, pp. 502–509 (1990).

**[Shivaratri et al. 1992]** Shivaratri, N. G., Krueger, P., and Singhal, M., "Load Distributing for Locally Distributed Systems," *IEEE Computer*, Vol. 25, No. 12, pp. 33–44 (1992).

**[Singhal and Shivaratri 1994]** Singhal, M., and Shivaratri, N. G., *Advanced Concepts in Operating Systems*, McGraw-Hill, New York (1994).

**[Smirni et al. 1995]** Smirni, E., Rosti, E., and Serrazi, G., "Performance Gains from Leaving Idle Processors in Multiprocessor Systems," In: *Proceedings of the 24th Annual International Conference on Parallel Processing*, CRC Press, Boca Raton, FL (August 1995).

**[Smith 1980]** Smith, R. G., "The Contract Net Protocol: High-Level Communication and Control in a Distributed Problem-Solver," *IEEE Transactions on Computers*, Vol. C-29, No. 12, pp. 1104–1113 (1980).

**[Srinivasan and Jha 1995]** Srinivasan, S., and Jha, N. K., "Task Allocation for Safety and Reliability in Distributed Systems," In: *Proceedings of the 24th Annual International Conference on Parallel Processing*, CRC Press, Boca Raton, FL (August 1995).

**[Stankovic 1984]** Stankovic, J. A., "Simulation of Three Adaptive, Decentralized Controlled, Job Scheduling Algorithms," *Computer Networks*, Vol. 8, No. 3, pp. 199–217 (1984).

**[Stankovic 1985]** Stankovic, J. A., "Stability and Distributed Scheduling Algorithms," *IEEE Transactions on Software Engineering*, Vol. SE-11, No. 10, pp. 1141–1152 (1985).

**[Stankovic and Sidhu 1984]** Stankovic, J. A., and Sidhu, I. S., "An Adaptive Bidding Algorithm for Processes, Clusters and Distributed Groups," In: *Proceedings of the 4th International Conference on Distributed Computing Systems*, IEEE, New York, NY, pp. 49–59 (May 1984).

**[Stone 1977]** Stone, H. S., "Multiprocessor Scheduling with the Aid of Network Flow Algorithms," *IEEE Transactions on Software Engineering*, Vol. SE-3, No. 1, pp. 85–93 (1977).

**[Stone 1978]** Stone, H. S., "Critical Load Factors in Two-Processor Distributed Systems," *IEEE Transactions on Software Engineering*, Vol. SE-4, No. 3, pp. 254–258 (1978).

**[Stumm 1988]** Stumm, M., "The Design and Implementation of a Decentralized Scheduling Facility for a Workstation Cluster," In: *Proceedings of the 2nd IEEE Conference on Computer Workstations*, IEEE, New York, NY, pp. 12–22 (March 1988).

**[Svensson 1990]** Svensson, A., "History—An Intelligent Load Sharing Filter," In: *Proceedings of the 10th International Conference on Distributed Computing Systems*, IEEE, New York, NY, pp. 546–553 (1990).

**[Tanenbaum 1995]** Tanenbaum, A. S., *Distributed Operating Systems*, Prentice-Hall, Englewood Cliffs, NJ (1995).

**[Tantawi and Towsley 1985]** Tantawi, A. N., and Towsley, D., "Optimal Static Load Balancing in Distributed Computer Systems," *Journal of ACM*, Vol. 32, No. 2, pp. 445–465 (1985).

**[Theimer and Lantz 1989]** Theimer, M. M., and Lantz, K. A., "Finding Idle Machines in a Workstation-Based Distributed System," *IEEE Transactions on Software Engineering*, Vol. 15, pp. 1444–1458 (1989).

**[Tilborg and Wittie 1984]** Tilborg, A. M., and Wittie, L. D., "Wave Scheduling—Decentralized Scheduling of Task Forces in Multicomputers," *IEEE Transactions on Computers*, Vol. C-33, pp. 835–844 (1984).

**[Wah 1984]** Wah, B. W., "A Comparative Study of Distributed Resource Sharing on Multiprocessors," *IEEE Transactions on Computers*, Vol. C-33, pp. 700–711 (1984).

**[Wah and Juang 1985]** Wah, B. W., and Juang, J-Y, "Resource Scheduling for Local Computer Systems with a Multiaccess Network," *IEEE Transactions on Computers*, Vol. C-34, No. 2, pp. 1144–1157 (1985).

**[Waldspurger et al. 1992]** Waldspurger, C. A., Hogg, T., Huberman, B. A., Kephart, J. O., and Stornetta, W. S., "Spawn: A Distributed Computational Economy," *IEEE Transactions on Software Engineering*, Vol. 18, No. 2, pp. 103–117 (1992).

**[Wang and Morris 1985]** Wang, Y. T., and Morris, R. J. T., "Load Sharing in Distributed Systems," *IEEE Transactions on Computers*, Vol. C-34, No. 3, pp. 204–217 (1985).

**[Wu and Liu 1980]** Wu, C. S., and Liu, M. T., "Assignment of Tasks and Resources for Distributed Processing," In: *Proceedings of the 1980 International Conference on Computers and Communications* (*COMPCON-80*), IEEE, New York, NY, pp. 655–662 (Fall 1980).

**[Zhou 1988]** Zhou, S., "A Trace-Driven Simulation Study of Dynamic Load Balancing," *IEEE Transactions on Software Engineering*, Vol. 14, pp. 1327–1341 (1988).

## POINTERS TO BIBLIOGRAPHIES ON THE INTERNET

Bibliographies containing references on the topics covered in this chapter can be found at:

ftp:ftp.cs.umanitoba.ca/pub/bibliographies/Parallel/Load.Balance.1.html

ftp:ftp.cs.umanitoba.ca/pub/bibliographies/Parallel/Load.Balance.2.html

ftp:ftp.cs.umanitoba.ca/pub/bibliographies/Parallel/load.balance.5.html

ftp:ftp.cs.umanitoba.ca/pub/bibliographies/Parallel/scheduling.html

ftp:ftp.cs.umanitoba.ca/pub/bibliographies/Distributed/dshell.html

# CHAPTER 8

# Process Management

## 8.1 INTRODUCTION

In a conventional (centralized) operating system, process management deals with mechanisms and policies for sharing the processor of the system among all processes. Similarly, in a distributed operating system, the main goal of process management is to make the best possible use of the processing resources of the entire system by sharing them among all processes. Three important concepts are used in distributed operating systems to achieve this goal:

1. *Processor allocation* deals with the process of deciding which process should be assigned to which processor.
2. *Process migration* deals with the movement of a process from its current location to the processor to which it has been assigned.
3. *Threads* deals with fine-grained parallelism for better utilization of the processing capability of the system.

The processor allocation concept has already been described in the previous chapter on resource management. Therefore, this chapter presents a description of the process migration and threads concepts.

## 8.2 PROCESS MIGRATION

*Process migration* is the relocation of a process from its current location (the *source node*) to another node (the *destination node*). The flow of execution of a migrating process is illustrated in Figure 8.1.

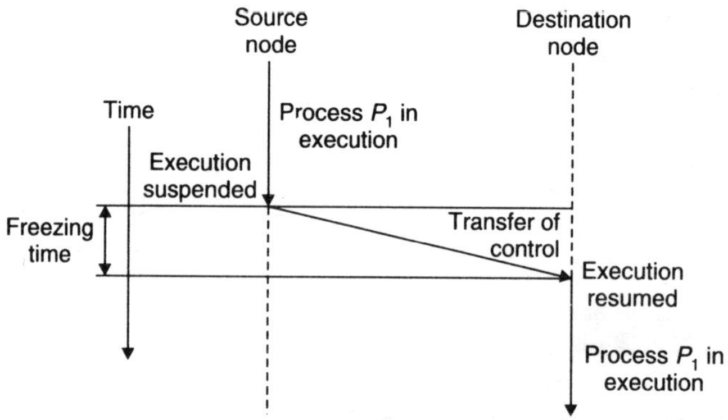


**Fig. 8.1** Flow of execution of a migrating process.

A process may be migrated either before it starts executing on its source node or during the course of its execution. The former is known as *non-preemptive* process migration and the latter is known as *preemptive* process migration. Preemptive process migration is costlier than non-preemptive process migration since the process environment must also accompany the process to its new node for an already executing process.

Process migration involves the following major steps:

1. Selection of a process that should be migrated
2. Selection of the destination node to which the selected process should be migrated
3. Actual transfer of the selected process to the destination node

The first two steps are taken care of by the process migration policy and the third step is taken care of by the process migration mechanism. The policies for the selection of a source node, a destination node, and the process to be migrated have already been described in the previous chapter on resource management. This chapter presents a description of the process migration mechanisms used by the existing distributed operating systems.

### 8.2.1 Desirable Features of a Good Process Migration Mechanism

A good process migration mechanism must possess transparency, minimal interferences, minimal residue dependencies, efficiency, robustness, and communication between coprocesses.

#### Transparency

Transparency is an important requirement for a system that supports process migration. The following levels of transparency can be identified:

1. *Object access level.* Transparency at the object access level is the minimum requirement for a system to support non-preemptive process migration facility. If a system supports transparency at the object access level, access to objects such as files and devices can be done in a location-independent manner. Thus, the object access level transparency allows free initiation of programs at an arbitrary node. Of course, to support transparency at object access level, the system must provide a mechanism for transparent object naming and locating.

2. *System call and interprocess communication level.* So that a migrated process does not continue to depend upon its originating node after being migrated, it is necessary that all system calls, including interprocess communication, are location independent. Thus, transparency at this level must be provided in a system that is to support preemptive process migration facility. However, system calls to request the physical properties of a node need not be location independent.

Transparency of interprocess communication is also desired for the transparent redirection of messages during the transient state of a process that recently migrated. That is, once a message has been sent, it should reach its receiver process without the need for resending it from the sender node in case the receiver process moves to another node before the message is received.

#### Minimal Interference

Migration of a process should cause minimal interference to the progress of the process involved and to the system as a whole. One method to achieve this is by minimizing the freezing time of the process being migrated. *Freezing time* is defined as the time period for which the execution of the process is stopped for transferring its information to the destination node.

#### Minimal Residual Dependencies

No residual dependency should be left on the previous node. That is, a migrated process should not in any way continue to depend on its previous node once it has started executing on its new node since, otherwise, the following will occur:

- The migrated process continues to impose a load on its previous node, thus diminishing some of the benefits of migrating the process.
- A failure or reboot of the previous node will cause the process to fail.

### Efficiency

Efficiency is another major issue in implementing process migration. The main sources of inefficiency involved with process migration are as follows:

- The time required for migrating a process
- The cost of locating an object (includes the migrated process)
- The cost of supporting remote execution once the process is migrated

All these costs should be kept to minimum as far as practicable.

### Robustness

The process migration mechanism must also be robust in the sense that the failure of a node other than the one on which a process is currently running should not in any way affect the accessibility or execution of that process.

### Communication between Coprocesses of a Job

One further exploitation of process migration is the parallel processing among the processes of a single job distributed over several nodes. Moreover, if this facility is supported, to reduce communication cost, it is also necessary that these coprocesses be able to directly communicate with each other irrespective of their locations.

## 8.2.2 Process Migration Mechanisms

Migration of a process is a complex activity that involves proper handling of several sub-activities in order to meet the requirements of a good process migration mechanism listed above. The four major subactivities involved in process migration are as follows:

1. Freezing the process on its source node and restarting it on its destination node
2. Transferring the process's address space from its source node to its destination node
3. Forwarding messages meant for the migrant process
4. Handling communication between cooperating processes that have been separated (placed on different nodes) as a result of process migration

The commonly used mechanisms for handling each of these subactivities are described below.

### Mechanisms for Freezing and Restarting a Process

In preemptive process migration, the usual process is to take a "snapshot" of the process's state on its source node and reinstate the snapshot on the destination node. For this, at some point during migration, the process is frozen on its source node, its state information is transferred to its destination node, and the process is restarted on its destination node using this state information. By freezing the process, we mean that the execution of the process is suspended and all external interactions with the process are deferred. Although the freezing and restart operations differ from system to system, some general issues involved in these operations are described below.

***Immediate and Delayed Blocking of the Process.*** Before a process can be frozen, its execution must be blocked. Depending upon the process's current state, it may be blocked immediately or the blocking may have to be delayed until the process reaches a state when it can be blocked. Some typical cases are as follows [Kingsbury and Kline 1989]:

1. If the process is not executing a system call, it can be immediately blocked from further execution.
2. If the process is executing a system call but is sleeping at an interruptible priority (a priority at which any received signal would awaken the process) waiting for a kernel event to occur, it can be immediately blocked from further execution.
3. If the process is executing a system call and is sleeping at a noninterruptible priority waiting for a kernel event to occur, it cannot be blocked immediately. The process's blocking has to be delayed until the system call is complete. Therefore, in this situation, a flag is set, telling the process that when the system call is complete, it should block itself from further execution.

Note that there may be some exceptions to this general procedure of blocking a process. For example, sometimes processes executing in certain kernel threads are immediately blocked, even when sleeping at noninterruptible priorities. The actual mechanism varies from one implementation to another.

***Fast and Slow I/O Operations.*** In general, after the process has been blocked, the next step in freezing the process is to wait for the completion of all fast I/O operations (e.g., disk I/O) associated with the process. The process is frozen after the completion of all fast I/O operations. Note that it is feasible to wait for fast I/O operations to complete before freezing the process. However, it is not feasible to wait for slow I/O operations, such as those on a pipe or terminal, because the process must be frozen in a timely manner for the effectiveness of process migration. Thus proper mechanisms are necessary for continuing these slow I/O operations correctly after the process starts executing on its destination node.

***Information about Open Files.*** A process's state information also consists of the information pertaining to files currently open by the process. This includes such information as the names or identifiers of the files, their access modes, and the current positions of their file pointers. In a distributed system that provides a network transparent execution environment, there is no problem in collecting this state information because the same protocol is used to access local as well as remote files using the systemwide unique file identifiers. However, several UNIX-based network systems uniquely identify files by their full pathnames [Mandelberg and Sunderam 1988, Alonso and Kyrimis 1988]. But in these systems it is difficult for a process in execution to obtain a file's complete pathname owing to UNIX file system semantics. A pathname loses significance once a file has been opened by a process because the operating system returns to the process a file descriptor that the process uses to perform all I/O operations on the file. Therefore, in such systems, it is necessary to somehow preserve a pointer to the file so that the migrated process could continue to access it. The following two approaches are used for this:

1. In the first approach [Mandelberg and Sunderam 1988], a link is created to the file and the pathname of the link is used as an access point to the file after the process migrates. Thus when the snapshot of the process's state is being created, a link (with a special name) is created to each file that is in use by the process.

2. In the second approach [Alonso and Kyrimis 1988], an open file's complete pathname is reconstructed when required. For this, necessary modifications have to be incorporated in the UNIX kernel. For example, in the approach described in [Alonso and Kyrimis 1988], each file structure, where information about open files is contained, is augmented with a pointer to a dynamically allocated character string containing the absolute pathname of the file to which it refers.

Another file system issue is that one or more files being used by the process on its source node may also be present on its destination node. For example, it is likely that the code for system commands such as *nroff*, *cc* is replicated at every node. It would be more efficient to access these files from the local node at which the process is executing, rather than accessing them across the network from the process's previous node [Agrawal and Ezzat 1987]. Another example is temporary files that would be more efficiently created at the node on which the process is executing, as by default these files are automatically deleted at the end of the operation. Therefore, for performance reasons, the file state information collected at the source node should be modified properly on the process's destination node in order to ensure that, whenever possible, local file operations are performed instead of remote file operations. This also helps in reducing the amount of data to be transferred at the time of address space transfer because the files already present on the destination node need not be transferred.

***Reinstating the Process on its Destination Node.*** On the destination node, an empty process state is created that is similar to that allocated during process creation. Depending upon the implementation, the newly allocated process may or may not have the same process identifier as the migrating process. In some implementations, this newly created copy of the process initially has a process identifier different from the migrating process in order to allow both the old copy and the new copy to exist and be accessible at the same time. However, if the process identifier of the new copy of the process is different from its old copy, the new copy's identifier is changed to the original identifier in a subsequent step before the process starts executing on the destination node. The rest of the system cannot detect the existence of two copies of the process because operations on both of them are suspended. Once all the state of the migrating process has been transferred from the source node to the destination node and copied into the empty process state, the new copy of the process is unfrozen and the old copy is deleted. Thus the process is restarted on its destination node in whatever state it was in before being migrated.

It may be noted here that the method described above to reinstate the migrant process is followed in the most simple and straightforward case. Several special cases may require special handling and hence more work. For example, when obtaining the snapshot, the process may have been executing a system call since some calls are not atomic. In particular, as described before, this can happen when the process is frozen while performing an I/O operation on a slow device. If the snapshot had been taken under such conditions, correct process continuation would be possible only if the system call is performed again. Therefore normally a check is made for these conditions and, if required, the program counter is adjusted as needed to reissue the system call.

### Address Space Transfer Mechanisms

A process consists of the program being executed, along with the program's data, stack, and state. Thus, the migration of a process involves the transfer of the following types of information from the source node to the destination node:

- Process's state, which consists of the execution status (contents of registers), scheduling information, information about main memory being used by the process (memory tables), I/O states (I/O queue, contents of I/O buffers, interrupt signals, etc.), a list of objects to which the process has a right to access (capability list), process's identifier, process's user and group identifiers, information about the files opened by the process (such as the mode and current position of the file pointer), and so on
- Process's address space (code, data, and stack of the program)

For nontrivial processes, the size of the process's address space (several megabytes) overshadows the size of the process's state information (few kilobytes). Therefore the cost of migrating a process is dominated by the time taken to transfer its address space. Although it is necessary to completely stop the execution of the migrant process while transferring its state information, it is possible to transfer the process's address space without stopping its execution. In addition, the migrant process's state information must be transferred to the destination node before it can start its execution on that node. Contrary to this, the process's address space can be transferred to the destination node either before or after the process starts executing on the destination node.

Thus in all the systems, the migrant process's execution is stopped while transferring its state information. However, due to the flexibility in transferring the process's address space at any time after the migration decision is made, the existing distributed systems use one of the following address space transfer mechanisms: total freezing, pretransferring, or transfer on reference.

***Total Freezing.*** In this method, a process's execution is stopped while its address space is being transferred (Fig. 8.2). This method is used in DEMOS/MP [Powell and Miller 1983], Sprite [Douglis and Ousterhout 1987], and LOCUS [Popek and Walker 1985] and is simple and easy to implement. Its main disadvantage is that if a process is suspended for a long time during migration, timeouts may occur, and if the process is interactive, the delay will be noticed by the user.

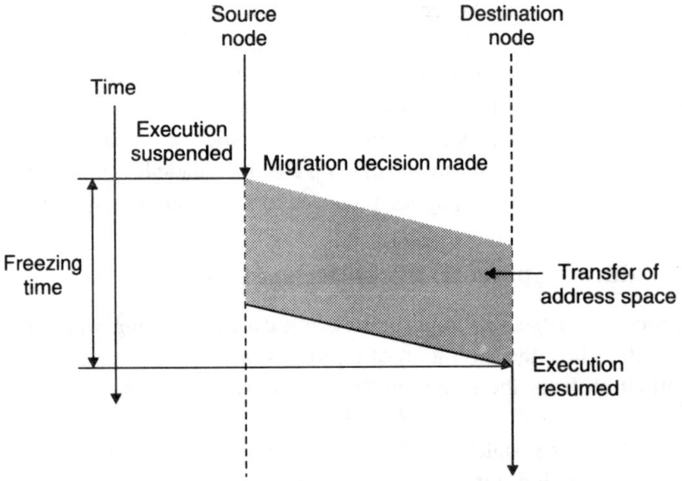


**Fig. 8.2** Total freezing mechanism.

***Pretransferring.*** In this method, the address space is transferred while the process is still running on the source node (Fig. 8.3). Therefore, once the decision has been made to migrate a process, it continues to run on its source node until its address space has been transferred to the destination node. Pretransferring (also known as *precopying*) is done as an initial transfer of the complete address space followed by repeated transfers of the pages modified during the previous transfer until the number of modified pages is relatively small or until no significant reduction in the number of modified pages (detected using dirty bits) is achieved. The remaining modified pages are retransferred after the process is frozen for transferring its state information [Theimer et al. 1985].

In the pretransfer operation, the first transfer operation moves the entire address space and takes the longest time, thus providing the longest time for modifications to the program's address space to occur. The second transfer moves only those pages of the address space that were modified during the first transfer, thus taking less time and presumably allowing fewer modifications to occur during its execution time. Thus subsequent transfer operations have to move fewer and fewer pages, finally converging to zero or very few pages, which are then transferred after the process is frozen. It may be noted here that the pretransfer operation is executed at a higher priority than all other

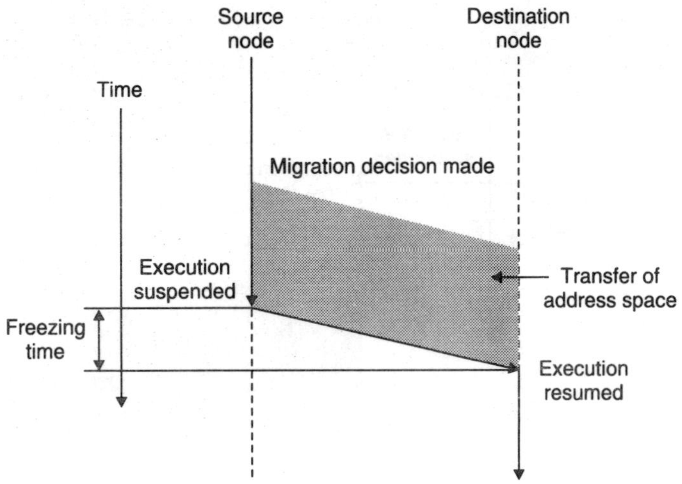


**Fig. 8.3** Pretransfer mechanism.

programs on the source node to prevent these other programs from interfering with the progress of the pretransfer operation.

This method is used in the V-System [Theimer et al. 1985]. In this method, the freezing time is reduced so migration interferes minimally with the process's interaction with other processes and the user. Although pretransferring reduces the freezing time of the process, it may increase the total time for migration due to the possibility of redundant page transfers. *Redundant pages* are pages that are transferred more than once during pretransferring because they become dirty while the pretransfer operation is being performed.

***Transfer on Reference.*** This method is based on the assumption that processes tend to use only a relatively small part of their address spaces while executing. In this method, the process's address space is left behind on its source node, and as the relocated process executes on its destination node, attempts to reference memory pages results in the generation of requests to copy in the desired blocks from their remote locations. Therefore in this demand-driven copy-on-reference approach, a page of the migrant process's address space is transferred from its source node to its destination node only when referenced (Fig. 8.4). However, Zayas [1987] also concluded through his simulation results that prefetching of one additional contiguous page per remote fault improves performance.

This method is used in Accent [Zayas 1987]. In this method, the switching time of the process from its source node to its destination node is very short once the decision about migrating the process has been made and is virtually independent of the size of the address space. However, this method is not efficient in terms of the cost of supporting remote execution once the process is migrated, and part of the effort saved in the lazy transfer of an address space must be expended as the process accesses its memory

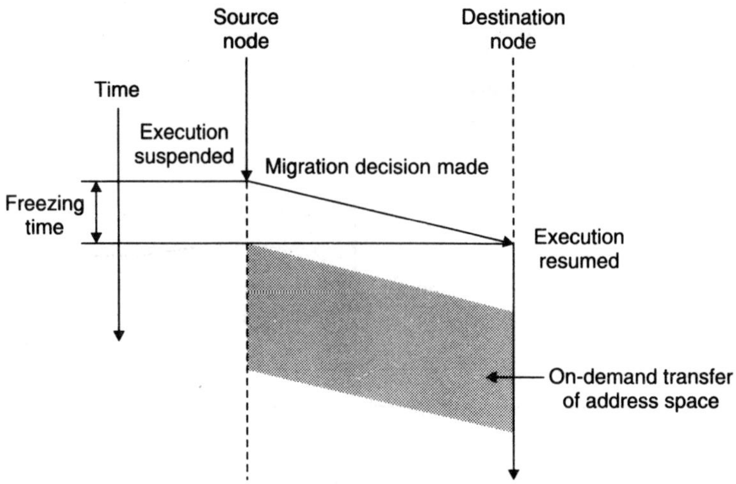


**Fig. 8.4** Transfer-on-reference mechanism.

remotely. Furthermore, this method imposes a continued load on the process's source node and results in failure of the process if the source node fails or is rebooted.

### Message-Forwarding Mechanisms

In moving a process, it must be ensured that all pending, en-route, and future messages arrive at the process's new location. The messages to be forwarded to the migrant process's new location can be classified into the following:

*Type* 1: Messages received at the source node after the process's execution has been stopped on its source node and the process's execution has not yet been started on its destination node

*Type* 2: Messages received at the source node after the process's execution has started on its destination node

*Type* 3: Messages that are to be sent to the migrant process from any other node after it has started executing on the destination node

The different mechanisms used for message forwarding in existing distributed systems are described below.

***Mechanism of Resending the Message.*** This mechanism is used in the V-System [Cheriton 1988, Theimer et al. 1985] and Amoeba [Mullender et al. 1990] to handle messages of all three types. In this method, messages of types 1 and 2 are returned to the sender as not deliverable or are simply dropped, with the assurance that the sender of the message is storing a copy of the data and is prepared to retransmit it.

For example, in V-System, a message of type 1 or 2 is simply dropped and the sender is prompted to resend it to the process's new node. The interprocess communication mechanism of V-System ensures that senders will retry until successful receipt of a reply. Similarly in Amoeba, for all messages of type 1, the source node's kernel sends a "try again later, this process is frozen" message to the sender. After the process has been deleted from the source node, those messages will come again at some point of time, but this time as type 2 messages. For all type 2 messages, the source node's kernel sends a "this process is unknown at this node" message to the sender.

In this method, upon receipt of a negative reply, the sender does a *locate* operation to find the new whereabouts of the process, and communication is reestablished. Both V-System and Amoeba use the broadcasting mechanism to locate a process (object locating mechanisms are described in Chapter 10). Obviously, in this mechanism, messages of type 3 are sent directly to the process's destination node.

This method does not require any process state to be left behind on the process's source node. However, the main drawback of this mechanism is that the message-forwarding mechanism of process migration operation is nontransparent to the processes interacting with the migrant process.

***Origin Site Mechanism.*** This method is used in AIX's TCF (Transparent Computing Facility) [Walker and Mathews 1989] and Sprite [Douglis and Ousterhout 1987]. The process identifier of these systems has the process's *origin site* (or *home node*) embedded in it, and each site is responsible for keeping information about the current locations of all the processes created on it. Therefore, a process's current location can be simply obtained by consulting its origin site. Thus, in these systems, messages for a particular process are always first sent to its origin site. The origin site then forwards the message to the process's current location. This method is not good from a reliability point of view because the failure of the origin site will disrupt the message-forwarding mechanism. Another drawback of this mechanism is that there is a continuous load on the migrant process's origin site even after the process has migrated from that node.

***Link Traversal Mechanism.*** In DEMOS/MP [Powell and Miller 1983], to redirect the messages of type 1, a message queue for the migrant process is created on its source node. All the messages of this type are placed in this message queue. Upon being notified that the process is established on the destination node, all messages in the queue are sent to the destination node as a part of the migration procedure.

To redirect the messages of types 2 and 3, a forwarding address known as *link* is left at the source node pointing to the destination node of the migrant process. The most important part of a link is the message process address that has two components. The first component is a systemwide, unique, process identifier. It consists of the identifier of the node on which the process was created and a unique local identifier generated by that node. The second component is the last known location of the process. During the lifetime of a link, the first component of its address never changes; the second, however, may. Thus to forward messages of types 2 and 3, a migrated process is located by traversing a series of links (starting from the node where the process was created) that form a chain ultimately leading to the process's current location. The second component of a link is updated when the corresponding process is accessed from a node. This is done to improve the efficiency of subsequent locating operations for the same process from that node.

The link traversal mechanism used by DEMOS/MP for message forwarding suffers from the drawbacks of poor efficiency and reliability. Several links may have to be traversed to locate a process from a node, and if any node in the chain of links fails, the process cannot be located.

***Link Update Mechanism.*** In Charlotte [Artsy and Finkel 1989], processes communicate via location-independent links, which are capabilities for duplex communication channels. During the transfer phase of the migrant process, the source node sends link-update messages to the kernels controlling all of the migrant process's communication partners. These link update messages tell the new address of each link held by the migrant process and are acknowledged (by the notified kernels) for synchronization purposes. This task is not expensive since it is performed in parallel. After this point, messages sent to the migrant process on any of its links will be sent directly to the migrant process's new node. Communication requests postponed while the migrant process was being transferred are buffered at the source node and directed to the destination node as a part of the transfer process. Therefore, messages of types 1 and 2 are forwarded to the destination node by the source node and messages of type 3 are sent directly to the process's destination node.

### Mechanisms for Handling Coprocesses

In systems that allow process migration, another important issue is the necessity to provide efficient communication between a process (parent) and its subprocesses (children), which might have been migrated and placed on different nodes. The two different mechanisms used by existing distributed operating systems to take care of this problem are described below.

***Disallowing Separation of Coprocesses.*** The easiest method of handling communication between coprocesses is to disallow their separation. This can be achieved in the following ways:

1. By disallowing the migration of processes that wait for one or more of their children to complete
2. By ensuring that when a parent process migrates, its children processes will be migrated along with it

The first method is used by some UNIX-based network systems [Alonso and Kyrimis 1988, Mandelberg and Sunderam 1988] and the second method is used by V-System [Theimer et al. 1985]. To ensure that a parent process will always be migrated along with its children processes, V-System introduced the concept of *logical host*. V-System address spaces and their associated processes are grouped into logical hosts. A V-System process identifier is structured as a (*logical-host-id*, *local-index*) pair. In the extreme, each program can be run in its own logical host. There may be multiple logical hosts associated with a single node; however, a logical host is local to a single node. In V-System, all subprocesses of a process typically execute within a single logical host. Migration of a process is actually migration of the logical host containing that process. Thus, typically, all subprocesses of a process are migrated together when the process is migrated [Theimer et al. 1985].

The main disadvantage of this method is that it does not allow the use of parallelism within jobs, which is achieved by assigning the various tasks of a job to the different nodes of the system and executing them simultaneously on these nodes. Furthermore, in the method employed by V-System, the overhead involved in migrating a process is large when its logical host consists of several associated processes.

***Home Node or Origin Site Concept.*** Sprite [Douglis and Ousterhout 1987] uses its home node concept (previously described) for communication between a process and its subprocess when the two are running on different nodes. Unlike V-System, this allows the complete freedom of migrating a process or its subprocesses independently and executing them on different nodes of the system. However, since all communications between a parent process and its children processes take place via the home node, the message traffic and the communication cost increase considerably. Similar drawbacks are associated with the concept of origin site of LOCUS [Popek and Walker 1985].

### 8.2.3 Process Migration in Heterogeneous Systems

When a process is migrated in a homogeneous environment, the interpretation of data is consistent on both the source and the destination nodes. Therefore, the question of *data translation* does not arise. However, when a process is migrated in a heterogeneous environment, all the concerned data must be translated from the source CPU format to the destination CPU format before it can be executed on the destination node. If the system consists of two CPU types, each processor must be able to convert the data from the foreign processor type into its own format. If a third CPU is added, each processor must be able to translate between its own representation and that of the other two processors. Hence, in general, a heterogeneous system having $n$ CPU types must have $n(n-1)$ pieces of translation software in order to support the facility of migrating a process from any node to any other node. An example for four processor types is shown in Figure 8.5($a$). This is undesirable, as adding a new CPU type becomes a more difficult task over time.

Maguire and Smith [1988] proposed the use of the *external data representation mechanism* for reducing the software complexity of this translation process. In this mechanism, a standard representation is used for the transport of data, and each processor needs only to be able to convert data to and from the standard form. This bounds the complexity of the translation software. An example for four processor types is shown in Figure 8.5($b$). The process of converting from a particular machine representation to external data representation format is called *serializing*, and the reverse process is called *deserializing*.

The standard data representation format is called *external data representation*, and its designer must successfully handle the problem of different representations for data such as characters, integers, and floating-point numbers. Of these, the handling of floating-point numbers needs special precautions. The issues discussed by Maguire and Smith [1988] for handling floating-point numbers in external data representation scheme are given below.

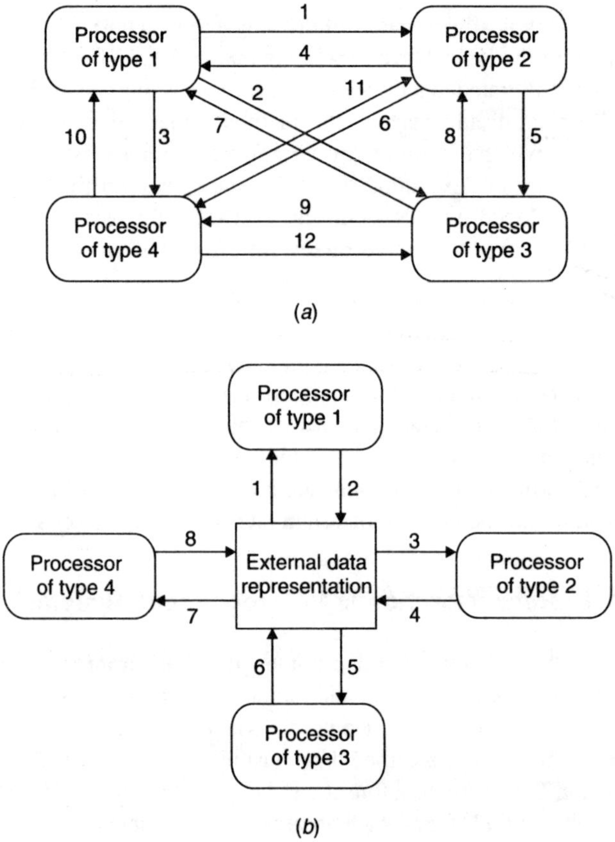


**Fig. 8.5** (*a*) Example illustrating the need for 12 pieces of translation software required in a heterogeneous system having 4 types of processors. (*b*) Example illustrating the need for only 8 pieces of translation software in a heterogeneous system having 4 types of processors when the external data representation mechanism is used.

A floating-point number representation consists of an exponent part, a mantissa part, and a sign part. The issue of proper handling of the exponent and the mantissa has been described separately because the side effects caused by an external data representation affect each of the two components differently.

### Handling the Exponent

The number of bits used for the exponent of a floating-point number varies from processor to processor. Let us assume that, for the exponent, processor *A* uses 8 bits, processor *B* uses 16 bits, and the external data representation designed by the users of processor architecture *A* provides 12 bits (an extra 4 bits for safety). Also assume that all three representations use the same number of bits for the mantissa.

In this situation, a process can be migrated from processor *A* to *B* without any problem in representing its floating-point numbers because the two-step translation process of the exponent involves the conversion of 8 bits of data to 12 bits and then 12 bits of data to 16 bits, having plenty of room for the converted data in both steps. However, a process that has some floating-point data whose exponent requires more than 12 bits cannot be migrated from processor *B* to *A* because this floating-point data cannot be represented in the external data representation, which has only 12 bits for the exponent. Note that the problem here is with the design of the external data representation, which will not even allow data transfer between two processors, both of which use 16 bits for the exponent, because the external data representation has only 12 bits for this purpose. This problem can be eliminated by guaranteeing that the external data representation have at least as many bits in the exponent as the longest exponent of any processor in the distributed system.

A second type of problem occurs when a floating-point number whose exponent is less than or equal to 12 bits but greater than 8 bits is transferred from processor *B* to *A*. In this case, although the external data representation has a sufficient number of bits to handle the data, processor *A* does not. Therefore, in this case, processor *A* must raise an overflow or underflow (depending on the sign of the exponent) upon conversion from the external data representation or expect meaningless results. There are three possible solutions to this problem:

1. Ensuring that numbers used by programs that migrate have a smaller exponent value than the smallest processor's exponent value in the system
2. Emulating the larger processor's value
3. Restricting the migration of the process to only those nodes whose processor's exponent representation is at least as large as that of the source node's processor

The first solution imposes a serious restriction on the use of floating-point numbers, and this solution may be unacceptable by serious scientific computations. The second solution may be prohibitively expensive in terms of computation time. Therefore, the third solution of restricting the direction of migration appears to be a viable solution. For this, each node of the system keeps a list of nodes that can serve as destinations for migrating a process from this node.

### Handling the Mantissa

The first problem in handling the mantissa is the same as that of handling the exponent. Let us assume that the exponent field is of the same size on all the processors, and for the mantissa representation, processor *A* uses 32 bits, processor *B* uses 64 bits, and the external data representation uses 48 bits. Due to similar reasons as described for handling the exponent, in this case also the migration of a process from processor *A* to *B* will have no problem, but the migration of a process from processor $B$ to $A$ will result in the computation being carried out in "half-precision." This may not be acceptable when accuracy of the result is important. As in handling the exponent, to overcome this problem, the external data representation must have sufficient precision to handle the largest mantissa, and the direction of migration should be restricted only to the nodes having a mantissa at least as large as the source node.

The second problem in handling the mantissa is the loss of precision due to multiple migrations between a set of processors, where our example processors $A$ and $B$ might be a subset. This is a concern only in the mantissa case because loss of one or more bits of the exponent is catastrophic, while loss of bits in the mantissa only degrades the precision of computation. It may appear that the loss in precision due to multiple migrations may be cumulative, and thus a series of migrations may totally invalidate a computation. However, if the external data representation is properly designed to be adequate enough to represent the longest mantissa of any processor of the system, the resulting precision will never be worse than performing the calculation on the processor that has the least precision (least number of bits for the mantissa) among all the processors of the system. This is because the remote computations can be viewed as "extra precision" calculations with respect to the floating point of the processor with least precision.

#### Handling Signed-Infinity and Signed-Zero Representations

Two other issues that need to be considered in the design of external data representation are the *signed-infinity* and *signed-zero* representations. Signed infinity is a value supported by some architectures that indicates that the generated result is too large (overflow) or too small (underflow) to store. Other architectures may use the sign bit of a value that would otherwise be zero, thus giving rise to a signed zero.

Now the problem is that these representations may not be supported on all systems. Therefore, while designing the translation algorithms, proper decisions must be made about how to deal with these situations. However, in a good design, the external data representation must take care of these values so that a given processor can either take advantage of this extra information or simply discard it.

### 8.2.4 Advantages of Process Migration

Process migration facility may be implemented in a distributed system for providing one or more of the following advantages to the users:

1. *Reducing average response time of processes.* The average response time of the processes of a node increases rapidly as the load on the node increases. Process migration facility may be used to reduce the average response time of the processes of a heavily loaded node by migrating and processing some of its processes on a node that is either idle or whose processing capacity is underutilized.

2. *Speeding up individual jobs*. Process migration facility may be used to speed up individual jobs in two ways. The first method is to migrate the tasks of a job to the different nodes of the system and to execute them concurrently. The second approach is to migrate a job to a node having a faster CPU or to a node at which it has minimum turnaround time due to various reasons (e.g., due to specific resource requirements of the job). Of course, the gain in execution time must be more than the migration cost involved.

3. *Gaining higher throughput*. In a system that does not support process migration, it is very likely that CPUs of all the nodes are not fully utilized. But in a system with process migration facility, the capabilities of the CPUs of all the nodes can be better utilized by using a suitable load-balancing policy. This helps in improving the throughput of the system. Furthermore, process migration facility may also be used to properly mix I/O and CPU-bound processes on a global basis for increasing the throughput of the system.

4. *Utilizing resources effectively*. In a distributed system, the capabilities of the various resources such as CPUs, printers, storage devices, and so on, of different nodes are different. Therefore, depending upon the nature of a process, it can be migrated to the most suitable node to utilize the system resources in the most efficient manner. This is true not only for hardware resources but also for software resources such as databases, files, and so on. Furthermore, there are some resources, such as special-purpose hardware devices, that are not remotely accessible by a process. For example, it may be difficult to provide remote access to facilities to perform fast Fourier transforms or array processing or this access may be sufficiently slow to prohibit successful accomplishment of real-time objectives [Smith 1988]. Process migration also facilitates the use of such resources by a process of any node because the process can be migrated to the resource's location for its successful execution.

5. *Reducing network traffic*. Migrating a process closer to the resources it is using most heavily (such as files, printers, etc.) may reduce network traffic in the system if the decreased cost of accessing its favorite resources offsets the possible increased cost of accessing its less favored ones. In general, whenever a process performs data reduction (it analyzes and reduces the volume of data by generating some result) on some volume of data larger than the process's size, it may be advantageous to move the process to the location of the data [Smith 1988]. Another way to reduce network traffic by process migration is to migrate and cluster two or more processes, which frequently communicate with each other, on the same node of the system.

6. *Improving system reliability*. Process migration facility may be used to improve system reliability in several ways. One method is to simply migrate a critical process to a node whose reliability is higher than other nodes in the system. Another method is to migrate a copy of a critical process to some other node and to execute both the original and copied processes concurrently on different nodes. Finally, in failure modes such as manual shutdown, which manifest themselves as gradual degradation of a node, the processes of the node, for their continued execution, may be migrated to another node before the dying node completely fails.

7. *Improving system security.* A sensitive process may be migrated and run on a secure node that is not directly accessible to general users, thus improving the security of that process.

## 8.3 THREADS

Threads are a popular way to improve application performance through parallelism. In traditional operating systems the basic unit of CPU utilization is a process. Each process has its own program counter, its own register states, its own stack, and its own address space. On the other hand, in operating systems with threads facility, the basic unit of CPU utilization is a thread. In these operating systems, a process consists of an address space and one or more threads of control [Fig. 8.6(*b*)]. Each thread of a process has its own program counter, its own register states, and its own stack. But all the threads of a process share the same address space. Hence they also share the same global variables. In addition, all threads of a process also share the same set of operating system resources, such as open files, child processes, semaphores, signals, accounting information, and so on. Due to the sharing of address space, there is no protection between the threads of a process. However, this is not a problem. Protection between processes is needed because different processes may belong to different users. But a process (and hence all its threads) is always owned by a single user. Therefore, protection between multiple threads of a process is not necessary. If protection is required between two threads of a process, it is preferable to put them in different processes, instead of putting them in a single process.

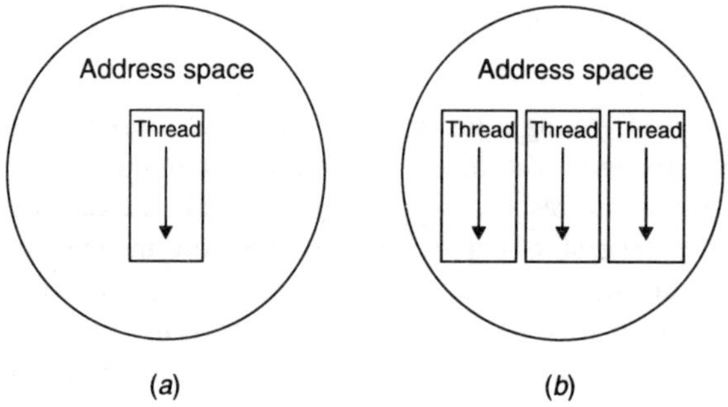


**Fig. 8.6** (*a*) Single-threaded and (*b*) multithreaded processes. A single-threaded process corresponds to a process of a traditional operating system.

Threads share a CPU in the same way as processes do. That is, on a uniprocessor, threads run in quasi-parallel (time sharing), whereas on a shared-memory multiprocessor, as many threads can run simultaneously as there are processors. Moreover, like traditional processes, threads can create child threads, can block waiting for system calls to complete, and can change states during their course of execution. At a particular instance of time, a thread can be in any one of several states: running, blocked, ready, or terminated. Due to these similarities, threads are often viewed as miniprocesses. In fact, in operating systems with threads facility, a process having a single thread corresponds to a process of a traditional operating system [Fig. 8.6(*a*)]. Threads are often referred to as *lightweight processes* and traditional processes are referred to as *heavyweight processes*.

### 8.3.1 Motivations for Using Threads

The main motivations for using a multithreaded process instead of multiple single-threaded processes for performing some computation activities are as follows:

1. The overheads involved in creating a new process are in general considerably greater than those of creating a new thread within a process.
2. Switching between threads sharing the same address space is considerably cheaper than switching between processes that have their own address spaces.
3. Threads allow parallelism to be combined with sequential execution and blocking system calls [Tanenbaum 1995]. Parallelism improves performance and blocking system calls make programming easier.
4. Resource sharing can be achieved more efficiently and naturally between threads of a process than between processes because all threads of a process share the same address space.

These advantages are elaborated below.

The overheads involved in the creation of a new process and building its execution environment are liable to be much greater than creating a new thread within an existing process. This is mainly because when a new process is created, its address space has to be created from scratch, although a part of it might be inherited from the process's parent process. However, when a new thread is created, it uses the address space of its process that need not be created from scratch. For instance, in case of a kernel-supported virtual-memory system, a newly created process will incur page faults as data and instructions are referenced for the first time. Moreover, hardware caches will initially contain no data values for the new process, and cache entries for the process's data will be created as the process executes. These overheads may also occur in thread creation, but they are liable to be less. This is because when the newly created thread accesses code and data that have recently been accessed by other threads within the process, it automatically takes advantage of any hardware or main memory caching that has taken place.

Threads also minimize context switching time, allowing the CPU to switch from one unit of computation to another unit of computation with minimal overhead. Due to the sharing of address space and other operating system resources among the threads of a process, the overhead involved in CPU switching among peer threads is very small as compared to CPU switching among processes having their own address spaces. This is the reason why threads are called lightweight processes.

To clarify how threads allow parallelism to be combined with sequential execution and blocking system calls, let us consider the different ways in which a server process can be constructed. One of the following three models may be used to construct a server process (e.g., let us consider the case of a file server) [Tanenbaum 1995]:

1. *As a single-thread process*. This model uses blocking system calls but without any parallelism. In this method, the file server gets a client's file access request from the request queue, checks the request for access permissions, and if access is allowed, checks whether a disk access is needed to service the request. If disk access is not needed, the request is serviced immediately and a reply is sent to the client process. Otherwise, the file server sends a disk access request to the disk server and waits for a reply. After receiving the disk server's reply, it services the client's request, sends a reply to the client process, and goes back to get the next request from the request queue.

In this method, the programming of the server process is simple because of the use of blocking system call; after sending its request, the file server blocks until a reply is received from the disk server. However, if a dedicated machine is used for the file server, the CPU remains idle while the file server is waiting for a reply from the disk server. Hence, no parallelism is achieved in this method and fewer client requests are processed per unit of time.

The performance of a server implemented as a single-thread process is often unacceptable. Therefore, it is necessary to overlap the execution of multiple client requests by allowing the file server to work on several requests simultaneously. The next two models support parallelism for this purpose.

2. *As a finite-state machine*. This model supports parallelism but with nonblocking system calls. In this method, the server is implemented as a single-threaded process and is operated like a finite-state machine. An event queue is maintained in which both client request messages and reply messages from the disk server are queued. Whenever the thread becomes idle, it takes the next message from the event queue. If it is a client request message, a check is made for access permission and need for disk access. If disk access is needed to service the request, the file server sends a disk access request message to the disk server. However, this time, instead of blocking, it records the current state of the client's request in a table and then goes to get the next message from the event queue. This message may either be a request from a new client or a reply from the disk server of a previous disk access request. If it is a new client request, it is processed as described above. On the other hand, if it is a reply from the disk server, the state of the client's request that corresponds to the reply is retrieved from the table, and the client's request is processed further.

Although the method achieves parallelism, it is difficult to program the server process in this method due to the use of nonblocking system calls. The server process must maintain entries for every outstanding client request, and whenever a disk operation completes, the appropriate piece of client state must be retrieved to find out how to continue carrying out the request.

3. *As a group of threads*. This model supports parallelism with blocking system calls. In this method, the server process is comprised of a single *dispatcher* thread and multiple *worker* threads. Either the worker threads can be created dynamically, whenever a request comes in, or a pool of threads can be created at start-up time to deal with as many simultaneous requests as there are threads. The dispatcher thread keeps waiting in a loop for requests from the clients. When a client request arrives, it checks it for access permission. If permission is allowed, it either creates a new worker

thread or chooses an idle worker thread from the pool (depending on whether the worker threads are created dynamically or statically) and hands over the request to the worker thread. The control is then passed on to the worker thread and the dispatcher thread's state changes from running to ready. Now the worker thread checks to see if a disk access is needed for the request or if it can be satisfied from the block cache that is shared by all the threads. If disk access is needed, it sends a disk access request to the disk server and blocks while waiting for a reply from the disk server. At this point, the scheduler will be invoked and a thread will be selected to be run from the group of threads that are in the ready state. The selected thread may be the dispatcher thread or another worker thread that is now ready to run.

This method achieves parallelism while retaining the idea of sequential processes that make blocking system calls. Therefore, a server process designed in this way has good performance and is also easy to program.

We saw the motivation for using threads in the design of server processes. Often there are some situations where client processes can also benefit from the concurrency made possible by threads. For example, a client process may use a divide-and-conquer algorithm to divide data into blocks that can be processed separately. It can then send each block to a server to be processed and finally collect and combine the results. In this case, a separate client thread may be used to handle each data block to interact with the different server processes. Similarly, when a file is to be replicated on multiple servers, a separate client thread can be used to interact with each server. Some client application user interfaces can also benefit by using threads to give the interface back to a user while a long operation takes place. Client processes that perform lots of distributed operations can also benefit from threads by using a separate thread to monitor each operation.

Finally, the use of threads is also motivated by the fact that a set of threads using a shared address space is the most natural way to program many applications. For example, in an application that uses the producer-consumer model, the producer and the consumer processes must share a common buffer. Therefore, programming the application in such a way that the producer and consumer are two threads of the same process makes the software design simpler.

## 8.3.2 Models for Organizing Threads

Depending on an application's needs, the threads of a process of the application can be organized in different ways. Three commonly used ways to organize the threads of a process are as follows [Tanenbaum 1995]:

1. *Dispatcher-workers model.* We have already seen the use of this model in designing a server process. In this model, the process consists of a single dispatcher thread and multiple worker threads. The dispatcher thread accepts requests from clients and, after examining the request, dispatches the request to one of the free worker threads for further processing of the request. Each worker thread works on a different client request. Therefore multiple client requests can be processed in parallel. An example of this model is shown in Figure 8.7(*a*).

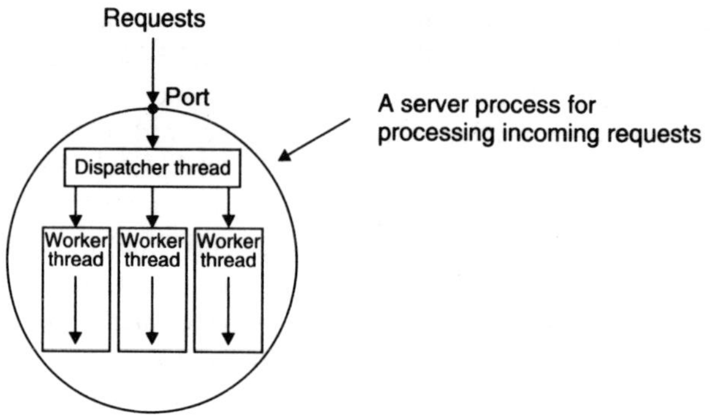


(*a*)

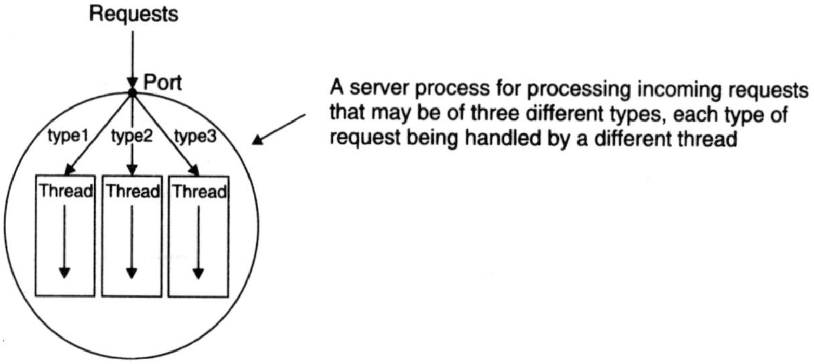


(*b*)

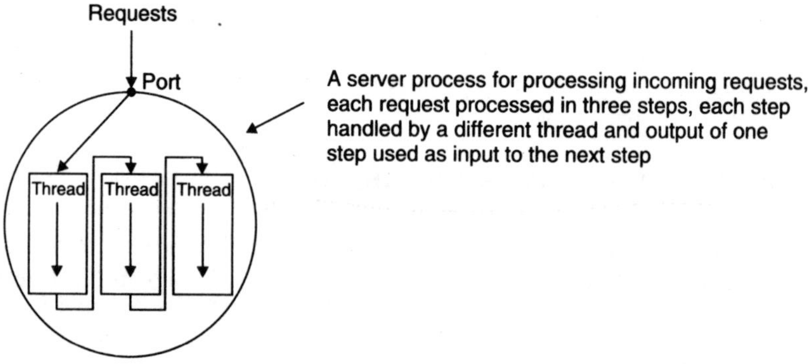


(*c*)

**Fig. 8.7** Models for organizing threads: (*a*) dispatcher-workers model; (*b*) team model; (*c*) pipeline model.

2. *Team model.* In this model, all threads behave as equals in the sense that there is no dispatcher-worker relationship for processing clients' requests. Each thread gets and processes clients' requests on its own. This model is often used for implementing specialized threads within a process. That is, each thread of the process is specialized in servicing a specific type of request. Therefore, multiple types of requests can be simultaneously handled by the process. An example of this model is shown in Figure 8.7(*b*).

3. *Pipeline model.* This model is useful for applications based on the producer-consumer model, in which the output data generated by one part of the application is used as input for another part of the application. In this model, the threads of a process are organized as a pipeline so that the output data generated by the first thread is used for processing by the second thread, the output of the second thread is used for processing by the third thread, and so on. The output of the last thread in the pipeline is the final output of the process to which the threads belong. An example of this model is shown in Figure 8.7(*c*).

### 8.3.3 Issues in Designing a Threads Package

A system that supports threads facility must provide a set of primitives to its users for threads-related operations. These primitives of the system are said to form a *threads package*. Some of the important issues in designing a threads package are described below.

#### Threads Creation

Threads can be created either statically or dynamically. In the static approach, the number of threads of a process remains fixed for its entire lifetime, while in the dynamic approach, the number of threads of a process keeps changing dynamically. In the dynamic approach, a process is started with a single thread, new threads are created as and when needed during the execution of the process, and a thread may destroy itself when it finishes its job by making an exit call. On the other hand, in the static approach, the number of threads of a process is decided either at the time of writing the corresponding program or when the program is compiled. In the static approach, a fixed stack is allocated to each thread, but in the dynamic approach, the stack size of a thread is specified as a parameter to the system call for thread creation. Other parameters usually required by this system call include scheduling priority and the procedure to be executed to run this thread. The system call returns a thread identifier for the newly created thread. This identifier is used in subsequent calls involving this thread.

#### Threads Termination

Termination of threads is performed in a manner similar to the termination of conventional processes. That is, a thread may either destroy itself when it finishes its job by making an exit call or be killed from outside by using the kill command and specifying the thread identifier as its parameter. In many cases, threads are never terminated. For example, we saw above that in a process that uses statically created threads, the number of threads remains constant for the entire life of the process. In such a process, all its threads are created immediately after the process starts up and then these threads are never killed until the process terminates.

### Threads Synchronization

Since all the threads of a process share a common address space, some mechanism must be used to prevent multiple threads from trying to access the same data simultaneously. For example, suppose two threads of a process need to increment the same global variable within the process. For this to occur safely, each thread must ensure that it has exclusive access for this variable for some period of time. A segment of code in which a thread may be accessing some shared variable is called a *critical region*. To prevent multiple threads from accessing the same data simultaneously, it is sufficient to ensure that when one thread is executing in a critical region, no other thread is allowed to execute in a critical region in which the same data is accessed. That is, the execution of critical regions in which the same data is accessed by the threads must be *mutually exclusive* in time. Two commonly used mutual exclusion techniques in a threads package are mutex variables and condition variables.

A *mutex variable* is like a binary semaphore that is always in one of two states, locked or unlocked. A thread that wants to execute in a critical region performs a *lock* operation on the corresponding mutex variable. If the mutex variable is in the unlocked state, the *lock* operation succeeds and the state of the mutex variable changes from unlocked to locked in a single atomic action. After this, the thread can execute in the critical region. However, if the mutex variable is already locked, depending on the implementation, the lock operation is handled in one of the following ways:

1. The thread is blocked and entered in a queue of threads waiting on the mutex variable.
2. A status code indicating failure is returned to the thread. In this case, the thread has the flexibility to continue with some other job. However, to enter the critical region, the thread has to keep retrying to lock the mutex variable until it succeeds.

A threads package may support both by providing different operations for actually locking and obtaining the status of a mutex variable.

In a multiprocessor system in which different threads run in parallel on different CPUs, it may happen that two threads perform lock operations on the same mutex variable simultaneously. In such a situation, one of them wins, and the loser is either blocked or returned a status code indicating failure.

When a thread finishes executing in its critical region, it performs an *unlock* operation on the corresponding mutex variable. At this time, if the blocking method is used and if one or more threads are blocked waiting on the mutex variable, one of them is given the lock and its state is changed from blocked to running while others continue to wait.

Mutex variables are simple to implement because they have only two states. However, their use is limited to guarding entries to critical regions. For more general synchronization requirements *condition variables* are used. A condition variable is associated with a mutex variable and reflects a Boolean state of that variable. *Wait* and *signal* are two operations normally provided for a condition variable. When a thread performs a *wait* operation on a condition variable, the associated mutex variable is unlocked, and the thread is blocked until a *signal* operation is performed by some other thread on the condition variable, indicating that the event being waited for may have occurred. When a thread performs a *signal* operation on the condition variable, the mutex variable is locked, and the thread that was blocked waiting on the condition variable starts executing in the critical region. Figure 8.8 illustrates the use of mutex variable and condition variable for synchronizing threads.

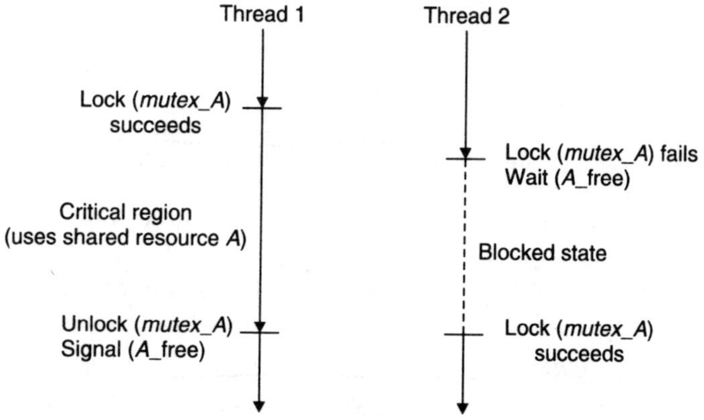


*Mutex_A* is a mutex variable for exclusive use of shared resource *A*.
*A_free* is a condition variable for resource *A* to become free.

**Fig. 8.8** Use of mutex variable and condition variable for synchronizing threads.

Condition variables are often used for cooperation between threads. For example, in an application in which two threads of a process have a producer-consumer relationship, the producer thread creates data and puts it in a bounded buffer, and the consumer thread takes the data from the buffer and uses it for further processing. In this case, if the buffer is empty when the consumer thread checks it, that thread can be made to wait on a *nonempty* condition variable, and when the producer thread puts some data in the buffer, it can signal the *nonempty* condition variable. Similarly, if the buffer is full when the producer thread checks it, that thread can be made to wait on a *nonfull* condition variable, and when the consumer thread takes out some data from the buffer, it can signal the *nonfull* condition variable. In this way, the two threads can work in cooperation with each other by the use of condition variables.

## Threads Scheduling

Another important issue in the design of a threads package is how to schedule the threads. Threads packages often provide calls to give the users the flexibility to specify the scheduling policy to be used for their applications. With this facility, an application programmer can use the heuristics of the problem to decide the most effective manner for scheduling. Some of the special features for threads scheduling that may be supported by a threads package are as follows:

1. *Priority assignment facility.* In a simple scheduling algorithm, threads are scheduled on a first-in, first-out basis or the round-robin policy is used to timeshare the CPU cycles among the threads on a quantum-by-quantum basis, with all threads treated as equals by the scheduling algorithm. However, a threads-scheduling scheme may provide the flexibility to the application programmers to assign priorities to the various threads of an application in order to ensure that important ones can be run on a higher priority basis.

   A priority-based threads scheduling scheme may be either non-preemptive or preemptive. In the former case, once a CPU is assigned to a thread, the thread can use it until it blocks, exits, or uses up its quantum. That is, the CPU is not taken away from the thread to which it has already been assigned even if another higher priority thread becomes ready to run. The higher priority thread is selected to run only after the thread that is currently using the CPU releases it. On the other hand, in the preemptive scheme, a higher priority thread always preempts a lower priority one. That is, whenever a higher priority thread becomes ready to run, the currently running lower priority thread is suspended, and the CPU is assigned to the higher priority thread. In this scheme, a thread can run only when no other higher priority thread is ready to run.

2. *Flexibility to vary quantum size dynamically.* A simple round-robin scheduling scheme assigns a fixed-length quantum to timeshare the CPU cycles among the threads. However, a fixed-length quantum is not appropriate on a multiprocessor system because there may be fewer runnable threads than there are available processors. In this case, it would be wasteful to interrupt a thread with a context switch to the kernel when its quantum runs out only to have it placed right back in the running state. Therefore, instead of using a fixed-length quantum, a scheduling scheme may vary the size of the time quantum inversely with the total number of threads in the system. This algorithm gives good response time to short requests, even on heavily loaded systems, but provides high efficiency on lightly loaded systems.

3. *Handoff scheduling.* A handoff scheduling scheme allows a thread to name its successor if it wants to. For example, after sending a message to another thread, the sending thread can give up the CPU and request that the receiving thread be allowed to run next. Therefore, this scheme provides the flexibility to bypass the queue of runnable threads and directly switch the CPU to the thread specified by the currently running thread. Handoff scheduling can enhance performance if it is wisely used.

4. *Affinity scheduling.* Another scheduling policy that may be used for better performance on a multiprocessor system is affinity scheduling. In this scheme, a thread is scheduled on the CPU it last ran on in hopes that part of its address space is still in that CPU's cache.

### Signal Handling

Signals provide software-generated interrupts and exceptions. Interrupts are externally generated disruptions of a thread or process, whereas exceptions are caused by the occurrence of unusual conditions during a thread's execution. The two main issues associated with handling signals in a multithreaded environment are as follows:

1. A signal must be handled properly no matter which thread of the process receives it. Recall that in UNIX a signal's handler must be a routine in the process receiving the signal.
2. Signals must be prevented from getting lost. A signal gets lost when another signal of the same type occurs in some other thread before the first one is handled by the thread in which it occurred. This happens because an exception condition causing the signal is stored in a processwide global variable that is overwritten by another exception condition causing a signal of the same type.

An approach for handling the former issue is to create a separate exception handler thread in each process. In this approach, the exception handler thread of a process is responsible for handling all exception conditions occurring in any thread of the process. When a thread receives a signal for an exception condition, it sends an exception occurrence message to the exception handler thread and waits until the exception is handled. The exception message usually includes information about the exception condition, the thread, and the process that caused the exception. The exception handler thread performs its function according to the type of exception. This may involve such actions as clearing the exception, causing the victim thread to resume, or terminating the victim thread.

On the other hand, an approach for handling the latter issue is to assign each thread its own private global variables for signaling exception conditions, so that conflicts between threads over the use of such global variables never occur. Such variables are said to be threadwide global because the code of a thread normally consists of multiple procedures. In this approach, new library procedures are needed to create, set, and read these threadwide global variables.

## 8.3.4 Implementing a Threads Package

A threads package can be implemented either in user space or in the kernel. In the description below, the two approaches are referred to as user-level and kernel-level, respectively. In the user-level approach, the user space consists of a runtime system that is a collection of threads management routines. Threads run in the user space on top of the runtime system and are managed by it. The runtime system also maintains a status information table to keep track of the current status of each thread. This table has one entry per thread. An entry of this table has fields for registers' values, state, priority, and other information of a thread. All calls of the threads package are implemented as calls to the runtime system procedures that perform the functions corresponding to the calls. These procedures also perform thread switching if the thread that made the call has to be suspended during the call. That is, two-level scheduling is performed in this approach. The scheduler in the kernel allocates quanta to heavyweight processes, and the scheduler of the runtime system divides a quantum allocated to a process among the threads of that process. In this manner, the existence of threads is made totally invisible to the kernel. The kernel functions in a manner similar to an ordinary kernel that manages only single-threaded, heavyweight processes. This approach is used by the SunOS 4.1 Lightweight Processes package.

On the other hand, in the kernel-level approach, no runtime system is used and the threads are managed by the kernel. Therefore, the threads status information table is maintained within the kernel. All calls that might block a thread are implemented as system calls that trap to the kernel. When a thread blocks, the kernel selects another thread to be run. The selected thread may belong to either the same process as that of the previously running thread or a different process. Hence, the existence of threads is known to the kernel, and single-level scheduling is used in this approach.

Figure 8.9 illustrates the two approaches for implementing a threads package. The relative advantages and disadvantages of the approaches are as follows:

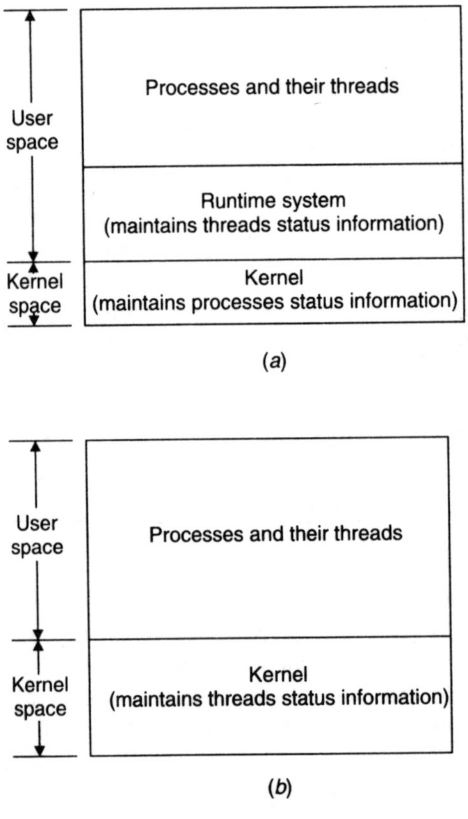


**Fig. 8.9** Approaches for implementing a threads package: (*a*) user level; (*b*) Kernel level.

1. The most important advantage of the user-level approach is that a threads package can be implemented on top of an existing operating system that does not support threads. This is not possible in the kernel-level approach because in this approach the concept of threads must be incorporated in the design of the kernel of an operating system.

2. In the user-level approach, due to the use of two-level scheduling, users have the flexibility to use their own customized algorithm to schedule the threads of a process. Therefore, depending on the needs of an application, a user can design and use the most appropriate scheduling algorithm for the application. This is not possible in the kernel-level approach because a single-level scheduler is used that is built into the kernel. Therefore, users only have the flexibility to specify through the system call parameters the priorities to be assigned to the various threads of a process and to select an existing algorithm from a set of already implemented scheduling algorithms.

3. Switching the context from one thread to another is faster in the user-level approach than in the kernel-level approach. This is because in the former approach context switching is performed by the runtime system, while in the latter approach a trap to the kernel is needed for it.

4. In the kernel-level approach, the status information table for threads is maintained within the kernel. Due to this, the scalability of the kernel-level approach is poor as compared to the user-level approach.

5. A serious drawback associated with the user-level approach is that with this approach the use of round-robin scheduling policy to timeshare the CPU cycles among the threads on a quantum-by-quantum basis is not possible [Tanenbaum 1995]. This is due to the lack of clock interrupts within a single process. Therefore, once a thread is given the CPU to run, there is no way to interrupt it, and it continues to run unless it voluntarily gives up the CPU. This is not the case with the kernel-level approach, in which clock interrupts occur periodically, and the kernel can keep track of the amount of CPU time consumed by a thread. When a thread finishes using its allocated quantum, it can be interrupted by the kernel, and the CPU can be given to another thread.
A crude way to solve this problem is to have the runtime system request a clock interrupt after every fixed unit of time (say every half a second) to give it control [Tanenbaum 1995]. When the runtime system gets control, the scheduler can decide if the thread should continue running or the CPU should now be allocated to another thread.

6. Another drawback of the user-level approach is associated with the implementation of blocking system calls. In the kernel-level approach, implementation of blocking system calls is straightforward because when a thread makes such a call, it traps to the kernel, where it is suspended, and the kernel starts a new thread. However, in the user-level approach, a thread should not be allowed to make blocking system calls directly. This is because if a thread directly makes a blocking system call, all threads of its process will be stopped, and the kernel will schedule another process to run. Therefore, the basic purpose of using threads will be lost.

A commonly used approach to overcome this problem is to use jacket routines. A *jacket routine* contains extra code before each blocking system call to first make a check to ensure if the call will cause a trap to the kernel. The call is made only if it is safe (will not cause a trap to the kernel); otherwise the thread is suspended and another thread is scheduled to run. Checking the safety condition and making the actual call must be done atomically.

With some success, few attempts have been made to combine the advantages of user-level and kernel-level approaches in the implementation of a threads package. For example, the FastThreads package [Anderson et al. 1991] and the threads package of the Psyche multiprocessor operating system [Marsh et al. 1991] provide kernel support for user-level thread scheduling. On the other hand, Mach [Black 1990] enables user-level code to provide scheduling hints to the kernel's thread scheduler. The details of threads implementation in Mach is given in Chapter 12.

### 8.3.5 Case Study: DCE Threads

The C Threads package developed for the Mach operating system and the Lightweight Processes package developed for the SunOS are two examples of commercially available threads packages. In addition, to avoid incompatibilities between threads designs, IEEE has drafted a POSIX (Portable Operating System Interface for Computer Environments) threads standard known as *P-Threads*. Two implementations of this standard are the DCE Threads developed by the Open Software Foundation (OSF) for the OSF/1 operating system and the GNU Threads developed by the Free Software Foundation for the SunOS. The DCE Threads package, which is based on the P1003.4a POSIX standard, is described below as a case study. A description of another threads package, the C Threads package, is given in Chapter 12 as a part of the description of the Mach operating system.

The user-level approach is used for implementing the DCE Threads package. That is, DCE provides a set of user-level library procedures for the creation, termination, synchronization, and so on, of threads. To access thread services from applications written in C, DCE specifies an application programming interface (API) that is compatible to the POSIX standard. If a system supporting DCE has no intrinsic support for threads, the API provides an interface to the DCE threads library that is linked to application procedures. On the other hand, if a system supporting DCE has operating system kernel support for threads, the DCE is set up to use this facility. In this case, the API serves as an interface to the kernel-supported threads facility.

#### Threads Management

The DCE Threads package has a number of library procedures for managing threads. Some of the important ones are as follows:

- *pthread_create* is used to create a new thread in the same address space as the calling thread. The thread executes concurrently with its parent thread. However, instead of executing the parent's code, it executes a procedure whose name is specified as an input parameter to the *pthread_create* routine.

- *pthread_exit* is used to terminate the calling thread. This routine is called by a thread when it has finished doing its work.
- *pthread_join* is used to cause the calling thread to block itself until the thread specified in this routine's argument terminates. This routine is similar to the *wait* system call of UNIX and may be used by a parent thread to wait for a child thread to complete execution.
- *pthread_detach* is used by a parent thread to disown a child thread. By calling *pthread_detach*, the parent thread announces that the specified child thread will never be *pthread_joined* (waited for). If the child thread ever calls *pthread_exit*, its stack and other state information are immediately reclaimed. In normal cases, this cleanup takes place after the parent has done a successful *pthread_join*.
- *pthread_cancel* is used by a thread to kill another thread.
- *pthread_setcancel* is used by a thread to enable or disable ability of other threads to kill it. It allows a thread to prevent it from getting killed by another thread at such times when killing the thread might have devastating effects, for example, if the thread has a mutex variable locked at the time.

### Threads Synchronization

The DCE Threads package provides support for both mutex variables and condition variables for threads synchronization. Mutex variables are used when access to a shared resource by multiple threads must be mutually exclusive in time. On the other hand, condition variables are used with mutex variables to allow threads to block and wait for a shared resource already locked by another thread until the thread using it unlocks it and signals the waiting thread.

The DCE Threads package supports the following mutex variables, which differ in how they deal with nested locks:

1. *Fast.* A fast mutex variable is one that causes a thread to block when the thread attempts to lock an already locked mutex variable. That is, nested locking of a fast mutex variable is not permitted. Note that fast mutex variables may lead to deadlock. For instance, if a thread tries to lock the same mutex variable a second time, a deadlock will occur.

2. *Recursive.* A recursive mutex variable is one that allows a thread to lock an already locked mutex variable. That is, nested locking of a recursive mutex variable is permitted with arbitrarily deep nestings. Notice that recursive mutex variables will never lead to deadlock. It is the responsibility of the application programmers to ultimately unlock a recursive mutex variable as many times as it is locked.

3. *Nonrecursive.* A nonrecursive mutex variable is one that neither allows a thread to lock an already locked mutex variable nor causes the thread to block. Rather, an error is returned to the thread that attempts to lock an already locked nonrecursive mutex variable. Notice that nonrecursive mutex variables avoid the deadlock problem associated with fast mutex variables.

Some of the main DCE thread calls for threads synchronization are as follows:

- *pthread_mutex_init* is used to dynamically create a mutex variable.
- *pthread_mutex_destroy* is used to dynamically delete a mutex variable.
- *pthread_mutex_lock* is used to lock a mutex variable. If the specified mutex variable is already locked, the thread that makes this call is blocked until the mutex variable is unlocked.
- *pthread_mutex_trylock* is used to make an attempt to lock a mutex variable. If the mutex variable is already locked, the call returns with an unsuccessful result rather than causing the thread to block.
- *pthread_mutex_unlock* is used to unlock a mutex variable.
- *pthread_cond_init* is used to dynamically create a condition variable.
- *pthread_cond_destroy* is used to dynamically delete a condition variable.
- *pthread_cond_wait* is used to wait on a condition variable. The calling thread blocks until a *pthread_cond_signal* or a *pthread_cond_broadcast* is executed for the condition variable.
- *pthread_cond_signal* is used to wake up a thread waiting on the condition variable. If multiple threads are waiting on the condition variable, only one thread is awakened; others continue to wait.
- *pthread_cond_broadcast* is used to wake up all the threads waiting on the condition variable.

Another area where mutual exclusion is needed is in the use of UNIX library procedures. The standard library procedures of UNIX are not reentrant. Therefore, to prevent inconsistencies that may be caused by threads switching occurring at arbitrary points in time, it is necessary to provide mutual exclusion for the individual calls.

DCE solves this problem by providing jacket routines for a number of nonreentrant UNIX system calls (mostly I/O procedures). Threads call the jacket routines instead of the UNIX system calls. The jacket routines take necessary action on behalf of the thread before or after invoking the system call to avoid any potential problem. For example, the jacket routines ensure that only one thread calls any particular service at a time.

For several other UNIX procedures, DCE provides a single global mutex variable to ensure that only one thread at a time is active in the library.

### Threads Scheduling

The DCE Threads package supports priority-based threads scheduling. It allows the users to specify not only the priorities for individual threads but also the scheduling algorithm to be used so that important threads can take priority over other threads, getting the necessary CPU time whenever they need it. A user can choose from one of the following threads-scheduling algorithms:

1. *First in, first out (FIFO)*. In this method, the first thread of the first nonempty highest priority queue is always selected to run. The selected thread continues to execute

until it either blocks or exits. After the thread finishes execution, the same method is used to select a new thread for CPU allocation. The algorithm may cause starvation of low-priority threads.

2. *Round robin* (*RR*). In this method, also, the first nonempty highest priority queue is located. However, instead of running the first thread on this queue to completion, all the threads on this queue are given equal importance by running each thread for a fixed quantum in a round-robin fashion. This algorithm may also cause starvation of low-priority threads.

3. *Default*. In this method, the threads on all the priority queues are run one after another using a time-sliced, round-robin algorithm. The quantum allocated to a thread varies depending on its priority; the higher the priority, the larger the quantum. Notice that in this algorithm there is no starvation because all threads get to run.

The following system calls allow users to select a scheduling algorithm of their choice and to manipulate individual threads priorities:

- *pthread_setscheduler* is used to select a scheduling algorithm.
- *pthread_getscheduler* is used to know which scheduling algorithm is currently in effect.
- *pthread_setprio* is used to set the scheduling priority of a thread.
- *pthread_getprio* is used to know the scheduling priority of a thread.

### Signal Handling

Signals may be generated due to either an exception condition occurring during a thread's execution, such as a segmentation violation, or a floating-point exception or due to an external interrupt, such as when the user intentionally interrupts the running process by hitting the appropriate key on the keyboard. In DCE, an exception condition is handled by the thread in which it occurs. However, an external interrupt is handled by all the concerned threads. That is, when an external interrupt occurs, the threads package passes it to all the threads that are waiting for the interrupt.

DCE also includes the POSIX *sigwait* and *sigaction* services that may be used for signal handling instead of catching signal handlers in the traditional way. These services operate at a different level than signal handlers but can achieve the same results. The *sigwait* service allows a thread to block until one of a specified set of interrupt-based signals (also known as asynchronous signals) is delivered. On the other hand, the *sigaction* service allows for per-thread handlers to be installed for catching exception-based signals (also known as synchronous signals).

### Error Handling

The UNIX system calls as well as the standard P1003.4a P-Threads calls report errors by setting a global variable, *errno*, and returning –1. In this method of handling errors, an error may get lost when the global *errno* variable is overwritten by an error occurring in some other thread before the previous *errno* value is seen and handled by the thread in which it occurred. To overcome this problem, each thread in DCE has its own private *errno* variable for storing its own error status. This variable is saved and restored along with other thread-specific items upon thread switches. The error-handling interface of DCE allows the programmers to inspect the value of this variable. Another method that may be used in DCE for error handling is to have system calls raise exceptions when errors occur.

## 8.4 SUMMARY

This chapter has presented a description of the two important process management concepts in distributed operating systems: process migration and threads.

Process migration deals with the transparent relocation of a process from one node to another in a distributed system. A process may be relocated before it starts executing or during the course of its execution. The former is called non-preemptive process migration and the latter is known as preemptive process migration. Preemptive process migration is costlier than non-preemptive process migration because the handling of the process's state, which must accompany the process to its new node, becomes much more complex after execution begins.

Process migration policy deals with the selection of a source node from which to migrate a process, a destination node to which the process will be migrated, and the migrant process. These selection decisions are taken by a suitable global scheduling algorithm used for the process migration policy. On the other hand, a process migration mechanism deals with the actual transfer of the process from its source node to its destination node and the forwarding and handling of related messages during and after migration. The commonly used method for preemptive process migration is to freeze the process on its source node, transfer its state information to its destination node, and restart the process on its destination node using this state information.

The cost of migrating a process is dominated by the time taken to migrate its address space. Total freezing, pretransferring, and transfer on reference are the mechanisms used by the existing systems for address space transfer. The different mechanisms used for message forwarding in the existing distributed systems are the mechanism of resending the message, the origin site mechanism, the link traversal mechanism, and the link update mechanism. The two different mechanisms for communication between a process and its subprocesses that might have been migrated and placed on different nodes are the logical host concept and the home node or origin site concept.

Process migration in heterogeneous systems becomes more complex than in homogeneous systems due to the need for data translation from the source node data format to the destination node data format. The external data representation mechanism helps in reducing the software complexity of this translation process. Of the various types of data, such as characters, integers, and floating-point numbers, the handling of floating-point numbers needs special precautions.

The existing implementations of process migration facility have shown that preemptive process migration is possible, although with higher overhead and complexity than originally anticipated. The cost of migration led some system designers to conclude that it is not a viable alternative, while others disagree. However, the topic is still an active research area with mixed reactions.

Threads are an increasingly popular way to improve application performance through parallelism. In operating systems with threads facility, a process consists of an address space and one or more threads of control. Each thread of a process has its own program counter, its own register states, and its own stack. But all the threads of a process share the same address space. Threads are often referred to as lightweight processes, and traditional processes are referred to as heavyweight processes.

A major motivation for threads is to minimize context switching time, allowing the CPU to switch from one unit of computation to another unit of computation with minimal overhead. Another important motivation for threads is to allow parallelism to be combined with sequential execution and blocking system calls. The use of threads is also motivated by the fact that a set of threads using a shared address space is the most natural way to program many applications.

The three commonly used ways to organize the threads of a process are the dispatcher-workers model, the team model, and the pipeline model.

The set of primitives provided to users for threads-related operations are said to form a threads package. Some of the important issues in designing a threads package are creation, termination, synchronization, and scheduling of threads and handling of signals and errors.

A threads package can be implemented either in user space or in the kernel. Both approaches have their own advantages and limitations.

## EXERCISES

**8.1.** Differentiate between preemptive and non-preemptive process migration. What are their relative advantages and disadvantages? Suppose you have to design a process migration facility for a distributed system. What factors will influence your decision to design a preemptive or a non-preemptive process migration facility?

**8.2.** What are some of the main issues involved in freezing a migrant process on its source node and restarting it on its destination node? Give a method for handling each of these issues.

**8.3.** What are the main similarities and differences between the implementation of the following two activities:

(a) Interrupting a process to execute a higher priority process and then restarting the interrupted process after some time on the same node

(b) Freezing a migrant process and then restarting it on a different node

**8.4.** From the point of view of supporting preemptive process migration facility, is a stateless or stateful file server preferable? Give reasons for your answer.

**8.5.** When a migrant process is restarted on its destination node after migration, it is given the same process identifier that it had on its source node. Is this necessary? Give reasons for your answer.

**8.6.** The cost of migrating a process is dominated by the time taken to transfer its address space. Suggest some methods that may be used to minimize this cost.

**8.7.** A distributed system supports DSM (Distributed Shared Memory) facility. Suggest a suitable address space transfer mechanism that you will use to design a process migration facility for this system.

**8.8.** Which one or more of the address space transfer mechanisms described in this chapter are suitable for a process migration facility with the following goals?
(a) High performance is the main goal.
(b) High reliability is the main goal.
(c) Effectiveness of process migration policy is the main goal.
(d) Simple implementation is the main goal.
(e) Both reliability and effectiveness of process migration policy are important goals.
If more than one mechanism is suitable for a particular case, which one will you prefer to use and why?

**8.9.** Which one or more of the message-forwarding mechanisms described in this chapter are suitable for a process migration facility with the following goals?
(a) Transparency is the main goal.
(b) Reliability is the main goal.
(c) Performance is the main goal.
(d) Simple implementation is the main goal.
If more than one mechanisms are suitable for a particular case, which one will you prefer to use and why?

**8.10.** Which of the mechanisms described in this chapter to handle communication among coprocesses are suitable for a process migration facility with the following goals?
(a) Performance is the main goal.
(b) Reliability is the main goal.
(c) Simple implementation is the main goal.
If more than one mechanisms are suitable for a particular case, which one will you prefer to use and why?

**8.11.** What are some of the main issues involved in designing a process migration facility for a heterogeneous distributed system?

**8.12.** The process migration facility of a distributed system does not allow free migration of processes from one node to another but has certain restrictions regarding which node's processes can be migrated to which other nodes of the system. What might be the reasons behind imposing such a restriction?

**8.13.** When should the external data representation mechanism be used in the design of a process migration facility? Suppose you have to design the external data representation format for a process migration facility. What important factors will influence your design decisions?

**8.14.** A distributed system has three types of processors *A*, *B*, and *C*. The numbers of bits used for the exponent of a floating-point number by processors of types *A*, *B*, and *C* are 8, 12, and 16, respectively; the numbers of bits used for the mantissa of a floating-point number by processors of types *A*, *B*, and *C* are 16, 32, and 64, respectively. In this system, from which processor type to which processor type should process migration be allowed and from which processor type to which processor type should processor migration not be allowed? Give reasons for your answer.

**8.15.** List some of the potential advantages and disadvantages of process migration.

**8.16.** In operating systems in which a process is the basic unit of CPU utilization, mechanisms are provided to protect a process from other processes. Do operating systems in which a thread is the basic unit of CPU utilization need to provide similar mechanisms to protect a thread from other threads? Give reasons for your answer.

**8.17.** The concept of threads is often used in distributed operating systems for better performance. Can this concept also be useful for better performance in other multiprocessor operating systems and in operating systems for conventional centralized time-sharing systems? Give reasons for your answer.

**8.18.** List the main differences and similarities between threads and processes.

**8.19.** What are the main advantages and disadvantages of using threads instead of multiple processes? Give an example of an application that would benefit from the use of threads and another application that would not benefit from the use of threads.

**8.20.** In a distributed system, parallelism improves performance and blocking system calls make programming easier. Explain how the concept of threads can be used to combine both advantages.

**8.21.** Give an example to show how a server process can be designed to benefit from the concurrency made possible by threads. Now give an example to show how a client process can be designed to benefit from the concurrency made possible by threads.

**8.22.** Give a suitable example for each of the following:
(a) An application in which a process uses multiple threads that are organized in the dispatcher-workers model
(b) An application in which a process uses multiple threads that are organized in the team model
(c) An application in which a process uses multiple threads that are organized in the pipeline model

**8.23.** A file server works in the following manner:
(a) It accepts a client request for file access.
(b) It then tries to service the request using data in a cache that it maintains.
(c) If the request cannot be serviced from the cached data, it makes a request to the disk server for the data and sleeps until a reply is received. On receiving the reply, it caches the data received and services the client's request.

Assume that the hit ratio for the cache is 0.7. That is, 70% of all the requests are serviced using cached data and access to disk server is needed only for serving 30% of all requests. Also assume that, on a cache hit, the request service time is 20 msec and on a cache miss the request service time is 100 msec. How many requests per second can be serviced if the file server is implemented as follows?
(a) A single-threaded process
(b) A multithreaded process

Assume that threads switching time is negligible.

**8.24.** Differentiate between handoff scheduling and affinity scheduling of threads. In your opinion, which of the two is a more desirable feature for a threads package and why?

**8.25.** Write pseudocode for a threads-scheduling algorithm that provides the flexibility to vary quantum size dynamically and also supports handoff scheduling.

**8.26.** What are the main issues in handling signals in a multithreaded environment? Describe a method for handling each of these issues.

**8.27.** Discuss the relative advantages and disadvantages of implementing a threads package in user space and in the kernel.

**8.28.** The operating system of a computer uses processes as the basic unit of CPU utilization. That is, it does not support threads. Can threads facility be provided in this computer system without modifying the operating system kernel? If no, explain why. If yes, explain how.

## BIBLIOGRAPHY

**[Agrawal and Ezzat 1987]** Agrawal, R., and Ezzat, A. K., "Location Independent Remote Execution in NEST," *IEEE Transactions on Software Engineering*, Vol. SE-13, No. 8 (1987).

**[Alonso and Kyrimis 1988]** Alonso, R., and Kyrimis, K., "A Process Migration Implementation for a UNIX System," In: *Proceedings of the Winter 1988 Usenix Conference*, Usenix Association, Berkeley, CA (February 1988).

**[Anderson et al. 1991]** Anderson, T. E., Bershad, B. N., Lazowska, E. D., and Levy, H. M., "Scheduler Activations: Effective Kernel Support for the User-Level Management of Parallelism," In: *Proceedings of the 13th ACM Symposium on Operating System Principles*, Association for Computing Machinery, New York, NY, pp. 95–109 (1991).

**[Artsy and Finkel 1989]** Artsy, Y., and Finkel, R., "Designing a Process Migration Facility," *IEEE Computer*, Vol. 22, pp. 47–56 (1989).

**[Black 1990]** Black, D., "Scheduling Support for Concurrency and Parallelism in the Mach Operating System," *IEEE Computer*, Vol. 23, pp. 35–43 (1990).

**[Butterfield and Popek 1984]** Butterfield, D. A., and Popek, G. J., "Network Tasking in the LOCUS Distributed UNIX System," In: *Proceedings of the Summer 1984 Usenix Conference*, Usenix Association, Berkeley, CA, pp. 62–71 (June 1984).

**[Cheriton 1988]** Cheriton, D. R., "The V Distributed System," *Communications of the ACM*, Vol. 31, No. 3, pp. 314–333 (1988).

**[Coulouris et al. 1994]** Coulouris, G. F., Dollimore, J., and Kindberg, T., *Distributed Systems Concepts and Design*, 2nd ed., Addison-Wesley, Reading, MA (1994).

**[Douglis and Ousterhout 1987]** Douglis, F., and Ousterhout, J., "Process Migration in the Sprite Operating System," In: *Proceedings of the 7th International Conference on Distributed Computing Systems*, IEEE, New York, NY, pp. 18–25 (September 1987).

**[Douglis and Ousterhout 1991]** Douglis, F., and Ousterhout, J., "Transparent Process Migration: Design Alternatives and the Sprite Implementation," *Software—Practice and Experience*, Vol. 21, pp. 757–785 (1991).

**[Draves et al. 1991]** Draves, R. P., Bershad, B. N., Rashid, R. F., and Dean, R. W., "Using Continuations to Implement Thread Management and Communication in Operating Systems," In: *Proceedings of the 13th ACM Symposium on Operating System Principles*, Association for Computing Machinery, New York, NY, pp. 122–136 (1991).

**[Ferrari and Sunderam 1995]** Ferrari, A., and Sunderam, V. S., "TPVM: Distributed Concurrent Computing with Lightweight Processes," In: *Proceedings of the 4th International Symposium on High Performance Distributed Computing* (August 1995).

**[Goscinski 1991]** Goscinski, A.,"Distributed Operating Systems, The Logical Design," Addison-Wesley, Reading, MA (1991).

**[Huang et al. 1995]** Huang, C., Huang, Y., and McKinley, P. K., "A Thread-Based Interface for Collective Communication on ATM Networks," In: *Proceedings of the 15th International Conference on Distributed Computing Systems*, IEEE, New York, NY (May–June 1995).

**[Hunter 1988]** Hunter, C., "Process Cloning: A System for Duplicating UNIX Processes," In: *Proceedings of the Winter 1988 Usenix Conference*, Usenix Association, Berkeley, CA (February 1988).

**[Jul 1989]** Jul, E., "Migration of Light-Weight Processes in Emerald," *TCOS Newsletter*, Vol. 3, No. 1, pp. 20–23 (1989).

**[Jul et al. 1988]** Jul, E., Levy, H., Norman, H., and Andrew, B., "Fine-Grained Mobility in the Emerald System," *ACM Transactions on Computer Systems*, Vol. 6, No. 1, pp. 109–133 (1988).

**[Kingsbury and Kline 1989]** Kingsbury, B. A., and Kline, J. T., "Job and Process Recovery in a UNIX-Based Operating System," In: *Proceedings of the Winter 1989 Usenix Conference*, Usenix Association, Berkeley, CA, pp. 355–364 (1989).

**[Litzkow 1987]** Litzkow, M. J., "Remote UNIX—Turning Idle Workstations into Cycle Servers," In: *Proceedings of the Summer 1987 Usenix Conference*, Usenix Association, Berkeley, CA (June 1987).

**[Lo 1989]** Lo, V. M., "Process Migration for Communication Performance," *TCOS Newsletter*, Vol. 3, No. 1, pp. 28–30 (1989).

**[Lockhart 1994]** Lockhart, Jr., H. W., *OSF DCE: Guide to Developing Distributed Applications*, IEEE Computer Society Press, Los Alamitos, CA (1994).

**[Maguire and Smith 1988]** Maguire, Jr., G. Q. and Smith, J. M., "Process Migration: Effects on Scientific Computation," *ACM-SIGPLAN Notices*, Vol. 23, No. 3, pp. 102–106 (1988).

**[Mandelberg and Sunderam 1988]** Mandelberg, K. I., and Sunderam, V. S., "Process Migration in UNIX Networks," In: *Proceedings of the Winter 1988 Usenix Conference*, Usenix Association, Berkeley, CA (February 1988).

**[Marsh et al. 1991]** Marsh, B. D., Scott, M. L., LeBlanc, T. J., and Markatos, E. P., "First-Class User-Level Threads," In: *Proceedings of the 13th ACM Symposium on Operating System Principles*, Association for Computing Machinery, New York, NY, pp. 110–121 (1991).

**[Mullender et al. 1990]** Mullender, S. J., Van Rossum, G., Tanenbaum, A. S., Van Renesse, R., and Van Staverene, H., "Amoeba: A Distributed Operating System for the 1990s," *IEEE Computer*, Vol. 23, No. 5, pp. 44–53 (1990).

**[Nutt 1991]** Nutt, G. J., *Centralized and Distributed Operating Systems*, Prentice-Hall, Englewood Cliffs, NJ (1991).

**[Popek and Walker 1985]** Popek, G. J., and Walker, B. J., *The LOCUS Distributed System Architecture*, MIT Press, Cambridge, MA (1985).

**[Powell and Miller 1983]** Powell, M. L., and Miller, B. P., "Process Migration in DEMOS/MP," In: *Proceedings of the 9th ACM Symposium on Operating System Principles*, Association for Computing Machinery, New York, NY, pp. 110–119 (November 1983).

**[Rosenberry et al. 1992]** Rosenberry, W., Kenney, D., and Fisher, G., *OSF DISTRIBUTED COMPUTING ENVIRONMENT, Understanding DCE*, O'Reilly & Associates, Sebastopol, CA (1992).

**[Schwan et al. 1991]** Schwan, K., Zhou, H., and Gheith, A., "Real-Time Threads," *ACM-SIGOPS Operating Systems Review*, Vol. 25, No. 4, pp. 35–46 (1991).

**[Sinha et al. 1991]** Sinha, P. K., Park, K., Jia, X., Shimizu, K., and Maekawa, M., "Process Migration Mechanism in the Galaxy Distributed Operating System," In: *Proceedings of the 5th International Parallel Processing Symposium*, IEEE, New York, NY, pp. 611–618 (April 1991).

**[Smith 1988]** Smith, J. M., "A Survey of Process Migration Mechanisms," *ACM-SIGOPS Operating Systems Review*, Vol. 22, pp. 28–40 (July 1988).

**[Stalling 1995]** Stalling, W., *Operating Systems*, 2nd ed., Prentice-Hall, Englewood Cliffs, NJ (1995).

**[Tanenbaum 1995]** Tanenbaum, A. S., *Distributed Operating Systems*, Prentice-Hall, Englewood Cliffs, NJ (1995).

**[Theimer et al. 1985]** Theimer, M. M., Lantz K. A., and Cheriton, D. R., "Preemptable Remote Execution Facilities for the V System," In: *Proceedings of the 10th ACM Symposium on Operating System Principles*, Association for Computing Machinery, New York, NY, pp. 2–12 (December 1985).

**[Thekkath and Eggers 1994]** Thekkath, R., and Eggers, S. J., "Impact of Sharing-Based Thread Placement on Multithreaded Architectures," In: *Proceedings of the 21st International Symposium on Computer Architecture*, Association for Computing Machinery, New York, NY, pp. 176–186 (1994).

**[Walker and Mathews 1989]** Walker, B. J., and Mathews, R. M., "Process Migration in AIX's Transparent Computing Facility (TCF)," *TCOS Newsletter*, Vol. 3, No. 1, pp. 5–7 (1989).

**[Zayas 1987]** Zayas, E. R., "Attacking the Process Migration Bottleneck," In: *Proceedings of the 11th ACM Symposium on Operating Systems Principles*, Association for Computing Machinery, New York, NY, pp. 13–22 (November 1987).

## POINTERS TO BIBLIOGRAPHIES ON THE INTERNET

Bibliographies containing references on *Process Migration* can be found at:

ftp:ftp.cs.umanitoba.ca/pub/bibliographies/Distributed/migrate.html

ftp:ftp.cs.umanitoba.ca/pub/bibliographies/Distributed/dshell.html

Bibliography containing references on *Threads and Multithreading* can be found at:

ftp:ftp.cs.umanitoba.ca/pub/bibliographies/Os/threads.html

CHAPTER 9

# Distributed File Systems

## 9.1 INTRODUCTION

In a computer system, a *file* is a named object that comes into existence by explicit creation, is immune to temporary failures in the system, and persists until explicitly destroyed. The two main purposes of using files are as follows:

1. *Permanent storage of information.* This is achieved by storing a file on a secondary storage media such as a magnetic disk.
2. *Sharing of information.* Files provide a natural and easy means of information sharing. That is, a file can be created by one application and then shared with different applications at a later time.

A *file system* is a subsystem of an operating system that performs file management activities such as organization, storing, retrieval, naming, sharing, and protection of files. It is designed to allow programs to use a set of operations that characterize the file abstraction and free the programmers from concerns about the details of space allocation and layout of the secondary storage device. Therefore, a file system provides an abstraction of a storage device; that is, it is a convenient mechanism for storing and retrieving information from the storage device.

A *distributed file system* provides similar abstraction to the users of a distributed system and makes it convenient for them to use files in a distributed environment. The design and implementation of a distributed file system, however, is more complex than a conventional file system due to the fact that the users and storage devices are physically dispersed.

In addition to the advantages of permanent storage and sharing of information provided by the file system of a single-processor system, a distributed file system normally supports the following:

1. *Remote information sharing*. A distributed file system allows a file to be transparently accessed by processes of any node of the system irrespective of the file's location. Therefore, a process on one node can create a file that can then be accessed at a later time by some other process running on another node.

2. *User mobility*. In a distributed system, user mobility implies that a user should not be forced to work on a specific node but should have the flexibility to work on different nodes at different times. This property is desirable due to reasons such as coping with node failures, suiting the nature of jobs of some users who need to work at different places at different times, and enabling use of any of the several nodes in those environments where workstations are managed as a common pool. A distributed file system normally allows a user to work on different nodes at different times without the necessity of physically relocating the secondary storage devices.

3. *Availability*. For better fault tolerance, files should be available for use even in the event of temporary failure of one and more nodes of the system. To take care of this, a distributed file system normally keeps multiple copies of a file on different nodes of the system. Each copy is called a *replica* of the file. In an ideal design, both the existence of multiple copies and their locations are hidden from the clients.

4. *Diskless workstations*. Disk drives are relatively expensive compared to the cost of most other parts in a workstation. Furthermore, since a workstation is likely to be physically placed in the immediate vicinity of a user, the noise and heat emitted from a disk drive are annoying factors associated with a workstation. Therefore, a diskless workstation is more economical, is less noisy, and generates less heat. A distributed file system, with its transparent remote file-accessing capability, allows the use of diskless workstations in a system.

A distributed file system typically provides the following three types of services. Each can be thought of as a component of a distributed file system.

1. *Storage service*. It deals with the allocation and management of space on a secondary storage device that is used for storage of files in the file system. It provides a logical view of the storage system by providing operations for storing and retrieving data in them. Most systems use magnetic disks as the secondary storage device for files. Therefore, the storage service is also known as *disk service*. Furthermore, several systems allocate disk space in units of fixed-size blocks, and hence, the storage service is also known as *block service* in these systems.

2. *True file service.* It is concerned with the operations on individual files, such as operations for accessing and modifying the data in files and for creating and deleting files. To perform these primitive file operations correctly and efficiently, typical design issues of a true file service component include file-accessing mechanism, file-sharing semantics, file-caching mechanism, file replication mechanism, concurrency control mechanism, data consistency and multiple copy update protocol, and access control mechanism. Note that the separation of the storage service from the true file service makes it easy to combine different methods of storage and different storage media in a single file system.

3. *Name service.* It provides a mapping between text names for files and references to files, that is, file IDs. Text names are required because, as described in Chapter 10, file IDs are awkward and difficult for human users to remember and use. Most file systems use directories to perform this mapping. Therefore, the name service is also known as a *directory service*. The directory service is responsible for performing directory-related activities such as creation and deletion of directories, adding a new file to a directory, deleting a file from a directory, changing the name of a file, moving a file from one directory to another, and so on.

The design and implementation of the storage service of a distributed file system is similar to that of the storage service of a centralized file system. Readers interested in the details of the storage service may refer to any good book on operating systems [Tanenbaum 1987, Silberschatz and Galvin 1994]. The design and implementation details of the name service will be presented in the next chapter. Therefore, this chapter will mainly deal with the design and implementation issues of the true file service component of distributed file systems.

## 9.2 DESIRABLE FEATURES OF A GOOD DISTRIBUTED FILE SYSTEM

A good distributed file system should have the features described below.

1. *Transparency.* The following four types of transparencies are desirable:

- *Structure transparency.* Although not necessary, for performance, scalability, and reliability reasons, a distributed file system normally uses multiple file servers. Each file server is normally a user process or sometimes a kernel process that is responsible for controlling a set of secondary storage devices (used for file storage) of the node on which it runs. In multiple file servers, the multiplicity of file servers should be transparent to the clients of a distributed file system. In particular, clients should not know the number or locations of the file servers and the storage devices. Ideally, a distributed file system should look to its clients like a conventional file system offered by a centralized, time-sharing operating system.

- *Access transparency.* Both local and remote files should be accessible in the same way. That is, the file system interface should not distinguish between local and remote files, and the file system should automatically locate an accessed file and arrange for the transport of data to the client's site.
- *Naming transparency.* The name of a file should give no hint as to where the file is located. Furthermore, a file should be allowed to move from one node to another in a distributed system without having to change the name of the file.
- *Replication transparency.* If a file is replicated on multiple nodes, both the existence of multiple copies and their locations should be hidden from the clients.

2. *User mobility.* In a distributed system, a user should not be forced to work on a specific node but should have the flexibility to work on different nodes at different times. Furthermore, the performance characteristics of the file system should not discourage users from accessing their files from workstations other than the one at which they usually work. One way to support user mobility is to automatically bring a user's environment (e.g., user's home directory) at the time of login to the node where the user logs in.

3. *Performance.* The performance of a file system is usually measured as the average amount of time needed to satisfy client requests. In centralized file systems, this time includes the time for accessing the secondary storage device on which the file is stored and the CPU processing time. In a distributed file system, however, this time also includes network communication overhead when the accessed file is remote. Although acceptable performance is hard to quantify, it is desirable that the performance of a distributed file system should be comparable to that of a centralized file system. Users should never feel the need to make explicit file placement decisions to improve performance.

4. *Simplicity and ease of use.* Several issues influence the simplicity and ease of use of a distributed file system. The most important issue is that the semantics of the distributed file system should be easy to understand. This implies that the user interface to the file system must be simple and the number of commands should be as small as possible. In an ideal design, the semantics of a distributed file system should be the same as that of a file system for a conventional centralized time-sharing system. Another important issue for ease of use is that the file system should be able to support the whole range of applications.

5. *Scalability.* It is inevitable that a distributed system will grow with time since expanding the network by adding new machines or interconnecting two networks together is commonplace. Therefore, a good distributed file system should be designed to easily cope with the growth of nodes and users in the system. That is, such growth should not cause serious disruption of service or significant loss of performance to users. In short, a scalable design should withstand high service load, accommodate growth of the user community, and enable simple integration of added resources.

6. *High availability.* A distributed file system should continue to function even when partial failures occur due to the failure of one or more components, such as a communication link failure, a machine failure, or a storage device crash. When partial failures occur, the file system may show degradation in performance, functionality, or

both. However, the degradation should be proportional, in some sense, to the failed components. For instance, it is quite acceptable that the failure causes temporary loss of service to small groups of users.

High availability and scalability are mutually related properties. Both properties call for a design in which both control and data are distributed. This is because centralized entities such as a central controller or a central data repository introduce both a severe point of failure and a performance bottleneck. Therefore, a highly available and scalable distributed file system should have multiple and independent file servers controlling multiple and independent storage devices. Replication of files at multiple servers is the primary mechanism for providing high availability.

7. *High reliability.* In a good distributed file system, the probability of loss of stored data should be minimized as far as practicable. That is, users should not feel compelled to make backup copies of their files because of the unreliability of the system. Rather, the file system should automatically generate backup copies of critical files that can be used in the event of loss of the original ones. Stable storage is a popular technique used by several file systems for high reliability.

8. *Data integrity.* A file is often shared by multiple users. For a shared file, the file system must guarantee the integrity of data stored in it. That is, concurrent access requests from multiple users who are competing to access the file must be properly synchronized by the use of some form of concurrency control mechanism. Atomic transactions are a high-level concurrency control mechanism often provided to the users by a file system for data integrity.

9. *Security.* A distributed file system should be secure so that its users can be confident of the privacy of their data. Necessary security mechanisms must be implemented to protect information stored in a file system against unauthorized access. Furthermore, passing rights to access a file should be performed safely; that is, the receiver of rights should not be able to pass them further if he or she is not allowed to do that.

A consequence of large-scale distributed systems is that the casual attitude toward security is not acceptable. A fundamental question is who enforces security. For this, the general design principle is that a system whose security depends on the integrity of the fewest possible entities is more likely to remain secure as it grows.

10. *Heterogeneity.* As a consequence of large scale, heterogeneity becomes inevitable in distributed systems. Heterogeneous distributed systems provide the flexibility to their users to use different computer platforms for different applications. For example, a user may use a supercomputer for simulations, a Macintosh for document processing, and a UNIX workstation for program development. Easy access to shared data across these diverse platforms would substantially improve usability. Therefore, a distributed file system should be designed to allow a variety of workstations to participate in the sharing of files via the distributed file system. Another heterogeneity issue in file systems is the ability to accommodate several different storage media. Therefore, a distributed file system should be designed to allow the integration of a new type of workstation or storage media in a relatively simple manner.

## 9.3 FILE MODELS

Different file systems use different conceptual models of a file. The two most commonly used criteria for file modeling are structure and modifiability. File models based on these criteria are described below.

### 9.3.1 Unstructured and Structured Files

According to the simplest model, a file is an unstructured sequence of data. In this model, there is no substructure known to the file server and the contents of each file of the file system appears to the file server as an uninterpreted sequence of bytes. The operating system is not interested in the information stored in the files. Hence, the interpretation of the meaning and structure of the data stored in the files are entirely up to the application programs. UNIX and MS-DOS use this file model.

Another file model that is rarely used nowadays is the structured file model. In this model, a file appears to the file server as an ordered sequence of records. Records of different files of the same file system can be of different size. Therefore, many types of files exist in a file system, each having different properties. In this model, a record is the smallest unit of file data that can be accessed, and the file system read or write operations are carried out on a set of records.

Structured files are again of two types—files with *nonindexed records* and files with *indexed records*. In the former model, a file record is accessed by specifying its position within the file, for example, the fifth record from the beginning of the file or the second record from the end of the file. In the latter model, records have one or more key fields and can be addressed by specifying the values of the key fields. In file systems that allow indexed records, a file is maintained as a B-tree or other suitable data structure or a hash table is used to locate records quickly.

Most modern operating systems use the unstructured file model. This is mainly because sharing of a file by different applications is easier with the unstructured file model as compared to the structured file model. Since a file has no structure in the unstructured model, different applications can interpret the contents of a file in different ways.

In addition to data items, files also normally have *attributes*. A file's attributes are information describing that file. Each attribute has a name and a value. For example, typical attributes of a file may contain information such as owner, size, access permissions, date of creation, date of last modification, and date of last access. Users can read and update some of the attribute values using the primitives provided by the file system. Notice, however, that although a user may read the value of any attribute, not all attributes are user modifiable. For example, a user may update the value of the access permissions attribute, but he or she cannot change the value of the size or date of creation attributes. The types of attributes that can be associated with a file are normally fixed by the file system. However, a file system may be designed to provide the flexibility to create and manipulate user-defined attributes in addition to those supported by the file system.

File attributes are normally maintained and used by the directory service because they are subject to different access controls than the file they describe. Notice that although file attributes are maintained and used by the directory service, they are stored with the corresponding file rather than with the file name in the directory. This is mainly because many directory systems allow files to be referenced by more than one name.

### 9.3.2 Mutable and Immutable Files

According to the modifiability criteria, files are of two types—mutable and immutable. Most existing operating systems use the mutable file model. In this model, an update performed on a file overwrites on its old contents to produce the new contents. That is, a file is represented as a single stored sequence that is altered by each update operation.

On the other hand, some more recent file systems, such as the Cedar File System (CFS) [Gifford et al. 1988], use the immutable file model. In this model, a file cannot be modified once it has been created except to be deleted. The file versioning approach is normally used to implement file updates, and each file is represented by a history of immutable versions. That is, rather than updating the same file, a new version of the file is created each time a change is made to the file contents and the old version is retained unchanged. In practice, the use of storage space may be reduced by keeping only a record of the differences between the old and new versions rather than creating the entire file once again.

Gifford et al. [1988] emphasized that sharing only immutable files makes it easy to support consistent sharing. Due to this feature, it is much easier to support file caching and replication in a distributed system with the immutable file model because it eliminates all the problems associated with keeping multiple copies of a file consistent. However, due to the need to keep multiple versions of a file, the immutable file model suffers from two potential problems—increased use of disk space and increased disk allocation activity. Some mechanism is normally used to prevent the disk space from filling instantaneously. For example, the CFS [Gifford et al. 1988] uses a *keep* parameter as the number of most current versions of a file to be retained. To keep track of the most current versions, each filename is suffixed with a version number, for example, "*demo.abc!6*" is a name for version 6 of the file with the base name of *demo.abc*. Therefore, if the value of the *keep* parameter of this file is 1, the creation of a new version of the file will cause the file *demo.abc!6* to be deleted and its disk space to be reused for the new file named *demo.abc!7*. When the value of the *keep* parameter is greater than 1 for a file, that is, when multiple versions of a file exist, users may use a particular version of the file by specifying its full name. However, when the version number part of a file is not specified, by default, CFS uses the lowest version number for some operations, such as *delete*, and highest version number for other operations, such as *open*.

## 9.4 FILE-ACCESSING MODELS

The manner in which a client's request to access a file is serviced depends on the file-accessing model used by the file system. The file-accessing model of a distributed file system mainly depends on two factors—the method used for accessing remote files and the unit of data access.

### 9.4.1 Accessing Remote Files

A distributed file system may use one of the following models to service a client's file access request when the accessed file is a remote file:

1. *Remote service model.* In this model, the processing of the client's request is performed at the server's node. That is, the client's request for file access is delivered to the server, the server machine performs the access request, and finally the result is forwarded back to the client. The access requests from the client and the server replies for the client are transferred across the network as messages. Notice that the data packing and communication overheads per message can be significant. Therefore, if the remote service model is used, the file server interface and the communication protocols must be designed carefully to minimize the overhead of generating messages as well as the number of messages that must be exchanged in order to satisfy a particular request.

2. *Data-caching model.* In the remote service model, every remote file access request results in network traffic. The data-caching model attempts to reduce the amount of network traffic by taking advantage of the locality feature found in file accesses. In this model, if the data needed to satisfy the client's access request is not present locally, it is copied from the server's node to the client's node and is cached there. The client's request is processed on the client's node itself by using the cached data. Recently accessed data are retained in the cache for some time so that repeated accesses to the same data can be handled locally. A replacement policy, such as the least recently used (LRU), is used to keep the cache size bounded.

   As compared to the remote access model, this model greatly reduces network traffic. However, in this model, there is a possibility that data of a particular file may simultaneously be available in different caches. Therefore, a write operation often incurs substantial overhead because, in addition to modifying the locally cached copy of the data, the changes must also be made in the original file at the server node and in any other caches having the data, depending on the relevant sharing semantics. The problem of keeping the cached data consistent with the original file content is referred to as the *cache consistency problem*. Methods to handle this problem will be described later in this chapter.

As compared to the remote service model, the data-caching model offers the possibility of increased performance and greater system scalability because it reduces network traffic, contention for the network, and contention for the file servers. Therefore, almost all existing distributed file systems implement some form of caching. In fact, many implementations can be thought of as a hybrid of the remote service and the data-caching models. For example, LOCUS [Popek and Walker 1985] and the Network File System (NFS) [Sandberg et al. 1985] use the remote service model but add caching for better performance. On the other hand, Sprite [Nelson et al. 1988] uses the data-caching model but employs the remote service method under certain circumstances.

### 9.4.2 Unit of Data Transfer

In file systems that use the data-caching model, an important design issue is to decide the unit of data transfer. Unit of data transfer refers to the fraction (or its multiples) of a file data that is transferred to and from clients as a result of a single read or write operation. The four commonly used data transfer models based on this factor are as follows:

1. *File-level transfer model.* In this model, when an operation requires file data to be transferred across the network in either direction between a client and a server, the whole file is moved.

In addition to its conceptual simplicity, this model has several advantages [Satyanarayanan et al. 1985]. First, transmitting an entire file in response to a single request is more efficient than transmitting it page by page in response to several requests because the network protocol overhead is required only once. Second, it has better scalability because it requires fewer accesses to file servers, resulting in reduced server load and network traffic. Third, disk access routines on the servers can be better optimized if it is known that requests are always for entire files rather than for random disk blocks. Fourth, once an entire file is cached at a client's site, it becomes immune to server and network failures. Hence the model also offers a degree of intrinsic resiliency. Finally, it also simplifies the task of supporting heterogeneous workstations. This is because it is easier to transform an entire file at one time from the form compatible with the file system of server workstation to the form compatible with the file system of the client workstation or vice versa.

On the other hand, the main drawback of this model is that it requires sufficient storage space on the client's node for storing all the required files in their entirety. Therefore, this approach fails to work with very large files, especially when the client runs on a diskless workstation. Even when the client's workstation is not diskless, files that are larger than the local disk capacity cannot be accessed at all. Furthermore, if only a small fraction of a file is needed, moving the whole file is wasteful.

Amoeba [Mullender and Tanenbaum 1984], CFS [Gifford et al. 1988], and the Andrew File System (AFS-2) [Satyanarayanan 1990b] are a few examples of distributed systems that use the file-level transfer model. AFS-3, which is an upgraded version of AFS-2, also allows files to be cached in large chunks (64 kilobytes) rather than in their entirety. This feature was later incorporated in AFS to allow a workstation to access files that are too large to fit on its local disk.

2. *Block-level transfer model.* In this model, file data transfers across the network between a client and a server take place in units of file blocks. A file block is a contiguous portion of a file and is usually fixed in length. For file systems in which block size is equal to virtual memory page size, this model is also called a page-level transfer model.

The advantage of this model is that it does not require client nodes to have large storage space. It also eliminates the need to copy an entire file when only a small portion of the file data is needed. Therefore, this model can be used in systems having diskless workstations. It provides large virtual memory for client nodes that do not have their own secondary storage devices. However, when an entire file is to be accessed, multiple server requests are needed in this model, resulting in more network traffic and more network protocol overhead. Therefore, this model has poor performance as compared to the file-level transfer model when the access requests are such that most files have to be transferred in their entirety. The Apollo Domain File System [Leach et al. 1983], Sun Microsystem's NFS [Sandberg 1987], LOCUS [Popek and Walker 1985], and Sprite [Nelson et al. 1988] are a few examples of distributed systems that use the block-level transfer model.

3. *Byte-level transfer model.* In this model, file data transfers across the network between a client and a server take place in units of bytes. This model provides maximum flexibility because it allows storage and retrieval of an arbitrary sequential subrange of a file, specified by an offset within a file, and a length. The main drawback of this model is the difficulty in cache management due to the variable-length data for different access requests. The Cambridge File Server [Dion 1980, Mitchell and Dion 1982, Needham and Herbert 1982] uses this model.

4. *Record-level transfer model.* The three file data transfer models described above are commonly used with unstructured file models. The record-level transfer model is suitable for use with those file models in which file contents are structured in the form of records. In this model, file data transfers across the network between a client and a server take place in units of records. The Research Storage System (RSS) [Gray 1978, Gray et al. 1981], which supports complex access methods to structured and indexed files, uses the record-level transfer model.

## 9.5 FILE-SHARING SEMANTICS

A shared file may be simultaneously accessed by multiple users. In such a situation, an important design issue for any file system is to clearly define when modifications of file data made by a user are observable by other users. This is defined by the type of file-sharing semantics adopted by a file system. Levy and Silberschatz [1990] defined the following types of file-sharing semantics:

1. *UNIX semantics.* This semantics enforces an absolute time ordering on all operations and ensures that every read operation on a file sees the effects of all previous write operations performed on that file [Fig. 9.1(*a*)]. In particular, writes to an open file by a user immediately become visible to other users who have this file open at the same time.

The UNIX semantics is commonly implemented in file systems for single-processor systems because it is the most desirable semantics and also because it is easy to serialize all read/write requests. However, implementing UNIX semantics in a distributed file system is not an easy task. One may think that this semantics can be achieved in a distributed system by disallowing files to be cached at client nodes and allowing a shared file to be managed by only one file server that processes all read and write requests for the file strictly in the order in which it receives them. However, even with this approach, there is a possibility that, due to network delays, client

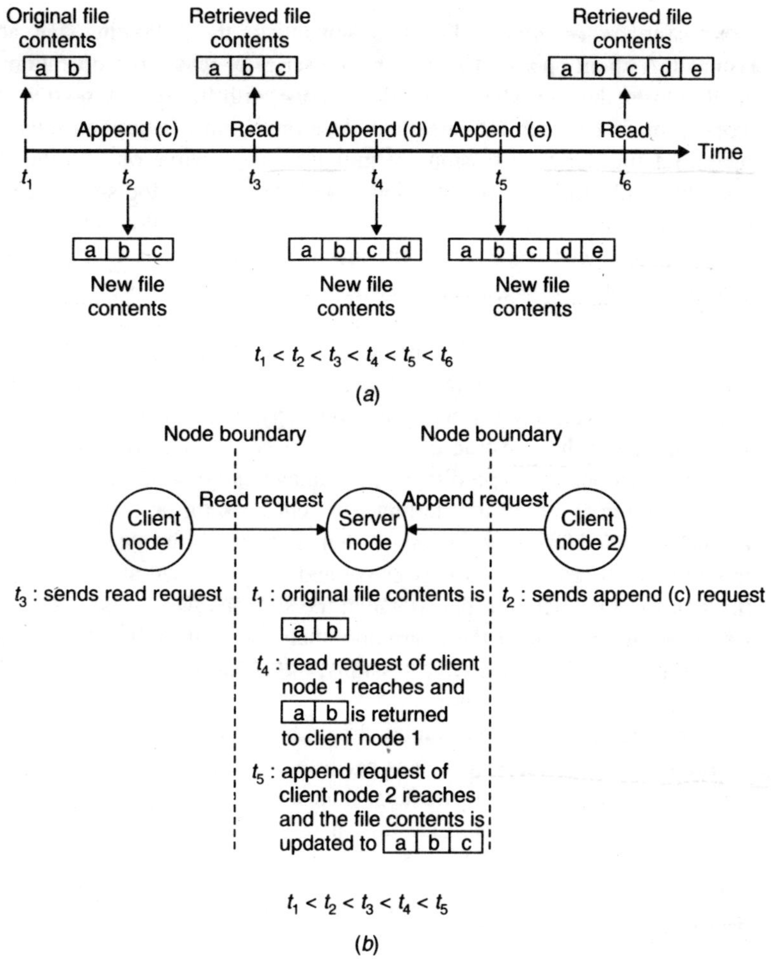


**Fig. 9.1** (*a*) Example of UNIX file-sharing semantics; (*b*) an example explaining why it is difficult to achieve UNIX semantics in a distributed file system even when the shared file is handled by a single server.

requests from different nodes may arrive and get processed at the server node in an order different from the actual order in which the requests were made [Fig. 9.1(*b*)]. Furthermore, having all file access requests processed by a single server and disallowing caching on client nodes is not desirable in practice due to poor performance, poor scalability, and poor reliability of the distributed file system. Therefore, distributed file systems normally implement a more relaxed semantics of file sharing. Applications that need to guarantee UNIX semantics for correct functioning should use special means (e.g., locks) for this purpose and should not rely on the underlying semantics of sharing provided by the file system.

2. *Session semantics*. For this semantics, the following file access pattern is assumed: A client opens a file, performs a series of read/write operations on the file, and finally closes the file when he or she is done with the file. A *session* is a series of file accesses made between the open and close operations. In session semantics, all changes made to a file during a session are initially made visible only to the client process (or possibly to all processes on the client node) that opened the session and are invisible to other remote processes who have the same file open simultaneously. Once the session is closed, the changes made to the file are made visible to remote processes only in later starting sessions. Already open instances of the file do not reflect these changes.

Notice that with session semantics multiple clients are allowed to perform both read and write accesses concurrently on the same file. In this case, each client maintains its own image of the file. When a client closes its session, all other remote clients who continue to use the file are actually using a stale copy of the file. Furthermore, using session semantics raises the question of what should be the final file image when multiple file sessions, each one having a different file image, are closed one after another. Notice that when a session is closed its file image is sent back to the server, so the final file image depends on who closes last. However, there is a possibility that due to network delays file images from different nodes may arrive and get processed at the server node in an order different from the actual order in which the sessions were closed. Therefore, in practice, it is easier to implement the alternative that says that the final file image is the image maintained by one of the active sessions; the actual one is left unspecified. That is, the final file image is nondeterministic.

Observe that session semantics should be used only with those file systems that use the file-level transfer model. This is because coupling the session semantics with caching parts of files may complicate matters, since a session is supposed to read the image of the entire file that corresponds to the time it was opened.

3. *Immutable shared-files semantics*. This semantics is based on the use of the immutable file model. Recall that an immutable file cannot be modified once it has been created. According to this semantics, once the creator of a file declares it to be sharable, the file is treated as immutable, so that it cannot be modified any more. Changes to the file are handled by creating a new updated version of the file. Each version of the file is treated as an entirely new file. Therefore, the semantics allows files to be shared only in the read-only mode. With this approach, since shared files cannot be changed at all, the problem of when to make the changes made to a file by a user visible to other users simply disappears.

4. *Transaction-like semantics*. This semantics is based on the transaction mechanism, which is a high-level mechanism for controlling concurrent access to shared, mutable data. A *transaction* is a set of operations enclosed in-between a pair of *begin_transaction*- and *end_transaction*-like operations. The transaction mechanism ensures that the partial modifications made to the shared data by a transaction will not be visible to other concurrently executing transactions until the transaction ends (its *end_transaction* is executed). Therefore, in multiple concurrent transactions operating on a file, the final file content will be the same as if all the transactions were run in some sequential order. In the Cambridge File Server [Needham and Herbert 1982], the

beginning and end of a transaction are implicit in the open and close file operations, and transactions can involve only one file. Thus, a file session in that system is actually a transaction.

## 9.6 FILE-CACHING SCHEMES

File caching has been implemented in several file systems for centralized time-sharing systems to improve file I/O performance (e.g., UNIX [McKusick et al. 1985]). The idea in file caching in these systems is to retain recently accessed file data in main memory, so that repeated accesses to the same information can be handled without additional disk transfers. Because of locality in file access patterns, file caching reduces disk transfers substantially, resulting in better overall performance of the file system. The property of locality in file access patterns can as well be exploited in distributed systems by designing a suitable file-caching scheme. In addition to better performance, a file-caching scheme for a distributed file system may also contribute to its scalability and reliability because it is possible to cache remotely located data on a client node. Therefore, every distributed file system in serious use today uses some form of file caching. Even AT&T's Remote File System (RFS) [Rifkin et al. 1986], which initially avoided caching to emulate UNIX semantics, now uses it.

In implementing a file-caching scheme for a centralized file system, one has to make several key decisions, such as the granularity of cached data (large versus small), cache size (large versus small, fixed versus dynamically changing), and the replacement policy. A good summary of these design issues is presented in [Smith 1982]. In addition to these issues, a file-caching scheme for a distributed file system should also address the following key decisions:

1. Cache location
2. Modification propagation
3. Cache validation

These three design issues are described below.

### 9.6.1 Cache Location

Cache location refers to the place where the cached data is stored. Assuming that the original location of a file is on its server's disk, there are three possible cache locations in a distributed file system (Fig. 9.2).

1. *Server's main memory.* When no caching scheme is used, before a remote client can access a file, the file must first be transferred from the server's disk to the server's main memory and then across the network from the server's main memory to the client's main memory. Therefore, the total cost involved is one disk access and one network

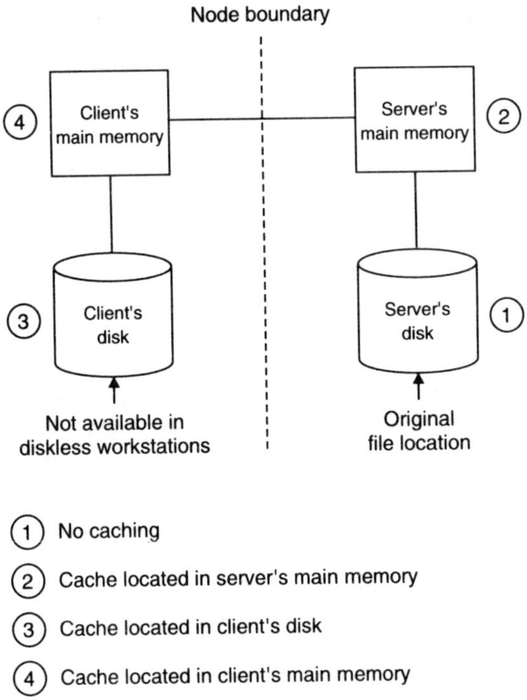


**Fig. 9.2** Possible cache locations in a file-catching scheme for a distributed file system.

access. A cache located in the server's main memory eliminates the disk access cost on a cache hit, resulting in a considerable performance gain as compared to no caching.

The decision to locate the cache in the server's main memory may be taken due to one or more of the following reasons. It is easy to implement and is totally transparent to the clients. It is easy to always keep the original file and cached data consistent since both reside on the same node. Furthermore, since a single server manages both the cached data and the file, multiple accesses from different clients can be easily synchronized to support UNIX-like file-sharing semantics.

However, having the cache in the server's main memory involves a network access for each file access operation by a remote client and processing of the access request by the server. Therefore, it does not eliminate the network access cost and does not contribute to the scalability and reliability of the distributed file system.

2. *Client's disk*. The second option is to have the cache in a client's disk. A cache located in a client's disk eliminates network access cost but requires disk access cost on a cache hit. A cache on a disk has several advantages. The first is reliability. Modifications to cached data are lost in a crash if the cache is kept in volatile memory. Moreover, if the cached data is kept on the client's disk, the data is still there during recovery and there is no need to fetch it again from the server's node. The second advantage is large storage capacity. As compared to a main-memory cache, a disk cache has plenty of storage space. Therefore, more data can be cached, resulting in a higher hit ratio. Furthermore, several

distributed file systems use the file-level data transfer model in which a file is always cached in its entirety. In these systems, if a file is too large to fit in a main-memory cache, the advantages of file caching cannot be availed for it. Therefore, disk cache is particularly useful for those systems that use the file-level transfer model because it allows the caching of most large files unless the file to be cached is larger than the available disk space. The third advantage is disconnected operation. A system may use a client's disk caching and the file-level transfer model to support disconnected operation. A client's disk cache also contributes to scalability and reliability because on a cache hit the access request can be serviced locally without the need to contact the server.

The main drawback of having cached data on a client's disk is that this policy does not work if the system is to support diskless workstations. Furthermore, with this caching policy, a disk access is required for each access request even when there is cache hit. Therefore, the access time is still considerably large. Notice that a server's main-memory cache eliminates disk access but requires network access on a cache hit. On the other hand, a client's disk cache eliminates network access but requires disk access on a cache hit. Therefore, when a decision has to be made whether to do caching in the server's main memory or the client's disk, the former is somewhat faster, and it is always much simpler [Tanenbaum 1995].

3. *Client's main memory.* The third alternative is to have the cache in a client's main memory. A cache located in a client's main memory eliminates both network access cost and disk access cost. Therefore, it provides maximum performance gain on a cache hit. It also permits workstations to be diskless. Like a client's disk cache, a client's main-memory cache also contributes to scalability and reliability because on a cache hit the access request can be serviced locally without the need to contact the server. However, a client's main-memory cache is not preferable to a client's disk cache when large cache size and increased reliability of cached data are desired.

The relative advantages of the three cache location policies are summarized in Figure 9.3. In conclusion, a main-memory cache and a disk cache emphasize different functionality. While a main-memory cache emphasizes reduced access time, a disk cache emphasizes increased reliability and autonomy of client machines. Furthermore, when faced with a choice between having a cache on the server node versus the client node, the latter is always preferable because it also contributes to scalability and reliability.

### 9.6.2 Modification Propagation

In file systems in which the cache is located on clients' nodes, a file's data may simultaneously be cached on multiple nodes. In such a situation, when the caches of all these nodes contain exactly the same copies of the file data, we say that the caches are *consistent*. It is possible for the caches to become *inconsistent* when the file data is changed by one of the clients and the corresponding data cached at other nodes are not changed or discarded.

Keeping file data cached at multiple client nodes consistent is an important design issue in those distributed file systems that use client caching. A variety of approaches to

Cost of remote access in case of no caching
= one disk access + one network access

| Cache location | Access cost on cache hit | Advantages |
|---|---|---|
| Server's main memory | One network access | 1. Easy to implement<br>2. Totally transparent to the clients<br>3. Easy to keep the original file and cached data consistent<br>4. Easy to support UNIX-like file-sharing semantics |
| Client's disk | One disk access | 1. Reliability against crashes<br>2. Large storage capacity<br>3. Suitable for supporting disconnected operation<br>4. Contributes to scalability and reliability |
| Client's main memory | — | 1. Maximum performance gain<br>2. Permits workstations to be diskless<br>3. Contributes to scalability and reliability |

**Fig. 9.3** Summary of the relative advantages of the three cache location policies.

handle this issue have been proposed and implemented. These approaches depend on the schemes used for the following cache design issues for distributed file systems:

1. When to propagate modifications made to a cached data to the corresponding file server
2. How to verify the validity of cached data

The modification propagation schemes are presented below and the cache validation schemes are presented in the next section.

A distributed file system may use one of the modification propagation schemes described below. The file-sharing semantics supported by the distributed file system depends greatly on the modification propagation scheme used. Furthermore, the modification propagation scheme used has a critical effect on the system's performance and reliability.

### Write-through Scheme

In this scheme, when a cache entry is modified, the new value is immediately sent to the server for updating the master copy of the file. This scheme has two main advantages—high degree of reliability and suitability for UNIX-like semantics. Since every modification is immediately propagated to the server having the master copy of the file, the risk of updated data getting lost (when a client crashes) is very low. A major drawback of this scheme is its poor write performance. This is because each write access has to wait until the information is written to the master copy of the server. Notice that with the write-through scheme the advantages of data caching are only for read accesses because the remote service method is basically used for all write accesses. Therefore, this scheme is suitable for use only in those cases in which the ratio of read-to-write accesses is fairly large.

### Delayed-Write Scheme

Although the write-through scheme helps on reads, it does not help in reducing the network traffic for writes. Therefore, to reduce network traffic for writes as well, some systems use the delayed-write scheme. In this scheme, when a cache entry is modified, the new value is written only to the cache and the client just makes a note that the cache entry has been updated. Some time later, all updated cache entries corresponding to a file are gathered together and sent to the server at a time.

Depending on when the modifications are sent to the file server, delayed-write policies are of different types. Three commonly used approaches are as follows:

1. *Write on ejection from cache*. In this method, modified data in a cache entry is sent to the server when the cache replacement policy has decided to eject it from the client's cache. This method can result in good performance, but some data can reside in the client's cache for a long time before they are sent to the server [Ousterhout et al. 1985]. Such data are subject to reliability problem.

2. *Periodic write*. In this method, the cache is scanned periodically, at regular intervals, and any cached data that have been modified since the last scan are sent to the server. Sprite [Nelson et al. 1988] uses this method with an interval of 30 seconds.

3. *Write on close*. In this method, the modifications made to a cached data by a client are sent to the server when the corresponding file is closed by the client. Notice that the write-on-close policy is a perfect match for the session semantics. However, it does not help much in reducing network traffic for those files that are open for very short periods or are rarely modified. Furthermore, the close operation takes a long time because all modified data must be written to the server before the operation completes. Therefore, this policy should be used only in cases in which files are open for long periods and are frequently modified. The ITC File System [Satyanarayanan et al. 1985] uses the write-on-close policy.

The delayed-write policy helps in performance improvement for write accesses due to the following reasons:

1. Write accesses complete more quickly because the new value is written only in the cache of the client performing the write.
2. Modified data may be deleted before it is time to send them to the server. For example, many programs create temporary files, use them, and then delete them soon after they are created. In such cases, modifications need not be propagated at all to the server, resulting in a major performance gain.
3. Gathering of all file updates and sending them together to the server is more efficient than sending each update separately.

Delayed-write schemes, however, suffer from reliability problems, since modifications not yet sent to the server from a client's cache will be lost if the client crashes. Another drawback of this approach is that delaying the propagation of modifications to the server results in fuzzier file-sharing semantics, because when another process reads the file, what it gets depends on the timing.

### 9.6.3 Cache Validation Schemes

A file data may simultaneously reside in the cache of multiple nodes. The modification propagation policy only specifies when the master copy of a file at the server node is updated upon modification of a cache entry. It does not tell anything about when the file data residing in the cache of other nodes is updated. Obviously, a client's cache entry becomes stale as soon as some other client modifies the data corresponding to the cache entry in the master copy of the file. Therefore, it becomes necessary to verify if the data cached at a client node is consistent with the master copy. If not, the cached data must be invalidated and the updated version of the data must be fetched again from the server. There are basically two approaches to verify the validity of cached data—the client-initiated approach and the server-initiated approach [Levy and Silberschatz 1990]. These are described below.

#### Client-Initiated Approach

In this approach, a client contacts the server and checks whether its locally cached data is consistent with the master copy. The file-sharing semantics depends on the frequency of the validity check. One of the following approaches may be used:

1. *Checking before every access.* This approach defeats the main purpose of caching because the server has to be contacted on every access. But it is suitable for supporting UNIX-like semantics.

2. *Periodic checking.* In this method, a check is initiated every fixed interval of time. The main problem of this method is that it results in fuzzier file-sharing semantics because the data on which an access operation is performed is timing dependent.

3. *Check on file open.* In this method, a client's cache entry is validated only when the client opens the corresponding file for use. This method is suitable for supporting session semantics. Observe that one method for implementing session semantics in a distributed file system is to use the file-level transfer model coupled with the write-on-close modification propagation policy and the check-on-file-open cache validation policy.

The validity check is performed by comparing the time of last modification of the cached version of the data with the server's master copy version. If the two are the same, the cached data is up to date. Otherwise, it is stale and hence the current version of the data is fetched from the server. Instead of using timestamps, version numbers or checksums can be used.

### Server-Initiated Approach

If the frequency of the validity check is high, the client-initiated cache validation approach generates a large amount of network traffic and consumes precious server CPU time. Owing to this reason, the AFS that initially used the client-initiated approach (in AFS-1) switched to the server-initiated approach (in AFS-2 and AFS-3) [Satyanarayanan 1990b, 1992].

In this method, a client informs the file server when opening a file, indicating whether the file is being opened for reading, writing, or both. The file server keeps a record of which client has which file open and in what mode. In this manner, the server keeps monitoring the file usage modes being used by different clients and reacts whenever it detects a potential for inconsistency. A potential for inconsistency occurs when two or more clients try to open a file in conflicting modes. For example, if a file is open for reading, other clients may be allowed to open it for reading without any problem, but opening it for writing cannot be allowed. Similarly, a new client should not be allowed to open a file in any mode if the file is already open for writing. When a client closes a file, it sends an intimation to the server along with any modifications made to the file. On receiving such an intimation, the server updates its record of which client has which file open in what mode.

When a new client makes a request to open an already open file and if the server finds that the new open mode conflicts with the already open mode, the server can be designed to deny the request or queue the request or disable caching and switch to the remote service mode of operation for that particular file by asking all the clients having the file open to remove that file from their caches. The method of disabling caching is used in Sprite [Nelson et al. 1988].

Although the server-initiated approach described above is quite effective, it has the following problems:

1. It violates the traditional client-server model in which servers simply respond to service request activities initiated by clients. This makes the code for client and server programs irregular and complex.
2. It requires that file servers be stateful. As explained later, stateful file servers have a distinct disadvantage over stateless file servers in the event of a failure.

3. A check-on-open, client-initiated cache validation approach must still be used along with the server-initiated approach. For example, a client may open a file, cache it, and then close it after use. Upon opening it again for use, the cache content must be validated because there is a possibility that some other client might have subsequently opened, modified, and closed the file.

In another server-initiated approach, known as the *callback policy* in AFS [Satyanarayanan 1990b], a cache entry is assumed to be valid unless otherwise notified by the server. In this method, instead of recording the access modes of all clients for an open file, the server only keeps a record of the clients who have cached a file (or a part of it). This record is maintained on a per-file basis, and corresponding to each file maintained by the server, the server maintains a list of the clients who have the file's data cached in their cache irrespective of whether the client currently has the file open for use or not. The server promises to notify all clients of a cached file before allowing any modification to the file by any other client.

In AFS, which implements session semantics, whenever a server receives a request to close a file that has been modified, it notifies all the clients having that file data in their caches to discard their cached data and consider it invalid. Clients having this file open at that time discard their copy when the current session is over. Other clients discard their copies at once. Notice that in this method the server need not be informed about *opens* of already cached files. It need only be informed about the *close* of a writing session. As a result, the server need not receive open validation requests of locally cached files. If the client machine crashes, it is assumed that all its local files may be inconsistent. Therefore, upon recovery from a cache, it generates a cache validation request for each file that is cached on its local disk.

## 9.7 FILE REPLICATION

High availability is a desirable feature of a good distributed file system and file replication is the primary mechanism for improving file availability. A *replicated file* is a file that has multiple copies, with each copy located on a separate file server. Each copy of the set of copies that comprises a replicated file is referred to as a *replica* of the replicated file.

### 9.7.1 Difference between Replication and Caching

Replication is often confused with caching, probably because they both deal with multiple copies of a data. However, the two concepts have the following basic differences:

1. A replica is associated with a server, whereas a cached copy is normally associated with a client.
2. The existence of a cached copy is primarily dependent on the locality in file access patterns, whereas the existence of a replica normally depends on availability and performance requirements.

3. As compared to a cached copy, a replica is more persistent, widely known, secure, available, complete, and accurate.
4. A cached copy is contingent upon a replica. Only by periodic revalidation with respect to a replica can a cached copy be useful.

Satyanarayanan [1992] distinguishes a replicated copy from a cached copy by calling them *first-class replicas* and *second-class replicas*, respectively.

### 9.7.2 Advantages of Replication

The replication of data in a distributed system offers the following potential benefits:

1. *Increased availability.* One of the most important advantages of replication is that it masks and tolerates failures in the network gracefully. In particular, the system remains operational and available to the users despite failures. By replicating critical data on servers with independent failure modes, the probability that one copy of the data will be accessible increases. Therefore, alternate copies of a replicated data can be used when the primary copy is unavailable.

2. *Increased reliability.* Many applications require extremely high reliability of their data stored in files. Replication is very advantageous for such applications because it allows the existence of multiple copies of their files. Due to the presence of redundant information in the system, recovery from catastrophic failures (such as permanent loss of data of a storage device) becomes possible.

3. *Improved response time.* Replication also helps in improving response time because it enables data to be accessed either locally or from a node to which access time is lower than the primary copy access time. The access time differential may arise either because of network topology or because of uneven loading of nodes.

4. *Reduced network traffic.* If a file's replica is available with a file server that resides on a client's node, the client's access requests can be serviced locally, resulting in reduced network traffic.

5. *Improved system throughput.* Replication also enables several clients' requests for access to the same file to be serviced in parallel by different servers, resulting in improved system throughput.

6. *Better scalability.* As the number of users of a shared file grows, having all access requests for the file serviced by a single file server can result in poor performance due to overloading of the file server. By replicating the file on multiple servers, the same requests can now be serviced more efficiently by multiple servers due to workload distribution. This results in better scalability.

7. *Autonomous operation.* In a distributed system that provides file replication as a service to their clients, all files required by a client for operation during a limited time period may be replicated on the file server residing at the client's node. This will facilitate

temporary autonomous operation of client machines. A distributed system having this feature can support detachable, portable machines.

### 9.7.3 Replication Transparency

Transparency is an important issue in file replication. A replicated file service must function exactly like a nonreplicated file service but exhibit improved performance and reliability. That is, replication of files should be designed to be transparent to the users so that multiple copies of a replicated file appear as a single logical file to its users. For this, the read, write, and other file operations should have the same client interface whether they apply to a nonreplicated file or to a replicated file. Two important issues related to replication transparency are naming of replicas and replication control.

#### Naming of Replicas

In systems that support object replication, a basic question is whether different replicas of an object should be assigned the same identifier or different identifiers. Obviously, the replication transparency requirement calls for the assignment of a single identifier to all replicas of an object. Assignment of a single identifier to all replicas of an object seems reasonable for immutable objects because a kernel can easily support this type of object. Any copy found by the kernel can be used, because all copies are immutable and identical; there is only one logical object with a given identifier. However, in mutable objects, different copies of a replicated object may not be the same (consistent) at a particular instance of time. In this case, if the same identifier is used for all replicas of the object, the kernel cannot decide which replica is the most up-to-date one. Therefore, the consistency control and management of the various replicas of a mutable object should be performed outside the kernel. Hence it is the responsibility of the naming system to map a user-supplied identifier into the appropriate replica of a mutable object. Furthermore, if all replicas are consistent, the mapping must provide the locations of all replicas and a mechanism to identify the relative distances of the replicas from the user's node.

#### Replication Control

Another transparency issue is providing replication control. Replication control includes determining the number and locations of replicas of a replicated file. That is, do the users play any role in determining how many copies of a replicated file should be created and on which server should each copy be placed? In a replication transparent system, the replication control is handled entirely automatically, in a user-transparent manner. However, under certain circumstances, it is desirable to expose these details to users and to provide them with the flexibility to control the replication process. For instance, if replication facility is provided to support autonomous operation of workstations, users should be provided with the flexibility to create a replica of the desired files on their local nodes. Similarly, because of the nature of job, if a user normally works on two or three different nodes at different times, it may be desirable to replicate some of the frequently used files on servers located on all his or her workstations.

Depending on whether replication control is user transparent or not, the replication process is of two types:

1. *Explicit replication.* In this type, users are given the flexibility to control the entire replication process. That is, when a process creates a file, it specifies the server on which the file should be placed. Then, if desired, additional copies of the file can be created on other servers on explicit request by the users. Users also have the flexibility to delete one or more replicas of a replicated file.

2. *Implicit/lazy replication.* In this type, the entire replication process is automatically controlled by the system without users' knowledge. That is, when a process creates a file, it does not provide any information about its location. The system automatically selects one server for the placement of the file. Later, the system automatically creates replicas of the file on other servers, based on some replication policy used by the system. The system must be intelligent enough to create and allow the existence of only as many replicas as are necessary and should automatically delete any extra copies when they are no longer needed. Lazy replication is normally performed in the background when the server has some free time.

### 9.7.4 Multicopy Update Problem

As soon as a file system allows multiple copies of the same (logical) file to exist on different servers, it is faced with the problem of keeping them mutually consistent. That is, a situation must not be allowed to arise whereby independent conflicting updates have been made to different copies of the same file. In fact, maintaining consistency among copies when a replicated file is updated is the major design issue of a file system that supports replication of files. Some of the commonly used approaches to handle this issue are described below.

#### Read-Only Replication

This approach allows the replication of only immutable files. Since immutable files are used only in the read-only mode and because mutable files cannot be replicated, the multicopy update problem does not arise. Files known to be frequently read and modified only once in a while (once in several months), such as files containing the object code of system programs, can be treated as immutable files for replication using this approach.

#### Read-Any–Write-All Protocol

The read-only replication approach is too restrictive in the sense that it allows the replication of only immutable files. Obviously, a replication scheme that can support the replication of mutable files as well is desirable. A simple multicopy update protocol that allows the replication of mutable files is the read-any–write-all protocol. In this method, a read operation on a replicated file is performed by reading any copy of the file and a write operation by writing to all copies of the file. Some form of locking has to be used to carry out a write operation. That is, before updating any copy, all copies are locked, then they are updated, and finally the locks are released to complete the write. The protocol is suitable for implementing UNIX-like semantics. Notice that, in this protocol, the availability of a write operation is severely restricted since all copies must be available for the operation to complete, but the read operation is responsive since the nearest copy can be used.

### Available-Copies Protocol

The main problem with the read-any–write-all protocol is that a write operation cannot be performed if any of the servers having a copy of the replicated file is down at the time of the write operation. The available-copies protocol relaxes this restriction and allows write operations to be carried out even when some of the servers having a copy of the replicated file are down. In this method, a read operation is performed by reading any available copy, but a write operation is performed by writing to all available copies. The basic idea behind the correct functioning of this protocol is that when a server recovers after a failure, it brings itself up to date by copying from other servers before accepting any user request. Failed servers (sites) are dynamically detected by high-priority status management routines and configured out of the system while newly recovered sites are configured back in. This protocol provides better availability than the read-any–write-all protocol but does not prevent inconsistencies in the presence of communication failures such as network partition. Only clean, detectable site crashes are handled correctly by this method.

### Primary-Copy Protocol

Another simple method to solve the multicopy update problem is the primary-copy protocol. In this protocol, for each replicated file, one copy is designated as the primary copy and all the others are secondary copies. Read operations can be performed using any copy, primary or secondary. But, all write operations are directly performed only on the primary copy. Each server having a secondary copy updates its copy either by receiving notification of changes from the server having the primary copy or by requesting the updated copy from it.

The consistency semantics implemented depends on when the secondary copies are updated. For instance, for UNIX-like semantics, when the primary-copy server receives an update request, it immediately orders all the secondary-copy servers to update their copies. Some form of locking is used and the write operation completes only when all the copies have been updated. Therefore, in this case, the primary-copy update protocol is simply another method of implementing the read-any–write-all protocol.

A fuzzier consistency semantics results if a write operation completes as soon as the primary copy has been updated. The secondary copies are then lazily updated either in the background or when requested for an updated version by their servers. In this way, all the secondary copies will ultimately get updated and reach a consistent state.

### Quorum-Based Protocols

The read-any–write-all and available-copies protocols cannot handle the network partition problem in which the copies of a replicated file are partitioned into two more active groups. Moreover, the primary-copy protocol is too restrictive in the sense that a write operation cannot be performed if the server having the primary copy is down. Gifford [1979a] presented a simple quorum protocol that is capable of handling the network partition problem and can increase the availability of write operations at the expense of read operations.

A quorum-based protocol works as follows. Suppose that there are a total of $n$ copies of a replicated file $F$. To read the file, a minimum $r$ copies of $F$ have to be consulted. This set of $r$ copies is called a *read quorum*. Similarly, to perform a write operation on the file, a minimum $w$ copies of $F$ have to be written. This set of $w$ copies is called a *write quorum*. The restriction on the choice of the values of $r$ and $w$ is that the sum of the read and write quorums must be greater than the total number of copies $n$ ($r + w > n$). This restriction guarantees that there is a nonnull intersection between every read quorum and every write quorum. That is, there is at least one common copy of the file between every pair of read and write operations resulting in at least one up-to-date copy in any read/write quorum.

Since the quorum protocol does not require that write operations be executed on all copies of a replicated file, some copies will be obsolete, and therefore, it becomes necessary to be able to identify a current (up-to-date) copy in a quorum. This is normally achieved by associating a version number attribute with each copy. The version number of a copy is updated every time the copy is modified. A copy with the largest version number in a quorum is current. The new version number assigned to each copy is one more than the version number associated with the current copy.

A read is executed as follows:

1. Retrieve a read quorum (any $r$ copies) of $F$.
2. Of the $r$ copies retrieved, select the copy with the largest version number.
3. Perform the read operation on the selected copy.

A write is executed as follows:

1. Retrieve a write quorum (any $w$ copies) of $F$.
2. Of the $w$ copies retrieved, get the version number of the copy with the largest version number.
3. Increment the version number.
4. Write the new value and the new version number to all the $w$ copies of the write quorum.

To further clarify how this protocol works, let us consider the example of Figure 9.4($a$). There are total of eight copies of the replicated file ($n = 8$) and the values of read and write quorums are 4 and 5, respectively ($r = 4$, $w = 5$). Therefore, the condition $r + w > n$ is satisfied. Now suppose a write operation is performed on the write quorum

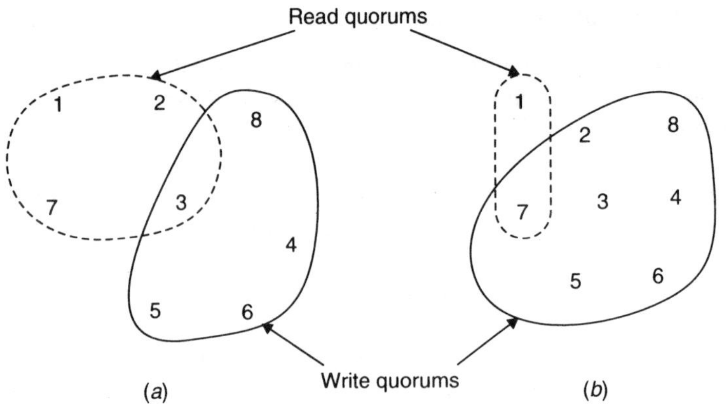


**Fig. 9.4** Examples of quorum consensus algorithm: (*a*) $n = 8$, $r = 4$, $w = 5$; (*b*) $n = 8$, $r = 2$, $w = 7$.

comprised of copies 3, 4, 5, 6, and 8. All these copies get the new version and the new version number. Now any subsequent read operation will require a read quorum of four copies because $r = 4$. Obviously any read quorum will have to contain at least one copy of the previous write quorum. For the read quorum shown in the figure, copy number 3 is the common copy. When the version numbers of the copies belonging to the read quorum are seen, the version number of copy number 3 is found to be larger than the other copies of the read quorum. Therefore, the read operation is performed using copy number 3. Another example in which $r = 2$ and $w = 7$ is shown in Figure 9.4(*b*).

The quorum protocol described above is a very general one, and several special algorithms can be derived from it. A few are described below.

1. *Read-any–write-all protocol.* The read-any–write-all protocol is actually a special case of the generalized quorum protocol with $r = 1$ and $w = n$. This protocol is suitable for use when the ratio of read to write operations is large.

2. *Read-all–write-any protocol.* For this protocol $r = n$ and $w = 1$. This protocol may be used in those cases where the ratio of write to read operations is large.

3. *Majority-consensus protocol.* In this protocol, the sizes of both the read quorum and the write quorum are made either equal or nearly equal. For example, if $n = 11$, a possible quorum assignment for this protocol will be $r = 6$ and $w = 6$. Similarly, when $n = 12$, a possible quorum assignment will be $r = 6$ and $w = 7$. This protocol is commonly used in those cases for which the ratio of read to write operations is nearly 1.

4. *Consensus with weighted voting.* In all the quorum-based protocols described above, all copies of a replicated file are given equal importance. In other words, all copies are assigned a single vote. The generalized quorum protocol can also be used to model the varying "importance" of different copies of a replicated file by assigning each copy some number of votes. The votes per copy can be adjusted for performance or reliability

reasons. For example, suppose that of the $n$ replicas of a replicated file, which are located on different nodes, the replica at node $A$ is accessed more frequently than other replicas. This fact can be modeled by assigning more votes to the copy at node $A$ than other replicas.

In this approach, a read quorum of $r$ votes is collected to read a file and a write quorum of $w$ votes to write a file. Since the votes assigned to each copy are not the same, the size of a read/write quorum depends on the copies selected for the quorum. The number of copies in the quorum will be less if the number of votes assigned to the selected copies is relatively more. On the other hand, the number of copies in the quorum will be more if the number of votes assigned to the selected copies is relatively less. Therefore, to guarantee that there is a nonnull intersection between every read quorum and every write quorum, the values of $r$ and $w$ are chosen such that $r+w$ is greater than the total number of votes ($v$) assigned to the file ($r+w>v$). Here, $v$ is the sum of the votes of all the copies of the file.

## 9.8 FAULT TOLERANCE

Fault tolerance is an important issue in the design of a distributed file system. Various types of faults could harm the integrity of the data stored by such a system. For instance, a processor loses the contents of its main memory in the event of a crash. Such a failure could result in logically complete but physically incomplete file operations, making the data that are stored by the file system inconsistent. Similarly, during a request processing, the server or client machine may crash, resulting in the loss of state information of the file being accessed. This may have an uncertain effect on the integrity of file data. Also, other adverse environmental phenomena such as transient faults (caused by electromagnetic fluctuations) or decay of disk storage devices may result in the loss or corruption of data stored by a file system. A portion of a disk storage device is said to be "decayed" if the data on that portion of the device are irretrievable.

The primary file properties that directly influence the ability of a distributed file system to tolerate faults are as follows [Levy and Silberschatz 1990]:

1. *Availability.* Availability of a file refers to the fraction of time for which the file is available for use. Note that the availability property depends on the location of the file and the locations of its clients (users). For example, if a network is partitioned due to a communication link failure, a file may be available to the clients of some nodes, but at the same time, it may not be available to the clients of other nodes. Replication is a primary mechanism for improving the availability of a file.

2. *Robustness.* Robustness of a file refers to its power to survive crashes of the storage device and decays of the storage medium on which it is stored. Storage devices that are implemented by using redundancy techniques, such as a stable storage device, are often used to store robust files. Note that a robust file may not be available until the faulty component has been recovered. Furthermore, unlike availability, robustness is independent of either the location of the file or the location of its clients.

3. *Recoverability.* Recoverability of a file refers to its ability to be rolled back to an earlier, consistent state when an operation on the file fails or is aborted by the client. Notice that a robust file is not necessarily recoverable and vice versa. Atomic update techniques such as a transaction mechanism are used to implement recoverable files.

The file replication technique has already been described in the previous section. The atomic transactions mechanism used for atomic update is described in the next section. The stable-storage technique and the effect of a service paradigm on the fault tolerance of distributed file systems are described below.

### 9.8.1 Stable Storage

In context of crash resistance capability, storage may be broadly classified into three types:

1. *Volatile storage*, such as RAM, which cannot withstand power failures or machine crashes. That is, the data stored in a volatile storage is lost in the event of a power failure or a machine crash.
2. *Nonvolatile storage*, such as a disk, which can withstand CPU failures but cannot withstand transient I/O faults and decay of the storage media. Although fairly reliable, nonvolatile storage media such as a disk have complicated failure modes and may prove to be insufficiently reliable for storing critical data.
3. *Stable storage*, which can even withstand transient I/O faults and decay of the storage media. It is a storage approach introduced by Lampson [1981].

The basic idea of stable storage is to use duplicate storage devices to implement a stable device and to try to ensure that any period when only one of the two component devices is operational is significantly less than the mean time between failures (MTBF) of a stable device. Therefore, a disk-based stable-storage system consists of a pair of ordinary disks (say disk 1 and disk 2) that are assumed to be decay independent. Each block on disk 2 is an exact copy of the corresponding block on disk 1. Unexpected faults that affect disk storage may occur, but effective fault tolerance facilities are provided to ensure that both the disks are not damaged at the same time. This is achieved by imposing restrictions on how the two disks are accessed.

As with conventional disks, the two basic operations related to a stable disk are read and write. A read operation first attempts to read from disk 1. If it fails, the read is done from disk 2. A write operation writes to both disks, but the write to disk 2 does not start until that for disk 1 has been successfully completed. This is to avoid the possibility of both disks getting damaged at the same time by a hardware fault. Read and write actions to each of the disks use retries of actions to tolerate the effects of transient hardware faults.

In addition, there is a crash recovery action that restores the internal consistency of data stored on the two disks after a crash has occurred. This recovery action compares the contents of the two disks block by block. Whenever two corresponding blocks differ, the block having incorrect data is regenerated from the corresponding block on the other disk. The correctness of a data block depends on the timing when the crash occurred. For instance, if the system crashes after disk 1 is updated but before disk 2 is updated or while disk 2 is being updated, the data block on disk 1 is the correct one. On the other hand, if the system crashes while disk 1 is being updated, the data block on disk 2 is the correct one. Of course, in the latter case, the update operation must be performed once again from the beginning.

Notice that a stable-storage system uses ordinary fallible disks and converts them into reliable virtual devices whose probability of failure is negligible. Stable storage is suitable for those applications that require a high degree of fault tolerance, such as atomic transactions.

### 9.8.2 Effect of Service Paradigm on Fault Tolerance

A server may be implemented by using any one of the following two service paradigms—stateful or stateless. The two paradigms are distinguished by one aspect of the client-server relationship—whether or not the history of the serviced requests between a client and a server affects the execution of the next service request. The stateful approach depends on the history of the serviced requests, but the stateless approach does not depend on it.

#### Stateful File Servers

A stateful file server maintains clients' state information from one access request to the next. That is, for two subsequent requests made by a client to a stateful server for accessing a file, some state information pertaining to the service performed for the client as a result of the first request execution is stored by the server process. This state information is subsequently used when executing the second request. To allow the file server to decide how long to retain the state information of a client, all access requests for a file by a client are performed within an open and a close operations called a *session*. The server creates state information for a client when the client starts a new session by performing an open operation, maintains the state information for the entire duration of the session, and discards the state information when the client closes the session by performing a close operation. To illustrate how a stateful file server works, let us consider a file server for byte-stream files that allows the following operations on files:

**Open** (*filename*, *mode*): This operation is used to open a file identified by *filename* in the specified *mode*. When the server executes this operation, it creates an entry for this file in a *file-table* that it uses for maintaining the file state information of all the open files. The file state information normally consists of the identifier of the file, the open mode, and the current position of a nonnegative integer pointer, called the *read-write pointer*. When a file is opened, its *read-write pointer* is set to zero and the server returns to the client a file identifier (*fid*) that is used by the client for subsequent accesses to that file.

**Read** (*fid*, *n*, *buffer*): This operation is used to get *n* bytes of data from the file identified by *fid* into the specified *buffer*.When the server executes this operation, it returns to the client *n* bytes of file data starting from the byte currently addressed by the *read-write pointer* and then increments the *read-write pointer* by *n*.

**Write** (*fid*, *n*, *buffer*): On execution of this operation, the server takes *n* bytes of data from the specified *buffer*, writes it into the file identified by *fid* at the byte position currently addressed by the *read-write pointer*, and then increments the *read-write pointer* by *n*.

**Seek** (*fid*, *position*): This operation causes the server to change the value of the *read-write pointer* of the file identified by *fid* to the new value specified as *position*.

**Close** (*fid*): This statement causes the server to delete from its *file-table* the file state information of the file identified by *fid*.

The file server mentioned above is stateful because it maintains the current state information for a file that has been opened for use by a client. Therefore, as shown in Figure 9.5, after opening a file, if a client makes two subsequent *Read* (*fid*, *100*, *buf*) requests, for the first request the first 100 bytes (bytes 0 to 99) will be read and for the second request the next 100 bytes (bytes 100 to 199) will be read.

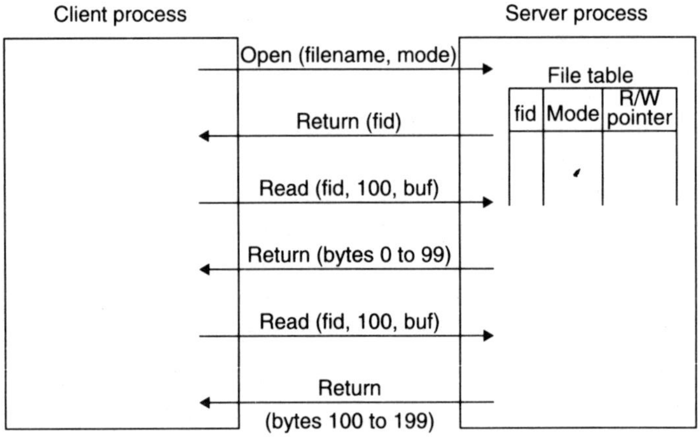


**Fig. 9.5** An example of a stateful file server.

### Stateless File Servers

A stateless file server does not maintain any client state information. Therefore every request from a client must be accompanied with all the necessary parameters to successfully carry out the desired operation. That is, each request identifies the file and the position in the file for the read/write access. For example, a server for byte-stream files that allows the following operations on files is stateless:

**Read** (*filename*, *position*, *n*, *buffer*): On execution of this operation, the server returns to the client *n* bytes of data of the file identified by *filename*. The returned data is placed in the specified *buffer*. The value of the actual number of bytes written is also returned to the client. The position within the file from where to begin reading is specified as the *position* parameter.

**Write** (*filename*, *position*, *n*, *buffer*): When the server executes this operation, it takes *n* bytes of data from the specified *buffer* and writes it into the file identified by *filename*. The *position* parameter specifies the byte position within the file from where to start writing. The server returns to the client the actual number of bytes written.

As shown in Figure 9.6, this file server does not keep track of any file state information resulting from a previous operation. Therefore, if a client wishes to have similar effect as that in Figure 9.5, the following two read operations must be carried out:

**Read** (*filename*, *0*, *100*, *buf*)
**Read** (*filename*, *100*, *100*, *buf*)

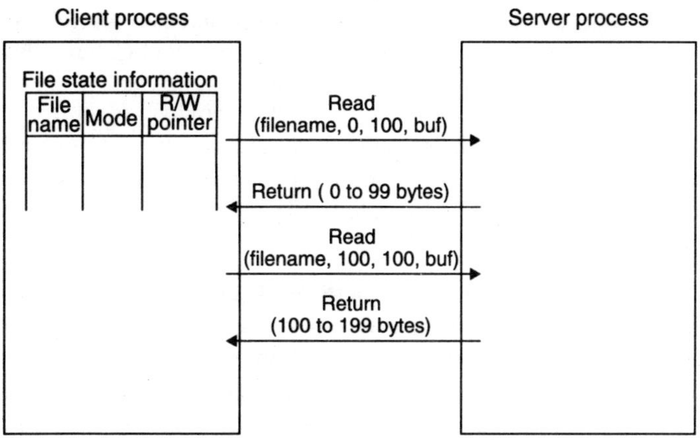


**Fig. 9.6** An example of a stateless file server.

Notice that in this case, there is no need to use the session concept with open and close operations because each file operation stands on its own. However, as shown in Figure 9.6, a client process normally keeps track of the state information of the files that are in use by it. Sun Microsystems' NFS uses stateless file servers [Sandberg et al. 1985].

### Advantages of Stateless Service Paradigm in Crash Recovery

The use of stateless file servers by many distributed file systems is justified by the fact that stateless servers have a distinct advantage over stateful servers in the event of a failure. For example, with stateful servers, if a server crashes and then restarts, the state information that it was holding may be lost and the client process might continue its task unaware of the crash, producing inconsistent results. Similarly, when a client process crashes and then restarts, the server is left holding state information that is no longer valid but cannot easily be withdrawn. Therefore, the stateful service paradigm requires complex crash recovery procedures. Both client and server need to reliably detect crashes. The server needs to detect client crashes so that it can discard any state it is holding for the client, and the client must detect server crashes so that it can perform necessary error-handling activities.

The stateless service paradigm makes crash recovery very easy because no client state information is maintained by the server and each request contains all the information that is necessary to complete the request. When a server crashes while serving a request, the client need only resend the request until the server responds, and the server does no crash recovery at all. When a client crashes during request processing, no recovery is necessary for either the client or the server. Therefore stateless servers can be constructed around repeatable operations. That is, if a client just resends a request until a response is received for it, data will never be lost due to a server crash.

The stateless service paradigm, however, imposes the following constraints on the design of the distributed file system [Silberschatz and Galvin 1994]:

1. Each request of the stateless service paradigm identifies the file by its *filename* instead of a low-level file identifier. If the translation of remote names to local names is done for each request, the request processing overhead will increase. To avoid the translation process, each file should have a systemwide unique low-level name associated with it.

2. The retransmission of requests by clients requires that the operations supported by stateless servers be idempotent. Recall that an idempotent operation has the same effect and returns the same output no matter how many times it is executed repeatedly. Self-contained read and write operations are idempotent, since they use an absolute byte count to indicate the position within a file and do not rely on an incremental offset. Similarly, operations to delete a file should also be made idempotent if the stateless service paradigm is used.

The stateless service paradigm also suffers from the drawbacks of longer request messages and slower processing of requests. Request messages are longer because every request must be accompanied with all the necessary parameters to successfully carry out the desired operation. On the other hand, request processing is slower because a stateless server does not maintain any state information to speed up the processing. Furthermore, in some cases, stateful service becomes necessary. For instance, in internetworks, messages may not be received in the same order in which they were sent. A stateful service is preferable in such a case, since by the maintained state it is possible to order the messages correctly (see Chapter 3). Similarly, if the file system uses the server-initiated cache validation approach, it cannot use the stateless service paradigm since the server has to maintain a record of which files are cached by which clients (see Section 9.6.3).

## 9.9 ATOMIC TRANSACTIONS

An *atomic transaction* (or just *transaction* for short) is a computation consisting of a collection of operations that take place indivisibly in the presence of failures and concurrent computations. That is, either all of the operations are performed successfully or none of their effects prevail, and other processes executing concurrently cannot modify or observe intermediate states of the computation. Transactions help to preserve the consistency of a set of shared data objects in the face of failures and concurrent access. They make crash recovery much easier, because a transaction can only end in two states—transaction carried out completely or transaction failed completely.

Transactions have the following essential properties:

1. *Atomicity.* This property ensures that to the outside world all the operations of a transaction appear to have been performed indivisibly. Two essential requirements for atomicity are atomicity with respect to failures and atomicity with respect to concurrent access. *Failure atomicity* ensures that if a transaction's work is interrupted by a failure, any partially completed results will be undone. Failure atomicity is also known as the *all-or-nothing property* because a transaction is always performed either completely or not at all. On the other hand, *concurrency atomicity* ensures that while a transaction is in progress, other processes executing concurrently with the transaction cannot modify or observe intermediate states of the transaction. Only the final state becomes visible to other processes after the transaction completes. Concurrency atomicity is also known as *consistency property* because a transaction moves the system from one consistent state to another.

2. *Serializability.* This property (also known as *isolation property*) ensures that concurrently executing transactions do not interfere with each other. That is, the concurrent execution of a set of two or more transactions is *serially equivalent* in the sense that the ultimate result of performing them concurrently is always the same as if they had been executed one at a time in some (system-dependent) order.

3. *Permanence.* This property (also known as *durability property*) ensures that once a transaction completes successfully, the results of its operations become permanent and cannot be lost even if the corresponding process or the processor on which it is running crashes.

To easily remember these properties, Harder and Reuter [1983] suggested the mnemonic ACID, where A, C, I, and D respectively stand for atomicity (failure atomicity), consistency (concurrency atomicity), isolation (serializability), and durability (permanence). Therefore, transaction properties are also referred to as *ACID properties.*

### 9.9.1 Need for Transactions in a File Service

The provision of transactions in a file service is needed for two main reasons:

1. For improving the recoverability of files in the event of failures. Due to the atomicity property of transactions, if a server or client process halts unexpectedly due to a hardware fault or a software error before a transaction is completed, the server subsequently restores any files that were undergoing modification to their original states. Notice that for a file service that does not support transaction facility, unexpected failure of the client or server process during the processing of an operation may leave the files that were undergoing modification in an inconsistent state. Without transaction facility, it may be difficult or even impossible in some cases to roll back (recover) the files from their current inconsistent state to their original state.

2. For allowing the concurrent sharing of mutable files by multiple clients in a consistent manner. If file access requests from multiple clients for accessing the same file are executed without synchronization, the sequences of read and write operations requested by different clients may be interleaved in many ways, some of which would not leave the file in the intended state. Therefore, unsynchronized execution of access requests from multiple clients, in general, results in unpredictable effects on the file. Transaction facility is basically a high-level synchronization mechanism that properly serializes the access requests from multiple clients to maintain the shared file in the intended consistent state.

The following examples illustrate how the transaction facility of a file service helps to prevent file inconsistencies arising from events beyond a client's control, such as machine or communication failures or concurrent access to files by other clients.

#### Inconsistency Due to System Failure

Consider the banking transaction of Figure 9.7, which is comprised of four operations ($a_1$, $a_2$, $a_3$, $a_4$) for transferring \$5 from account $X$ to account $Z$. Suppose that the customer account records are stored in a file maintained by the file server. Read/write access to customer account records are done by sending access requests to the file server. In the base file service without transaction facility, the job of transferring \$5 from account $X$ to account $Z$ will be performed by the execution of operations $a_1$, $a_2$, $a_3$, and $a_4$ in that order. Suppose the initial balance in both the accounts is \$100. Therefore, if all the four operations are performed successfully, the final balances in accounts $X$ and $Z$ will be \$95 and \$105, respectively. Now suppose a system failure occurs after operation $a_3$ has been successfully performed but before operation $a_4$ has been performed. In this situation, account $X$ will have

$a_1$: read balance ($x$) of account $X$
$a_2$: read balance ($z$) of account $Z$
$a_3$: write ($x - 5$) to account $X$
$a_4$: write ($z + 5$) to account $Z$

**Fig. 9.7** A set of operations to transfer \$5 from account $X$ to account $Z$.

been debited but account $Z$ will not have been credited. Therefore \$5 vanishes because the final balances in accounts $X$ and $Z$ are \$95 and \$100, respectively (Fig. 9.8). Successful reexecution of the four operations will cause the final balances in accounts $X$ and $Z$ to become \$90 and \$105, respectively, which is not what was intended.

Let the initial balance in both the accounts of Figure 9.7 be \$100.

<table>
<tr><th>Successful execution</th><th colspan="2">Unsuccessful execution</th></tr>
<tr><td>$a_1$: $x = 100$<br>$a_2$: $z = 100$<br>$a_3$: $x = 95$<br>$a_4$: $z = 105$</td><td colspan="2">$a_1$: $x = 100$<br>$a_2$: $z = 100$<br>$a_3$: $x = 95$<br>System crashes</td></tr>
<tr><th>Final result</th><th colspan="2">Final result</th></tr>
<tr><td rowspan="2">$x = 95$<br>$z = 105$</td><td>When the four operations are not treated as a transaction</td><td>When the four operations are treated as a transaction</td></tr>
<tr><td>$x = 95$<br>$z = 100$</td><td>$x = 100$<br>$z = 100$</td></tr>
</table>

**Fig. 9.8** Possible final results in successful and unsuccessful executions with and without transaction facility of the operations of Figure 9.7.

On the other hand, in a file service with transaction facility, the four operations $a_1$, $a_2$, $a_3$, and $a_4$ can be treated as a single transaction so that they can be performed indivisibly. In this case, if the transaction gets executed successfully, obviously the final balances of accounts $X$ and $Z$ will be \$95 and \$105, respectively. However, if the transaction fails in-between, the final balances in accounts $X$ and $Z$ will be rolled back to \$100 each, irrespective of what was the intermediate state of the balances in the two accounts when the failure occurred (Fig. 9.8). Therefore, in case of a failure, the balances of the two accounts remain unchanged and the reexecution of the transaction will not cause any inconsistency.

### Inconsistency Due to Concurrent Access

Consider the two banking transactions $T_1$ and $T_2$ of Figure 9.9. Transaction $T_1$, which is meant for transferring \$5 from account $X$ to account $Z$, consists of four operations $a_1$, $a_2$, $a_3$, and $a_4$. Similarly, transaction $T_2$, which is meant for transferring \$7 from account $Y$

$a_1$: read balance ($x$) of account $X$
$a_2$: read balance ($z$) of account $Z$
$a_3$: write ($x -$ 5) to account $X$
$a_4$: write ($z + 5$) to account $Z$

$T_1$ : Transfer $5 from account $X$ to account $Z$.

$b_1$: read balance ($y$) of account $Y$
$b_2$: read balance ($z$) of account $Z$
$b_3$: write ($y -$ 7) to account $Y$
$b_4$: write ($z + 7$) to account $Z$

$T_2$ : Transfer $7 from account $Y$ to account $Z$.

**Fig. 9.9** Two banking transactions.

to account $Z$, consists of four operations $b_1$, $b_2$, $b_3$, and $b_4$. The net effects of executing the two transactions should be the following:

- To decrease the balance in account $X$ by $5
- To decrease the balance in account $Y$ by $7
- To increase the balance in account $Z$ by $12

Assuming that the initial balance in all the three accounts is $100, the final balances of accounts $X$, $Y$, and $Z$ after the execution of the two transactions should be $95, $93, and $112, respectively.

In a base file service without transaction facility, if the operations corresponding to the two transactions are allowed to progress concurrently and if the file system makes no attempt to serialize the execution of these operations, unexpected final results may be obtained. This is because the execution of the operations corresponding to the two transactions may get interleaved in time in an arbitrary order. Two such possible interleavings that produce unexpected final results are shown in Figure 9.10. The cause of the error is that both clients are accessing the balance in account $Z$ and then altering it in a manner that depends on its previous value.

In a file service with transaction facility, the operations of each of the two transactions can be performed indivisibly, producing correct results irrespective of which transaction is executed first. Therefore, a transaction facility serializes the operations of multiple transactions to prevent file inconsistencies due to concurrent access. However, notice that the complete serialization of all transactions (completing one before the next one is allowed to commence) that access the same data is unnecessarily restrictive and can produce long delays in the completion of tasks. In many applications, it is possible to allow some parts of multiple concurrent transactions to be interleaved in time and still produce the correct result. For instance, two possible interleavings of the operations of the two transactions of Figure 9.9 that produce correct results are shown in Figure 9.11.

Let the initial balance in all the three accounts of the two transactions of Figure 9.9 be $100.

| An illegal schedule | Another illegal schedule |
|---|---|
| $a_1$: $x = 100$ | $b_1$: $y = 100$ |
| $b_1$: $y = 100$ | $b_2$: $z = 100$ |
| $a_2$: $z = 100$ | $a_1$: $x = 100$ |
| $b_2$: $z = 100$ | $a_2$: $z = 100$ |
| $a_3$: $x = 95$ | $b_3$: $y = 93$ |
| $b_3$: $y = 93$ | $b_4$: $z = 107$ |
| $a_4$: $z = 105$ | $a_3$: $x = 95$ |
| $b_4$: $z = 107$ | $a_4$: $z = 105$ |
| **Final result** | **Final result** |
| $x = 95$ | $x = 95$ |
| $y = 93$ | $y = 93$ |
| $z = 107$ | $z = 105$ |

Time

**Fig. 9.10** Two interleavings of the operations of the two transactions of Figure 9.9 that produce unexpected final results.

Let the initial balance in all the three accounts of the two transactions of Figure 9.9 be $100.

| A legal schedule | Another legal schedule |
|---|---|
| $a_1$: $x = 100$ | $b_1$: $y = 100$ |
| $b_1$: $y = 100$ | $b_2$: $z = 100$ |
| $a_2$: $z = 100$ | $a_1$: $x = 100$ |
| $a_3$: $x = 95$ | $b_3$: $y = 93$ |
| $a_4$: $z = 105$ | $b_4$: $z = 107$ |
| $b_2$: $y = 105$ | $a_2$: $z = 107$ |
| $b_3$: $z = 93$ | $a_3$: $x = 95$ |
| $b_4$: $z = 112$ | $a_4$: $z = 112$ |
| **Final result** | **Final result** |
| $x = 95$ | $x = 95$ |
| $y = 93$ | $y = 93$ |
| $z = 112$ | $z = 112$ |

Time

**Fig. 9.11** Two interleavings of the operations of the two transactions of Figure 9.9 that produce correct final results.

Any interleaving of the operations of two or more concurrent transactions is known as a *schedule*. All schedules that produce the same final result as if the transactions had been performed one at a time in some serial order are said to be serially equivalent. Serial equivalence is used as a criteria for the correctness of concurrently executing transactions. It is up to the system to ensure that a serially equivalent schedule is always selected to execute a set of concurrently executing transactions. By allowing the system the freedom to choose any ordering of the operations it wants to, provided it produces the correct final result, we eliminate the need for programmers to do their own mutual exclusion, thus simplifying the programming task.

### 9.9.2 Operations for Transaction-Based File Service

In a file system that provides a transaction facility, a transaction consists of a sequence of elementary file access operations such as read and write. The actual operations and their sequence that constitute a transaction is application dependent, and so it is the client's responsibility to construct transactions. Therefore, the client interface to such a file system must include special operations for transaction service. The three essential operations for transaction service are as follows:

**begin_transaction** → *returns* (*TID*): Begins a new transaction and returns a unique transaction identifier (TID). This identifier is used in other operations of this transaction. All operations within a *begin_transaction* and an *end_transaction* form the body of the transaction.

**end_transaction** (TID) → *returns* (*status*): This operation indicates that, from the viewpoint of the client, the transaction completed successfully. Therefore the transaction is terminated and an attempt is made to commit it. The returned status indicates whether the transaction has *committed* or is inactive because it was *aborted* by either the client or the server. If the transaction commits, all of its changes are made permanent and subsequent transactions will see the results of all the changes to files made by this transaction. On the other hand, if the transaction was aborted, none of the changes requested so far within the transaction will become visible to other transactions. A transaction is aborted either on explicit request by the client or in the event of system failures that disrupt the execution of the transaction.

**abort_transaction** (TID): Aborts the transaction, restores any changes made so far within the transaction to the original values, and changes its status to inactive. A transaction is normally aborted in the event of some system failure. However, a client may use this primitive to intentionally abort a transaction. For instance, consider the transaction of Figure 9.12, which consists of three write operations on a file. In Figure 9.12(*a*), all three operations are performed successfully, and after the *end_transaction* operation, the transaction makes the new file data visible to other transactions. However, in Figure 9.12(*b*), the third write operation could not succeed because of lack of sufficient disk space. Therefore, in this situation, the client may use the *abort_transaction* operation to abort the transaction so that the results of the two write operations are undone and the file contents is restored back to the value it

TID = **begin_ transaction**
**write**(TID, file, position, n, buffer) ⟶ returns (ok)
**write**(TID, file, position, n, buffer) ⟶ returns (ok)
**write**(TID, file, position, n, buffer) ⟶ returns (ok)
**end _ transaction** (TID)

(*a*)

TID = **begin_transaction**
**write**(TID, file, position, n, buffer) ⟶ returns (ok)
**write**(TID, file, position, n, buffer) ⟶ returns (ok)
**write**(TID, file, position, n, buffer) ⟶ returns (disk full error)
**abort _ transaction** (TID)

(*b*)

**Fig. 9.12** Illustrating the use of **abort_transaction** operation: (*a*) all three operations are performed successfully so the transaction commits; (*b*) all three operations could not be performed successfully so the transaction was aborted.

had before the transaction started. Notice that, once a transaction has been committed or aborted in the server, its state cannot be reversed by the client or the server. Consequently, an *abort_transaction* request would fail if a client issued it after that transaction had been committed.

In a file system with transaction facility, in addition to the three transaction service operations described above, the transaction service also has file access operations. Each file access operation of the transaction service corresponds to an elementary file service operation. The parameters of the file access operations of the transaction service are the same as those of the elementary file service operations except for an additional argument to specify the transaction identifier (TID) of the transaction to which the operation belongs. For instance, the following are file access operations for transaction service of the stateless server for the byte-stream files of Section 9.8.2:

**Tread** (*TID, filename, position, n, buffer*): Returns to the client *n* bytes of the tentative data resulting from the *TID* if any has been recorded; otherwise it has the same effect as **Read** (*filename, position, n, buffer*).

**Twrite** (*TID, filename, position, n, buffer*): Has the same effect as **Write** (*filename, position, n, buffer*) but records the new data in a tentative form that is made permanent only when the *TID* commits.

### 9.9.3 Recovery Techniques

From the point of view of a server, a transaction has two phases (Fig. 9.13). The first phase starts when the server receives a *begin_transaction* request from a client. In this phase, the file access operations in the transaction are performed and the client adds changes to file items progressively. On execution of the *end_transaction* or *abort_transaction* operation, the first phase ends and the second phase starts. In the second phase, the transaction is either committed or aborted. In a commit, the changes made by the transaction to file items are made permanent so as to make them visible to other transactions as well. On the other hand, in an abort, the changes made by the transaction to file items are undone to restore the files to the state they were in before the transaction started.

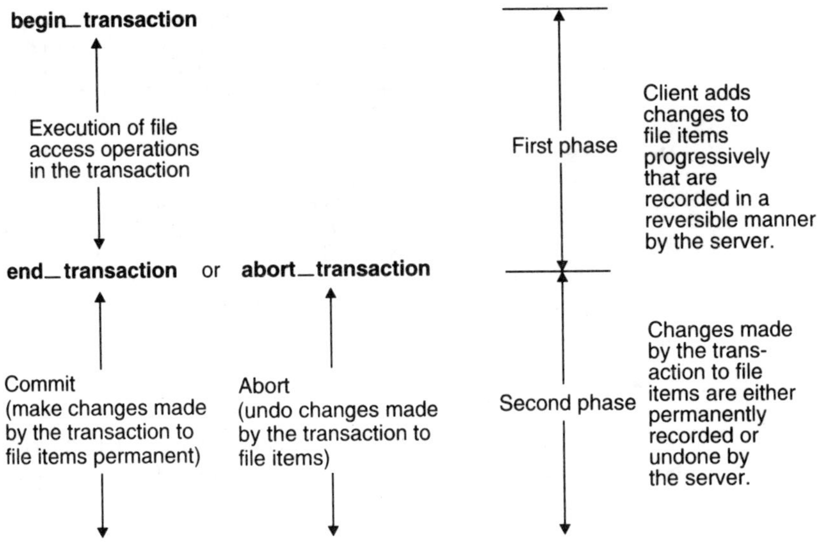


**Fig. 9.13** The two phases of a transaction.

The fact that in the second phase the transaction may either be committed or aborted requires that the file update operations in the first phase must be performed in such a way that they may be either permanently recorded or undone. Therefore, while a transaction is in its first phase, and hence subject to abortion, its updates must be recorded in a reversible manner. The two commonly used approaches for recording file updates in a reversible manner are the file versions approach and the write-ahead log approach.

### File Versions Approach

A basic technique to ensure file recoverability is to avoid overwriting the actual data in physical storage. The file versions approach is based on this technique. As shown in Figure 9.14, in this approach, when a transaction begins, the current file version is used for all file access operations (within the transaction) that do not modify the file. Recall that as soon as a transaction commits, the changes made by it to a file become public. Therefore, the current version of a file is the version produced by the most recently committed transaction.

When the first operation that modifies the file is encountered within the transaction, the server creates a tentative version of the file for the transaction from the current file version and performs the update operation on this version of the file. From now on, all subsequent file access operations (read or write) within the transaction are performed on this tentative file version. When the transaction is committed, the tentative file version is made the new current version and the previous current version of the file is added to the sequence of old versions. On the other hand, if the transaction is aborted, the tentative file version is simply discarded and the current file version continues to remain the current version.

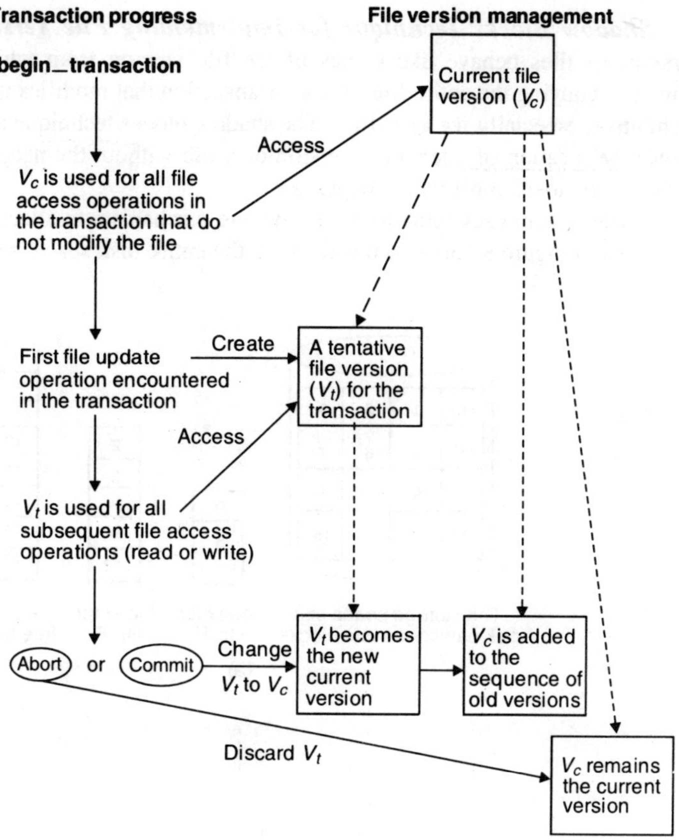


**Fig. 9.14** The file versions approach for recording file updates in a reversible manner.

Notice that a transaction can modify more than one file. In this situation, there is a tentative version of each file for the transaction. Furthermore, since a file may be involved in several concurrent transactions, it may have several tentative versions existing at the same time. In this situation, when one of the concurrent transactions commits, the tentative version corresponding to that transaction becomes the current version of the file. Since the remaining tentative versions of the file are no longer based on the current version, they are handled as follows. When the next transaction out of the concurrent transactions commits, and if there are no serializability conflicts between this transaction and the previously committed transactions, the tentative version corresponding to this transaction is merged with the current version, creating a new current version that includes the changes made by all of the transactions that have already committed. On the other hand, if there are serializability conflicts, all the transactions that are involved except the first one to commit are aborted. A *serializability conflict* occurs when two or more concurrent transactions are allowed to access the same data items in a file and one or more of these accesses is a write operation.

***Shadow Blocks Technique for Implementing File Versions.*** The tentative versions of files behave like copies of the file version from which they are derived. However, copying the entire file for each transaction that modifies it may be wasteful and prohibitive, especially for large files. The shadow blocks technique is an optimization that allows the creation of a tentative version of a file without the need to copy the full file. In fact, it removes most of the copying.

A file system uses some form of indexing mechanism to allocate disk space to files. As shown in Figure 9.15($a$), in this method, the entire disk space is partitioned into fixed-

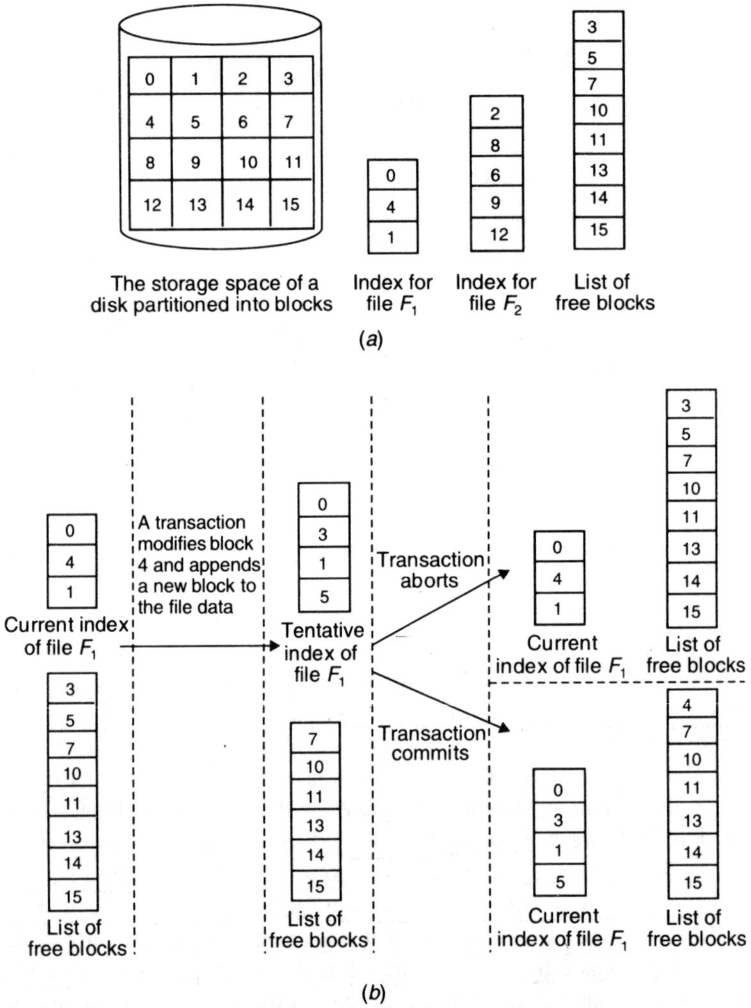


**Fig. 9.15** The shadow blocks technique for implementing file versions: ($a$) example of disk blocks, file indices, and list of free blocks; ($b$) allocation and deallocation of blocks as the transaction progresses.

length byte sequences called blocks. The file system maintains an index for each file and a list of free blocks. The index for a particular file specifies the block numbers and their exact sequence used for storing the file data. For example, in Figure 9.15(*a*), file $F_1$ uses the blocks numbered 0, 4, 1 in that sequence and file $F_2$ uses the blocks numbered 2, 8, 6, 9, 12 in that sequence. On the other hand, the list of free blocks contains the block numbers that are currently free and may be allocated to any file for storing new data.

In the shadow blocks technique, a tentative version of a file is created simply by copying the index of the current version of that file. That is, a tentative index of the file is created from its current index. Now when a file update operation affects a block, a new disk block is taken from the free list, the new tentative value is written in it, and the old block number in the tentative index is replaced by the block number of the new block [see Fig. 9.15(*b*)]. File update operations that append new data to the file are also handled in the same way by allocating new blocks from the free list for the appended data and extending the tentative index of the file. The new blocks allocated to a tentative version of a file are called *shadow blocks*. Subsequent writes to the same file block by the transaction are performed on the same shadow block.

All file access operations in the transaction are performed by using the tentative index while file access operations of other processes are performed by using the current index. Therefore, the process running the transaction sees the modified file version, but all other processes continue to see the original file version. Notice that unmodified file blocks are shared between these two file versions.

As shown in Figure 9.15(*b*), if the transaction aborts, the shadow blocks of the tentative version of the file are returned to the list of free blocks and the tentative index is simply discarded. On the other hand, if the transaction commits, the tentative index is made the current index of the file, and if there is no need to retain the old file version, the blocks of the original file version whose data were modified by the transaction are added to the list of free blocks and the old current index is discarded.

### The Write-Ahead Log Approach

Another commonly used technique for recording file updates in a recoverable manner is the write-ahead log approach. In this method, for each operation of a transaction that modifies a file, a record is first created and written to a log file known as a *write-ahead log*. After this, the operation is performed on the file to modify its contents.

A write-ahead log is maintained on stable storage and contains a record for each operation that makes changes to files. Each record contains the identifier of the transaction that is making the modification, the identifier of the file that is being modified, the items of the file that are being modified, and the old and new values of each item modified.

To illustrate how the log works, let us again consider the transaction for transferring $5 from account *X* to account *Z*. As shown in Figure 9.16, for each operation of the transaction that makes changes to file items, a record is first created and written to the write-ahead log. In each record, the old and new values of each item modified by the operation are separated by a slash.

When the transaction commits, a commit record is written to the write-ahead log. Notice that since the changes due to update operations were made on the file itself, there

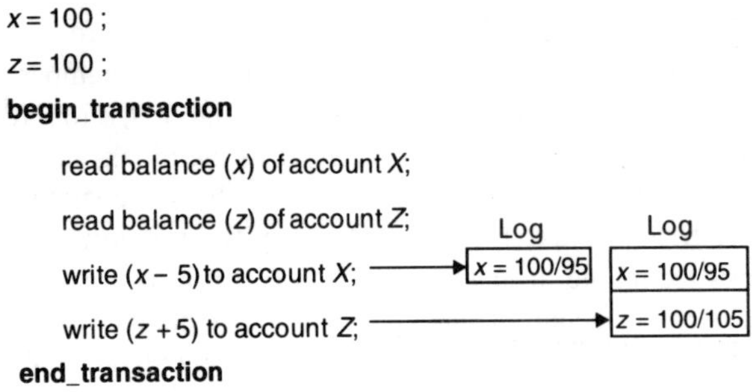
x = 100 ;
z = 100 ;
begin_transaction
read balance (x) of account X;
read balance (z) of account Z;
write (x − 5) to account X;
write (z + 5) to account Z;
end_transaction
Log
x = 100/95
Log
x = 100/95
z = 100/105

**Fig. 9.16** An example of creation of write-ahead log records.

is no need to change the file items when the transaction commits. On the other hand, if the transaction aborts, the information in the write-ahead log is used to roll back the individual file items to their initial values, thus bringing the files affected by the transaction to their original state. For rollback, the write-ahead log records are used one by one, starting from the last record and going backward, to undo the changes described in them.

The write-ahead log also facilitates recovery from crashes. For instance, suppose the server process handling the transaction of Figure 9.16 crashes after writing the log record for the second write operation in the transaction. After the server's machine is restarted, the write-ahead log is used to identify the exact point of failure. For this, the value of the changed data item in the last record of the log (in this case $z$) is compared with its value in the file. One of the following actions are taken depending on the status of the file:

1. If the value in the file is 100, it means that the crash occurred before the file was updated. Therefore, the value of the data item in the file is changed to 105.
2. On the other hand, if the value in the file is 105, it means that the crash occurred after the file was updated, so nothing needs to be done in this case.

### 9.9.4 Concurrency Control

Serializability is an important property of atomic transactions that ensures that concurrently executing transactions do not interfere with each other. However, we have seen in the example of Figure 9.10 that if the operations of two or more concurrent transactions accessing the same data item are allowed to progress uncontrolled, the operations of these transactions may get interleaved in time in an arbitrary order, producing unexpected final results. Therefore, to prevent data inconsistency due to concurrent access by multiple transactions, every transaction mechanism needs to implement a concurrency control algorithm.

A good concurrency control mechanism allows maximum concurrency with minimum overhead while ensuring that transactions are run in a manner so that their effects on shared data are serially equivalent. The simplest approach for concurrency control would be to allow the transactions to be run one at a time so that two transactions never run concurrently and hence there is no conflict. However, this approach is not good because it does not allow any concurrency. Total elimination of concurrency is neither acceptable nor necessary because a transaction normally accesses only a few of the large number of files available in a system. This observation gives rise to another simple approach to concurrency control. Two transactions should be allowed to run concurrently only if they do not use a common file (or data item in general). Although better than the previous approach, this approach is also unnecessarily restrictive because a pair of transactions may access the same data item in a manner that does not cause any conflict (inconsistency of the data item). Furthermore, it is usually not possible to predict which data items will be used by a transaction. Therefore, more flexible concurrency control algorithms are normally used by a transaction mechanism. The most commonly used ones are locking, optimistic concurrency control, and timestamps. Descriptions of these three approaches follow.

### Locking

This is the oldest and the most widely used approach. In the basic locking mechanism, a transaction locks a data item before accessing it. Each lock is labeled with the transaction identifier and only the transaction that locked the data item can access it any number of times. Other transactions that want to access the same data item must wait until the data item is unlocked. All data items locked by a transaction are unlocked as soon as the transaction completes (commits or aborts). Locking is performed by the transaction service as a part of the data access operations, and clients have no access to operations for locking or unlocking data items.

***Optimized Locking for Better Concurrency.*** The basic locking scheme is too restrictive and some optimizations have been proposed for better concurrency. Two of them are described below.

1. *Type-specific locking*. A simple lock that is used for all types of accesses to data items reduces concurrency more than is necessary. Better concurrency can be achieved by using type-specific locking scheme in which more than one type of locks are used based on the semantics of access operations. For instance, let us consider the simple case of two types of access operations *read* and *write*. Notice that multiple transactions that read the same data item but never write on it do not conflict. Therefore, when a transaction is accessing a data item in the read-only mode, there is no reason to keep those transactions waiting that also want to access the data item in the read-only mode. Therefore, instead of using a single lock for both read and write accesses, separate locks (read locks and write locks) should be used for the two operations. With these two types of locks, the locking rules are given in Figure 9.17. If a read lock is set on a data item, other read locks are permitted but write locks are not permitted. Therefore, an item locked with a read lock cannot have its value changed by other transactions. On the other hand, when a write lock is set, no other locks of any kind are permitted. Therefore, a data item locked with a write lock cannot be accessed (read or written) by another transaction.

2. *Intention-to-write locks*. Recall that a transaction has two phases and the updates made by a transaction to a data item are tentative in the first phase and are made permanent only in the second phase. Each transaction is unable to observe the other

| Type of lock already set | Type of lock to be set | |
|---|---|---|
| | Read | Write |
| None | Permitted | Permitted |
| Read | Permitted | Not permitted |
| Write | Not permitted | Not permitted |

**Fig. 9.17** Locking rules in case of read locks and write locks.

transactions' tentative values. Therefore, when a read lock is set, instead of preventing any other transaction from writing the locked data item, a transaction should be allowed to proceed with its tentative writes until it is ready to commit. The value of the item will not actually change until the writing transaction commits, so, if it is suspended at that point, the item remains unchanged until the reading transaction releases its lock.

Based on the observation above, for better concurrency, Gifford [1979b] proposed the use of an "intention-to-write lock" (*I-write*) and a *commit* lock instead of a write lock. Therefore, three types of locks are used in this scheme, and the locking rules for them are given in Figure 9.18. Notice that if a read lock is set, an I-write lock is permitted on the data item and vice versa. This is because the effects of write are not observable by any other transaction until the writing transaction commits. If an I-write lock is set, no other transaction is allowed to have an I-write lock on the same data item. A commit lock is not permitted if any other type of lock is already set on the data item. Therefore, when a

| Type of lock already set | Type of lock to be set | | |
|---|---|---|---|
| | Read | I-write | Commit |
| None | Permitted | Permitted | Permitted |
| Read | Permitted | Permitted | Not permitted |
| I-write | Permitted | Not permitted | Not permitted |
| Commit | Not permitted | Not permitted | Not permitted |

**Fig. 9.18** Locking rules in case of read locks, I-write locks, and commit locks.

transaction having an I-write lock commits, its I-write lock is converted to a commit lock, so that if there are any outstanding read locks, the transaction must wait until it is possible to set the commit lock.

***Two-Phase Locking Protocol.*** Because of the potential for increased concurrency, it is tempting to lock a data item for use by a transaction only for the period during which the transaction actually works on it and to release the lock as soon as the access operation is over. However, locking and unlocking data items precisely at the moment they are needed (or no longer needed) can lead to inconsistency problems. For instance, two commonly encountered problems due to early release (releasing immediately after the access operation finishes) of read locks and write locks are as follows:

1. Possibility of reading inconsistent data in case of two or more read accesses by the same transaction. This is because when read locks and write locks are released early, between two subsequent read accesses to the same data item by a transaction, another transaction may update the same data item and commit. Therefore, the second read may not see the same value of the data item as the first read. Notice that if a transaction reads a data item only once per transaction, there is no harm in releasing its read lock early.

2. Need for cascaded aborts. Suppose a transaction releases a write lock early and then some other transaction locks the same data item, performs all its work, and commits before the first transaction. Afterward, suppose the first transaction aborts. In this situation, the already committed transaction must now be undone because its results are based on a value of the data item that it should never have seen. Aborting of already committed transactions when a transaction aborts is known as *cascaded aborting*. Because of the large overhead involved in cascaded aborting, it is better to avoid it.

To avoid the data inconsistency problems, transaction systems use the two-phase locking protocol. In the first phase of a transaction, known as the *growing phase*, all locks needed by the transaction are gradually acquired. Then in the second phase of the transaction, known as the *shrinking phase*, the acquired locks are released. Therefore, once a transaction has released any of its locks, it cannot request any more locks on the same or other data items. It has been proved [Eswaran et al. 1976] that if all transactions use the two-phase locking protocol, all schedules formed by interleaving their operations are serializable.

***Granularity of Locking.*** The granularity of locking refers to the unit of lockable data items. In a file system supporting transactions, this unit is normally an entire file, a page, or a record. If many transactions share files, the granularity of locking can have a significant impact on how many transactions can be executed concurrently. For instance, if locks can be applied only to whole files, concurrency gets severely restricted due to the increased possibility of false sharing. *False sharing* occurs when two different transactions access two unrelated data items that reside in the same file (Fig. 9.19). In such a situation, even though the two data items can be accessed concurrently by the two transactions, this is not allowed because the granularity of locking is a file. Notice that the locking granularity increases concurrency by reducing the possibility of false sharing.

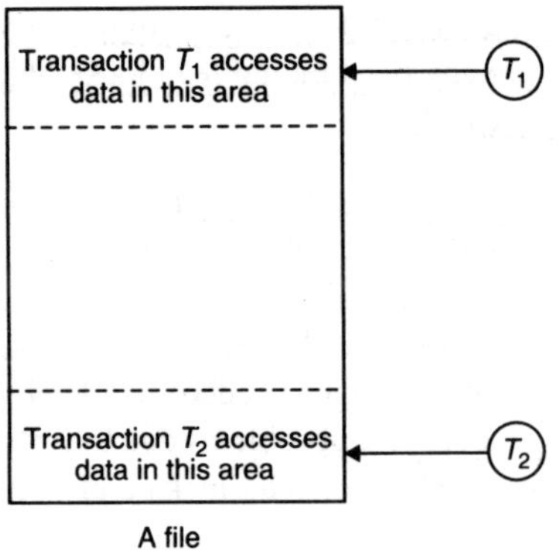


**Fig. 9.19** False sharing.

However, finer locking granularity leads to larger lock management overhead, complicates implementation of recoverable files, and is more likely to lead to deadlocks.

***Handling of Locking Deadlocks.*** The locking scheme can lead to deadlocks. A *deadlock* is a state in which a transaction waits for a data item locked by another transaction that in turn waits, perhaps via a chain of other waiting transactions, for the first transaction to release some of its locks. Since a transaction cannot release any lock until it finishes, none of the transactions involved in such a circular wait can proceed unless one of them is aborted. For example, suppose two transactions $T_1$ and $T_2$ have locked data items $D_1$ and $D_2$, respectively. Now suppose that $T_1$ requests a lock on $D_2$ and $T_2$ requests a lock on $D_1$. A deadlock results because each transaction has an item of data locked that the other needs to access.

A detailed description of the commonly used techniques for handling deadlocks was presented in Chapter 6. In transactions, one of the following techniques may be used:

1. *Avoidance*. One method to handle the deadlock problem is to prevent deadlocks. Deadlocks can be prevented by enforcing that requests to lock data items be always made in a predefined order so that there can be no cycle in the who-waits-for-whom graph. Although the method is quite effective, it may cause data items to be locked too soon, resulting in reduced concurrency.

2. *Detection*. Deadlocks can be detected by constructing and checking who-waits-for-whom graph. A cycle in the graph indicates the existence of a deadlock. When such a cycle is detected, the server must select and abort a transaction out of the transactions involved in the cycle.

3. *Timeouts*. Associating a timeout period with each lock is another method for handling deadlocks. That is, a lock remains invulnerable for a fixed period, after which it becomes vulnerable. A data item with a vulnerable lock remains locked if no other transaction is waiting for it to get unlocked. Otherwise, the lock is broken (the data item is unlocked) and the waiting process is permitted to lock the data item for accessing it. The transaction whose lock has been broken is normally aborted.

Three major drawbacks of the timeout approach are (a) it is hard to decide the length of the timeout period for a lock; (b) in an overloaded system, the number of transactions getting aborted due to timeouts will increase, resulting in increased overhead for rerunning the aborted transactions; and (c) the method favors short transactions over long transactions because transactions taking a long time are more likely to be penalized.

## Optimistic Concurrency Control

This approach for concurrency control by Kung and Robinson [1981] is based on the observation that access conflicts in concurrently executing transactions are very rare. Therefore, in this approach, transactions are allowed to proceed uncontrolled up to the end of the first phase. However, in the second phase, before a transaction is committed, the transaction is validated to see if any of its data items have been changed by any other transaction since it started. The transaction is committed if found valid; otherwise it is aborted.

For the validation process, two records are kept of the data items accessed within a transaction—a *read set* that contains the data items read by the transaction and a *write set* that contains the data items changed, created, or deleted by the transaction. To validate a transaction, its read set and write set are compared with the write sets of all of the concurrent transactions that reached the end of their first phase before it. The validation fails if any data item present in the read set or write set of the transaction being validated is also present in the write set of any of the concurrent transactions mentioned above.

Two main advantages of the optimistic concurrency control approach are as follows:

1. It allows maximum parallelism because all transactions are allowed to proceed independently in parallel without any need to wait for a lock.
2. It is free from deadlock.

However, it suffers from the following drawbacks:

1. It requires that old versions of files corresponding to recently committed transactions be retained for the validation process. This is not necessary either with locking or timestamping.

2. Although the approach is free from deadlock, it may cause the starvation of a transaction. This is because a transaction that fails validation is aborted and then restarted all over again. But if the transaction comes into conflict with other transactions for the use of data items each time it is restarted, it can never pass the validation checks.

To solve the starvation problem, Kung and Robinson suggested that the server should detect a transaction that has been aborted several times. When such a transaction is detected, it should be given exclusive access to the data items it uses by the use of a critical section protected by a semaphore.

3. In an overloaded system, the number of transactions getting aborted due to access conflicts may go up substantially, resulting in increased overhead for rerunning the

aborted transactions. Optimistic concurrency control is not a suitable approach for such situations.

Mullender and Tanenbaum [1985] suggested that locking should be used in transactions in which several files are changed and where the chance of two transactions using the same data item is high. On the other hand, optimistic concurrency control should be used for transactions using one file and in which the likelihood of two transactions accessing the same data item is low.

### Timestamps

In the optimistic concurrency control approach, a transaction is validated only after it has completed its first phase. If the validation fails because some conflict is detected, the transaction is aborted and restarted all over again. Execution of operations of the transaction that follow the operation that caused the conflict is actually a waste in this case. Notice that the overhead involved in executing the operations of the transaction that follow the operation that caused the conflict can be totally avoided if it is possible to detect the conflict right at the time when the operation causing it is executed. This is because the transaction can be aborted immediately at the point where the conflict occurs and it can then be restarted. This has been made possible in the timestamps approach, in which each operation in a transaction is validated when it is carried out. If the validation fails, the transaction is aborted immediately and it can then be restarted.

To perform validation at the operation level, each transaction is assigned a unique timestamp at the moment it does *begin_transaction*. In addition, every data item has a *read timestamp* and a *write timestamp* associated with it. When a transaction accesses a data item, depending on the type of access (read or write), the data item's read timestamp or write timestamp is updated to the transaction's timestamp.

As usual, the write operations of a transaction are recorded tentatively and are invisible to other transactions until the transaction commits. Therefore, when a transaction is in progress, there will be a number of data items with tentative values and write timestamps. The tentative values and timestamps become permanent when the transaction commits.

Before performing a read operation or a write operation on a data item, the server performs a validation check by inspecting the timestamps on the data item, including the timestamps on its tentative values that belong to incomplete transactions. The rules for validation are as follows:

***Validation of a Write Operation.*** If the timestamp of the current transaction (transaction that requested the write operation) is either equal to or more recent than the read and (committed) write timestamps of the accessed data item, the write operation passes the validation check. Therefore a tentative write operation is performed in this case. On the other hand, if the timestamp of the current transaction is older than the timestamp of the last read or committed write of the data item, the validation fails. This is because another transaction has accessed the data item since the current transaction started. Therefore the current transaction is aborted in this case.

***Validation of a Read Operation.*** If the timestamp of the current transaction (transaction that requested the read operation) is more recent than the write timestamps of all committed and tentative values of the accessed data item, the read operation passes the validation check. However, the read operation can be performed immediately only if there are no tentative values of the data item; otherwise it must wait until the completion of the transactions having tentative values of the data item. On the other hand, the validation check fails and the current transaction is aborted in the following cases:

1. The timestamp of the current transaction is older than the timestamp of the most recent (committed) write to the data item.
2. The timestamp of the current transaction is older than that of a tentative value of the data item made by another transaction, although it is more recent than the timestamp of the permanent data item.

Notice that in the approach described above, a transaction can complete its first phase only if all its operations have been consistent with those of earlier transactions. Therefore, if a transaction completes its first phase, it can always be committed, although it may have to wait for earlier transactions that have tentative copies of shared data items to commit.

The timestamp-based concurrency control scheme described above is used in the SDD-1 database system [Bernstein et al. 1980]. A similar scheme using timeouts is described in [Reed 1983]. Timestamp-based concurrency control schemes are deadlock free.

### 9.9.5 Distributed Transaction Service

Distributed file systems having transaction facility need to support distributed transaction service. A distributed transaction service is an extension of the conventional transaction service, which can support transactions involving files managed by more than one server. When a transaction involves multiple servers, all the servers need to communicate with one another to coordinate their actions during the processing of the transaction so as to achieve recoverability and concurrency control over the entire set of file operations in the transaction.

A simple approach to coordinate the actions of multiple servers involved in a distributed transaction would be to enforce that all client requests pass through a single server. However, to avoid unnecessary communication overhead, a distributed transaction service normally allows client requests to be sent directly to the server that holds the relevant file instead of directing them via a single server. This approach is described below. The description is based on the concepts introduced in [Israel et al. 1978] and used in the XDFS file service [Mitchell and Dion 1982, Sturgis et al. 1980].

In a distributed transaction service, a client begins a transaction by sending a *begin_transaction* request to any server. The contacted server executes the *begin_transaction* request and returns the resulting TID to the client. This server becomes the *coordinator* for the transaction and is responsible for aborting or committing it and for adding other servers called *workers*.

Workers are dynamically added to the transaction. For this, a distributed transaction service has a new operation in addition to the operations of a traditional transaction service: The request

**add_transaction** (TID, server_id of coordinator)

informs a server that it is involved in the TID.

Before an access request is sent to a server that has not yet joined the transaction, an *add_transaction* request is sent to the server. When the server receives the *add_transaction* request, it records the server identifier of the coordinator, makes a new transaction record containing the TID, and initializes a new log to record the updates to local files from the transaction. It also makes a call to the coordinator to inform it of its intention to join the transaction. In this manner, each worker comes to know about the coordinator and the coordinator comes to know about and keeps a list of all the workers involved in the transaction. This information enables the coordinator and the workers of the transaction to coordinate with each other at commit time.

### Two-Phase Multiserver Commit Protocol

The most crucial part in the design of a distributed transaction service is the committing of distributed transactions. In a distributed transaction, since the files changed within the transaction are stored on multiple servers, the commit protocol becomes more complicated. A crash of one server does not normally affect other servers, and hence the commit protocol must ensure that the transaction is not committed and its changes to the files are completed on some servers if it cannot be completed on all servers involved.

The general protocol for committing distributed transactions has two phases. The two-phase multiserver commit protocol given in [Gray 1978] is described below.

When the client of a distributed transaction makes an *end_transaction* request, the coordinator and the workers in the transaction have tentative values in their logs describing the operations that affect their own files. The coordinator is responsible for deciding whether the transaction should be aborted or committed; if any server is unable to commit, the whole transaction must be aborted. Therefore, the *end_transaction* operation is performed in two phases—preparation phase and commitment phase. The actions involved in each phase are described below.

***Preparation Phase.***

1. The coordinator makes an entry in its log that it is starting the commit protocol.
2. It then sends a *prepare* message to all the workers telling them to prepare to commit. The message has a timeout value associated with it.
3. When a worker gets the message, it checks to see if it is ready to commit (i.e., it has not previously aborted its part of the transaction). If so, it makes an entry in its log and replies with a *ready* message. Otherwise, it replies with an *abort* message.

***Commitment Phase.*** At this point, the coordinator has received a *ready* or *abort* reply from each worker or the *prepare* message has timed out:

1. If all the workers are ready to commit, the transaction is committed. For this, the coordinator makes an entry in its log indicating that the transaction has been committed. It then sends a *commit* message to the workers asking them to commit. At this point, the transaction is effectively completed, so the coordinator can report success to the client.

   On the other hand, if any of the replies was *abort* or the *prepare* message of any worker got timed out, the transaction is aborted. For this, the coordinator makes an entry in its log indicating that the transaction has been aborted. It then sends an *abort* message to the workers asking them to abort and reports failure to the client.

2. When a worker receives the *commit* message, it makes a *committed* entry in its log and sends a *committed* reply to the coordinator. At this point, the part of the transaction with the worker is treated as completed and its records maintained by the worker are erased.

3. When the coordinator has received a *committed* reply from all the workers, the transaction is considered complete, and all its records maintained by the coordinator are erased. The coordinator keeps resending the *commit* message until it receives the *committed* reply from all the workers.

### 9.9.6 Nested Transactions

*Nested transactions* are a generalization of traditional transactions in which a transaction may be composed of other transactions called *subtransactions*. A subtransaction may in turn have its own subtransactions. In this way, transactions can be nested arbitrarily deep, forming a family of transactions.

Tree terminology is normally used in describing relationships among the transactions belonging to the same family. When a transaction starts, it consists of only one transaction (process) called the *top-level transaction*. This transaction may fork off children, giving rise to subtransactions. Each of these children may again fork off its own children, giving rise to a further level of subtransactions. When a transaction forks a subtransaction, it is called the *parent* of the subtransaction and the subtransaction is referred to as its *child*. The terms *ancestors* and *descendants* are also used. A transaction is an ancestor and a descendant of itself.

#### Committing of Nested Transactions

In a nested-transactions system, a transaction may commit only after all its descendants have committed. However, a transaction may abort at any time. Therefore, in order for an entire transaction family to commit, its top-level transaction must wait for other transactions in the family to commit.

A subtransaction appears atomic to its parent. That is, the operations it performs take place indivisibly with respect to both failures and concurrent computations just as for traditional transactions. Therefore, the changes made to data items by the subtransaction become visible to its parent only after the subtransaction commits and notifies this to its parent. As a result, the actual committing of any updates performed by the subtransaction is contingent upon the commit of each ancestor transaction all the way up to the top-level transaction.

On the other hand, if a failure occurs that causes a subtransaction to abort before its completion, all of its tentative updates are undone, and its parent is notified. The parent may then choose to continue processing and try to complete its task using an alternative method or it may abort itself. Therefore, the abort of a subtransaction may not necessarily cause its ancestors to abort. However, if a failure causes an ancestor transaction to abort, the updates of all its descendant transactions (that have already committed) have to be undone. Thus no updates performed within an entire transaction family are made permanent until the top-level transaction commits. Only after the top-level transaction commits is success reported to the client.

### Advantages of Nested Transactions

Nested-transactions facility is considered to be an important extension to the traditional transaction facility (especially in distributed systems) due to its following main advantages:

1. It allows concurrency within a transaction. That is, a transaction may generate several subtransactions that run in parallel on different processors. Notice that all children of a parent transaction are synchronized so that the parent transaction still exhibits serializability.

2. It provides greater protection against failures, in that it allows checkpoints to be established within a transaction. This is because the subtransactions of a parent transaction fail independently of the parent transaction and of one another. Therefore, when a subtransaction aborts, its parent can still continue and may fork an alternative subtransaction in place of the failed subtransaction in order to complete its task.

## 9.10 DESIGN PRINCIPLES

Based on his experience with the AFS and other distributed file systems, Satyanarayanan [1992] has stated the following general principles for designing distributed file systems:

1. *Clients have cycles to burn.* This principle says that, if possible, it is always preferable to perform an operation on a client's own machine rather than performing it on a server machine. This is because a server is a common resource for all clients, and hence cycles of a server machine are more precious than the cycles of client machines. This principle aims at enhancing the scalability of the design, since it lessens the need to increase centralized (commonly used) resources and allows graceful degradation of system performance as the system grows in size.

2. *Cache whenever possible*. Better performance, scalability, user mobility, and site autonomy motivate this principle. Caching of data at clients' sites frequently improves overall system performance because it makes data available wherever it is being currently used, thus saving a large amount of computing time and network bandwidth. Caching also enhances scalability because it reduces contention on centralized resources.

3. *Exploit usage properties*. This principle says that, depending on usage properties (access and modification patterns), files should be grouped into a small number of easily identifiable classes, and then class-specific properties should be exploited for independent optimization for improved performance. For example, files known to be frequently read and modified only once in a while can be treated as immutable files for read-only replication. Files containing the object code of system programs are good candidates for this class.

Notice that the use of different mechanisms for handling files belonging to different classes for improved performance makes the design of a file system complex. Hence, for simplicity of design, some designers prefer to use a single mechanism for handling all files.

4. *Minimize systemwide knowledge and change*. This principle is aimed at enhancing the scalability of design. The larger is a distributed system, the more difficult it is to be aware at all times of the entire state of the system and to update distributed or replicated data structures in a consistent manner. Therefore, monitoring or automatically updating of global information should be avoided as far as practicable. The callback approach for cache validation and the use of negative rights in an access control list (ACL) based access control mechanism (described in Chapter 11) are two instances of the application of this principle. The use of hierarchical system structure is also an application of this principle.

5. *Trust the fewest possible entities*. This principle is aimed at enhancing the security of the system. For example, it is much simpler to ensure security based on the integrity of the much smaller number of servers rather than trusting thousands of clients. In this case, it is sufficient to only ensure the physical security of these servers and the software they run.

6. *Batch if possible*. Batching often helps in improving performance greatly. For example, grouping operations together can improve throughput, although it is often at the cost of latency. Similarly, transfer of data across the network in large chunks rather than as individual pages is much more efficient. The full file transfer protocol is an instance of the application of this principle.

## 9.11 CASE STUDY: DCE DISTRIBUTED FILE SERVICE

Two of the popular commercial file systems for distributed computing systems are Sun Microsystems' Network File System (NFS) and Open Software Foundation's Distributed File Service (DFS). DFS is one of the many services supported by Distributed Computing Environment (DCE).

As a case study of how the concepts and the mechanisms described in this chapter can be used to build a distributed file system, DFS is briefly described below. A good description of NFS can be found in [Khanna 1994, Sandberg 1987, Sandberg et al. 1985]. However, in the following description of DFS, the major differences with NFS have also been pointed out.

DCE's DFS has several attractive features and promises to play a major role in future distributed computing environments. It is derived from the CMU Andrew File System (AFS) but possesses many new features. For instance, AFS supports session semantics for shared files, but DFS supports more accurate single-site UNIX semantics.

DFS is basically a DCE application that makes use of other services of DCE. It uses DCE threads to handle multiple file access requests simultaneously, Remote Procedure Call (RPC) for client-server communication during file access operations, Distributed Time Service (DTS) for synchronization of the clocks of multiple servers, security service for client-server authentication and authorization at the time of file access requests, and directory service to provide a single global name space for all files so that any file in the entire system can be accessed by any client from any cell by simply specifying the file name.

DFS has been designed to allow multiple file systems to simultaneously exist on a node of a DCE system. For example, UNIX, NFS, and DFS's own file system can coexist on a node to provide three different types of file systems to the users of that node. The local file system of DFS that provides DFS on a single node is called *Episode* [Chutani et al. 1992]. As may be expected, when multiple file systems coexist on a node, features specific to DFS are available only to those users who use the Episode file system. DFS features are not available to the users of other file systems.

### 9.11.1 DFS File Model

Like UNIX, DFS uses the unstructured file model in which a file is an unstructured sequence of data. A DFS file server handles the contents of a file as an uninterpreted sequence of bytes. A single file can contain up to $2^{42}$ bytes.

Like UNIX, DFS also uses the mutable file model. That is, for each file there is just one stored sequence that is altered by update operations. Note that although DFS uses the mutable file model, it has a facility called *cloning* (described later) that allows two stored sequences of a file to exist simultaneously; one of these is the version of the file before cloning and the other contains the changes made to the file after cloning.

### 9.11.2 DFS File System Model

As shown in Figure 9.20, the DFS file system model has four levels of aggregation. At the lowest level are individual *files*. At the next level are *directories*. Each directory usually contains several files. Above directories are *filesets*. Each fileset usually contains several directories. Finally, at the highest level is an *aggregate* that usually contains multiple filesets. Each disk partition holds exactly one aggregate.

Like a file system of UNIX, a fileset is a group of files that are administered (moved, replicated, backed up, etc.) as a set. However, unlike UNIX, a fileset is normally a subtree of a file system and not the entire file system tree. For example, a fileset may contain all the files of a single user, or all the files of a group of related

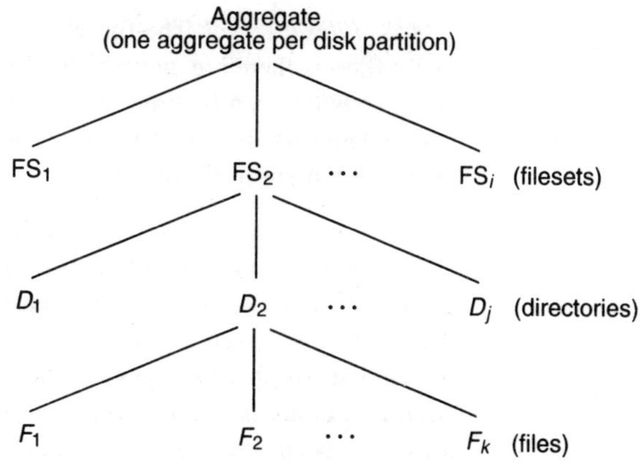


**Fig. 9.20** Four levels of aggregation in the DFS file system model.

users. With this difference, DFS allows multiple filesets per disk partition, a management advantage over UNIX or NFS, which allow only a single file system per disk partition. The main advantage is that disk space can be more efficiently utilized by dynamically rebalancing the space occupancy of different partitions by moving filesets from nearly full partitions to relatively empty partitions as and when needed.

### 9.11.3 DFS File-Accessing Model

Distributed File Service relies on a client-server architecture and uses the data-caching model for file accessing. A machine in a DCE system is a DFS client, a DFS server, or both. A DFS client is a machine that uses files in filesets managed by DFS servers. The main software component of a DFS client machine is the DFS *cache manager*, which caches parts of recently used files to improve performance.

On the other hand, a DFS server is a machine having its own disk storage that manages files in the filesets stored on its local disk and services requests received from DFS clients. A DFS server machine has the following software components:

1. *Episode*. This is the DFS local file system.

2. *Token manager*. The token manger is used to implement the token-based approach for handling multicache consistency problems (this approach is described later).

3. *File exporter*. The file exporter accepts file access requests from clients and returns replies to them. The interaction between clients and the file exporter is done using DCE RPC. In addition to handling requests for the Episode files, the file exporter also handles requests for all the other file systems that exist on that node. It also handles client authentication for establishing secure communication channels between clients and the DFS server. The file exporter is multithreaded so that several client requests can be handled simultaneously.

4. *Fileset server.* The fileset server manages the local filesets. It keeps track of how many filesets there are and which fileset belongs to which disk partition. It also provides commands that can be used by the system administrator to obtain fileset information, to manipulate disk quotas of filesets, and to create, delete, duplicate, move, backup, clone, or restore an entire fileset.

5. *Fileset location server.* The fileset location server keeps information about which DFS servers are managing which filesets in the cell. If a fileset is moved from one DFS server to another or is replicated on another DFS server, the fileset location server records these changes. Given the name of a file, the fileset location server returns the address of the DFS server that manages the fileset that contains the file. If a fileset is replicated, the addresses of all the DFS servers that manage it are returned. When a DFS client accesses a file by specifying its name, its cache manager gets the address of the DFS server that manages the fileset of the file from the fileset location server. The cache manager caches this information for future use.

6. *Replication server.* The replication server maintains the consistency of the replicas of filesets.

Of the above mentioned six components of a DFS server, the former three reside in the kernel space and the latter three reside in the user space.

When a DFS client makes a file access request, the cache manager of the client's machine first checks to see if the requested data is already present in its cache. If the data is found in the cache, the file access operation is performed locally without contacting a DFS server. Otherwise, the cache manager does an RPC with the appropriate DFS server asking for the data. The data received from the DFS server is cached by the cache manager for future use.

DFS uses the block-level transfer model for the unit of data transfer. The block size is 64 kilobytes, so many (in some environments most) files will be transferred and cached in their entirety.

To mention about file accessing in NFS, NFS also uses the data-caching model for file accessing and the block-level transfer model for the unit of data transfer. The block size in NFS is 8 kilobytes. For performance improvement, in addition to data caching, NFS also uses a *read-ahead* mechanism. In this mechanism, after the file system component on the client machine receives the block that contains the needed data, it automatically issues a request for the next block, so that it will be available locally in case it is needed shortly.

### 9.11.4 DFS File-Sharing Semantics

The strongest feature of DFS is that, in spite of using the data-caching model, it supports the single-site UNIX semantics. That is, every read operation on a file sees the effects of all previous write operations performed on that file. This is achieved in the manner described below.

Recall that each DFS server has a component called token manger. The job of the token manager is to issue tokens to clients for file access requests and to keep track of which clients have been issued what types of tokens for which files. A client cannot perform the desired file operation on a piece of file data until it possesses the proper token.

The use of a token-based approach to implement the single-site UNIX file-sharing semantics can best be illustrated with the help of an example (see Fig. 9.21). For simplicity, in this example we assume that there is only one type of token for all types of file access operations.

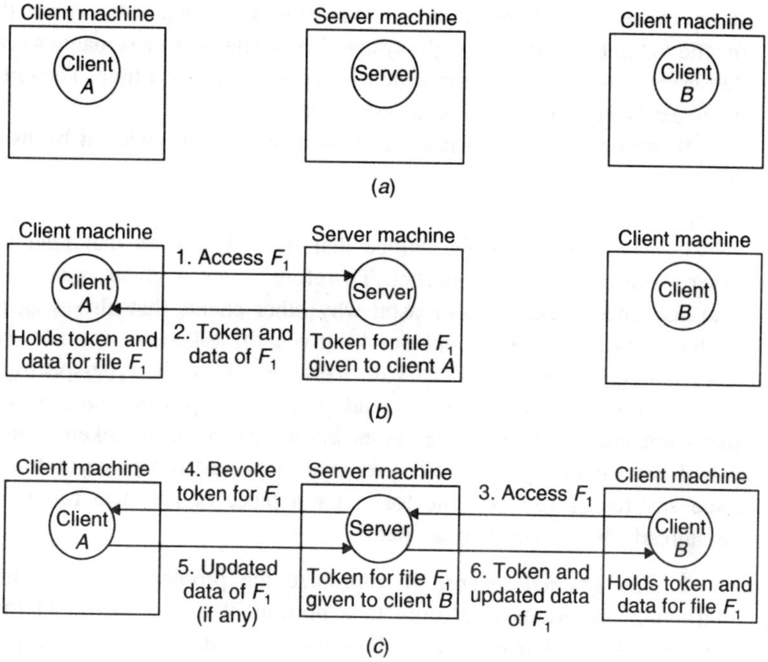


**Fig. 9.21** Token-based approach of DFS for implementing the UNIX file-sharing semantics: (*a*) initial state of a server machine and two client machines; (*b*) state after client *A* receives the token and data for file $F_1$; (*c*) state after client *B* receives the token and data for file $F_1$.

Figure 9.21(*a*) shows the initial state of a server and two client machines. At this time, client *A* makes a request to the server for accessing file $F_1$. The server checks its state information to see if the token for file $F_1$ has been given to any other client. It finds that it has not been given to any other client, so it sends the token and data of file $F_1$ to client *A* and makes a record of this information for future use. Client *A* caches the received file data and then continues to perform file access operations on this data as many times as needed. Figure 9.21(*b*) shows the state of the server and client machines after client A receives the token and data for file $F_1$.

Now suppose after some time that client $B$ makes a request to the server for accessing the same file $F_1$. The server checks its state information and finds that the token for file $F_1$ has been given to client $A$. Therefore, it does not immediately send the token and data for file $F_1$ to client $B$. Rather it first sends a message to client $A$ asking back the token for file $F_1$. On receiving the revocation message, client $A$ returns the token along with updated data of file $F_1$ (if any updates were made) and invalidates its cached data for file $F_1$. The server then updates its local copy of file $F_1$ (if needed) and now returns the token and up-to-date data of file $F_1$ to client $B$. Client $B$ caches the received file data and then continues to perform file access operations on this data as many times as needed. Figure 9.21($c$) shows the state of the server and client machines after client $B$ receives the token and data for file $F_1$. In this way, the single-system UNIX file-sharing semantics is achieved because the server issues the token for a file to only one client at a time. The client that possesses the token is assured exclusive access to the file.

To maximize performance, better concurrency is achieved by using the following techniques:

1. *Type-specific tokens.* Notice that multiple clients that read the same file but never write on it do not conflict. Therefore, when a client is accessing a file in the read-only mode, there is no reason why other clients that also want to access the file in the read-only mode should not be given the token for the file. Hence, instead of using a single token for all types of operations on a file, type-specific tokens are used. Separate tokens exist for open, read, write, lock, check file status, and update file status operations on files. The server knows the rules for token compatibility. That is, it will issue multiple read tokens for read accesses to a piece of file data but will not issue any read token or write token for a piece of file data for which a write token has already been issued to a client.

2. *Fine-grained tokens.* To minimize the problem of false sharing, tokens for conflicting operations refer only to a portion of a file instead of the entire file. For instance, tokens for open, check file status, and update file status operations apply to the entire file, but tokens for read, write, and lock operations apply only to a portion of a file.

Every token has an expiration time of 2 minutes. Therefore, if a client does not respond (either due to a crash or some other reason) to a token revocation message from a server, the server just waits for 2 minutes and then acts as if the token has been returned by the client.

To mention the file-sharing semantics in NFS, NFS does not support the UNIX semantics for file sharing. It has been widely criticized for having a fuzzy file-sharing semantics in which a write to a file performed by a client on its cached copy of the file data may or may not be seen when another client reads the file, depending on timing. This is because in NFS each cached data block has a timer of 3 seconds associated with it. A cached data block is discarded when its timer expires. In addition, whenever a cached file is opened, the client contacts the server to find out when the file was last modified. If the last modification was done after the client's copy was cached, the client discards the old copy from its cache, gets the updated copy from the server, and caches this copy in its cache. Finally, NFS uses the periodic write modification propagation scheme with a 30-second interval. That is, once every 30 seconds all the modified blocks of a cache are sent to the server. Due to the use of timer-based mechanisms for discarding cached entries and for modification propagation, NFS does not make good use of data caching.

Another important difference between NFS and DFS that is worth mentioning here is that NFS allows every machine to be both a client and a server at the same time. That is, any client may also be a server and any server may also be a client. All machines are independent and exist in different administrative environments. However, in DFS, a server assumes the dependency of clients in the same cell. Therefore, the server-client relationship in DFS is much more a convention for master-slave than NFS.

### 9.11.5 File-Caching Scheme in DFS

We have already seen that in DFS recently accessed file data are cached by the cache manager of client machines. The local disk of a client machine is used for this purpose. However, in a diskless client machine, the local memory is used for caching file data.

As shown in Figure 9.21, in DFS, modifications made to a cached file data are propagated to the file server only when the client receives a token revocation message for the file data. The same is true for cache validation scheme. That is, a cached file data of a client machine is invalidated (its cache entry is discarded) only when the client receives a token revocation message for the file data from the file server. As long as the client possesses the token for the specified operation on the file data, the cached data is valid and the client can continue to perform the specified operation on it. In effect, the approach used for cache validation is a server-initiated approach.

The NFS schemes for modification propagation and cache validation have already been described in the previous section.

### 9.11.6 Replication and Cloning in DFS

Distributed File Service provides the facility to replicate files on multiple file servers. The unit of replication is a fileset. That is, all files of a fileset are replicated together.

The existence of multiple replicas of a file is transparent to normal users (client applications). That is, a filename is mapped to all file servers having a replica of the file. Therefore, given a filename, the fileset location server returns the addresses of all the file servers that have a replica of the fileset containing the file. DFS uses the explicit replication mechanism for replication control. That is, the number of replicas for a fileset and their locations are decided by the system administrator. The fileset server has a single command for replicating an entire fileset.

The replication server of a server machine is responsible for maintaining the consistency of the replicas of filesets. The primary-copy protocol is used for this purpose. That is, for each replicated fileset, one copy is designated as the primary copy and all the others are secondary copies. Read operations on a file in a replicated fileset can be performed using any copy of the fileset, primary or secondary. But all update operations on a file in the fileset are directly performed only on the primary copy of the fileset. The replication server of the primary copy periodically sends the updated versions of modified files to the replication servers of the secondary copies, which then update their own replicas of the fileset.

NFS does not provide the facility to replicate files on multiple servers.

In addition to allowing replication of filesets, DFS also provides the facility to clone filesets. This facility allows the creation of a new virtual copy of the fileset in another disk partition and the old copy is marked read only. This facility may be used by the system administrator to maintain an old version of a fileset, allowing the recovery of the old version of an inadvertently deleted file. For example, the system administrator might instruct the system to clone a fileset every day at midnight so that the previous day's work always remains intact in an old version of all files. If a user inadvertently deletes a file, he or she can always get the old version of the file and once again perform the current day's updates on it.

Cloning of a fileset does not take much time because only a virtual copy of the fileset is made. That is, only the data structures for the files in the fileset are copied to the new partition and the file data is not copied. The old data structures in the original partition are marked read only. Therefore, both sets of data structures point to the same data blocks. When a file in the new fileset is updated, new data blocks are allocated for writing the updated version of the data and the corresponding file data structure in the new partition is updated to point to the new data blocks. A request to update a file in the original fileset is refused with an error message.

### 9.11.7 Fault Tolerance

In addition to allowing replication of filesets, another important feature of DFS that helps in improving its fault tolerance ability is the use of the write-ahead log approach for recording file updates in a recoverable manner. In DFS, for every update made to a file, a log is written to the disk. A log entry contains the old value and the new value of the modified part of the file. When the system comes up after a crash, the log is used to check which changes have already been made to the file and which changes have not yet been made. Those that have not been made are the ones that were lost due to system crash. These changes are now made to the file to bring it to a consistent state. If an update is lost because the crash occurred before the log for the update was recorded on the disk, it does not create any inconsistency because the lost update is treated as if the update was never performed on the file. Therefore the file is always in a consistent state after recovery.

Notice that in the log-based crash recovery approach used in DFS, the recovery time is proportional to the length of the log and is independent of the size of the disk partition. This allows faster recovery than traditional systems like UNIX, in which the recovery time of a file system is proportional to the size of its disk partition.

For fault tolerance, the main approach used by NFS is to use stateless file servers. Notice from Figure 9.21 that DFS servers are stateful because they have to keep track of the tokens issued to the clients.

### 9.11.8 Atomic Transactions

The DCE does not provide transaction processing facility either as a part of DFS or as an independent component. This is mainly because DCE currently does not possess services needed for developing and running mission critical, distributed on-line transaction processing (OLTP) applications. For instance, OLTP applications require guaranteed data integrity, application programming interface with simplified transaction semantics, and the ability to extend programs to support RPCs that allow multiple processes to work together over the network to perform a common task. Such services are not currently supported by DCE. However, users of DCE who need transaction processing facility can use Transarc Corporation's *Encina* OLTP technology. Encina expands on the DCE framework and provides a set of standards-based distributed services for simplifying the construction of reliable, distributed OLTP systems with guaranteed data integrity. In particular, the services offered by Encina for distributed OLTP include full data integrity with a transactional two-phase commit protocol, a high-level application programming interface with simplified transaction semantics, and additional transactional semantics required for achieving deterministic results with RPCs.

In addition to Encina, two other transaction processing environments gaining popularity are *Customer Information Control System* (*CICS*) and *Information Management System* (*IMS*), both from IBM. CICS is already being used by more than 20,000 customers in more than 90 countries worldwide. Encina offers interoperability with IBM's CICS. Therefore, CICS can be implemented on top of the DCE and Encina technology.

### 9.11.9 User Interfaces to DFS

Distributed File Service supports the following types of user interfaces for different types of users:

1. *File service interface*. DFS uses native operating system commands for directory and file operations so that users do not need to learn new commands. For example, users on UNIX systems will use *cd* to change directory, *ls* to list directory contents, *mkdir* to create a new directory, and so on. DFS also has several commands that work only for its own file system (Episode). These include commands to check quotas of different filesets, to locate the server of a file, and so on. To access a file, a client may specify the file by its global name or by its cell relative name. Details of the object-naming mechanism of DCE are given in Chapter 10.

2. *Application programming interface*. The application programming interface to DFS is very similar to UNIX. Therefore, application programmers can use standard file system calls like *fopen ()* for opening a file, *fread ()* to read from a file, *fwrite ()* to write to a file, *fclose ()* to close a file, and so on. In fact, most existing software will work immediately by simply recompiling with the DFS libraries.

3. *Administrative interface*. The administrative interface of DFS provides commands that allow the system administrator to handle filesets, to install or remove DFS file servers,

and to manipulate ACLs associated with files and directories. The commands for handling filesets are used by the system administrator to create, delete, move, replicate, clone, back up, or restore filesets. For example, the system administrator may move filesets from one server machine to other server machines to balance the load across all file server machines in a cell.

On the other hand, the commands to install or remove file servers allow the system administrator to dynamically reconfigure the system as needs change. For example, the system administrator may notice that the DFS performance of a cell is not so good because there are too many clients and only a few file servers. In this case, he or she may install a new file server in the cell and move some of the filesets from already existing file servers of the cell to this file server.

Finally, the commands to manipulate ACLs are used by the system administrator to revoke some of the access permissions already given to some users or to give additional permissions to some users.

## 9.12 SUMMARY

A file is a named object that comes into existence by explicit creation, is immune to temporary failures in the system, and persists until explicitly destroyed. A file system is a subsystem of an operating system that performs file management activities such as organization, storing, retrieval, naming, sharing, and protection of files. A distributed file system is a distributed implementation of the classical time-sharing model of a file system. In addition to the advantages of permanent storage and sharing of information provided by the file system of a single-processor system, a distributed file system normally supports the following: remote information sharing, user mobility, availability, and diskless workstations.

The desirable features of a good distributed file system are—transparency (structure transparency, access transparency, naming transparency, and replication transparency), user mobility, performance, simplicity and ease of use, scalability, high availability, high reliability, data integrity, security, and heterogeneity.

From the viewpoint of structure, files are of two types—unstructured and structured. On the other hand, according to modifiability criteria, files may be mutable or immutable.

The two complementary models for accessing remote files are remote service model and data-caching model. In file systems that use the data-caching model, an important design issue is to decide the unit of data transfer. The four commonly used units for this purpose are file, block, byte, and record.

In shared files, the file-sharing semantics defines when modifications of file data made by a user are observable by other users. The four commonly used file-sharing semantics are UNIX semantics, session semantics, immutable shared-files semantics, and transaction-like semantics.

Every distributed file system in serious use today uses some form of file caching because, in addition to better performance, it also contributes to its scalability and reliability. In a distributed file system, a cache may be located in a server's main memory, a client's disk, or a client's main memory. Keeping file data cached at multiple client nodes consistent is an important design issue in distributed file systems that use client caching. The approaches for handling this issue depend on the schemes used to propagate modifications made to cached data to the corresponding file server and to verify the validity of cached data. The write-through scheme and the delayed-write scheme are the two commonly used schemes for modification propagation. The cache validation approaches may either be client initiated or server initiated.

A replicated file is a file that has multiple copies, with each copy located on a separate file server. Each copy of the set of copies that comprises a replicated file is referred to as a replica of the replicated file. Replication of files in a distributed system offers the following potential benefits: increased availability, increased reliability, improved response time, reduced network traffic, improved system throughput, better scalability, and autonomous operation. Maintaining consistency among copies when a replicated file is updated is the major design issue of a file system that supports replication of files. Some of the commonly used approaches to handle this issue are read-only replication, read-any—write-all protocol, available-copies protocol, primary-copy protocol, and quorum-based protocols.

Fault tolerance is an important issue in the design of a distributed file system. The three primary file properties that directly influence the ability of a distributed file system to tolerate faults are availability, robustness, and recoverability. Replication is a primary mechanism for improving the availability of a file. Robust files are implemented by redundancy techniques such as stable storage. Recoverable files are realized by atomic update techniques.

A server may be implemented by using either a stateful or a stateless service paradigm. A stateful file server maintains clients' state information from one access request to the next. On the other hand, a stateless file server does not maintain any client state information. Therefore, every request from a client must be accompanied with all the necessary parameters to successfully carry out the desired operation. The stateless service paradigm makes crash recovery very easy because no client state information is maintained by the server and each request contains all the needed information.

An atomic transaction (or just transaction for short) is a computation consisting of a collection of operations that take place indivisibly in the presence of failures and concurrent computations. The three essential properties of transactions are atomicity, serializability, and permanence. A distributed transaction service is an extension of the traditional transaction service, which can support transactions involving files managed by more than one server. Nested transactions are a generalization of traditional transactions in which a transaction may be composed of other transactions called subtransactions.

The general principles for designing distributed file systems as proposed by Satyanarayanan are—know that clients have cycles to burn, cache whenever possible, exploit usage properties, minimize systemwide knowledge and change, trust the fewest possible entities, and batch if possible.

## EXERCISES

**9.1.** In what aspects is the design of a distributed file system different from that of a file system for a centralized time-sharing system?

**9.2.** Name the main components of a distributed file system. What might be the reasons for separating the various functions of a distributed file system into these components?

**9.3.** In the design of a distributed file system, high availability and high scalability are mutually related properties. Discuss.

**9.4.** In the design of a distributed file system, high performance and high reliability are conflicting properties. Discuss.

**9.5.** What is an immutable file? Can a file system be designed to function correctly by using only immutable files? If no, explain why. If yes, explain how the basic file operations (create, read, write, delete) can be performed in this file system for shared files.

**9.6.** Discuss the relative advantages and disadvantages of using full-file caching and block caching models for the data-caching mechanism of a distributed file system.

**9.7.** Of the four data transfer models that may be used in a distributed file system that uses the data-caching model for file accessing, which models are suitable for each of the following types of distributed systems:

(a) A distributed system that supports diskless workstations

(b) A distributed system in which each node has large disk storage space

(c) A distributed system that uses the structured file model in which each file is a group of records

If more than one model is suitable for a particular case, which model will you prefer to use and why?

**9.8.** In your opinion, where (in server memory, in client disk, or in client memory) should a cache for caching data be located in the following types of distributed file systems (give reasons for your answer):

(a) One that supports diskless workstations

(b) One that uses the file-level transfer model as unit of data access

(c) One that uses session semantics

(d) One that is designed to occasionally support disconnected operation

(e) One in which the ratio of number of clients to number of file servers is very large

(f) One that has to handle fairly large files

(g) One that supports UNIX-like file-sharing semantics

If more than one location is suitable for a particular case, which one will you prefer to use and why?

**9.9.** Suppose you have to design the caching scheme of a distributed file system that has to support session semantics. Suggest a suitable solution for each of the following issues in your design:

(a) Where to locate a cache?

(b) What should be the unit of data caching?

(c) When should modification to a cached data be propagated to its master copy?

(d) When should the validation to check if a cached copy of a data is consistent with its master copy be performed?

Give reasons for your answer.

**9.10.** A distributed operating system designer is of the opinion that since both replication and caching of objects provide more or less similar advantages to a distributed system, both concepts need not be implemented in the same distributed system. Is he or she correct? Give reasons for your answer. Now differentiate among the following types of distributed operating systems by listing their relative advantages and disadvantages:
(a) One that implements object caching but no object replication
(b) One that implements object replication but no object caching
(c) One that implements both object caching and object replication

**9.11.** In the design of a distributed operating system, the data-caching mechanism may be used for caching many different types of data. A separate cache can be maintained for each type of data. In your opinion, is it necessary to always keep a cached data up to date? If yes, explain why. If no, give an example in which a system can function correctly even when processes access cached data that are not always up to date.

**9.12.** Suppose a file system uses the client-initiated approach for validating the contents of client caches. Also suppose that the validity check is performed by comparing the time of last modification of the cached version of the data with the server's master copy version. This file system will not function correctly in a system in which the clocks of various nodes are not synchronized. Suggest a scheme that can be used with the client-initiated approach for cache validation in systems in which clocks of various nodes are not synchronized.

**9.13.** Differentiate among the following properties of a distributed file system:
(a) High degree of availability
(b) High degree of recoverability
(c) High degree of robustness
Name a suitable mechanism that may be used for implementing each of these properties.

**9.14.** Explain how a stable-storage system converts fallible disks into reliable devices. In the discussion in this chapter, we saw a stable-storage system designed with two conventional disks. Can this idea be extended to three disks for better crash resistance capability? If no, explain why. If yes, explain how.

**9.15.** A stateful file server records state information for its clients. What problems are associated with this type of file server? Give two examples where it might be necessary to use stateful file servers.

**9.16.** A distributed system based on the workstation-server model provides on-line help facility to its users by allowing the users to read the on-line manuals by using the *man* command. Suggest different possible locations for storing the manuals in the system and discuss their relative advantages and disadvantages.

**9.17.** What is a transaction? What are the two main factors that threaten the atomicity of transactions? Describe how atomicity is ensured for a transaction in both commit and abort.

**9.18.** Why are transactions needed in a file service? Give suitable examples to illustrate how transactions help in doing the following:
(a) Improving the recoverability of files in the event of failures
(b) Allowing the concurrent sharing of mutable files by multiple clients in a consistent manner

**9.19.** Discuss the need for serializability property in transactions. What is the main goal in devising a mechanism for satisfying this property? Describe at least three mechanisms that may be used in the implementation of a transaction facility for satisfying this property. Now compare the mechanisms described by you to show how close each of them is to the main goal.

**9.20.** Give two methods that may be used in the design of a file system to record updates to a file in a reversible manner. That is, the file system provides the flexibility to the users to cancel the updates made to a file within an open-close session and revert the file back to the state that it was in before the start of the session.

**9.21.** Let the initial balance in all the three accounts of the two banking transactions of Figure 9.9 be $100. For these two transactions, enumerate all the schedules that produce different final values of $z$. Which of these are legal schedules?

**9.22.** An application consists of three transactions $T_1$, $T_2$, and $T_3$ that are defined below:

$T_1$: begin_transaction
read($x$); read($z$); write($x$–5); write($z$+5);
end_transaction

$T_2$: begin_transaction
read($z$); write($z$–8); read($y$); write($y$+8);
end_transaction

$T_3$: begin_transaction
read($x$); write($x$+4); read($y$); write($y$–4);
end_transaction

Describe how the concurrency of these three transactions can be controlled by using the following:

(a) Same type of locks for both read and write operations
(b) Type-specific locks
(c) Intention-to-write locks
(d) Optimistic concurrency control scheme
(e) Timestamp-based concurrency control scheme

**9.23.** What are serially equivalent schedules? For the three transactions of the previous exercise give at least six schedules that are serially equivalent.

**9.24.** Figure 9.10 shows two schedules of the operations of the two transactions of Figure 9.9 that produced unexpected final results. Show that if both transactions use the two-phase locking protocol, these schedules produce correct results.

**9.25.** Prove that if all transactions of an application use the two-phase locking protocol, all schedules formed by interleaving their operations are serializable.

**9.26.** What is false sharing? Discuss the importance of granularity of locks in combating the false-sharing problem.

**9.27.** What is a transaction deadlock? Give an example to illustrate how a transaction deadlock occurs when:

(a) The same type of locks are used for both read and write operations.
(b) Type-specific locks are used.

Now give a method that may be used to avoid transaction deadlocks and apply the method to your examples to show how it prevents the deadlocks that occurred in cases (a) and (b).

**9.28.** Suppose the optimistic concurrency control mechanism is used in the implementation of the transaction mechanism of a file system. Give two examples of concurrently executing transactions in this system:

(a) One in which the validation check is successful for all transactions and they are committed successfully
(b) One in which the validation check fails and a transaction has to be aborted

**9.29.** In what manner is the timestamp-based concurrency control scheme better than the optimistic concurrency control scheme? For the example given by you for case (b) of the previous exercise, use the timestamp-based concurrency control scheme and show that the transaction that was aborted cannot complete its first phase in this case.

**9.30.** What advantages does nested transactions facility have over traditional transaction facility in a distributed system? Answer the following questions for a nested transactions family:
(a) Can a transaction commit independent of other transactions in the family?
(b) Can a transaction abort independent of other transactions in the family?
(c) When do the changes made to data items by a transaction become visible to other transactions in the family?
(d) What happens if a transaction in the family fails?
(e) When are the updates performed by a transaction made permanent?
(f) When does the entire transaction family commit and success is reported to the client?
Give reasons for your answer.

**9.31.** In a distributed system based on the workstation-server model, a server machine is dedicated to work as a file server. The file system uses the remote service model for processing clients' requests. With the passage of time, the number of workstations gradually increases in the system, and it is found that the system performance has degraded because the file server is often overloaded by requests from clients. As an expert of distributed operating systems, you are contacted to solve this problem. Describe three different solutions that may be used to solve this problem.

**9.32.** Describe the two-phase, multiserver commit protocol. In the banking transaction given below, suppose accounts *X* and *Y* belong to two different branches of a bank. The local records of the two branches are managed by file servers $S_1$ and $S_2$, respectively.
$a_1$: begin_transaction
$a_2$: read balance $(x)$ of account *X*
$a_3$: read balance $(y)$ of account *Y*
$a_4$: write $(x-5)$ to account *X*
$a_5$: write $(y+5)$ to account *Y*
$a_6$: end_transaction
For the above transaction, if $S_1$ is the coordinator and $S_2$ is the worker, give the list of messages exchanged among the client and file servers $S_1$ and $S_2$ for the successful execution of this transaction. What will happen if $S_2$ crashes after performing operation $a_5$?

## BIBLIOGRAPHY

**[Agrawal and Jalote 1995]** Agrawal, G., and Jalote, P., "Coding-Based Replication Schemes for Distributed Systems," *IEEE Transactions on Parallel and Distributed Systems*, Vol. 6, No. 3, pp. 240–251 (1995).

**[Ahamad et al. 1991]** Ahamad, M., Ammar, M. H., and Cheung, S. Y., "Multi-dimensional Voting," *ACM Transactions on Computer Systems*, pp. 399–431 (November 1991).

**[Barghouti and Kaiser 1991]** Barghouti, N. S., and Kaiser, G. E., "Concurrency Control in Advanced Database Applications," *ACM Computing Surveys*, Vol. 23, No. 3, pp. 269–318 (1991).

**[Bernstein and Goodman 1981]** Bernstein, P. A., and Goodman, N., "Concurrency Control in Distributed Database Systems," *ACM Computing Surveys*, Vol. 13, No. 2, pp. 185–221 (1981).

**[Bernstein and Goodman 1984]** Bernstein, P. A., and Goodman, N., "An Algorithm for Concurrency Control and Recovery in Replicated Distributed Databases," *ACM Transactions on Database Systems*, Vol. 9, No. 4, pp. 596–615 (1984).

**[Bernstein et al. 1980]** Bernstein, P. A., Shipman, D. W., and Rothnie, J. B., "Concurrency Control in a System for Distributed Databases (SDD-1)," *ACM Transactions on Database Systems*, Vol. 5, No. 1, pp. 18–51 (1980).

**[Bernstein et al. 1987]** Bernstein, P. A., Hadzilacos, V., and Goodman, N., *Concurrency and Recovery in Database Systems*, Addison-Wesley, Reading, MA, pp. 289–307 (1987).

**[Brown et al. 1985]** Brown, M., Kolling, K., and Taft, E., "The Alpine File System," *ACM Transactions on Computer Systems*, Vol. 3, No. 4, pp. 261–293 (1985).

**[Chen et al. 1995]** Chen, K., Bunt, R. B., and Eager, D. L., "Write Caching in Distributed File Systems," In: *Proceedings of the 15th IEEE International Conference on Distributed Computing Systems*, IEEE, New York, NY (May–June 1995).

**[Chutani et al. 1992]** Chutani, S., Anderson, O. T., Kazar, M. L., Leverett, B. W., Mason, W. A., and Sidebotham, R. N., "The Episode File System," In: *Proceedings of the 1992 USENIX Winter Conference*. USENIX Association, Berkeley, CA, pp. 43–60 (1992).

**[Claybrook 1992]** Claybrook, B., *OLTP: Online Transaction Processing Systems*, John Wiley, New York (1992).

**[Coulouris et al. 1994]** Coulouris, G. F., Dollimore, J., and Kindberg, T., *Distributed Systems Concepts and Design*, 2nd ed., Addison-Wesley, Reading, MA (1994).

**[Davcev and Burkhard 1985]** Davcev, D., and Burkhard, W. A., "Consistency and Recovery Control for Replicated Files," In: *Proceedings of the 10th ACM Symposium on Operating Systems Principles*, Association for Computing Machinery, New York, NY, pp. 87–96 (December 1985).

**[Dion 1980]** Dion, J., "The Cambridge File Server," *ACM Operating Systems Review*, Vol. 14, No. 4, pp. 26–35 (1980).

**[Eswaran et al. 1976]** Eswaran, K. P., Gray, J. N., Lorie, R. A., and Traiger, I. L., "The Notions of Consistency and Predicate Locks in a Database System," *Communications of the ACM*, Vol. 19, No. 11, pp. 624–633 (1976).

**[Fridrich and Older 1985]** Fridrich, M., and Older, W., "Helix: The Architecture of the XMS Distributed File System," *IEEE Computer*, pp. 21–29 (1985).

**[Gifford 1979a]** Gifford, D. K., "Weighted Voting for Replicated Data," In: *Proceedings of the 7th ACM Symposium on Operating Systems Principles*, Association for Computing Machinery, New York, NY, pp. 150–159 (December 1979).

**[Gifford 1979b]** Gifford, D. K., "Violet: An Experimental Decentralized System," *ACM Operating Systems Review*, Vol. 13, No. 5 (1979).

**[Gifford et al. 1988]** Gifford, D. K., Needham, R. M., and Schroeder, M. D., "The Cedar File System," *Communications of the ACM*, Vol. 31, No. 3, pp. 288–298 (1988).

**[Goscinski 1991]** Goscinski, A., *Distributed Operating Systems, The Logical Design*, Addison-Wesley, Reading, MA (1991).

**[Gray 1978]** Gray, J. N., "Notes on Database Operating Systems," *Lecture Notes in Computer Science*, Vol. 60, Springer-Verlag, Berlin, pp. 393–481 (1978).

**[Gray and Cheriton 1989]** Gray, C., and Cheriton, D., "Leases: An Efficient Fault-Tolerant Mechanism for Distributed File System Consistency," In: *Proceedings of the 11th ACM Symposium on Operating Systems Principles*, Association for Computing Machinery, New York, NY, pp. 202–210 (1989).

**[Gray and Reuter 1993]** Gray, J., and Reuter, A., *Transaction Processing: Concepts and Techniques*, Morgan Kaufmann, San Francisco, CA (1993).

**[Gray et al. 1981]** Gray, J. N., McJones, P., Blasgen, M. W., Lorie, R. A., Price, T. G., Putzulu, G. F., and Traiger, I. L., "The Recovery Manager of the System R Database Manager," *ACM Computing Surveys*, Vol. 13, No. 2, pp. 223–242 (1981).

**[Harder and Reuter 1983]** Harder, T., and Reuter, A., "Principles of Transaction-Oriented Database Recovery," *Computing Surveys*, Vol. 15, No. 4 (1983).

**[Herlihy 1986]** Herlihy, M., "A Quorum-Consensus Replication Method for Abstract Data Types," *ACM Transactions on Computer Systems*, Vol. 4, No. 1, pp. 32–53 (1986).

**[Howard et al. 1988]** Howard, J. H., Kazar, M. L., Menees, S. G., Nichols, D. A., Satyanarayanan, M., Sidebotham, R. N., and West, M. J., "Scale and Performance in a Distributed File System," *ACM Transactions on Computer Systems*, Vol. 6, No. 1, pp. 51–81 (1988).

**[Israel et al. 1978]** Israel, J. E., Mitchell, J. G., and Sturgis, H. E., "Separating Data from Function in a Distributed File System," In: D. Lanciaux (Ed.), *Operating Systems: Theory and Practice*, North Holland, Amsterdam, pp. 17–22 (1978).

**[Jalote 1994]** Jalote, P., *Fault Tolerance in Distributed Systems*, Prentice-Hall, Englewood Cliffs, NJ (1994).

**[Kazar et al. 1990]** Kazar, M. L., Leverett, B. W., Anderson, O. T., Apostolides, V., Bottos, B. A., Chutani, S., Everhart, C. F., Mason, W. A., Tu, S. T., and Zayas, E. R., "Decorum File System Architectural Overview," In: *Proceedings of the 1990 USENIX Summer Conference*, USENIX Association, Berkeley, CA, pp. 151–163 (1990).

**[Khanna 1994]** Khanna, R. (Ed.), *Distributed Computing: Implementation and Management Strategies*, Prentice-Hall, Englewood Cliffs, NJ (1994).

**[Kistler 1995]** Kistler, J. J., *Disconnected Operation in a Distributed File System*, Springer-Verlag, New York, NY (1995).

**[Kistler and Satyanarayanan 1992]** Kistler, J. J., and Satyanarayanan, M., "Disconnected Operation in the Coda File System," *ACM Transactions on Computer Systems*, Vol. 10, No. 1 (1992).

**[Kotz and Ellis 1993]** Kotz, D., and Ellis, C. S., "Caching and Writeback Policies in Parallel File Systems," *Journal of Parallel and Distributed Computing*, Vol. 17, Nos. 1 and 2, pp. 140–145 (1993).

**[Kumar 1991]** Kumar, A., "Hierarchical Quorum Consensus: A New Algorithm for Managing Replicated Data," *IEEE Transactions on Computers*, Vol. 40, No. 9, pp. 996–1004 (1991).

**[Kung and Robinson 1981]** Kung, H. T., and Robinson, J. T., "On Optimistic Methods for Concurrency Control," *ACM Transactions on Database Systems*, Vol. 6, No. 2, pp. 213–226 (1981).

**[Ladin et al. 1992]** Ladin, R., Liskov, B., Shrira, L., and Ghemawat, S., "Providing Availability Using Lazy Replication," *ACM Transactions on Computer Systems*, Vol. 10, No. 4, pp. 360–391 (1992).

**[Lampson 1981]** Lampson, B. W., "Atomic Transactions in Distributed Systems—Architecture and Implementation," In: B. W. Lampson, M. Paul, and H. J. Siegart (Eds.), *An Advanced Course, Lecture Notes in Computer Science*, Vol. 105, Springer-Verlag, New York, NY, pp. 246–264 (1981).

**[Lazowska et al. 1986]** Lazowska, E. D., Zahorjan, J., Cheriton, D., and Zwaenepoel, W., "File Access Performance of Diskless Workstations," *ACM Transactions on Computer Systems*, Vol. 4, No. 3, pp. 238–268 (1986).

**[Leach et al. 1983]** Leach, P. J., Levine, P. H., Douros, B. P., Hamilton, J. A., Nelson, D. L., and Stumpf, B. L., "The Architecture of an Integrated Local Network," *IEEE Journal on Selected Areas in Communication*, Vol. SAC-1, No. 5, pp. 842–857 (1983).

**[Levine 1986]** Levine, P. H., "The Apollo DOMAIN Distributed File System," In Y. Parker et al., (Eds.), *Distributed Operating Systems: Theory and Practice*, NATO ASI Series, Springer-Verlag, New York, NY, Vol. F28, pp. 241–260 (1986).

**[Levy and Silberschatz 1990]** Levy, E., and Silberschatz, A., "Distributed File Systems: Concepts and Examples," *ACM Computing Surveys*, Vol. 22, No. 4, pp. 321–374 (1990).

**[Liskov et al. 1991]** Liskov, B., Ghemawat, S., Gruber, R., Johnson, P., Shrira, L., and Williams, M., "Replication in the Harp File System," In: *Proceedings of the 13th ACM Symposium on Operating Systems Principles*, Association for Computing Machinery, New York, NY, pp. 226–238 (1991).

**[Lockhart Jr. 1994]** Lockhart, Jr., H. W., *OSF DCE: Guide to Developing Distributed Applications*, IEEE Computer Society Press, Los Alamitos, CA (1994).

**[Lyon et al. 1985]** Lyon, B., Sager, G., Chang, J. M., Goldberg, D., Kleiman, S., Lyon, T., Sandberg, R., Walsh, D., and Weiss, P., "Overview of the SUN Network File System," In: *Proceedings of the USENIX Conference*, USENIX Association, Berkeley, CA, pp. 1–8 (January 1985).

**[McKusick et al. 1985]** McKusick, M. K., Karels, M. J., and Leffler, S. J., "Performance Improvements and Functional Enhancements in 4.3BSD," In: *Proceedings of the 1985 USENIX Summer Conference*, USENIX Association, Berkeley, CA, pp. 519–531 (1985).

**[Mitchell and Dion 1982]** Mitchell, J. G., and Dion, J., "A Comparison of Two Network- Based File Servers," *Communications of the ACM*, Vol. 25, No. 4, pp. 233–245 (1982).

**[Morris et al. 1986]** Morris, J. H., Satyanarayanan, M., Conner, M. H., Howard, J. H., Rosenthal, D. S. H., and Smith, F. D., "Andrew: A Distributed Personal Computing Environment," *Communications of the ACM*, Vol. 29, No. 3, pp. 184–201 (1986).

**[Moss 1985]** Moss, E., *Nested Transactions, An Approach to Reliable Distributed Computing*, MIT Press, Cambridge, MA (1985).

**[Mueller et al. 1983]** Mueller, E. T., Moore, J. D., and Popek, G. J., "A Nested Transaction Mechanism for LOCUS," In: *Proceedings of the 9th ACM Symposium on Operating Systems Principles*, Association for Computing Machinery, New York, NY, pp. 71–85 (1983).

**[Mullender and Tanenbaum 1984]** Mullender, S. J., and Tanenbaum, A. S., "Immediate Files," *Software Practice and Experience*, Vol. 14, No. 4, pp. 365–368 (1984).

**[Mullender and Tanenbaum 1985]** Mullender, S. J., and Tanenbaum, A. S., "A Distributed File Service Based on Optimistic Concurrency Control," In: *Proceedings of the 10th ACM Symposium on Operating Systems Principles*, Association for Computing Machinery, New York, NY, pp. 51–62 (December 1985).

**[Needham and Herbert 1982]** Needham, R. M., and Herbert, A. J., *The Cambridge Distributed Computing System*, Addison-Wesley, Reading, MA (1982).

**[Nelson et al. 1988]** Nelson, M. N., Welch, B. B., and Ousterhout, J. K., "Caching in the Sprite Network File System," *ACM Transactions on Computer Systems*, Vol. 6, No. 1, pp. 134–154 (1988).

**[Ousterhout et al. 1985]** Ousterhout, J. K., Costa, D., Harrison, D., Kunze, J. A., Kupfler, M., and Thompson, J. G., "A Trace-Driven Analysis of the UNIX 4.2 BSD File System," In: *Proceedings of the 10th ACM Symposium on Operating Systems Principles*, Association for Computing Machinery, New York, NY, pp. 15–24 (December 1985).

**[Popek and Walker 1985]** Popek, G. J., and Walker, B. J., *The LOCUS Distributed System Architecture*, MIT Press, Cambridge, MA (1985).

**[Ramamritham and Chrysanthis 1996]** Ramamritham, K., and Chrysanthis, P. K. (Eds.), *Advances in Concurrency Control and Transaction Processing*, IEEE Computer Society Press, Los Alamitos, CA (1996).

**[Rangarajan et al. 1995]** Rangarajan, S., Setia, S., and Tripathi, S. K., "A Fault-Tolerant Algorithm for Replicated Data Management," *IEEE Transactions on Parallel and Distributed Systems*, Vol. 6, No. 12, pp. 1271–1282 (1995).

**[Reed 1983]** Reed, D. P., "Implementing Atomic Actions on Decentralized Data," *ACM Transactions on Computer Systems*, Vol. 1, No. 1, pp. 3–23 (1983).

**[Rifkin et al. 1986]** Rifkin, A. P., Forbes, M. P., Hamilton, R. L., Sabrio, M., Shar, S., and Yueh, K., "RFS Architectural Overview," In: *Proceedings of the USENIX Conference,* Atlanta, GA, USENIX Association, Berkeley, CA, pp. 248–259 (1986).

**[Rosenberry et al. 1992]** Rosenberry, W., Kenney, D., and Fisher, G., *OSF DISTRIBUTED COMPUTING ENVIRONMENT, Understanding DCE*, O'Reilly, Sebastopol, CA (1992).

**[Sandberg 1987]** Sandberg, R., "The Sun Network File System: Design, Implementation and Experience," In: *Proceedings of the USENIX Summer Conference*, USENIX Association, Berkeley, CA, pp. 300–314 (June 1987).

**[Sandberg et al. 1985]** Sandberg, R., Goldberg, D., Kleinman, S., Walsh, D., and Lyon, B., "Design and Implementation of the SUN Network File System," In: *Proceedings of the USENIX Summer Conference*, Portland, OR, USENIX Association, Berkeley, CA, pp. 119–130 (June 1985).

**[Santifaller 1994]** Santifaller, M., *TCP/IP and ONC/NFS, Internetworking in a UNIX Environment*, 2nd ed., Addison-Wesley, Reading, MA (1994).

**[Satyanarayanan 1990a]** Satyanarayanan, M., "A Survey of Distributed File Systems," *Annual Review of Computer Science*, Vol. 4, pp. 73–104 (1990).

**[Satyanarayanan 1990b]** Satyanarayanan, M., "Scalable, Secure, and Highly Available Distributed File Access," *IEEE Computer*, Vol. 23, No. 5, pp. 9–21 (May 1990).

**[Satyanarayanan 1992]** Satyanarayanan, M., "The Influence of Scale on Distributed File System Design," *IEEE Transactions on Software Engineering*, Vol. 18, No. 1 (January 1992).

**[Satyanarayanan 1993]** Satyanarayanan, M., "Distributed File Systems," In: S. Mullender (Ed.), *Distributed Systems*, 2nd ed., Association for Computing Machinery, New York, NY, pp. 353–383 (1993).

**[Satyanarayanan et al. 1985]** Satyanarayanan, M., Howard, J. H., Nichols, D. A., Sidebotham, R. N., Spector, A. Z., and West, M. J., "The ITC Distributed File System: Principles and Design," In: *Proceedings of the 10th ACM Symposium on Operating Systems Principles*, Association for Computing Machinery, New York, NY, pp. 35–50 (December 1985).

**[Satyanarayanan et al. 1990]** Satyanarayanan, M., Kistler, J. J., Kumar, P., Okasaki, M. E., Siegel, E. H., and Steere, D. C., "Coda: A Highly Available File System for a Distributed Workstation Environment," *IEEE Transactions on Computers*, Vol. 39, No. 4, pp. 447–459 (April 1990).

**[Schroeder et al. 1985]** Schroeder, M. D., Gifford, D. K., and Needham, R. M., "A Caching File System for a Programmer's Workstation," In: *Proceedings of the 10th ACM Symposium on Operating Systems Principles*, Association for Computing Machinery, New York, NY, pp. 25–34 (December 1985).

**[Silberschatz and Galvin 1994]** Silberschatz, A., and Galvin, P. B., *Operating System Concepts*, 4th ed., Addison-Wesley, Reading, MA (1994).

**[Singhal and Shivaratri 1994]** Singhal, M., and Shivaratri, N. G., *Advanced Concepts in Operating Systems*, McGraw-Hill, New York (1994).

**[Smith 1982]** Smith, A. J., "Cache Memories," *ACM Computing Surveys*, Vol. 14, No. 3, pp. 473–530 (1982).

**[Stalling 1995]** Stalling, W., *Operating Systems*, 2nd ed., Prentice-Hall, Englewood Cliffs, NJ (1995).

**[Sturgis et al. 1980]** Sturgis, H., Mitchell, J. G., and Israel, J., "Issues in the Design and Use of a Distributed File System," *ACM Operating Systems Review*, Vol. 14, No. 3, pp. 55–69 (1980).

**[Svobodova 1984]** Svobodova, L., "File Servers for Network-Based Distributed Systems," *ACM Computing Surveys*, Vol. 16, No. 4, pp. 353–398 (1984).

**[Tanenbaum 1987]** Tanenbaum, A. S., *Operating Systems: Design and Implementation*, Prentice-Hall, Englewood Cliffs, NJ (1987).

**[Tanenbaum 1995]** Tanenbaum, A. S., *Distributed Operating Systems*, Prentice-Hall, Englewood Cliffs, NJ (1995).

**[Terry 1987]** Terry, D. B., "Caching Hints in Distributed Systems," *IEEE Transactions on Software Engineering*, Vol. SE-13, No. 1, pp. 48–54 (1987).

**[Tichy and Ruan 1984]** Tichy, W. F., and Ruan, Z., "Towards a Distributed File System," In: *Proceedings of the Summer USENIX Conference*, USENIX Association, Berkeley, CA, pp. 87–97 (June 1984).

**[Tomlinson et al. 1985]** Tomlinson, G. M., Keeffe, D., Wand, I. C., and Wellings, A. J., "The PULSE Distributed File System," *Software Practice and Experience*, Vol. 15, No. 11, pp. 1087–1101 (1985).

**[Turek and Shasha 1992]** Turek, J., and Shasha, D., "The Many Faces of Consensus in Distributed Systems," *IEEE Computer*, Vol. 25, No. 6, pp. 8–17 (1992).

**[Van Renesse and Tanenbaum 1988]** Van Renesse, R., and Tanenbaum, A. S., "Voting with Ghosts," In: *Proceedings of the 8th IEEE International Conference on Distributed Computing Systems*, IEEE Press, New York, NY, pp. 456–461 (June 1988).

**[Weihl 1993]** Weihl, W. E., "Transaction-Processing Techniques," In: S. Mullender (Ed.), *Distributed Systems*, 2nd ed., Association for Computing Machinery, New York, NY, pp. 329–352 (1993).

**[Weikum 1991]** Weikum, G., "Principles and Realization of Multilevel Transaction Management," *ACM Transactions on Database Systems*, Vol. 16, No. 1, pp. 132–140 (1991).

## POINTERS TO BIBLIOGRAPHIES ON THE INTERNET

Bibliographies containing references on *Distributed File Systems* can be found at:

ftp:ftp.cs.umanitoba.ca/pub/bibliographies/Distributed/distfs.html

ftp:ftp.cs.umanitoba.ca/pub/bibliographies/Distributed/dist.sys.html

Bibliography containing references on *Object Replication in Distributed Systems* can be found at:

ftp:ftp.cs.umanitoba.ca/pub/bibliographies/Distributed/Dist.Sys.html

Bibliography containing references on *AFS* (*Andrew File System*) can be found at:

http:www.transarc.com/Product/AFS/FAQ/faq.html#sub6

# CHAPTER 10

# Naming

## 10.1 INTRODUCTION

A distributed system supports several types of objects such as processes, files, I/O devices, mail boxes, and nodes. The *naming facility* of a distributed operating system enables users and programs to assign character-string names to objects and subsequently use these names to refer to those objects. The *locating facility*, which is an integral part of the naming facility, maps an object's name to the object's location in a distributed system. The naming and locating facilities jointly form a *naming system* that provides the users with an abstraction of an object that hides the details of how and where an object is actually located in the network. It provides a further level of abstraction when dealing with object replicas. Given an object name, it returns a set of the locations of the object's replicas.

The naming system plays a very important role in achieving the goal of location transparency in a distributed system. In addition to facilitating transparent migration and replication of objects, the naming system also facilitates object sharing. If various computations want to act upon the same object, they are enabled to do so by each containing a name for the object. Although the names contained in each computation may not necessarily be the same, they are mapped to the same object in this case.

This chapter presents a description of the various approaches in the design and implementation of naming systems for distributed systems.

## 10.2 DESIRABLE FEATURES OF A GOOD NAMING SYSTEM

A good naming system for a distributed system should have the features described below.

1. *Location transparency.* Location transparency means that the name of an object should not reveal any hint as to the physical location of the object. That is, an object's name should be independent of the physical connectivity or topology of the system, or the current location of the object.

2. *Location independency.* For performance, reliability, availability, and security reasons, distributed systems provide the facility of object migration that allows the movement and relocation of objects dynamically among the various nodes of a system. Location independency means that the name of an object need not be changed when the object's location changes. Furthermore, a user should be able to access an object by its same name irrespective of the node from where he or she accesses it. Therefore, the requirement of location independency calls for a global naming facility with the following two features:

- An object at any node can be accessed without the knowledge of its physical location (location independency of request-receiving objects).
- An object at any node can issue an access request without the knowledge of its own physical location (location independency of request-issuing objects). This property is also known as *user mobility.*

A location-independent naming system must support a dynamic mapping scheme so that it can map the same object name to different locations at two different instances of time. Therefore, location independency is a stronger property than location transparency [Levy and Silberschatz 1990].

3. *Scalability.* Distributed systems vary in size ranging from one with a few nodes to one with many nodes. Moreover, distributed systems are normally open systems, and their size changes dynamically. Therefore, it is impossible to have an a priori idea about how large the set of names to be dealt with is liable to get. Hence a naming system must be capable of adapting to the dynamically changing scale of a distributed system that normally leads to a change in the size of the name space. That is, a change in the system scale should not require any change in the naming or locating mechanisms.

4. *Uniform naming convention.* In many existing systems, different ways of naming objects, called naming conventions, are used for naming different types of objects. For example, filenames typically differ from user names and process names. Instead of using such nonuniform naming conventions, a good naming system should use the same naming convention for all types of objects in the system.

5. *Multiple user-defined names for the same object.* For a shared object, it is desirable that different users of the object can use their own convenient names for accessing it. Therefore, a naming system must provide the flexibility to assign multiple user-defined names to the same object. In this case, it should be possible for a user to change or delete his or her name for the object without affecting those of other users.

6. *Group naming.* A naming system should allow many different objects to be identified by the same name. Such a facility is useful to support broadcast facility or to group objects for conferencing or other applications.

7. *Meaningful names.* A name can be simply any character string identifying some object. However, for users, meaningful names are preferred to lower level identifiers such as memory pointers, disk block numbers, or network addresses. This is because meaningful names typically indicate something about the contents or function of their referents, are easily transmitted between users, and are easy to remember and use. Therefore, a good naming system should support at least two levels of object identifiers, one convenient for human users and one convenient for machines.

8. *Performance.* The most important performance measurement of a naming system is the amount of time needed to map an object's name to its attributes, such as its location. In a distributed environment, this performance is dominated by the number of messages exchanged during the name-mapping operation. Therefore, a naming system should be efficient in the sense that the number of messages exchanged in a name-mapping operation should be as small as possible.

9. *Fault tolerance.* A naming system should be capable of tolerating, to some extent, faults that occur due to the failure of a node or a communication link in a distributed system network. That is, the naming system should continue functioning, perhaps in a degraded form, in the event of these failures. The degradation can be in performance, functionality, or both but should be proportional, in some sense, to the failures causing it.

10. *Replication transparency.* In a distributed system, replicas of an object are generally created to improve performance and reliability. A naming system should support the use of multiple copies of the same object in a user-transparent manner. That is, if not necessary, a user should not be aware that multiple copies of an object are in use.

11. *Locating the nearest replica.* When a naming system supports the use of multiple copies of the same object, it is important that the object-locating mechanism of the naming system should always supply the location of the nearest replica of the desired object. This is because the efficiency of the object accessing operation will be affected if the object-locating mechanism does not take this point into consideration. This is illustrated by the example given in Figure 10.1, where the desired object is replicated at nodes $N_2$, $N_3$, and $N_4$ and the object-locating mechanism is such that it maps to the replica at node $N_4$ instead of the nearest replica at node $N_2$. Obviously this is undesirable.

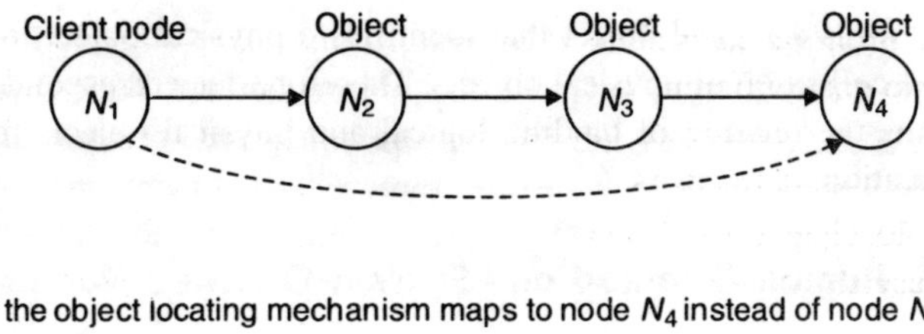


**Fig. 10.1** Illustrating the importance of locating the nearest replica of an object.

12. *Locating all replicas*. In addition to locating the nearest replica of an object, it is also important from a reliability point of view that all replicas of the desired object be located by the object-locating mechanism. A need for this property is illustrated in Figure 10.2, where the nearest replica at node $N_5$ is currently inaccessible due to a communication link failure in the network. In this case, another replica of the object at a farther node $N_4$ can be used.

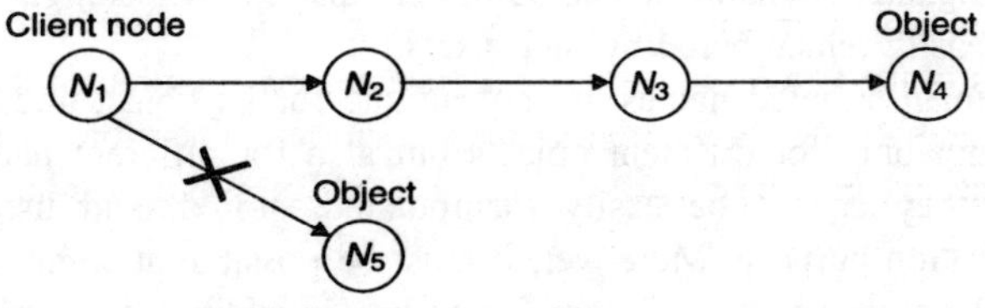


**Fig. 10.2** Illustrating the importance of locating all the replicas of an object.

## 10.3 FUNDAMENTAL TERMINOLOGIES AND CONCEPTS

The naming system is one of the most important components of a distributed operating system because it enables other services and objects to be identified and accessed in a uniform manner. In spite of the importance of names, no general unified treatment of them exists in the literature. This section defines and explains the fundamental terminologies and concepts associated with object naming in distributed systems.

### 10.3.1 Name

A *name* is a string composed of a set of symbols chosen from a finite alphabet. For example, *SINHA*, *#173#4879#5965*, *node-1!node-2!node-3!sinha*, */a/b/c*, *25A2368DM197*, etc. eare all valid names composed of symbols from the ASCII character set. A name is also called an *identifier* because it is used to denote or identify an object. A name may also be thought of as a logical object that identifies a physical object to which it is bound from among a collection of physical objects. Therefore, the correspondence between names and objects is the relation of binding logical and physical objects for the purpose of object identification.

### 10.3.2 Human-Oriented and System-Oriented Names

Names are used to designate or refer to objects at all levels of system architecture. They have various purposes, forms, and properties depending on the levels at which they are defined. However, an informal distinction can be made between two basic classes of names widely used in operating systems—human-oriented names and system-oriented names.

A human-oriented name is generally a character string that is meaningful to its users. For example, */user/sinha/project-1/file-1* is a human-oriented name. Human-oriented names are defined by their users. For a shared object, different users of the object must have the flexibility to define their own human-oriented names for the object for accessing it. Flexibility must also be provided so that a user can change or delete his or her own name for the object without affecting those of other users. For transparency, human-oriented names should be independent of the physical location or the structure of objects they designate. Human-oriented names are also known as *high-level names* because they can be easily remembered by their users.

Human-oriented names are not unique for an object and are normally variable in length not only for different objects but also for different names for the same object. Hence, they cannot be easily manipulated, stored, and used by the machines for identification purpose. Moreover, it must be possible at some level to uniquely identify every object in the entire system. Therefore, in addition to human-oriented names, which are useful for users, system-oriented names are needed to be used efficiently by the system. These names generally are bit patterns of fixed size that can be easily manipulated and stored by machines. They are automatically generated by the system. They should be generated in a distributed manner to avoid the problems of efficiency and reliability of a centralized unique identifier generator. They are basically meant for use by the system but may also be used by the users. They are also known as *unique identifiers* and *low-level names*.

Figure 10.3 shows a simple naming model based on these two types of names. In this naming model, a human-oriented name is first mapped (translated) to a system-oriented name that is then mapped to the physical locations of the corresponding object's replicas.

### 10.3.3 Name Space

A naming system employs one or more naming conventions for name assignment to objects. For example, a naming system may use one naming convention for assigning human-oriented names to objects and another naming convention for assigning system-oriented names to objects. The syntactic representation of a name as well as its semantic interpretation depends on the naming convention used for that name. The set of names complying with a given naming convention is said to form a *name space* [Terry 1984].

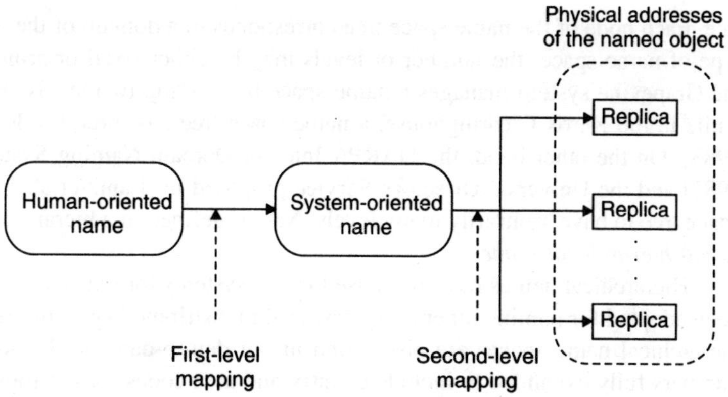


**Fig. 10.3** A simple naming model based on the use of human-oriented and system-oriented names in a distributed system.

### 10.3.4 Flat Name Space

The simplest name space is a flat name space where names are character strings exhibiting no structure. Names defined in a flat name space are called *primitive* or *flat names*. Since flat names do not have any structure, it is difficult to assign unambiguous meaningful names to a large set of objects. Therefore, flat names are suitable for use either for small name spaces having names for only a few objects or for system-oriented names that need not be meaningful to the users.

### 10.3.5 Partitioned Name Space

When there is a need to assign unambiguous meaningful names to a large set of objects, a naming convention that partitions the name space into disjoint classes is normally used. When partitioning is done syntactically, which is generally the case, the name structure reflects physical or organizational associations. Each partition of a partitioned name space is called a *domain* of the name space.

Each domain of a partitioned name space may be viewed as a flat name space by itself, and the names defined in a domain must be unique within that domain. However, two different domains may have a common name defined within them. A name defined in a domain is called a *simple name*. In a partitioned name space, all objects cannot be uniquely identified by simple names, and hence compound names are used for the purpose of unique identification. A *compound name* is composed of one or more simple names that are separated by a special delimiter character such as /, $, @, %, and so on (following the UNIX file system convention, the delimiter character / will be used for the examples and discussion presented in this chapter). For example, */a/b/c* is a compound name consisting of three simple names a, b, and c.

A commonly used type of partitioned name space is the hierarchical name space, in which the name space is partitioned into multiple levels and is structured as an inverted tree. Each node of the name space tree corresponds to a domain of the name space. In this type of name space, the number of levels may be either fixed or arbitrary. For instance, the Grapevine system manages a name space tree having two levels [Birrell et al. 1982], while in the Xerox Clearinghouse, a name space tree has three levels [Oppen and Dalal 1983]. On the other hand, the DARPA Internet Domain Naming System [Su and Postel 1982] and the Universal Directory Service proposed in [Lantz et al. 1985] allow a name space tree to have arbitrarily many levels. Names defined in a hierarchical name space are called *hierarchical names*.

Hierarchical names have been used in file systems for many years and have recently been adopted for naming other objects as well in distributed systems. Several examples of hierarchical name spaces are also found in our day-to-day life. For instance, telephone numbers fully expanded to include country and area codes form a four-level hierarchical name space and network addresses in computer networks form a three-level hierarchical name space where the three levels are for network number, node number, and socket number.

### 10.3.6 Name Server

Name spaces are managed by name servers. A *name server* is a process that maintains information about named objects and provides facilities that enable users to access that information. It acts to bind an object's name to some of its properties, including the object's location [Terry 1984].

In practice, several name servers are normally used for managing the name space of object names in a distributed system. Each name server normally has information about only a small subset of the set of objects in the distributed system. The name servers that store the information about an object are called the *authoritative name servers* of that object [Terry 1984]. To determine the authoritative name servers for every named object, the name service maintains *authority attributes* that contain a list of the authoritative name servers for each object.

Partitioned name spaces are easier to manage efficiently as compared to flat name spaces because they enable the amount of configuration data required in each name server to be reduced since it need only be maintained for each domain and not for each individual object. For example, in a hierarchical name space, it is sufficient that each name server store only enough information to locate the authoritative name servers for the root domain of the name tree. The authoritative name servers of the root domain, in turn, should know the locations of the authoritative name servers of the domains that branch out from the root domain. In general, the authoritative name servers of a domain should know the locations of the authoritative name servers of only those domains that branch out from that domain. For example, in the name space tree of Figure 10.4, all name servers must know the locations of the authoritative name servers of domain $D_1$; the authoritative name servers of domain $D_1$ need only know the locations of the authoritative name servers of domains $D_2$, $D_3$, and $D_4$; and the authoritative name servers of domain $D_2$ need only know the locations of the authoritative name servers of domains $D_5$ and $D_6$. Therefore, the amount of configuration data that must be maintained by name servers at the various levels of the hierarchy is proportional to the degree of branching of the name space tree. For this

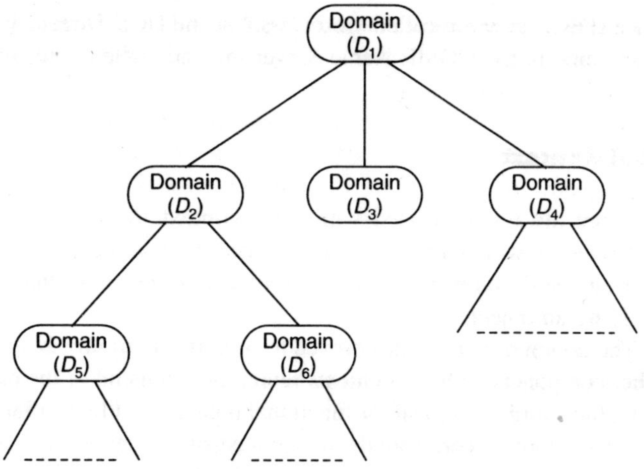


**Fig. 10.4** Domains of a hierarchical name space.

reason, hierarchical naming conventions with several levels are often better suited for naming large number of objects.

It is important to note that the internal representation of a name server need not necessarily reflect the structure of the abstract naming system. For example, rather than adopt to a hierarchical internal structure, a name server may compress hierarchical names into a flat data structure and do string comparisons of entire compound names instead of matching a sequence of simple-name components. In fact, some name servers use a procedure-based strategy rather than table-based strategy to implement the bindings in a given domain of the name space. However, one-to-one correspondence between name servers and domains facilitates easy management of partitioned name spaces.

### 10.3.7 Name Agent

The distribution of the name service and the locations of the name servers should be transparent to the clients of a name service. This transparency is achieved through *name agents* that act between name servers and their clients. A name agent maintains a knowledge of existing name servers. When a client requests for a name service, the name agent uses the proper communication protocol to transfer the user's request to a proper name server. On receiving a reply from the server, it forwards it to the client.

Name agents may be of two types: (a) private, which work for a single client, and (b) shared, which work for several clients. A private name agent is structured as a set of subroutines that are linked to the client program. On the other hand, a shared name agent is structured as a part of an operating system kernel, with system calls to invoke name service operations, or as a separate process that is accessed via interprocess communication primitives.

Name agents are known by various names. For instance, in the CSNET Name Server they are called "name server agent programs," in the DARPA Internet Domain Name

Service (DNS) they are called "resolvers," in the DCE Directory Service they are called "clerks," and in the COSIE Name Server they are called "user interfaces."

### 10.3.8 Context

Names are always associated with some context. A *context* can be thought of as the environment in which a name is valid. Because all names are interpreted relative to some context, a *context/name* pair is said to form a *qualified name* that can be used for uniquely identifying an object.

The notion of context has proved to be very useful for partitioning a name space into smaller components. Often, contexts represent a division of the name space along natural geographical, organizational, or functional boundaries [Terry 1986]. In a partitioned name space, each domain corresponds to a context of the name space. Names in a context can be generated independently of what names exist in any other context. Therefore, a name may occur in more than one context. Contexts may also be nested, as in the case of hierarchical name spaces. For example, in the name space tree of Figure 10.5, context $C_3$ is nested within context $C_2$, which in turn is nested within context $C_1$. In nested contexts, a qualified name consists of a series of names identifying, respectively, a context, a subcontext, a sub-subcontext followed by a name inside the last sub-sub-. . . context. For example, in Figure 10.5, the qualified name for object $O_1$ that is associated with context $C_3$ will be $C_1/C_2/C_3/O_1$.

For the purpose of name management, contexts provide a means of partitioning the naming information database so that it may be distributed among multiple name servers. Contexts represent indivisible units for storage and replication of information regarding named objects [Terry 1986].

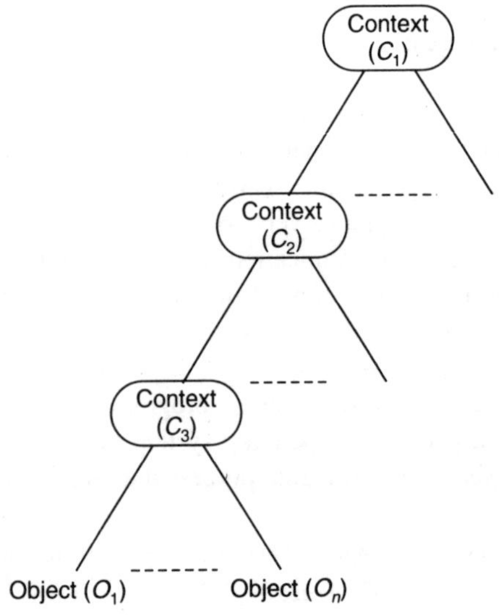


**Fig. 10.5** Nested contexts.

### 10.3.9 Name Resolution

*Name resolution* is the process of mapping an object's name to the object's properties, such as its location. Since an object's properties are stored and maintained by the authoritative name servers of that object, name resolution is basically the process of mapping an object's name to the authoritative name servers of that object. Once an authoritative name server of the object has been located, operations can be invoked to read or update the object's properties.

Each name agent in a distributed system knows about at least one name server a priori. To get a name resolved, a client first contacts its name agent, which in turn contacts a known name server, which may in turn contact other name servers. Because name servers must be able to identify each other, they are also treated as objects and are assigned names. However, to avoid potential cycles, name servers at a given level of a naming system generally identify each other with system-oriented, low-level names.

In a partitioned name space, the name resolution mechanism traverses a resolution chain from one context to another until the authoritative name servers of the named object are encountered. As shown in Figure 10.6, a given name is first interpreted in the context to which it is associated. The interpretation either provides the authoritative name servers of the named object or returns a new name and a new context to interpret that name. In the former case the name resolution process ends, while in the latter case the interpretation process continues as before until the authoritative name servers of the named object are encountered. Notice that if all the contexts involved in the resolution of a name are managed by a single name server, then the complete name resolution operation is carried out by a single name server; otherwise more than one name server is involved in the name resolution operation.

### 10.3.10 Abbreviation/Alias

In case of partitioned name spaces, a qualified name, which is normally a compound name, may consist of several simple names and may be very long. It may be inconvenient for a user to specify the qualified name of an object every time he or she wants to use it. Therefore, in a naming convention for partitioned name spaces, users are generally allowed to specify and use their own short-form substitutes for qualified names called *abbreviations*. All abbreviations defined by a user form a private context of that user. A mapping of abbreviations to qualified names is maintained on a per private context basis. When a user specifies an abbreviation, it is first converted to a qualified name by using the mapping associated with the private context of that user. Therefore, different users may use the same abbreviation to identify different objects. For example, two users, *user-1* and *user-2*, may use the same abbreviation *my-object-1* to identify their objects having the qualified names */user-1/project-1/group-1/object-1* and */user-2/project-5/group-3/object-1*, respectively. Abbreviations are also know as *aliases*. Notice that aliases are generally simple names that need to be unique only in a single private context. The symbolic links facility of the UNIX file system is an example of aliasing facility in a naming system.

In case of aliasing, a binding associates a single simple name with a qualified name. However, a user may wish to identify an object by one of two or more simple names. A

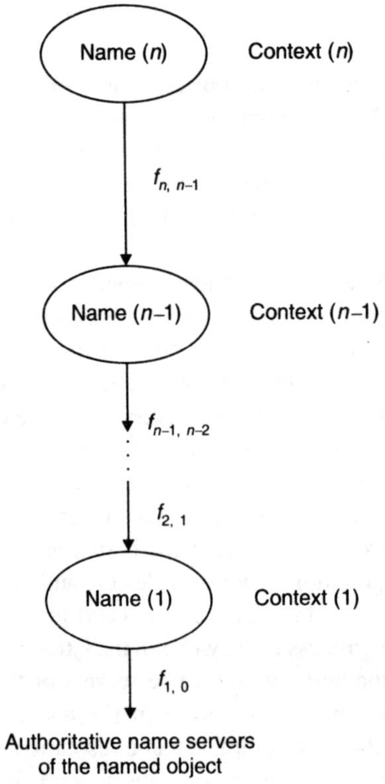


Context ($i$) = context at level $i$
Name ($i$) = valid name in context at level ($i$)
$f_{i,j}$ = mapping function from the name in context ($i$) to a new name in context ($j$)

**Fig. 10.6** Context-by-context name resolution mechanism.

naming system may provide this flexibility to its users by allowing many-to-one bindings within a context. That is, more than one simple name may be bound to the same qualified name within a given context. If this facility is provided, the simple names bound to the same qualified name are called *synonyms* or *nicknames*.

### 10.3.11 Absolute and Relative Names

Another method to avoid the necessity to specify the full qualified name of an object in tree-structured name spaces is the use of the concept of *current working context*. A current working context is also known by the shorter names *current context* or *working context*. According to this concept, a user is always associated with a context that is his or her current context. A user can change his or her current context whenever he or she desires.

In this method, object names can be of two types—absolute or relative. An *absolute name* begins at the root context of the name space tree and follows a path down to the specified object, giving the context names on the path. On the other hand, a *relative name* defines a path from the current context to the specified object. It is called a relative name because it is "relative to" (starts from) the user's current context. For example, in the tree-structured name space of Figure 10.7, if the user's current context is *root-context/context-1/context-3*, the relative name *context-5/object-1* refers to the same object as does the absolute name *root-context/context-1/context-3/context-5/object-1*. Means are also provided in this method to refer to the parent context of a context. For example, in the UNIX file-naming convention, which uses tree-structured name space, two periods (.., pronounced "dot dot") refer to a directory's parent directory (a directory is basically a context). The root directory is its own parent.

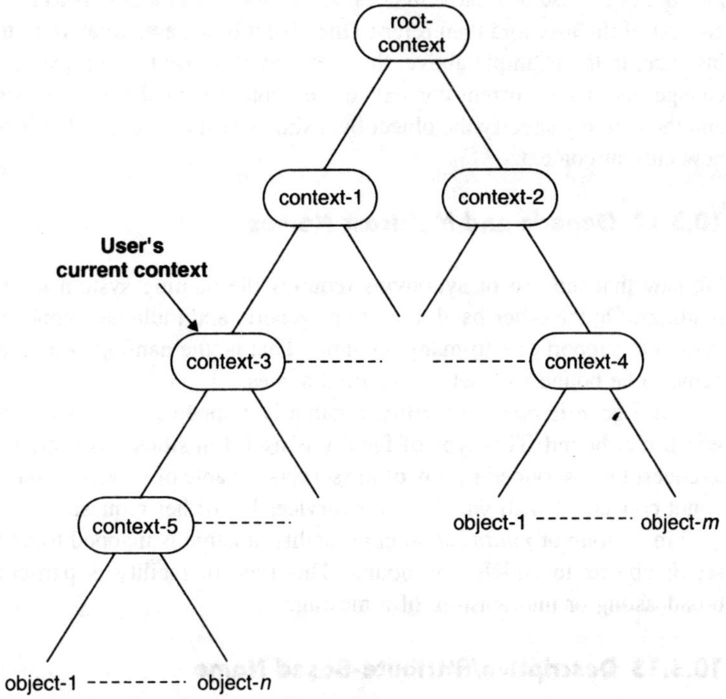


**Fig. 10.7** A tree-structured name space to illustrate absolute and relative names.

In this method, a user may specify an object in any of the following ways:

1. Using the full (absolute) name
2. Using a relative name
3. Changing the current context first and then using a relative name

For example, in Figure 10.7, if the user whose current context is *root-context/context-1/context-3* wants to specify the object *root-context/context-2/context-4/object-1*, he or she can do so in the following ways:

1. Specify the absolute name of the object, which is *root-context/context-2/context-4/object-1*.

2. Specify the name of the object relative to his or her current context as *../../context-2/context-4/object-1*. In this relative name, the first dot dot refers to the parent context of the user's current context, which is *context-1*, and the second dot dot refers to the parent context of *context-1*, which is *root-context*.

3. Notice from the above two name specification methods that a relative name may be equally long or even longer than the absolute name in some cases. This defeats the main purpose of the use of relative names. Hence the third method is to first change the current context of the user and then refer to the object by a name relative to the new context. For instance, in the example above, the user may first use the context-changing command to change his or her current context to the context named *root-context/context-2/context-4* and then simply specify the object by a simple name *object-1* that is relative to the user's new current context.

### 10.3.12 Generic and Multicast Names

We saw that the use of synonyms requires the naming system to support many-to-one bindings. On the other hand, the use of generic and multicast names requires the naming system to support one-to-many bindings. That is, the naming system must allow a simple name to be bound to a set of qualified names.

In a *generic naming* facility, a name is mapped to any one of the set of objects to which it is bound. This type of facility is useful in situations such as when a user wants a request to be serviced by any of the servers capable of servicing that request and the user is not concerned with which server services his or her request.

In a *group* or *multicast naming* facility, a name is mapped to all the members of the set of objects to which it is bound. This type of facility is particularly useful for the broadcasting or multicasting of a message.

### 10.3.13 Descriptive/Attribute-Based Name

A naming system that supports descriptive/attribute-based names allows an object to be identified by a set of attributes or properties that describe the object and uniquely identify it among the group of objects in the name space. A partitioned name space having a rigid structure (a rigid set of attributes) is an example of a descriptive naming convention. In this case, each domain of the name space is used to define an attribute of the objects. An attribute has both a type and a value. The type indicates the format and meaning of the value field. For example, a typical set of attributes that may be used for uniquely identifying a file object may be *User = Sinha, Creation date = 1995/04/06, File type = Source, Language = Pascal, Name = Quicksort.*

Note that an attribute value may be the same for several objects, but all attributes considered together refer to a single object. Moreover, it is not always necessary to specify all the attributes of a naming convention to identify an object. Attribute-based naming systems usually work based on the idea that a query must supply enough attributes so that the target object can be uniquely identified. Also notice that in a partitioned name space using descriptive naming convention, domains can be arranged in any arbitrary manner.

Multicast or group naming facility can be easily provided with attribute-based naming by constructing an attribute for a list of names. Group names are particularly useful in forming mail distribution lists and access control lists.

### 10.3.14 Source-Routing Name

Many name spaces mirror the structure of the underlying physical network. When the structure of a name space has the same form as the underlying network of a distributed system, the name space defines *source-routing names*. A source-routing name identifies a path through the network of a distributed system. The UNIX-to-UNIX Copy (UUCP) name space that defines names of the form *host-1!host-2!host-3!sinha* is an example of a source-routing name space. The UUCP style names are called source-routing names because the route through the network is specified at the source computer. For instance, in the example above, the specified route is from *host-1* to *host-2* to *host-3* to *sinha*. The UUCP style names are relative names because they must be interpreted relative to the starting point.

## 10.4 SYSTEM-ORIENTED NAMES

System-oriented names normally have the following characteristic features:

1. They are large integers or bit strings. For example, in a typical naming system, system-oriented names may be members of some large set of integers, such as the integers up to $2^{128}-1$.

2. They are also referred to as *unique identifiers* because in most naming systems they are guaranteed to be unique in both space and time. That is, these names do not change during their lifetime, and once used, they are never reused. Therefore, in the naming system discussed above, a 128-bit pattern refers either to nothing or, if it refers to anything, to the same thing at all times. This is the main reason why unique identifiers are so large.

3. Unlike human-oriented names that are variable in length, all system-oriented names of a naming system are of the same size irrespective of the type or location of the object identified by these names. This allows the naming of all objects uniformly.

4. Since all the system-oriented names of a naming system are of uniform size and also are normally shorter than human-oriented names, manipulations like hashing, sorting, and so on, can be easily performed on them. Hence, they are suitable for efficient handling by machines.

5. They are hard to guess and hence are sometimes also used for security-related purposes. For example, they may be used as tickets of permission to access objects. A computation that presents a valid name may be assumed to have been given it deliberately rather than to have guessed or invented it. This is an example of use of protected names or capabilities, one of the classical approaches to access control management.

6. System-oriented names are automatically generated by the system.

An important issue associated with system-oriented names is how to create a unique name for each object in the system. Before describing the methods to handle this issue, it is useful to mention that system-oriented names can be either unstructured or structured (see Fig. 10.8 for an example of each type). Unstructured names have a single field of large integers or bit strings that uniquely identifies an object but does not provide any other information about the object. On the other hand, structured names contain more than one component, some of which provide information about the properties of the object identified by its name. For example, a structured name may have a component that specifies the node on which the object was created or the node on which the object is currently located. The two basic approaches for the creation of these two types of system-oriented names are discussed below.

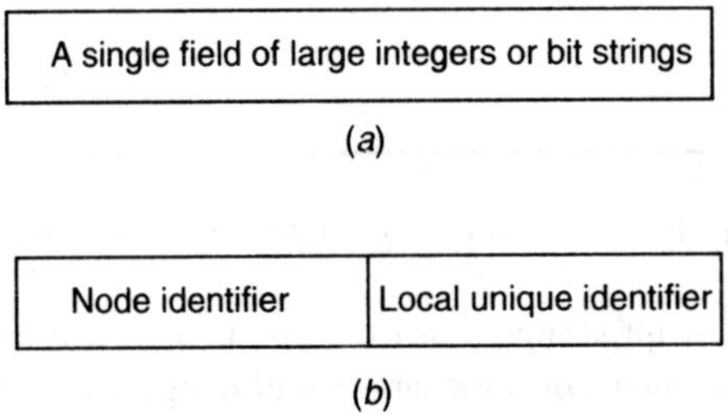

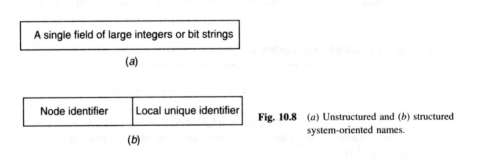

**Fig. 10.8** (*a*) Unstructured and (*b*) structured system-oriented names.

### 10.4.1 Centralized Approach for Generating System-Oriented Names

Although the centralized approach may be used for the generation of both unstructured as well as structured system-oriented names, it is mainly used by a naming system that uses unstructured names. In this method, a standard, uniform global identifier is generated for each object in the system by a centralized global unique identifier generator, and some method is used to partition this global name space among the local domains of each node. Each node either directly binds these global identifiers to the locally created objects or it maps its local identifiers for the locally created objects to these global identifiers. In the latter case, binding of local identifiers to global identifiers can be permanent or temporary.

The centralized approach has the advantages that it is simple and easy to implement and is the only method for generating unstructured global unique identifiers. However, it suffers from the drawbacks of poor efficiency and poor reliability. The single global unique identifier generator may become a bottleneck for large name spaces. Also, the continuous generation of global unique identifiers is totally dependent on the reliability of the centralized global unique identifier generator.

### 10.4.2 Distributed Approach for Generating System-Oriented Names

To overcome the drawbacks of poor efficiency and poor reliability of the centralized approach, several naming systems use the distributed approach for the generation of system-oriented names. However, distributed generation forces the naming system to use structured object identifiers. In the distributed approach, the *hierarchical concatenation* strategy is used to create global unique identifiers. In this strategy, each identification domain is assigned a unique identifier, and a global unique identifier for an object is created by concatenating the unique identifier of a domain with an identifier used within this domain. Therefore, global unique identifiers generated in this manner basically consist of two components—the domain identifier and an identifier within this domain. Notice that each component may in turn consist of two or more subcomponents. For example, the domain identifier for a wide area network may consist of two subcomponents—network identifier and node identifier within this network.

The next question that arises is how to generate unique identifiers within a domain in an efficient manner. One method to do this is to treat each node of the system as a domain of the name space and treat a reading from the real-time clock (called timestamp) of a node as a unique identifier within the node. With this, global unique identifiers take the form of the pair (*node-ID*, *timestamp*). Another method is to treat each server as a domain and then to allow a server to generate object identifiers for the objects it serves in a server-specific manner. In this case, global unique identifiers take the form of the pair (*server-ID*, *server-specific-unique-identifier*).

Although the distributed approach has better efficiency and reliability as compared to the centralized approach, it suffers from the following drawbacks:

1. In a heterogeneous environment, the form and length of identifiers may be different for different computers (nodes), resulting in nonuniform global unique identifiers. It may be awkward or inefficient for applications to be prepared to deal with the nonuniformity of these low-level identifiers.
2. Node boundaries or servers are explicitly visible in this scheme.

### 10.4.3 Generating Unique Identifiers in the Event of Crashes

Another important problem related with the creation of unique identifiers (whether global or local) is to be able to create unique identifiers in the face of crashes. A crash may lead to loss of the state information of a unique identifier generator. Therefore, upon recovery, the unique identifier generator may not function correctly, which may result in the generation of nonunique identifiers. Two basic approaches are used to solve this problem [Watson 1981]:

1. *Using a clock that operates across failures*. In this method, a clock is used at the location of the unique identifier generator. This clock is guaranteed to continue operating across failures, and it will not recycle during the period within which the needed identifiers must be unique. However, to implement this method, one may require rather long identifiers, depending on the granularity of the clock interval needed.

2. *Using two or more levels of storage*. In this method, two or more levels of storage are used and the unique identifiers are structured in a hierarchical fashion with one field for each level. A counter associated with each level contains the highest value of the corresponding field assigned. The current values of these fields are cached in main memory. When a lower level field is about to cycle or the associated storage device crashes, the next higher level counter is incremented and the lower level counters are reset. If a stable storage (the information on which can survive crashes) is used, two levels of storage (the upper level being the main-memory storage and the lower level being the stable storage) are sufficient for creating a safe and efficient unique identifier generator. As compared to the first mechanism, this mechanism can yield shorter identifiers, but it is more complex to implement.

## 10.5 OBJECT-LOCATING MECHANISMS

*Object locating* is the process of mapping an object's system-oriented unique identifier (UID for short) to the replica locations of the object. It may be noted here that the *object-locating operation* is different and independent of the *object-accessing operation*. In a distributed system, object locating is only the process of knowing the object's location, that is, the node on which it is located. On the other hand, object accessing involves the process of carrying out the desired operation (e.g., read, write) on the object. Therefore, the object-accessing operation starts only after the object-locating operation has been carried out successfully.

Several object-locating mechanisms have been proposed and are being used by various distributed operating systems. These mechanisms are briefly described below. The suitability of a particular mechanism for a distributed system depends on various factors such as the scale of the system, the type of UID being used by its naming system, whether the system supports object migration, whether the system supports location transparency of objects, and so on.

### 10.5.1 Broadcasting

In this method, an object is located by broadcasting a request for the object from a client node. The request is processed by all nodes and then the nodes currently having the object reply back to the client node. Amoeba [Mullender and Tanenbaum 1986] uses this method for locating a remote port.

The method is simple and enjoys a high degree of reliability because it supplies all replica locations of the target object. However, it suffers from the drawbacks of poor efficiency and scalability because the amount of network traffic generated for each request is directly proportional to the number of nodes in the system and is prohibitive for large networks. Therefore, this method is suitable only when the number of nodes is small, communication speed is high, and object-locating requests are not so frequent.

### 10.5.2 Expanding Ring Broadcast

Pure broadcasting is expensive for large networks. Moreover, direct broadcasting to all nodes may not be supported by wide-area networks. Therefore, a modified form of broadcasting, called expanding ring broadcast (ERB) [Wiebe 1986], is normally employed in an internetwork that consists of local area networks (LANs) connected by gateways. In this method, increasingly distant LANs are systematically searched until the object is found or until every LAN has been searched unsuccessfully. The distance metric used is a *hop*. A hop corresponds to a gateway between processors. For example, if a message from processor $A$ to processor $B$ must pass through at least two gateways, $A$ and $B$ are two hops distant. Processors on the same LAN are zero hop distant. A *ring* is the set of LANs a certain distance away from a processor. Thus, $Ring_0[A]$ is $A$'s local network, $Ring_1[A]$ is the set of LANs one hop away, and so on.

An ERB search works as follows. Suppose that processor $A$ needs to locate object $X$. Beginning with $i = 0$, a request message is broadcast to all LANs in $Ring_i[A]$. If a response is received, the search ends successfully. Otherwise, after a timeout period has elapsed, $i$ is incremented by 1 and the request broadcast is repeated. The ring size $i$ is bounded from above by the diameter of the internetwork.

Notice that this method does not necessarily supply all the replica locations of an object simultaneously, although it does supply the nearest replica location. Furthermore, the efficiency of an object-locating operation is directly proportional to the distance of the object from the client node at the time of locating it.

### 10.5.3 Encoding Location of Object within Its UID

This scheme uses structured object identifiers. One field of the structured UID is the location of the object. Given a UID, the system simply extracts the corresponding object's location from its UID by examining the appropriate field of the structured UID. The extracted location is the node on which the object resides.

This is a straightforward and efficient scheme. One restriction of the scheme, however, is that an object is not permitted to move once it is assigned to a node, since this would require its identifier to change. Consequently, an object is fixed to one node throughout its lifetime. Another limitation of the scheme is that it is not clear how to support multiple replicas of an object. Therefore, the use of this object-locating scheme is limited to those distributed systems that do not support object migration and object replication.

### 10.5.4 Searching Creator Node First and Then Broadcasting

This scheme is a simple extension of the previous scheme. The included extension is basically meant for supporting object migration facility. The method is based on the assumption that it is very likely for an object to remain at the node where it was created (although it may not be always true). This is because object migration is an expensive operation and objects do not migrate frequently.

In this scheme, the location field of the structured UID contains the identifier of the node on which the object was created. Given a UID, the creator node information is extracted from the UID and a request is sent to that node. If the object no longer resides on its creator node, a failure reply is returned back to the client node. In case of failure, the object is located by broadcasting the request from the client node. This method of object locating is used in Cronus [Schantz et al. 1986].

As compared to the broadcasting scheme, this method helps in reducing the network traffic to a great extent. Furthermore, the scheme is more flexible than the method of encoding the location of an object within its UID because it allows the system to support object migration. However, the use of broadcast protocol to locate those objects that are not found on their creator nodes limits the scalability of this mechanism.

### 10.5.5 Using Forward Location Pointers

This scheme is an extension of the previous scheme. The goal of this extension is to avoid the use of broadcast protocol. A *forward location pointer* is a reference used at a node to indicate the new location of an object. Whenever an object is migrated from one node to another, a forward location pointer is left at its previous node. Therefore, to locate an object, the system first contacts the creator node of the object and then simply follows the forward pointer or chain of pointers to the node on which the object currently resides.

The method has the advantages of totally avoiding the use of broadcast protocol and allowing the support of object migration facility. However, the method practically has the following major drawbacks:

1. The object-locating cost is directly proportional to the length of the chain of pointers to be traversed and grows considerably as the chain becomes longer.
2. It is difficult, or even impossible, to locate an object if an intermediate pointer has been lost or is unavailable due to node failures. Therefore, the reliability of the mechanism is poor.
3. The method introduces additional system overhead for upkeep.

### 10.5.6 Using Hint Cache and Broadcasting

Another commonly used approach is the cache-broadcast scheme. In this method, a cache is maintained on each node that contains the (*UID*, *last known location*) pairs of a number of recently referenced remote objects. Given a UID, the local cache is examined to determine if it has an entry for the UID. If an entry is found, the corresponding location information is extracted from the cache. The object access request is then sent to the node specified in the extracted location information. If the object no longer resides at that node, however, the request is returned with a negative reply, indicating that the location information extracted from the cache was outdated. If the specified UID is not found in the local cache or if the location information of the object in the local cache is found to be outdated, a message is broadcast throughout the network requesting the current location of the object. Each node that receives the broadcast request performs an internal search for the specified object. A reply message is returned to the client node from the node on which the object is found. This location of the object is then recorded in the client node's cache. Notice that a cache entry only serves as a hint because it is not always correct.

This scheme can be very efficient if a high degree of locality is exhibited in locating objects from a node. It is also flexible since it can support object migration facility. Furthermore, the method of on-use update of cached information avoids the expense and delay of having to notify other nodes when an object migrates. One problem with this scheme, however, is that broadcast requests will clutter up the network, disturbing all the nodes even though only a single node is directly involved with each object-locating operation.

This is the most commonly used object-locating mechanism in modern distributed operating systems. It is used in Amoeba [Mullender et al. 1990], V-System [Cheriton and Mann 1989], DOMAIN [Leach et al. 1983], NEXUS [Tripathi et al. 1987], Mach [Rashid 1987], and Chorus [Rozier et al. 1988].

Figure 10.9 summarizes the various object-locating mechanisms discussed above. Note that schemes (*c*), (*d*), and (*e*) require structured UID whereas schemes (*a*), (*b*), and (*f*) can work with both unstructured and structured UIDs. Also notice that only scheme (*c*) facilitates the object-locating operation to be carried out without the need to exchange any message with any other node. However, it is inflexible because it does not support object migration and object replication facilities.

## 10.6 HUMAN-ORIENTED NAMES

System-oriented names such as *31A5 2B5F AD19 B1C8*, though useful for machine handling, are not suitable for use by users. Users will have a tough time if they are required to remember these names or type them in. Furthermore, each object has only a single system-oriented name, and therefore all the users sharing an object must remember and use its only name. To overcome these limitations, almost all naming systems provide the facility to the users to define and use their own suitable names for the various objects in the system. These user-defined object names, which form a name space on top of the name space for system-oriented names, are called human-oriented names.

Human-oriented names normally have the following characteristics:

1. They are character strings that are meaningful to their users.
2. They are defined and used by the users.

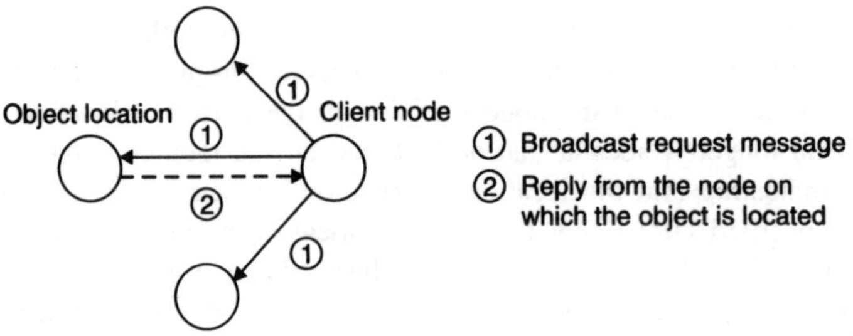
Object location
Client node
1
1
2
1
1 Broadcast request message
2 Reply from the node on which the object is located

(*a*)

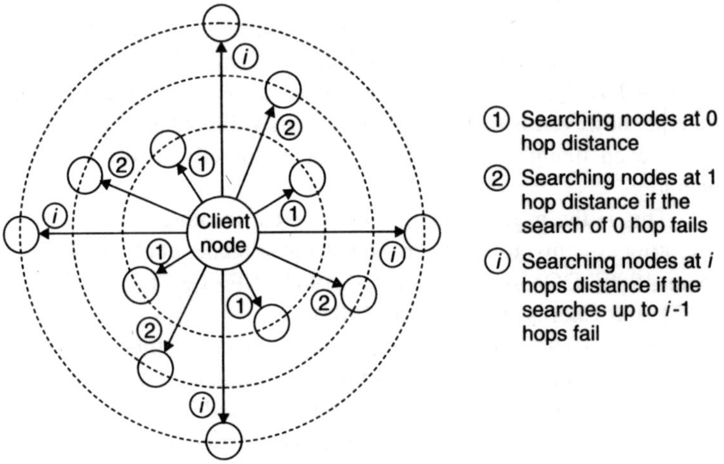
Client node
1 Searching nodes at 0 hop distance
2 Searching nodes at 1 hop distance if the search of 0 hop fails
i Searching nodes at i hops distance if the searches up to i-1 hops fail

(*b*)

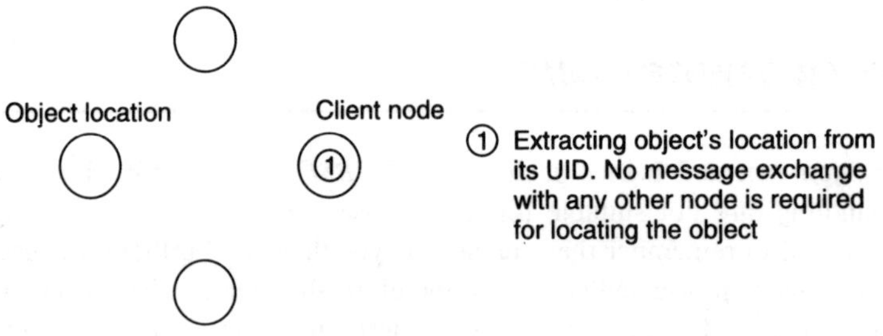
Object location
Client node
1
1 Extracting object's location from its UID. No message exchange with any other node is required for locating the object

(*c*)

**Fig. 10.9** Object-locating mechanisms: (*a*) broadcasting; (*b*) expanding-ring broadcast; (*c*) encoding the location of an object within its UID; (*d*) searching the creator node first and then broadcasting; (*e*) using forward location pointers; (*f*) using hint cache and broadcasting. (Continued on next page.)

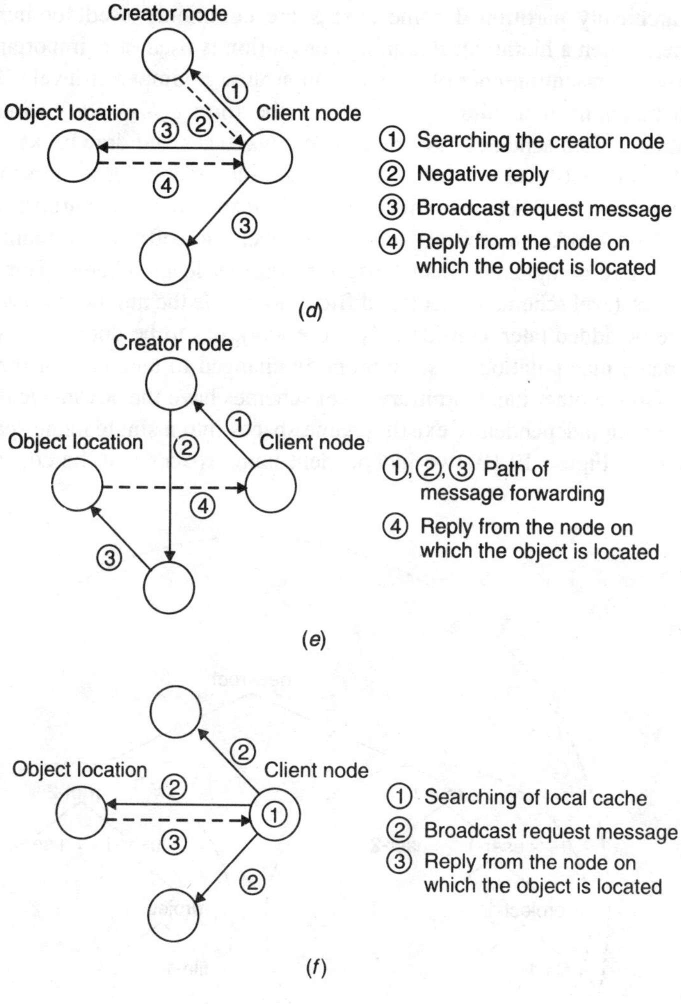


**Fig. 10.9** (Continued.)

3. Different users can define and use their own suitable names for a shared object. That is, the facility of aliasing is provided to the users.
4. Human-oriented names are variable in length not only in names for different objects but even in different names for the same object.
5. Due to the facility of aliasing, the same name may be used by two different users at the same time to refer to two different objects. Furthermore, a user may use the same name at different instances of time to refer to different objects. Therefore, human-oriented names are not unique in either space or time.

Because of the advantages of easy and efficient management of name space, hierarchically partitioned name spaces are commonly used for human-oriented object names. When a hierarchical naming convention is used, it is important to decide whether to use a constant number of levels or an arbitrary number of levels. That is, if the names of a hierarchical naming system are of the form $c_1/c_2/\ldots/c_i$, should $i$ be constant or arbitrary? Both schemes have their own advantages and drawbacks. The main advantage of the constant-level scheme is that it is simpler and easier to implement as compared to the arbitrary-level scheme. This is because all software in the arbitrary-level scheme must be able to handle an arbitrary number of levels, so software for manipulating names tend to be more complicated than those for constant-level scheme. The disadvantage of the constant-level scheme is that it is difficult to decide the number of levels, and if new levels are to be added later, considerably more work has to be done because all the algorithms for name manipulation must be properly changed to take care of the new levels.

On the other hand, arbitrary-level schemes have the advantage of easy expansion by combining independently existing name spaces into a single name space. For example, as shown in Figure 10.10, two independent name spaces may be combined into one name

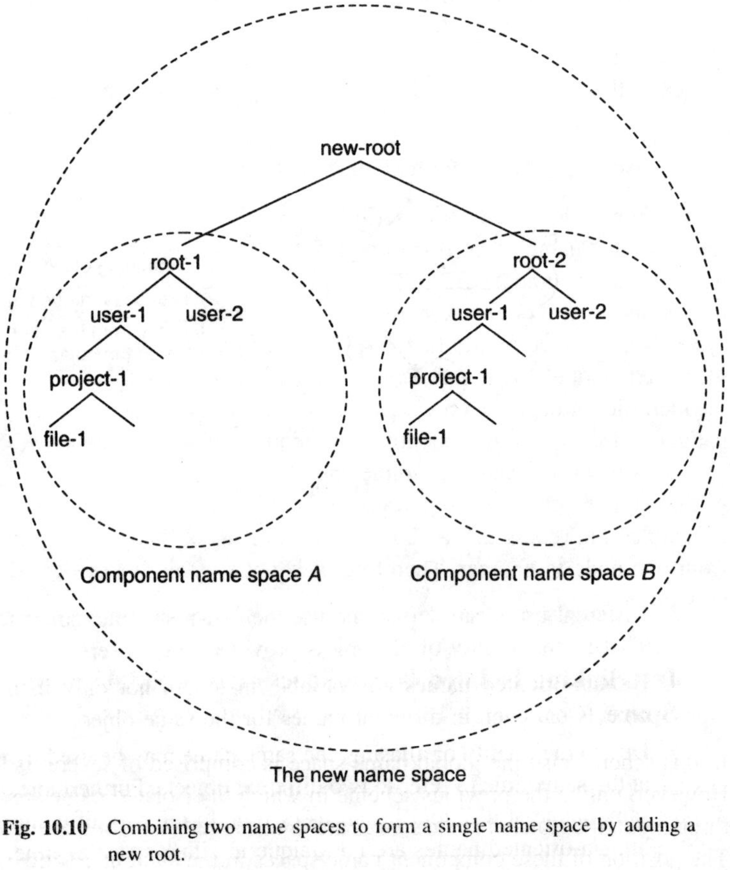


**Fig. 10.10** Combining two name spaces to form a single name space by adding a new root.

space by adding a new root, making the existing roots its children. The major advantage is that if a name was unambiguous within its old name space, it is still unambiguous within its new name space, even if the name also appeared in some other name space that was combined. There is no need to change any of the algorithms for manipulating names.

Arbitrary-level schemes, being more flexible than constant-level schemes, are used by most recent distributed systems. Hence, subsequent sections of this chapter deal with arbitrary-level hierarchical name spaces.

The major issues associated with human-oriented names are as follows:

1. Selecting a proper scheme for global object naming
2. Selecting a proper scheme for partitioning a name space into contexts
3. Selecting a proper scheme for implementing context bindings
4. Selecting a proper scheme for name resolution

These issues are described in the next section.

### 10.6.1 Human-Oriented Hierarchical Naming Schemes

Basically there are four approaches for assigning systemwide unique human-oriented names to the various objects in a distributed system. These are described below.

#### Combining an Object's Local Name with Its Host Name

This naming scheme uses a name space that is comprised of several isolated name spaces. Each isolated name space corresponds to a node of the distributed system, and a name in this name space uniquely identifies an object of the node. In the global system, objects are named by some combination of their host name and local name, which guarantees a systemwide unique name. In Ibis [Tichy and Ruan 1984], for instance, file objects are identified uniquely by names having the form *host-name:local-name*, where *host-name* is the identifier of the node on which the file resides and *local-name* is a UNIX-like absolute pathname for the file that identifies it uniquely on its host node.

This naming scheme is simple and easy to implement. Its main drawback, however, is that it is neither location transparent nor location independent. Furthermore, it is inflexible in the sense that an object's absolute name changes every time an object moves from one node to another. Therefore, it is not suitable for modern distributed operating systems.

#### Interlinking Isolated Name Spaces into a Single Name Space

In this scheme also the global name space is comprised of several isolated name spaces. However, unlike the previous scheme in which the isolated name spaces remain isolated throughout, the isolated name spaces are joined together to form a single naming structure. The position of these component name spaces in the naming hierarchy is arbitrary. In the naming structure, a component name space may be placed below any other component name space either directly or through other component name spaces. In this scheme there is no notion of absolute pathname. Each pathname is relative to some context, either to the current working context or to the current component name space.

This naming scheme is used in UNIX United [Brownbridge et al. 1982] to join any number of UNIX systems to compose a UNIX United system. In the single naming structure of UNIX United, each component system is a complete UNIX directory tree belonging to a certain node. The root of each component name space is assigned a unique name so that they become accessible and distinguishable externally. A component's own root is still referred to as / and still serves as the starting point of all pathnames starting with a /. The UNIX notation ../ is used to refer to the parent of a component's own root. Therefore, there is only one root that is its own parent and that is not assigned a string name, namely, the root of the composite structure, which is just a virtual root needed to make the whole structure a single tree.

A simple example of such a naming structure is shown in Figure 10.10, in which the composite name structure is comprised of two component name spaces *A* and *B* whose roots are named *root-1* and *root-2*, respectively. As an illustration of relative path naming in this scheme, note that from within the component name space *A*, *file-1* of the two component name spaces *A* and *B* will be referred to as */user-1/project-1/file-1* and *../root-2/user-1/project-1/file-1*, respectively. Similarly, if the current working directory of a client is *project-1* of the component name space *B*, *file-1* of the two component name spaces *A* and *B* will be referred to as *../../../root-1/user-1/project-1/file-1* and *file-1*, respectively.

The main advantage of this naming scheme is that it is simple to join existing name spaces into a single global name space. However, in naming systems that employ this scheme for global object naming, an important issue that needs to be handled is to allow clients to continue to use names that were valid in the independent name spaces without the need to update them to match the new name space structure. For example, in Figure 10.10, */user-1/project-1/file-1* is a name used by clients before the two component name spaces were integrated. Before integration, this name referred to *file-1* of component name space *A* for clients of component name space *A* and to *file-1* of component name space *B* for clients of component name space *B*. Therefore, it is desirable that after integration of the two component name spaces, this name should still refer to the same object for the clients of the two component name spaces. The Global Name Service (GNS), which was designed and implemented by Lampson and colleagues at the DEC Systems Research Center [Lampson 1986], provides an interesting solution to this problem. Its approach, which is based on the use of directory identifiers (DIs) and a table of well-known directories, is described below.

A GNS has two parts *<directory name, value name>*. The first part identifies a directory and the second part refers to a value tree or some portion of a value tree. Each directory has a unique DI associated with it. Figure 10.10 has been redrawn in Figure 10.11(*a*) to illustrate the GNS naming scheme.

In the GNS naming convention, *file-1* of both the component name spaces *A* and *B*, before their integration, will be referred to as *</user-1, project-1/file-1>*. After integration of the two component name spaces, when a client of component name space

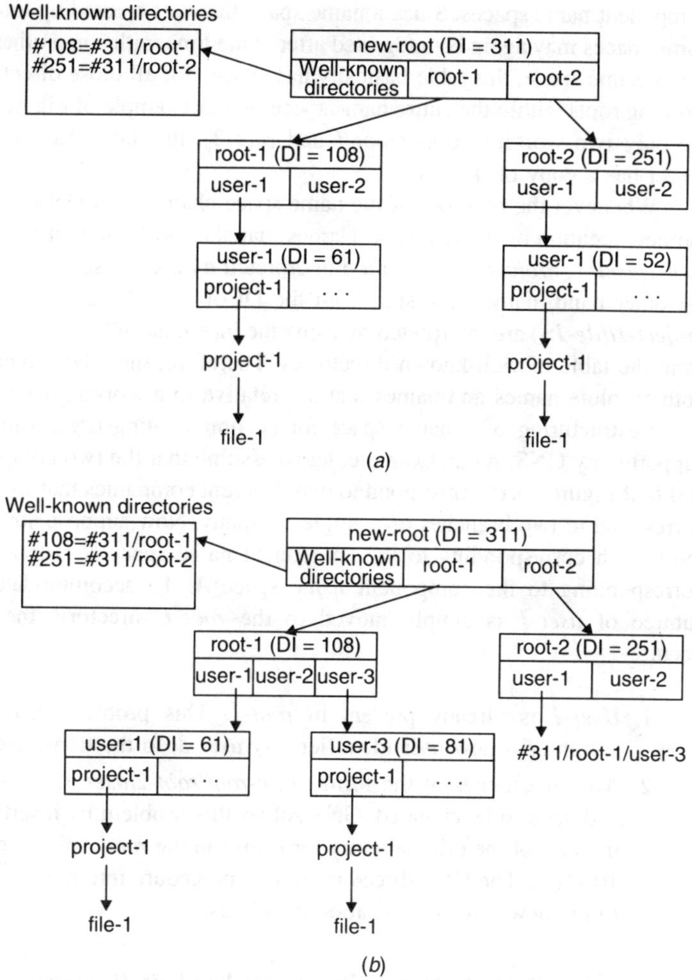


**Fig. 10.11** The GNS approach of accommodating changes in existing name spaces: (*a*) combining two name spaces to form a single name space; (*b*) restructuring a name space.

*A* uses this name, its local name agent, which is aware of the local root directory's DI, prefixes the DI (*#108*), thus producing the name <*#108/user-1, project-1/file-1*>. On the other hand, when a client of component name space *B* uses the same name, its local name agent prefixes the DI (*#251*) of the root directory of component name space *B*, thus producing the name <*#251/user-1, project-1/file-1*>. The name agent then passes this derived name in a lookup request to a GNS server. Relative names are similarly converted into local absolute names by a local name agent before being passed to a GNS server for lookup.

To allow a GNS server to locate a directory given its DI (such as *#108*), GNS uses a table of well-known directories. This table contains a list of the root directories of all component name spaces. Since a name space that was created by integrating two or more name spaces may again be integrated after some time with some other name space to form a new name space, this table basically has entries for all those directories that are used as working roots within the entire name space. In our example of Figure 10.11(*a*), since there are only two working roots (*root-1* and *root-2*), this table has two entries. Each GNS server has a copy of this table.

Whenever the real root of the name space changes, all GNS servers are informed of the new location of the real root. Names that start with the real root (such as <*new-root/root-1/user-1, project-1/file-1*>) are interpreted by a GNS server in the usual manner. On the other hand, names that start with the DI of a working root (such as <*#108/user-1, project-1/file-1*>) are interpreted by using the information for the corresponding DI's entry from the table of well-known directories. Therefore, the GNS scheme allows the use of both absolute names and names that are relative to a working root.

Restructuring of a name space for accommodating organizational changes is also supported by GNS. As an example, let us assume that the two component name spaces *A* and *B* of Figure 10.10 correspond to two different companies that were integrated and now correspond to two branches of a single company. Now suppose sometime later *user-1* of the branch corresponding to the component name space *B* is transferred to the branch corresponding to the component name space *A*. To accommodate this change, if the subtree of *user-1* is simply moved to the *root-1* directory, the following problems occur:

1. *User-1* is already present in *root-1*. This problem can be easily solved by assigning a new user identifier, say *user-3*, to the transferred user.
2. Absolute names of the form <*new-root/root-2/user-1, . . .*> will no longer work and need to be changed. GNS solves this problem by inserting a "symbolic link" in place of the original entry for *user-1* in the *root-2* directory, as shown in Figure 10.11(*b*). The GNS directory lookup procedure interprets the link as a redirection to the new directory location of this user.

### Sharing Remote Name Spaces on Explicit Request

This scheme, popularized by Sun Microsystems' Network File System (NFS) [Sandberg et al. 1985], is also based on the idea of attaching the isolated name spaces of various nodes to create a new name space. However, unlike the previous scheme in which a single naming structure is created by the system, in this scheme users are given the flexibility to attach a context of a remote name space to one of the contexts of their local name spaces. Once a remote context is attached locally, its objects can be named in a location-transparent manner. The goal is to allow some degree of sharing among the name spaces of various nodes in a transparent manner on explicit request by the users. Therefore, the global view of the resulting name structure is a forest of trees, one for each node, with some overlapping due to the shared subtrees. Notice that, unlike the previous scheme in which the entire name space of each node is attached to the single naming structure, in this scheme the users have the flexibility to attach to their local name space tree either a complete remote name space tree or a part of it (subtree). Also notice that a request to share a remote name space affects only the node from which the request was made and no other node. This ensures node independence. The naming of file objects in NFS is described below as an illustration of this scheme.

In NFS, the *mount* protocol is used to attach a remote name space directory to a local name space. Therefore, to make a remote directory accessible in a transparent manner from a node, a mount operation has to be performed from the node. The node that performs the mount operation is called a client node and the node whose name space directory is mounted is called a server node. NFS allows every machine to be both a client and a server at the same time. A server must export all those directories of its name space tree that are to be made accessible to remote clients. The complete subtree rooted at an exported directory is exported as a unit. Therefore, all directories below an exported directory automatically become accessible to a client when the exported directory is mounted on the client's local name space. This is because when a client mounts a server's directory, the mounting process sets up a link between the mount point of the client's local name space and the exported directory of the server's name space. To allow directories to be automatically exported by a server when it is booted, the list of directories to be exported by the server is maintained in the */etc/ exports* file.

The semantics of the mount operation are that a server's file system directory exported by the server is mounted over a directory of the client's file system. The mounted directory's subtree of the server file system appears to be an integral part of the client's file system, replacing the subtree descending from the client's local directory on which the server's directory was mounted. The local directory becomes the name of the root of the newly mounted directory. Hence, after the mount operation, local users can access files in the mounted remote directory in a totally transparent manner. To programs running on the client machine, there is (almost) no difference between a file located on a remote file server and a file located on the local disk.

A client can mount a directory in one of the following ways:

1. *Manual mounting*. In this case, the client uses the *mount* command any time a server's directory is to be mounted on the client's local name space. The *umount* command allows the client to unmount the directory when the client no longer needs to access the files in the subtree of the server's directory. A client must be a superuser to use the *mount* and *umount* commands. This method provides the flexibility to the clients to dynamically mount or unmount servers' directories depending on changing needs.

2. *Static mounting*. In the manual mounting scheme, a *mount* command is to be used every time a server's directory is to be mounted by a client. The static mounting scheme allows clients to automatically mount the directories of their choice out of the directories exported by servers without manual intervention. In this method, the shell script for the commands to mount the desired directories are written in a file called */etc/rc* on the client machine. This shell script is automatically executed when the client machine is booted. Therefore, all mountings automatically take place at boot time.

3. *Automounting*. In the static mounting scheme, since mounting is done at boot time, all servers' directories listed in the */etc/rc* file of a client are mounted even when not

being used by the client. The automounting scheme allows a server's directory to be mounted only when the client needs it. That is, in this scheme servers' directories are mounted and unmounted automatically on a need basis.

In this scheme, a server's directory is associated with a client's local directory, but actual mounting is performed only at the time the client invokes a command to access a file in the name space below the server's directory. Once mounted, the server's directory remains mounted for as long as it is needed. Whenever 5 minutes have elapsed without the name space below the server's directory being accessed by the client, the server's directory is automatically unmounted.

Another important feature of this scheme is that instead of a single server's directories, a set of servers' directories may also be simultaneously associated with a directory of the client's local name space. In this case, when the client accesses a file in the name space below the mounted directory for the first time, the operating system sends a message to each of the servers whose directories are associated. The first one to reply wins, and its directory is mounted.

The automounting scheme helps achieve fault tolerance because a server need be up and working only when the client actually needs it. Moreover, when a set of servers are associated instead of a single server, only one of them need be up.

For an illustration of the file-mounting mechanism of NFS, consider the example given in Figure 10.12 based on the example given in [Silberschatz and Galvin 1994]. Figure 10.12(*a*) and (*b*) shows parts of the name trees of nodes $N_1$ and $N_2$, respectively, that are of interest here. The triangles represent subtrees of directories that are of interest. Since no mounting has been done yet, only local files can be accessed at each node. Figure 10.12(*c*) shows the structure of the portion of interest of the name tree of node $N_1$ after mounting the directory */user2/dir2* of node $N_2$ over the directory */user1/dir1* of node $N_1$. After this mounting, *dir2* becomes a shared directory, being shared by the users of nodes $N_1$ and $N_2$. Users on node $N_1$ can access any file within the *dir2* directory by using the prefix */user1/dir1/dir2*. Notice that the original subtree below the directory */user1/dir1* on node $N_1$ is no longer visible.

An advantage of this scheme is that it provides the flexibility to a user to attach only the necessary portions of remote name spaces on his or her local node's name space. Another advantage of this scheme is that it is simple to implement as a modification to UNIX. However, it suffers from several drawbacks. The main drawback is that the scheme does not provide a consistent global name space for all nodes. Thus the same object may have different "absolute" names when viewed from different nodes. For example, Figure 10.12(*c*) and (*d*) shows the name tree structures of nodes $N_1$ and $N_2$, respectively, after some mountings done on user requests. Now the absolute names of an object in the directory *dir2* will have the prefixes */user1/dir1/dir2* and */user2/dir2* on nodes $N_1$ and $N_2$, respectively. This lack of absolute naming facility can cause difficulties for distributed application programs, since processes running on different nodes are in different naming domains. For example, an application using several nodes to process a data file would run into trouble if the file name were specified as */user1/project1/data1*; rather than opening the same file, participating processes on nodes having identifiers *rome* and *paris* would respectively open */rome/*

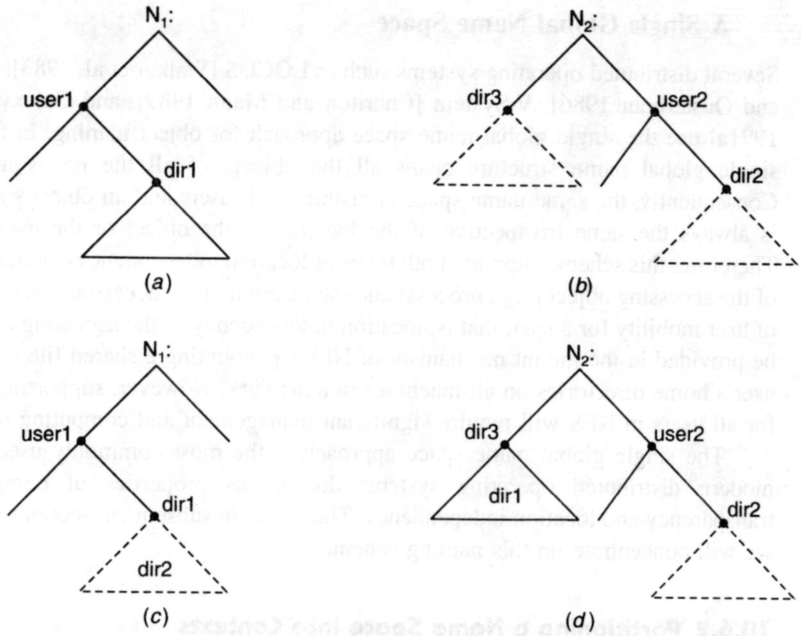


**Fig. 10.12** Illustrating the file-mounting mechanism of NFS naming scheme: (*a*) a part of the name tree of node $N_1$; (*b*) a part of the name tree of node $N_2$; (*c*) structure of name tree of node $N_1$ after mounting dir2 of node $N_2$ over dir1; (*d*) structure of name tree of node $N_2$ after mounting dir1 of node $N_1$ over dir3.

*user1/project1/data1* and */paris/user1/project1/data1*. Even if the user were to explicitly specify */paris/user1/project1/data1*, the program would fail if *rome* did not have *paris*'s file system mounted, or worse, had some other node's file system mounted under the name */paris*. The only way to ensure that all nodes use the same name for the same object is by careful manual management of each node's mount table. Systems using this approach do not scale well, because if every node mounts every other, the number of mount points in the system is proportional to $n^2$ ($n$ = total number of nodes), producing a significant management and computing overhead.

Another serious drawback of this scheme is its administrative complexity. The effects of a failed node, or taking a node off-line, are that some arbitrary set of directories on different nodes become unavailable. Likewise, migrating objects from one node to another requires changes in the name spaces of all the affected nodes. Furthermore, the scheme does not provide complete transparency because the specification of a remote directory as an argument for the mount operation is done in a nontransparent manner; the location (that is, node identifier) of the remote directory has to be provided. Location independency is also not supported by the scheme because, as discussed above, the absolute name of an object depends on the node from which it is being accessed.

### A Single Global Name Space

Several distributed operating systems such as LOCUS [Walker et al. 1983], Sprite [Welch and Ousterhout 1986], V-System [Cheriton and Mann 1989], and Galaxy [Sinha et al. 1991a] use the single global name space approach for object naming. In this scheme, a single global name structure spans all the objects of all the nodes in the system. Consequently, the same name space is visible to all users and an object's absolute name is always the same irrespective of the location of the object or the user accessing it. Therefore, this scheme supports both types of location independency—that of the location of the accessing object (e.g., process) and the location of the accessed object. The property of user mobility for a user, that is, location independency of the accessing object, can also be provided in the mount mechanism of NFS by mounting a shared file system over the user's home directories on all machines in a network. However, supporting this property for all users in NFS will require significant management and computing overhead.

The single global name space approach is the most commonly used approach by modern distributed operating systems due to its properties of complete location transparency and location independency. Therefore, in subsequent sections of this chapter we will concentrate on this naming scheme.

## 10.6.2 Partitioning a Name Space into Contexts

Name space management involves the storage and maintenance of *naming information*, which consists of object names, object attributes, and the bindings between the two. Due to reliability and space overhead problems in a distributed system, storing the complete naming information at a centralized node or replicating it at every node is not desirable. Therefore, the naming information is usually decentralized and replicated. That is, instead of one global name server, there are many name servers, each storing a copy of a portion of the complete naming information. These name servers interact among themselves to maintain the naming information and to satisfy the name resolution requests of the users. A basic problem is how to decompose the naming information database to be distributed among the name servers. The main goal of a decomposition mechanism for this purpose is to minimize the overhead involved in the maintenance of naming information and the resolution of names.

The notion of *context* is used for partitioning a name space into smaller components. Contexts represent indivisible units for storage and replication of information regarding named objects. A name space is partitioned into contexts by using clustering conditions. A *clustering condition* is an expression that, when applied to a name, returns either a true or false value, depending on whether the given name exists in the context designated by the clustering condition. The three basic clustering methods are algorithmic clustering, syntactic clustering, and attribute clustering. These are discussed below.

### Algorithmic Clustering

In this method, names are clustered according to the value that results from applying a function to them. Therefore, in algorithmic clustering, the clustering condition is a predicate of the form *function*(*name*) = *value*. For instance, a hash function that clusters names into buckets is a good example of a clustering condition for algorithmic clustering.

As an illustration, a simple example of algorithmic clustering of names is given in Figure 10.13. In this example, at first, *func-1* is applied to the names in the name space to partition them into two contexts. One of the two contexts is still found to be too large. Therefore, a second function (*func-2*) is applied to the names of this context to further partition the context into smaller contexts. Thus starting with the complete name space as a single context, a sequence of clustering conditions can be applied to yield a group of reasonably sized contexts.

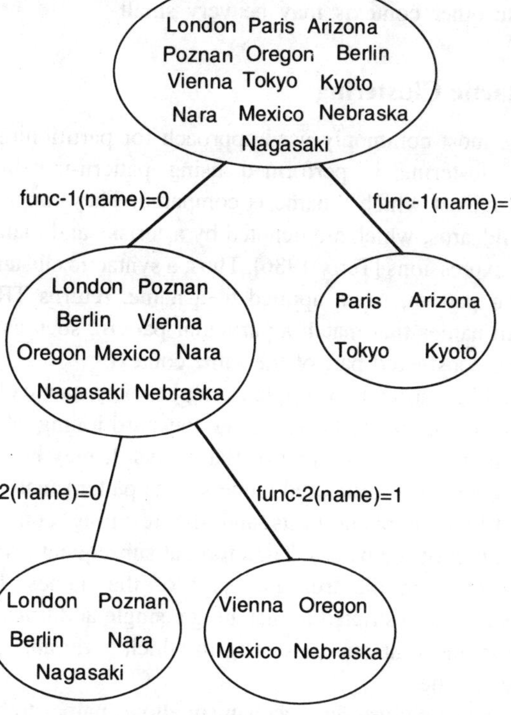

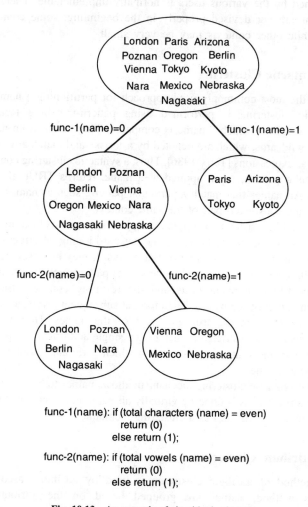

```
func-1(name): if (total characters (name) = even)
                  return (0)
              else return (1);

func-2(name): if (total vowels (name) = even)
                  return (0)
              else return (1);
```

**Fig. 10.13** An example of algorithmic clustering.

The main advantage of algorithmic clustering mechanism is that it supports structure-free name distribution. A *structure-free name distribution* is one that places no restriction on the administrative control over parts of a name space. The partitions of such a name space do not correspond to the structure of the names, such as their sizes, or the number of component names, or the order of the component names or characters within a name, and so on. In particular, the owner of an object may choose its authoritative name servers, subject to administrative constraints, independent of the object's name. This permits maximum flexibility in the administration assignment (and reassignment) of authoritative name servers to a given object. Algorithmic clustering also has the advantage that it allows a healthy name resolution tree to be built even for flat name spaces. However, the main drawback of the method is difficulty in devising proper clustering functions. This is because the characteristics of the names to be defined by the various users is normally unpredictable. Therefore, if the clustering functions are not devised properly in the beginning, some contexts may become too large while other contexts may be very small.

### Syntactic Clustering

This is the most commonly used approach for partitioning a name space into contexts. Syntactic clustering is performed using pattern-matching techniques. *Patterns* are templates against which a name is compared. They range from names that may simply contain wildcards, which are denoted by asterisks and match any sequence of characters, to regular expressions [Terry 1986]. Thus, a syntactic clustering condition that is meant for a particular pattern, when applied to a name, returns TRUE if the name matches the pattern. All names that match a particular pattern, such as names with a common prefix *prefix**, are considered part of the same context.

As an illustration, two simple examples of syntactic clustering of names are given in Figure 10.14. Figure 10.14(*a*) shows the partitioning of structured names and Figure 10.14(*b*) shows the partitioning of flat names. It may be observed from Figure 10.14(*a*) that in hierarchically structured name spaces pattern matching is usually performed on a component-by-component basis and the resulting contexts usually contain only the unmatched part of the names. Therefore, at subsequent levels, a new clustering condition is applied only on the truncated part of the names. However, syntactic clustering conditions are not restricted to matching a single additional component in each step. This leads to variable syntactic clustering in which a variable number of components can be matched at a time.

The syntactic clustering mechanism allows names to be resolved in a manner similar to their structure, as is done by virtually all name management systems. This means that simple matching suffices as a clustering technique.

### Attribute Clustering

The method of attribute clustering is used by attribute-based naming conventions. In this method, names are grouped based on the attributes possessed by the names. An attribute has both a type and a value, where the type indicates the

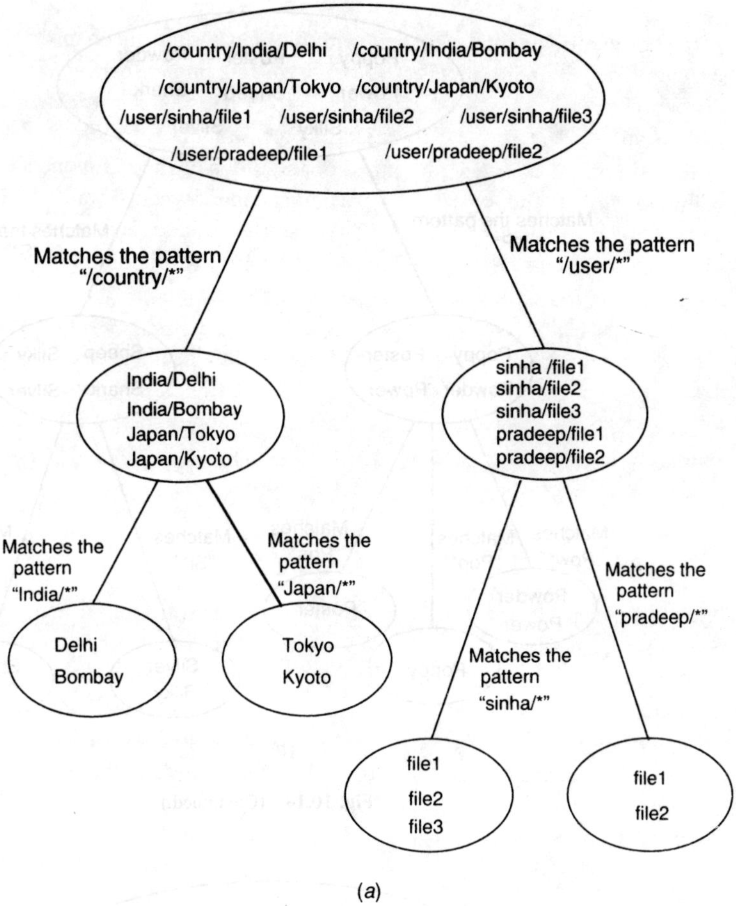


**Fig. 10.14** Examples of syntactic clustering: (*a*) partitioning of structured names; (*b*) partitioning of flat names. (Continued on next page.)

format and meaning of the value field. Therefore, all names having the same attribute (type, value) pair are placed in the same partition in the attribute clustering mechanism.

As an illustration, a simple example of attribute clustering of names is given in Figure 10.15. Observe that in a hierarchically structured name space, attribute clustering is usually performed on an attribute-by-attribute basis, and the resulting contexts usually contain only the unmatched attributes of the names. Therefore, at subsequent levels, a new clustering condition is applied only on the remaining attributes of the names. However, attribute clustering conditions are not restricted to matching a single additional attribute in each step and several attributes may be matched in a single step.

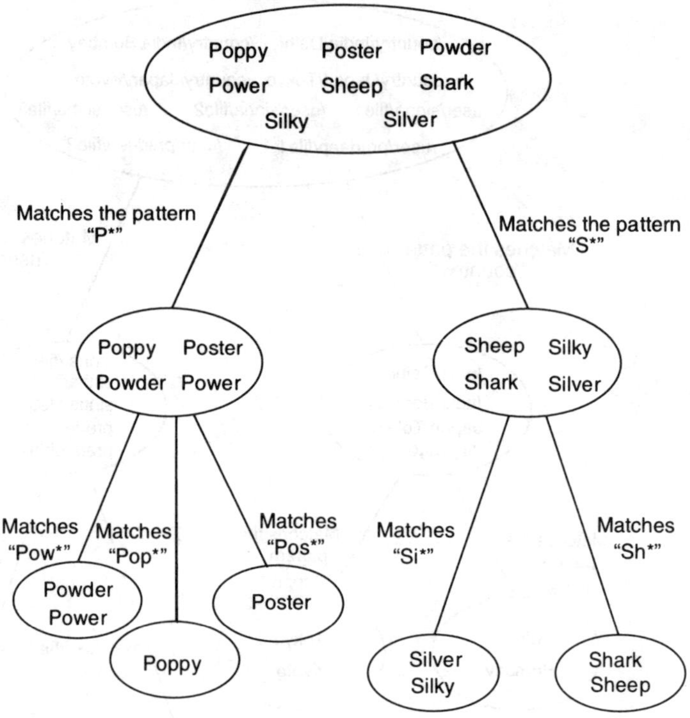


(b)

**Fig. 10.14** (Continued.)

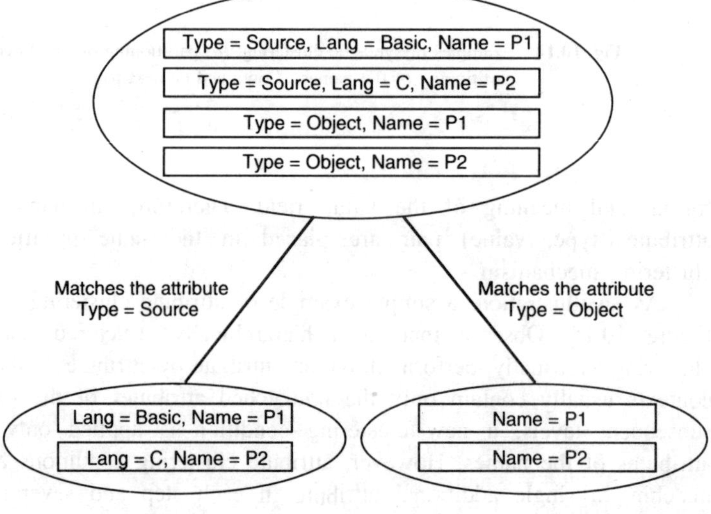


**Fig. 10.15** Example of attribute clustering.

### 10.6.3 Context Binding

The contexts of a name space are distributed among the various name servers managing that name space. That is, a name server normally stores only a small subset of the set of contexts of the name space. Therefore, when presented with a name to be resolved, a server first looks in local contexts for an authority attribute for the named object. Recall that an authority attribute contains a list of the authoritative name servers for a named object. If the authority attribute for the named object is not found in a local context, additional configuration data, called *context bindings*, must exist locally for the name resolution to proceed. A context binding associates the context within which it is stored to another context, that is more knowledgeable about the named object, and the name servers that store that context. The two strategies commonly used to implement context bindings in naming systems are table-based strategy and procedure-based strategy. These are discussed below.

#### Table-Based Strategy

This is the most commonly used approach for implementing context bindings in hierarchical tree-structured name spaces. In this method, each context is a table having two fields; the first field stores a component name of the named object and the second field either stores context binding information or authority attribute information. An entry corresponding to the last component of a name contains the authority attribute information while other entries contain context bindings. The context bindings reflect the delegation of authority for managing parts of the name space. Note that the amount of configuration data that must be stored in context objects at the various levels of the hierarchy is proportional to the degree of branching of the name space tree. The contexts of a table-based strategy are also known as *directories*.

As an illustration, an example of table-based strategy for implementing context bindings is given in Figure 10.16. The figure also illustrates how an object can have two different human-oriented names in this implementation strategy. Therefore, the users of a shared object can specify their own suitable names for accessing it.

#### Procedure-Based Strategy

Name servers may also use procedure-based strategy rather than table-based strategy to implement the bindings in a given context. In this method, a context binding takes the form of a procedure, which, when executed, supplies information about the next context to be consulted for the named object. For instance, in the examples of Figure 10.14, the syntactic clustering condition used by each context can also be used as the procedure for supplying context bindings for the names defined within that context. Notice that no configuration data is required by this scheme and hence the data management overhead is zero. This scheme, however, is less flexible than the table-based strategy because, if required, the context bindings cannot be changed dynamically and independently for each object. Changing of context bindings will require changes in the clustering procedures. Therefore, almost all naming systems use the table-based strategy for implementing context bindings.

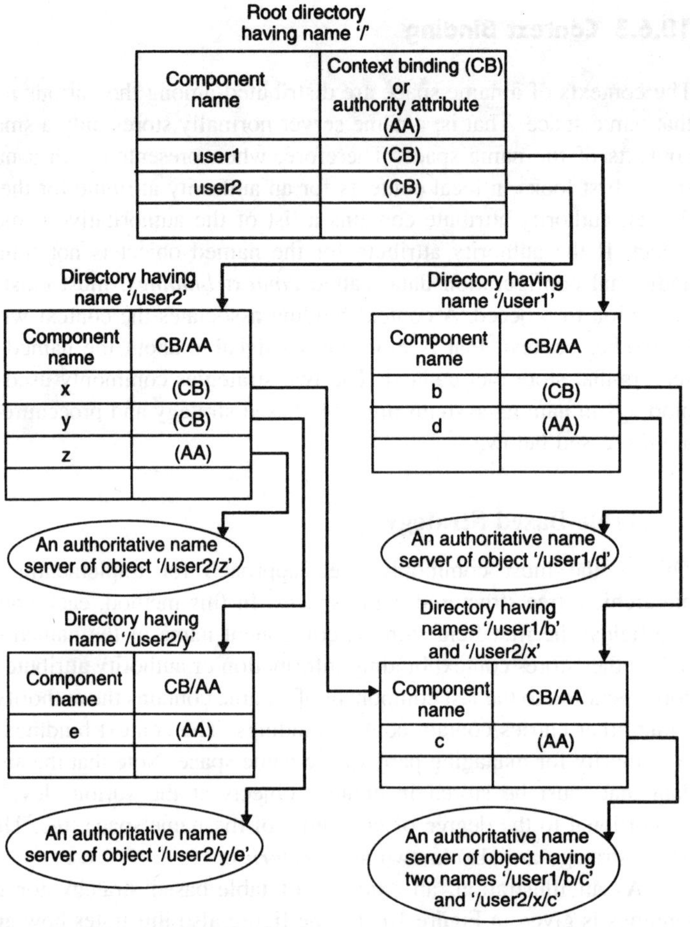


**Fig. 10.16** An example of table-based strategy for implementing context bindings.

### 10.6.4 Distribution of Contexts and Name Resolution Mechanisms

Name resolution is the process of mapping an object's name to the authoritative name servers of the object. The process basically involves traversal of a resolution chain of contexts (using the context binding information of each context in the chain) until the authority attribute of the named object is found. Obviously, the traversal of the resolution chain of contexts for a name is greatly influenced by the locations of these contexts in a distributed system. Therefore, the name resolution mechanism of a naming system depends on the policy used for distributing the contexts of the name space of the naming system. Some of the commonly used name resolution mechanisms are described below.

### Centralized Approach

In this method, a single name server in the entire distributed system is located at a centralized node. This name server is responsible for storing all contexts and maintaining the name-mapping information in them up to date. The location of the centralized name server is known to all other nodes. Therefore, name resolution requests from all nodes are first sent to the centralized name server's node. The name server resolves a name by traversing the complete resolution chain of contexts locally and finally returns the attributes of the named object to the client node. An example of a system with a centralized name service is the early DARPA Domain Name System [Mockapetris and Dunlap 1988, Cerf and Cain 1983].

The main advantage of this scheme is that it is simple and easy to implement. It is also efficient because any name resolution request involves only two messages (a request and a reply) to be passed across the network. The scheme, however, suffers from several drawbacks. For instance, it does not scale well because the performance of the centralized name server may become a serious bottleneck for large systems. Furthermore, the reliability of this mechanism is also very poor. The inability of a node to communicate with the centralized name server's node due to a link failure of the network will create a situation in which none of the name resolution requests of that node can be carried out. An even worse situation occurs if the centralized name server's node fails, in which case none of the name resolution requests from any node of the system can be carried out.

### Fully Replicated Approach

In this method, there is a name server located on each node of the distributed system and all contexts are replicated at every node. That is, the name space database is fully replicated, and therefore each name server has the name-mapping information for all object names. Obviously, all name resolution requests of any node are serviced locally by the local name server. The Pup name service [Boggs 1983] and the DDLCN (Distributed Double-Loop Computer Network) system [Lin et al. 1982] use this approach.

The method is simple and efficient because all name resolution requests can be serviced locally without the need to communicate with any other node. The method, however, involves large overhead in maintaining consistency of naming information in all servers and hence is not suitable for large name spaces.

### Distribution Based on Physical Structure of Name Space

This is the most commonly used approach for hierarchical tree-structured name spaces. In this method, the name space tree is divided into several subtrees that are known by different names in different systems, such as *domains* in Sprite [Welch and Ousterhout 1986] and *file groups* in LOCUS [Walker et al. 1983]. To differentiate this concept with other terminologies used before, the term *zones* will be used here to refer to such subtrees. In this scheme, there are several name servers in the distributed system, with each server providing storage for one or more of these zones. An example is shown in Figure 10.17.

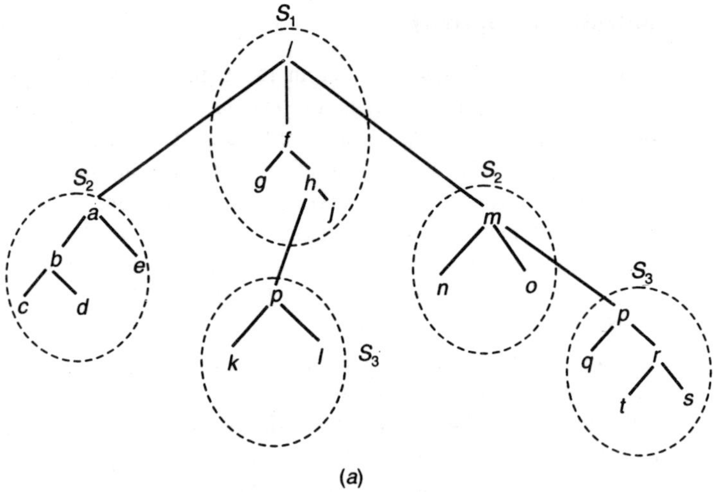


(a)

| Name prefix | Zone identifier | |
|---|---|---|
| | Server identifier | Specific zone identifier |
| / | $S_1$ | 12 |
| /a | $S_2$ | 19 |
| /f/h/p | $S_3$ | 33 |
| /m | $S_2$ | 87 |
| /m/p | $S_3$ | 61 |

(b)

**Fig. 10.17** Distribution and management of contexts based on the physical structure of the name space: (*a*) hierarchical name space tree partitioned into zones; (*b*) sample name prefix table/cache for the zones of the name tree of (*a*).

Note that each node of the name space tree corresponds to a context, and therefore the contexts belonging to the same zone are grouped together in this scheme. Hence, in this scheme, instead of contexts, zones represent indivisible units for storage and replication regarding named objects.

In this scheme, the resolution of an object name basically involves the sending of the name resolution request to the server that manages the subtree (zone) to which the last component of the name belongs. For instance, in Figure 10.17, the name resolution requests for the object names */a/b/c*, */f/h*, */f/g*, */f/h/p/k*, */m/n*, */m/p/r*, and */m/p/r/s/* must be sent to servers $S_2$, $S_1$, $S_1$, $S_3$, $S_2$, $S_3$, and $S_3$, respectively. To facilitate the mapping of names to servers, each client maintains a *name prefix table* (also known as a *name prefix cache*) that is built and updated dynamically. Each entry in the name prefix table corresponds to one of the zones of the name space tree. It contains the name of the topmost context (directory) in the zone (called the *name prefix* for the zone) and a *zone identifier*. A *zone identifier* consists of two fields—*server identifier* and *specific zone identifier*—where the specific zone identifier is assigned to the zone by the server. It helps in differentiating among the various zones maintained by the same server. For example, in Figure 10.17, server $S_3$ maintains two zones both of whose roots have the same name *p* but different zone identifiers 33 and 61. A server's identifier has its location embedded in it.

When a name is to be resolved, the client searches its own name prefix table for a matching name prefix of the object name to be resolved. Notice that any one of */*, */a*, */a/b*, or */a/b/c* is a matching name prefix for an object named */a/b/c*. If more than one matching name prefixes are found, the longest one is selected and the client uses the corresponding zone identifier information to send its request directly to the server that stores that zone. The specific zone identifier of the table entry is also sent along with the request.

When the server receives the request, it uses the specific zone identifier associated with the request to carry out the requested name resolution. It then maps the rest of the component names of the named object with the contexts (directories) of the selected zone. If all the remaining components are mapped, the name resolution operation completes and the object's attributes are returned by the server to the client. On the other hand, if only a part of the remaining component names is resolved in the selected zone, then some other zone has to be used for further resolution of the name; that is, a zone crossing is necessary. In this case, the server returns the next zone's name prefix to the client for further processing. The client then broadcasts the new prefix to obtain the zone identifier of the next zone. The servers that store that zone respond to the broadcast message. Using the responses, the new zone's details are entered into the name prefix table and the name resolution proceeds as before by sending the request to a server of the new zone.

The name prefix table is built and updated dynamically with a broadcast protocol. Initially, each client starts with an empty name prefix table. Entries are added to the name prefix table of a client only when needed. That is, the name prefix of a zone that has never been accessed by a client will not appear in its name prefix table. In some systems, the name prefix of the zone containing the root directory of the name space tree is known to all nodes and is entered into a name prefix table at the time of its creation. With this approach, a client never experiences a complete miss while searching a name prefix for any name in the name prefix table.

Notice that in this scheme the name prefix of a zone may simultaneously exist in multiple name prefix tables of the same or different nodes. Furthermore, the servers of a zone may change dynamically, providing increased availability, security, and efficiency. Therefore, an important issue of this scheme is the updating of entries in name prefix tables to keep them consistent. Instead of informing all clients when the server of a zone they are storing in their name prefix tables changes, the consistency of name prefix table entries is maintained by detecting and discarding/updating stale table entries on use. That is, the server information stored in a name prefix table is made up of hints that are corrected when they are found to be wrong. A *hint* is a piece of information that can substantially improve performance if correct but has no semantically negative consequence if incorrect. For maximum performance benefit a hint should nearly always be correct. Of course, only information that is self-validating upon use is amenable to this strategy. When a client tries to use a stale name prefix table entry, it ends up sending its name request to the wrong server. If the server no longer exists, the client receives no reply and times out. If the server exists but no longer stores the given zone, the server reports that fact back to the client. In either case, the client recognizes that its table entry is stale, deletes the entry, and issues a broadcast for up-to-date server information for the zone to which the context corresponding to the named object's last component name belongs.

This scheme has the following advantages:

1. Matching on a name prefix rather than on the full name allows a small number of table entries to cover a large number of names, resulting in good performance. For example, in Figure 10.17, a single table entry for */a* allows every name of objects in this zone to go directly to the correct server without the overhead of a broadcast or global directory lookup. The zone having prefix name */a* can reasonably contain the attribute information for hundreds or thousands of objects.

2. As compared to global directory lookup, in which all directories starting from the root down to the last component name of the named object are searched one by one, the name prefix table helps in bypassing part of the directory lookup mechanism. The directory bypass has advantages in performance and reliability because a crash on one name server does not prevent clients from resolving names in zones on other servers. To illustrate this, let us see the example given in [Welch and Ousterhout 1986]. In a system with two zones / and */a*, the server for / need not be available for resolving the name */a/b/c*. If a client already has an entry for */a* in its name prefix table, then it will use it and communicate directly with the server for that zone; otherwise it will broadcast the name */a/b/c* and the server for */a* will respond directly to the client with zone identifier information. In neither case is the server for / involved. This bypassing mechanism reduces contention for the upper level directories. However, the bypassing of upper level directories has consequences on the system's security mechanism. To illustrate this, once again let us see the example given in [Welch and Ousterhout 1986]. If there is a name prefix */a/b/c* and the client looks up the name */a/b/c/d*, neither */a* nor */a/b* is examined; the client communicates directly with the server containing */a/b/c*. This means that any access controls in directories */a* or */a/b* will be ignored. The effect is that all programs implicitly have search permission along the paths to all the directories. If access to a directory is to be restricted, it must be restricted with access controls at the level of the directory or below.

3. The on-use consistency checking of a name prefix table entry results in considerable saving of consistency control overheads because there is no need to inform all clients when a table entry they are storing becomes invalid.

### Structure-Free Distribution of Contexts

Name services should be able to be reconfigured if the present servers become overworked or overburdened with data or if the system scale changes due to addition or removal of workstations (nodes). Reconfiguration often requires changing an object's authoritative name server. In the zone-based context distribution approach, changing an object's authoritative name server will require changing its name, storing all the contexts in the zone that corresponds to the object and is managed by the object's current authoritative name server on the new name server, or creating a new zone for storage with the object's new authoritative name server. The new zone will be a subzone of the zone that corresponds to the object and is managed by the object's old authoritative name server. The first two solutions are obviously not acceptable. The third solution may require duplication of some of the contexts in the old as well as the new zones, resulting in the need to store such contexts on both the object's old and new authoritative name servers. For example, in Figure 10.17(*a*), if the authoritative name server for the object named */a/b/c* is to be changed from $S_2$ to $S_4$, a new zone containing the contexts named */a*, */a/b*, and */a/b/c* or the contexts named */a/b* and*/a/b/c* will have to be created for storage at $S_4$. Notice that in the former case two contexts (*/a* and */a/b*) will have to be stored at both $S_2$ and $S_4$, while in the latter case one context (*/a/b*) needs duplication. In large name spaces, such changes may require the duplication of many contexts. Therefore, the zone-based scheme has limited flexibility in the assignment/changing of an object's authoritative name server.

To overcome this limitation of the approach of distributing contexts based on the physical structure of the name space, some systems use the structure-free name distribution scheme. A structure-free name distribution is one that places no restriction on the administrative control over parts of a name space. Therefore, in this scheme, any context of the name space can be freely stored/moved at any name server independently of any other context. That is, in this approach, each context may be considered to belong to its own zone. A name service based on this approach permits maximum flexibility in the assignment/changing of an object's authoritative name server. Furthermore, this scheme also simplifies name management because name servers need not agree on what zones make up the name space.

In systems using this scheme, some policy is used for the partitioning and distribution of contexts among name servers. For example, in Galaxy [Sinha et al. 1991a], the distribution and replication of contexts among name servers of various nodes are based on the idea of improving the reliability of the name resolution mechanism. The details of this policy is given in [Sinha et al. 1992]. Also notice that in this scheme name space structure need not but can be exploited to partition and distribute the contexts among name servers.

In this scheme, the name resolution operation for a given object name is carried out by traversing the complete resolution chain of contexts on a context-by-context basis until the named object's authoritative name server is encountered. For example, the pathname */a/b/c* of an object is resolved by first consulting the root context (*/*) to obtain the location of the pathname's next context (*/a*). Recall that this is stored in the root context as a context-binding information. With the location information obtained, the context */a* is consulted next to obtain the location of the pathname's next context (*/a/b*). Finally, the named object's authoritative name server's information is obtained by consulting the context */a/b*. Notice that since each context can be freely placed at any server, so a name resolution operation may migrate from server to server, possibly hopping from one node to another if the servers involved are located on different nodes.

The are two important questions to be addressed in this type of name resolution mechanism:

1. How should context objects be located?
2. How should one interact with name servers while resolving a name?

Methods to handle these questions are described below.

***Locating Context Objects During Name Resolution.*** Recall that a qualified name consists of a *context/name* pair. That is, a name is always associated with some context. Therefore, when a user specifies a name to be resolved, its resolution should start in the context to which it is associated. Hence, the first step in the resolution process is to locate the context. However, locating a context involves resolving its name. That is, a context-locating operation is triggered by the resolution of a name in the first place. Thus, we observe an infinite recursion that must be solved using some special technique. Two commonly used methods to tackle this problem are described below.

1. *Using a metacontext.* In this method, a special context, called a *metacontext*, is used that contains the name and authority attribute pairs for all context objects in the name space. The size of the metacontext depends on the number of contexts in the name space. If it is small, it can be stored at all name server nodes. However, if it is large, it is stored only at some name server nodes, and other name servers only store pointers to the servers that store the metacontext. Therefore, given a name to be resolved in a context, the metacontext is first consulted to obtain the authority attribute of the context. The name is then sent for resolution to one of the authoritative name servers of the context.

2. *Always starting the resolution from the root context.* This method is used in those naming systems in which the name space is structured as a single global hierarchical name tree. In this method, the root context is replicated at all name server nodes. Given a name to be resolved in a context, we say that the name is relative to that context. A relative name can be converted to an absolute name by prepending the context name to it. Recall that an absolute name begins at the root context of the name space. Therefore, in this method, given a name to be resolved in a context, the name is first converted to its absolute form and then its resolution starts from the root context. Since the root context is available at all name server nodes, the resolution of any name can be started at any name server node.

***Interacting with Name Servers During Name Resolution.*** We saw that the various contexts of a given pathname may be stored at different name servers. Therefore, the resolution of a pathname in such a situation will involve interacting with all the name servers that store one or more contexts of the pathname. During name resolution, a name agent may interact with the name servers in one of the following manners:

1. *Recursive.* In this method, the name agent forwards the name resolution request to the name server that stores the first context needed to start the resolution of the given name. After this, the name servers that store the contexts of the given pathname are

recursively activated one after another until the authority attribute of the named object is extracted from the context corresponding to the last component name of the pathname. The last name server returns the authority attribute to its previous name server, which then returns it to its own previous name server, and so on. Finally, the first name server that received the request from the name agent returns the authority attribute to the name agent. Figure 10.18($a$) illustrates the method of recursive interaction.

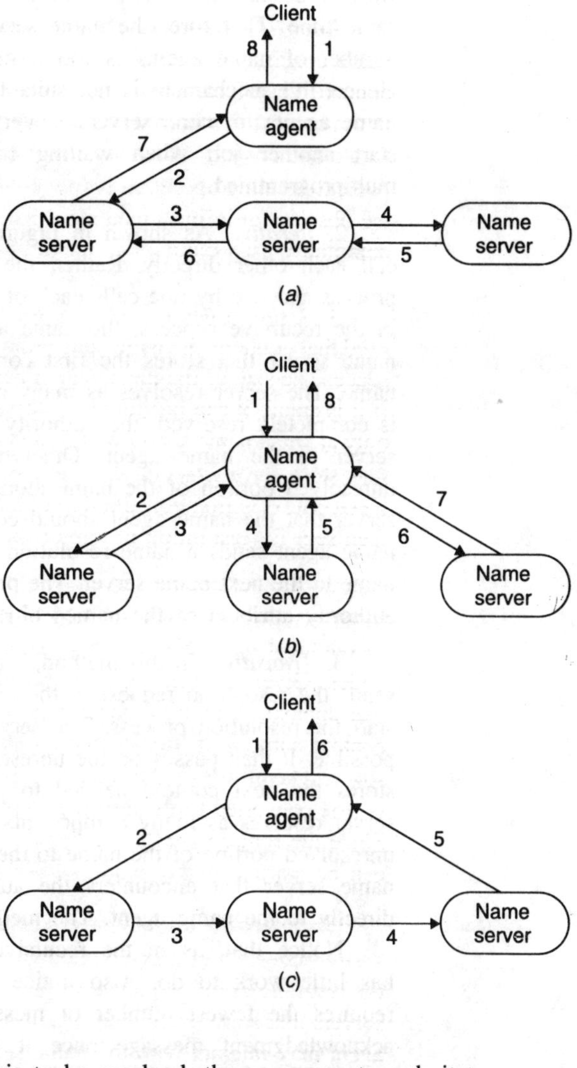


**Fig. 10.18** Methods of interacting with name servers during name resolution: ($a$) recursive; ($b$) iterative; ($c$) transitive.

As an example, if the name /a/b/c is to be resolved, the name agent sends it to the name server (say $S_1$) of the root context (/) and waits for a reply. Then $S_1$ searches for the component name $a$ in the root context, extracts the corresponding binding information, sends the remaining pathname b/c to the name server (say $S_2$) of the next context (*/a*), and waits for a reply. Then $S_2$ extracts from context */a* the binding information corresponding to the component name *b*, sends the remaining pathname *c* to the name server (say $S_3$) of the next context (*/a/b*), and waits for a reply. Then $S_3$ extracts from context */a/b* the authority attribute corresponding to the component name *c* and returns it to $S_2$, which in turn returns it to $S_1$, and finally $S_1$ returns it to the name agent.

Notice that in the recursive name resolution mechanism, the name agent has little work to do but the name servers may be involved in processing several requests at the same time. Therefore, the name servers may get overloaded in situations where the number of name agents is too large as compared to the number of name servers. Hence, this mechanism is not suitable for use in those systems in which the ratio of name agents to name servers is very high. Furthermore, to allow a name server to start another job when waiting for a response, the name servers have to be multiprogrammed.

2. *Iterative*. As shown in Figure 10.18(*b*), in this method, name servers do not call each other directly. Rather, the name agent retains control over the resolution process and one by one calls each of the servers involved in the resolution process. As in the recursive process, the name agent first sends the name to be resolved to the name server that stores the first context needed to start the resolution of the given name. The server resolves as many components of the name as possible. If the name is completely resolved, the authority attribute of the named object is returned by the server to the name agent. Otherwise, the server returns to the name agent the unresolved portion of the name along with the location information of another name server that the name agent should contact next. To continue the name resolution, the name agent sends a name resolution request along with the unresolved portion of the name to the next name server. The process continues until the name agent receives the authority attribute of the named object.

3. *Transitive*. In this method, a name is resolved as follows. The name agent first sends the resolution request to the name server that stores the first context needed to start the resolution process. The server resolves as many components of the name as possible. It then passes on the unresolved portion of the name to the name server that stores the next context needed to proceed with the resolution process. This name server resolves as many components of the name as possible and then passes on the unresolved portion of the name to the next name server. The process continues and the name server that encounters the authority attribute of the named object returns it directly to the name agent. The method is illustrated in Figure 10.18(*c*).

Notice that, as in the recursive method, in this method also the name agent has little work to do. Also notice from Figure 10.18 that the transitive approach requires the fewest number of messages. However, a sender does not receive any acknowledgment message once it passes on the resolution operation to another server. Therefore, this approach should be used in systems with reliable communication. On the other hand, recursive and iterative approaches can be efficiently supported by RPC-based communication systems because they use a "call-response" model.

## 10.7 NAME CACHES

Readers might have observed that name resolution operations are not likely to be especially cheap. Based on the measurements made by few researchers in the past, it has been found that in operating systems that provide a flexible, hierarchical name space, the system overhead involved in name resolution operations is considerably large. For instance, Leffler et al. [1984] attribute 40% of the system call overhead in UNIX to file name resolution. Also, Mogul's measurements of the UNIX system call frequency indicate that name-mapping operations (*open*, *stat*, *lstat*) constitute over 50% of the file system calls [Mogul 1986]. Sheltzer et al. [1986] also made an observation that in a large distributed system a substantial portion of network traffic is naming related. Hence it is very desirable for a client to be able to cache the result of a name resolution operation for a while, rather than repeating it every time the value is needed.

Work has been carried out in the past by some researchers [Sheltzer et al. 1986, Cheriton and Mann 1989] to investigate whether a distributed name cache is a suitable solution to improve the performance of name service as well as to reduce the overall system overhead. The conclusion drawn by these researchers is that a simple distributed name cache can have a substantial positive effect on distributed system performance. This is mainly due to the following characteristics of name service related activities:

1. *High degree of locality of name lookup*. The property of "locality of reference" has been observed in program execution, file access, as well as database access. Measurements made by Sheltzer et al. [1986] and Cheriton and Mann [1989] clearly show that a high degree of locality also exists in the use of pathnames for accessing objects. Due to this locality feature, a reasonable size name cache, used for caching recently used naming information, can provide excellent hit ratios.

2. *Slow update of name information database*. It has also been found that naming data does not change very fast, so inconsistencies are rare. The activity of most users is usually confined to a small, slowly changing subset of the entire name information database. Furthermore, most naming data have a high read-to-modify ratio. This behavior implies that the cost of maintaining the consistency of cached data is significantly low.

3. *On-use consistency of cached information is possible*. An attractive feature of name service related activity is that it is possible to find that something does not work if one tries to use obsolete naming data, so that it can be attended to at the time of use. That is, name cache consistency can be maintained by detecting and discarding stale cache entries on use. With on-use consistency checking, there is no need to invalidate all related cache entries when a naming data update occurs, yet stale data never causes a name to be mapped to the wrong object.

Some issues specific to the design of name caches are discussed in the next section.

### 10.7.1 Types of Name Caches

Depending on the type of information stored in each entry, a name cache may be of one of the following types:

1. *Directory cache.* In this type of name cache, each entry consists of a directory page. This type of cache is normally used in those systems that use the iterative method of name resolution. All recently used directory pages that are brought to the client node during name resolution are cached for a while. For example, LOCUS [Sheltzer et al. 1986] uses name caches of this type. The argument given by LOCUS designers in favor of caching directory pages is that common tasks such as listing the contents of a directory, expanding wild card arguments, and accessing parent directories all use information found in directory pages. However, this means that for only one useful entry of a directory an entire page of the directory blocks a large area of precious cache space requiring large-sized name caches.

2. *Prefix cache.* This type of name cache is used in those naming systems that use the zone-based context distribution mechanism. In this type of name cache, each entry consists of a name prefix and the corresponding zone identifier. Recall that a name prefix corresponds to a zone in the zone-based context distribution approach. Details of the use of this type of name cache has already been presented in Section 10.6.4. Sprite [Welch and Ousterhout 1986] and V-System [Cheriton and Mann 1989] use this type of name cache. This type of name cache is not suitable for use with the structure-free context distribution approach.

3. *Full-name cache.* In this type of name cache, each entry consists of an object's full pathname and the identifier and location of its authoritative name server. Therefore requests for accessing an object whose name is available in the local cache can be directly sent to the object's authoritative name server. This type of name cache can be conveniently used with any naming mechanism, although it is mainly used by the naming systems that use the structure-free context distribution approach. Notice that in a prefix cache an entry usually serves as a mapping information for several objects, but in a full-name cache each entry serves as a mapping information for only a single object. Therefore, full-name caches are usually larger in size as compared to prefix caches. This type of name cache is used in Galaxy [Sinha et al. 1991b].

### 10.7.2 Approaches for Name Cache Implementation

The two commonly used approaches for name cache implementation are as follows:

1. A cache per process
2. A single cache for all processes of a node

Both approaches have their own advantages and drawbacks. In the first approach, a separate name cache is maintained for each process. Each cache is maintained in the corresponding process's address space and is usually small in size. Therefore, accessing of cached information is fast and no memory area of the operating system is occupied by the name caches. However, a process-oriented name cache vanishes with the process. Therefore every new process must create its name cache from scratch. Hence, if the processes are short lived, the caches will have short lifetimes, and the true hit ratio will be fairly low for process-oriented caches due to *start-up misses*, which are initial misses that occur when a new, empty cache is created. Furthermore, the use of a process-oriented cache is limited only to a single process due to which there is a possibility that the same naming information is duplicated in several caches of the same node. To alleviate the problem of start-up misses, V-System implementation [Cheriton and Mann 1989] uses *cache inheritance* to give cached data a long lifetime. In this method, each process inherits its initial cache contents from its parent process (usually the V-System command interpreter or "shell").

In the second approach, a single name cache is maintained at each node for all the processes of that node. As compared to the process-oriented name caches, these caches are larger in size and are located in the memory area of the operating system. Accessing of cached information is slower as compared to that of process-oriented caches. However, cached information in a single-name cache is long lived and is removed only when the cache replacement policy finds it suitable for being removed. Therefore the problem of start-up misses is not associated with the single-name cache approach, resulting in higher average hit ratio as compared to the process-oriented caches. The possibility of duplicating cached information on the same node is also not there in this approach.

Sprite and V-System use process-oriented name caches, whereas LOCUS and Galaxy use the single-name cache approach.

### 10.7.3 Multicache Consistency

When a naming data update occurs, related name cache entries become stale and must be invalidated or updated properly. Two commonly used methods for multicache consistency of name caches are immediate invalidate and on-use update.

#### Immediate Invalidate

In this method, all related name cache entries are immediately invalidated when a naming data update occurs. There are two ways of doing this. In the first approach, whenever a naming data update operation is performed, an invalidate message identifying the data to be invalidated is broadcast to all the nodes in the system. Each node's name caches are then examined for the presence of the updated data, and if it is present, the corresponding cache entry is invalidated. Although this approach may work well for a system having a few nodes, its use becomes prohibitive for very large networks having many nodes.

To avoid the use of broadcast protocol, in the second approach, the storage node of naming data (for example, the storage node of a directory) keeps a list of nodes against each data that corresponds to the nodes on which the data is cached. When a storage node receives a request for a naming data update, only the nodes in the corresponding list are notified to invalidate their corresponding cache entry. This method is acceptable only if there is a low rate of update to naming data that are shared among nodes and only if a small number of nodes share a naming data when that data is modified.

### On-Use Update

This is the more commonly used method for maintaining name cache consistency. In this method, no attempt is made to invalidate all related cache entries when a naming data update occurs. Rather, when a client uses a stale cached data, it is informed by the naming system that the data being used is either incorrectly specified or stale. On receiving a negative reply, necessary steps are taken (either by broadcasting or multicasting a request or by using some other implementation dependent approach) to obtain the updated data, which is then used to refresh the stale cache entry.

## 10.8 NAMING AND SECURITY

An important job of the naming system of several centralized and distributed operating systems is to control unauthorized access to both the named objects and the information in the naming database. Many different security mechanisms have been proposed and are used by operating systems to control unauthorized access to the various resources (objects) of the system. Chapter 11 fully addresses security issues. This section describes only those security issues that are pertinent to object naming. Three basic naming-related access control mechanisms are described below.

### 10.8.1 Object Names As Protection Keys

In this method, an object's name acts as a protection key for the object. A user who knows the name of an object (i.e., has the key for the object) can access the object by using its name. Notice that an object may have several keys in those systems that allow an object to have multiple names. In this case, any of the keys can be used to access the object.

In systems using this method, users are not allowed by the system to define a name for an object that they are not authorized to access. Obviously, if a user cannot name an object, he or she cannot operate on it. This scheme is based on the assumption that object names cannot be forged or stolen. That is, there is no way for a user to obtain the names of other user's objects and the names cannot be guessed easily. However, in practice, since object names are generally picked to be mnemonic, they can often be guessed easily. Therefore, the scheme does not guarantee a reliable access control mechanism. Another limitation of this scheme is that it does not provide the flexibility of specifying the modes of access control. That is, a user having a name for an object usually has all types of possible access rights for the object. For instance, providing only read access to a file object to one user and both read and write accesses to another user is not possible by this scheme alone.

### 10.8.2 Capabilities

This is a simple extension of the above scheme that overcomes its limitations. As shown in Figure 10.19, a *capability* is a special type of object identifier that contains additional information redundancy for protection. It may be considered as an unforgeable ticket that

**Fig. 10.19** The two basic parts of a capability.

| Object identifier | Rights information |
|---|---|

allows its holders to access the object (identified by its object identifier part) in one or more permission modes (specified by its access control information part). Therefore, capabilities are object names having the following properties:

1. A capability is a system-oriented name that uniquely identifies an object.
2. In addition to identifying an object, it is also used to protect the object it references by defining operations that may be performed on the object it identifies.
3. A client that possesses a capability can access the object identified by it in the modes allowed by it.
4. There are usually several capabilities for the same object. Each one confers different access rights to its holders. The same capability held by different holders provides the same access rights to all of them.
5. All clients that have capabilities to a given object can share this object. The exact mode of sharing depends on the capability possessed by each client of the same object.
6. Capabilities are unforgeable protected objects that are maintained by the operating system and only indirectly accessed by the users. Capability-based protection relies on the fact that the capabilities are never allowed to migrate into any address space directly accessible by a user process (where they could be modified). If all capabilities are secure, the objects they protect are also secure against unauthorized access.

When a process wants to perform an operation on an object, it must send to the name server a message containing the object's capability. The name server verifies if the capability provided by the client allows the type of operation requested by the client on the relevant object. If not, a "permission denied" message is returned to the client process. If allowed, the client's request is forwarded to the manager of the object. Notice that in the capability-based approach, there is no checking of user identity. If this is required, some user authentication mechanism must be used. Chapter 11 deals with these issues in greater detail.

### 10.8.3 Associating Protection with Name Resolution Path

Protection can be associated either with an object or with the name resolution path of the name used to identify the object. The more common scheme provides protection on the name resolution path.

Systems using this approach usually employ access control list (ACL) based protection, which controls access dependent on the identity of the user (described in Chapter 11). The mechanism based on ACL requires, in addition to the object identifier, another trusted identifier representing the accessing principal, the entity with which access rights are associated. This trusted identifier might be a password, address, or any other identifier form that cannot be forged or stolen. An ACL is associated with an object and specifies the user name (user identifier) and the types of access allowed for each user of that object. When a user requests access to an object, the operating system checks the ACL associated with that object. If that user is listed for the requested access, the access is allowed. Otherwise, a protection violation occurs and the user job is denied access to the object.

By associating an ACL with each context (directory) of the name space, access can be controlled to both the named objects and the information in the naming database. When a name server receives an access request for a directory, it first verifies if the accessing process is authorized for the requested access. With this approach, name servers do not provide information to clients that are not authorized to have it, and at the same time name servers do not accept unauthorized updates to naming information stored in the contexts of the name space.

Regarding access control to an object, a client accesses an object by specifying its name. A name is first resolved using the context objects to find out the named object's authoritative name server. If the ACL associated with any of the contexts that correspond to the name of the object does not allow the client to access context information, the name specified by the client cannot be resolved and the client will automatically not be allowed to access the object by using that name.

Notice that, to allow access to an object in this scheme, a user must be allowed access to both the directories of the object's pathname and the object itself. Therefore, associating protection with the name resolution path of an object name provides an additional layer of protection to the named object. Also notice that, in systems where objects may have multiple pathnames (such as acyclic or general graphs), a given user may have different access rights to an object depending on the pathname used.

## 10.9 CASE STUDY: DCE DIRECTORY SERVICE

As a case study of how the naming concepts and mechanisms described in this chapter can be used to build a naming system for a distributed computing system, the DCE Directory Service is briefly described below.

Recall from Chapter 1 that in a DCE system, users, machines, and other resources are grouped into cells. Therefore, the DCE Directory Service mainly has the following types of components for intracell and intercell naming:

1. *Cell Directory Service* (*CDS*), which controls the naming environment used within a cell. Every cell has at least one CDS server.
2. *Global Directory Service* (*GDS*), which controls the global naming environment outside (between) cells. It links cells together so that any cell can be located from any other cell. GDS implementation is based on the X.500 directory service, which is an international standard for naming defined by the CCITT and ISO standards organizations. Therefore, X.500-style names (described later) are used in DCE for naming cells.

Since many DCE users use the Internet, DCE also supports the standard Internet *Domain Name System* (*DNS*) for cell naming. Therefore, cell names in DCE can also be specified in DNS notation (described later).

### 10.9.1 DCE Name Space and Naming Convention

The DCE uses the single global name space approach for object naming. That is, the DCE name space is a single, worldwide structure, with a global root denoted by the symbol /.... Below this root appears the GDS name space, used to name each cell. If DNS names are also used to name cells in the same DCE system, its name space also appears below the DCE global root, sitting by the side of the GDS name space. Finally, each cell contains its own internal name space, starting from the cell root. An example of the DCE name space structure is shown in Figure 10.20.

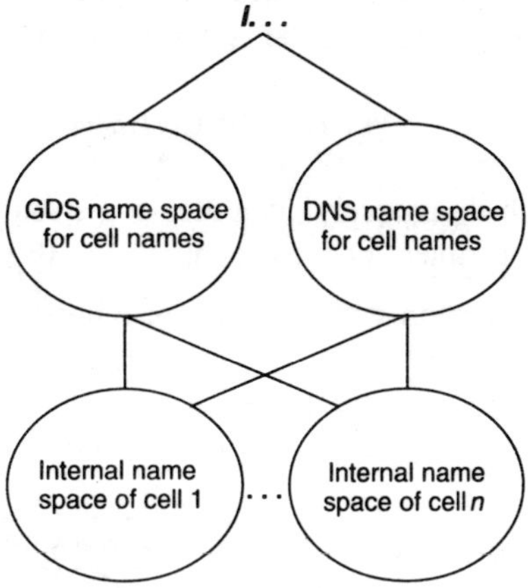


**Fig. 10.20** The name space structure of a DCE system having *n* cells that uses both X.500 and DNS notations for cell naming.

Each object in DCE has a unique name that mainly consists of the following parts each of which is separated by a slash (see Fig. 10.21):

1. *A prefix*. This part indicates whether the name is local to the current cell or global to the entire DCE name space. The prefix /.: is used to denote a local name, whereas the prefix /... is used to denote a global name.

| Prefix | Cell name | Local name |
|---|---|---|
| /... means global<br>/.: means local | in X.500 notation or in DNS notation | UNIX-like hierarchical name |

Object name = prefix/cell name/local name

**Fig. 10.21** The DCE naming convention.

2. *Cell name*. This is an optional part specified only when the prefix /... is used for the first part of the name. This part can be specified either in X.500 notation or in DNS notation. A global name must contain this part, whereas a local name must not contain this part.
3. *Local name*. This part uniquely identifies an object within a cell. The UNIX-like hierarchical naming scheme is used for local names.

The X.500 and DNS notations for cell naming are briefly described below.

### The X.500 Notation

The OSI X.500 is an international standard for naming people, computers, resources, services, or anything else that needs a unique name. It uses the hierarchical, attribute-based naming scheme (see Fig. 10.22). Therefore, in the X.500 notation, a name is represented by a set of attributes separated by slashes. Each attribute has an attribute type and one or more values. The type and value of an attribute are separated by an equal sign. Therefore, a typical X.500 name may be of the form

*/Country=US/OrgType=COM/OrgName=IBM/Dept=ENG/Person=Nancy/*

which uniquely identifies a person named Nancy who belongs to the engineering department of a company named IBM in the United States. In X.500 terminology, each

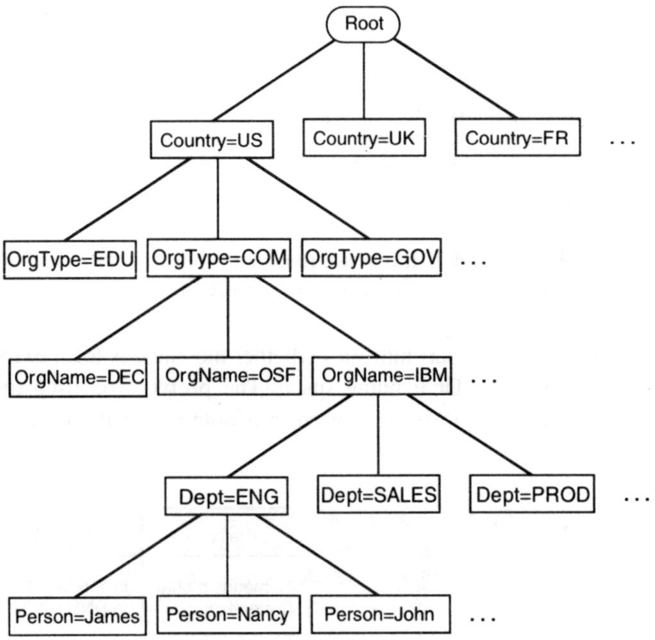


**Fig. 10.22** Part of an X.500 directory information tree.

component of a name is called the *relative distinguished name* (*RDN*) and the full name is called the *distinguished name* (*DN*).

X.500 also provides the facility to define and use aliases, which are similar to symbolic links in a file system.

The X.500 name tree is called the *Directory Information Tree* (*DIT*) and the entire directory structure including the data associated with the nodes is called the *Directory Information Base* (*DIB*). A DIB entry consists of a set of attributes described in the OSI ASN.1 notation (a standard notation for syntax definitions). For each attribute type, the description includes a type description and a syntax definition defining representations for all permissible values of the type. New attributes can be defined as and when required.

X.500 uses an object-oriented information model for grouping DIB entries into classes. Each DIB entry has an *ObjectClass* attribute that determines the class (or classes) of the object to which an entry refers. For instance, in the DIT of Figure 10.22, *Country*, *OrgType*, *OrgName*, *Dept*, and *Person* are all examples of values of *ObjectClass* attribute. The definition of a class determines which attributes are mandatory and which are optional for entries of the given class. The *ObjectClass* attribute is always mandatory, whose value must be the name of one or more classes. If the *ObjectClass* attribute of an object has two or more values, that object inherits the mandatory and optional attributes of each of the corresponding classes.

X.500, being a standard, does not address implementation issues. Readers interested in a more detailed description of X.500 and methods for its implementation may refer to [Rose 1992].

### The DNS Notation

The DNS is the standard scheme for naming hosts and other resources on the Internet. It uses a hierarchical, tree-structured name space partitioned into domains. In this scheme, a name consists of one or more strings called *labels* separated by the delimiter ".". There is no delimiter at the beginning or end of a name. Names are written with the highest level domain on the right.

The Internet DNS name space is partitioned both organizationally and according to geography. It divides the world up into top-level domains consisting of country names such as *us* (United States) (this is the default top-level domain and is often omitted in the qualified name of an object belonging to this domain), *uk* (United Kingdom), *fr* (France), and *jp* (Japan). Different countries then have their own organizational domains that form the next level of domains of the name space tree. For example, in the United States, the organizational domains are *edu* (educational institutions), *com* (commercial organizations), *gov* (government agencies), *mil* (military organizations), *net* (network support centers), *int* (international organizations), and *org* (organizations not included in any of the above-mentioned domains). The organizational domains in turn have subdomains such as *stanford.edu*, *ibm.com*, *anl.gov*, and *ieee.org*. These subdomains in turn have sub-subdomains such as *cs.stanford.edu*.

Registration authorities responsible for the registration of names in a domain at a particular level are different. For example, the domain *cs.stanford.edu.us*, which stands for the department of Computer Science at Stanford educational institution of the United

States, can contain any name the department wishes. But the name *cs* in the domain *stanford.edu.us* has to be agreed with the Stanford University authorities, who manage the domain *stanford.edu.us*. Similarly, the name *stanford* in the domain *edu.us* has to be agreed with the registration authorities who manage the domain *edu.us*, and so on.

In summary, Figure 10.23 shows the three different ways that may be used to refer to an object in DCE.

/.../ENG.IBM.COM.US/nancy/letters/to/lucy

(*a*)

/.../Country=US/OrgType=COM/OrgName=IBM/Dept=ENG/nancy/letters/to/lucy

(*b*)

/.:/nancy/letters/to/lucy

(*c*)

**Fig. 10.23** Three different ways to refer to the same object in DCE Directory Service. Global object name with cell name specified in (*a*) Internet format (DNS notation) and (*b*) GDS format (× 500 notation); (*c*) local object name within a cell.

### 10.9.2 Intracell Naming in DCE

All names within a cell are managed by the CDS, whose functions and implementation are briefly described below.

#### CDS Directories

The CDS of a cell basically manages the CDS directories of the cell that are organized in a hierarchical tree structure. These directories collectively contain the names and attributes of all the objects within the cell. Each *CDS directory* has a number of directory entries. Each directory entry consists of a name and a set of attributes. For example, a directory entry for a printer might contain its name, its location, and its characteristics, such as type and speed.

DCE uses the approach of associating protection with the name resolution path of an object name. Therefore, each directory entry also has protection information associated with it that specifies which users have what types of access rights (such as read, delete) for the entry. The CDS manages this protection information. Note that permission to access a directory entry does not imply permission to access the named object. Protection information for the named object is managed by the server that manages the object.

Therefore, the server knows which users have what types of access rights for the object.

### Replication of Naming Information

For better performance and reliability, CDS supports replication of its information, with the unit of replication being a directory. A collection of directories forms a *clearinghouse*. A clearinghouse is a physical database managed by a CDS server. While every DCE cell must run at least one CDS server, most will choose to run two or more, with critical information replicated among them. Each CDS server maintains one or more clearing houses. Each replica of a directory resides in a different clearinghouse. The root directory is replicated in all clearinghouses to allow a search for any name to be begun by any CDS server. This is because when a new directory is created, CDS automatically creates an entry for this directory in its parent directory (the directory immediately above the new directory in the hierarchical tree-structured name space). This entry is used to track the location of the child directory even when the parent and child directories are located in different clearinghouses. The root directory contains entries for all its children directories. Those directories, in turn, contain entries for their own children directories, and so on. Therefore, given the root directory, this path of connectivity enables CDS servers to find every directory (and thus every entry) in the name space.

### Consistency of Replicated Naming Information

To maintain the consistency of the naming information in replicated directories, DCE uses the primary-copy protocol for directory update operations. That is, for each replicated directory, one copy is designated as the primary copy and all others are secondary copies. Read operations can be performed using any copy of a replicated directory, primary or secondary. But all update operations are directly performed only on the primary copy. One of the following two approaches is used to update the secondary copies:

1. *Update propagation*. In this method, when the primary copy of a directory is updated, the changes are immediately sent to all the secondary copies. This method is used for updating the naming information that must be kept consistent all the time.
2. *Skulking*. In this method, the changes made to the primary copy are accumulated and are periodically sent together in a single message. This method is used for updating less critical naming information.

### CDS Implementation

The CDS implementation uses the client-server model. That is, there are *CDS server* daemon processes and *CDS client* daemon processes. A CDS server runs on a server machine, stores and manages one or more clearinghouses, and handles requests to create, modify, or look up names in its local clearinghouse. On the other hand, a CDS client, called a *CDS clerk*, runs on every client machine that uses CDS. A CDS clerk receives a request from a client application, interacts with one or more CDS servers to carry out the request, and returns the resulting information to the client. A CDS clerk also maintains a name cache in which it saves the results of name resolution requests for future use. The cache is written to disk periodically so that the information in it can survive a system reboot or the restart of an application.

### How CDS Clerks Learn about CDS Servers

A CDS clerk learns about the existence of a CDS server in one of the following ways:

1. *By broadcasting*. CDS servers periodically broadcast their existence. CDS clerks learn about CDS servers by listening to these broadcast messages. This method allows CDS clerks to learn about all those CDS servers that reside on the same LAN as that of the CDS clerk.

2. *During a name resolution*. During a name resolution, if a contacted CDS server cannot completely resolve the name with the information in its local clearinghouse, it returns to the requesting CDS clerk the location of another CDS server that has more information about resolving the given name. Such a reply from a CDS server during name resolution helps a CDS clerk to learn the existence of another CDS server that it was unaware of until now.

3. *By management command*. A DCE administrator can use the CDS control program to create information about a CDS server in a CDS clerk's cache. This method is normally used when the CDS clerk and the CDS server reside on different LANs so that broadcast messages sent by the CDS server on its own LAN cannot be received by the CDS clerk on a different LAN.

### Name Resolution

A name resolution operation (called *lookup* in CDS) is performed in the manner described below. The steps of this description correspond to the steps of Figure 10.24, which shows how a simple name resolution operation is performed in DCE:

1. A client application sends a lookup request to its local CDS clerk in an RPC message.
2. The CDS clerk checks its cache for the name. If it is found in the cache, the CDS clerk returns a reply to the client and the name resolution operation completes.
3. If the name is not found in the cache, the CDS clerk does an RPC with a CDS server that it knows about.
4. With the directories available in its local clearinghouse, the CDS server tries to resolve as many components of the name as possible.
5. If the name can be completely resolved, the CDS server returns the result of name resolution to the CDS clerk.

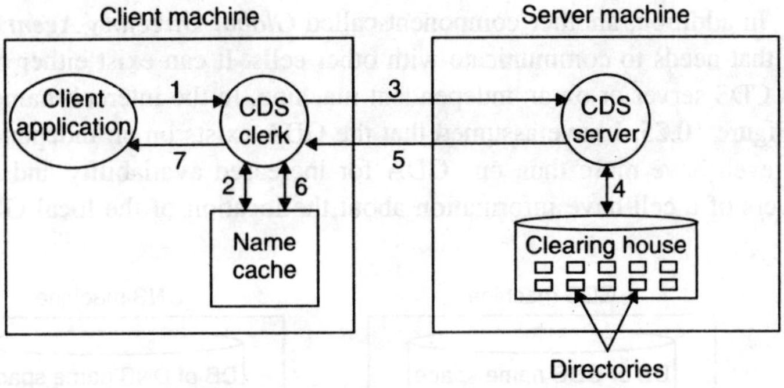


**Fig. 10.24** Steps of a simple name resolution in DCE. Complex name resolutions involving multiple CDS servers use the iterative approach of Figure 10.18(b).

6. The CDS clerk caches this information in its cache for future use.
7. The CDS clerk finally returns a reply to the client and the name resolution operation completes.

If the name can only be partially resolved by the contacted CDS server in Step 4 above (remember that partial name resolution is always possible since the root directory is replicated in every clearinghouse), the CDS server returns to the CDS clerk the location of another CDS server that has more information about resolving the given name. The CDS clerk then interacts with this newly learned CDS server for getting the name resolved. This step is repeated until the name gets resolved and the CDS clerk receives the result of name resolution from the last contacted CDS server. That is, the iterative approach of interaction among the name agent and name servers is used during name resolution. The CDS clerk caches the result of name resolution and the information of newly learned CDS servers and returns a reply to the client.

Notice from the description above that CDS only performs the name resolution operation. It does not perform an object-accessing operation. To access the object after successful name resolution, a client must do an RPC with the server that manages the named object.

### 10.9.3 Intercell Naming in DCE

A client in one cell may want to access an object that belongs to another cell. To resolve names that point to objects in other cells, CDS clerks must have a way to locate CDS servers in other cells. We have already seen that a DCE system has a GDS name space for cell names stored in X.500 notation. This name space is managed by a *GDS server.* We also saw that in addition to a GDS name space for cell names, a DCE system may also have a DNS name space for cell names in DNS notation. This name space is managed by a *DNS server.* These two name spaces map a cell name to a CDS server within that cell.

In addition, another component called *Global Directory Agent* (*GDA*) exists in any cell that needs to communicate with other cells. It can exist either on the same machine as a CDS server or on an independent machine. In the intercell name resolution example of Figure 10.25, I have assumed that the GDA exists on an independent machine. A cell can even have more than one GDA for increased availability and reliability. The CDS servers of a cell have information about the location of the local GDA.

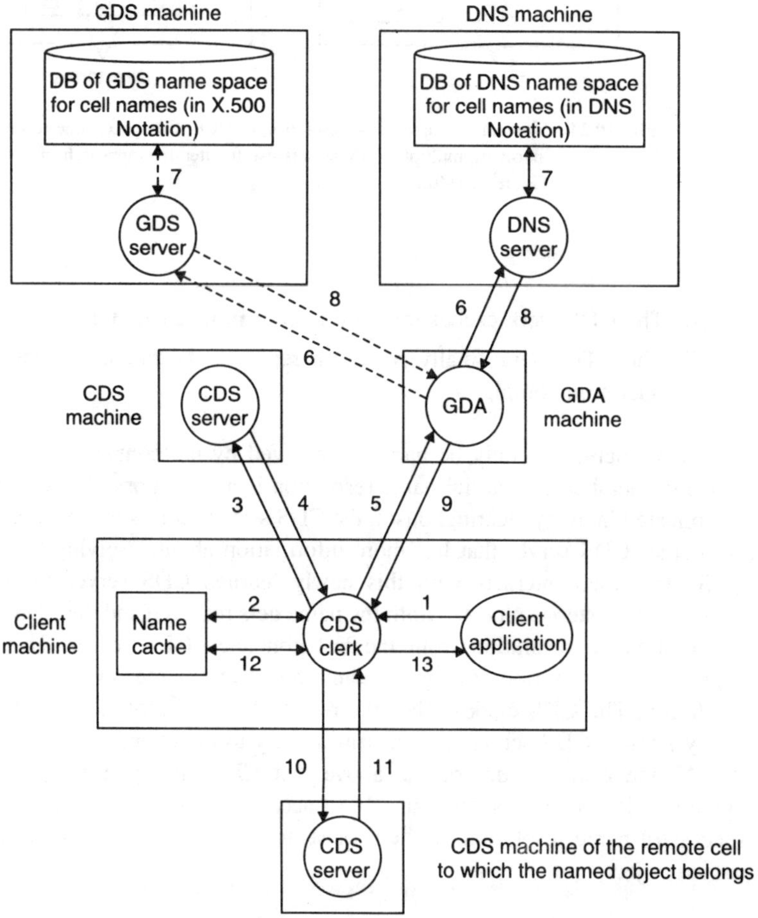


**Fig. 10.25** Intercell name resolution in DCE.

Now let us see the steps involved in the resolution of a name that points to an object in another cell. The steps in the following description correspond to the steps of Figure 10.25, which shows how intercell name resolution is performed in DCE:

1. A client application sends a lookup request to its local CDS clerk in an RPC message.

2. The CDS clerk checks its cache for the name. If it is found in the cache, the CDS clerk returns a reply to the client and the name resolution operation completes.
3. If the name is not found in the cache, the CDS clerk does an RPC with a CDS server asking for the location of the GDA. Recall that a global name must have a cell name and a local name must not have a cell name. Therefore, by seeing the name supplied by the client, the CDS clerk knows that it is a global name and the GDA must be contacted to resolve its cell name.
4. The CDS server returns the location of the GDA to the CDS clerk.
5. The CDS clerk then does an RPC with the GDA, sending it the cell name embedded in the name to be resolved.
6. The GDA checks to see which notation has been used to name the cell. If it is X.500 notation, the GDA does an RPC with the GDS server. On the other hand, if the notation used is DNS notation, the GDA does an RPC with the DNS server.
7. The GDS or DNS server looks up the cell name in its database.
8. It returns to the GDA the address of a CDS server in the named cell.
9. The GDA forwards this information to the CDS clerk.
10. The CDS clerk now uses this information to send its name lookup request to the CDS server of the cell to which the named object belongs. The CDS server resolves the name using the directories in its clearinghouse. In this example, we assume that the contacted CDS server can completely resolve the name with the directories in its clearinghouse. If this is not the case, an iterative approach is used by the CDS clerk to interact with other CDS servers of the remote cell.
11. The CDS server returns the result of name resolution to the CDS clerk.
12. The CDS clerk caches this information in its cache for future use.
13. The CDS clerk finally returns a reply to the client and the name resolution operation completes.

### 10.9.4 User Interfaces to the DCE Directory Service

DCE Directory Service supports the following types of user interfaces for users having different access privileges for the naming information:

1. *Browsing interface*. This interface is for users having the least privilege for the naming information. It allows the users to only view the content and structure of cell directories. The interface takes the form of a browser tool that runs on workstations with windowing software based on the OSF/Motif graphical user interface. The browser can display an overall directory structure as well as show the contents of directories. It can also be customized so that it displays only specific kinds of entries. Recall that each directory entry has protection information associated with it that specifies which users have what types of access rights for the entry. When a user uses the browser tool, only

those directory entries are displayed for which the user has read permission. Other entries are not displayed.

2. *XDS application programming interface*. Users can create, modify, and delete directory entries by using the *XDS* (*X/Open Directory Server*) application programming interface to write an application that makes direct calls to the DCE Directory Service. The XDS application programming interface is consistent with the standard interface to X.500, called *XOM* (*X/Open Object Management*). The XDS interface has 13 calls for manipulating directory objects and for setting up and initializing connections between clients and directory servers. Some of the calls for directory manipulation are *add_entry* for adding a new entry to a directory, *remove_entry* for deleting an entry from a directory, *list* for listing all entries of a directory, *read* for reading the attributes of an object, *modify_entry* for changing the attributes of an object, and *modify_rdn* for renaming an object.

3. *Administrative interface*. This interface is for users having maximum privilege to the naming information. It allows the administrators to configure or reconfigure the naming information within the system. That is, based on the idea of where a directory is most likely to be used, an administrator decides the distribution and replication of various directories in the clearinghouses of different CDS servers. For replicated directories, administrators also specify the mechanism (update propagation or skulking) to be used for consistency control of the information in each of these directories. Furthermore, an administrator can also change the access control rights associated with a directory entry for controlling access to it.

## 10.10 SUMMARY

A naming system of a distributed operating system enables users and programs to assign character-string names to objects and subsequently use these names to refer to those objects. It provides the users with an abstraction of an object that hides the details of how and where an object is actually located in the network.

The desirable features of a good naming system for a distributed system are location transparency, location independency, scalability, uniform naming convention, provision for multiple user-defined names for the same object, group naming facility, assignment of meaningful names to objects, good performance, fault tolerance, replication transparency, locating the nearest replica, and locating all replicas.

A name is a string composed of a set of symbols chosen from a finite alphabet. Two basic classes of names widely used in operating systems are human-oriented names and system-oriented names.

A naming system employs one or more naming conventions for name assignment to objects. The set of names complying with a given naming convention is said to form a name space. A name space may either be flat or partitioned. Each partition of a partitioned name space is called a domain of the name space. A name defined in a domain is called a simple name. A compound name is composed of one or more simple names that are separated by a special delimiter character.

A name server is a process that maintains information about named objects and provides facilities that enable users to access that information. A name space of a distributed system is usually managed by several name servers. Each name server normally has information about only a small subset of the set of objects in the distributed system. The name servers that store the information about an object are called the authoritative name servers of that object.

The distribution of the name service and the locations of the name servers should be transparent to the clients of a name service. This transparency is achieved through name agents that act between name servers and their clients.

Names are always associated with some context. A context can be thought of as the environment in which a name is valid. A "context/name" pair is said to form a qualified name that uniquely identifies an object.

Name resolution is the process of mapping an object's name to the authoritative name servers of that object.

For ease of use, a naming system usually provides the facility of abbreviations, relative names, generic names, and multicast names for its human-oriented names.

A naming system that supports descriptive/attribute-based names allows an object to be identified by a set of attributes or properties that describe the object and uniquely identify it among the group of objects in the name space.

Object locating is the process of mapping an object's system-oriented unique identifier to the replica locations of the object. The commonly used object-locating mechanisms in a distributed system are broadcasting, expanding ring broadcast, encoding the location of an object within its identifier, searching the creator node first and then broadcasting, using forward location pointers, and using hint cache and broadcasting.

The four basic approaches for assigning systemwide unique human-oriented names to the various objects in a distributed system are combining an object's local name with its host name, interlinking isolated name spaces into a single name space, full/partial replication of remote name spaces on explicit request, and a single global name space.

A name space is partitioned into contexts by using clustering conditions. A clustering condition is an expression that, when applied to a name, returns either a true or a false value, depending on whether the given name exists in the context designated by the clustering condition. The three basic clustering methods are algorithmic clustering, syntactic clustering, and attribute clustering.

A context binding associates the context within which it is stored to another context that is more knowledgeable about the named object and the name servers that store that context. Two commonly used strategies to implement context bindings are table-based strategy and procedure-based strategy. The contexts of a table-based strategy are also known as directories.

The name resolution mechanism of a naming system depends on the policy used for distributing the contexts of the name space of the naming system. Some of the commonly used approaches for the distribution of contexts for name resolution are the centralized approach, the fully replicated approach, distribution of contexts based on the physical structure of the name space, and structure-free distribution of contexts.

Research results have shown that a simple distributed name cache can have substantial positive effect on distributed system performance. The three types of name caches used in distributed systems are directory cache, prefix cache, and full-name cache. The two commonly used approaches for name cache implementation are a cache per process and a single cache at each node for all processes of the node. The two commonly used methods for multicache consistency are immediate invalidate and on-use update.

An important job of the naming system of several centralized and distributed operating systems is to control unauthorized access to both the named objects and the information in the naming database. The three basic naming-related access control mechanisms are object names as protection keys, capabilities, and associating protection with the name resolution path of an object name.

## EXERCISES

**10.1.** What are the main jobs performed by the naming subsystem of a distributed operating system? Is a naming subsystem also needed in an operating system for a centralized time-sharing system? If no, explain why. If yes, in what aspects does the naming subsystem of a distributed operating system differ from that of a centralized time-sharing operating system?

**10.2.** Differentiate between the terms "location transparency" and "location independency." Which is a more powerful feature and why?

**10.3.** The object-locating mechanism of a distributed operating system is designed to return the locations of all the replicas of an object. Suggest a mechanism that can be used in this system to allow a name agent to find out the relative distances of the replicas from the obtained locations so that the object-accessing request can be sent to the nearest available replica location.

**10.4.** Differentiate between human-oriented and system-oriented names used in operating systems. Is it possible to design a system in which objects are identified only by their system-oriented names and there are no human-oriented names for objects? If no, explain why. If yes, explain what problems may occur in such a system.

**10.5.** What is a name space? For a hierarchically structured name space, discuss the relative advantages and disadvantages of using a fixed number of levels and allowing an arbitrary number of levels for the hierarchy.

**10.6.** Give an example of each of the following types of name spaces:
- (a) A flat name space having 10 names.
- (b) A nonhierarchical name space having four domains with each domain having three names.
- (c) A hierarchical name space having four domains with each domain having three names.
- (d) A name space having two nonnested contexts and four qualified names.
- (e) A name space having two contexts and four qualified names. One of the contexts is nested within the other.

**10.7.** Give an example of a flat name space having 20 names. Use the following to partition this name space into contexts such that none of the contexts contain more than eight names:
- (a) The algorithmic clustering method
- (b) The syntactic clustering method

Specify the clustering conditions used in each case.

**10.8.** The object-locating operation can be greatly simplified if the location of an object is embedded in its unique identifier. In spite of this advantage, why is it undesirable to include the location of an object in its unique identifier?

**10.9.** In what ways does the creation of system-oriented names in distributed operating systems differ from their creation in centralized operating systems? Give three different methods that may be used to create system-oriented names in distributed operating systems.

**10.10.** Suppose a distributed system uses a single global hierarchical name space for its human-oriented names. The qualified names in this name space are likely to be long, having too many component names. Therefore, it may be inconvenient for a user to specify the qualified name of an object every time he or she wants to use it. Suggest two methods that may be used to solve this problem and discuss the relative advantages and disadvantages of both methods.

**10.11.** In what manner will the design of the naming systems of the following types of distributed operating systems differ?

(a) One that does not permit object migration and object replication
(b) One that permits object migration but does not permit object replication
(c) One that permits object replication but does not permit object migration
(d) One that permits both migration and replication of objects

**10.12.** Suppose you have to design an object-locating mechanism for the naming system of a distributed system. What factors will influence your design decision?

**10.13.** Which one or more of the object-locating mechanisms discussed in the chapter are suitable for a naming system for the following types of distributed systems:

(a) A LAN-based system having few nodes
(b) A LAN-based system having a large number of nodes
(c) A WAN-based system
(d) A system that does not permit object migration and object replication
(e) A system that permits object migration but does not permit object replication
(f) A system that permits object replication but does not permit object migration
(g) A system that permits both migration and replication of objects

If more than one mechanism is suitable for a particular case, which one will you prefer to use and why?

**10.14.** What is a "meta-context"? Is it needed in the design of all naming systems that use name spaces partitioned into contexts? If yes, explain why. If no, explain in what type of naming systems it is needed.

**10.15.** For a distributed system, suppose you have to design a naming system that uses a single global hierarchical name space for its human-oriented names and directories for maintaining context-binding information. To simplify the design and programming, suppose that you have decided to separate the part of the naming system that deals with the management of directories and to implement it in the form of a directory server. Specify the set of primitives that you will provide to allow interaction with the directory server.

**10.16.** Suppose you have to design a name-caching scheme for a naming system. What are the main issues involved in the design? What features of the naming system will influence the manner in which you will handle each of these issues in your design?

**10.17.** Suppose a user inputs the command *open* (file_name, mode), where *file_name* is specified as */edu/users/sinha/project1/file1*. Assume that the naming subsystem of this system uses the following:

(a) Table-based strategy for context bindings
(b) Structure-free distribution of contexts
(c) Transitive approach of interaction among name agent and name servers during name resolution
(d) A full name cache for each process on a node

List all the main steps in sequential order that the naming subsystem of the operating system has to perform to carry out this command. You may make any other assumptions if needed, but state your assumptions.

**10.18.** Explain the on-use consistency control mechanism. In what respect is this mechanism better than other commonly used mechanisms for cache consistency? Can this mechanism be used to maintain the consistency of all types of cached data? Give reasons for your answer.

**10.19.** In a distributed system, system-oriented names of objects are to be used to control access to objects. That is, in this system, a subject that possesses the system-oriented name of an object will be allowed to access the object in all possible modes. An important issue in the design of this system is that system-oriented names must be hard to guess. Suggest some methods that can be used to handle this issue.

**10.20.** In a distributed system, system-oriented names of objects are to be used as capabilities for controlling access to objects. Think of a method that can be used for creating system-oriented names that can also be used as capabilities to grant different access permissions to different users of the same object.

## BIBLIOGRAPHY

**[Birrell et al. 1982]** Birrell, A. D., Levin, R., Needham, R. M., and Schroeder, M. D., "Grapevine: An Exercise in Distributed Computing," *Communications of the ACM*, Vol. 25, No. 4, pp. 260–274 (1982).

**[Boggs 1983]** Boggs, D. R., "Internet Broadcasting," Ph.D. Dissertation, Stanford University, Technical Report No. CSL-83-3, Palo Alto Research Center (1983).

**[Brownbridge et al. 1982]** Brownbridge, D. R., Marshall, L. F., and Randell, B., "The Newcastle Connection or UNIXes of the World Unite!" *Software Practice and Experience*, Vol. 12, No. 12, pp. 1147–1162 (1982).

**[Cerf and Cain 1983]** Cerf, V. G., and Cain, E., "The DoD Internet Architecture Model," *Computer Networks*, Vol. 7, No. 5, pp. 307–318 (1983).

**[Cheriton and Mann 1989]** Cheriton, D. R., and Mann, T. P., "Decentralizing a Global Naming Service for Improved Performance and Fault Tolerance," *ACM Transactions on Computer Systems*, Vol. 7, No. 2, pp. 147–183 (1989).

**[Comer and Murtagh 1986]** Comer, D., and Murtagh, T. P., "The Tilde File Naming Scheme," In: *Proceedings of the 6th International Conference on Distributed Computing Systems*, IEEE Press, New York, NY, pp. 509–514 (1986).

**[Comer and Peterson 1986]** Comer, D., and Peterson, L. L., "A Model of Name Resolution in Distributed Systems," In: *Proceedings of the 6th International Conference on Distributed Computing Systems*, IEEE Press, New York, NY, pp. 523–530 (1986).

**[Coulouris et al. 1994]** Coulouris, G. F., Dollimore, J., and Kindberg, T., *Distributed Systems Concepts and Design*, 2nd ed., Addison-Wesley, Reading, MA (1994).

**[Goscinski 1991]** Goscinski, A., *Distributed Operating Systems, The Logical Design*, Addison-Wesley, Reading, MA (1991).

**[Kille 1992]** Kille, S., *Implementing X.400 and X.500: The PP and QUIPU Systems*, Artech House, Norwood, MA (1992).

**[Lampson 1986]** Lampson, B. W., "Designing a Global Name Service," In: *Proceedings of the 5th Annual Symposium on Principles of Distributed Computing*, Calgary, Canada, Association for Computing Machinery, New York, NY, pp. 1–10 (August 1986).

**[Lantz et al. 1985]** Lantz, K., Edighoffer, J., and Hitson, B., "Towards a Universal Directory Service," In: *Proceedings of the 4th Annual Symposium on Principles of Distributed Computing*, Minaki, Canada, Association for Computing Machinery, New York, NY, pp. 250–260 (August 1985).

**[Leach et al. 1982]** Leach, P. J., Stump, B. L., Hamilton, J. A., and Levine, P. H., "UIDs as Internal Names in a Distributed File System," In: *Proceedings of the 1st Annual Symposium on Principles of Distributed Computing*, Ontario, Canada, Association for Computing Machinery, New York, NY, pp. 34–41 (August 1982).

**[Leach et al. 1983]** Leach, P. J., Levine, P. H., Douros, B. P., Hamilton, J. A., Nelson, D. L., and Stumpf, B. L., "The Architecture of an Integrated Local Network," *IEEE Journal on Selected Areas in Communication*, Vol. SAC-1, No. 5, pp. 842–857 (1983).

**[Leffler et al. 1984]** Leffler, S., Karels, M., and McKusick, M., "Measuring and Improving the Performance of 4.2BSD," In: *Proceedings of the 1984 USENIX Summer Conference*, USENIX Association, Berkeley, CA, pp. 237–252 (1984).

**[Levy and Silberschatz 1990]** Levy, E., and Silberschatz, A., "Distributed File Systems: Concepts and Examples," *ACM Computing Surveys*, Vol. 22, No. 4, pp. 321–374 (1990).

**[Lin et al. 1982]** Lin, M. T., Tsoy, D. P., and Lian, R. C., "Design of a Network Operating System for the Distributed Double-Loop Computer Network (DDLCN)," *Local Computer Networks*, North-Holland Co., IFIP (1982).

**[Lockhart, Jr. 1994]** Lockhart, Jr., H. W., *OSF DCE: Guide to Developing Distributed Applications*, IEEE Computer Society Press, Los Alamitos, CA (1994).

**[Mockapetris 1984]** Mockapetris, P. V., "The Domain Name System," In: *Proceedings IFIP 6.5, International Symposium on Computer Messaging*, Nottingham, England (May 1984).

**[Mockapetris and Dunlap 1988]** Mockapetris, P. V., and Dunlap, K. J., "Development of the Domain Name System," In: *Proceedings of the SIGCOMM'88 Symposium on Communications Architectures and Protocols*, Stanford, CA, Association for Computing Machinery, New York, NY, pp. 123–133 (1988).

**[Mogul 1986]** Mogul, J. C., "Representing Information About Files," Ph.D. Dissertation, Stanford University, Computer Science Technical Report, STAN-CS-86-1103 (March 1986).

**[Mullender and Tanenbaum 1986]** Mullender, S. J., and Tanenbaum, A. S., "The Design of a Capability Based Distributed Operating System," *The Computer Journal*, Vol. 29, No. 4, pp. 289–300 (1986).

**[Mullender et al. 1990]** Mullender, S. J., Van Rossum, G., Tanenbaum, A. S., Van Renesse, R., and Van Staverene, H., "Amoeba: A Distributed Operating System for the 1990s," *IEEE Computer*, Vol. 23, No. 5, pp. 44–53 (1990).

**[Needham 1993]** Needham, R. M., "Names," In: S. Mullender (Ed.), *Distributed Systems*, 2nd ed., Association for Computing Machinery, New York, NY, pp. 315–327 (1993).

**[Oppen and Dalal 1983]** Oppen, D. C., and Dalal, Y. K., "The Clearinghouse: A Decentralized Agent for Locating Named Objects in a Distributed Environment," *ACM Transactions on Office Information Systems*, Vol. 1, No. 3, pp. 230–253 (1983).

**[Peterson 1988]** Peterson, L., "The Profile Naming Service," *ACM Transactions on Computer Systems*, Vol. 6, No. 4, pp. 341–364 (1988).

**[Rashid 1987]** Rashid, R. F., "Mach: A New Foundation for Multiprocessor Systems Development," In: *Proceedings of COMPCON'87—Digest of Papers*, IEEE Press, New York, NY, pp. 192–193 (1987).

**[Rose 1992]** Rose, M. T., *The Little Black Book: Mail Bonding with OSI Directory Services*, Prentice-Hall, Englewood Cliffs, NJ (1992).

**[Rosenberry et al. 1992]** Rosenberry, W., Kenney, D., and Fisher, G., *OSF DISTRIBUTED COMPUTING ENVIRONMENT, Understanding DCE*, O'Reilly & Associates, Sebastopol, CA (1992).

**[Rozier et al. 1988]** Rozier, M., Abrossimov, V., Armand, F., Boule, I., Gien, M., Guillemont, M., Herrmann, F., Kaiser, C., Leonard, P., Langlois, S., and Neuhauser, W., "Chorus Distributed Operating System," *Computing Systems*, Vol. 1, pp. 305–379 (1988).

**[Saltzer 1982]** Saltzer, J. H., "On the Naming and Binding of Network Destinations," In: *Proceedings of IFIP/TC6 International Symposium on Local Computer Networks*, Florence, Italy, pp. 311–317 (April 1982).

**[Sandberg et al. 1985]** Sandberg, R., Goldberg, D., Kleinman, S., Walsh, D., and Lyon, B., "Design and Implementation of the SUN Network File System," In: *Proceedings of the USENIX Conference*, Portland, OR, USENIX Association, Berkeley, CA, pp. 119–130 (1985).

**[Schantz et al. 1986]** Schantz, R. E., Thomas, R. H., and Bono, G., "The Architecture of the Cronus Distributed Operating System," In: *Proceedings of the 6th International Conference on Distributed Computing Systems*, IEEE Press, New York, NY, pp. 250–259 (1986).

**[Schickler 1982]** Schickler, P., "Naming and Addressing in a Computer Based Mail Environment," *IEEE Transactions on Communications*, Vol. COM-30, No. 1 (1982).

**[Schroeder et al. 1984]** Schroeder, R., Birrell, A. D., and Needham, R. M., "Experience with Grapevine: The Growth of a Distributed System," *ACM Transactions on Computer Systems*, Vol. 2, No. 1, pp. 3–23 (1984).

**[Schwartz et al. 1987]** Schwartz, M., Zahorjan, J., and Notkin, D., "A Name Service for Evolving Heterogeneous Systems," In: *Proceedings of the 11th ACM Symposium on Operating Systems Principles*, Association for Computing Machinery, New York, NY, pp. 52–62 (November 1987).

**[Sheltzer et al. 1986]** Sheltzer, A. B., Lindell, R., and Popek, G. J., "Name Service Locality and Cache Design in a Distributed Operating System," In: *Proceedings of the 6th International Conference on Distributed Computing Systems*, IEEE Press, New York, NY, pp. 515–522 (1986).

**[Silberschatz and Galvin 1994]** Silberschatz, A., and Galvin, P. B., *Operating Systems, Concepts*, 4th ed., Addison-Wesley, Reading, MA (1994).

**[Sinha et al. 1991a]** Sinha, P. K., Maekawa, M., Shimizu, K., Jia, X., Ashihara, H., Utsunomiya, N., Park, K. S., and Nakano, H., "The Galaxy Distributed Operating System," *IEEE Computer*, Vol. 24, No. 8, pp. 34–41 (1991).

**[Sinha et al. 1991b]** Sinha, P. K., Shimizu, K., Utsunomiya, N., Nakano, H., and Maekawa, M., "Network Transparent Object Naming and Locating in the Galaxy Distributed Operating System," *Journal of Information Processing*, Vol. 14, No. 3, pp. 310–324 (1991).

**[Sinha et al. 1992]** Sinha, P. K., Maekawa, M., and Shimizu, K., "Improving the Reliability of Name Resolution Mechanism in Distributed Operating Systems," In: *Proceedings of the 12th International Conference on Distributed Computing Systems*, Yokohama, Japan, pp. 589–596 (June 1992).

**[Su and Postel 1982]** Su, Z., and Postel, J., "The Domain Naming Convention for Internet User Applications," Network Information Center, SRI International, RFC 819 (August 1982).

**[Terry 1984]** Terry, D. B., "An Analysis of Naming Conventions for Distributed Computer Systems," In: *Proceedings of the 6th International Conference on Distributed Computing Systems*, IEEE Press, New York, NY, pp. 502–508 (1984).

**[Terry 1986]** Terry, D. B., "Structure-Free Name Management for Evolving Distributed Environments," In: *Proceedings of the ACM SIGCOMM'84*, Montreal, Quebec, Association for Computing Machinery, New York, NY, pp. 218–224 (June 1986).

**[Tichy and Ruan 1984]** Tichy, W. F., and Ruan, Z., "Towards a Distributed File System," In: *Proceedings of the Summer USENIX Conference*, USENIX Association, Berkeley, CA, pp. 87–97 (June 1984).

**[Tripathi et al. 1987]** Tripathi, A., Ghonami, A., and Schmitz, T., "Object Management in the NEXUS Distributed Operating System," In: *Proceedings of IEEE COMPCON'87*, IEEE Press, New York, NY, pp. 50–53 (February 1987).

**[Walker et al. 1983]** Walker, B., Popek, G., English, R., Kline, C., and Thiel, G., "The LOCUS Distributed Operating System," In: *Proceedings of the 9th ACM SIGOPS Symposium on Operating Systems Principles*, Association for Computing Machinery, New York, NY, pp. 49–70 (1983).

**[Watson 1981]** Watson, R., "Identifiers (Naming) in Distributed Systems," In: B. W. Lampson, M. Paul, and H. Siegert (Eds.), *Lecture Notes in Computing Science: Distributed Systems—Architecture and Implementation*, Springer-Verlag, New York, NY, pp. 191–210 (1981).

**[Welch and Ousterhout 1986]** Welch, B., and Ousterhout, J. K., "Prefix Tables: A Simple Mechanism for Locating Files in a Distributed System," In: *Proceedings of the 6th International Conference on Distributed Computing Systems*, IEEE Computer Society Press, Los Alamitos, CA, pp. 184–189 (1986).

**[Wiebe 1986]** Wiebe, D., "A Distributed Repository for Immutable Persistent Objects," In: *Proceedings of OOPSLA'86*, Association for Computing Machinery, New York, NY, pp. 453–465 (1986).

## POINTERS TO BIBLIOGRAPHIES ON THE INTERNET

I could not find a bibliography dedicated only to *Naming*. However, the following bibliographies contain references on the topics covered in this chapter:

ftp:ftp.cs.umanitoba.ca/pub/bibliographies/Os/IMMD_IV.html

ftp:ftp.cs.umanitoba.ca/pub/bibliographies/Misc/misc.1.html

ftp:ftp.cs.umanitoba.ca/pub/bibliographies/Distributed/rfc.html

# CHAPTER 11

# Security

## 11.1 INTRODUCTION

Computer systems store large amounts of information, some of which is highly sensitive and valuable to their users. Users can trust the system and rely on it only if the various resources and information of a computer system are protected against destruction and unauthorized access. Obviously, the security requirements are different for different computer systems depending on the environment in which they are supposed to operate. For example, security requirements for systems meant to operate in a military environment are different from those for systems that are meant to operate in an educational environment. The security goals of a computer system are decided by its security policies, and the methods used to achieve these goals are called security mechanisms. While designing the security of a system, it is often useful to distinguish between security policies and security mechanisms because security policies can be decided independent of the available technology but security mechanisms are influenced by the available technology. It may be difficult to implement the desired security policies with a selected set of security mechanisms. But new security mechanisms can be later added to the set to implement the desired security policies.

Irrespective of the operation environment, some of the common goals of computer security are as follows [Mullender 1985]:

1. *Secrecy.* Information within the system must be accessible only to authorized users.
2. *Privacy.* Misuse of information must be prevented. That is, a piece of information given to a user should be used only for the purpose for which it was given.
3. *Authenticity.* When a user receives some data, the user must be able to verify its authenticity. That is, the data arrived indeed from its expected sender and not from any other source.
4. *Integrity.* Information within the system must be protected against accidental destruction or intentional corruption by an unauthorized user.

A total approach to computer security involves both external and internal security. *External security* deals with securing the computer system against external factors such as fires, floods, earthquakes, stolen disks/tapes, leaking out of stored information by a person who has access to the information, and so on. For external security, the commonly used methods include maintaining adequate backup copies of stored information at places far away from the original information, using security guards to allow the entry of only authorized persons into the computer center, allowing the access to sensitive information to only trusted employees/users, and so on.

*Internal security,* on the other hand, mainly deals with the following two aspects:

1. *User authentication.* Once a user is allowed physical access to the computer facility, the user's identification must be checked by the system before the user can actually use the facility.

2. *Access control.* A computer system contains many resources and several types of information. Obviously, not all resources and information are meant for all users. Therefore, even when a user passes the authentication phase and is allowed to use the computer facility, a way is needed to prohibit the user from accessing those resources/ information that he or she is not authorized to access. In fact, a secure system requires that at any time a subject (person or program) should be allowed to access only those resources that it currently needs to complete its task. This requirement is commonly referred to as the *need-to-know principle* or the *principle of least privilege.*

We saw that the security needs of a computer system are intricately linked with that system's environment, use, and implementation. Therefore, in addition to the two aspects mentioned above, internal security in distributed systems has a third aspect called communication security.

3. *Communication security.* In a distributed system, the communication channels that are used to connect the computers are normally exposed to attackers who may try to breach the security of the system by observing, modifying, or disrupting the communications. Wireless networks are even more vulnerable to monitoring by intruders

because anyone with a scanner can pluck the radio signals out of the air without being detected. Communication security safeguards against unauthorized tampering of information while it is being transmitted from one computer to another through the communication channels. Two other aspects of communication security are *authenticity of communicating entities* and *integrity of messages*. That is, the sender of a message wants to know that the message was received by the intended receiver, and the receiver wants to know that the message was sent by the genuine sender. Obviously, both the sender and the receiver also want to be guaranteed that the contents of the message were not changed while it was in transfer.

Providing both external and internal security is more difficult in distributed systems than in centralized systems because of the lack of a single point of control and the use of insecure networks for data communication. Although external security is as important as internal security, the policies and mechanisms used at the operating system level for computer security deal only with the internal security aspects. Therefore, this chapter deals mainly with the commonly used mechanisms for providing different types of internal security in distributed systems.

## 11.2 POTENTIAL ATTACKS TO COMPUTER SYSTEMS

The first step in the provision of appropriate computer security is to identify the potential threats/attacks to computer systems. The term *intruder* or *attacker* is commonly used to refer to a person or program trying to obtain unauthorized access to data or a resource of a computer system. An intruder may be a threat to computer security in many ways that are broadly classified into two categories—passive attacks and active attacks. A *passive attack* does not cause any harm to the system being threatened, whereas an *active attack* does. Therefore, passive attacks are inherently undetectable by the system and can only be dealt with by using preventive measures. On the other hand, active attacks are combated by a combination of prevention, detection, and recovery techniques. A description of these attacks and some other related problems are presented below.

### 11.2.1 Passive Attacks

In passive attacks, an intruder somehow tries to steal unauthorized information from the computer system without interfering with the normal functioning of the system. Some commonly used methods of passive attack are described below:

1. *Browsing*. In this method, intruders attempt to read stored files, message packets passing by on the network, other processes' memory, and so on, without modifying any data. Access control mechanisms are used to prevent unauthorized reading of stored files and other processes' memory contents, and message encryption is used to prevent eavesdropping of messages transmitted over network links.

2. *Leaking*. In this method, an intruder uses an accomplice (a legitimate user having authority to access the information to be stolen) who leaks the information to him or her. Prevention of leaking is a difficult problem to solve and requires preventing all types of communication between the accomplice and the intruder. The problem of ensuring that it is impossible for a potential accomplice to leak any information to the outside world is called the *confinement problem* [Lampson 1973]. As described later, leaking of information between processes that in theory cannot communicate at all is relatively straightforward. Therefore, the confinement problem is in general unsolvable.

3. *Inferencing*. In this method, an intruder tries to draw some inference by closely observing and analyzing the system's data or the activities carried out by the system. For example, if information is encrypted to protect unauthorized access, an intruder may try to derive the encryption key by analyzing several pieces of encrypted data. Since the derived key can be used for stealing information from the system, it is valuable and may be sold to other intruders. Another example of inferencing is traffic analysis in distributed systems. In this case, an intruder observes when and where interprocess messages flow in the system, and by analyzing the frequency of message exchanges between various communicating partners, the intruder tries to draw some inference. For example, in a business environment, traffic analysis may provide useful clues to negotiations taking place between different organizations.

4. *Masquerading*. In this method, an intruder masquerades as an authorized user or program in order to gain access to unauthorized data or resources. For instance, many systems have mechanisms for allowing programs written by users to be used by other users. These programs can improperly use the access rights of an executing user and leak information. For example, an intruder may write an editor program that works perfectly as an editor but also creates a copy of the edited file to a special area accessible to the intruder. This editor program is then compiled and read into the *bin* directory of a user, whose files the intruder is interested in. From then on, the intruder gets a copy of all the files edited by the user. The user is ignorant of the theft being made because the editor program performs all his or her editing jobs in a perfectly normal fashion.

Penetrating computer security in this manner is known as the *Trojan horse attack*. That is, a *Trojan horse program* is a program that consists of clandestine code to do nasty things in addition to its usual function but appears to be benign. It is often offered as a gift or sometimes for a nominal price to prevent suspicion. A user normally accepts it into his or her system because of the useful function performed by it. However, once inside the user's computer, code hidden in the program becomes active and either executes malicious acts or creates a way of subverting system security so that unauthorized personnel can gain access to the system resources. Note that a Trojan horse attack may either be passive or active depending on the activities performed by the clandestine code. For example, if the clandestine code simply steals information, then it is of the passive type. But if it does something more harmful like destroying/corrupting files, then it is of the active type.

An intruder can also masquerade as a trusted server to a client requesting a service from the system. This action is known as *spoofing*.

### 11.2.2 Active Attacks

Active intruders are more malicious than passive intruders. Unlike passive attacks, active attacks interfere with the normal functioning of the system and often have damaging effects. The most common types of damage that active attacks cause are corrupting files, destroying data, imitating hardware errors, slowing down the system, filling up memory or disk space with garbage, causing the system to crash, confounding a receiver into accepting fabricated messages, and denial/delay of message delivery. Some commonly used forms of active attacks are described below. In the following, the description of viruses, worms, and logic bombs is based on the material presented in [Bowles and Pelaez 1992].

#### Viruses

A *computer virus* is a piece of code attached to a legitimate program that, when executed, infects other programs in the system by replicating and attaching itself to them. In addition to this replicating effect, a virus normally does some other damage to the system, such as corrupting/erasing files. Therefore, due to its spreading nature, a virus can cause severe damage to a system. Notice that virus attacks are active-type Trojan horse attacks.

A typical virus works as follows. The intruder writes a new program that performs some interesting or useful function (such as some game or utility) and attaches the virus to it in such a way that when the program is executed the viral code also gets executed. The intruder now uploads this infected program to a public bulletin board system or sends it by mail to other users of the system or offers it for free or for a nominal charge on floppy disks. Now if anyone uses the infected program, its viral code gets executed. When the viral code of the infected program executes, it randomly selects an executable file on the hard disk and checks to see if it is already infected. Most viruses include a string of characters that acts as a marker showing that the program has been infected. If the selected file is already infected, the virus selects another executable file. When an uninfected program is found, the virus infects it by attaching a copy of itself to the end of that program and replacing the first instruction of the program with a jump to the viral code. When the viral code is finished executing, it executes the instruction that had previously been first and then jumps to the second instruction so that the program now performs its intended function. Notice that a virus spreads because every time an infected program is executed, it tries to infect more programs. Also notice that a virus does not infect an already infected file in order to prevent an object file from growing ever longer. This allows the virus to infect many programs without noticeably increasing disk space usage.

Recovery from a virus infection is a difficult task that often requires partial or complete shutdown for long periods of time of the computer system under attack. Therefore, it is always better to take necessary precautions to prevent virus problems. Some precautionary steps include (a) buying software only from respectable stores, (b) refusing to accept software in unsealed packages or from untrusted sources, (c) avoiding borrowing programs from someone whose security standards are less rigorous than one's own, and (d) avoiding uploading of free software from public domain, bulletin boards, and programs sent by electronic mail.

When a computer system suffers from virus infection, it has to be cured. The simplest way to cure a computer from virus infection is to shut it down, purge its memory and all its disks, and rebuild its files from scratch using the original manufacturer's copy. Disinfection utilities may also be used to cure a computer from virus infection. These utilities first identify the virus type with which the computer is infected by matching its marker against the markers of well-known viruses. Once the type is known, the original programs are restored from their infected versions by applying a detailed knowledge of the infection method used by the virus. For example, in viruses that modify jump instructions at the beginning of the host program, recovering can be done simply by restoring the original jump to the start of the host program code. However, notice that these disinfection utilities can only cure specific known viruses. They cannot cure a newly encountered type of virus. A good disinfection utility can normally cure several hundred types of viruses and its power can be regularly improved by frequently updating it as new viruses are discovered.

Notice that the longer a virus remains in a system, the more time it has to spread and the tougher recovery from it becomes. Therefore, it is important to detect a virus as soon as possible. An effective method to detect viruses is to use a snapshot program and a check routine. The snapshot program is used to log all critical system information at the time of the initial installation and the check routine is periodically executed to compare the system's current state with the original snapshot. If signs of infection are detected, the affected area of the computer is identified and the user is notified.

Curing a distributed system from virus infection is much more difficult because if the infection is not removed from every workstation at the same time, reinfection will occur. This is because an infected file on the network server can infect every workstation on the network.

### Worms

Worms are programs that spread from one computer to another in a network of computers. They spread by taking advantage of the way in which resources are shared on a computer network and, in some cases, by exploiting flaws in the standard software installed on network systems. A worm program may perform destructive activities after arrival at a network node. Even when not directly destructive, worms often cripple a network by subverting the operation of computers on the network to their own purposes, monopolizing their resources, and saturating the communications links in a network. Often, it is necessary to shut down the entire system (all computers of the network) to recover from a worm problem.

To illustrate how a worm propagates in a network, the famous Internet Worm attack by a Cornell graduate student, Robert Tappan Morris, on November 2, 1988, that infected thousands of UNIX machines all over the Internet is described here. This worm program had two types of code, the bootstrap code and the code forming the main body of the worm. The bootstrap code was compiled and executed on the system under attack. When executed, the bootstrap code established a communications link between its new host and the machine from which it came, copied the main body of the worm to the new host, and executed it. Once installed on a new host, the worm's first few actions were to hide its existence. For this, it unlinked the binary version of itself, killed its parent process, read its files into memory and encrypted them, and deleted the files created during its entry into the system. After finishing its hiding operations, the worm's next job was to look into its host's routing tables to collect information about other hosts to which its current host was connected. Using this information, it then attempted to spread its bootstrap code to those machines by trying the following three methods one by one:

1. The first method was to try to spawn a remote shell on the target machine using the *rsh* command of UNIX. This method sometimes works because some machines trust other machines and willingly run *rsh* without authenticating the remote machine. If successful, the remote shell uploaded the worm program on the target machine and continued spreading to new machines from there.

2. If the first method failed, the second method was tried. This method took advantage of a bug in the *finger* program that runs as a daemon process at every BSD site. A user anywhere on the Internet can type

*finger user_name@host_name*

to obtain general information about a person at a particular site, such as the person's real name, home address, office address, telephone number, and so on. The *finger* utility uses the C library function *gets* to read input data. A problem with *gets* is that it reads the entire input string without checking for buffer overflows. The worm exploited this flaw and called *finger* with a specially constructed 536-byte string as a parameter. The overflow caused an area of the system stack to be overwritten, allowing the worm to put its own suitable instructions (a procedure to execute */bin/sh*) on the stack. Now when the *finger* daemon returned from the procedure it was in at the time it got the request, it returned to and executed the procedure inside the 536-byte string on the stack instead of returning to *main*. If this method succeeded, the worm had a shell running on the target machine.

3. If the first two methods failed, the worm tried a third method that takes advantage of a loophole in the UNIX electronic mail utility *sendmail*. The *sendmail* program has a *DEBUG* option, which allows program testers to verify that mail has arrived at a site without having to invoke the mailer's address resolution routines. Many vendors and site administrators leave the debug option compiled into the *sendmail* code to facilitate configuring the mailer for local conditions. What the worm did was to execute the *sendmail* program with the *DEBUG* option and then enact a sequence of commands to mail the bootstrap code to the target machine.

Once established on a new machine, the worm tried to break into user accounts by exploiting the accessibility of the UNIX password file and the tendency of users to choose common words as their passwords. Each broken password allowed the worm to masquerade as the user corresponding to that password and gain access to any remote machine where that user had an account.

The worm was designed to act intelligently to prevent being spotted. It periodically *forked* itself and killed its parent, so that its process ID was constantly changing. This prevented any one process from accumulating a large amount of CPU time that might create suspicion or cause its scheduling priority to be degraded. Furthermore, after every 12 hours, the worm erased its record of the machines it had infected, so that already infected hosts were put back on the list of potential targets. Whenever the worm gained access to a new machine, it first checked to see if the machine already had a copy of the worm. If so, the new copy exited, except one time in seven. The use of one in seven possibly was to allow the worm to spread even on a machine on which the system administrator might have started its own version of the worm to fool the real worm.

Although viruses and worms both replicate and spread themselves, the two differ in the following aspects:

1. A virus is a program fragment whereas a worm is a complete program in itself.
2. Since a virus is a program fragment, it does not exist independently. It resides in a host program, runs only when the host program runs, and depends on the host program for its existence. On the other hand, a worm can exist and execute independently.
3. A virus spreads from one program to another whereas a worm spreads from one computer to another in a network.

### Logic Bombs

A logic bomb is a program that lies dormant until some trigger condition causes it to explode. On explosion, it destroys data and spoils system software of the host computer. A trigger condition may be an event such as accessing a particular data file, a program being run a certain number of times, the passage of a given amount of time, or the system clock reaching some specific date (for instance, Friday the 13th or April Fool's Day). The trigger condition is normally selected so that the logic bomb explodes at the moment when it can do maximum damage to the system. Logic bombs can be embedded in a Trojan horse or carried about by a virus.

### Active Attacks Associated with Message Communications

In a distributed system, communication channels are used to carry information from one node to another in the system in the form of messages. These communication channels may be exposed to attackers who may try to breach the security of the system by observing, modifying, deleting, inserting, delaying, redirecting, or replaying the messages that travel through the communication channels. The commonly known active attacks associated with message communications are of the following types:

1. *Integrity attack.* For secure communication, the integrity requirement specifies that every message is received exactly as it was sent or a discrepancy is detected. However, an intruder may change the contents of a message while it is traveling through a communication channel and the receiver may not be aware of this and accept it as the original message.

2. *Authenticity attack.* An intruder may illegally connect his or her own computer system to a communication channel and impersonate a legal network site. The intruder can then synthesize and insert bogus messages with valid addresses into the system so that they are delivered as genuine messages. If an integrity attack is possible, an intruder may also cause an authenticity attack by changing the protocol control information (addresses) of the messages so that they are delivered to wrong destinations.

3. *Denial attack.* In this case, the intruder either completely blocks the communication path between two processes so that the two processes cannot communicate at all or observes all messages exchanged between the two processes and prevents only selected messages from delivery. That is, the intruder causes complete or partial denial of message delivery.

4. *Delay attack.* Several messages have time value. Therefore, instead of using a denial attack, an intruder may simply delay the delivery of message passing in an association between two communicating processes to fulfill his or her motive.

5. *Replay attack.* In this case, an intruder retransmits old messages that are accepted as new messages by their recipients.

*Cryptography* deals with the encryption of sensitive data to prevent its comprehension and is the only practical means for protecting information sent over an insecure channel, be it telephone line, microwave, satellite, or any other transmission media. This is because an encrypted message provides no information regarding the original message, hence guaranteeing secrecy; and an encrypted message, if tampered with, would not decrypt into a legal message, hence guaranteeing integrity. Cryptography can also be used for secure identification of communicating entities, hence guaranteeing authenticity. Furthermore, encryption, in conjunction with protocols, can also be used to prevent denial, delay, and replay of messages. For instance, replay of old messages can be countered by using nonces or timestamps. A *nonce* is an information that is guaranteed to be fresh; that is, it has not been used or appeared before. Therefore, a reply that contains some function of a recently sent nonce should be considered timely because the reply could have been generated only after the nonce was sent. Perfect random numbers are suitable for use as nonces. In summary, the only way to prevent attacks associated with message communications is by the application of cryptographic techniques.

### 11.2.3 Confinement Problem

In a client-server model, a single server program may be shared by multiple clients. In situations where programs are shared, a security problem is considerably more complex than if only data objects are shared. One reason that we have already seen is a Trojan horse. A Trojan horse is just one way in which a shared program could leak classified information to other unclassified subjects. There may be several other ways in which a shared program could leak confidential information to unauthorized subjects.

A program that cannot retain or leak confidential information is said to be *memoryless* or *confined*, and the prevention of such leakage is called the *confinement problem* [Lampson 1973]. That is, the confinement problem deals with the problem of eliminating every means by which an authorized subject can release any information contained in the object to which it has access to some subjects that are not authorized to access that information. According to Lampson, as long as a program does not have to retain or output any information, confinement can be implemented by restricting the access rights of the program. But if a program must retain or output information, access control alone is not sufficient to ensure security.

Lampson identified the following kinds of channels that can be used by a program to leak information:

1. *Legitimate channels.* Legitimate channels are those that the program uses to convey the results of its computation, such as messages or printed output. The program may hide additional information in these channels along with the actual result. Some form of encoding that is meaningful to the person or process receiving the result is used to convey the additional information. For example, in a printed output, two different space lengths that are not discernible to normal persons but visible if observed minutely may be used between words to mean 0 and 1 bits. This type of printed output can be used to convey additional information to a person who knows about the hidden bits between two words.

2. *Storage channels.* Storage channels are those that utilize system storage such as shared variables or files to leak information to other processes. Notice that when a process ($A$) wants to leak information to another process ($B$) by using a storage channel, it is not necessary that both processes must have access rights to the shared object. For example, if the system provides a way of locking files, process $A$ can lock some file to indicate a 1 and unlock it to indicate a 0. It may be possible for process $B$ to detect the status of a lock even on a file that $B$ cannot access. Similarly, in UNIX, process $A$ could create a file to indicate a 1 and remove it to indicate a 0. Even though process $B$ has no permission to access the file created by $A$, it can use the *access* system call to see if the file exists.

3. *Covert channels.* Covert channels are paths that are not normally intended for information transfer at all but could be used to send some information. For example, a process may use one of the following methods to leak information to some other process that is carefully monitoring its activities [Tanenbaum 1992]:

   - *By modulating paging rate*. For example, during a fixed time period, many page faults caused by the process may be used to convey a 1, and no page faults for a 0.
   - *By modulating CPU usage*. For example, usage of CPU for a fixed time period by the process may be used to convey a 1, and sleeping of the process for the same period may be used to convey a 0.
   - *By acquiring and releasing dedicated resources.* For example, the process may acquire the resource to convey a 1 and release it to convey a 0.

To solve the confinement problem, it is important to block all channels that a program may use to communicate with other processes. However, finding all such channels and trying to block them is extremely difficult. In practice, there is little that can be done. Therefore, the confinement problem is in general unsolvable.

## 11.3 CRYPTOGRAPHY

Cryptography is a means of protecting private information against unauthorized access in those situations where it is difficult to provide physical security. The basic idea behind this security technique is that if it is not possible to prevent copying of information, it is better to prevent comprehension.

### 11.3.1 Basic Concepts and Terminologies

Two primitive operations employed by cryptography are *encryption* and *decryption*. Encryption (also called *enciphering*) is the process of transforming an intelligible information (called *plaintext* or *cleartext*) into an unintelligible form (called *ciphertext*). Decryption (also called *deciphering*) is the process of transforming the information back from ciphertext to plaintext. When cryptography is employed for protecting information transmitted through communication channels, plaintext is also called a *message*.

Encryption is basically a mathematical function (encryption algorithm) having the following form:

$$C = E\,(P, K_e)$$

where $P$ is the plaintext to be encrypted, $K_e$ is an encryption key, and $C$ is the resulting ciphertext. Decryption of $C$ is performed by a matching function (decryption algorithm) that has the following form:

$$P = D\,(C, K_d)$$

where $K_d$ is the decryption key. Note that the decryption function $D$ is the inverse of the encryption function $E$. Therefore we have

$$D\,(E\,(P, K_e), K_d) = P$$

To prevent the plaintext from being easily revealed, it must be possible to transform a given plaintext into a large variety of possible ciphertexts selected by a specific parameter. The keys $K_e$ and $K_d$ serve as this parameter. That is, the function parts remain the same but the keys are changed as often as necessary.

The above described general structure of a cryptosystem is illustrated with an example in Figure 11.1, where a message is encrypted for secure transmission over an insecure channel from a sender node to a receiver node.

### 11.3.2 Basic Requirements

To be practically useful, a cryptosystem must fulfill the following basic requirements:

1. It must be easy to use and its encryption and decryption algorithms should be efficient for computer application.

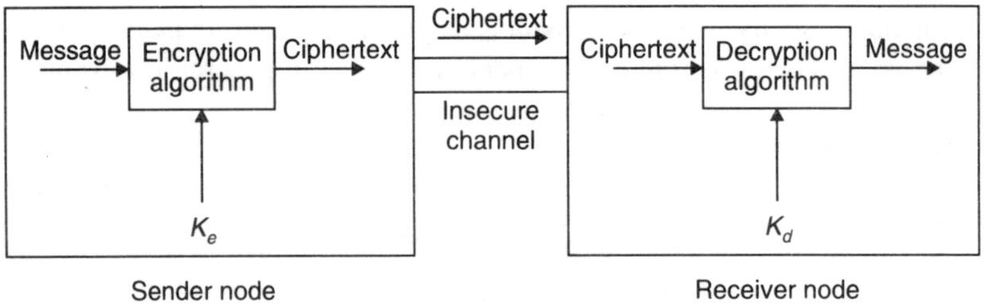


**Fig. 11.1** General structure of a cryptosystem.

2. There are two methods to achieve security. In the first method, the encryption algorithm is kept secret and is rather complex to make it difficult to guess. In the second method, the encryption algorithm is made public but the keys are kept secret and they are long enough to make it practically impossible to guess a key. The second method is preferred for practically useful systems. That is, the security of the system should depend only on the secrecy of the keys and not on the secrecy of the algorithms.

3. The system must be computationally (practically) secure. That is, the determination of $K_d$ must be computationally infeasible for an attacker (also called a *cryptanalyst*). Note that the strength of a cryptosystem is measured by the level of difficulty (usually measured either by the time or number of elementary operations) of determining $K_d$. Depending on the amount of information available to an intruder, in a cryptosystem, attacks are mainly of three types—ciphertext only, known plaintext, and chosen plaintext [Bright 1977].

In *ciphertext-only* attack, an intruder is able to intercept ciphertext and tries to derive $K_d$ from the ciphertext. A system whose security is not resistant to a ciphertext-only attack is considered to be totally insecure and is useless.

In *known-plaintext* attack, an intruder has considerable amount of both ciphertext and corresponding plaintext and tries to derive $K_d$ from them. A system that can resist a known-plaintext attack is considered to be secure.

In *chosen-plaintext* attack, an intruder has access to ciphertext for any plaintext of his or her choice. The intruder tries to derive $K_d$ by examining several ciphertexts for the carefully thought plaintexts of his or her choice. It is most appropriate nowadays to evaluate cryptosystems by their ability to withstand chosen-plaintext attacks.

Another important way by which a cryptosystem is demonstrated to be secure is the test of time. If no known successful attacks have been reported since a system is published and in use for a significant amount of time (measured in years), the cryptosystem is considered to probably provide pretty good security.

### 11.3.3 Symmetric and Asymmetric Cryptosystems

There are two broad classes of cryptosystems, symmetric and asymmetric. In a *symmetric cryptosystem*, either both the encryption key ($K_e$) and decryption key ($K_d$) are the same or one is easily derivable from the other. Usually, a common key ($K$) is used for both enciphering and deciphering. For security, it is important that the key of a symmetric cryptosystem be easily alterable and must always be kept secret. This implies that the key is known only to authorized users. Symmetric cryptosystems are also known as *shared-key* or *private-key cryptosystems*.

Symmetric cryptosystems are useful in those situations where both encryption and decryption of information are performed by a trusted subsystem. For example, a password-based user authentication system may use this scheme for saving passwords in encrypted form. When a user declares a password, the operating system uses the encryption key for encrypting the password before storing it internally. At the time of authentication, the operating system again uses the same key to decrypt the stored password to compare it to the password supplied by the user.

In an *asymmetric cryptosystem*, on the other hand, the decryption key ($K_d$) is not equal to the encryption key ($K_e$). Furthermore, it is computationally impractical to derive $K_d$ from $K_e$. Because of this property, only $K_d$ needs to be kept secret and $K_e$ is made publicly known. Asymmetric cryptosystems are also known as *public-key cryptosystems*.

Public-key cryptosystems are computationally expensive and hence are not suitable for bulk data encryption. A typical use of a public-key cryptosystem in distributed systems is for establishing connection between two communicating entities ($A$ and $B$) for the exchange of messages using a symmetric cryptosystem. Let us suppose that $A$ and $B$ want to establish a connection between themselves for initiating message transfers using a symmetric cryptosystem whose key is $K$. Note that it is insecure to send the key $K$ over a normal communication channel for the purpose of sharing it with $A$ and $B$. Therefore, a public-key cryptosystem is first used to establish a connection between $A$ and $B$ in the following manner:

- Entity $A$ posts the encryption key ($K_e$) of a public-key cryptosystem on, say, an electronic bulletin board, so that it is obtainable by $B$.
- Entity $B$ uses $A$'s public key to encrypt the key $K$ and transmits it to $A$.
- Entity $A$ decrypts $B$'s message using the decryption key ($K_d$) of the public-key cryptosystem. Only $A$ can decrypt this message because $K_d$ is available only with $A$.
- Now that $A$ also has the key $K$, both $A$ and $B$ can safely communicate with each other using the symmetric cryptosystem scheme. Any eavesdropper would only have the public key ($K_e$), the encrypted form of key $K$, and the encrypted form of the messages being communicated between $A$ and $B$.

One pitfall here is that someone else could masquerade as $A$ or $B$. This can be overcome by using digital signatures (described later in this chapter).

The relative advantages and disadvantages of symmetric and asymmetric cryptosystems are as follows:

1. Symmetric cryptosystems require that both encryption and decryption of information be performed by a trusted subsystem, whereas this is not necessary with asymmetric cryptosystems. Therefore, general security policies need asymmetric cryptosystems.

2. When employed for the security of messages in a communication system, a symmetric cryptosystem requires a secure channel by which the sender can inform the receiver of the key used to encipher the messages. The encrypted messages may, however, be transmitted through an insecure channel. On the other hand, in an asymmetric cryptosystem, both the public-key and the messages can be transmitted through an insecure channel. Therefore, there is no need for a special secure channel for key transmission. Due to this reason, asymmetric cryptosystems are considered to be more secure than symmetric cryptosystems.

3. In general, asymmetric cryptosystems are computationally much more expensive than symmetric cryptosystems and are inefficient for bulk data encryption. Hence, in practice, for data communications, asymmetric cryptosystems are often used only for initialization/control functions, while symmetric cryptosystems are used for actual data transfer.

The Data Encryption Standard (DES) cryptosystem [NBS 1977, Seberry and Pieprzyk 1989] is the best known and most widely used symmetric cryptosystem today. On the other hand, the Rivest–Shamir–Adleman (RSA) cryptosystem [Rivest et al. 1978, Seberry and Pieprzyk 1989] is the first published and practically the most satisfactory asymmetric cryptosystem today.

### 11.3.4 Key Distribution Problem

When cryptography is employed for secure communications in distributed systems, a need for key distribution arises because two communicating entities can securely communicate only when they obtain matching keys for encryption and decryption of the transmitted messages. A matching pair of keys held by two communicating entities forms an independent, private logical channel between them. The key distribution problem deals with how to securely supply the keys necessary to create these logical channels. The key distribution problem in symmetric and asymmetric cryptosystems are described below.

#### Key Distribution in Symmetric Cryptosystems

When two users (persons or programs) of two different nodes want to communicate securely by using a symmetric cryptosystem, they must first share the encryption/decryption key. For this, the key must be transmitted from one of the two users to the other user. However, there is no special transmission medium for the key transfer and the key must be transmitted using the same insecure physical medium by which all exchanged messages are transmitted. This requires that the key must itself be encrypted before transmission because if the key is compromised by an intruder while being transmitted over the insecure medium, the intruder can decrypt all encrypted messages exchanged between the two users. Therefore, a circularity exists in symmetric cryptosystems. This circularity can only be broken through prior distribution of a small number of keys by some secure means. The usual approach is to use a server process that performs the job of a *key distribution center* (*KDC*). Each user in the system shares with the KDC a prearranged pair of unique keys.

The KDC is a generally trusted entity and is shared by all communicating users of the system. On request by a user, it generates a new secret key to be used by the user to communicate with another user. In actual implementation, there may be several KDCs in the system. The three commonly used implementation approaches are as follows:

- Centralized approach
- Fully distributed approach
- Partially distributed approach

Below we describe how key distribution takes place in each approach between two users who want to communicate securely with each other.

***Centralized Approach.*** In this approach, a single centralized KDC is used that maintains a table of secret keys for each user (see Fig. 11.2). A user's secret key is known only to the user and KDC. Suppose that the secret keys of users $A$ and $B$ are $K_a$ and $K_b$, respectively, and that a secure logical communication channel is to be established for exchanging encrypted messages between them. The following protocol was proposed in [Needham and Schroeder 1978] for performing this task (see Fig. 11.2):

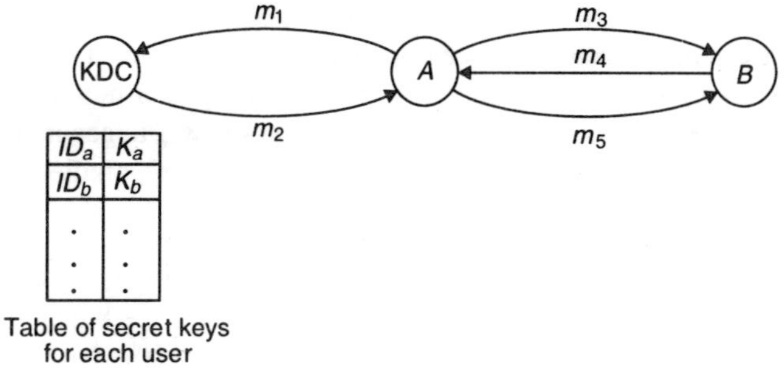

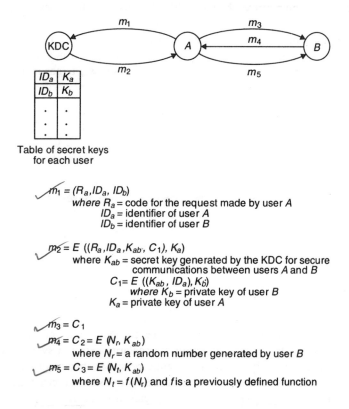

$m_1 = (R_a, ID_a, ID_b)$
where $R_a$ = code for the request made by user $A$
$ID_a$ = identifier of user $A$
$ID_b$ = identifier of user $B$

$m_2 = E\ ((R_a, ID_a, K_{ab}, C_1), K_a)$
where $K_{ab}$ = secret key generated by the KDC for secure communications between users $A$ and $B$
$C_1 = E\ ((K_{ab}, ID_a), K_b)$
where $K_b$ = private key of user $B$
$K_a$ = private key of user $A$

$m_3 = C_1$

$m_4 = C_2 = E\ (N_r, K_{ab})$
where $N_r$ = a random number generated by user $B$

$m_5 = C_3 = E\ (N_t, K_{ab})$
where $N_t = f(N_r)$ and $f$ is a previously defined function

**Fig. 11.2** The method of key distribution in the centralized approach.

1. User $A$ sends a request message ($m_1$) to the KDC indicating that it wants to establish a secure logical communication channel with user $B$. The message contains a code for the request ($R_a$), the user identifier of $A$ ($ID_a$), and the user identifier of $B$ ($ID_b$). This message is transmitted from user $A$ to KDC in plaintext form.

2. On receiving $m_1$, the KDC extracts from its table the keys $K_a$ and $K_b$, which correspond respectively to the user identifiers $ID_a$ and $ID_b$ in the message. It then creates a secret key $K_{ab}$ for secure communications between users $A$ and $B$. By using key $K_b$, the KDC encrypts the pair ($K_{ab}$, $ID_a$) to generate a ciphertext $C_1 = E((K_{ab}, ID_a), K_b)$. Finally, it sends a message ($m_2$) to user $A$ that contains $R_a$, $ID_a$, $K_{ab}$, and $C_1$. The message $m_2$ is encrypted with the key $K_a$ so that only user $A$ can decrypt it.

3. On receiving $m_2$, user $A$ decrypts it with its private key $K_a$ and checks whether $R_a$ and $ID_a$ of the message match with the originals to get confirmed that $m_2$ is the reply for $m_1$. If so, user $A$ keeps the key $K_{ab}$ with it for future use and sends a message $m_3$ to user $B$. This message contains the ciphertext $C_1$. Note that only user $B$ can decrypt $C_1$ because it was generated using key $K_b$.

4. On receiving $m_3$, user $B$ decrypts $C_1$ with its private key $K_b$ and retrieves both $K_{ab}$ and $ID_a$. At this stage, both users $A$ and $B$ have the same key $K_{ab}$ that can be used for secure communications between them because no other user has this key. At this point, user $B$ needs to verify if user $A$ is also in possession of the key $K_{ab}$. Therefore, user $B$ initiates an authentication procedure that involves sending a nonce to user $A$ and receiving a reply that contains some function of the recently sent nonce. For this, user $B$ generates a random number $N_r$, encrypts $N_r$ by using the key $K_{ab}$ to generate a ciphertext $C_2 = E(N_r, K_{ab})$, and sends $C_2$ to user $A$ in a message $m_4$. The random number $N_r$ is used as a nonce.

5. On receiving $m_4$, user $A$ decrypts $C_2$ with the key $K_{ab}$ and retrieves $N_r$. It then transforms $N_r$ to a new value $N_t$ by a previously defined function ($f$). User $A$ encrypts $N_t$ by using the key $K_{ab}$ to generate a ciphertext $C_3 = E(N_t, K_{ab})$, and sends $C_3$ to user $B$ in a message $m_5$.

6. On receiving $m_5$, user $B$ decrypts $C_3$, retrieves $N_t$, and applies the inverse of function $f$ to $N_t$ to check if the value obtained is $N_r$. If so, user $B$ gets confirmed that a secure channel can be created between users $A$ and $B$ by using the key $K_{ab}$. This is sufficient to achieve mutual confidence, and from now on, the exchange of actual messages encrypted with key $K_{ab}$ can take place between users $A$ and $B$.

That there is a problem in the protocol was pointed out by Denning and Sacco [1981]. They observed that during the transfer of message $m_3$, if an intruder copies $C_1$ and by unspecified means came to know $K_{ab}$, that intruder can in future always pretend to $B$ that it was $A$. The basic problem here is that $B$ never had the chance to offer a nonce to the KDC and, therefore, has no means of deducing the freshness of the quantity ($K_{ab}$) that came from the KDC. Note that only the KDC and $A$ know that $K_{ab}$ is fresh. One method to correct this problem is to add a timestamp ($T$) to the ciphertext $C_1$, so that it becomes $E((K_{ab}, ID_a, T), K_b)$. User $B$ decrypts this message and checks that $T$ is recent. This solution is adopted in the Kerberos system (described later in this chapter).

Notice that in the centralized KDC approach, if there are $n$ users in the system, $n$ prearranged key pairs are needed to provide secure communications. The approach is simple and easy to implement. However, it suffers from the drawbacks of poor reliability and performance bottleneck of the single KDC. That is, fresh key distributions cannot take place if the node on which the KDC resides crashes, and the KDC may get overloaded in a large system with too many users. Two other approaches described below may be used to overcome these drawbacks of the centralized approach.

***Fully Distributed Approach.*** In this approach, there is a KDC at each node of the distributed system. The prior distribution of secret keys allows each KDC to communicate securely with all other KDCs. That is, each KDC has a table of secret keys having private keys of all other KDCs. Therefore, in a system having $n$ nodes, each KDC keeps $n$–1 keys, resulting in a total of $n(n-1)/2$ key pairs in the system.

Suppose that a secure logical communication channel is to be established between user $A$ of node $N_1$ and user $B$ of node $N_2$. Also suppose that $K_1$ and $K_2$ are the private keys of the KDCs of nodes $N_1$ and $N_2$, respectively. The desired connection can be established in the following manner (see Fig. 11.3):

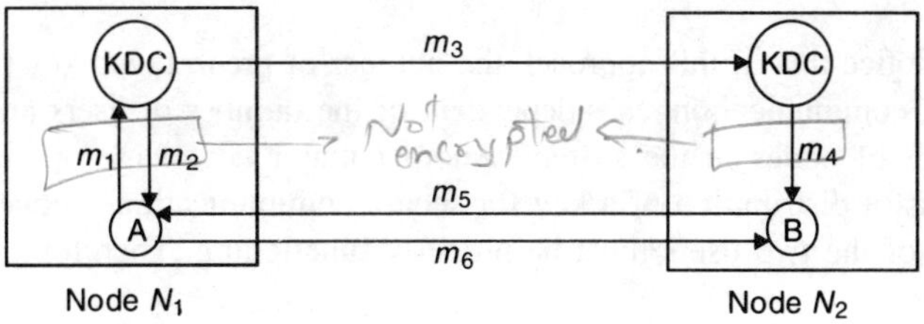


$m_1 = (R_a, ID_a, ID_b)$
where $R_a$ = code for the request made by user $A$
$ID_a$ = identifier of user $A$
$ID_b$ = identifier of user $B$

$m_2 = (R_a, ID_a, K_{ab})$
where $K_{ab}$ = secret key generated by the KDC of node $N_1$ for secure communications between users $A$ and $B$

$m_3 = C_1 = E((K_{ab}, ID_a, ID_b), K_2)$
where $K_2$ = private key of KDC of node $N_2$

$m_4 = (K_{ab}, ID_a)$

$m_5 = C_2 = E(N_r, K_{ab})$
where $N_r$ = a random number generated by user $B$

$m_6 = C_3 = E(N_t, K_{ab})$
where $N_t = f(N_r)$ and $f$ is a previously defined function

**Fig. 11.3** The method of key distribution in the fully distributed approach.

1. User $A$ sends a request message ($m_1$) to its local KDC. The message contains a code for the request ($R_a$), the user identifier of $A$ ($ID_a$), and the user identifier of $B$ ($ID_b$). It is assumed that all local communications are secure and hence local messages can be securely transmitted in plaintext form.

2. On receiving $m_1$, the KDC of node $N_1$ consults the name server to get the location ($N_2$) of the user having identifier $ID_b$. It then extracts the private key ($K_2$) of the KDC of node $N_2$ from its table. Next, it creates a secret key $K_{ab}$ for secure communications between users $A$ and $B$. By using key $K_2$, it encrypts the triplet ($K_{ab}$, $ID_a$, $ID_b$) to generate a ciphertext $C_1 = E((K_{ab}, ID_a, ID_b), K_2)$. Finally, it sends a message ($m_2$) to user $A$ that contains $R_a$, $ID_a$, $K_{ab}$ and a message ($m_3$) to the KDC of node $N_2$ that contains $C_1$.

3. On receiving $m_2$, user $A$ checks whether $R_a$ and $ID_a$ of the message match with the originals to get confirmed that $m_2$ is the reply for $m_1$. If so, user $A$ keeps the key $K_{ab}$ with it for future use.

4. On the other hand, on receiving message $m_3$, the KDC of node $N_2$ decrypts it with its private key $K_2$ and forwards the pair ($K_{ab}$, $ID_a$) to the user with identifier $ID_b$ in the form of message $m_4$.

5. On receiving $m_4$, user $B$ initiates an authentication procedure and authenticates user $A$ exactly in the same way as done in the centralized approach.

Notice that in this approach the number of prearranged key pairs needed to provide secure communications is independent of the number of users and depends only on the number of nodes in the system. Another major advantage of this approach is that for successful distribution of a key for secure communications between two users, only the nodes of the two users must be properly functioning. Therefore, the approach is highly reliable.

***Partially Distributed Approach.*** In this approach, the nodes of the system are partitioned into regions and, instead of having a KDC for each node, there is a KDC only for each region that resides on one of the nodes of that region. The prior distribution of secret keys allows each KDC to communicate securely with each user of its own region and with the KDCs of all other regions. That is, each KDC has a table of secret keys that contains private keys of all users of its own region and of all other KDCs.

In this approach, the distribution of a key for the establishment of a secure logical communication channel between two users $A$ and $B$ depends on the locations of the two users. If both the users $A$ and $B$ reside on nodes that belong to the same region, the key is distributed exactly in the same manner as is done in the centralized approach. In this case, the KDC of that region plays the role of the centralized KDC. On the other hand, if the users $A$ and $B$ reside on nodes belonging to different regions, the key distribution is performed in a manner similar to that in the case of the fully distributed approach. The only difference is that, in this case, messages $m_2$ and $m_4$ are also encrypted because they are transmitted from one node to another. That is, $m_2$ is encrypted with the private key of user $A$, and $m_4$ is encrypted with the private key of user $B$. The complete process of key distribution in this approach is shown in Figure 11.4. Notice that, in this approach, the

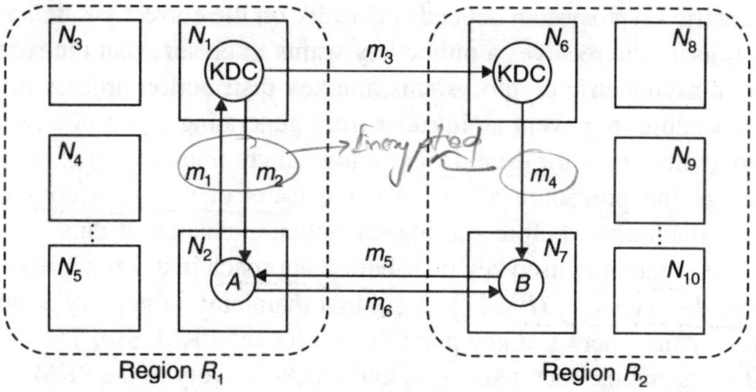


Let there be 10 nodes in the system that are partitioned into two regions $R_1$ and $R_2$ as shown above. The KDCs of regions $R_1$ and $R_2$ are located on nodes $N_1$ and $N_6$, respectively.

$m_1 = (R_a, ID_a, ID_b)$
where $R_a$ = code for the request made by user $A$
$ID_a$ = identifier of user $A$
$ID_b$ = identifier of user $B$

$m_2 = C_1 = E\ ((R_a, ID_a, K_{ab}), K_a)$
where $K_{ab}$ = secret key generated by the KDC of region $R_1$ for secure communications between users $A$ and $B$
$K_a$ = private key for user $A$

$m_3 = C_2 = E\ ((K_{ab}, ID_a, ID_b), K_2)$
where $K_2$ = private key of KDC of region $R_2$

$m_4 = C_3 = E\ (K_{ab}, ID_a), K_b)$
where $K_b$ = private key of user $B$

$m_5 = C_4 = E\ (N_r, K_{ab})$
where $N_r$ = a random number generated by user $B$

$m_6 = C_5 = E\ (N_t, K_{ab})$
where $N_t = f(N_r)$ and f is a previously defined function.

**Fig. 11.4** The method of key distribution in the partially distributed approach.

failure of the KDC of a particular region will only disrupt key distribution activities that involve a user of that region. Key distribution involving users of other regions can still be carried out successfully. Therefore, the reliability of this approach lies in between the reliabilities of the centralized and the fully distributed approaches.

### Key Distribution in Asymmetric Cryptosystems

In an asymmetric cryptosystem only public keys are distributed. Since public keys need not be kept secret, there is no problem of key transmission through an insecure physical medium. Therefore, one might conclude that the key distribution problem does not exist in asymmetric cryptosystems. However, this is not correct since the safety of an asymmetric cryptosystem depends critically on the correct public key being selected by a user. A user who receives a public key wants to be sure that the received key is genuine. Thus, in asymmetric cryptosystems, the key distribution process involves an authentication procedure to prevent an intruder from generating a pair of keys and sending a public key to another user for establishing a logical communication channel with that user. The authentication procedure allows the two users of a logical communication channel to identify themselves before starting the actual exchange of data.

The commonly used key distribution approach in asymmetric cryptosystems is to use a *public-key manager (PKM)* process that maintains a directory of public keys of all users in the system. There is a key pair ($P_k$, $S_k$) for the PKM also. The public key $P_k$ is known to all users and the secret key $S_k$ is known exclusively to the PKM. The protocol based on this approach for establishing a logical communication channel between two users is described below.

Let us assume that a logical communication channel is to be established between users $A$ and $B$. Also assume that ($P_a$, $S_a$) is the key pair of user $A$ and ($P_b$, $S_b$) is the key pair of user $B$. The public keys $P_a$ and $P_b$ are stored with the PKM and the secret keys $S_a$ and $S_b$ are known exclusively to users $A$ and $B$, respectively. The desired connection can be established in the following manner (see Fig. 11.5):

1. User $A$ sends a request message ($m_1$) to the PKM indicating that it wants to establish a secure logical communication channel with user $B$. The message contains a code for the request ($R_a$), a timestamp ($T_1$), the user identifier of $A$ ($ID_a$), and the user identifier of $B$ ($ID_b$). This message is encrypted by using $P_k$. That is, $m_1$ contains the ciphertext $C_1 = E((R_a, T_1, ID_a, ID_b), P_k)$.

2. On receiving $m_1$, the PKM decrypts $C_1$ by using $S_k$. It then extracts the public keys $P_a$ and $P_b$ from its table that correspond respectively to the user identifiers $ID_a$ and $ID_b$ of the message. By using key $P_a$, the PKM encrypts the triplet ($R_a$, $T_1$, $P_b$) to generate a ciphertext $C_2 = E((R_a, T_1, P_b), P_a)$. Finally, it sends $C_2$ to user $A$ in the form of a message ($m_2$).

3. On receiving $m_2$, user $A$ decrypts $C_2$ by using $S_a$ and retrieves its contents. The retrieved values of $R_a$ and $T_1$ are compared with the originals to get confirmed that $m_2$ is the reply for $m_1$ and that it is not a replay of an old message. User $A$ then generates a random number $N_a$, encrypts the pair ($ID_a$, $N_a$) by using user $B$'s public key $P_b$ to generate a ciphertext $C_3 = E((ID_a, N_a), P_b)$, and sends $C_3$ to user $B$ in a message ($m_3$).

4. On receiving $m_3$, user $B$ decrypts $C_3$ by using $S_b$ and retrieves its contents. By seeing $ID_a$ in the message, user $B$ knows that user $A$ wants to establish a logical communication channel with it. In order to get the authentic public key of user $A$, user $B$ contacts the PKM. For this, it sends a message ($m_4$) to the PKM requesting for user $A$'s public key. The message contains a code for the request ($R_b$), a timestamp ($T_2$), the user identifier of $A$ ($ID_a$), and the user identifier of $B$ ($ID_b$). This message is encrypted by using $P_k$. That is, $m_4$ contains the ciphertext $C_4 = E((R_b, T_2, ID_a, ID_b), P_k)$.

5. On receiving $m_4$, the PKM decrypts $C_4$ by using $S_k$. It then extracts the public keys $P_a$ and $P_b$ that correspond respectively to the user identifiers $ID_a$ and $ID_b$ of the

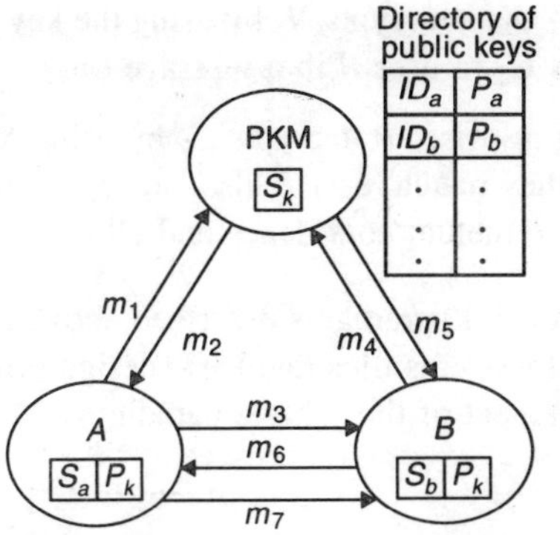


$P_k$ = public key of PKM
$S_k$ = secret key of PKM
$P_a$ = public key of user $A$
$S_a$ = secret key of user $A$

$P_b$ = public key of user $B$
$S_b$ = secret key of user $B$
$ID_a$ = user identifier of $A$
$ID_b$ = user identifier of $B$

$m_1 = C_1 = E\ ((R_a, T_1, ID_a, ID_b), P_k)$
where $R_a$ = code for the request made by user $A$
$T_1$ = a timestamp

$m_2 = C_2 = E\ ((R_a, T_1, P_b), P_a)$

$m_3 = C_3 = E\ ((ID_a, N_a), P_b)$
where $N_a$ = a random number generated by user $A$

$m_4 = C_4 = E\ ((R_b, T_2, ID_a, ID_b), P_k)$
where $R_b$ = code for the request made by user $B$
$T_2$ = a timestamp

$m_5 = C_5 = E\ ((R_b, T_2, P_a), P_b)$

$m_6 = C_6 = E\ ((N_a, N_b), P_a)$
where $N_b$ = a random number generated by user $B$

$m_7 = C_7 = E\ (N_b, P_b)$

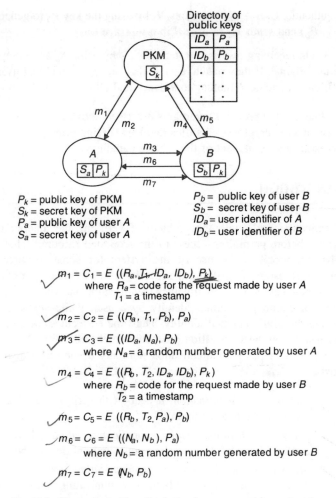

**Fig. 11.5** The method of key distribution in an asymmetric cryptosystem.

message. By using key $P_b$, the PKM encrypts the triple $(R_b, T_2, P_a)$ to generate a ciphertext $C_5 = E\ ((R_b, T_2, P_a), P_b)$. Finally it sends $C_5$ to user $B$ in the form of a message $(m_5)$.

6. On receiving $m_5$, user $B$ decrypts $C_5$ by using $S_b$, retrieves its contents, and compares $R_b$ and $T_2$ with the originals to get confirmed that $m_5$ is really the reply of $m_4$. User $B$ then generates a random number $N_b$, encrypts the pair $(N_a, N_b)$ by using the key $P_a$ to generate a ciphertext $C_6 = E\ ((N_a, N_b), P_a)$, and sends $C_6$ to user $A$ in a message $(m_6)$.

7. On receiving $m_6$, user $A$ decrypts $C_6$ by using $S_a$, retrieves its contents, and compares the received $N_a$ with the original. If they match, user $A$ becomes sure that user

$B$ is authentic. User $A$ then encrypts $N_b$ by using the key $P_b$ to generate a ciphertext $C_7 = E(N_b, P_b)$ and sends $C_7$ to user $B$ in a message ($m_7$).

8. On receiving $m_7$, user $B$ decrypts $C_7$ by using $S_b$ and compares the received $N_b$ with the original. If they match, user $B$ also gets confirmed that user $A$ is authentic. This is sufficient to achieve mutual confidence and allows regular communication to start.

Note that the protocol paradigms described above for key distribution in symmetric and asymmetric cryptosystems illustrate basic design principles only. A realistic protocol is necessarily a refinement of these basic paradigms.

## 11.4 AUTHENTICATION

Authentication deals with the problem of verifying the identity of a user (person or program) before permitting access to the requested resource. That is, an authentication mechanism prohibits the use of the system (or some resource of the system) by unauthorized users by verifying the identity of a user making a request.

Authentication basically involves identification and verification. *Identification* is the process of claiming a certain identity by a user, while *verification* is the process of verifying the user's claimed identity. Thus, the correctness of an authentication process relies heavily on the verification procedure employed.

The main types of authentication normally needed in a distributed system are as follows:

1. *User logins authentication.* It deals with verifying the identity of a user by the system at the time of login.
2. *One-way authentication of communicating entities.* It deals with verifying the identity of one of the two communicating entities by the other entity.
3. *Two-way authentication of communicating entities.* It deals with mutual authentication, whereby both communicating entities verify each other's identity.

A description of the authentication mechanisms that are commonly used to perform these types of authentication is presented below. Note that the authentication protocol paradigms described below illustrate basic design principles only. A realistic protocol is necessarily a refinement of these basic paradigms and addresses weaker environment assumptions, stronger postconditions, or both.

### 11.4.1 Approaches to Authentication

The basic approaches to authentication are as follows [Shankar 1977, Woo and Lam 1992]:

1. *Proof by knowledge.* In this approach, authentication involves verifying something that can only be known by an authorized principal. Authentication of a user

based on the password supplied by him or her is an example of proof by knowledge. Authentication methods based on the concept of proof by knowledge are again of two types—direct demonstration method and challenge-response method. In the *direct demonstration* method, a user claims his or her identity by supplying information (like typing in a password) that the verifier checks against prestored information. On the other hand, in the *challenge-response* method, a user proves his or her identity by responding correctly to the challenge questions asked by the verifier. For instance, when signing up as a user, the user picks a function, for example, $x + 18$. When the user logs in, the system randomly selects and displays a number, say 105, in which case the user must type 123 for authentication to be successful. For further security improvement, several functions may be used by the same user. At the time of login, the function to be used will depend on when the login is made. For example, a user may use seven different functions, one for each day of the week. In another variation of this method, a list of questions such as what is the name of your father, what is the name of your mother, what is the name of your street on which your house is located, is maintained by the system. When signing up as a user, the user has to reply to all these questions and the system stores the answers. At login, the system asks one of these questions at random and verifies the answer supplied by the user.

2. *Proof by possession.* In this approach, a user proves his or her identity by producing some item that can only be possessed by an authorized principal. The system is designed to verify the produced item to confirm the claimed identity. For example, a plastic card with a magnetic strip on it that has a user identifier number written on it in invisible, electronic form may be used as the item to be produced by the user. The user inserts the card in a slot meant for this purpose in the system's terminal, which then extracts the user identifier number from the card and checks to see if the card produced belongs to an authorized user. Obviously, security can be ensured only if the item to be produced is unforgeable and safely guarded.

3. *Proof by property.* In this approach, the system is designed to verify the identity of a user by measuring some physical characteristics of the user that are hard to forge. The measured property must be distinguishing, that is, unique among all possible users. For example, a special device (known as a biometric device) may be attached to each terminal of the system that verifies some physical characteristic of the user, such as the person's appearance, fingerprints, hand geometry, voice, signature. In deciding the physical characteristic to be measured, an important factor to be considered is that the scheme must be phycologically acceptable to the user community. Biometric systems offer the greatest degree of confidence that a user actually is who he or she claims to be, but they are also generally the most expensive to implement. Moreover, they often have user acceptance problems because users see biometric devices as unduly intrusive.

Of the three authentication approaches described above, proof by knowledge and possession can be applied to all types of authentication needs in a secure distributed system, while proof by property is generally limited to the authentication of human users by a system equipped with specialized measuring instruments. Moreover, in practice, a system may use a combination of two or more of these authentication methods. For example, the authentication mechanism used by automated cash-dispensing machines usually employ a combination of the first two approaches. That is, a user is allowed to withdraw money only if he or she produces a valid identification card and specifies the correct password corresponding to the identification number on the card.

### 11.4.2 User Login Authentication

As in centralized systems, a user gains access to a distributed system by logging in a host in the system. User identity is established at login, and all subsequent user activities are attributed to this identity. Correct user identification at the time of login is crucial to the functioning of a secure system because all access-control decisions and accounting functions are based on this identity. Although any of the three basic approaches to authentication can be employed for user login authentication, the proof by knowledge is the most widely used method. In particular, most systems employ the direct demonstration method based on passwords.

In the authentication scheme based on passwords, the system maintains a table of authorized users' login names and their corresponding passwords. When a user wants to log in, the system asks the user to type his or her name and password. If the password supplied by the user matches the password stored in the system against his or her name, it is assumed that the user is legitimate and login is permitted; otherwise it is refused.

To provide good security and be practically useful, a password-based authentication system must have mechanisms for the following:

1. Keeping passwords secret
2. Making passwords difficult to guess
3. Limiting damages done by a compromised password
4. Identifying and discouraging unauthorized user logins
5. Single sign-on for using all resources in the system

The commonly used mechanisms for dealing with these issues are described below.

#### Keeping Passwords Secret

A user is responsible for keeping his or her password secret outside the computer system (external world). How to keep passwords secret in the external world is not of concern to operating system designers except for the fact that while a password is being typed in, it should not be displayed on the terminal, to prevent it from being seen by prying eyes near the terminal. The main concern, however, is to prevent an intruder from obtaining somebody's password by having access to the system's password table. The password table is of course protected and is accessible only to the authentication program. However, there is a great chance that the password table is exposed by accident or that the system administrator has access to the table. Therefore, instead of storing the names and passwords in plaintext form, they are encrypted and stored in ciphertext form in the table. In this case, instead of directly using a user-specified name and password for table lookup, they are first encrypted and then the results are used for table lookup. Notice that for implementing this scheme, the main requirement is that even if both the encryption function and the password table are known, it is impossible to find the original password. That is, a noninvertible function is needed for encryption because in the scheme we never need to decrypt a ciphertext. This is an example of the use of *one-way cipher*. In cryptography we use the function

$$C = E(P, K)$$

where $K$ is a key, $P$ is a plaintext, and $C$ is the resulting ciphertext. A one-way cipher can be implemented by letting the plaintext $P$ serve as the key to $E$ such that

$$C = E(P, P)$$

In a one-way cipher, it is very difficult to invert the encryption function ($E$) even if the intruder knows the key. Furthermore, if the key is not known (as in the case of password security scheme in which a password itself is used as the key), the inversion becomes much more difficult because the intruder cannot know which functions (and how many times of them) are used.

To keep passwords secret in a distributed environment, it is important that passwords should never be sent across the network in plain text form. Moreover, they should not be stored on normal servers but should only be stored on trusted servers that are well protected. Notice that due to these requirements, authentication of a user by simply sending his or her password to an authentication server for approval does not work in a distributed environment. The Kerberos authentication system (described later in this chapter) provides an interesting solution to this problem.

### Making Passwords Difficult to Guess

Use of mechanisms to keep passwords secret does not guarantee that the system's security cannot be broken. It only says that it is difficult to obtain passwords. The intruder can always use a trial-and-error method. Virtually, in case of passwords, break-ins usually consist of guessing a user name and password combination. How successful an intruder can be in guessing passwords is obvious from the study made by Morris and Thompson [1979] of passwords on UNIX systems. They compiled a list of likely passwords that contained first and last names of persons, names of cities and streets, words from a small dictionary spelled correctly and backward, short strings of random characters, and license plate numbers. These passwords were then encrypted using the known password encryption algorithm to obtain a list of encrypted guessed passwords. Then another list of encrypted passwords was prepared by using entries in password tables of various UNIX systems. The entries in the two lists were then compared to find matching entries. Surprisingly, it was found that over 86% of actual passwords had a match in the list of guessed passwords.

A test of only a limited set of potential strings tends to reveal most passwords because there is a strong tendency for people to choose relatively short and simple passwords that they can remember. Some techniques that may be used to make the task of guessing a password difficult are as follows:

1. *Longer passwords*. The length of a password determines the ease with which a password can be found by exhaustion. For example, a three-digit password provides 1000 variations whereas a four digit password provides 10,000 variations. Longer passwords are less susceptible to enumeration because the work involved in enumerating all possible passwords increases by increasing the length of the password. Use of longer passwords can be enforced or encouraged by providing a password entry program that asks a user to enter a longer password if he or she enters a short one.

2. *Salting the password table*. Another technique to make the task of guessing passwords difficult is to artificially lengthen passwords by associating an $n$-bit random number with each password when it is first entered. The random number is changed whenever the password is changed. Instead of just storing the encrypted password in the password table, the password and the random number are first concatenated and then encrypted together. This encrypted result is stored in the password table. In this scheme, the password table has an additional field that contains the random number in its unencrypted form. At the time of login, this random number is concatenated with the entered password, encrypted, and then compared with the stored encrypted value. Guessing of a password becomes difficult because if an intruder suspects that *Tokyo* might be the password of a user, it is no longer enough to just encrypt *Tokyo* and compare the encrypted result with the value stored in the password table. Rather, for each guess made, the intruder has to try out $2^n$ strings, such as *Tokyo0000*, *Tokyo0001*, *Tokyo0002*, and so forth, for $n = 4$. This increases the encryption and comparison time for each guess made. UNIX uses this method with $n = 12$.

3. *System assistance in password selection*. A password can be either system generated or user selected. User-selected passwords are often easy to guess. A system can be designed to assist users in using passwords that are difficult to guess. This can be done in two ways. One way is to store a list of easy-to-guess passwords within the system and to first compare a user-selected password with the entries in the list. If a match is found, the system refuses to accept the selected password and asks the user to select another password informing him or her that the selected password is easy to guess. Another way of providing system assistance is to have a password generator program that generates random, easy-to-remember, meaningless words, such as *mounce*, *bulbul*, *halchal*, that can be used as passwords. The user selects a password suggested by the system and uses it with his or her own choice of a mixture of upper- and lowercase letters of that word, such as *hAlCHal*.

### Identifying and Discouraging Unauthorized User Logins

Some management techniques should be used to improve the security of a system against unauthorized user logins. Three such techniques are as follows:

1. *Threat monitoring*. This technique detects security violations by checking for suspicious patterns of activity. For example, the system may count the number of incorrect passwords given when a user is trying to log in, and after, say, three failed login attempts, the system notifies security personnel by setting an alarm.

2. *Audit logs.* In this technique, the system maintains a record of all logins. That is, the time at which login was done, the duration of login, the accessed objects and the types of accesses made, etc., are recorded for each login. When a user logs in successfully, the system reports to the user some of the recorded information (such as time and duration) of the previous login. This may be helpful for the user to detect possible break-ins. After a security violation has been detected, the audit log can be used to detect which objects were accessed by the intruder and the amount of damage done. This information can be useful for recovery from the damages done by the intruder.

3. *Baited traps.* Intruders may also be caught by laying baited traps. For example, the system may maintain some special login names with easy passwords, such as login name: user, password: user. Whenever anyone logs in using any of these names, the system security personnel are immediately notified.

### Single Sign-on

In a distributed client-server environment, a user might have several client programs running on his or her host node that access different server programs on remote nodes. In such an environment, the servers must authenticate that the clients run on behalf of a legitimate user. If a simple password-based authentication scheme is used, the user's password must be presented each time a server wants to authenticate a client program running on behalf of the user. This is cumbersome and inconvenient because a user will certainly not want to enter a password each time he or she accesses a new service. This is also not desirable from the point of view of transparency, which aims to provide a virtual single system image. A simple way to solve this problem is to cache the user's password on his or her host computer and use it from the cache every time a new service is accessed. However, this solution does not work because it is dangerous to keep passwords in cache from the point of view of keeping passwords secret. Once again, the Kerberos authentication system (described later in this chapter) provides an interesting solution to this problem.

### Limiting Damages Done by a Compromised Password

It is suggested that a user should change his or her password frequently so that an intruder who has been successful in guessing the current password will have to guess a new one after the current password is changed by the user. In this way, the damage done by the intruder can be reduced. The extreme form of this approach is the use of *one-time passwords*. There are three different methods to implement the idea of one-time passwords. In the first method, the user gets a book containing a list of passwords. For each login, the user must use the next password in the list. Obviously, the user must keep the password book in a secure place. In the second method, every time a user logs out, the system asks to select a new password for the next login and replaces the old password with the new one. The user either remembers the new password or notes it down somewhere for use at the time of next login. The third method relies on the use of a special equipment such as smart cards or synchronized password generators. For example, a synchronized password generator device generates a pseudorandom alphanumeric word or number that changes every minute or so and is time synchronized to a database stored in the computer. To log in, a user types in the word or number displayed on the card at the time of login. This results in a one-time password that is good only at that particular point in time and for only one login. One such device is the SecureID from Security Dynamics (Cambridge, Massachusetts). This method has not been very successful thus far, primarily due to the inconvenience and cost of the additional hardware required. It requires that all users purchase the hardware device. However, it has the advantage that once set up, it is fairly easy to administer (as opposed to a manual password list that requires frequent updating for all users).

### 11.4.3 One-Way Authentication of Communicating Entities

When an entity $A$ wants to communicate with another entity $B$, $B$ may like to verify the identity of $A$ before allowing $A$ to communicate with it. For example, a server may be designed to first verify the identity of any client that wants to communicate with it. The commonly used authentication protocols for one-way authentication of communicating entities are described below.

The following description is based on the material presented in [Woo and Lam 1992]. Since the authentication protocol paradigms directly use cryptosystems, their basic design principles also follow closely the type of cryptosystem used. Therefore, the protocols can be broadly classified into two categories—those based on symmetric cryptosystems and those based on asymmetric cryptosystems. Authentication protocols of both categories are based on the proof-by-knowledge principle.

#### Protocols Based on Symmetric Cryptosystems

In a symmetric cryptosystem, the knowledge of the shared key allows an entity to encrypt or decrypt arbitrary messages. Without such knowledge, it is not possible for the entity to encrypt a message or to decrypt an encrypted message. Hence, in authentication protocols based upon symmetric cryptosystems, the verifier verifies the identity of a claimant by checking if the claimant can correctly encrypt a message by using a key that the verifier believes is known only to an entity with the claimed identity (outside the entities used in the verification process).

Let us assume that user $A$ wants to communicate with user $B$ but $B$ wants to authenticate $A$ before starting the communication. Also assume that $K$ is the key of a symmetric cryptosystem that is shared between users $A$ and $B$. The authentication protocol for this consists of the following steps:

1. User $A$ encrypts its identifier ($ID_a$) by using key $K$ to obtain a ciphertext $C_1 = E(ID_a, K)$. It then sends a message $m_1$ to user $B$, which contains $ID_a$ and $C_1$.
2. On receiving $m_1$, user $B$ decrypts $C_1$ by using key $K$ and compares the obtained result with $ID_a$ of the message. If they match, user $A$ is accepted; otherwise it is rejected.

One major weakness of this protocol is its vulnerability to replays. That is, an intruder could masquerade as $A$ by recording the message $m_1$ and later replay it to $B$. Replay attacks can be countered by using nonces or timestamps. A nonce-based challenge-response protocol that overcomes the problem of replay of messages works as follows (see Fig. 11.6):

1. User $A$ sends its identifier ($ID_a$) to user $B$ in plaintext form in a message $m_1$.
2. On receiving $m_1$, user $B$ generates a random number $N_r$ and sends $N_r$ to user $A$ in plaintext form in a message $m_2$.
3. On receiving $m_2$, user $A$ encrypts $N_r$ by using key $K$ to obtain a ciphertext $C_1 = E(N_r, K)$. It then sends $C_1$ to $B$ in a message $m_3$.
4. On receiving $m_3$, user $B$ decrypts $C_1$ by using key $K$ and compares the obtained result with the original value of $N_r$. If they are equal, user $A$ is accepted; otherwise it is rejected.

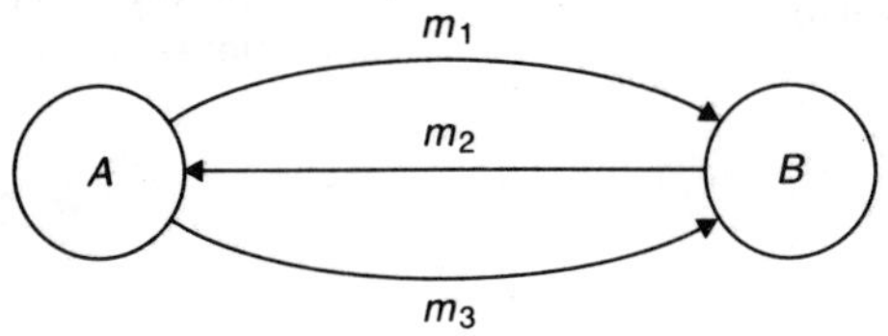


$m_1 = ID_a$ = identifier of user $A$

$m_2 = N_r$ = a random number grenerated by user $B$

$m_3 = C_1 = E(N_r, K)$

where $K$ is the symmetric key shared between users $A$ and $B$

$B$ decrypts $C_1$ using $K$ and compares the result with original $N_r$.
If they are equal, $A$ isaccepted, otherwise rejected.

**Fig. 11.6** One-way authentication protocol based on symmetric cryptosystem.

In this protocol, the freshness of $N_r$ (whose value is different for each conversation) guarantees that an intruder cannot masquerade as $A$ by replaying a recording of an old authentication conversation between $A$ and $B$.

Although the above-described protocol functions correctly, it is impractical for a general large-scale system due to the following reasons:

1. Notice that the scheme requires that each user must store the secret key for every other user it would ever want to authenticate. This may not be practically feasible in a large system having too many users and in which the number of users keeps changing frequently.
2. The compromise of one user can potentially compromise the entire system.

To overcome these problems, the use of a centralized *authentication server* (*AS*) was proposed in [Needham and Schroeder 1978]. Each user in the system shares with the AS a prearranged secret key. The AS is a generally trusted entity and is shared by all communicating users of the system. When the AS is used, the authentication protocol takes the form shown in Fig. 11.7 (it has been assumed that $K_a$ and $K_b$ are the secret keys of users $A$ and $B$, respectively, that are shared with the AS).

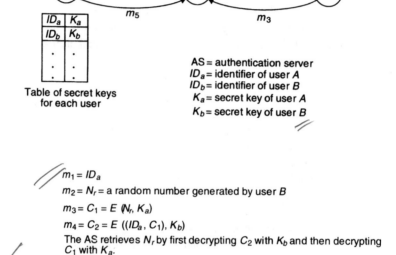

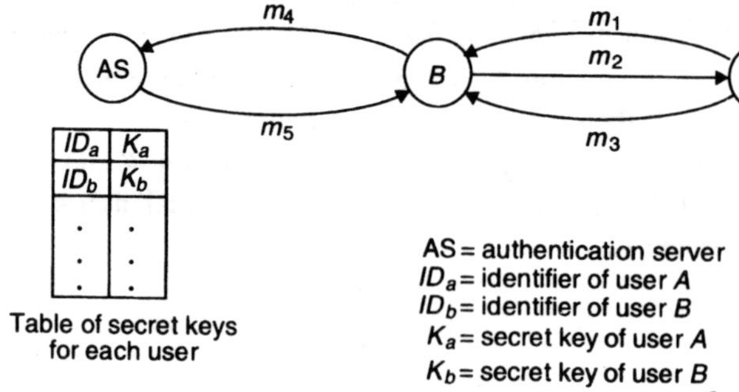


$m_1 = ID_a$

$m_2 = N_r =$ a random number generated by user $B$

$m_3 = C_1 = E\ (N_r, K_a)$

$m_4 = C_2 = E\ ((ID_a, C_1), K_b)$

The AS retrieves $N_r$ by first decrypting $C_2$ with $K_b$ and then decrypting $C_1$ with $K_a$.

$m_5 = C_3 = E\ (N_r, K_b)$

$B$ decrypts $C_3$ with $K_b$ and compares the result with original $N_r$. If they are equal, then $A$ is accepted, otherwise rejected.

**Fig. 11.7** One-way authentication protocol based on symmetric cryptosystem and the use of a centralized authentication server.

1. User $A$ sends its identifier ($ID_a$) to user $B$ in plaintext form in a message $m_1$.
2. On receiving $m_1$, user $B$ generates a random number $N_r$ and sends $N_r$ to user $A$ in plaintext form in a message $m_2$.
3. On receiving $m_2$, user $A$ encrypts $N_r$ by using its secret key $K_a$ to obtain a ciphertext $C_1 = E\ (N_r, K_a)$. It then sends $C_1$ to $B$ in a message $m_3$.
4. On receiving $m_3$, user $B$ encrypts the pair ($ID_a$, $C_1$) by using its secret key $K_b$ to generate a ciphertext $C_2 = E\ ((ID_a, C_1), K_b)$. It then sends $C_2$ to the AS in a message $m_4$.
5. On receiving $m_4$, the AS decrypts $C_2$ with key $K_b$ and retrieves the pair ($ID_a$, $C_1$). It then extracts from its database the key ($K_a$) that corresponds to $ID_a$ and decrypts

$C_1$ with key $K_a$ and retrieves $N_r$. Next, it encrypts $N_r$ by using key $K_b$ to generate a ciphertext $C_3 = E\ (N_r,\ K_b)$. Finally, it sends $C_3$ to $B$ in a message $m_5$.

6. On receiving $m_5$, user $B$ decrypts it by using its secret key $K_b$, retrieves $N_r$, and compares it with the original value of $N_r$. If they are equal, user $A$ is accepted; otherwise it is rejected.

As compared to the previous protocol, the key distribution and storage problems are greatly alleviated because now each user needs to keep only one key. Moreover, the system's security can be greatly improved simply by tightening security for the AS because the risk of compromise is mostly shifted to the AS. The centralized AS, however, suffers from the same drawbacks as the centralized KDC. These drawbacks can also be solved by using fully/partially distributed ASs in a similar manner as described for the key distribution problem in Section 11.3.4.

## Protocols Based on Asymmetric Cryptosystems

In an asymmetric cryptosystem, the public key of each user is published while the secret key of each user is known only to the user and no one else. Hence, in authentication protocols based upon asymmetric cryptosystems, the verifier verifies the identity of a claimant by checking if the claimant can correctly encrypt a message by using the secret key of the user whose identity is being claimed.

Let us assume that user $A$ wants to communicate with user $B$ but $B$ wants to authenticate $A$ before starting the communication. Also assume that $P_a$ and $S_a$ are the public and secret keys of user $A$, and $P_b$ and $S_b$ are the public and secret keys of user $B$. The authentication protocol for this consists of the following steps (see Fig. 11.8):

1. User $A$ sends its identifier ($ID_a$) to user $B$ in plaintext form in a message $m_1$.
2. On receiving $m_1$, user $B$ generates a random number $N_r$ and sends $N_r$ to user $A$ in plaintext form in a message $m_2$.

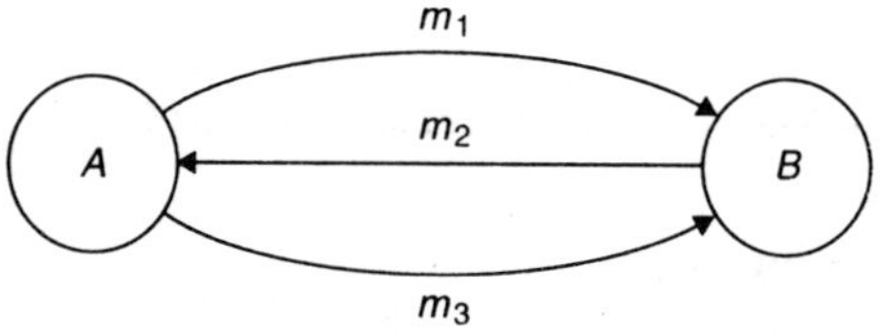


$m_1 = ID_a$ = identifier of user $A$

$m_2 = N_r$ = a random number generated by user $B$

$m_3 = C_1 = E\ (N_r,\ S_a)$

where $S_a$ = secret key of user $A$

$B$ decrypts $C_1$ by using the public key of user $A$ and compares the result with original $N_r$. If they are equal, $A$ isaccepted, otherwise rejected.

**Fig. 11.8** One-way authentication protocol based on asymmetric cryptosystem.

3. On receiving $m_2$, user $A$ encrypts $N_r$ by using its secret key $S_a$ to obtain a ciphertext $C_1 = E(N_r, S_a)$. It then sends $C_1$ to $B$ in a message $m_3$.
4. On receiving $m_3$, user $B$ decrypts $C_1$ by using the public key of user $A$ ($P_a$) and compares the obtained result with the original value of $N_r$. If they are equal, user $A$ is accepted; otherwise it is rejected.

As in the case of protocols based upon symmetric cryptosystems, in this case also a centralized AS may be used to greatly alleviate the key distribution and storage problems. In this case, the AS maintains a database of all published public keys and each user in the system keeps a copy of the public key ($P_s$) of the AS. When the AS is used, the authentication protocol takes the following form (see Fig. 11.9):

1. User $A$ sends its identifier ($ID_a$) to user $B$ in plaintext form in a message $m_1$.

2. On receiving $m_1$, user $B$ generates a random number $N_r$ and sends $N_r$ to user $A$ in plaintext form in a message $m_2$.

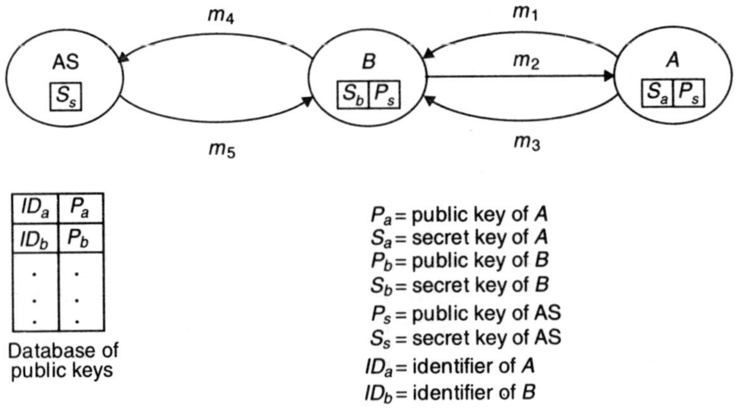


$m_1 = ID_a$

$m_2 = N_r$ = a random number generated by $B$

$m_3 = C_1 = E(N_r, S_a)$

$m_4 = (R_b, ID_a)$

where $R_b$ = code for requesting the public key of a user

$m_5 = C_2 = E((ID_a, P_a), S_s)$

$B$ retrieves $N_r$ by first decrypting $C_2$ with $P_s$ and then decrypting $C_1$ with $P_a$. The value of $N_r$ obtained in this way is compared with the original value of $N_r$. If they are equal, then $A$ isaccepted, otherwise rejected.

**Fig. 11.9** One-way authentication protocol based on asymmetric cryptostem and the use of a centralized authentication server.

3. On receiving $m_2$, user $A$ encrypts $N_r$ by using its secret key $S_a$ to obtain a ciphertext $C_1 = E(N_r, S_a)$. It then sends $C_1$ to $B$ in a message $m_3$.

4. On receiving $m_3$, user $B$ sends the pair $(R_b, ID_a)$ to the AS in plaintext form in a message $m_4$, where $R_b$ is a request code for requesting the public key of the user whose identifier is specified in the second element of the message.

5. On receiving $m_4$, the AS extracts from its database the public key $(P_a)$ of the user whose identifier is $ID_a$. It then encrypts the pair $(ID_a, P_a)$ by using its own secret key $S_s$ to generate a ciphertext $C_2 = E((ID_a, P_a), S_s)$. Finally, it sends $C_2$ to $B$ in a message $m_5$.

6. On receiving $m_5$, user $B$ decrypts $C_2$ by using the public key of the AS $(P_s)$ and retrieves the pair $(ID_a, P_a)$. Now by using the key $P_a$, it decrypts $C_1$ and compares the obtained result with the original value of $N_r$. If they are equal, user $A$ is accepted; otherwise it is rejected.

Notice that in this case each user needs to keep only one public key, the public key of the AS. Also notice that in the above protocol it has been assumed that the asymmetric cryptosystem is commutative. That is, the public and secret keys function in either order. Therefore, if the public key is used for encryption, then the secret key can be used for decryption, whereas if the secret key is used for encryption, then the public key can be used for decryption.

### 11.4.4 Two-Way Authentication of Communicating Entities

In a distributed system, tasks are often distributed over multiple hosts to achieve a higher throughput or more balanced utilization of resources than centralized systems. Correctness of such a distributed task depends on whether peer processes participating in the task can correctly identify each other. Two-way authentication protocols allow both communicating entities to verify each other's identity before establishing a secure logical communication channel between them.

Obviously, mutual authentication can be achieved by performing one-way authentication twice. That is, if two communicating users $A$ and $B$ want to authenticate each other, $A$ can first authenticate $B$ by performing one-way authentication, and then $B$ can authenticate $A$ by repeating the same process, but with the roles of $A$ and $B$ reversed. However, this may turn out to be costlier than a protocol designed specially for two-way authentication. For example, if the protocol of Figure 11.9 is repeated twice for performing two-way authentication, a total of 10 messages will be required. However, a protocol for mutual authentication of communicating entries that requires only seven messages and that is also based upon an asymmetric cryptosystem and uses a centralized AS is described below. In the description, it has been assumed that two users $A$ and $B$ want to authenticate each other. Here, $P_a$ and $S_a$ are the public and secret keys of user $A$, and $P_b$ and $S_b$ are the public and secret keys of user $B$. Moreover, $P_s$ and $S_s$ are the public and secret keys of the AS. The authentication protocol consists of the following steps (see Fig. 11.10):

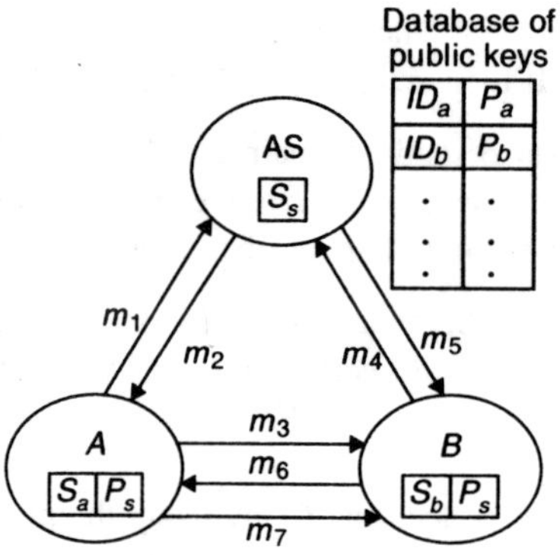

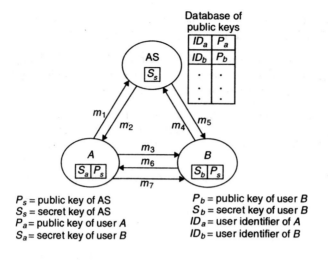

$P_s$ = public key of AS
$S_s$ = secret key of AS
$P_a$ = public key of user $A$
$S_a$ = secret key of user $B$

$P_b$ = public key of user $B$
$S_b$ = secret key of user $B$
$ID_a$ = user identifier of $A$
$ID_b$ = user identifier of $B$

$m_1 = (R_a, ID_a, ID_b)$
where $R_a$ = code for the request made by user $A$

$m_2 = C_1 = E\ ((ID_b, P_b), S_s)$

$m_3 = C_2 = E\ ((ID_a, N_a), P_b)$
where $N_a$ is a random number generated by user $A$

$m_4 = C_3 = E\ ((R_b, ID_a, ID_b, N_a), P_s)$

$m_5 = (C_4, C_6)$
where $C_4 = E\ ((ID_a, P_a), S_s)$ and
$C_6 = E\ (C_5, P_b)$
where $C_5 = (ID_b, K, N_a), S_s)$
where $K$ is a session key generated by the AS for users $A$ and $B$.

$m_6 = C_7 = E\ ((C_5, N_b), P_a)$
where $N_b$ is a random number generated by user $B$

$m_7 = C_8 = E\ (N_b, K)$

$B$ decrypts $C_8$ with the session key $K$ and compares the result with the original value of $N_b$. If they are equal, this is sufficient to prove that the logical communication channel established between $A$ and $B$ with key $K$ is a newly established channel and is secure.

**Fig. 11.10** Two-way authentication protocol based on asymmetric cryptosystem and the use of a centralized authentication server.

1. User $A$ sends a request message ($m_1$) to the AS indicating that it wants to establish a secure logical communication channel with user $B$. The message contains a code for the request ($R_a$), the identifier of user $A$ ($ID_a$), and the identifier of user $B$ ($ID_b$). This message is sent in plaintext form.

2. On receiving $m_1$, the AS extracts from its database the public key $P_b$ that corresponds to the user identifier $ID_b$ of the message. By using its secret key $S_s$, the AS encrypts the pair ($ID_b$, $P_b$) to generate a ciphertext $C_1 = E((ID_b, P_b), S_s)$. It then sends $C_1$ to $A$ in a message $m_2$.

3. On receiving $m_2$, user $A$ decrypts $C_1$ by using the public key of the AS ($P_s$) and retrieves its contents. It then generates a random number $N_a$, encrypts the pair ($ID_a$, $N_a$) by using the public key of user $B$ ($P_b$) to generate a ciphertext $C_2 = E((ID_a, N_a), P_b)$, and sends $C_2$ to $B$ in a message $m_3$.

4. On receiving $m_3$, user $B$ decrypts $C_2$ by using its secret key $S_b$ and retrieves its contents. It then sends a message $m_4$ to the AS requesting for the public key of user $A$ and a session key for the secure logical communication channel between $A$ and $B$. The message contains the request code ($R_b$), $ID_a$, $ID_b$, and $N_a$. Before being sent, the message is encrypted with the public key of the AS ($P_s$). That is, the message contains the ciphertext $C_3 = E((R_b, ID_a, ID_b, N_a), P_s)$.

5. On receiving $m_4$, the AS decrypts $C_3$ with its secret key ($S_s$) and retrieves its contents. It generates a new session key $K$ for $A$ and $B$. Next it generates three ciphertexts: $C_4 = E((ID_a, P_a), S_s)$, $C_5 = E((ID_b, K, N_a), S_s)$, and $C_6 = E(C_5, P_b)$. Finally, it sends $C_4$ and $C_6$ to $B$ in a message $m_5$.

6. On receiving $m_5$, user $B$ decrypts $C_4$ and $C_6$ with $P_s$ and $S_b$, respectively, and retrieves their contents. It then generates a random number $N_b$ and creates a ciphertext $C_7 = E((C_5, N_b), P_a)$. Finally, it sends $C_7$ to $A$ in a message $m_6$. Notice that $C_5$ is obtained by decrypting $C_6$.

7. On receiving $m_6$, user $A$ first decrypts $C_7$ by using its secret key $S_a$ and then decrypts $C_5$ by using the public key of the AS ($P_s$). Now both users $A$ and $B$ have the session key $K$. User $A$ next generates a ciphertext $C_8 = E(N_b, K)$ and sends $C_8$ to $B$ in a message $m_7$.

8. On receiving $m_7$, user $B$ decrypts $C_8$ by using the session key $K$ and compares the result with the original value of $N_b$. If they are equal, this is sufficient to prove that the logical communication channel established between $A$ and $B$ with key $K$ is a newly established channel and is secure. Both users $A$ and $B$ are now sure of each other's identity.

Notice that although the authentication protocol is based upon an asymmetric cryptosystem, the actual communications between users $A$ and $B$, after the secure logical communication channel is established between them, take place by a symmetric cryptosystem.

### 11.4.5 Case Study: Kerberos Authentication System

The need for secure authentication in distributed computing systems has led to the design of authentication standards and systems for this purpose. For example, X.509 identifies the CCITT X.500 directory authentication framework standard [Smart 1994], Kerberos is a network authentication system developed at MIT [Neuman and Theodore 1994, Stallings 1994], and SPX is an experimental authentication system developed by the Digital Equipment Corporation [Khanna 1994]. Of several authentication systems developed to date, the Kerberos system is the most popular one and is continuing to evolve. It has been declared the Internet standard and has become the de facto standard for remote authentication in networked client-server environments. Therefore, a description of this system is presented here.

Kerberos was developed at MIT as part of its project Athena [Champine et al. 1990]. It is named after the three-headed dog of Greek mythology that guards the entrance to Hades. Its design is based on the ideas of Needham and Schroeder [1978] for key distribution and authentication that we have already seen in Sections 11.3.4 and 11.4.3, respectively. It is now available in both commercial and public-domain implementations and is widely used at MIT and elsewhere to provide secure access to resources in distributed environments. It is used by Transarc's AFS file system and is the underlying component of the OSF's DCE Security Server (described later in this chapter). Several vendors, including DEC, Hewlett-Packard, and IBM, now offer Kerberos implementations as part of their standard middleware offerings on commercial UNIX and midrange server platforms. Version 5, the most recent version of Kerberos, is described here.

#### Kerberos System Architecture

The system architecture of Kerberos is shown in Figure 11.11. It consists of the following basic components:

1. *Kerberos server*. The key component of a Kerberos system is a Kerberos server that acts as a key distribution center. Each Kerberos server has an authentication database, an authentication server, and a ticket-granting server. The authentication database has the user ID and password of all users of the system. Moreover, the Kerberos server shares a unique secret key with each server in the system. Therefore, the authentication database also has the server ID and secret key for all servers in the system. The passwords and secret keys are distributed physically or in some other secure manner as part of the Kerberos installation. Kerberos uses the DES algorithm to generate the keys and encrypt messages, but this is implemented as a separate module that can be easily replaced by any other suitable algorithm.

The authentication server performs the task of verifying user's identity at the time of login without requiring the password to travel over the network. Kerberos has single sign-on facility. Therefore, a user has to enter his or her password only once at the time of login no matter how many different resources are accessed by the user after that.

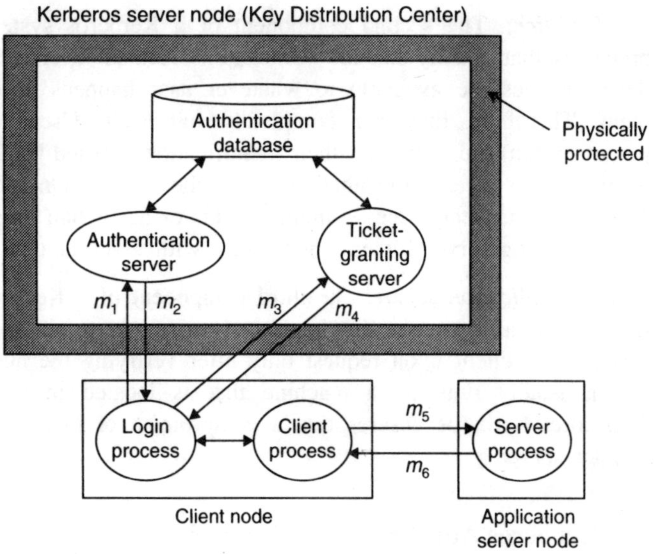


$ID_g$ = ticket-granting server's identifier
$ID_c$ = client's identifier
$ID_s$ = applicationserver's identifier
$N_i$ = a nonce
$K_c$ = client's secret key
$K_s$ = applicationserver's secret key

$K_g$ = ticket-granting server's secret key
$K_1$ = ticket-granting ticket session key
$K_2$ = service-granting ticket session key
$T_{si}$ = starting time of validityof ticket
$T_{ei}$ = ending time of validityof ticket
$T_i$ = a timestamp

$m_1 = (ID_c, N_1)$

$m_2 = C_2 = E((N_1, K_1, C_1), K_c)$, where $C_1 = E((ID_c, ID_g, T_{s1}, T_{e1}, K_1), K_g)$

$m_3 = (ID_s, N_2, C_1, C_3)$, where $C_3 = E((ID_c, T_1), K_1)$

$m_4 = C_5 = E((N_2, K_2, C_4), K_1)$, where $C_4 = E((ID_c, ID_s, T_{s2}, T_{e2}, K_2), K_s)$

$m_5 = (C_4, C_6)$, where $C_6 = E((ID_c, T_2), K_2)$

$m_6 = C_7 = E(T_3, K_2)$, where $T_3 = T_{2+1}$

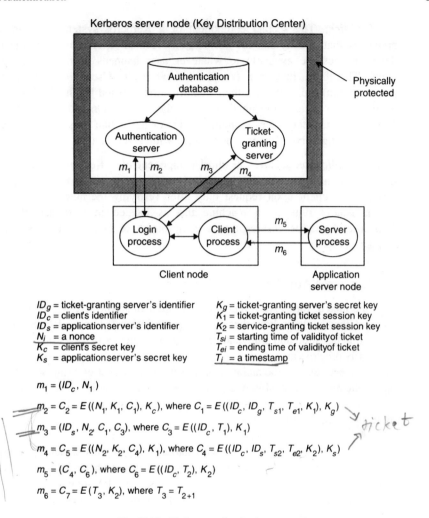

**Fig. 11.11** Kerberos authentication protocol.

The ticket-granting server performs the task of supplying tickets to clients for permitting access to other servers in the system. These tickets are used to establish secure logical communication channels between clients and servers by performing mutual authentication.

Since the Kerberos server has valuable information in its authentication database that must be kept secret, it is extremely important that it be installed on a carefully protected and physically secure machine. Although there is no technical problem in installing the Kerberos server on the same machine that has another application, it is always better for security reasons to have a dedicated machine for the Kerberos server. The number of users having access permission to this machine should be extremely limited.

2. *Client*. The second component of a Kerberos system is comprised of client processes that usually run on workstations located in effectively public places where their consoles are available to whatever user happens to be physically in front of them. Therefore, they are completely untrusted. Users (on whose behalf client processes run) must first get their identification verified by the Kerberos server before attempting to access any other server in the system. Once a user's identity has been verified, each client process running on his or her behalf must obtain a ticket from the ticket-granting server for communicating with a server that it wants to access.

3. *Application server*. The third component of a Kerberos system is the application server, also known simply as the server. A server provides a specific type of service to a client upon request only after verifying the authenticity of the client. A server usually runs on a machine that is located in a moderately secure room. Therefore, Kerberos ensures that a compromise of one server does not compromise another server.

### Kerberos Authentication Protocol

With the idea of the basic components and their functions, we will now see the Kerberos protocol that explains how these components interact with each other to perform user login authentication and mutual authentication of client and server processes. The protocol is described below and is summarized in Figure 11.11. In the description, $A$, $G$, $C$, and $S$ stand respectively for the authentication server, the ticket-granting server, the client, and the application server. Moreover, let $K_a$, $K_g$, and $K_s$ be the secret keys of $A$, $G$, and $S$, respectively, and $K_c$ be the secret key of $C$ (this key is generated from the user's password by using a one-way function).

1. When a user logs on to a workstation by typing his or her login name, the login program sends a request to the authentication server for what is known as a ticket-granting ticket in a message $m_1$. Message $m_1$ contains the user's ID (login name) ($ID_c$) and a nonce $N_1$ that is used to check the validity of the reply. This message is sent in plaintext form.

2. On receiving $m_1$, the authentication server extracts the password of this user from the authentication database. It then generates a random number for use as a session key ($K_1$). After this, it creates a ticket-granting ticket that contains the user's ID ($ID_c$), the ticket-granting server's ID ($ID_g$), the starting time for validity of the ticket ($T_{s1}$), the ending time for validity of the ticket ($T_{e1}$) (typically on the order of 8 hours), and a copy of the session key ($K_1$). Making the ticket-granting ticket time sensitive prevents an unauthorized user from capturing it and using it at a later time. Now it encrypts this ticket by using the ticket-granting server's secret key ($K_g$) to generate a ciphertext $C_1 = E((ID_c, ID_g, T_{s1}, T_{e1}, K_1), K_g)$. This encryption ensures that no one (not even the client) can tamper with the ticket-granting ticket and only the Kerberos server can decode it. Next it uses the client's secret key ($K_c$) (generated from the user's password) to generate another ciphertext $C_2 = E((N_1, K_1, C_1), K_c)$. It then returns $C_2$ to the login program in a message $m_2$.

3. On receiving $m_2$, the login program prompts the user for his or her password. The entered password is run through a one-way function that generates the client's secret key ($K_c$) from the password. Immediately after obtaining $K_c$, the password is removed from the computer's memory to minimize the chance of password disclosure in the event of a client crash. The login program then attempts to decrypt $C_2$ by using $K_c$. If the user supplied the correct password, $C_2$ is successfully decrypted and the login program obtains the nonce, the session key, and the encrypted ticket from the message. It checks the nonce for validity of the reply and stores the session key and the encrypted ticket for subsequent use when communicating with the ticket-granting server. When this has been done, the client's secret key can also be erased from memory, since the ticket now serves to authenticate the user. A login session is then started for the user on the user's workstation.

Notice that user authentication is done without requiring the password to travel over the network. Moreover, if an intruder intercepts the reply message, it will be unable to decrypt it and thus be unable to obtain the session key and the ticket inside it.

4. Now when a client process running on the client workstation on behalf of the authenticated user wants to access the application server, it requests the ticket-granting server for a service-granting ticket that can be used to communicate with the application server. For this, the client creates an authenticator that contains the client's ID ($ID_c$) and a timestamp ($T_1$). It encrypts this authenticator by using the session key ($K_1$) to obtain a ciphertext $C_3 = E((ID_c, T_1), K_1)$. Unlike the ticket-granting ticket, which is reusable, this authenticator is intended for one-time use and has a very short life span (typically on the order of a few minutes). The client next sends the encrypted authenticator ($C_3$), the encrypted ticket-granting ticket ($C_1$), the ID of the application server ($ID_s$), and a nonce ($N_2$) to the ticket-granting server in a message $m_3$.

5. On receiving $m_3$, the ticket-granting server decrypts $C_1$ by using its secret key ($K_g$) and makes sure that it has not expired by comparing $T_{e1}$ with the current time. It extracts the session key ($K_1$) from it and uses it to decrypt $C_3$ to obtain $ID_c$ and $T_1$. The obtained $ID_c$ is compared with the value of $ID_c$ in the ticket-granting ticket to authenticate the source of the request. On the other hand, $T_1$ is used to ascertain the freshness of the request. If all verifications pass successfully, the ticket-granting server gets assured that the sender of the ticket is indeed the ticket's real owner.

Notice here that it is the authenticator and not the ticket-granting ticket that proves the client's identity. Therefore, the use of a ticket-granting ticket is merely a way to distribute keys securely. Moreover, since the authenticator can be used only once and has a very short life span, it is nearly impossible for an intruder to steal both the ticket-granting ticket and an authenticator for later use. Each time a client applies to the ticket-granting server for a new service-granting ticket, it sends its reusable ticket-granting ticket plus a fresh authenticator. Also notice that the reusability of the ticket-granting ticket allows support of a single sign-on facility in which a user need not enter his or her password every time it needs to access a new server.

After successful authentication of the client, the ticket-granting server generates a new random session key ($K_2$) and then creates a reusable service-granting ticket for access to the requested server. This ticket contains the client's ID ($ID_c$), the application server's

ID ($ID_s$), the starting time for validity of the ticket ($T_{s2}$), the ending time for validity of the ticket ($T_{e2}$), and a copy of the new session key ($K_2$). It then encrypts the service-granting ticket with the secret key of the application server ($K_s$) to obtain a ciphertext $C_4 = E((ID_c, ID_s, T_{s2}, T_{e2}, K_2), K_s)$. This encryption ensures that no one (not even the client) can tamper with the service-granting ticket and only the application server or the Kerberos server can decode it. Next it uses the old session key ($K_1$) to generate another ciphertext $C_5 = E((N_2, K_2, C_4), K_1)$. It then returns $C_5$ to the client in a message $m_4$.

6. On receiving $m_4$, the client decrypts $C_5$ by using the old session key ($K_1$) and obtains the nonce, the new session key, and the encrypted service-granting ticket. It checks the nonce for validity of the reply and stores the new session key and the encrypted ticket for subsequent use when communicating with the application server. The client is now ready to issue request messages to the application server. However, if mutual authentication is desired, before proceeding with its transaction or request for service, the client creates an authenticator that contains the client's ID ($ID_c$) and a timestamp ($T_2$). It encrypts this authenticator by using the session key ($K_2$) to obtain a ciphertext $C_6 = E((ID_c, T_2), K_2)$. The client next sends to the application server, in a message $m_5$, the encrypted authenticator ($C_6$), the encrypted service-granting ticket ($C_4$), and a request that the server reply with the value of the timestamp from the authenticator, incremented by 1, and encrypted in the session key.

7. On receiving $m_5$, the application server decrypts $C_4$ by using its secret key ($K_s$) and extracts the copy of the session key ($K_2$). It then uses it to decrypt $C_6$ to obtain $ID_c$ and $T_2$. Next, it increments $T_2$ by 1 and encrypts the obtained value ($T_3$) with the session key $K_2$ to obtain a ciphertext $C_7 = E(T_3, K_2)$. It returns $C_7$ to the client in a message $m_6$.

8. On receiving $m_6$, the client decrypts $C_7$ by using the session key $K_2$ to obtain $T_3$. If $T_3 = T_2 + 1$, the client gets assured that the server is genuine. This mutual authentication procedure prevents any possibility of an intruder impersonating a server in attempt to gain access information from a client.

At the conclusion of this process, the client and server are assured of the establishment of a secure communication channel in between them. They also now share a session key ($K_2$), which they can use (if required) to encrypt future messages.

### Interrealm Authentication in Kerberos

In a system that crosses organizational boundaries, it is not appropriate for all users and servers to be registered with a single Kerberos server. Therefore, in such an environment, multiple Kerberos servers exist, each responsible for a subset of the users and servers in the system. A subset of users and servers along with the Kerberos server with which they are registered is called a *realm* in Kerberos. In a typical implementation, networks of clients and servers belonging to different organizations usually constitute different realms. In such an environment, interrealm authentication facility is needed to allow a client to securely interact with a server belonging to a different realm. For this, a Kerberos server of one realm is registered (shares a secret key) with the Kerberos servers of all other realms. The interrealm authentication protocol is shown in Figure 11.12 and is described below:

1. A client that wants to access a server in a different realm first makes a request for a service-granting ticket from its own ticket-granting server to access the ticket-granting server of the other realm.
2. With the obtained service-granting ticket, the client then makes a request for another service-granting ticket from the ticket-granting server of the other realm to access the application server of that realm.

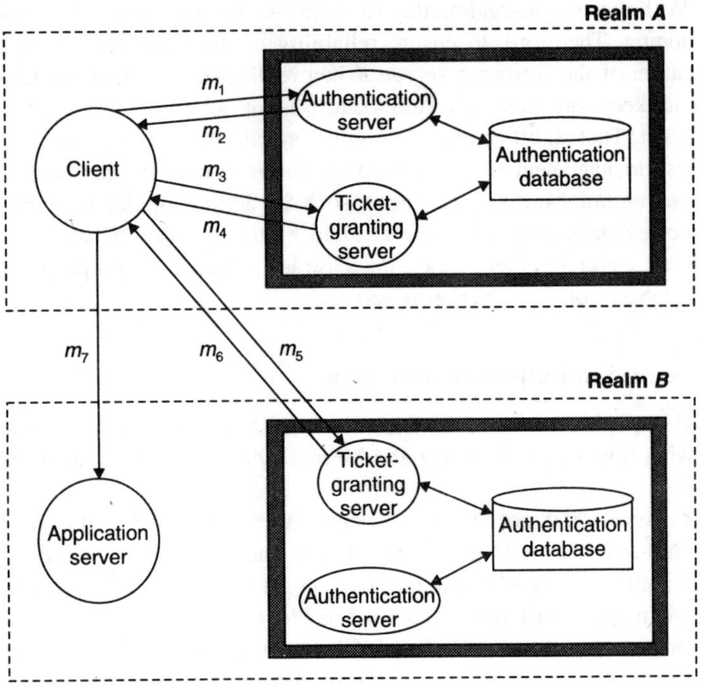


$m_1$ = request for ticket-granting ticket

$m_2$ = reply for $m_1$

$m_3$ = request for service-granting ticket to access the remote ticket-granting server

$m_4$ = reply for $m_3$

$m_5$ = request for service-granting ticket to access the remote application server

$m_6$ = reply for $m_5$

$m_7$ = access request

**Fig. 11.12** Interrealm authentication protocol of Kerberos.

3. With the newly obtained service-granting ticket, the client now sends its request to the desired application server of the other realm. The remote server then chooses whether to honor the client's request.

In the above approach for interrealm authentication, if it is desired that each Kerberos realm be able to operate with all other Kerberos realms, in a system having $n$ realms, there must be $n(n-1)/2$ secure key exchanges. Therefore, this approach does not scale well. It creates a lot of overhead on the network and the Kerberos servers themselves. Thus, it is suggested that Kerberos implementations should use a few relatively large realms rather than too many small realms. The latest version of Kerberos (Version 5) also supports multihop interrealm authentication, allowing keys to be shared hierarchically [Neuman and Theodore 1994].

Within a single realm, the Kerberos server is a critical component for smooth functioning. Therefore, to ensure reliability of the Kerberos server, Kerberos supports replication of the Kerberos server. When replicated, a simple master-slave technique is used to keep the authentication databases of all the replicas of a Kerberos server consistent. That is, all changes are only applied to the master copy by a single Kerberos database management server (KDBMS) that runs only on the master Kerberos server's machine. Administrative operations such as adding or deleting users or requests for password change from users are handled by the KDBMS. Changes made to the master Kerberos server's authentication database are periodically propagated to the authentication databases of slave Kerberos servers.

### Some Limitations of Kerberos

For all its popularity, however, Kerberos is not a complete security solution because of the following limitations [Bellovin and Merritt 1990, Neumann and Theodore 1994]:

1. Kerberos is not effective against password-guessing attacks. If a user chooses a password that is easy to guess, an intruder guessing that password can impersonate the user. Another way by which an intruder can get to know a user's password is by modifying the login program (a Trojan horse) that resides on the user's workstation. In this case, also, the intruder may obtain sufficient information to impersonate the user. To address these limitations, it is suggested that Kerberos should be combined with a one-time password technique. Commercial products that combine a one-time password technique with Kerberos are available.

2. The Kerberos protocol depends upon loose synchronization of clocks of the nodes present in a system. It may not be very difficult to meet this requirement, but the problem is that the synchronization protocol used for this purpose must itself be secure against security attacks. A Kerberos protocol that does not rely on synchronized clocks has been presented in [Kehne et al. 1992].

3. Another problem with Kerberos is that it is difficult to decide the appropriate lifetime of the tickets, which is generally limited to a few hours. For better security, it is desirable that this lifetime should be short so that users who have been unregistered or

downgraded will not be able to continue to use the resources for a long time. However, for user transparency, the lifetime should be as long as the longest possible login session, since the use of an expired ticket will result in the rejection of service requests. Once rejected, the user must reauthenticate the login session and then request new server tickets for all the services in use. Interrupting an application at an arbitrary point for reauthentication might not be acceptable in commercial environments.

4. Finally, client-server applications must be modified to take advantage of Kerberos authentication. This process is called *Kerberization*. Kerberizing an application is the most difficult part of installing Kerberos. Many large organizations may find it almost impossible to Kerberize their applications and turn to other solutions. Fortunately, the availability of Kerberized applications has improved with time and is expected to improve further. More and more vendors are now producing new Kerberized versions of their popular products.

## 11.5 ACCESS CONTROL

Once a user or a process has been authenticated, the next step in security is to devise ways to prohibit the user or the process from accessing those resources/information that he or she or it is not authorized to access. This issue is called *authorization* and is dealt with by using access control mechanisms. Access control mechanisms (also known as protection mechanisms) used in distributed systems are basically the same as those used in centralized systems. The main difference is that since all resources are centrally located in a centralized system, access control can be performed by a central authority. However, in a distributed client-server environment, each server is responsible for controlling access to its own resources.

When talking about access control in computer systems, it is customary to use the following terms:

1. *Objects*. An object is an entity to which access must be controlled. An object may be an abstract entity, such as a process, a file, a database, a semaphore, a tree data structure, or a physical entity, such as a CPU, a memory segment, a printer, a card reader, a tape drive, a site of a network.

Each object has a unique name that differentiates it from all other objects in the system. An object is referenced by its unique name. In addition, associated with each object is a "type" that determines the set of operations that may be performed on it. For example, the set of operations possible on objects belonging to the type "data file" may be *Open*, *Close*, *Create*, *Delete*, *Read*, and *Write*, whereas for objects belonging to the type "program file," the set of possible operations may be *Read*, *Write*, and *Execute*. Similarly, for objects of type "semaphore," the set of possible operations may be *Up* and *Down*, and for objects of type "tape drive," the set of possible operations may be *Read*, *Write*, and *Rewind*.

2. *Subjects*. A subject is an active entity whose access to objects must be controlled. That is, entities wishing to access and perform operations on objects and to which access authorizations are granted are called subjects. Examples of subjects are processes and

users. Note that subjects are also objects since they too must be protected. Therefore, each subject also has a unique name.

3. *Protection rules*. Protection rules define the possible ways in which subjects and objects are allowed to interact. That is, protection rules govern the subjects' access to objects. Therefore, associated with each (subject, object) pair is an *access right* that defines the subset of the set of possible operations for the object type that the subject may perform on the object. The complete set of access rights of a system defines which subjects can perform what operations on which objects. At any particular instance of time, this set defines the *protection state* of the system at that time.

The exact manner in which the protection rules are imposed to control the subjects' access to objects depends on the access control model used by the system. The following access control models have been proposed in the literature:

1. The access matrix model [Lampson 1971, Graham and Denning 1972, Harrison et al. 1976]
2. The information flow control model [Denning 1976, Bell and LaPadula 1973]
3. The security kernel model [Ames et al. 1983, Rushby and Randell 1983]

Of these, the access matrix model is the most popular one and is widely used in existing centralized and distributed systems. The other two models are mainly of theoretical interest. A description of the access control mechanisms based on the access matrix model is presented below.

### 11.5.1 Protection Domains

We saw that the principle of least privilege requires that at any time a subject should be able to access only those objects that it currently requires to complete its task. Therefore, from time to time, subjects may need to change the set of access rights they have to objects, depending on the particular task that they have to do at any time. The concept of a domain is commonly used to provide this type of flexibility of access control in a security system.

A *domain* is an abstract definition of a set of access rights. It is defined as a set of (object, rights) pairs. Each pair specifies an object and one or more operations that can be performed on the object. Each one of the allowed operations is called a *right*.

A security system based on the concept of domain defines a set of domains with each domain having its own set of (object, rights) pairs. At any instance of time, each process executes in one of the protection domains of the system. Therefore, at a particular instance of time, the access rights of a process are equal to the access rights defined in the domain in which it is at that time. A process can also switch from one domain to another during execution.

Figure 11.13 shows an example of a system having three protection domains $D_1$, $D_2$, $D_3$. The following points may be observed from this example:

1. Domains need not be disjoint. That is, the same access rights may simultaneously exist in two or more domains. For instance, access right (*Semaphore-1*, {*Up*, *Down*}) is in both domains $D_1$ and $D_2$. This implies that a subject in either of the two domains can perform *Up* and *Down* operations on *Semaphore-1*.

2. The same object can exist in multiple domains with different rights in each domain. For instance, rights for *File-1* and *File-2* are different in $D_1$ and $D_2$, and rights for *TapeDrive-1* are different in $D_2$ and $D_3$. Considering *File-1*, a subject in domain $D_1$ can *Read*, *Write*, and *Execute* it, but a subject in domain $D_2$ can only perform *Read* and *Write* operations on it. Therefore, in order to execute *File-1*, a subject must be in domain $D_1$.

3. If an object exists only in a single domain, it can be accessed only by the subjects in that domain. For instance, *File-3* can only be accessed by the subjects in domain $D_3$.

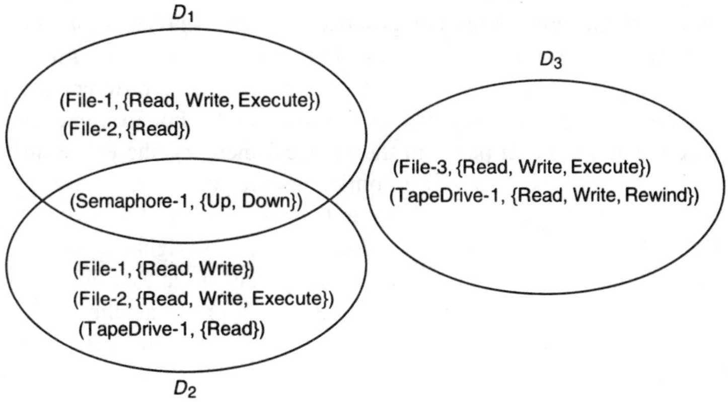


**Fig. 11.13** A system having three protection domains.

Since a domain is an abstract concept, its realization and the rules for domain switching are highly system dependent. For instance, some ways of realizing a domain may be the following:

1. *Each user as a domain.* In this case, processes are assigned to domains according to the identity of the user on whose behalf they are executed. A domain switching occurs when a user logs out and another user logs in.
2. *Each process as a domain.* In this case, the access rights of a process are limited to the access rights of its own domain. A domain switching occurs when one process sends a message to another process and then waits for a response.
3. *Each procedure as a domain.* In this case, each procedure has its own set of access rights and a domain switching occurs when a procedure calls another procedure during the course of its execution.

In the protection scheme of UNIX, both the concepts of user-oriented domains and procedure-oriented domains are employed. Let us first see the use of the concept of user-oriented domains. In UNIX, a *user-id* (*uid*) and a *group-id* (*gid*) are associated with each user. A (*uid*, *gid*) pair identifies the list of objects and the types of operations that can be performed on these objects. The domain of a process depends on the user on whose behalf it is executed. Therefore, the domain of a process is defined by its (*uid*, *gid*) pair. That is, two processes with the same (*uid*, *gid*) pair will have exactly the same access rights and two processes with different (*uid*, *gid*) pairs will have different access rights. In the latter case, several of the access rights may be the same for the two processes. A process switches domains by acquiring a new *uid* or *gid* by executing the *setuid* or *setgid* commands. Furthermore, it is also worth mentioning here that the *superuser* in a UNIX system is not a person but a name for a special domain within which the most privileged processes, needing access to all of the objects in the system, may run.

Now let us see the use of the concept of procedure-oriented domains in UNIX. In UNIX, all the procedures are grouped into two classes—user procedures and kernel procedures. These two classes form two domains called the *user mode* and the *kernel mode*. A process running in the kernel mode has a different set of access rights as compared to a process running in the user mode. For example, in the kernel mode, a process can access all pages in the physical memory, the entire disk area, and all other protected resources. In this two-domain architecture, when a user process does a system call, it switches from the user mode to the kernel mode. Therefore, at a particular instance of time, the domain of a process and hence its access rights depend on whether the process is executing a user procedure or a kernel procedure at that time.

Multics [Schroeder et al. 1977] used a more generalized form of the procedure-oriented domains. Unlike UNIX, which uses two domains (user mode and kernel mode), the Multics architecture had the flexibility to support up to 64 domains. Each domain of Multics was called a *ring*. As shown in Figure 11.14, the rings were concentric and the procedures in the innermost ring, the operating system kernel, were most powerful, having maximum access rights. Moving outward from the innermost ring, the rings became successively less powerful having fewer access rights. In fact, the access privileges of ring $i$ were a subset of those for ring $j$ for all $i > j$ when the ring numbers started from the innermost ring and increased for each ring as we moved outward. That is, $j < i$ implied that the procedures in ring $j$ had more access rights than the procedures in ring $i$. A process could operate in multiple domains (rings) during its lifetime. A domain switching occurred when a procedure in one domain (ring) made a call to a procedure in another domain (ring). Obviously, domain switching was done in a controlled manner; otherwise, a process could start executing in the innermost ring and no protection would be provided.

### 11.5.2 Access Matrix

In the domain-based protection approach, the system must keep track of which rights on which objects belong to a particular domain. In the access matrix model, this information is represented as a matrix, called an *access matrix*, that has the following form:

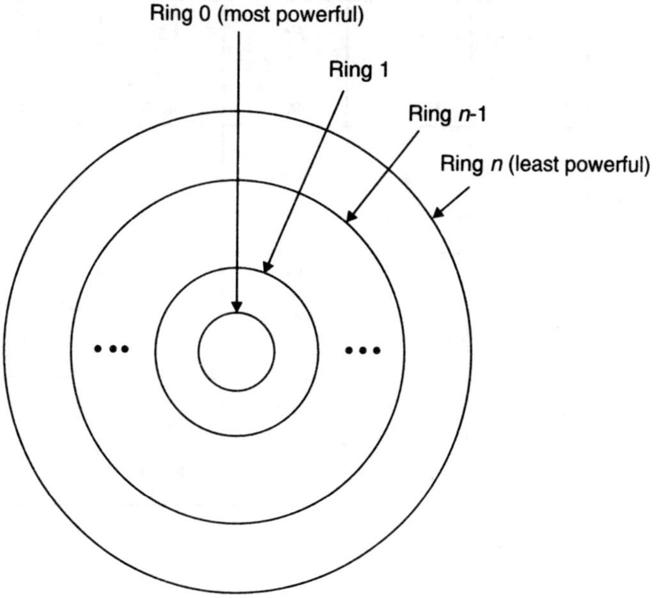


**Fig. 11.14** The ring architecture of Multics protection domains.

1. The rows represent domains.
2. The columns represent objects.
3. Each entry in the access matrix consists of a set of access rights.
4. The $(i, j)$th entry of the access matrix defines the set of operations that a process, executing in domain $D_i$, can perform on object $O_j$.

At any instance of time, the *protection state* of the system is defined by the contents of the access matrix. The access matrix of Figure 11.15 shows the protection state of the system in Figure 11.13.

When an access matrix is used to represent the protection state of a system, the following issues must be resolved:

1. How to decide the contents of the access matrix entries.
2. How to validate access to objects by subjects.
3. How to allow subjects to switch domains in a controlled manner.
4. How to allow changes to the protection state of the system in a controlled manner.

The normally used methods to handle these issues are described below.

| Domain \ Object | $F_1$ (File-1) | $F_2$ (File-2) | $F_3$ (File-3) | $S_1$ (Semaphore-1) | $T_1$ (Tape drive-1) |
|---|---|---|---|---|---|
| $D_1$ | Read<br>Write<br>Execute | Read | | Up<br>Down | |
| $D_2$ | Read<br>Write | Read<br>Write<br>Execute | | Up<br>Down | Read |
| $D_3$ | | | Read<br>Write<br>Execute | | Read<br>Write<br>Rewind |

**Fig. 11.15** The access matrix for the protection state of the system in Figure 11.13.

## Deciding the Contents of the Access Matrix Entries

Policy decisions concerning which rights should be included in the $(i, j)$th entry are system dependent. However, in general, the contents of the access matrix entries corresponding to user-defined objects are decided by the users, whereas the contents of the entries corresponding to system-defined objects are decided by the system. For example, when a user creates a new object $O_j$, column $j$ is added to the access matrix with suitable entries as decided by the user's specification of access control for the object.

## Validating Access to Objects by Subjects

Given the access matrix, how can access to objects by subjects be allowed only in the manner permitted by the protection state of the matrix? For this, an *object monitor* is associated with each type of object, and every attempted access by a subject to an object is validated in the following manner:

1. A subject $S$ in domain $D$ initiates $r$ access to object $O$, where $r$ belongs to the set of operations that may be performed on $O$.
2. The protection system forms the triple $(D, r, O)$ and passes it to the object monitor of $O$.
3. The object monitor of $O$ looks for the operation $r$ in the $(D, O)$th entry of the access matrix. If present, the access is permitted; otherwise, a protection violation occurs.

### Allowing Controlled Domain Switching

The principle of least privilege requires that a process should be allowed to switch from one domain to another during its lifetime so that at any instance of time the process is given only as many rights as are necessary for performing its task at that time. However, domain switching by processes must be done in a controlled manner; otherwise, a process may switch to a powerful domain and violate the protection policies of the system.

Domain switching can be controlled by treating domains as objects on which the only possible operation is *switch*. Therefore, for allowing domain switching in a controlled manner, the domains are also included among the objects of the access matrix.

Figure 11.16 shows the access matrix of Figure 11.15 with the three domains as objects themselves. In the modified access matrix, domain switching from domain $D_i$ to domain $D_j$ is permitted if and only if the right *switch* is present in the $(D_i, D_j)$th entry of the access matrix. Thus in Figure 11.16, a process executing in domain $D_1$ can switch to domain $D_2$ or to domain $D_3$, a process executing in domain $D_2$ can switch only to domain $D_3$, and a process executing in domain $D_3$ cannot switch to any other domain.

| Domain \ Object | $F_1$ | $F_2$ | $F_3$ | $S_1$ | $T_1$ | $D_1$ | $D_2$ | $D_3$ |
|---|---|---|---|---|---|---|---|---|
| $D_1$ | Read<br>Write<br>Execute | Read | | Up<br>Down | | | Switch | Switch |
| $D_2$ | Read<br>Write | Read<br>Write<br>Execute | | Up<br>Down | Read | | | Switch |
| $D_3$ | | | Read<br>Write<br>Execute | | Read<br>Write<br>Rewind | | | |

**Fig. 11.16** The access matrix of Figure 11.15 with the domains included as objects.

### Allowing Controlled Change to the Protection State

In a flexible design, the protection system should also allow the content of a domain to be changed. However, this facility is not essential because if the content of a domain cannot be changed, the same effect can be provided by creating a new domain with the changed contents and switching to that new domain when we want to change the domain contents. Although not essential, the facility of allowing controlled change to the protection state is normally provided in a protection system for greater flexibility.

In an access matrix model, this facility can be provided by treating the access matrix itself as an object to be protected. In fact, since each entry in the access matrix may be individually modified, each entry must be considered as an object to be protected. For allowing controlled change, the possible rights defined for this new object are *copy*, *owner*, and *control*. To simplify the description, we will categorize the changes to be allowed to the content of the access matrix entries into two types—allowing changes to the column entries and allowing changes to the row entries.

***Allowing Changes to the Column Entries.*** The *copy* and *owner* rights allow a process to change the entries in a column. The ability to copy an access right from one domain (row) to another is denoted by appending an asterisk (*) to the access right. For example, Figure 11.17 shows the access rights of only the first three objects ($F_1$, $F_2$, and $F_3$) of the access matrix of Figure 11.15 with some copy rights. A process executing in domain $D_1$ can copy the *Read* and *Write* operations on $F_1$ to any other domain (any other entry in column $F_1$), whereas a process executing in domain $D_2$ can copy the *Read* operation on $F_1$ and *Read* and *Execute* operations on $F_2$ to any other domain. None of the operations on $F_3$ can be copied to any other domain.

| Domain \ Object | $F_1$ | $F_2$ | $F_3$ |
|---|---|---|---|
| $D_1$ | Read*<br>Write*<br>Execute | Read | |
| $D_2$ | Read*<br>Write | Read*<br>Write<br>Execute* | |
| $D_3$ | | | Read<br>Write<br>Execute |

**Fig. 11.17** An access matrix with copy rights.

The copy right may have the following three variants:

1. *Transfer.* In this case, when a right is copied from the $(i, j)$th entry to the $(k, j)$th entry of the access matrix, it is removed from the $(i, j)$th entry.
2. *Copy with propagation not allowed.* In this case, when the right $R*$ is copied from the $(i, j)$th entry to the $(k, j)$th entry, only the right $R$ (not $R*$) is created in the $(k, j)$th entry. The implication of this is that a process executing in domain $D_k$ cannot further copy the right $R$.

3. *Copy with propagation allowed.* In this case, when the right $R^*$ is copied from the $(i, j)$th entry to the $(k, j)$th entry, the right $R^*$ is created in the $(k, j)$th entry, so that a process executing in domain $D_k$ can further copy the right $R^*$ or $R$.

On the other hand, the *owner* right is used to allow the adding/deleting of rights to column entries in a controlled manner. If the *owner* right is included in the $(i, j)$th entry of the access matrix, a process executing in domain $D_i$ can add and delete any right in any entry in column $j$. Figure 11.18 shows the access matrix of Figure 11.17 with *owner* rights included for the three objects. In the figure, domains $D_1$, $D_2$, and $D_3$ have the *owner* rights for objects $F_1$, $F_2$, and $F_3$, respectively. Therefore, a process executing in domain $D_1$ can add and delete any valid right of $F_1$ in any entry in column $F_1$. Similarly, a process executing in domain $D_2$ can add and delete any valid right of $F_2$ in any entry in column $F_2$, and a process executing in domain $D_3$ can add and delete any valid right of $F_3$ in any entry in column $F_3$.

| Domain \ Object | $F_1$ | $F_2$ | $F_3$ |
|---|---|---|---|
| $D_1$ | Read*<br>Write*<br>Execute<br>Owner | Read | |
| $D_2$ | Read*<br>Write | Read*<br>Write<br>Execute*<br>Owner | |
| $D_3$ | | | Read<br>Write<br>Execute<br>Owner |

**Fig. 11.18** An access matrix with owner rights.

***Allowing Changes to the Row Entries.*** The *control* right, which is only applicable to domain objects, is used to allow a process to change the entries in a row. If the control right is present in the $(D_i, D_j)$th entry of the access matrix, a process executing in domain $D_i$ can remove any access right from row $D_j$. For example, Figure 11.19 shows the access matrix of Figure 11.16 with *control* rights included. In this figure, since the entries $(D_1, D_2)$ and $(D_1, D_3)$ have *control* rights, a process executing in domain $D_1$ can delete any right from rows $D_2$ and $D_3$. Similarly, since the entry $(D_2, D_3)$ has *control* right, a process executing in domain $D_2$ can delete any right from row $D_3$.

| Domain \ Object | $F_1$ | $F_2$ | $F_3$ | $S_1$ | $T_1$ | $D_1$ | $D_2$ | $D_3$ |
|---|---|---|---|---|---|---|---|---|
| $D_1$ | Read Write Execute | Read | | Up Down | | | Switch Control | Switch Control |
| $D_2$ | Read Write | Read Write Execute | | Up Down | Read | | | Switch Control |
| $D_3$ | | | Read Write Execute | | Read Write Rewind | | | |

**Fig. 11.19** An access matrix with control rights.

### 11.5.3 Implementation of Access Matrix

In practice, an access matrix is large and sparse. Most domains have no access at all to most objects, that is, most of the entries are empty. Therefore, a direct implementation of an access matrix as a two-dimensional matrix would be very inefficient and expensive (wastage of disk space). Moreover, in distributed systems, subjects and objects may be located on different sites, which further complicates the implementation issue. The two most commonly used methods that have gained popularity in contemporary distributed systems for implementing an access matrix are access control lists (ACLs) and capabilities. For instance, Andrew [Satyanarayanan 1989], Apollo [Levine 1986], and Butler [Dannenberg and Hibbard 1985] use ACLs and Accent [Rashid and Robertson 1981], Amoeba [Mullender and Tanenbaum 1986], and Mach [Sansom et al. 1986] use capabilities. These two methods are described below.

#### Access Control Lists

In this method, the access matrix is decomposed by columns, and each column of the matrix is implemented as an access list for the object corresponding to that column. The empty entries of the matrix are not stored in the access list. Therefore, for each object, a list of ordered pairs (*domain*, *rights*) is maintained, which defines all domains with a nonempty set of access rights for that object. Further details of the working and properties of a security system based on ACLs are presented below.

***Access Validation.*** Whenever a subject in domain $D$ executes an operation $r$ on an object $O$, the access list for object $O$ is first searched for the list element whose domain field is $D$. Then the rights field of this element is searched for $r$. If found, the operation is allowed to continue; otherwise, a protection violation occurs.

In this method, the access list is checked on every access. This is a very desirable feature from a security point of view. However, consulting the access list on every access could cause substantial overhead, especially when the access list is long. This drawback can be overcome by maintaining a cache for the access list entries of only the active domains.

***Granting Rights.*** Access right $r$ for object $O$ is granted to domain $D$ in the following manner:

1. The access list for object $O$ is first searched for the list element whose domain field is $D$.
2. If found, right $r$ is added to the rights field of this list element. Otherwise, a new list element is added to the access list for the object $O$. The domain field and rights field of this list element are set to $D$ and $r$, respectively.

***Passing Rights.*** Access right $r$ for object $O$ is passed (propagated) from a domain $D_1$ to another domain $D_2$ in the following manner:

1. Access list for object $O$ is first checked to ensure that $D_1$ possesses either *owner* right for object $O$ or *copy* right for access right $r$.
2. If $D_1$ possesses any of the above two rights, access right $r$ for object $O$ is granted to domain $D_2$ in the manner described above. Otherwise, a protection violation occurs.

***Rights Revocation.*** Access right $r$ for object $O$ is revoked from domain $D$ simply by deleting $r$ from the rights set of domain $D$ in the access list for $O$.

For file protection, several systems use user-oriented domains like that of UNIX in which a (*uid*, *gid*) pair forms a domain. Revocation of a user's access right becomes more complicated in these systems because access revocation requires the deletion of the user's *uid* (if present) from the access list of the object in question and also the cancellation of the user's membership from all the groups that belong to a domain that has access to that object. In a large distributed system, the process of discovering all groups that the user should be removed from and performing the actual removal operation may take a significant amount of time that may be unacceptable in emergencies. The concept of *negative rights* is used to overcome this problem [Satyanarayanan 1989, 1990]. This concept is based on the idea that to revoke a user's access right to an object, the user can be given negative rights on that object. Negative rights indicate denial of the specified rights, with denial overriding possession in case of conflict. With this extension, the ACLs may contain negative rights, so that it is possible to express facts, such as every user of a domain except *user-i* and *user-j* may exercise right $r$ on object $O$. The union of all the negative rights specified for a user subtracted from his or her positive rights gives his or her actual total rights. Negative rights thus act as a mechanism for rapid and selective revocation and are particularly valuable in a large distributed system.

---

The main advantage of the method of ACLs is that for a given object the set of domains from which it can be accessed can be determined efficiently. However, the main drawback of the method is that for a given domain the set of access rights cannot be determined efficiently.

### Capabilities

Rather than decomposing the access matrix by columns, in this method the access matrix is decomposed by rows, and each row is associated with its domain. Obviously, the empty entries are discarded. Therefore, for each domain, a list of ordered pairs (*object*, *rights*) is maintained, which defines all objects for which the domain possesses some access rights. Each (*object*, *rights*) pair is called a *capability* and the list associated with a domain is called a *capability list*.

A capability is used for the following two purposes:

- To uniquely identify an object
- To allow its holder to access the object it identifies in one or more permission modes

Therefore, as shown in Figure 11.20, a capability is composed of two basic parts—an object identifier part and a rights information part. The object identifier part usually contains a pointer to the object and acts as a globally unique system-oriented name for the object. On the other hand, the rights information part is usually a set of bits that determine which operations are allowed on the object with this capability. Further details of the working and properties of a security system based on capabilities are presented below. For ease of presentation, in the following description we will assume that each user/process forms a domain of the system.

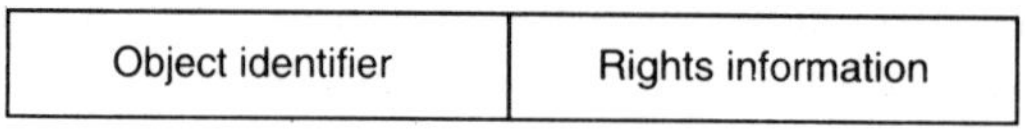


**Fig. 11.20** The two basic parts of a capability.

***Access Validation.*** A capability is considered as an unforgeable ticket that allows its holder to access the object (identified by its object identifier part) in one or more permission modes (specified by its rights information part). A process that possesses a capability can access the object identified by it in the modes permitted by it. There are usually several capabilities for the same object. Each one confers different access rights to its holders. The same capability held by different holders provides the same set of access rights to all of them.

Since simple possession of a capability means that access is permitted in the modes associated with the capability, to execute an operation *r* on an object *O*, a process executes the operation *r*, specifying the capability for object *O* as a parameter. When the monitor for object *O* receives the access request (with the capability), it need only verify that the rights information part of the capability has permission for operation *r*.

Notice that in a capability-based security system, there is no need to search a list to verify that access is allowed. Rather, the security system need only verify that the capability supplied by a process is valid for the desired operation on the object. Therefore, once a process establishes the possession of a capability for an object, it can access the object in one of the modes allowed by the capability without any further check by the security system. For these reasons, capability-based security systems are more efficient than security systems based on ACLs. Also notice that in the capability-based approach, there is no checking of user identity. If this is required for access validation, some user authentication mechanism must be used.

***Granting and Passing of Rights.*** In the capability-based security scheme, each user maintains a list of capabilities that identifies all objects that the user can access and the associated access permissions. But how does a user get a capability in the first place?

In a capability-based system, there are usually one or more object managers for each type of object. A request to create an object or to perform some operation on an object is sent to one of the object managers of that object type. When a new object is created, the object manager that creates the object generates (as a part of the object creation process) a capability with all rights of access for the object. The generated capability is returned to the owner for use. Now the owner may give the capability to other users with whom the object is to be shared. However, the owner may want to restrict the access modes in a different manner for different users who share the object. Therefore, before the owner gives the capability to other users, it may be necessary to restrict the capability by removing some of the rights. The usual way to do this is to have a function in the object manager for restricting capabilities. When called, this function generates a new capability for the object with only the desired access permissions and returns the newly generated capability to the caller. This capability is then given to the user(s) for whom it was generated.

***Protecting Capabilities against Unauthorized Access.*** To ensure that in a capability-based security system the objects are protected against unauthorized access, the following basic requirements must be met:

1. A capability must uniquely identify an object in the entire system. Even after the object associated with a given capability is deleted, it is important that the capability is not reused because some users may retain obsolete capabilities. Use of an obsolete capability should produce an error instead of allowing access to a different object.

2. Capabilities must be protected from user tampering. For this, it is necessary that capabilities be treated as unforgeable protected objects that are maintained by the operating system and only indirectly accessed by the users.

3. Guessing of a valid capability should be impossible or at least very difficult. This is because in the capability-based scheme the degree of protection is probabilistic and proportional to the difficulty of guessing a valid capability.

The following methods are normally used to meet these requirements:

1. *Tagged architecture*. In this method, each object has a tag to denote its type as either a capability or an ordinary accessible data such as integer, pointer, character, or instruction. Tags are normally implemented in hardware by associating a tag with units of memory, usually words. In this case, each memory word has a tag field that tells whether

the word contains a capability or not. The tag field is not directly accessible by an application program, and it can be modified only by programs running in the kernel mode (i.e., the operating system). Although only one bit is necessary for the tag field to distinguish between capabilities and other objects, tagged architecture machines typically use $n$ bits for the tag field to allow the software to distinguish among $2^n$ different types of objects (memory contents).

2. *Partitioned implementation.* Another method to preserve the integrity of capabilities is to store them separately from data in special segments that can only be accessed by the operating system. One way to implement this is to partition the address space of a user process into two parts—one accessible to the process and the other accessible only to the operating system. The former contains the process's normal data and instructions, whereas the latter contains its capabilities.

3. *Encryption of sparse capabilities.* The tagged and partitioned methods of protecting capabilities from unauthorized access are oriented toward centralized computer systems. These methods are not suitable for use in a distributed system because in a distributed system the security mechanism used should allow capabilities to be safely transferred from one node to another. The third method, which does not require capabilities to be distinguished from other objects either by separation or by tagging, is particularly suited to distributed systems. In addition to preventing capabilities from user tampering, this method also makes capabilities unique and difficult to guess.

In this method, a large name space that is sufficiently sparse is used for the capabilities. Uniqueness is achieved by using the methods described in Section 10.4 for the creation of unique system-oriented identifiers that form the object identifier part of the capabilities. On the other hand, to make the capabilities difficult to guess or forge, the rights information part of each capability is combined with an extra field containing a random number, thereby rending the task of a malicious user wishing to generate any valid capability so lengthy as to be impractical. Furthermore, the rights information part and the random-number part are encrypted by the object manager before a capability is issued to a user. The secret key is available only with the object manager. When a process presents the capability along with a request for object accessing, the object manager uses the key to decrypt the encrypted part of the capability before using it. In this way, the rights information part of a capability that confers restricted permissions cannot be forged by its possessors to convert it to one with more permissions.

***Rights Amplification.*** The concept of rights amplification was introduced in Hydra [Cohen and Jefferson 1975]. We saw that in a capability-based system objects are typed and recognize a set of predefined operations. The set of predefined operations for an object type is known as *auxiliary rights* in Hydra. In addition to the auxiliary rights, each object type has a set of *kernel rights*, such as *get*, *put*, and *add* to manipulate the data part of an object and *load*, *store*, *append*, *delete*, *copy*, and *create* to manipulate the capability list part of an object. The kernel rights are implemented within the kernel and are transparent to the user processes.

A request to perform an operation on an object is sent to the object manager of that object type. The request contains the capability for the object as a parameter. This capability may include an auxiliary right to invoke some operation on the object but would not include any of the kernel rights for the object. A problem arises here because the object manager is itself an ordinary program. It is essential that the object manager be able to invoke kernel operations in order to perform the requested operation successfully. The rights amplification technique of Hydra solves this problem by giving a rights template to object managers that gives them more rights to an object than the capability itself allows. Additional rights given to the object managers allow them to perform kernel operations on the objects.

When a process $P$ invokes an operation $r$ on an object $O$, the capability $C$ supplied by $P$ may get amplified to $C_a$ when the object manager $M$ starts performing the operation $r$ on the object. This may be necessary in order to allow $M$ to access the storage segment representing $O$ for performing operation $r$ on it. That is, $M$ is allowed to perform kernel operations on $O$ directly, even though the calling process $P$ cannot. After completion of the operation $r$ on $O$, the capability $C_a$ for $O$ is restored to its original, unamplified state $C$. This is a typical case in which the rights held by a process for access to a protected segment must change dynamically, depending on the task to be performed.

Notice that in the rights amplification scheme, the object managers are treated as "trustworthy" procedures and are allowed to perform kernel operations on the objects of a specified type, on behalf of any process that holds an auxiliary right for an object of that type. Therefore, the rights held by an object manager are independent of and normally exceed the rights held by the subjects that access the object. However, an object manager is not a universally trustworthy procedure because it is not allowed to act on other types of objects and cannot extend its rights to any other procedure.

***Rights Revocation.*** In a security system based on ACLs, revocation of rights is easy because for a given object it is possible to easily and efficiently determine which subjects have what rights for the object. However, in a security system based on capabilities, revocation of rights is a much more difficult problem because for a given object it is difficult to determine which subjects have what rights for the object. This is because the capabilities for an object may be stored in several capability lists that are distributed throughout the system, and we must first find them before we can revoke them. Some commonly used methods for implementing revocation for capabilities are described below.

1. *Back pointers.* One way is to keep track of all the capabilities for an object and to change/delete them selectively depending on the desired revocation of access rights. A simple method to keep track of all the capabilities for an object is to maintain a list of pointers with the object, pointing to all capabilities associated with the object. This method has been used in the Multics system. The method is quite general but very costly to implement.

2. *Indirection.* Another approach is to use indirect addressing. In this method each capability points to an indirect object (such as a table entry) rather than to the object itself. The indirect object in turn points to the real object. Revocation is implemented by deleting the indirect object to break the connection between the real object and the capabilities for it. When an access is attempted with a capability whose indirect object has been deleted,

access operation fails because the real object is unknown due to the broken connection. A drawback of this method is that it does not allow selective revocation.

3. *Use of keys*. In this method, in addition to the object identifier and rights information fields, each capability has a field that contains a unique bit pattern. The contents of this field is called a "key." A capability's key is defined when the capability is created and it cannot be modified or inspected by a process owning that capability. Each object has a *master key* associated with it that can be dynamically defined or changed with a special *set_key* operation. Normally, only the owner of an object is given the right to invoke the *set_key* operation for changing the master key of the object.

When a new capability for an object is created, the key field of the capability is set to the current master key for the object. When an access is attempted with a capability, the capability's key is compared to the master key of the corresponding object. If the two keys match, access to the object is allowed; otherwise, a protection violation occurs. Revocation involves replacement of the master key with a new value by using the *set_key* operation, invalidating all previous capabilities for this object.

This revocation scheme is used in Amoeba, in which random numbers are used as keys. A drawback of this scheme is that it does not allow selective revocation, since only one master key is associated with each object. However, this drawback can be overcome by associating a list of keys with each object.

### Hybrid Approach

As compared to the capability-based scheme, the scheme based on ACLs is more suited to the implementation of security systems because ACLs correspond directly to the needs of the users. When users create objects, they can specify which domains can access the objects as well as the operations allowed. However, we saw that a security system based on ACLs is normally less efficient than capability-based security systems because of the need to search the access list on every access. To overcome the drawbacks of the two schemes and to combine their advantages, most systems use a hybrid approach for designing their security system.

In the hybrid approach, both ACLs and capabilities are employed along with the concept of a session. A *session* is a logical concept of a period during which a process accesses an object. When a process first tries to start a session for accessing an object, it specifies the access modes (types of operations) that it may perform on the object during the session. The ACL of the object is searched for the types of operations desired. If access is denied, a protection violation occurs. Otherwise, the system creates a new capability for the object and attaches it to the process. After this, all accesses to the object by this process during the session are made using the capability so that an access control check can be performed efficiently. After the session is over, the capability is destroyed.

The UNIX file system employs this scheme, with a session being the period between the *open* and *close* operations of a file by a process. Each file has an associated ACL. When a process opens a file, its ACL is checked for the mode specified in the *open* command. If access in the specified mode is permitted, a new entry is allocated in a file table, the access mode is recorded in this entry, and an index to this entry is returned to the process. All subsequent operations on the file are made by this process by specifying the index into the file table. The entry in the file table points to the file. When the process executes the *close* operation on the file, the session is closed by deleting the file table entry. A new session must be started after this if the process wants to access the same file at some later time.

The file table is maintained by the operating system, so that it cannot be corrupted by the user. Security is ensured because access is validated at the time a session is started and a process can access only those files for which a session has been started but not yet closed.

## 11.6 DIGITAL SIGNATURES

Message integrity, which guarantees that the contents of a message were not changed when it was in transfer, is also an important security requirement in a distributed system. The concept of digital signature, which is based upon asymmetric cryptosystems, is the most commonly used method to handle this issue.

Recall that in an asymmetric cryptosystem the secret key of a user is known only to that user and no one else. Therefore, the sender of a message can use its secret key for signing the message by encrypting it with the key. That is, the sender can uniquely "seal" the message with his or her own signature (secret key). The sealed message can be sent to anyone with the corresponding public key. Using digital signatures assures the receiver of the message not only that the message content has not been manipulated but also that the message was indeed sent by the claimed sender. Thus, digital signatures are applicable to both user authentication and message integrity.

A *digital signature* is basically a code, or a large number, that is unique for each message and to each message originator. It is obtained by first processing the message with a hash function (called a *digest function*) to obtain a small digest dependent on each bit of information in the message and then encrypting the digest by using the originator's secret key. To avoid duplicity problems, a digest function ($D$) must have the property that $D(M)$ is different from $D(M')$ for all possible pairs of $M$ and $M'$. Rivest [1992] proposed a message digest function (known as *MD5*) for use in secure mail and other applications on the Internet.

To illustrate how the digest of a message can be obtained from the message, the example given in [Adam 1992] is presented here. In this example, it is assumed that a message is a digital string of 0's and 1's and is divided into blocks of 64 bits. The bitwise Exclusive-OR of the first two blocks is performed to obtain a new block of 64 bits. The newly obtained block is again Exclusive-ORed with the third block of the message, again resulting in a new block of 64 bits. This process is continued one by one with all the other blocks of the message. The end result is a 64-bit digest that depends on each bit of data in the whole message stream. In other words, to alter the message, even by 1 bit, would alter the 64-bit digest. Moreover, it should be essentially impossible to forge a message that would result in the same digest.

A protocol based on a digital signature for ensuring message integrity works as follows:

1. A sender ($A$) computes the digest ($D$) of a message ($M$). It then encrypts the digest $D$ by using its secret key ($S_a$) to obtain a ciphertext $C_1 = E(\text{D}, S_a)$. A signed message is then created that consists of the sender's identifier, the message $M$ in its plaintext form, and the ciphertext $C_1$. The signed message, which has the form ($ID_a$, $C_1$, $M$), is then sent to a receiver.

2. On receiving the signed message, the receiver decrypts $C_1$ by using the public key of the sender to recover the digest $D$. It then calculates a digest for $M$ (by using the same digest function) and compares the calculated digest with the digest recovered by decrypting $C_1$. If the two are equal, message $M$ is considered to be correct; otherwise it is considered incorrect.

Notice that the protocol does not require a message to be hidden from unauthorized users. Rather, it allows a message to be read openly by anyone who receives or intercepts it. But a forged message is successfully detected by the protocol.

An application may require that the first receiver retransmit the signed message to another receiver, which may have to subsequently retransmit it to other receivers. In such a situation, it is important that each of the recipients should be able to verify that the signed message indeed originated from the claimed originator and that its contents were not changed by any of the intermediate recipients or by an intruder. A digitally signed message meets these requirements because it has the originator's identifier included in it and the digest of the message can only be decrypted by using the originator's public key.

In the actual implementation, a key distribution server may be used that maintains a database of the public keys of all users. If the receiver of a digitally signed message does not already have the public key of the message originator, it can request it from the key distribution server. This avoids the need to send a new user's public key to all other user's in the system. The new user's public key can be simply registered with the key distribution server.

*Privacy Enhanced Mail* (*PEM*) scheme, designed for adding privacy to Internet mail applications, is a good example of use of cryptography and digital signature techniques. PEM offers confidentiality, authentication, and message integrity. These features are intended to provide sufficient trust so that the general Internet user population will feel comfortable using the Internet for business correspondence and sending messages that contain sensitive information. PEM is completely implemented at the application level by end systems so that it can be incorporated on a site-by-site or user-by-user basis. This approach imposes no special requirements on message transfer systems at intermediate relay sites or endpoints. That is, network routers and mail relays treat PEM messages as an ordinary piece of mail. How PEM provides privacy to electronic mails is briefly described below. Readers interested in its detail description may refer to [Linn 1993, Kent 1993b, Balenson 1993, Kaliski 1993, Kent 1993a].

PEM assumes that the network is not trusted but that each user of PEM trusts his or her own local computer. Mail users obtain a public/secret key pair from a local PEM program and publish their public keys with their mail addresses. The PEM program maintains a database of the secret keys of its local users and the public keys of remote users. Currently, the Rivest-Shamir-Adleman (RSA) algorithm is used to generate the public/secret key pairs for users. PEM provides the following types of facilities:

1. *Confidentiality.* Sending a message in encrypted form so that sensitive information within it cannot be read by an intruder.
2. *Message integrity.* Sending a signed message so that the receiver can be ensured that the contents of the message were not changed.

Both facilities also possess an authentication feature because the encryption and decryption of the message or the digital signature can only be done by a user having the proper key.

Let us first see how PEM sends a secret message ($M$) for ensuring confidentiality:

1. The PEM program of the sender's computer first generates a random secret key ($K$) and encrypts the message ($M$) by using this key to obtain a ciphertext $C_1 = E(M, K)$. Currently, the DES algorithm is used for this purpose, but others may as well be used in the future. The secret key ($K$) is then encrypted by using the recipient's public key (say, $P_r$) to obtain a ciphertext $C_2 = E(K, P_r)$. Now $C_1$ and $C_2$ are sent to the recipient in a message $m_1$.

2. On receiving $m_1$, the PEM program of the recipient's computer fetches the recipient's secret key ($S_r$) from its database and decrypts $C_2$ by using $S_r$ to obtain $K$. Now by using $K$, it decrypts $C_1$ to obtain the original message $M$, which it then stores in the recipient's mailbox.

Notice that the PEM scheme retains the efficiency of symmetric cryptography for the bulk encryption but avoids the need for a secure key distribution server.

Now let us see how PEM sends a signed message ($M$) for ensuring message integrity:

1. The PEM program of the sender's computer computes the digest ($D$) of the message ($M$) by using a message digest function. The digest ($D$) is then encrypted by using the sender's secret key ($S_s$) to obtain a ciphertext $C_1 = (D, S_s)$. The sender's ID, $C_1$, and $M$ are then sent to the recipient in a message $m_1$.

2. On receiving $m_1$, the PEM program of the recipient's computer fetches the sender's public key ($P_s$) from its database and uses it to decrypt $C_1$ to obtain the digest $D$. It then applies the same message digest function to $M$ and compares the result with $D$. If the two are equal, message $M$ is considered to be correct; otherwise it is considered incorrect. The message $M$ is then stored in the recipient's mailbox with a proper note from the PEM program's side about the result of its integrity check.

## 11.7 DESIGN PRINCIPLES

Based on their experience with Multics, Saltzer, and Schroeder [1975] identified some design principles that can be used as a guide to designing secure systems. Although these design principles were proposed for centralized systems, they hold good for distributed systems as well [Kent 1981]. These and some other design principles are summarized below. Designers of security components of a distributed operating system should use them as basic guidelines.

1. *Least privilege*. The principle of least privilege (also known as the need-to-know principle) states that any process should be given only those access rights that enable it to access, at any time, what it needs to accomplish its function and nothing more and nothing less. That is, the security system must be flexible enough to allow the access rights of a process to grow and shrink with its changing access requirements. This principle serves to limit the damage when a system's security is broken. For example, if an editor is given the right to access only the file that has to be edited, even if the editor has a Trojan horse, it will not be able to access other files of the user and hence cannot do much damage.

2. *Fail-safe defaults*. Access rights should be acquired by explicit permission only and the default should be no access. This principle requires that access control decisions should be based on why an object should be accessible to a process rather than on why it should not be accessible.

3. *Open design*. This principle requires that the design of the security mechanisms should not be secret but should be public. It is a mistake on the part of a designer to assume that the intruders will not know how the security mechanism of the system works.

4. *Built in to the system*. This principle requires that security be designed into the systems at their inception and be built in to the lowest layers of the systems. That is, security should not be treated as an add-on feature because security problems cannot be resolved very effectively by patching the penetration holes detected in an existing system.

5. *Check for current authority*. This principle requires that every access to every object must be checked using an access control database for authority. This is necessary to have immediate effect of revocation of previously given access rights. For instance, in some file systems, a check for access permission is made only when a file is opened and subsequent accesses to the file are allowed without any check. In these systems, a user can keep a file open for several days and continue to have access to its contents, even if the owner of the file changes the access permission and revokes the user's right to access its contents.

6. *Easy granting and revocation of access rights*. For greater flexibility, a security system must allow access rights for an object to be granted or revoked dynamically. It should be possible to restrict some of the rights and to grant to a user only those rights that are sufficient to accomplish its functions. On the other hand, a good security

system should allow immediate revocation with the flexibility of selective and partial revocation. With *selective revocation* facility, it is possible to revoke access rights to an object only from a selected group of users rather than from all users who posses access rights for the object. And with *partial revocation* facility, only a subset of the rights granted to a user for an object can be revoked instead of always revoking all its rights for the object.

7. *Never trust other parties.* For producing a secure distributed system, the system components must be designed with the assumption that other parties (people or programs) are not trustworthy until they are demonstrated to be trustworthy. For example, clients and servers must always be designed to view each other with mutual suspicion.

8. *Always ensure freshness of messages.* To avoid security violations through the replay of messages, the security of a distributed system must be designed to always ensure freshness of messages exchanged between two communicating entities.

9. *Build firewalls.* To limit the damage in case a system's security is compromised, the system must have firewalls built into it. One way to meet this requirement is to allow only short-lived passwords and keys in the system. For example, a shared secret key used to build a logical communication channel between a client and a server should be fairly short-lived, perhaps being changed with every communication session between them.

10. *Efficient.* The security mechanisms used must execute efficiently and be simple to implement.

11. *Convenient to use.* To be psychologically acceptable, the security mechanisms must be convenient to use. Otherwise, they are likely to be bypassed or incorrectly used by the users.

12. *Cost effective.* It is often the case that security needs to be traded off with other goals of the system, such as performance or ease of use. Therefore, in designing the security of a system, it is important to come up with the right set of trade-offs that take into account the likelihood that the system will be compromised with the cost of providing the security, both in terms of money and personnel experience.

## 11.8 CASE STUDY: DCE SECURITY SERVICE

As a case study of how the various security concepts described in this chapter can be integrated to provide security in a single system, the DCE Security Service is briefly described below.

In DCE, a user or a process (client or server) that needs to communicate securely is called a *principal*. For convenience of access control, principals are assigned membership in one or more *groups* and *organizations*. All principals of the same group or organization have the same access rights. Groups generally correspond to work groups or departments, and organizations typically include multiple groups having some common properties. Typically, a principal is a member of one organization but may simultaneously be a member of multiple groups. Each principal has a unique identifier associated with it.

Together, a principal's identifier, group, and organization membership are known as the principal's *privilege attributes*.

The main components of the DCE Security Service for a single cell are shown in Figure 11.21. These components collectively provide authentication, authorization, message integrity, and security administration services. Let us consider these services one by one.

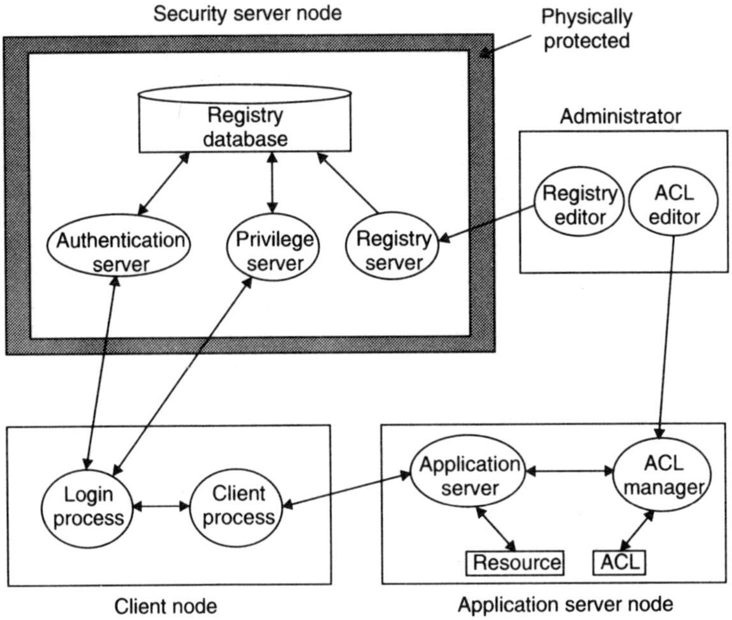


**Fig. 11.21** Main components of DCE Security Service for a single cell.

### 11.8.1 Authentication in DCE

The DCE authentication service uses the Kerberos system described in Section 11.4.5. The authentication server, ticket-granting server, and authentication database of Kerberos are respectively called authentication server, privilege server, and registry database in DCE. The information registered in the registry database includes each principal's secret key and privilege attributes. The protocols for authenticating a user at the time of login and for mutual authentication of a client and a server are the same as that of Kerberos (the intercell client-server authentication protocol in DCE is the same as the interrealm authentication protocol of Kerberos). The only difference is that the service-granting ticket in DCE also contains the group and organization membership information of a client. This information is used by the application server to verify the access rights of the client before providing the requested service.

The establishment of a secure logical communication channel between a client and a server by using the authentication protocol is known as *authenticated RPC* in DCE. This is because in DCE clients and servers communicate by using RPCs. Once authenticated RPC has been established, it is up to the client and the server to determine how much security is desired. That is, subsequent RPC messages may or may not be encrypted depending on the security needs of the application.

### 11.8.2 Authorization in DCE

Authorization in DCE is based on ACLs. Associated with each application server is an ACL and an ACL manager. The ACL contains complete information about which principals have what rights for the resources managed by the server. When a client's request comes to the server, it extracts the client's ID and its group and organization membership information from the received encrypted ticket. It then passes the client's ID, membership, and the operation desired to the ACL manager. Using this information, the ACL manager checks the ACL to make a decision if the client is authorized to perform the requested operation. It returns an access granted or denied reply to the server, after which the server acts accordingly.

Note that in DCE groups are effective only within cells. Therefore, a principal belonging to a different cell can be granted access based solely on its unique identifier, not on group membership. That is, if access is to be granted to principals of remote cells, their unique identifiers have to be entered in the ACL along with the access rights.

### 11.8.3 Message Integrity in DCE

As already mentioned above, once authenticated RPC has been established, it is up to the client and server to determine how much security is desired. Therefore, if message integrity is desired, it can be ensured by the use of a digital signature technique. That is, applications can ensure data integrity by including an encrypted digest of the message data passed between clients and servers. The digest must be encrypted and decrypted by using the session key that a client and a server share for secure communication between them.

### 11.8.4 Security Administration in DCE

The administrator, registry server, and ACL manager jointly perform security administration tasks. Two programs are used by the administrator for performing administration tasks. One is the registry editor program and the other is the ACL editor program.

The registry editor program may be used by the system administrator to view, add, delete, and modify information in the registry database. Even system administrators do not have direct access to the registry database, and they access the registry database only by making requests to the registry server. This is much safer, for although an administrator can change any password, he or she cannot obtain the password of any user.

On the other hand, the ACL editor program may be used by an application administrator to view, add, delete, and modify entries in ACLs for applications or ACLs for objects (resources) controlled by them. Once again, all requests for updates to ACLs are sent to the ACL manager and not performed directly on ACLs.

In DCE, system administrators use organization membership to apply global security policies, such as deciding the lifetime of tickets and passwords of different principals. For example, the lifetime of tickets and passwords is kept smaller for principals of an organization that handles highly sensitive information as compared to the lifetime of tickets and passwords of principals of an organization that does not handle sensitive information.

## 11.9 SUMMARY

Computer security deals with protecting the various resources and information of a computer system against destruction and unauthorized access. The main goals of computer security are secrecy, privacy, authenticity, and integrity.

A total approach to computer security involves both external and internal security. The three main aspects of internal security in distributed systems are authentication, access control, and communication security.

An intruder is a person or program that tries to obtain unauthorized access to data or a resource of a computer system. An intruder may be a threat to computer security in many ways that are broadly classified into two categories—passive attacks and active attacks. In passive attacks, an intruder somehow tries to steal unauthorized information from the computer system without interfering with the normal functioning of the system. Some commonly used methods of passive attack are browsing, leaking, inferencing, and masquerading. On the other hand, active attacks interfere with the normal functioning of the system and often have damaging effects. Some commonly used forms of active attacks are viruses, worms, and logic bombs. Active attacks associated with message communications are integrity attack, authenticity attack, denial attack, delay attack, and replay attack.

Three kinds of channels that can be used by a program to leak information are legitimate channels, storage channels, and convert channels. The confinement problem deals with the problem of eliminating every means by which an authorized subject can release any information contained in the object to which it has access to some subjects that are not authorized to access that information. The confinement problem is in general unsolvable.

Cryptography is a means of protecting private information against unauthorized access in those situations where it is difficult to provide physical security. There are two broad classes of cryptosystems—symmetric and asymmetric. When cryptography is employed for secure communications in distributed systems, a need for key distribution arises. The mechanisms and protocols for key distribution in symmetric and asymmetric cryptosystems have been described in the chapter.

An authentication mechanism prohibits the use of the system (or some resource of the system) by unauthorized users by verifying the identity of a user making a request. The main types of authentication normally needed in a distributed system are user login authentication, one-way authentication of communicating entities, and two-way authentication of communicating entities. The three basic approaches to authentication are proof by knowledge, proof by possession, and proof by property. The proof-by-knowledge method based on passwords is the most widely used method for user login authentication. For one-way and two-way authentication of communicating entities, the protocols based on cryptosystems have been described in the chapter. The Kerberos authentication system has also been described as a case study.

Access control deals with the ways that are used in a computer system to prohibit a user (or a process) from accessing those resources/information that he or she is not authorized to access. The three access control models proposed in the literature are the access matrix model, the information flow control model, and the security kernel model. Of these, the access matrix model is the most popular one and is widely used in existing centralized and distributed systems.

In the access matrix model, the access rights of each subject to each object are defined as entries in a matrix, called the access matrix. The two most widely used methods that have gained popularity in contemporary distributed systems for implementing an access matrix are ACLs and capabilities.

The concept of digital signatures, which is based upon asymmetric cryptosystems, is the most commonly used method to handle the issue of message integrity in distributed systems.

Some design principles that can be used as a guide to designing secure systems are least privilege, fail-safe defaults, open design, security built in to the system, checking for current authority, easy to grant and revoke access rights, not to trust other parties, always ensuring freshness of messages, building of firewalls, cost effective, efficient, convenient to use, and right set of trade-offs.

## EXERCISES

**11.1.** List some of the common goals of computer security.

**11.2.** What are the additional security problems that a distributed operating system designer must deal with as compared to the designer of an operating system for a centralized time-sharing system? Can we ensure the same degree of security in a distributed system as we have in a centralized time-sharing system? Give reasons for your answer.

**11.3.** What is the "need-to-know" principle in computer security? Think of some security problems that may occur if this principle is not taken care of in the design of the security component of a computer system.

**11.4.** Differentiate between passive and active attacks. Which of the two is more harmful and why?

**11.5.** What are some of the commonly used methods for passive attack? Comment on the relative complexity of each of these methods from the point of view of the following:
(a) An intruder
(b) The designer of a security system

**11.6.** What is a Trojan horse program? Give an example (in pseudocode) of both a passive type and an active type Trojan horse program.

**11.7.** List necessary precautions for preventing a computer system from virus infection. How can an already infected computer system be cured of virus infection? Why is curing of a distributed system from virus infection much more difficult than curing a centralized system?

**11.8.** List the important differences between computer viruses and worms. How do they each reproduce? A security system is to be designed that prevents virus programs from replicating in an uncontrolled manner but allows worm programs to be run. Suggest a suitable security scheme for this.

**11.9.** What are the common types of active attacks associated with message communications in a distributed system? Comment on the relative complexities of these types of attacks from the point of view of the following:
(a) An intruder
(b) The designer of the security system of a distributed system

**11.10.** What is a nonce? Give examples of some items that can be used as a nonce.

**11.11.** What is a confinement problem in computer security? Explain why this problem is in general unsolvable.

**11.12.** List the different types of channels that may be used by a program to leak information. Explain how these channels are used to leak information. Is it possible to totally prevent the leakage of information?

**11.13.** Discuss the relative complexity of designing the security component of a system that allows only data objects to be shared and a system that allows both data objects and program objects to be shared.

**11.14.** What is cryptography? What are some of its common uses in a distributed system?

**11.15.** What are some of the basic requirements that a good cryptosystem must fulfill?

**11.16.** Differentiate among ciphertext-only, known-plaintext, and chosen-plaintext attacks with respect to a cryptosystem.

**11.17.** Explain how symmetric and asymmetric cryptosystems work. Discuss their relative advantages and disadvantages. Which of the two is more suitable for each of the following cases (give reasons for your answer):
(a) Where both encryption and decryption of information are performed by a trusted subsystem
(b) Where different subjects perform the encryption and decryption of information
(c) Where bulk data encryption is involved
(d) For establishing connection between two communicating entities in a distributed system
(e) For exchange of messages between two communicating entities in a distributed system

**11.18.** What is a key distribution problem? How does it differ for symmetric and asymmetric cryptosystems?

**11.19.** Describe two methods for solving the key distribution problem for a symmetric cryptosystem and discuss their relative advantages and disadvantages.

**11.20.** Describe a method for solving the key distribution problem for an asymmetric cryptosystem.

**11.21.** What are the commonly used approaches for user authentication in computer systems? Explain how a user is authenticated in each of these approaches.

**11.22.** Explain the password-based approach for user logins authentication. What are the problems associated with this approach? Suggest solutions to overcome these problems.

**11.23.** In a distributed system it is desired that a server process should serve any client that needs its service only after verifying the identity of the client. Describe how to implement this authentication requirement.

**11.24.** In the preceding exercise, suppose that both the client and the server should verify each other's authenticity before a communication session can be started between them. Describe how to implement this authentication requirement.

**11.25.** The password mechanism is used in a distributed system to authenticate users at login time. State the most suitable locations (according to you) for storing the login program and the password file in the following cases:

(a) The distributed system is based on the workstation-server model with each workstation having a small hard disk of about 20 megabytes capacity.

(b) The distributed system is based on the workstation-server model. Some of the workstations are diskless and others have a small hard disk of about 20 megabytes capacity.

(c) The distributed system is based on the processor-pool model.

Assume that any user is free to use any of the user terminals or workstations.

**11.26.** What is an access matrix? Explain how the following issues can be handled in a security system that uses access matrix for access control:

(a) Deciding the contents of the access matrix entries

(b) Validating access to objects by subjects

(c) Allowing subjects to switch domains in a controlled manner

**11.27.** What are the commonly used methods for implementing an access matrix? Explain their relative advantages and disadvantages.

**11.28.** What is a domain? State three different ways in which domains can be realized in the design of the security component of an operating system and explain how domain switching will be done in each case. Explain how domains are formed and how domain switching takes place in UNIX and Multics operating systems.

**11.29.** What is a capability? Answer the following questions for a capability-based security system:

(a) When a subject accesses an object, how is the validation check made whether the subject is allowed to access the object in the requested mode?

(b) How does a subject get a capability for an object? Consider both the case in which the subject is the owner of the object and another one in which the subject is not the owner of the object.

(c) The owner of an object wants to share the object with another subject allowing it restricted access rights to the object. How can this be made possible?

(d) How can it be ensured that a capability is never reused for identifying some other object in the system?

(e) How can capabilities be protected against unauthorized access?

(f) How can capabilities be made difficult to guess?

(g) How can capabilities be made difficult to forge?

(h) How can selective revocation of capabilities be performed?

**11.30.** Answer the following questions for an ACL-based security system:

(a) When a subject accesses an object, how is the validation check made whether the subject is allowed to access the object in the requested mode?

(b) How is access right for an object granted to a subject?

(c) The owner of an object wants to share the object with another subject allowing it restricted access rights to the object. How can this be made possible?

(d) How are ACLs protected against user tampering?

(e) How can an access right given to a subject be revoked?

**11.31.** In a distributed system, it is desired that servers should check the access right of clients for every access request made. Explain how can this be implemented by using the following:

(a) Only ACLs

(b) Only capabilities

(c) Both ACLs and capabilities

Which approach is preferable and why?

**11.32.** A distributed operating system uses the ACL-based access control mechanism but does not use the negative rights concept. What type of access control activity is difficult to perform in this system? Why is this difficulty not faced in a centralized system that uses the ACL-based access control mechanism?

**11.33.** A system has a large number of users. In this system, it is desired that a file be accessible to all except five users. Describe how this security requirement can be specified:

(a) If the system uses the ACL-based security scheme without negative rights facility

(b) If the system uses the ACL-based security scheme with negative rights facility

(c) If the system uses the capability-based security scheme

**11.34.** What is a digital signature? What are its uses in the security of a distributed system? Give a method to create a digital signature. Describe how digital signature can be used for ensuring message integrity in a distributed system.

**11.35.** What are the important design principles that should normally be used as a guideline to designing secure computer systems? Explain why these design principles are important.

## BIBLIOGRAPHY

**[Abrams et al. 1995]** Abrams, M. D., Podell, H. J., and Jajodia, S. (Eds.), *Information Security: An Integrated Collection of Essays*, IEEE Computer Society Press, Los Alamitos, CA (1995).

**[Adam 1992]** Adam, J. A., "Cryptography = privacy," *IEEE Spectrum*, pp. 29–35 (August 1992).

**[Akl 1983]** Akl, S. G., "Digital Signatures: A Tutorial Survey," *IEEE Computer*, Vol. 16, No. 2, pp. 15–24 (1983).

**[Ames et al. 1983]** Ames, S. R., Gasser, M., and Schell, R. R., "Security Kernel Design and Implementation: An Introduction," *IEEE Computer*, Vol. 16, No. 7, pp. 14–22 (1983).

**[Amoroso 1994]** Amoroso, E., *Fundamentals of Computer Security Technology*, Prentice-Hall, Englewood Cliffs, NJ (1994).

**[Anderson 1994]** Anderson, R. J., "Why Cryptosystems Fail," *Communications of the ACM*, Vol. 37, No. 11, pp. 32–40 (1994).

**[Balenson 1993]** Balenson, D. M., "Privacy Enhancement for Internet Electronic Mail. Algorithms, Modes, and Identifiers," Internet RFC 1423 (Part 3) (1993).

**[Bauer et al. 1983]** Bauer, R. K., Berson, T. A., and Feirtag, R. J., "A Key Distribution Protocol Using Event Markers," *ACM Transactions on Computer Systems*, Vol. 1, No. 3, pp. 249–255 (1983).

**[Bell and LaPadula 1973]** Bell, D. E., and LaPadula, L. J., "Secure Computer Systems: Mathematical Foundations," ESD-TR-278, 1, ESD/AFSC, Hanscom AFB, Bedford, MA (1973).

**[Bellovin and Cheswick 1994]** Bellovin, S. M., and Cheswick, W. R., "Network Firewalls," *IEEE Communications Magazine*, pp. 50–57 (September 1994).

**[Bellovin and Merritt 1990]** Bellovin, S. M., and Merritt, M., "Limitations of the Kerberos Authentication System," *ACM Computer Communications Review*, Vol. 20, No. 5, pp. 119–132 (1990).

**[Bowles and Pelaez 1992]** Bowles, J. B., and Pelaez, C. E., "Bad Code," *IEEE Spectrum*, pp. 36–40 (August 1992).

**[Bright 1977]** Bright, H. S., "Cryptanalytic Attack and Defense: Ciphertext-Only, Known-Plaintext, Chosen-Plaintext," *Cryptologia*, Vol. 1, No. 4, pp. 366–370 (1977).

**[Brown 1994]** Brown, P. W., "Digital Signatures: Are They Legal for Electronic Commerce?" *IEEE Communications Magazine*, pp. 76–80 (September 1994).

**[Burrows et al. 1990]** Burrows, M., Abadi, M., and Needham, R. M., "A Logic of Authentication," *ACM Transactions on Computer Systems*, Vol. 8, No. 1, pp. 18–36 (1990).

**[Champine et al. 1990]** Champine, G. A., Geer, Jr., D. E., and Ruh, W. N., "Project Athena as a Distributed Computer System," *IEEE Computer*, Vol. 23, No. 9, pp. 40–51 (1990).

**[Chess 1989]** Chess, D. M., "Computer Viruses and Related Threats to Computer and Network Integrity," *Computer Networks and ISDN Systems*, Vol. 17, pp. 141–148 (1989).

**[Clark and Hoffman 1994]** Clark, P. C., and Hoffman, L. J., "BITS: A Smartcard Protected Operating System," *Communications of the ACM*, Vol. 37, No. 11, pp. 66–70 (1994).

**[Cohen 1987]** Cohen, F., "Computer Viruses: Theory and Experiments," *Computers and Security*, Vol. 6, pp. 22–35 (1987).

**[Cohen and Jefferson 1975]** Cohen, E., and Jefferson, D., "Protection in the Hydra Operating System," In: *Proceedings of the 5h ACM Symposium on Operating Systems Principles*, Association for Computing Machinery, New York, NY, pp. 141–160 (November 1975).

**[Dannenberg and Hibbard 1985]** Dannenberg, R. B., and Hibbard, P. G., "A Butler Process for Resource Sharing on Spice Machines," *ACM Transactions on Office Information Systems*, Vol. 3, No. 3, pp. 234–252 (1985).

**[Denning 1976]** Denning, D. E., "A Lattice Model for Secure Information Flow," *Communications of the ACM*, Vol. 19, No. 5, pp. 236–243 (1976).

**[Denning and Sacco 1981]** Denning, D. E., and Sacco, G. M., "Timestamps in Key Distribution Protocols," *Communications of the ACM*, Vol. 24, No. 8, pp. 533–536 (1981).

**[Dolev and Yao 1983]** Dolev, D., and Yao, A. C., "On the Security of Public Key Protocols," *IEEE Transactions on Information Theory*, Vol. IT-30, No. 2, pp. 198–208 (1983).

**[Ganesan and Sandhu 1994]** Ganesan, R., and Sandhu, R., "Securing Cyberspace," *Communications of the ACM*, Vol. 37, No. 11, pp. 29–31 (1994).

**[Glasgow et al. 1992]** Glasgow, J., McEwan, G., and Pananageden, P., "A Logic for Reasoning about Security," *ACM Transactions on Computer Systems*, Vol. 10, No. 3, pp. 265–310 (1992).

**[Graham and Denning 1972]** Graham, G. S., and Denning, P. J., "Protection—Principles and Practice," In: *AFIPS Proceedings of the Spring Joint Computer Conference*, Vol. 40, pp. 417–429 (1972).

**[Harrison et al. 1976]** Harrison, M. A., Ruzzo, W. L., and Ullman, J. D., "Protection in Operating Systems," *Communications of the ACM*, Vol. 19, No. 8, pp. 461–471 (1976).

**[Hellman 1978]** Hellman, M. E., "An Overview of Public-Key Cryptography," *IEEE Transactions on Computers*, Vol. C-16, No. 6, pp. 24–32 (1978).

**[Hendry 1995]** Hendry, M., *Practical Computer Network Security*, Artech House, Boston, MA (1995).

**[Hruska 1993]** Hruska, J., *Computer Viruses and Anti-Virus Warfare*, 2nd ed., Prentice-Hall, Englewood Cliffs, NJ (1993).

**[Hu 1995]** Hu, W., *DCE Security Programming*, O'Reilly, Sebastopol, CA (1995).

**[Hutt et al. 1995]** Hutt, A. E., Bosworth, S., and Hoyt, D. B. (Eds.), *Computer Security Handbook*, 3rd ed., Wiley, New York, NY (1995).

**[Kak 1983]** Kak, S. C., "Data Security in Computer Networks," *IEEE Computer*, Vol. 16, No. 2, pp. 8–10 (1983).

**[Kaliski 1993]** Kaliski, B. S., "Privacy Enhancement for Internet Electronic Mail. Key Certification and Related Services," Internet RFC 1424 (Part 4) (1993).

**[Kehne et al. 1992]** Kehne, A., Schonwalder, J., and Langendorfer, H., "A Nonce-Based Protocol for Multiple Authentications," *ACM Operating System Review*, Vol. 26, No. 4, pp. 84–89 (1992).

**[Kent 1981]** Kent, S. T., "Security in Computer Networks," *Protocols and Techniques for Data Communication Networks*, Prentice-Hall, Englewood Cliffs, NJ, pp. 369–432 (1981).

**[Kent 1993a]** Kent, S. T., "Internet Privacy Enhanced Mail," *Communications of the ACM*, Vol. 36, No. 8, pp. 48–60 (1993).

**[Kent 1993b]** Kent, S. T., "Privacy Enhancement for Internet Electronic Mail. Certificate Based Key Management," Internet RFC 1422 (Part 2) (1993).

**[Khanna 1994]** Khanna, R. (Ed.), *Distributed Computing: Implementation and Management Strategies*, Prentice-Hall, Englewood Cliffs, NJ (1994).

**[Kluepfel 1994]** Kluepfel, H. M., "Securing a Global Village and Its Resources," *IEEE Communications Magazine*, pp. 82–89 (September 1994).

**[Lampson 1971]** Lampson, B. W., "Protection," In: *Proceedings of the 5th Princeton Symposium on Information Sciences and Systems*, Princeton University, Princeton, NJ, pp. 437–443 (March 1971).

**[Lampson 1973]** Lampson, B. W., "A Note on the Confinement Problem," *Communications of the ACM*, Vol. 6, No. 10, pp. 613–615 (1973).

**[Lampson 1993]** Lampson, B. W., "Authentication in Distributed Systems," In: S. Mullender (Ed.), *Distributed Systems*, 2nd ed., Association for Computing Machinery, New York, NY, pp. 543–580 (1993).

**[Lampson et al. 1992]** Lampson, B. W., Abadi, M., Burrows, M., and Wobber, E., "Authentication in Distributed Systems: Theory and Practice," *ACM Transactions on Computer Systems*, Vol. 10, No. 4, pp. 265–310 (1992).

**[Levine 1986]** Levine, P., "The Apollo Domain Distributed File System," *Distributed Operating Systems: Theory and Practice*, NATO Advanced Study Institute, Turkey, Springer-Verlag, New York, NY (1986).

**[Linn 1993]** Linn, J., "Privacy Enhancement for Internet Electronic Mail. Message Encipherment and Authentication Procedures," Internet RFC 1421 (Part 1) (1993).

**[Lockhart, Jr. 1994]** Lockhart, Jr., H. W., *OSF DCE: Guide to Developing Distributed Applications*, IEEE Computer Society Press, Los Alamitos, CA (1994).

**[Milenkovic 1992]** Milenkovic, M., *Operating Systems: Concepts and Design*, 2nd ed., McGraw-Hill, New York, NY (1992).

**[Mitchell et al. 1992]** Mitchell, C. J., Piper, F., and Wild, P., "Digital Signatures," In: G. J. Simmons (Ed.), *Contemporary Cryptology*, IEEE, New York, NY (1992).

**[Morris and Thompson 1979]** Morris, M., and Thompson, K., "Password Security: A Case History," *Communications of the ACM*, Vol. 22, No. 11, pp. 594–597 (1979).

**[Mullender 1985]** Mullender, S. J., "Principles of Distributed Operating System Design," Ph.D. Dissertation, Mathematisch Centrum, Amsterdam (1985).

**[Mullender and Tanenbaum 1984]** Mullender, S. J., and Tanenbaum, A. S., "Protection and Resource Control in Distributed Operating Systems," *Computer Networks*, Vol. 8, pp. 421–432 (1984).

**[Mullender and Tanenbaum 1986]** Mullender, S. J., and Tanenbaum, A. S., "The Design of a Capability-Based Distributed Operating System," *Computer Journal*, Vol. 29, No. 4, pp. 289–300 (1986).

**[NBS 1977]** National Bureau of Standards, *Federal Information Processing Standards*, Publ. p. 46, Washington, DC (1977).

**[Needham 1993]** Needham, R. M., "Cryptography and Secure Channels," In: S. Mullender (Ed.), *Distributed Systems*, 2nd ed., Association for Computing Machinery, New York, NY, pp. 531–541 (1993).

**[Needham 1994]** Needham, R. M., "Denial of Service: An Example," *Communications of the ACM*, Vol. 37, No. 11, pp. 42–46 (1994).

**[Needham and Schroeder 1978]** Needham, R. M., and Schroeder, M. D., "Using Encryption for Authentication in Large Networks of Computers," *Communications of the ACM*, Vol. 21, No. 12, pp. 993–999 (1978).

**[Needham and Schroeder 1987]** Needham, R. M., and Schroeder, M. D., "Authentication Revisited," *ACM Operating System Review*, Vol. 21, No. 1, p. 7 (1987).

**[Nessett 1983]** Nessett, D. M., "A Systematic Methodology for Analyzing Security Threats to Interprocess Communication in a Distributed System," *IEEE Transactions on Communications*, Vol. COM-31, pp. 1055–1063 (1983).

**[Nessett 1987]** Nessett, D. M., "Factors Affecting Distributed System Security," *IEEE Transactions on Software Engineering*, Vol. SE-13, No. 2, pp. 233–248 (1987).

**[Neuman and Theodore 1994]** Neuman, B. C., and Theodore, T., "Kerberos: An Authentication Service for Computer Networks," *IEEE Communications Magazine*, pp. 33–38 (September 1994).

**[Otway and Rees 1987]** Otway, D., and Rees, O., "Efficient and Timely Mutual Authentication," *ACM Operating System Review*, Vol. 21, No. 1, pp. 8–10 (1987).

**[Pfleeger 1989]** Pfleeger, C. P., *Security in Computing*, Prentice-Hall, Englewood Cliffs, NJ (1989).

**[Rashid and Robertson 1981]** Rashid, R. F., and Robertson, G. G., "Accent: A Communication Oriented Network Operating System Kernel," In: *Proceedings of the 8h ACM Symposium on Operating Systems Principles*, Association for Computing Machinery, New York, NY (1981).

**[Rivest 1992]** Rivest, R. L., "The MD5 Message-Digest Algorithm," Technical Report RFC 1321, available for anonymous ftp from the Internet Network Information Center, Internet host: nic.ddn.mil, directory/usr/pub/RFC (1992).

**[Rivest et al. 1978]** Rivest, R. L., Shamir, A., and Adleman, L. M., "A Method for Obtaining Digital Signatures and Public-Key Cryptosystems," *Communications of the ACM*, Vol. 21, No. 2, pp. 120–126 (1978).

**[Rosenberry et al. 1992]** Rosenberry, W., Kenney, D., and Fisher, G.,' *OSF DISTRIBUTED COMPUTING ENVIRONMENT, Understanding DCE*, O'Reilly, Sebastopol, CA (1992).

**[Rushby and Randell 1983]** Rushby, J. M., and Randell, B., "A Distributed Secure System," *IEEE Computer*, Vol. 16, No. 7, pp. 55–67 (1983).

**[Saltzer and Schroeder 1975]** Saltzer, J. H., and Schroeder, M. N., "The Protection of Information in Computer Systems," In: *Proceedings of the IEEE*, Vol. 63, pp. 1278–1308 (1975).

**[Sandhu and Samarati 1994]** Sandhu, R. S., and Samarati, P., "Access Control: Principles and Practice," *IEEE Communications Magazine*, pp. 40–48 (September 1994).

**[Sansom et al. 1986]** Sansom, R. D., Julin, D. P., and Rashid, R. F., "Extending a Capability Based System into a Network Environment," Technical Report No. CMU-CS-86-115, Computer Science Department, Carnegie-Mellon University, Pittsburgh, PA (1986).

**[Satyanarayanan 1989]** Satyanarayanan, M., "Integrating Security in a Large Distributed System," *ACM Transactions on Computer Systems*, Vol. 7, No. 3, pp. 247–280 (1989).

**[Satyanarayanan 1990]** Satyanarayanan, M., "Scalable, Secure, and Highly Available Distributed File Access," *IEEE Computer*, Vol. 23, No. 5, pp. 9–21 (1990).

**[Schneier 1996]** Schneier, B., *Applied Cryptography: Protocols, Algorithms, and Source Code in C*, 2nd ed., Wiley, New York, NY (1996).

**[Schroeder et al. 1977]** Schroeder, M. D., Clark, D. D., and Saltzer, J. H., "The MULTICS Kernel Design Project," In: *Proceedings of the 6th ACM Symposium on Operating Systems Principles*, Association for Computing Machinery, New York, NY, pp. 43–56 (November 1977).

**[Seberry and Pieprzyk 1989]** Seberry, J., and Pieprzyk, J., *Cryptography: An Introduction to Computer Security*, Prentice-Hall, Englewood Cliffs, NJ (1989).

**[Shankar 1977]** Shankar, K. S., "The Total Computer Security Problem: An Overview," *IEEE Computer*, Vol. 10, pp. 50–62, 71–73 (1977).

**[Silberschatz and Galvin 1994]** Silberschatz, A., and Galvin, P. B., *Operating System Concepts*, 4th ed., Addison-Wesley, Reading, MA (1994).

**[Simmons 1992]** Simmons, G. J. (Ed.), *Contemporary Cryptology*, IEEE, New York (1992).

**[Simmons 1994]** Simmons, G. J., "Cryptanalysis and Protocol Failures," *Communications of the ACM*, Vol. 37, No. 11, pp. 56–65 (1994).

**[Singhal and Shivaratri 1994]** Singhal, M., and Shivaratri, N. G., *Advanced Concepts in Operating Systems*, McGraw-Hill, New York (1994).

**[Skardhamar 1996]** Skardhamar, R., *Virus Detection and Elimination*, Academic Press, San Diego, CA (1996).

**[Smart 1994]** Smart, R. K., "The X.509 Extended File System," In: *Proceedings of the ISOC Symposium on Network and Distributed System Security*, Internet Society, Reston, VA (February 1994).

**[Stallings 1994]** Stallings, W., "Kerberos Keeps the Enterprise Secure," *Data Communications Magazine*, pp. 103–111 (October 1994).

**[Stallings 1995]** Stallings, W., *Network and Internetwork Security: Principles and Practice*, Prentice-Hall, Englewood Cliffs, NJ (1995).

**[Stallings 1996]** Stallings, W. (Ed.), *Practical Cryptography for Data Internetworks*, IEEE Computer Society Press, Los Alamitos, CA (1996).

**[Steiner et al. 1988]** Steiner, J. G., Neuman, B. C., and Schiller, J. I., "Kerberos: An Authentication Service for Open Network Systems," In: *Proceedings of the Winter 1988 USENIX Conference*, USENIX, Berkeley, CA, pp. 191–202 (February 1988).

**[Tardo and Alagappan 1991]** Tardo, J. J., and Alagappan, K., "SPX: Global Authentication Using Public Key Certificates," In: *Proceedings of the IEEE Symposium on Research in Security and Privacy*, IEEE Press, New York, NY, pp. 232–244 (1991).

**[Tanenbaum 1987]** Tanenbaum, A. S., *Operating Systems: Design and Implementation*, Prentice-Hall, Englewood Cliffs, NJ (1987).

**[Tanenbaum 1992]** Tanenbaum, A. S., *Modern Operating Systems*, Prentice-Hall, Englewood Cliffs, NJ (1992).

**[Tanenbaum et al. 1986]** Tanenbaum, A. S., Mullender, S. J., and van Renesse, R., "Using Sparse Capabilities in a Distributed Operating System," In: *Proceedings of the 6th International Conference on Distributed Computing Systems*, IEEE Press, New York, NY, pp. 558–563 (May 1986).

**[Tsai et al. 1990]** Tsai, C., Gligor, V. D., and Chandersekaran, C. S., "On the Identification of Covert Storage Channels in Secure Systems," *IEEE Transactions on Software Engineering*, Vol. SE-16, No. 6, pp. 569–580 (1990).

**[White et al. 1996]** White, G. B., Fisch, E. A., and Pooch, U. W., *Computer System and Network Security*, CRC, Boca Raton, FL (1996).

**[Wobber et al. 1994]** Wobber, E., Abadi, M., Burrows, M., and Lampson, B., "Authentication in the Taos Operating System," *ACM Transactions on Computer Systems*, Vol. 12, pp. 3–32 (1994).

**[Woo and Lam 1992]** Woo, T. Y. C., and Lam, S. S., "Authentication for Distributed Systems," *IEEE Computer*, Vol. 25, No. 1, pp. 39–52 (1992).

**[Worm 1989]** "Special Section on the Internet Worm," *Communications of the ACM*, Vol. 32, No. 6, pp. 677–710 (1989).

## POINTERS TO BIBLIOGRAPHIES ON THE INTERNET

Bibliographies containing references on *Computer Security* can be found at:

ftp:ftp.cs.umanitoba.ca/pub/bibliographies/Misc/security.html

ftp:ftp.cs.umanitoba.ca/pub/bibliographies/Misc/security.1.html

ftp:ftp.cs.umanitoba.ca/pub/bibliographies/Misc/security.2.html

http:julmara.ce.chalmers.se/Security/sec_bib.html

http:www.telstra.com.au/pub/docs/security

A list of books on *Security in Computer Networks* can be found at:

http:www.crpht.lu/CNS/html/PubServ/Security/bibliography.html

Bibliography containing references on *Cryptography* can be found at:

http:mnementh.cs.adfa.oz.au/htbin/bib_lpb

(This is a gateway to the index into Lawries Cryptography Bibliography, which contains references on various aspects of cryptography and computer security.)

An index of bibliographies containing references on *Cryptography, Internet Security,* and *Kerberos* can be found at:

http:www.comp.vuw.ac.nz/~sai/docs

COAST (Computer Operations, Audit, and Security Technology) is a multiple project, multiple investigator laboratory in computer security research in the Computer Science Department at Purdue University. A list of documents on various COAST projects, and some other security-related papers by COAST personnel can be found at:

http:www.cs.purdue.edu/coast/coast-library.html

# CHAPTER 12

# Case Studies

## 12.1 INTRODUCTION

This chapter aims to consolidate the reader's understanding of the various concepts described in the preceding chapters of this book by describing real distributed operating systems. The systems described are Amoeba, V-System, Mach, and Chorus. The first two are university research projects. The latter two also started as research projects but have now been commercialized. These systems are still in various stages of development and refinement. Therefore, an exhaustive and detailed description of each system has not been presented. For each system, only the design goals, system architectures, and most important and noteworthy aspects and features have been highlighted. Furthermore, the order of presentation is not strictly chronological and does not reflect the relative importance of the systems. The bibliography provides references for several other systems that may be of interest to researchers performing research activities in the area of distributed operating systems.

## 12.2 AMOEBA

Amoeba is a microkernel-based distributed operating system developed at Vrije University and the Center for Mathematics and Computer Science in Amsterdam, The Netherlands. It was started in 1981 by Andrew S. Tanenbaum as a research project in distributed and parallel computing. Since then, it has evolved over the years to acquire several attractive features. The following description of Amoeba is based on [Tanenbaum 1995, Coulouris et al. 1994, Mullender et al. 1990, Mullender and Tanenbaum 1986].

### 12.2.1 Design Goals and Main Features

Amoeba's design was influenced by the research and design goals given below.

#### Transparency

Providing a single-system image to the users was one of the main goals of Amoeba. The most important design decision that was taken to achieve this goal was to use the processor-pool model in which there is no concept of a "home machine" and all resources belong to the system as a whole.

#### Parallel Programming Support

Although transparency is a useful feature for most users of a distributed system, some users are interested in using the system as a testbed for experimenting with distributed and parallel algorithms, languages, tools, and applications. Amoeba supports such users by making the underlying parallelism available to them. For this, the Orca language [Bal et al. 1992] has been designed and implemented on Amoeba.

#### Capability-Based, Object-Oriented Approach

Another major goal of Amoeba was to investigate the possibility of using the capability-based, object-oriented approach for building an operational distributed system. To achieve this goal, objects and capabilities are used in a uniform way in the design of Amoeba. In particular, the Amoeba software is based on objects, and objects are named and protected by using capabilities.

#### Small-Kernel Approach

Another goal in Amoeba's design was to minimize the kernel size and enhance flexibility. To achieve this goal, its design was based on the microkernel approach. That is, in Amoeba, several of the standard services, such as a file service, are built outside the kernel in user space. This helps in enhancing flexibility because these services can be easily modified, and multiple versions of a service can be simultaneously run on the same system to suit the needs of different users.

### High Performance

High performance was also a goal in Amoeba. Three design decisions that were influenced by this goal are the use of the processor-pool model, the use of multithreaded processes, and the use of a bullet file service that stores immutable files as contiguous byte strings both on disk and in its cache.

### High Reliability

Amoeba has also been designed to have a high degree of reliability. The following design decisions helped in improving the overall reliability of the system:

1. *Use of the processor-pool model.* In the processor-pool model, processors can be dynamically added to the pool or removed from the pool. Therefore, when a few processors crash, some jobs may have to be restarted and the computing power of the system is temporarily lowered, but otherwise the system continues to function normally, providing a high degree of fault tolerance.

2. *Support for reliable interprocess communication.* RPC is the basic IPC mechanism in Amoeba. Amoeba's RPC supports at-most-once semantics, so that an RPC is never carried out more than once, even in the face of server crashes and rapid reboots.

3. *Making the directory service reliable.* The directory service, whose primary function is to provide a mapping from human-oriented object names to system-defined capabilities, is a critical component in Amoeba because almost every application depends on it for finding the capabilities it needs. If the directory service stops, everything else will also come to a halt. So that no single-site failure can bring it down, it has been implemented in a fault-tolerant way by using the stable-storage technique.

### UNIX Emulation

Amoeba was developed from scratch rather than starting with an existing system (e.g., UNIX). The motivation behind this design approach was to experiment with new ideas without having to worry about backward compatibility with any existing system. However, the result of this design was that Amoeba's interface turned out to be quite different from that of UNIX. Therefore, to avoid writing hundreds of utility and application programs for Amoeba from scratch, a UNIX emulation package was later added to Amoeba. This package, which is in the form of a library, allows most UNIX programs to run on Amoeba with little or no modification. Further details of UNIX emulation in Amoeba can be found in [Mullender et al. 1990].

### 12.2.2 System Architecture

#### Hardware Architecture

As Figure 12.1 shows, the Amoeba hardware consists of the following principal components:

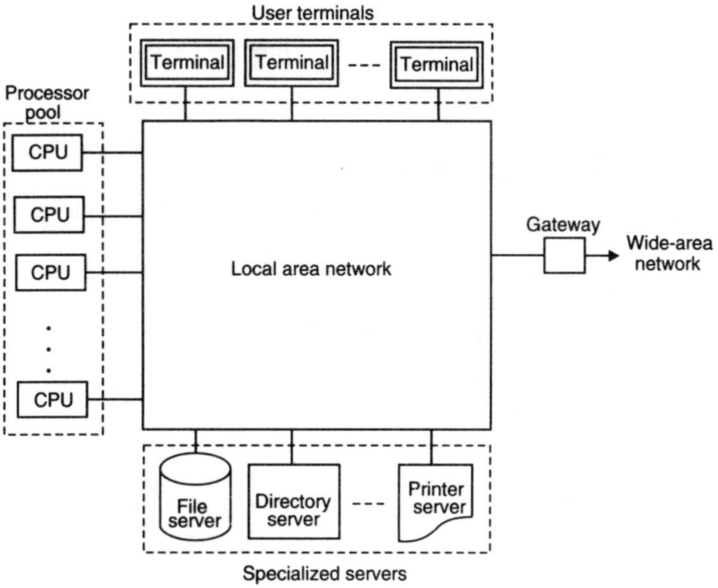


**Fig. 12.1** Hardware architecture of the Amoeba system.

1. *Processor pool.* Amoeba is based on the processor-pool model. An Amoeba system can have one or more processor pools. The CPUs in a pool belong to the system as a whole and have no specific "owners." Therefore, a user does not log on to a specific machine but to the system as a whole. When a user has an application to run, the operating system dynamically allocates one or more CPUs from the pool to that application. When the user's application completes, the CPUs are returned to the pool for allocation to other work. If no CPU is free when a user has an application to run, the CPUs are time shared, and a newly arrived job is assigned to the most lightly loaded CPU at that time. Amoeba has been designed to support heterogeneity. Therefore, the CPUs in a pool can be of different architectures.

2. *Terminals.* Terminals provide an interface to the users for accessing the system resources. A terminal may either be an ordinary X terminal or a personal computer or workstation running X windows. When a personal computer or a workstation is used as a terminal, the processes that require intense user interaction (such as command interpreters and editors) are executed at the terminals. Most applications, however, do not

interact much with the user and are run on one or more of the CPUs of a processor pool.

3. *Specialized servers.* Specialized servers are machines for running dedicated processes with unusual resource demands. For example, it is natural to run a file server process on a machine having one or more disks and a print server process on a machine having one or more printers. The main servers are directory, file, and block servers, database servers, and boot servers.

4. *Gateways.* Gateways are used to link two or more Amoeba systems over wide-area networks into a single, uniform system.

### Software Architecture

The Amoeba software consists of the following principal components:

1. *A microkernel.* The microkernel that runs on all machines of an Amoeba system provides low-level memory management support, manages processes containing multiple threads, supports interprocess communication, and handles low-level I/O.

2. *A collection of servers.* All other services (functions not included in the microkernel) are provided by user-level processes called servers. Servers provide most of the traditional operating system functionality. Servers are typically written by the systems programmers, but users are free to write their own servers if they wish. Some standard servers in Amoeba are the bullet server, which manages files; the directory server, which handles naming of files and other objects; the replication server, which takes care of automatic replication of objects; and the run server, which decides which process should run on which processor. All standard servers have stub procedures in the library. To use a server, a client normally just calls the stub, which marshals the parameters, sends the message, and blocks until the reply comes back. This mechanism hides all the implementation details of a server from its clients.

## 12.2.3 Objects and Their Management

Amoeba is an object-based system in which the entire software is structured as objects. An object is like an abstract data type that consists of some encapsulated data with certain operations defined on it. Amoeba objects are passive in nature. That is, they cannot do anything on their own. Therefore, each object is managed by a server process that performs the operations defined on the objects it manages. Typical examples of objects supported in this manner are files, directories, memory segments, screen windows, processors, disks, and tape drives.

### Object Naming and Protection

Each object in Amoeba is both identified and protected by a capability. As Figure 12.2 shows, a capability in Amoeba is composed of the following fields:

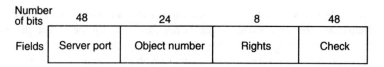

| | | | | |
|---|---|---|---|---|
| Number of bits | 48 | 24 | 8 | 48 |
| Fields | Server port | Object number | Rights | Check |

**Fig. 12.2** An Amoeba capability.

1. *Server port.* This is a 48-bit logical address that identifies the server that manages the object referred to by the capability. In Amoeba, the only way a server can be accessed is via its port. It may be noted here that a server port is a logical address that is associated not with a specific machine but with a particular server (or a set of servers providing the same service). Therefore, when a server is relocated on a new machine, it takes its server port with it. A server can choose its own port address.

2. *Object number.* A server typically manages several objects of the same type. For example, a file server usually manages hundreds of files. The object number field is a 24-bit identifier used by the server to identify the specific object in question from among the objects managed by it. The server port and object number fields together uniquely identify an object in the entire system.

3. *Rights.* This 8-bit field is a bitmap telling which of the allowed operations the holder of this capability can perform on the object identified by the capability. The meaning of this field is different for each object type since the legal operations themselves also vary from one object type to another.

4. *Check.* This field is used for validating the capability. It contains a 48-bit number that is used to protect the capability against forging.

Capabilities are managed entirely by user processes and are protected cryptographically. In particular, to create an object, a client sends a request message to the appropriate server. The server then creates the object and returns a capability to the client. This capability is called the *owner capability*, and all its rights bits are initially on. When creating the capability for the newly created object, the server picks a 48-bit random number and stores it both in the check field of the capability and also in its own internal table. The client must send this capability along with any request for an operation on this object. Before performing the requested operation, the server compares the contents of the check field in the capability with that stored in its internal table for validating the supplied capability.

When the owner of an object wants to pass restricted access rights for the object to other users, it sends a message to the server requesting to create a capability with restricted rights. This message, among other things, contains the owner capability for the object and a bit mask for the new rights. The server EXCLUSIVE-ORs the new rights with the original value of the check field from its internal table and then encrypts the obtained result ($x$) by using a one-way function [$y = f(x)$], which has the property that given $x$ it is easy to find $y$, but given $y$, $x$ can only be found by an exhaustive search of all possible values of $x$. The server then creates a new capability whose server port and object number fields have the same values as the owner capability for the object, the rights field contains the new rights bits, and the check field contains the output of the one-way function. This new capability is returned to the caller, which then sends it to another process for passing to it restricted access rights for the object.

It may be noted here that the capability-based naming scheme of Amoeba is fully location transparent because to perform an operation on an object, it is not necessary to know the location of the object or the location of the server that manages the object. The protocol for talking to a server, whether local or remote, is identical in all cases. Thus a client is entirely concerned with what it wants to do, not where objects are stored and where servers run.

The capability-based protection scheme of Amoeba has the advantage that it requires almost no administrative overhead. However, notice that it is possible to create an object in Amoeba and then lose its capability. Therefore, some mechanism is needed to identify and destroy those objects that are no longer accessible. For this, each server in Amoeba periodically runs a garbage collector, which removes all objects that have not been used in $n$ garbage collection cycles. Furthermore, in an insecure environment, to keep capabilities from getting disclosed to intruders on the network, additional cryptographic measures (e.g., link encryption) will be necessary [Tanenbaum 1995].

### Server-Locating Mechanism

To perform an operation on an object, a client process presents a capability for the object to the system. The system must forward this request to the appropriate server for performing the operation on the object. However, notice that, although the server port field in the capability specifies the server that manages the object, it does not carry any information about the whereabouts of the associated server process. Therefore, a locating mechanism is necessary to find the location of the appropriate server.

The mechanism used in Amoeba for locating a server is based on broadcast queries. That is, for locating a server, a message "where are you" that contains the port address of the server is broadcast on the network. The location of the server is known only after a reply for the broadcast message is received from the server whose port address was contained in the broadcast message. The reply message contains the network address of the server. The kernel doing the broadcasting records the (*port*, *network address*) pair in a cache for future use. Therefore, broadcasting is done only when a server's port is not found in the cache.

### Name Resolution Mechanism

Capabilities are low-level, system-oriented object names. They are hard for people to remember and use. Therefore, objects in Amoeba also have human-oriented ASCII names. The process of mapping a human-oriented object name to its system-oriented name (capability) is known as name resolution. In Amoeba, *directory servers* are used to perform the name resolution operations. Directory servers manage directory objects for this purpose. In its simplest form, a directory is a set of (*ASCII name*, *capability*) pairs.

*Lookup*, *enter*, and *delete* are the three basic operations allowed on directory objects. The first operation looks up an object's ASCII name in a directory and returns its capability. The other two operations are meant for entering and deleting entries from a directory. Since directories themselves are objects, a directory can contain capabilities for other directories, thus allowing users to build hierarchical directory trees and other more general graph structures [Mullender et al. 1990].

The directory-based object-naming scheme of Amoeba is very flexible and can be used to implement sharing of objects in various different ways. For instance, consider the following examples:

1. Different users of a shared object can use their own suitable ASCII names for the object. For this, each user can enter his or her own (*ASCII name*, *capability*) pair in a directory. Note that the (*ASCII name*, *capability*) pairs of different users need not necessarily be entered in the same directory. They can be placed in two or more directories to create multiple links to the object. Moreover, the capabilities for different users may have different rights so that different users have different access permissions for the shared object.

2. Objects shared among a group of users can be stored in a directory whose capability is given only to the group members, making the directory and hence the shared objects accessible only to the group members. In this manner, a directory capability can serve as a capability for many other capabilities [Mullender et al. 1990].

3. Instead of implementing a directory as a two-column table, each row of which is an (*ASCII name*, *capability*) pair, a directory can be implemented as an $(n+1)$-column table with ASCII names in column 0 and capabilities in columns 1 through $n$ [Mullender et al. 1990]. In this generalized model, each of the $n$ capabilities of an object forms a different protection domain, having different access rights for the object. For example, a directory may have one column for the owner capability, one for the owner's group capability, and one for public capability, to simulate the UNIX protection scheme [Mullender et al. 1990].

Amoeba designers felt that the directory service is a critical component in the system because almost all applications depend on it for finding the capabilities they need. If the directory service fails, the entire system will stop functioning. Therefore, in order that no single-site failure can cause the directory service to fail, it has been implemented in a fault-tolerant way. In particular, directory servers come in pairs, each with its own array of capability pairs (on different disks), to prevent loss of information if the disk of one of the directory servers is damaged. The two servers communicate to keep synchronized.

### 12.2.4 Process Management

#### Process Model

A process in Amoeba consists of a segmented virtual address space and one or more threads. Therefore, the process abstraction in Amoeba is realized by three kinds of basic objects—process, segment, and thread. They are briefly described below.

1. *Process*. A process is defined by its state. Each process has a *process descriptor* associated with it that defines its state at any instance of time. The four main parts of a process descriptor are the host descriptor, the capabilities, the segment descriptors, and the thread descriptors.

The host descriptor describes the processor type(s) suitable for running the process and the memory requirements of the process. Processor type(s) can be specified as a particular CPU architecture, a group of CPUs, or a predefined class of CPUs. The process can be run only on a processor whose processor type matches the processor type(s) specified in the process's host descriptor and which has sufficient memory for running the process.

The capabilities part mainly consists of a process capability and a handler capability. Every client manipulating the process must possess the process capability. On the other hand, the handler capability is needed to communicate the exit status of the process to its owner. That is, when the process terminates or is stunned (process states are explained later), the handler capability is used to do an RPC with the owner process to report this event.

The segment descriptors part describes the segments of the process. It has a segment descriptor for each segment in the process's address space. A segment's descriptor contains information such as its virtual address, its length, and its access control.

The thread descriptors part describes the threads of the process. It has a thread descriptor for each thread in the process. Among other things, a thread's descriptor contains the thread's program counter and stack pointer. The exact contents of a thread descriptor is CPU architecture dependent.

2. *Segment*. A segment is a named linear section of memory. A process can have one or more segments. The number of segments can keep changing during the lifetime of the process as it executes.

To create a segment, a process makes a request to the kernel specifying the initial size of the segment and optionally specifying a segment or a file whose contents should be used as an initial value of the segment. The kernel then allocates the necessary amount of memory and returns to the requester a capability for the newly created segment. This capability is used by the requester to perform any subsequent operation on the segment. The initial size of the segment may change during process execution.

System calls are provided to allow processes to create, read, write, map, unmap, and destroy their segments. Of these, the map and unmap operations can be used for various different purposes. For instance, they can be used by a process to add new segments to its address space by mapping them and to remove segments from its address space by unmapping them. An unmapped segment remains in memory (but is not a part of the address space of any process) and can be either read or written like a file or can even be remapped to any part of the same process's address space or to a different process's address space. For this, the unmap operation returns a capability for the segment. Due to this feature, the map and unmap operations can also be used for interprocess communication; the sender process unmaps a segment of its address space and passes the capability returned by the unmap operation to the receiver process, which then maps the segment to its own address space. Finally, these two operations can also be used to allow two or more processes to operate on shared memory by simultaneously mapping a segment into the address spaces of all these processes.

3. *Thread.* A process has one or more threads, all of which share the process's address space. Each thread has its own stack and stack pointer, its own copy of the CPU registers, and its own set of "glocal" variables. A thread's *glocal variables* are global to all its procedures but are not accessible to other threads. Amoeba has library procedures to allow threads to create and use glocal variables.

A process can create new threads and can terminate existing threads as it executes. Hence, the number of threads in a process can keep changing during its lifetime. The parameters to the call for creating a new thread specify the initial procedure to be run and the size of the initial stack.

Threads are managed by the kernel, and a priority-based threads-scheduling scheme is used in which kernel threads have higher priority than user threads.

The three different mechanisms that may be used for threads synchronization are signals, mutex variables, and counting semaphores. Signals are used to send an asynchronous interrupt from one thread to another in the same process. Mutex variables are like binary semaphores, and they have the same purpose as described in Chapter 8. Counting semaphores are useful for more general synchronization requirements that cannot be handled by using mutex variables.

In Amoeba, a process creates a new (child) process by first making a *CreateSegment* request three times for the three segments (text, data, and stack) of the child process and gets back one capability for each segment. It then performs *write* operations for each segment to fill each one with that segment's initial data (this may not be done as a separate step if the pointer to the initial data for each segment is provided as a parameter in the *CreateSegment* requests). Finally, the process does a *MakeProcess* request with the capabilities of the child's segments as parameters. *MakeProcess* creates the child process and returns a capability for it. The parent process continues to execute in parallel with the newly created child process. It can use the child process's capability to suspend, restart, or destroy the child process. Note that a process can create an arbitrary number of children, which in turn can create their own children. This flexibility allows the creation of an arbitrarily large tree of processes.

At any time, a process is in one of two states—running or stunned (suspended). A running process can be stunned by executing a library procedure called *stun*, with the capability of the process as a parameter. A process can be stunned directly by its parent or by any other process that has a capability for the process with rights to stun it. For example, a process being interactively debugged switches between running and stunned states. For this, the parent gives the process's capability to the debugger process, which can then change the process's state as it likes during interactive debugging. When a process is in the stunned state, for all attempts to communicate with the process, the low-level communication protocols in the kernel respond with a message saying "this process is stunned."

### Choosing a Processor for a New Process

In the processor-pool model of Amoeba, when a new process has to be created, the system must choose from the pool the most suitable processor for running the process. There are special servers called *run servers* to make this decision. Each run server manages one or more processor pools. For simplicity, let us assume that each run server manages only one processor pool.

When the shell wants to run a program, it does an RPC, with the run server sending to it the process descriptors for the program and asking it to pick a processor for it from the pool. The run server uses the following method to select a processor for executing the program:

1. The process descriptors contain information about the CPU architectures on which the corresponding process can run. Therefore, the run server takes the intersection of the CPU architectures in the process descriptors and the CPU architectures in the processor pool that it manages. To facilitate this, a processor pool is represented by a directory called a *pooldir*, which contains subdirectories for each of the CPU architectures in the pool. The subdirectories contain capabilities for accessing the process servers on each of the CPUs in the pool. The processors that result from the intersection are chosen as possible candidates for running the process.

2. Next, the run server checks to see which of the selected processors have sufficient memory for executing the program. For this, the run server maintains a table containing the speed, current load, and amount of currently free memory for each processor. The information in this table is continuously refreshed by executing a library procedure called *getload* for each processor in the pool. Those processors that do not have enough memory for the program are removed from the set of possible candidates.

3. Finally, for each of the remaining processors, the run server estimates the computing power that the processor can devote to the new program. For this, it uses a heuristic that takes as input the known total computing power of the processor and the number of currently active threads running on it. The processor that can deliver the maximum computing power is finally selected as the most suitable candidate for executing the program.

The run server returns the capability of the process server of the selected processor to the caller. The caller then uses this capability to create the process on the selected processor.

### Process Migration Mechanism

Although Amoeba does not currently support process migration, the designers have thought about it, and it has been mentioned in the literature that a process migration mechanism for migrating a process from its old node to a new node can be easily implemented in the future in the following manner [Mullender et al. 1990]:

1. At first, the process server at the old node of the migrant process will stun it.
2. It will then pass the process descriptor of the process to the process server at the new node in a *RunProcess* request.
3. The process server at the new node will then fetch the address space of the process from the old node by making a series of *ReadSegment* requests.
4. After this, it will start the process at the new node with a *CreateProcess* request. With this, the process starts executing on its new node.
5. The process server of the new node then returns a "success" reply for the *RunProcess* request made by the process server of the old node. On receiving this reply, the process server at the old node will delete the process by making a *DeleteProcess* request to the kernel. With this, the migration of the process will complete.

Note that while the migration of a process is in progress, it is frozen (stunned) on its old node. Therefore, processes communicating with the process will receive "this process is stunned" replies to their attempts until the process on the old node is killed. They will then get a "process not here" reply for their attempts to communicate with the deleted process. As a result of this reply, a sender will start a *locate* operation to find the process. After it finds the process on its new node, it can resume communication with the process in normal fashion.

### 12.2.5 File Management

Amoeba is designed to support multiple file systems at the same time. It has a built-in standard file system, but those users who do not like it are free to write and use their own file system. Therefore, in the same Amoeba system, files of different users may be managed by different and incompatible file systems. The main reason for this flexibility is that a file system in Amoeba runs as a collection of server processes. A description of the standard file system of Amoeba is presented below.

The standard file system of Amoeba is comprised of the following types of servers:

1. *Bullet server.* It deals with the storage and manipulation of files.
2. *Directory server.* It takes care of object naming (including files) and directory management.
3. *Replication server.* It handles automatic replication of objects (including files) managed by the directory server.

A description of the directory server has already been presented in Section 12.2.3. Therefore, only the bullet server and the replication server are described below.

#### Bullet Server

The bullet server is so called because it was designed to be very fast. In fact, high performance and simple design were the two main goals in the design of the standard file system of Amoeba. The following design decisions were made to achieve these goals:

1. *Use of immutable files*. A file cannot be modified once it has been created except to be deleted. Therefore, the bullet server supports only three principal file operations—*read*, *create*, and *delete*. To modify an existing file, a client makes a *read* request to the bullet server specifying its capability. In reply to this request, the server sends to the client the entire file that is loaded into the client's memory. The client now performs all the modifications on the local copy of the file. It then makes a *create* request to the bullet server, sending a pointer to the memory location that contains the modified file as a parameter. The server creates a new file and returns a new capability to the client. Either the original file can be left for use as a backup copy or the client can make a *delete* request to the bullet server to destroy it.

Notice from the description above that for an immutable file a file modification typically requires a client to perform three RPCs (one each for *read*, *create*, and *delete* operations) with the bullet server. This makes file modifications complicated and slow. To solve this problem, the bullet server supports two kinds of files—uncommitted and committed. An *uncommitted file* is one that is in the process of being created and can be directly modified by sending modification requests (such as to change, insert, or delete bytes) to the bullet server. When all the changes have been completed, the file can be committed, at which point it becomes immutable. Notice that an uncommitted file is transient in nature and hence cannot be read. On the other hand, a *committed file* is permanent in nature. It can be read but cannot be modified because it is immutable. A *create* request must specify whether the file is to be committed immediately or not. In either case, a copy of the file is made at the server and a capability for the file is returned to the client.

2. *Storing files as contiguous byte strings*. The final size of an immutable file is always known at creation time because it cannot be modified after its creation. Due to this property, files in Amoeba are stored contiguously, both on the disk and in the main-memory cache. Although this strategy wastes space due to external fragmentation, both in memory and on disk, it helps in achieving the goals of high performance and simple design. This is because a contiguously stored file can be read into memory in a single disk operation and can be sent to users in a single RPC reply message. Furthermore, in this strategy, a file can be simply represented by an initial address and length, which simplifies the administration of storage space, both in memory and on disk.

As Figure 12.3 shows, the bullet server maintains a file table that is entirely memory resident while the bullet server is running. The entire file table is loaded into memory when the bullet server is loaded.

The file table has one entry for each file being managed by the bullet server. The entries are indexed by a file number field. Since the initial address and size are sufficient to represent a file, each entry of the file table also has the following three fields:

- A length field that has the file size.
- A disk address field that contains the initial address of the file on disk.
- A memory address field. If the file is currently present in the main-memory cache, this field contains the starting address of the file in main memory.

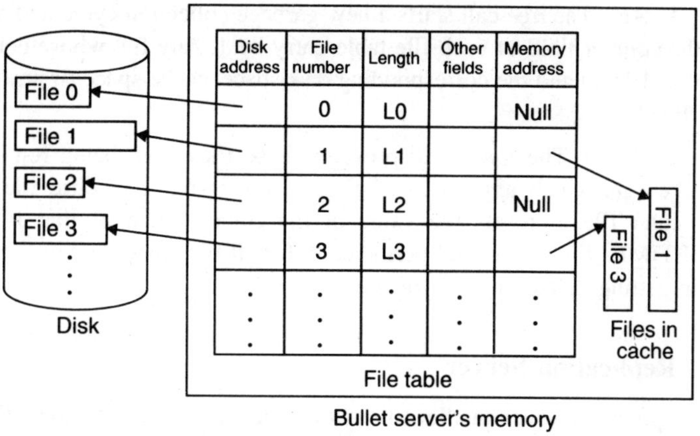


**Fig. 12.3** Bullet server implementation.

In addition to these fields, there are other fields containing information that are used for access control and administration purpose.

To read a file, a client does an RPC with the bullet server, sending it the capability for the file. The server then extracts the file number from the object number field of the capability and uses it to reach at the appropriate file table entry. Each file table entry also has a field containing the random number used in the check field of the capability. This information is used to validate the capability. If the capability is found to be valid, the server first checks the information in the memory address field of the file table to see if the file is currently present in the main-memory cache. If not, the server next uses the information in the disk address and length fields of the file table to fetch the entire file from the disk into the main-memory cache. Finally, it returns the entire file to the client as a reply of the RPC message. The least recently used (LRU) scheme is used to manage the cache space.

If a file's capability is lost, it will remain forever in the system as an inaccessible file. Uncommitted and committed files are handled differently to prevent this situation. For an uncommitted file, if it has not been accessed for 10 minutes, it is simply deleted and the corresponding entry in the file table is freed. If a request for accessing the deleted file is received after the deleted file's entry is reused for another file, the check field will detect the fact that the file has changed, and the operation on the already deleted file will be rejected. This approach is based on the designers' assumption that files normally exist in the uncommitted state for only a few seconds.

For committed files, a garbage collector is run periodically, removing all files that have not been used in *n* garbage collection cycles. This idea is implemented as follows. The file table entry has a counter field for each file that is initialized to a predetermined constant MAX_LIFETIME. Now the following two calls are made periodically to detect and remove committed files that can never be accessed:

1. *Age*. The *age* call starts a new garbage collection cycle and decrements the value of the counter field of each file table entry by 1. Any file whose counter value becomes zero is deleted and the corresponding disk space, cache space (if any), and file table entry are freed.

2. *Touch*. The *touch* call prevents those files from being removed that are in use. Unlike *age*, which applies to all files, *touch* is for a specific file. When called for a particular file, it resets the value of the counter field of that file's entry to MAX_LIFETIME. *Touch* is called periodically for all files listed in any directory, to keep them from getting deleted by the *age* call.

### Replication Server

The replication server handles automatic replication of objects (including files) managed by the directory server. It always keeps running in the background and uses the lazy replication approach for creating object replicas. It scans specified parts of the directory system periodically to check if replica creation for any object in the directory system is needed. In particular, if there is a directory entry that is supposed to contain $n$ capabilities but contains only $m$ ($m < n$), then $n - m$ additional copies of the corresponding object must be created. Therefore, when the replication server finds such a directory entry, it contacts the relevant servers and arranges for the creation of additional replicas of the corresponding object.

In addition to creating object replicas, the replication server is also responsible for garbage collection. That is, it periodically makes a *touch* call for each object in the directory system to refresh their lifetime so that they will not be removed by the garbage collector. Periodically, it also sends the *age* message to the servers of different object types to cause them to make the *age* call to decrement the value of the counter field for all their objects and to remove those objects whose counter value reaches zero.

## 12.2.6 Interprocess Communication

### Basic IPC Mechanism

Amoeba uses the client-server model for operations on objects. That is, client processes send requests to server processes (object managers) for carrying out operations on objects. A server accepts a client's request message, carries out the requested operation, and returns a reply to the client. Each standard server is defined by a set of stub procedures that clients can call. The stub procedures precisely define the services and their parameters that the server provides. When a stub procedure is called by a client, it packs the parameters into a message and invokes the kernel primitives to actually send the message. The kernel provides the following three basic IPC primitives:

- *trans* is used by a client to send a request message to a server for getting some work done by the server.
- *get_request* is used by a server to announce its willingness to accept messages addressed to a specific port.
- *send_reply* is used by a server to send a reply to a client.

Although these primitives are actually related to message passing, the procedural interface provided by stub procedures makes the basic IPC mechanism appear as RPC (Remote Procedure Call) to the programmers. Therefore, the basic IPC mechanism of Amoeba is also referred to as RPC. This RPC mechanism has the following properties:

1. It supports only synchronous type of communication. That is, after making a *trans* call, a client thread blocks until the corresponding reply comes back from the called server. Similarly, after making a *get_request* call, a server goes to sleep, waiting for an incoming request message. The server is unblocked only when a request message arrives.

2. Messages are unbuffered. Hence a message is simply discarded if its receiver is not in a state ready to receive it. In this case, the sending kernel will time out and retransmit the message. Flexibility is provided to the users to specify the maximum duration for retransmissions, after which the kernel should give up and report failure.

3. It supports at-most-once semantics. That is, the system guarantees that an RPC will never be carried out more than once, even if the server crashes and is rapidly rebooted.

4. Stateless servers are used. Therefore, each RPC is completely self contained and does not depend on any previous information stored in the server's memories.

### Group Communication

In addition to the RPC mechanism, Amoeba also supports group communication facility. A group consists of multiple processes that cooperate to provide some service. Amoeba uses the concept of closed groups. That is, the information regarding the size and the member processes of a group are not known to processes outside the group. Therefore, for accessing a service provided by a group, a client process simply performs an RPC with one of its members. That member then uses group communication within the group to service the client's request in cooperation with other members of the group.

Processes can join and leave a group dynamically and can be members of multiple groups at the same time. The system provides primitives for creating a new group, allowing a process to dynamically join or leave a group, sending a message to all members of a group, and receiving a message from a group. The group communication mechanism of Amoeba has the following properties:

1. It ensures ordered delivery of messages. That is, if two processes send messages to a group almost simultaneously, the system ensures that all group members will receive the messages in the same order. A sequencer process is used for properly sequencing the messages received by a group. The sequencer process is chosen by using an election algorithm.

2. It ensures reliable delivery of messages. That is, when a user process broadcasts a message, the message is correctly delivered to all members of the group, even though the hardware may lose packets. The basic mechanisms used to ensure reliable message

delivery are timeout-based retransmissions for retransmitting lost messages; use of unique message identifiers to detect duplicate messages; and the use of a history buffer to store messages for which acknowledgments have not yet been received.

3. It can withstand the loss of an arbitrary collection of *k* processors (including the sequencer), where *k* (the degree of resilience) is specified by the user as a parameter in the primitive for creating a group [Tanenbaum 1995]. The larger is the value of *k*, the more redundancy is required, and the slower the group communication becomes. Therefore, the user must carefully choose the value of *k*.

Further details of the group communication facility of Amoeba may be found in [Kaashoek and Tanenbaum 1991].

### Low-Level Communication Protocols

Both RPC and the group communication facilities of Amoeba use a custom protocol, called FLIP (Fast Local Internet Protocol), for actual message transmission. The details of FLIP have already been presented in Chapter 2 and hence will not be repeated here.

FLIP is used in Amoeba for achieving high performance. However, there are occasions when Amoeba users need to use the standard TCP/IP instead of FLIP. For instance, TCP/IP must be used to communicate with X terminals, to send and receive mails to non-Amoeba machines, and to interact with other Amoeba systems via the Internet [Tanenbaum 1995]. To facilitate communications of these types, Amoeba has a TCP/IP server. For TCP/IP-based communications, a client performs an RPC with the TCP/IP server giving it a TCP/IP address. The TCP/IP server establishes a connection with the desired process and returns a capability to the client process. This capability allows the client to use the established connection. Once the connection is established, subsequent RPCs between the two processes can be done without the Amoeba process having to know that TCP/IP is being used.

### Communication Security

***Ensuring Genuine Clients.*** Amoeba has two levels of protection to ensure the genuineness of a client—ports for protecting access to servers and capabilities for protecting access to individual objects [Mullender et al. 1990]. That is, the knowledge of a server's port and the possession of a valid capability is taken by the system as sufficient evidence that the sender has a right to communicate with the server and to perform operations allowed by the capability on the object identified by the capability. The ports used by an ordinary user process will, in general, be known only to the processes that have the right to communicate with the user process. However, the port of a server process providing some public service, such as a file server, will be known to all users. Therefore, for public servers, capabilities serve as the basic mechanism to ensure the genuineness of a client.

***Ensuring Genuine Servers.*** Since ports for public servers are known to all users, it is easy for an intruder to impersonate a server just by doing a *get_request* on the server's port. A one-way encryption technique is used in Amoeba to solve this problem.

In this approach, each port is defined as a pair of ports, *get-port* and *put-port*, related by *put-port* = *F*(*get-port*). The function *F* is a publicly known one-way encryption function. Therefore, it is easy to compute put-port for a given get-port, but finding get-port for a given put-port is not practically feasible. Here, *F* need not be the same one-way function as that used for protecting capabilities since the two concepts are unrelated.

As a part of its creation process, a server chooses a get-port that it keeps secret with it. It computes the corresponding put-port and makes it publicly known. When the server is ready to accept client requests, it makes a *get_request* (*get-port*, ...) call. The kernel computes the corresponding put-port and stores it in a table of ports being listened to. When a client wants to send a message to the server, it makes a *trans* (*put-port*, ...) call. The kernel of the client machine then sends a message containing put-port in a header field to the server. On the server side, the kernel compares the put-port in the message header to the put-ports in its table for a match and then forwards the message to the corresponding server.

This scheme ensures that only genuine servers can receive client requests because get-ports never appear on the network and cannot be derived from the publicly known put-ports.

## 12.3 V-SYSTEM

V-System is a microkernel-based distributed operating system designed for a cluster of workstations connected by a high-performance network. It started as a research project on distributed systems at Stanford University under the direction of David Cheriton. It is basically an outgrowth of the experience acquired with an earlier system called Thoth [Cheriton et al. 1979]. Its development was motivated by the growing availability and functionality of relatively low-cost, high-performance workstations and local area networks.

V-System has been in active use at Stanford University for the last several years. The V-System environment at Stanford mainly consists of a collection of powerful Sun and VAX workstations connected by Ethernet. V-System is also distributed under license by Stanford and is in use at several other universities, research laboratories, and companies. The following description of V-System is based on [Cheriton 1984, 1987, 1988, Cheriton et al. 1990, Berglund 1986].

### 12.3.1 Design Goals and Main Features

V-System's design was influenced by the research and design goals mentioned below.

#### High-Performance Communication

V-System designers were of the opinion that high performance of interprocess communication is necessary in a distributed system for better performance and simpler design of resulting application systems and also for true network transparency. In a system with fast communication facility, better performance of application systems is obvious.

Simpler design of application systems is due to the reason that there is no need to highly optimize the use of communication to prevent performance degradation. Finally, true network transparency can be achieved because fast communication allows resource accessing without concern for location.

Fast interprocess communication in V-System is achieved by the following [Cheriton 1988]:

1. Using relatively simple and basic interprocess communication primitives
2. Using a transport protocol called VMTP (Versatile Message Transaction Protocol) that is carefully designed to support these primitives
3. Optimizing for the performance-critical common cases
4. Internally structuring the kernel for efficient communication

### Uniform Interface and Protocol

V-System designers were also of the opinion that the protocols and interfaces, not the software modules, define the system. That is, a device- and network-independent uniform interface and protocol can be defined to build an open-system architecture. Thus, V-System designers mainly focused their work on designing the protocols and interfaces. The result was a set of protocols for data transport, naming, I/O, remote execution, migration, and so on, which provides a basis for standardization.

### Relatively Small Kernel

Another important design goal of V-System was to have a relatively small kernel that can provide a software backplane for distributed systems analogous to what a good hardware backplane provides for hardware systems and to implement the rest of the system at a user level in a machine- and network-independent fashion. Consequently, most of the facilities found in traditional operating systems, such as a file system, resource management, and protection, are provided in V-System by servers outside the kernel.

### High Performance

High performance was also an important goal in V-System because the designers were of the opinion that no one will use a slow system, independent of its elegance. Some of the important techniques used in the design of V-System for high performance are as follows:

1. Making the interprocess communication fast by already mentioned methods
2. Allowing application programs to make use of concurrency by using multi-threaded processes
3. Maintaining a name prefix cache for each program for efficient resolution of object names

4. Using the problem-oriented approach for shared-memory coherence that implements a relaxed form of consistency to improve performance, with the potential inconsistencies handled in an application-specific fashion

### Network Transparency

Similar to other distributed operating systems, network transparency was also a goal in V-System. To achieve this goal, the naming facility of V-System was based on a three-level model, structured as character-string names, object identifiers, and entity identifiers.

### Support for Conventional Programming Models

Another goal in V-System design was to provide support for conventional programming models so that applications programmers can access the system services through a set of procedural interfaces. To achieve this goal, each system-provided service procedure is made a part of one of the runtime libraries of V-System. When an application process invokes a procedure for accessing some system service, if possible, the invoked procedure itself performs the requested operation. Otherwise, it uses the kernel-provided interprocess communication to communicate with the proper service module(s) of V-System to get the operation performed. In either case, it is the invoked procedure that returns a reply to the application process, and hence the actual mechanism used to perform the operation is transparent to the application process.

### UNIX Emulation

A relatively new goal of V-System was to provide binary compatibility with a UNIX system so that existing UNIX programs can be run on V-System. For this, a UNIX emulation package was later added to V-System. Its details can be found in [Cheriton et al. 1990].

## 12.3.2 System Architecture

### Hardware Architecture

As Figure 12.4 shows, the hardware architecture of V-System consists of a collection of workstations interconnected by a communications network, such as an Ethernet. The workstations are broadly classified into the following categories:

1. *User machines*. A workstation belonging to this category supports an interactive user. It has most of the processing resources for its user in addition to display, keyboard, and mouse.

2. *Server machines*. A workstation belonging to this category functions as a dedicated server providing services such as file service, print service, authentication service, and other kinds of services. Each workstation of this category may provide one

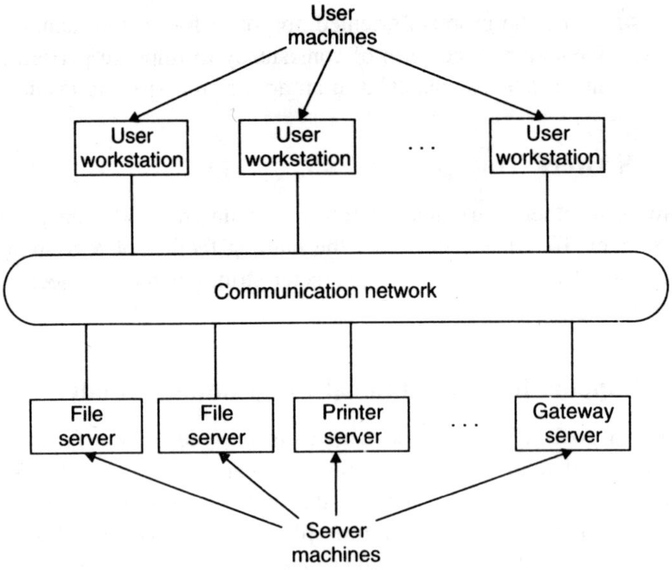


**Fig. 12.4** Hardware architecture of the V-System.

or more types of services. For instance, a workstation with secondary storage may run the V-System file server software and exclusively offer file service. The kernel's interprocess communication makes this service and others available in a network-transparent fashion to all workstations on the network.

### Software Architecture

From a software point of view, V-System architecture mainly consists of the following layers (Fig. 12.5):

1. *The kernel layer.* The V-System kernel forms the lowest layer of the software architecture. To keep it small, the kernel is designed using a minimalist philosophy. That is, only those facilities that are just sufficient and powerful enough to build all other system functions and features are placed in the kernel. Hence, the kernel performs only such functions as management of lightweight processes, management of address spaces, and interprocess communication. A separate copy of the kernel executes on each workstation, and all of them cooperate to provide a single system image at the application process level.

2. *Service modules layer.* The modules at this layer use the basic access to hardware resources provided by the kernel for implementing various types of services for the users. For instance, the file server module at this layer implements a UNIX-like file system using the raw disk access supported by the kernel. Some other service modules of this layer are a pipe server that implements UNIX-like pipes, an Internet server that implements the

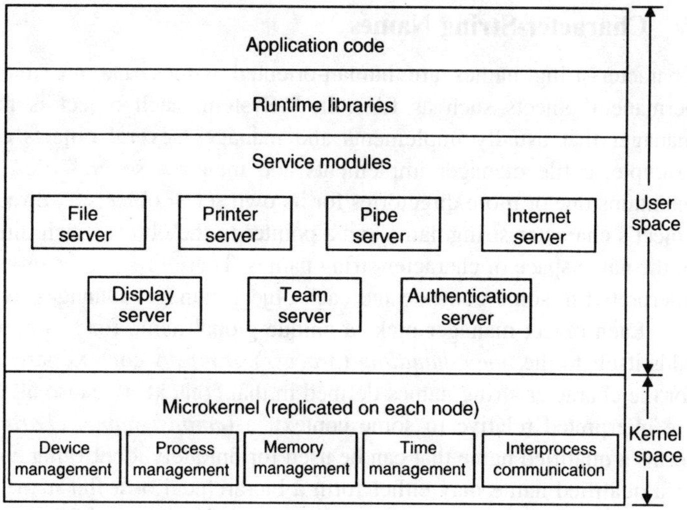


**Fig. 12.5** Software architecture of the V-System.

TCP/IP suite, a printer server that supports spooling of print jobs, and a display server that implements multiwindow facilities using a bitmap display. In this way, V-System allows many traditional kernel-based functions to be implemented as user-level server processes.

3. *Runtime libraries.* This layer implements conventional language or application-to-operating-system interface. Most V-System applications and commands are written in terms of these conventional interfaces and are unaware of the distributed nature of the underlying system. Therefore, the software at this layer causes V-System to appear to the applications programmers as a set of procedural interfaces that provide access to the system services. It also allows many programs that originated in nondistributed systems to be ported to V-System with little or no modification by simply linking the original source with the runtime libraries at this layer.

4. *Application code layer.* This layer contains the code for the application programs.

### 12.3.3 Object Naming

The object-naming facility of V-System is based on a three-level model structured as character-string names, object identifiers, and entity identifiers. The usage and management of the names and the method of locating an object given its name are described below.

### Character-String Names

Character-string names are human-oriented names that are mainly used for naming permanent objects such as files. In V-System, each object is managed by an object manager that usually implements and manages several objects of the same kind. For example, a file manager implements and manages several files. Each object manager maintains one or more directories for its own set of objects. A directory entry contains an object's character-string name and a pointer to the object. Each directory forms a context of the name space of character-string names. Therefore, character-string names are always interpreted in some context, and each object manager manages its own contexts.

Each object manager picks a unique global name for a context that it manages and adds itself to the *name-handling (process) group*. A context name acts as a name prefix for the character-string names defined in that context. Because all character-string names are interpreted relative to some context, a (*context name*, *character-string name*) pair forms a qualified name that can be used for uniquely identifying an object. Both the parts of a qualified name may either form a hierarchical or a flat name space.

To access an object, a client process specifies the qualified name of the object. The appropriate object manager is then located by multicasting the name along with the access request to all the object managers in the name-handling group. Each object manager extracts the context name part of the qualified name to check if the named object belongs to a context managed by it. Only the appropriate object manager then performs the requested access operation on the named object and responds to the client.

To reduce the number of multicast queries mentioned above, each process maintains a name prefix cache that has context-name-to-object-manager bindings. The cache is initialized on process initiation to avoid start-up name cache misses. Furthermore, an on-use update mechanism is used for the consistency of name prefix caches.

The name management approach described above takes advantage of the fact that a name is generally only mapped as part of an operation on the corresponding object. V-System designers mentioned that, in general, integrating naming with object management in this way has following advantages [Cheriton and Mann 1989]:

1. It leads to efficiency because when an operation on an object is requested by specifying its name, both the name resolution operation and the requested operation on the object can be completed in a single set of message exchange. This contrasts with those systems that use separate name servers, in which case one set of message exchange is needed for name resolution to locate the object (its manager) and then another set of message exchange is needed for performing the desired operation on the object.

2. It leads to consistent reliability of both the name resolution and object-accessing operations. That is, in this scheme, an object's name can always be resolved when the object (its manager) is available for use. This contrasts with those systems that use separate name servers, in which case it is quite likely that an object is available for use but cannot be accessed because the name server is down.

3. It leads to simpler design because the availability of all information of an object (names, properties, data, etc.) in one server makes it easier to maintain their consistency.

For example, when an object is deleted, all its related information can be deleted without the need to communicate with any other server.

4. The design also allows the automatic application of the security mechanism for communicating with the object manager and controlling access to information to the naming operations as well.

### Object Identifiers

Object identifiers are system-oriented names. They are used to identify transient objects such as open files, address spaces, and contexts or directories to avoid the overhead of character-string name handling and lookup each time an object is accessed. For example, a process uses the character-string name of a file at the time of opening it for use, when the system assigns an object identifier to the opened file and returns the object identifier to the process. The process uses the object identifier to refer to the file in subsequent operations on it.

An object identifier is structured as a (*manager-id*, *local-object-id*) pair. The *manager-id* identifies the object manager that implements the object, and the *local-object-id* identifies the object among all the objects managed by this object manager. The *manager-id* part of an object identifier is used to efficiently send a client's request to the correct object manager for operation on the object. On the other hand, the *local-object-id* part is used by the object manager to perform the requested operation on the correct object.

Note that the life of an object (transient object) identified by an object identifier must not exceed the lifetime of the embedded *manager-id*. This is because the *manager-id* of an object manager is invalidated when the corresponding process crashes (an object manager is assigned a new *manager-id* on reboot).

When an object manager is replicated or distributed across multiple nodes, the process group mechanism (described later) is used to identify the entire group of server instances, implementing the object manager, by a single group identifier. In this case, a particular server of the group can be addressed by using the coresident addressing (qualifier) facility of the group addressing mechanism (described later).

### Entity Identifiers

Entity identifiers are used to identify processes, process groups, and transport-level communication endpoints. Therefore, *manager-id* and *group-id* are basically entity identifiers.

Entity identifiers are fixed-length (64-bit) binary values that are host address independent (host addresses are network or internetwork dependent). Hence, when a process migrates from one host to another, there is no need to change its *process-id*. The mapping of an object's identifier to its host address is done by the kernel. For this, the kernel uses a cache of such mappings along with a multicast mechanism to query other kernels for mappings not found in the cache. When an entity identifier is used to identify a process group, the entity identifier contains an embedded subfield that, when hashed to a base multicast address, generates the multicast host address for the group.

### 12.3.4 Process Management

The three basic abstractions used in V-System for process management are *process*, *team*, and *team space*, which respectively correspond to the concepts of "thread," "process," and "a process's address space" presented in this book. To avoid any confusion, in the description that follows, the terms *thread*, *process*, and *address space* will be used instead of *process*, *team*, and *team space*, except in V-System calls.

In V-System, process management activities are mainly performed by two modules— the *kernel process server* and the *program manager*. Each node of the system has these two modules. The kernel process server executes inside the kernel, whereas the program manager executes in the user space. One of the goals of V-System designers was to minimize the kernel process management activities so that the kernel can be kept as small as possible. Therefore, the kernel process server performs only the basic low-level process management functions and the rest are performed by the user-level program manager. The role of these two modules in process creation, destruction, scheduling, migration, and so on, are described below.

#### Process Creation and Termination

Threads and processes are dynamically created and destroyed by using the primitives *CreateProcess*, *CreateTeam*, and *DestroyProcess*. When a thread is created, it is created as part of the same process as that of its creator. When a thread is destroyed, all the threads created by it are also destroyed. Creation of a process is similar to the creation of a thread, except that in this case the newly created thread is created as a separate process and not as a part of its parent process. Also notice that there is no explicit operation for destroying a process because a process is automatically destroyed when the last thread in that process is destroyed.

To minimize the kernel's job in the process creation activity, V-System separates process initiation from address space creation and initialization. Therefore, as far as the kernel process server is concerned, creation of a new process simply involves allocating and initializing a new process descriptor. The address space allocation and initialization is performed by using V-System's virtual memory system, which is described below.

In V-System, an address space is a range of addresses, called *regions*, bound to some portion of an open file or a uniform input output (UIO) object. (A UIO object corresponds to an open file in conventional systems.) Accessing a memory address that falls within a region corresponds to accessing the corresponding data in the open file bound to the region. The *kernel memory server* module manages the physical memory as a cache of pages from open files. A page fault occurs when a portion of a region that corresponds to an uncached portion of the bound object is accessed. To handle a page fault, the kernel maps from the virtual address to a block in the bound UIO or open file and then either locates that block in the kernel page frame cache or else causes the faulting process to send a read request requesting the data block to the server implementing the open file. File-like read/write access may also be performed on address spaces by using the standard UIO interface.

Creation and initialization of address space of a process becomes a simple task by using the virtual memory system. For this, an address space descriptor is allocated and the program file of the process is bound to this address space. Now as the process references portions of this address space, the program file pages are transferred and mapped into the address space dynamically on demand. Hence, the V-System kernel has no special mechanism for program loading.

The kernel's job in process termination activity is simplified in the following manner. In V-System, most operating system resources such as open files are managed by user-level server modules. Therefore, there are few resources at the kernel level to reclaim when a process terminates. Furthermore, when a process terminates, the kernel does not inform the concerned servers because each server is responsible for keeping track of the resources it has allocated to a client process and for checking periodically whether the client exists, reclaiming the resource if not. For example, the file server has a garbage collector process that closes files that are associated with processes that do not exist any more.

### Remote Program Execution

In V-System, one of the following primitives may be used at the command interpreter level to execute a program on a remote machine [Theimer et al. 1985]:

- *<program-name> <arguments>* @ *<machine-name>*
- *<program-name> <arguments>* @ *

In the former case, the specified program is executed on the specified machine, but in the latter case, the system becomes responsible for selecting an appropriate machine for executing the specified program. The selection of an appropriate machine is done by the method described below.

In V-System, the program managers of all the nodes are grouped into a well-known *program manager (process) group*. When a user uses the latter primitive for making a request for remote program execution, the processor allocation module on the user's machine multicasts a "remote program execution request" message to the program manager group. Only program managers whose machines have permission from their users for remote program execution and sufficient amounts of processor and memory resources available reply to this message. The processor allocation module then uses a policy to select the most appropriate machine from the replies received. In the current policy, the machine whose program manager responds first is selected since this is generally the least loaded one and also because this policy is simple and inexpensive to implement.

Except for the selection of a program manager, remote program execution is the same as local program execution because processes in V-System are provided with a network-transparent execution environment. Furthermore, the kernel and the program manager of a machine provide identical services to both locally originated programs and remote programs executing on this machine.

Initiation of a program execution (either local or remote) involves sending a request to the appropriate program manager (of the local or remote machine) to create a new address space and load the image file of the specified program into this address space. The program manager, in cooperation with the kernel process server and kernel memory server, sets up the address space and creates an initial process that awaits reply from its creator. The program manager then turns over control of the newly created process to the requester by forwarding the newly created process to it. The requester initializes the new program space with program arguments, default I/O, and various "environment variables." Finally, it starts the execution of the program by replying to its initial process.

Note that a program can be executed remotely only if it does not require low-level access to the hardware devices of the machine on which it originated. That is, the program should not access such hardware devices as disks, frame buffers, network interfaces, and serial lines by directly accessing a device server of its originating node.

### Process Scheduling

In V-System, processes are scheduled using a priority discipline. To simplify the task of the kernel, two-level scheduling is used to allocate the processor of a node to the processes assigned to that node. A kernel-level scheduler provides a very simple and efficient priority-based scheduling. It simply takes the highest priority process in the ready state and allocates it to the processor. On the other hand, a process-level scheduler that runs outside the kernel manipulates priorities to effectively implement time slicing among interactive and background processes. V-System gives special treatment to real-time processes by reserving a number of high-priority levels for them.

### Process Migration

***Process Migration Policy.*** In V-System, a process may be selected for migration either by the system or on explicit request by a user. In the former case, processes are selected for migration between processors by a periodically invoked kernel procedure that attempts to balance the processing load across the processors. On the other hand, in the latter case, all the processes corresponding to a program are migrated together by invoking [Theimer et al. 1985]

*migrateprog [-n]* [<*program-name*>]

The selection of an appropriate destination node for a migrant process (or group of processes) is done in exactly the same manner as is done for selecting a machine for remote execution of a program when the meta machine name "*" is specified. The processes of the specified program are not migrated if an appropriate destination node cannot be found for the program. However, if the "*-n*" option is present, the processes of the program are destroyed if they cannot be migrated. Furthermore, if the program name is not specified, an attempt is made to migrate the processes of all remote programs that are executing on this node.

***Process Migration Mechanisms.***

1. *Address space transfer mechanism.* V-System uses the pretransfer mechanism for address space transmission. This mechanism is described in Chapter 8.

2. *Message-forwarding mechanism.* The three types of messages (type 1, type 2, and type 3) to be forwarded to the migrant process's destination node are described in Chapter 8. V-System uses the mechanism of resending the message to forward messages of all three types. This mechanism is described in Chapter 8.

3. *Mechanism for handling coprocesses.* V-System ensures that when a parent process migrates, its children processes will be migrated along with it. Therefore, the method of disallowing separation of parent and child processes is used in V-System's process migration to handle coprocesses.

**Exception Handling**

In V-System, all exceptions are handled by a user-level server process called the *exception server.* When an exception condition occurs, the kernel causes the faulting process to send a message describing its problem to the exception server. The exception server then takes over and initiates necessary actions to deal with the problem by using the facilities of the kernel and other higher level servers. The main advantage of this approach is that it allows the implementation of a powerful, flexible, and network-transparent exception-handling mechanism with very little kernel complexity [Cheriton 1988].

### 12.3.5 Device Management

In V-System, most of the device management activities are performed by user-level server processes. However, some device support must be provided in the kernel because device interrupts go to the kernel, some device control operations are privileged, and kernel control of some device operations is required for kernel integrity [Cheriton 1988]. Therefore, the V-System kernel has a *kernel device server* module designed to provide efficient, reliable, machine-independent, and secure access to a wide variety of devices. The kernel device server provides only minimum device support for a particular device and has device-independent code that interfaces between the user-level processes and the driver modules for the individual devices.

The interface provided by the kernel device server is called the *UIO interface.* It allows client processes to use the standard I/O runtime support for device I/O. It also allows the user-level server processes to implement extended abstractions of devices for application programmers. For example, the kernel device server provides access to each disk drive as a raw block device, and the user-level file server implements files using this basic interface. Similarly, for network connections, the kernel device server provides a block interface to the Ethernet, providing the ability to read and write raw Ethernet packets, and the user-level Internet server implements TCP/IP, UDP, and X.25 protocols.

Device I/O is accomplished by creating a UIO object that is viewed as a sequence of data blocks that are read or written. The UIO interface defines the syntax and semantics of read, write, query, and modify operations that can be performed on UIO objects. With the supported operations and the use of a block-oriented data access model, the UIO interface is general enough to handle a wide variety of devices such as disk, tape, printer, network interface, serial line, terminal, and even a mouse.

### 12.3.6 Interprocess Communication

Interprocess communication is an important facility provided by the V-System kernel. Special care has been taken in the design of interprocess communication facility to provide fast exchange of messages between client and server processes using RPC-like semantics. The three basic forms of interprocess communication provided by the kernel are communication for fixed-length message transfer, communication for passing access to a data segment, and multicast communication. These are described below.

#### Fixed-Length Message Transfer

This form of communication is used by processes to send, receive, and reply to requests by using fixed-length messages. The three primitives provided for this purpose are *Send*, *Receive*, and *Reply*. The *Send* primitive is used by a client process to pass the equivalent of a procedure argument. On the other hand, the *Receive* and *Reply* primitives are used respectively by a server process to receive a client's request and to return the result of a request execution to the client. All messages are exchanged in a strictly synchronous manner. That is, the process that has sent a message is blocked awaiting for the reply until the message it sent has been received and replied to by the receiving process. On the other hand, after replying to a client's request, a server performs a *Receive* and blocks waiting for a message to be sent by a client. All these messages are of fixed length (32 bytes).

#### Passing Access to a Data Segment

In this form of communication, a process uses the *Send* primitive to send a pseudopointer to one of its memory segments (a contiguous range of addresses) in a fixed-length message to a receiver process. The segment size and access modes are also specified in the message. On receiving this message, the recipient process can access this segment for reading and/or writing, depending on the access mode specified in the message, while the sender is awaiting reply from the recipient. Such reads and writes are handled by kernel primitives *CopyFrom* and *CopyTo* (Fig. 12.6). The receiver can execute these primitives several times before replying. Furthermore, the receiver may forward the message to another process, passing to it the segment access and the right to reply. The sender is blocked until it receives a reply for the message that it sent. This facility allows parameters to be passed by reference.

The communication semantics for exchange of messages in the two forms of communication described above is illustrated in Figure 12.6. Notice that in both cases the sender and receiver interact in a strictly synchronous manner. Moreover, the receiver can

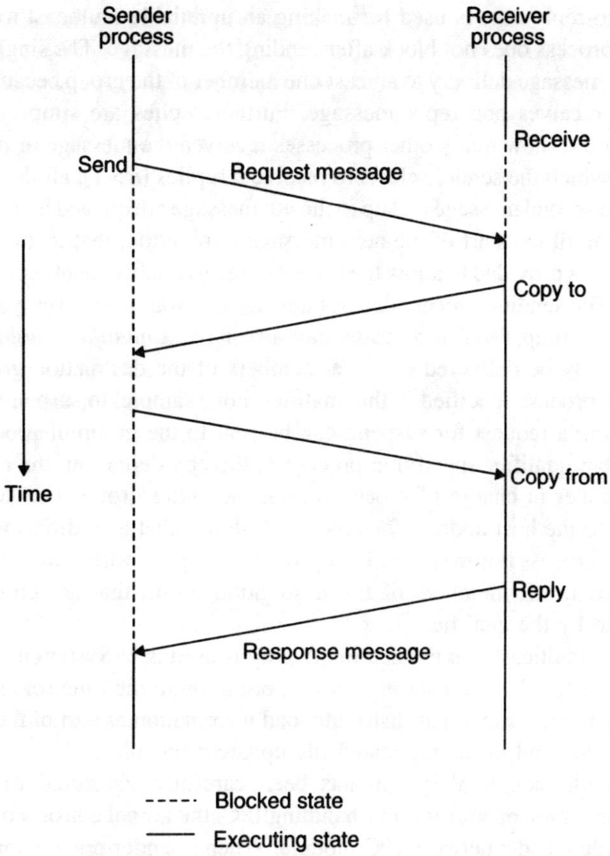


**Fig. 12.6** Communication semantics for exchange of messages in the V-System.

receive and queue multiple messages and can reply to a message when it wants. This flexibility allows writing of applications that need sophisticated scheduling of message handling and replies.

## Multicast Communication

The third form of interprocess communication in V-System provides group (one-to-many) communication facility. V-System supports the notion of a *process group* (or simply a group), which is a set of processes identified by a group identifier. A process can simultaneously belong to multiple groups and can freely join or leave groups.

Any process, including one that is not a member of a group, can send a message to a group by specifying a group identifier instead of a process identifier in the parameter for *Send*. After sending, the sender may block or continue executing depending on whether it selects to receive zero, one, or more than one reply message for the message that it has sent.

The zero-reply case is used for making an unreliable multicast to the group because the sender process does not block after sending the message. The single-reply case is used for reliable message delivery to at least one member of the group because the sender is blocked until it receives one reply message. Further replies are simply discarded without any indication of how many other processes received the message or replied it. Finally, in the case in which the sender selects to receive $n$ replies ($n > 1$), all the reply messages starting from the second message and up to the $n$th message are queued in the kernel for the sender to retrieve until the start of the next message transaction, that is, the next *Send*. A primitive *GetReply* is provided to allow the sender to receive subsequent replies that are queued in the kernel. The sending process decides how long to wait for the reply messages.

In a group *Send*, a message can also have a *qualifier*, indicating that the message should only be delivered to those members of the destination group that are coresident with the process specified in the qualifier. For example, to suspend a process *P*, a message containing a request for suspend can be sent to the group of process managers with the coresident qualifier specifying process *P*, thereby delivering the request message to only the manager in charge of process *P*, not the entire group. The kernel simply routes the request to the host address for process *P*. Notice that a qualifier need not always identify a single process but may also be a process group identifier, in which case the message is delivered to all members of the destination group that are coresident with the group specified by the qualifier.

The multicast communication facility is used in V-System in a number of ways, such as to transmit clock synchronization information to the time servers in the kernel of each node, to request as well as distribute load information as part of the distributed scheduling mechanism, and in the replicated file update protocol.

The kernel of V-System has been carefully structured to minimize the cost of communication operations. For handling IPC, the kernel consists of two modules—a local IPC module and a network IPC module. When a sender process makes a *Send* call to send a message to a receiver process, the call is trapped into the kernel and processed by the local IPC module if the receiver process is local. Otherwise, it is processed by the network IPC module using the VMTP to communicate with the remote kernel and the remote receiver process. It may be noted here that fast IPC in V-System is achieved not only by using relatively simple and basic IPC primitives but also due to the use of VMTP, which is optimized for request-response behavior. VMTP supports multicast, datagrams, forwarding, streaming, security, and priority of messages. The details of VMTP have already been presented in Chapter 2 and hence will not be repeated here.

### 12.3.7 V-System Servers

We saw that the V-System kernel provides only minimum functionality that serves as a basic framework for implementing many traditional kernel-based functions as user-level server processes. This allows the users to design and implement their own server processes for their applications. However, there are several services that are commonly used by most applications. V-System provides servers for such services so that the users need not design their own servers for these services. The services provided by some of the most important V-System servers are briefly described below.

### Program Manager

The program manager (also known as the *team server*) performs most of the process management activities. It performs jobs that are normally performed by the kernel in traditional time-sharing operating systems, such as process creation and termination, process scheduling, and maintaining resource consumption statistics for various processes. It also manipulates priorities of processes to efficiently implement time slicing among interactive, background, and guest processes (those that originated on some other node but are being executed on this node). In addition, it serves as a user-level exception handler and invokes an interactive debugger on faulting programs. Moreover, the program managers of different nodes cooperate for implementing automatic load-balancing facility and for process migration activities.

### File Server

The file server performs most of the file management activities performed by the kernel in traditional operating systems. In particular, it provides an abstraction of the physical storage devices by allowing the users to store and access data from these devices in the form of read and write operations on files. The file server usually runs on a dedicated server machine with mass disk storage. Since most workstations in V-System are diskless, the file server also provides file access facility for clients on the network.

The file server is multithreaded for efficiency, so that when one thread blocks waiting for a disk block, some other thread can be executed. Furthermore, all threads belonging to the file server process share a common buffer cache, which is used to keep heavily used blocks in main memory.

### Internet Server

The Internet server implements the TCP/IP suite on top of the basic network interface device provided by the kernel device server. It has a multithreaded, modular structure for efficiency and flexibility. Moreover, for better performance, it makes direct use of several kernel facilities such as real-time scheduling, accurate timing, and fast IPC. It is not permanently configured in the standard system and is loaded only when required.

### Printer Server

The printer server spools print files. In general, print files are submitted to the printer server by using the IPC facility and UIO interface of V-System. However, when the printer server runs an instance of the Internet server, print files can also be submitted by using TCP connections.

### Display Server

The display server implements multiwindow facilities using a bitmap display. It also provides a high-level graphics representation at the client interface, allowing commonly used operations to be performed local to the display server, rather than relying on application facilities. For instance, the display server supports multiple views, zooming, and redraw, making these facilities available for all applications.

## 12.4 MACH

Mach is a microkernel-based operating system developed at Carnegie-Mellon University (CMU) under the leadership of Richard Rashid and with the support of DARPA, the U.S. Department of Defense Advanced Research Projects Agency. It is based on a previously developed operating system at CMU called Accent [Rashid and Robertson 1981]. Therefore, many of the basic concepts in Mach are based on Accent work. However, as compared to Accent, Mach has many improved features, including finer grained parallelism by the use of threads, multiprocessor support, a better interprocess communication mechanism, and a more flexible and efficient memory management scheme.

The first version of Mach was released in 1986 for the DEC VAX computer family, including the VAX 11/784, a four-CPU multiprocessor. By 1987, versions for the IBM RT PC, SUN 3, PERQ, Sequent, and Encore machines were also available. At this time, Mach was mainly considered to be an operating system for shared-memory multiprocessor systems, rather than a distributed operating system for a collection of machines interconnected by a network. This was because most of the machines running Mach were tightly coupled shared-memory multiprocessor systems. An extended version (Mach 2.5) was later released that was also suitable for loosely coupled distributed-memory multiprocessor systems. This version also provided compatibility with the 4.2 BSD UNIX by including most of the 4.2 BSD UNIX into the Mach kernel. Due to the presence of a large amount of BSD UNIX code in the kernel, the Mach 2.5 kernel was quite large and monolithic. In 1989, a new version (Mach 3.0) was released in which all the BSD UNIX code was removed from the kernel and put in the user space. Therefore, Mach 3.0 has a microkernel that consists of pure Mach.

In 1989, the Open Software Foundation (OSF), a consortium of computer vendors, selected Mach as the basis of its first operating system, called OSF/1. OSF has such important companies as IBM, DEC, and Hewlett-Packard as its members. The NeXT workstation also uses Mach as its operating system.

The following description of Mach is based on [Rashid 1987, Accetta et al. 1986, Jones and Rashid 1986, Black 1990, Fitzgerald and Rashid 1986, Rashid et al. 1988, Coulouris et al. 1994, Tanenbaum 1995, Silberschatz and Galvin 1994].

### 12.4.1 Design Goals and Main Features

Mach's design was influenced by the research and design goals described below.

#### Open-System Architecture

One of the main goals of Mach was to design an open system that could provide a base for building new operating systems and emulating existing ones. To achieve this goal, the design philosophy used in Mach was to have a minimal microkernel that would provide a small set of basic abstractions sufficient for deriving other functionality and to implement many traditional kernel-based functions as user-level servers. With this approach, it is both possible and rational to think of traditional operating systems such as UNIX and MS-DOS not as operating system kernels but as application programs—servers or a set of servers that can provide client programs with specific programming abstractions. Note that the microkernel-based design of Mach allows multiple emulators to be run simultaneously. This makes it possible to run programs written for different operating systems such as UNIX and MS-DOS on the same machine at the same time.

### Compatibility with BSD UNIX

From the very beginning, an important goal of Mach was to provide full compatibility with BSD UNIX systems so that it could receive wide acceptance in the research and academic communities. This goal was initially achieved by combining Mach and the 4.2 BSD UNIX into a single kernel. Although this design guaranteed absolute compatibility with the 4.2 BSD UNIX, it led to a large kernel. The open-system design strategy was later employed, and all the BSD UNIX code was removed from the kernel and put in the user space. This redesign reduced the Mach kernel to a minimal microkernel consisting of pure Mach that could be used as a base for emulating not only BSD UNIX but also other existing operating systems and designing new operating systems on it.

### Network Transparency

Similar to any other distributed operating system, network transparency was also a goal in Mach. To achieve this goal, a higher level networkwide naming system is used in Mach. It is implemented by user-level servers called *network message servers* that are involved in transparent sending of messages between two processes that are located on different nodes of the system. This facility allows transparent access to networkwide resources.

### Flexible Memory Management

Another important goal of Mach was to support a powerful and flexible memory management system. To achieve this goal, Mach provides an elaborate virtual-memory system that is implemented in terms of fixed-size pages. Some of the attractive features of Mach's memory management system are as follows:

1. It clearly separates the machine-independent parts of the memory management system from the machine-dependent parts, making the memory management system far more portable than in other systems.

2. It is integrated with the communication system, allowing the realization of fast local IPC.

3. It has a *copy-on-write* mechanism for efficient sharing of data between two or more processes. In this mechanism, data are physically copied only when they are

changed. Hence, it provides the potential to eliminate much data movement between the kernel, block I/O devices, clients, and servers.

4. It has an *inheritance* mechanism that allows a parent process to declare which regions of memory are to be inherited by its children and which are to be read-writable. This mechanism provides for various sharing policies to enforce protection between the parent and its children processes.

5. It has an *external memory manager* concept, which allows the implementation and use of multiple user-level memory managers for handling different memory managers. Each user-level memory manager can implement its own semantics and paging algorithm suitable to the object it is backing. The external memory manager concept also lends itself well to implementing a page-based distributed shared-memory system.

### Flexible IPC

Another goal of Mach was to provide a flexible IPC system that can allow processes to communicate in a reliable and efficient manner. To achieve this goal, Mach uses a message-based IPC that is based on ports, which are kernel objects that hold messages. This IPC system has the following features:

1. It supports both synchronous and asynchronous message passing.
2. It guarantees reliable and sequenced delivery of messages.
3. It ensures secure message communication by using a capability-based access control mechanism for controlling access to ports. All messages are sent to and received from ports.
4. It supports network transparency by allowing a sender to send a message to a receiver on another node without the necessity to know the receiver's location.
5. When both the sender and receiver of a message are located on the same node of the system, it provides a way to transfer bulk data without doing any copying.
6. It supports heterogeneity by translating data types from one machine's representation to another's when the data is transferred between two machines of different types.

### High Performance

High performance was also a goal of Mach. However, the use of the microkernel-based design approach in Mach is subject to a performance penalty because message passing between serving processes and the microkernel requires context switches, slowing down the system. Some of the important techniques used in the design of Mach to obtain high performance are as follows:

1. Use of multithreaded processes to take advantage of fine-grained parallelism for multiprocessing.

2. Use of hand-off thread scheduling policy for fast local IPC. For example, a client can "hand off" to a server and a server can "hand back" at the completion of a local IPC. With this approach, although the context switch is unavoidable, the path through the scheduler is optimized or avoided.

3. Use of copy-on-write mechanism to minimize the copying of data. Notice that the largest CPU cost of many operations in a traditional kernel is the copying of data (in and out of buffers, for instance). Mach's copy-on-write mechanism can be used to greatly reduce the data-copying cost.

4. Use of a transparent shared library in the user space to perform server work in the client address space. In Mach, many kernel activities are effectively moved out of the kernel directly into the client's address space by being placed in a transparent shared library. With this approach, to the extent possible, the requirements of a server are implemented in the library, thus avoiding the need for either a message or a kernel trap.

#### Simple Programmer Interface

Another goal of Mach was to provide a simple interface to the programmers. To achieve this goal, Mach provides an interface generator called *Mach Interface Generator* (*MIG*). MIG is basically a compiler that generates stub procedures from a service definition. The stub procedures for all services are placed in a transparent shared library. It is these procedures that are described in the manuals and called by application programs. This approach allows the application programmers to use a service by simply making a procedure call, rather than making a system call or writing code for sending and receiving messages.

### 12.4.2 System Architecture

As Figure 12.7 shows, the Mach system architecture mainly consists of the following layers:

1. *The microkernel layer.* The lowest layer is the minimal microkernel that is replicated on each node of the system. It is minimal because it consists of a small set of basic abstractions that are just sufficient and powerful enough to derive all other functionality and features. In particular, this layer is concerned with IPC, memory management, process management, and I/O services. To carry out these functions, it supports five basic abstractions—tasks, threads, memory objects, ports, and messages. Tasks and threads are abstractions for process management, memory objects is an abstraction used in memory management, and ports and messages are abstractions for interprocess communication.

2. *User-level server layer.* In Mach, many traditional kernel-based functions are implemented as user-level servers. These servers form the next layer of the overall system architecture. The servers at this layer may be broadly classified into two categories—

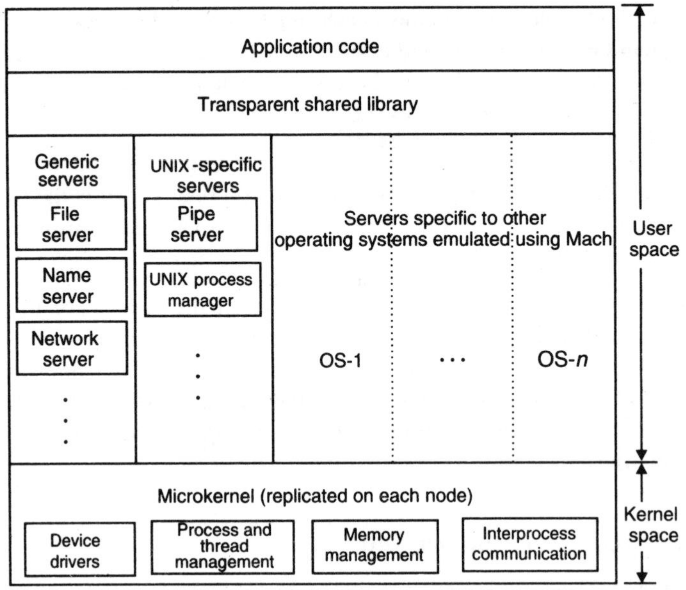


**Fig. 12.7** Mach system architecture.

generic and specific. *Generic servers* provide services of general interest. For instance, there may be generic servers for services such as user authentication, distributed file management, transparent naming of objects, network protocols, and device allocation. On the other hand, *specific servers* are used to provide particular behavior in a node. For instance, a set of specific servers may be used to deliver the functionality of an existing operating system, such as UNIX. As shown in Figure 12.7, multiple sets of specific servers may be used at a single node to emulate the functionality of different operating systems at the same node.

3. *Transparent shared-library layer.* This layer contains the stub procedures generated by MIG for all services, so that the application programmers can use a service by simply making a procedure call, rather than making a system call or writing code for sending and receiving messages.

4. *Application code layer.* This layer contains the code for the application programs.

### 12.4.3 Process Management

#### Basic Abstractions

The two basic abstractions used for process management in Mach are task and thread, which basically correspond to the concepts of "process" and "thread" presented in Chapter 8. That is, a *task* is an execution environment and a *thread* is the basic unit of execution. Resources are allocated to and owned by a task, and all threads of a task share its resources. To avoid any confusion, the term "process" will be used instead of "task" in the following description of Mach.

### Process and Thread States

At any instance of time, a thread may be in one of the following states:

1. *Running.* A thread that is in the running state either is executing on some processor or is eligible for execution and waiting in the run queue for the allocation of a processor to it. A thread that is blocked within the kernel (for example, while waiting for a page fault to be satisfied) is also considered to be in the running state.

2. *Suspended.* A thread that is in the suspended state is neither executing on a processor nor waiting in the run queue for processor allocation. The thread will not execute until it is returned to the running state.

Similar to a thread, a process can also be in the running or suspended state. A process can be running or suspended, independent of the state of its threads. However, the state of a process affects all threads of that process. Therefore, if a process is suspended, its threads cannot execute, irrespective of their current state. That is, a thread can execute only when both it and its process are in the running state.

Processes and threads can be suspended and resumed under program control. For this, each process and each thread has a *suspend* counter associated with it. Primitives *process_suspend* and *thread_suspend* are provided to increment a suspend counter and *process_resume* and *thread_resume* to decrement it. When the suspend counter of a thread (or process) is positive, it is suspended, and when it becomes zero, its state becomes running. This mechanism allows multiple suspend calls to be executed on a thread (or process), and only when an equal number of resume calls occur is the thread (or process) resumed. Therefore, using a counter provides greater flexibility than using a bit and helps avoid race conditions.

### Operations on Processes and Threads

Each process owns a *process port* and each thread owns a *thread port*. These ports provide the mechanism to operate on processes and threads. In particular, an operation on a thread (or process) is invoked by sending a message to the thread port (or process port) of the thread (or process). Access to a process port indirectly permits access to all threads within that process, but not vice versa.

Process management primitives provided in Mach include those for creating a process, killing a process, suspending or resuming a process, controlling which threads of a process can run on which processor or group of processors, setting the priority of a process for scheduling of its current and future threads, getting a list of all threads in a process, and getting statistical information about a process.

In Mach, threads are managed by the kernel. That is, thread creation and destruction are done by the kernel and involve updating kernel data structures. The basic kernel interface provides a variety of primitives for operations on threads. They provide the basic mechanisms for handling multiple activities within a single address space. However, rather than making programmers work with these low-level primitives, Mach provides many higher level interfaces for programming in C and other languages. One such interface is the *C-threads package* that is briefly described below.

### The C-threads Package

The C-threads package allows the programmers to use the kernel thread primitives in a simple and convenient manner. Although it does not provide the full power of the kernel interface, it is good enough for the average programmers. In particular, it has routines for directly controlling threads, for enforcing mutual exclusion for critical sections of threads, and for general synchronization of threads.

The routines for direct thread manipulation are given below:

- *cthread_fork* is used to create a new thread in the same address space as the calling thread. The thread executes concurrently with its parent thread. However, instead of executing the parent's code, it executes a procedure that is specified as an input parameter to this routine.
- *cthread_exit* is used to terminate the calling thread. This routine is called by a thread when it has finished doing its work.
- *cthread_join* is used to cause the calling thread to suspend itself until a specific child thread terminates.
- *cthread_detach* is used to announce that a particular thread will never be *cthread_joined* (waited for). If that thread ever calls *cthread_exit*, its stack and other state information is immediately deleted. Normally, this cleanup takes place after the parent has done a successful *cthread_join*.
- *cthread_yield* is used by a thread to voluntarily relinquish the CPU to the scheduler when it has nothing to do. The scheduler can then schedule another thread to run on that CPU.

Since all the threads of a process share a common address space, the execution of critical regions by the threads must be mutually exclusive in time. In Mach, the mutex-variable technique is used for this purpose; the associated C-threads package routines are given below:

- *mutex_alloc* is used to dynamically create a mutex variable.
- *mutex_free* is used to deallocate a mutex variable.
- *mutex_lock* is used to lock a mutex variable. If the mutex variable is already locked, the thread keeps trying to lock it until it succeeds. Notice that a deadlock will result if a thread with a lock tries to lock the same mutex variable. The C-threads package does not guarantee bounded waiting. Rather, it is dependent on the hardware instructions used to implement the mutex routines.
- *mutex_unlock* is used to unlock a mutex variable.

Finally, the condition-variables technique is used in Mach for general synchronization of threads; the associated C-threads package routines are given below. Recall from Chapter 8 that a condition variable is associated with a mutex variable:

- *condition_alloc* is used to dynamically allocate a condition variable.
- *condition_free* is used to delete a condition variable that was previously allocated.
- *condition_wait* is used to unlock the mutex variable associated with the condition variable and block the calling thread.
- *condition_signal* is used to indicate to a thread blocked on a condition variable that the event being waited for may have occurred. The associated mutex variable is then locked, and the thread starts executing in the critical region. Note that a *condition_signal* does not guarantee that the condition still holds when the unblocked thread finally returns from its *condition_wait* call, so the awakened thread must keep executing the *condition_wait* routine in a loop until it is unblocked and the condition holds.

### Threads Scheduling

The threads-scheduling scheme of Mach is illustrated in Figure 12.8. It uses the concept of *processor sets*, in which all the processors of the system are grouped into disjoint sets by software. Depending on the computation needs of a thread and workload on each

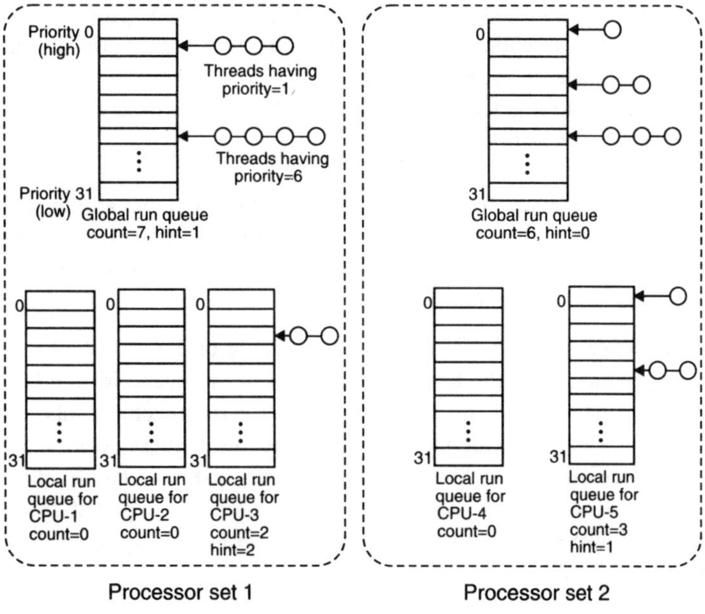


**Fig. 12.8** Threads scheduling in Mach.

processor set, each thread is assigned to one of the processor sets by software. Thus each processor set has a collection of CPUs and a collection of threads. For the purpose of scheduling, the CPUs and the threads of a processor set are totally independent of all other processor sets. That is, the scheduling algorithm is mainly concerned with assigning the threads of a processor set to the CPUs of the processor set in a fair and efficient manner. For fairness and efficiency, the scheduling algorithm uses a priority-based scheme with dynamically variable quantum size. Its details are given below.

In Mach, each thread has an associated priority from 0 to 31, with 0 being the highest priority and 31 being the lowest priority. Moreover, as Figure 12.8 shows, associated with each CPU is a *local run queue* and associated with each processor set is a *global run queue*. Each of these queues is an array of 32 queues, with each queue corresponding to priorities 0–31. Both the local and global run queues have two variables associated with them—a count and a hint. The count variable contains the number of threads on all the 32 queues of that run queue, and the hint variable contains the number of the queue out of the 32 queues that currently has the highest priority thread. The hint variable allows the search for the highest priority thread to be performed efficiently by avoiding the checking of higher priority empty queues. In addition to these two variables, each global run queue has a mutex variable associated with it that is used to lock the queue to ensure that only one CPU at a time manipulates it.

The global run queue of a processor set holds those threads that can be assigned to any of the CPUs of the processor set. On the other hand, each local run queue holds those threads that are permanently bound to the corresponding CPU. For instance, a thread that is a device driver for a device connected to an individual CPU must run only on that CPU. Putting such a thread on the global run queue is incorrect because in that case it may be picked up for execution by some other CPU of the same processor set. With respect to a particular CPU, threads in its local run queue have higher priority than the threads in the global run queue of its processor set.

With this arrangement of queues and threads in a processor set, the basic scheduling algorithm works as follows:

1. When the state of a thread with priority *n* becomes *running*, it is put at the end of queue *n* of either the local run queue of a particular CPU (if it is permanently bound to that CPU) or the global run queue. Notice that a thread that is not in the running state is not present on any run queue.

2. When a thread that is currently running on a CPU blocks, exits, yields, or uses up its quantum, the CPU first inspects its local run queue for the highest priority thread. For this, it first checks the count variable. If it is nonzero, it takes the value of the hint variable and begins searching the queue for the highest priority thread, starting at the queue specified by the hint. If the local run queue is empty (the value of its count variable is found to be zero), the CPU searches the global run queue in the same manner. However, this time it first locks the global run queue before starting the search operation.

3. If no runnable thread is found on either queue, a special idle thread is run until some thread becomes ready to run.

4. On the other hand, if the CPU finds a runnable thread, it runs the thread for one quantum. When the quantum finishes, a check is made to see if any other threads having higher or equal priority than the just-run thread have become runnable. The check involves searching both the local and global run queues. If such a thread is found, the CPU is taken away from the current thread and assigned to that thread, and the current thread is put at the end of its priority queue in the appropriate run queue. Otherwise, the same thread is run for another quantum.

In addition to the basic scheduling algorithm described above, Mach's scheduling scheme has several other important features:

1. To provide high efficiency when the system is lightly loaded and good response time to small jobs when the system is heavily loaded, the size of the time quantum is varied inversely with the total number of threads that are runnable.

2. Threads may also be scheduled preemptively. For example, if the quantum size is suddenly reduced due to sudden increase in the load of a processor set, the currently running thread (that was given the previously valid long quantum size) can be preempted before it has fully utilized its allocated quantum. This feature allows fair CPU utilization in a situation in which the system load suddenly increases. A thread may also relinquish the CPU voluntarily before the quantum expires if it currently has no use for the CPU (e.g., the *cthread_yield* routine).

3. The priority value of a thread is dynamically changed to prevent the monopolization of a CPU by a high-priority thread. This feature allows fair utilization of the available computing power by all threads.

4. Handoff scheduling facility may be used to bypass the run queues and to directly switch the CPU to the thread specified by the currently running thread.

5. On a multiprocessor, Mach can also be configured to do affinity scheduling.

Further details of the threads-scheduling scheme of Mach can be found in [Black 1990].

### Exception Handling

The exception-handling facility of Mach classifies the uses of exceptions into the following categories:

1. For error handling
2. For debugging

The two classes of exceptions are handled in different ways. Exceptions of the former class are handled on a per-thread basis, whereas exceptions of the latter class are handled by a single exception handler that has a special port, called the *exception port*, associated with it. When an exception occurs, the kernel sends a message describing the exception to the appropriate exception handler. The two types of exceptions are handled differently because it makes little sense to try to debug only one thread or to have exceptions from multiple threads invoking multiple debuggers.

In debugging, the exception-handling facilities of a process are inherited by its children processes, allowing a debugger to manipulate an entire tree of processes. On the other hand, in error handling, no exception-handling facility of a process is inherited by its children processes, and the default assumption is that a process has no exception-handling facility.

In Mach, if exceptions of both types occur simultaneously, error handlers take precedence over debuggers. This is because error handlers are normally part of the process and therefore should execute normally even in the presence of a debugger.

### 12.4.4 Memory Management

#### Virtual-Memory Management

In Mach, the memory is modeled as a linear virtual address space supported by paging. Each process has its own virtual address space within which its threads execute. The virtual address space of a process is generally sparse, consisting of holes of unallocated space between sections of the virtual address space in use. This is because Mach makes no attempt to compress the address space to remove the holes of unallocated memory that appear in the address space as new items are mapped or removed from the address space.

The commonly used approach to maintain the virtual address space for each process is to keep a linear page table from 0 to the highest used page in the kernel. Since the virtual address space of a process in Mach is sparse, for a reasonable page size, this approach would require excessive amounts of memory for fairly large page tables, making it expensive. To overcome this problem, the concept of *regions* is used in Mach, which is a contiguous area of an address space represented as a base address and a size. A region must be aligned on a page boundary. The size of the table used to maintain the virtual address space of a process is kept manageable by keeping information about only currently allocated regions in it. A virtual address is valid only if it falls in an allocated region. Accessing an address that is in an unallocated region (unused virtual address space) will result in a trap, which, however, can be caught by the process if it so desires.

Mach provides a number of calls for manipulating virtual address spaces. For instance, the *vm_allocate* call allocates a new region of virtual memory. The caller can specify either both a base address and a size or only a size. In the former case, the system allocates the indicated region, whereas in the latter case, the system finds and allocates a suitable region and returns its base address to the caller. The *vm_deallocate* call removes a region from a process's address space and makes it no longer valid for the process. The *vm_read* and *vm_write* calls allow a process to access the virtual memory of another process. The *vm_copy* call causes a memory region to be copied onto a new region. In addition to these calls, there are other calls that may be used for such purposes as to control access protection of a region of memory, to control inheritance of memory regions by a child process from its parent process when new processes are created, and to get information about a region in a process's address space.

### External Memory Managers

In traditional operating systems, management of secondary storage (such as a disk) is usually based around a kernel-supplied file system that determines the paging scheme, sharing semantics, and other implementation details of the corresponding objects (such as file). The schemes built into the system for managing such objects may be suitable for a large variety of objects but may not be the best for all types of objects. Therefore, Mach's memory management system is designed in such a way that it allows users to implement and use their own special-purpose memory managers, having their own object management scheme, for objects with special requirements. These special-purpose, user-level memory managers are called *external memory managers*.

For the realization of the idea of external memory managers, an important abstraction used in the memory management system of Mach is the *memory object*. A memory object is an abstract object that represents a collection of data on which a set of operations are defined (for example, read and write). It can be mapped into an unused portion of the virtual address space of a process, forming a new region.

Memory objects are created and managed by external memory managers. As Figure 12.9 shows, for every memory object that is mapped in a process's address space, there is an external memory manager that controls it. The Mach kernel simply acts as a cache manager for these memory objects. It maintains a cache of memory-resident pages of all mapped objects, as in other virtual-memory implementations. However, since the external memory managers are user-level processes, it is possible to have different memory managers for handling different classes of memory objects. This provides the flexibility to have different sets of operations, different sharing semantics, and different rules about what becomes of objects after they are mapped out for different classes of memory objects. This flexibility also allows user-written memory managers to have their own paging scheme for the memory objects they manage. Each memory manager can

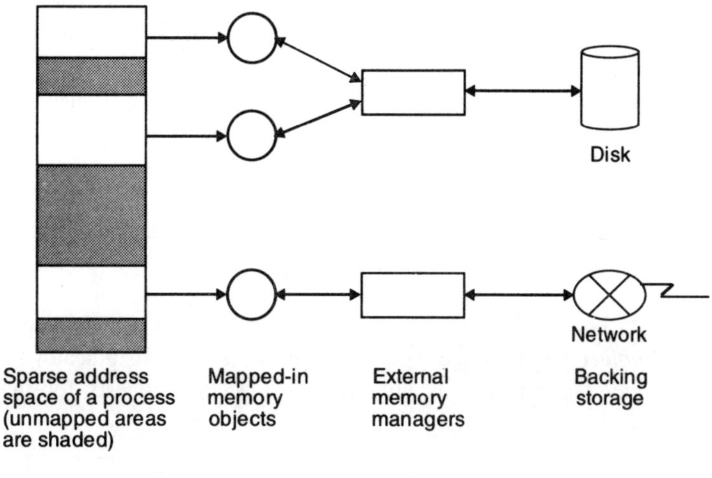


**Fig. 12.9** External memory managers and memory objects.

determine on its own where to store pages that are not in memory and whether to write back any changed pages to secondary storage when a memory object is destroyed. Note that memory objects are independent of the kernel in the sense that no assumptions are made by Mach as to the content or importance of memory objects.

To make it possible for users to write and use their own memory managers, Mach provides a well-defined interface between the kernel and the memory managers. This interface takes the form of a communication protocol that consists of a set of message types that can be exchanged between the kernel and the memory managers. These message types can be classified into two categories—those that the kernel sends to memory managers and those that memory managers send to the kernel. Some examples of those the kernel sends to memory managers are as follows:

- *memory_object_init*. This message is sent when a memory object is to be mapped for the first time. When a memory manager receives this message, it initializes itself. The message contains the control and name ports (these port types are described later) for the memory object being mapped. These ports are used later by the memory manager to send messages to the kernel in connection with the memory object.
- *memory_object_data_request*. This message is sent to a memory manager to request data of a memory object managed by it when a page fault occurs on the memory object. The message contains the range of the desired data.
- *memory_object_data_write*. This message is sent when the kernel needs to remove one or more dirty pages of a memory object from resident memory, for instance, due to page aging. The updated data to be written on the secondary storage is included in the message.
- *memory_object_data_unlock*. This message is sent to request the memory manager of a memory object to unlock a locked page of the object so that it can be used for another process.
- *memory_object_lock_completed*. This message is sent to a memory manager in reply to its *memory_object_data_lock* request (described below) made to the kernel.
- *memory_object_terminate*. This message is sent to a memory manager to inform it that the memory object named in the message is no longer in use and can be removed from memory.

Some examples of message types the memory managers send to the kernel are as follows:

- *memory_object_set_attributes*. This message is sent in response to the *memory_object_init* message received from the kernel. It indicates to the kernel that the memory manager is now ready to accept requests for the newly mapped-in object.
- *memory_object_data_provided*. This message is sent in response to the *memory_object_data_request* message to return the requested page to the kernel.

- *memory_object_data_unavailable.* This message is sent in response to the *memory_object_data_request* message when the requested data is not available.
- *memory_object_data_lock.* This message is sent to make a request to the kernel to change the protection mode on pages. The message contains a *lock_value* that specifies the new protection mode (read, write, execute) on the data specified in the message.
- *memory_object_data_clean.* This message is sent by a memory manager to make a request to the kernel to send it the pages specified in the message so that they can be made clean by writing them to disk.
- *memory_object_data_cache.* This message is sent to tell the kernel whether it may retain cached data of the memory object even when no process has it mapped in to its address space.
- *memory_object_destroy.* This message is sent to tell the kernel that a certain memory object is no longer needed and its information in the kernel can be destroyed.

All messages from the kernel to the memory managers are sent asynchronously because it is not reasonable for the kernel to block any of its threads waiting for a user process that may not reply. The messages are exchanged between the kernel and the memory managers by using the port-based interprocess communication mechanism of Mach (described later). For this, the following types of ports are used:

1. *Object port.* Every memory object has an object port associated with it. This port is created by the memory manager that manages the object. It is used by the memory manager for receiving messages from the kernel about page faults and other events relating to the object.

2. *Control port.* For each memory object, a control port is created by the kernel. It is used by the kernel to receive messages related to the object from the memory manager of the object.

3. *Name port.* For each memory object, the kernel also creates a name port. It is used as a kind of name to identify the object. Name ports are not used for receiving messages but rather are used as a point of reference. For example, each region of an address space may be treated as an object, in which case the kernel has a name port for each region. Now when a thread gives an address to the kernel asking it which region the address belongs to, the kernel returns the name port of that region as an answer. Notice that all addresses belonging to the same region will be identified by the same name port.

Now let us look at how a memory manager and the kernel interact to manage a memory object and to satisfy user access requests for data in the memory object. The call *vm_map* provided in Mach (along with other calls for manipulating virtual address spaces) is used to map a memory object into the virtual address space of the calling process. When a thread needs access to data in a memory object, it makes a *vm_map* call. If this is the first *vm_map* call on the memory object, the kernel creates the control and name ports for the memory object and sends a *memory_object_init* message to the object port included in the *vm_map* call. The memory manager that manages the memory object provides this object port as a part of its support of the object. In reply, the memory manager sends a *memory_object_set_attributes* message telling the kernel what the object's attributes are. Initially, all the pages of the object are marked as unreadable/unwriteable, so that the first access to the object will result in a trap. The thread that made the *vm_map* call is now unblocked and allowed to execute.

When the thread attempts to read/write some data of the memory object, a page fault occurs, and the kernel sends a *memory_object_data_request* message to the memory manager via the object port of the memory object. On receiving this message, the memory manager fetches the page by whatever method is appropriate for the concerned object and returns a pointer to the page in the *memory_object_data_provided* message or returns an appropriate error to the kernel. The kernel then maps the page into the faulting thread's address space and unblocks the thread allowing it to continue with its execution.

In addition to the user-written specialized memory managers, there is a *default memory manager* provided by the Mach system. This memory manager is needed for several reasons, such as for taking care of the system's own memory needs, for managing those regions of an address space that do not have a memory manager assigned to them, and for managing a memory object in the default manner when the specialized memory manager of that object crashes due to a bug in it. The default memory manager has an interface identical to that of user-written memory managers. However, it uses the standard file system to store data that must be written to disk. Unlike UNIX, which uses a separate swap area, the default memory manager uses a temporary file for swap space. Notice that when a process makes the *vm_allocate* call to allocate a region of virtual address space, it is in fact mapping an object managed by the default memory manager that provides zero-filled pages in response to the call.

To ensure that there is always sufficient free-page frames, Mach also provides a *pageout daemon* that is a part of the kernel. It runs as a thread within the kernel and uses a first-in, first-out (FIFO) algorithm to select victims for page replacement. It wakes up from time to time and checks the number of free-page frames. If there are not enough free-page frames, it selects one or more pages to be replaced. If a page selected for replacement is dirty, it is sent to the memory manager in charge of the page's object in a *memory_object_data_write* message. On receiving this message, the memory manager writes the page to disk and informs the kernel when it is done.

### Memory Sharing

The use of threads in Mach automatically allows the threads of a process to share the same address space. Therefore, no special mechanism is needed to share memory among the threads of a single process. However, for sharing memory among two or more processes, Mach provides the three mechanisms described below.

***Copy-on-Write Sharing.*** We have seen that each process in Mach, including the kernel, has its own paged address space managed by the kernel. Therefore, two processes of the same node can share a memory region by having entries for the memory region in the page tables of both processes. This technique is used in the copy-on-write memory-sharing mechanism. In this mechanism, two or more processes share common memory pages by having entries for these pages in the page table of each of these processes and making them read-only. The sharing continues until one of the processes attempts to write into its own logical copy of a shared page; this causes an actual copy of the page to be created for that process, so that it has its own version of the page that is marked writable in the page table of the process. Other processes that were sharing that page continue to use the old version of the page in the read-only mode.

***Controlled Inheritance of Address Space.*** This mechanism allows selective memory sharing at the time of process creation. As in UNIX, a new process in Mach is basically created as a copy of an existing process. However, Mach's process creation mechanism is different from that of UNIX in the following aspects:

1. In UNIX, the child process is always a clone of the process that executes the *fork* system call, but in Mach the child process can be a clone of a different process called the *prototype*.

2. In UNIX, the child process inherits the entire address space of its parent process, but Mach allows controlled inheritance of address space. For controlled inheritance of address spaces, Mach allows a process to assign one of the following three inheritance attributes to each region in its address space:

(a) *No access*. A region with this attribute is not inherited by the child process. That is, it is not a part of the child's address space.

(b) *Shared access*. A region with this attribute is shared between the prototype process and the child. That is, the pages in the region are present in the address spaces of both the prototype and child processes. Changes made by either process are visible to the other process.

(c) *Copy access*. A region with this attribute is copied and mapped into the child's address space. The *fork* system call of UNIX can be simulated by using this option. However, in Mach, the region is not copied when the child is created, but the copy-on-write mechanism is used for efficiency.

***Distributed Shared Memory.*** Mach does not provide a direct mechanism for sharing memory among processes on separate machines that do not have any common shared memory. However, the external memory manager concept of Mach allows users to implement their own distributed shared-memory system. For example, to implement a page-based distributed shared-memory system, a new memory object, the shared page, can be defined. To manage these objects, one or more special memory managers can be implemented. The memory managers could be as simple or as complicated as needed, depending on which coherence protocol and data-locating mechanism, among those described in Chapter 5, are used in the implementation.

## 12.4.5 Interprocess Communication

### Basic Abstractions

The two basic abstractions used for interprocess communication in Mach are ports and messages. A *port* in Mach is a one-way communication channel, logically a bounded message queue. A *message* is a typed collection of data objects. To communicate with another process, a process sends a message to a port associated with the receiver process. The message is queued at the port until the receiver retrieves it from the port. The sender and receiver must have permission to access the port. This permission takes the form of a capability. For instance, a sender must have a capability with *send* right for a port to send a message to the port, and a receiver needs a capability with *receive* right to retrieve messages from the port. Ports support reliable, sequenced, message streams in the sense that the system guarantees the delivery of messages sent to a port in the order sent.

### Management of Ports

Ports are managed and protected by the kernel. They are kept track of on a per-process basis rather than per thread. Therefore, all ports created by the threads of a process are unique within the process. The kernel keeps no record of which thread created which port.

Protection is ensured by keeping ports information safely inside the kernel, where user processes cannot modify it. Furthermore, the threads of a process can send or receive messages from a port only if the process possesses the appropriate port capability. A port capability consists of a port identifier (pointer to the port) and a rights field telling what access the holder of the capability has to the port. The three types of rights that may be defined on a port are *send*, *send_once*, and *receive*. A capability with *send* right allows the holder to send messages to the specified port any number of times. The *send_once* right allows the capability holder to send only one message to the port, after which the kernel destroys the capability (this mechanism is useful for request–reply protocols). The *receive* right allows the capability holder to read messages from the port. At any instance of time, there can be only one process with *receive* right to a port, but many processes may simultaneously have *send* right. A process having a port capability with *receive* right may send that capability in a message to another process. However, by doing so, the sender loses its *receive* right for the port and the receiver gains that right. For each process, the kernel maintains a capability list that contains complete information about what rights the process possesses for different ports. Since ports are kept track of on a per-process basis, all the threads in a process are equally considered holders of the process's port capabilities.

When a process holding a port capability with *receive* right exits or is killed, the port can no longer be used and is therefore destroyed by the kernel, even if it contains any undelivered messages. The kernel then searches for all the *send* capabilities of the port and marks them as dead. Any attempt to send a message with a capability that has been marked as dead by the kernel fails, and the kernel returns an appropriate error code to the sender. On the other hand, when there are no processes having a capability with *send* right for a port, the kernel (optionally) sends a message to the process having *receive* right capability for the port, notifying it that there are no senders left.

The message queue associated with a port is of finite length and may become full. Several options are provided for handling problems associated with message transmission to a full queue. For instance, if a queue is full, a sender may abort the send, block until a slot becomes available in the queue, or have the kernel deliver the message for it. In the latter case, the kernel acts as a single-message queue and cannot accept any message from the sender until it has delivered the already queued message of the sender.

Mach provides the facility to group a number of ports into a *port set*. A port may belong to at most one port set at a time. It is possible to only receive messages from a port set; sending messages to a port set is not possible. Furthermore, a port that belongs to a port set cannot be used directly to receive messages. This is because all messages sent to any port in a port set are queued in a common queue, the port set's queue. When a receive is performed on a port set, the kernel returns one message from the port set's queue. If the queue is empty, one of the options described above may be selected to handle this problem. The facility to create a port set is particularly useful for writing server processes that can service requests coming in on multiple ports, such as for a server that supports multiple objects. Such a server can maintain a different port for each of the many objects that it supports and get messages for any of them without having to dedicate a thread to each one.

### Message Passing

The basic interprocess communication mechanism involves the sender process sending a message to a port and the receiver process receiving it from the same port. Messages may be sent and received either synchronously or asynchronously. An RPC mechanism is also implemented in which the sender blocks after sending a message until a reply comes back.

A message consists of a fixed-length header and a variable number of typed data objects. The header contains such information as capability name for the destination port, capability name for the reply port to which return messages should be sent, message size, and several types of options such as whether synchronous, asynchronous, or RPC type communication is desired, what to do if the *send* or *receive* cannot complete successfully, and what to do if the message queue at the port is full.

The data part of a message consists of a variable number of typed data objects. Each data object may be represented either as an *in-line data* or an *out-of-line data*. In the former representation, the data object is included in the body of the message, whereas in the latter representation, the message body contains a pointer to the data object. Associated with each data object in the message is a descriptor that contains such information as the type of data object and its size. This information is needed so that the receiver can unpack the data correctly. It is also useful to do conversions between machines, when the source and destination machines have different internal representations. A data field of a message may also contain a port capability when a process wants to send a capability to another process.

The facility to use out-of-line data representation in a message body provides the means to transfer the entire address space of a process in a single message. Furthermore, when both the sender and receiver processes are on the same node,

Mach uses the copy-on-write mechanism to transfer out-of-line data from the sender to the receiver. That is, instead of copying the data physically from the sender's address space to the receiver's address space, the kernel simply updates the receiver's page table by placing information about all the pages of the data object in it and making them copy-on-write. Depending on the bit in the descriptor for the data object, the region corresponding to the data object is either removed from the sender's address space (by deleting the corresponding entries from the sender's page table) or kept there. In the latter case, a page of the data is physically copied in the receiver's address space when the receiver attempts to write on it, and the corresponding entry in the receiver's page table is appropriately updated. This is done to ensure that any modifications do not affect the original version of the data that the sender is still using.

With the use of copy-on-write mechanism, message passing becomes very efficient because no copying of data is required in most cases. In essence, message passing is implemented by using the virtual-memory management mechanism.

### Networkwide IPC

For networkwide IPC, Mach uses user-level servers called *network message servers* and *network ports* that are ports for receiving messages from other nodes of the system. There is a network message server at each node of the system. All the network message servers work together to handle internode messages in a transparent manner. The three main jobs performed by network message servers are as follows:

1. Making the networkwide IPC mechanism network transparent.
2. Supporting heterogeneity by translating message data from the sender's computer format to the receiver's computer format. The type information in the descriptor for each data object in the message is used for this purpose.
3. Performing authentication of other network message servers to prevent message data from falling into the hands of unauthorized users.

Processes of a node automatically inherit *send* right to a port created by the local network message server for receiving messages from local processes. The network message server of a node allows local processes to register network ports with it, and the network message servers of all the nodes communicate with each other to maintain a distributed database of all network ports in the system. A process can gain *send* right to a network port by asking its local network message server to look up a name in its database or by receiving a port capability in a message.

The basic method by which a message is sent from a process $P_1$ on node $A$ to a process $P_2$ on node $B$ is illustrated in Figure 12.10. It involves the following steps:

1. Process $P_1$ prepares the header and body of the message to be sent and executes the *message_send* system call for sending the message, just as in the case of a local IPC.

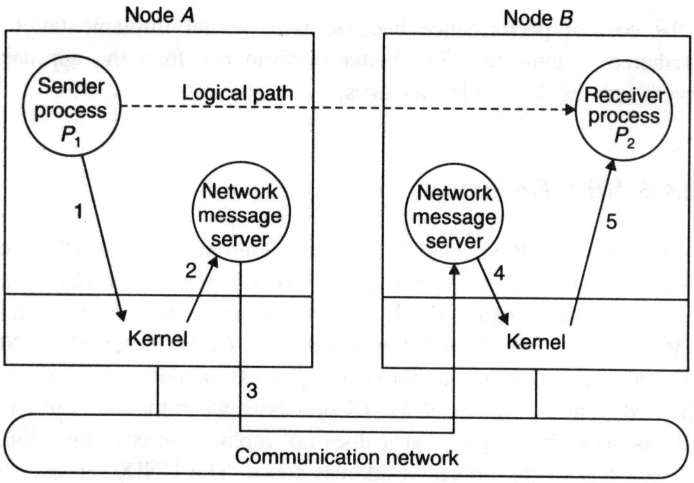


**Fig. 12.10** Networkwide IPC mechanism in Mach.

2. The system call causes a trap to the kernel. The kernel extracts the receiver's port number from the message header, and after determining that this port is nonlocal, it forwards the message to the local network message server.

3. The network message server of node *A* then consults the database of network ports to find out the node to which the message should be forwarded. It then constructs a network message containing the message of process $P_1$ and sends it across the network to the network message server of node *B*. In some cases, the message between the two network message servers is encrypted for security.

4. The network message server of node *B* looks up the network port number contained in the message and maps it to its equivalent local port number by using a mapping table that it maintains. When needed, it also translates message data from the representation of the computer at node *A* to its own computer representation. It then executes the *message_send* system call for sending this message to the extracted local port.

5. The system call causes a trap to the kernel. The kernel extracts the receiver's port number from the message header, and after determining that this port is local with process $P_2$ having *receive* right for it, it provides the message to process $P_2$ when it executes a *message_receive* call. In this way, the message is transferred from the sender to the receiver in a transparent manner.

Notice that since network message servers are user-level processes, they can be designed by the users to allow for a flexible choice of data type representations, the amount or type of security to be used on a network, and the use of a specific protocol depending on the network to which they are attached. However, this flexibility is achieved at the cost of performance because pure kernel implementation (which most other distributed systems use) has better performance than the approach having user-level servers forward internode messages.

### 12.4.6 UNIX Emulation

Mach emulates 4.3BSD UNIX. The basic approach used for UNIX emulation in Mach is briefly described below. Its further details can be found in [Golub et al. 1990].

As shown in Figure 12.11, the two software components used for UNIX emulation in Mach are the *UNIX emulation library* and *UNIX server*. The UNIX emulation library is linked as a distinct region into every process emulating a UNIX process. This region is inherited from */etc/init* by all UNIX processes when they are forked off. The *exec* system call has been changed so that it does not replace the emulation library but just the user program part of the process's address space. The UNIX server, which contains a large amount of UNIX code, has the routines corresponding to the UNIX system calls. It is implemented as a collection of C threads.

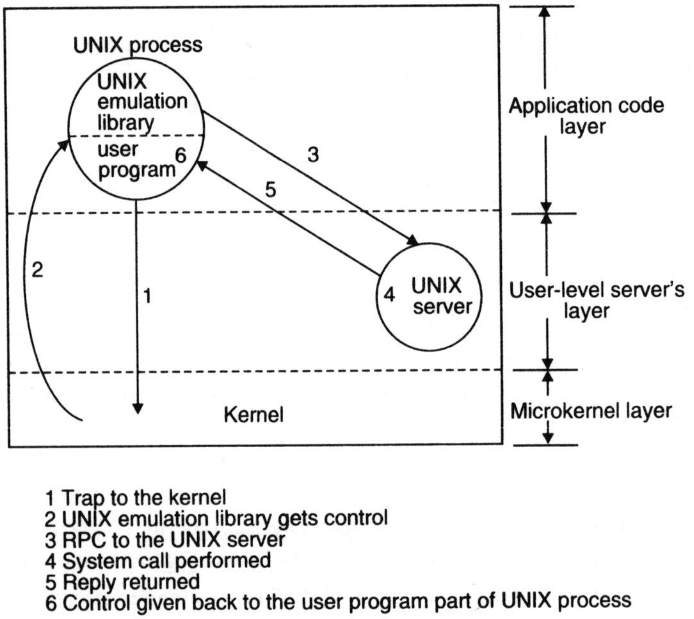


**Fig. 12.11** UNIX emulation in Mach.

The *trampoline mechanism* [Tanenbaum 1995] is used to invoke the code in the emulation library. In this mechanism, the code in the emulation library is not directly invoked by user applications, but the emulation library gets control from the kernel when a system call causes a trap to the kernel. For this, Mach provides a call named *task_set_emulation*, which assigns the address of a handler in the emulation library to a given system call number. At the time of system initialization, this is called for each UNIX system call so that all of them get registered in a system call redirection table maintained by the kernel.

With this setup, when a UNIX process makes a system call and traps to the kernel, the kernel uses the system call redirection table and immediately transfers control back to the emulation library of the same process. When the emulation library gets control, it examines the machine registers to determine which system call was invoked (note that at this time all machine registers have the same values that they had at the time of the trap). The emulation library then packs the system call number and necessary parameters into a message and does an RPC with the UNIX server. On receiving the RPC message, the UNIX server extracts the system call number and parameters from it, carries out the system call, and sends back a reply to the emulation library. On receiving the reply, the emulation library directly transfers control to the user program without going through the kernel. The entire process is summarized in Figure 12.11.

### 12.4.7 Mach Interface Generator

A programmer can write applications for the Mach system by directly using the system call interface (several system calls of Mach were described in the sections above). However, working at the system call level makes many programming tasks tedious and repetitive. For instance, any client program that requests for a service from a server process must have code to create and send messages to the server and to wait to receive a reply. Similarly, any server program that provides service to client processes must have code to accept messages, unpack them, dispatch them to the proper routine, and reply after the routine finishes processing the data. A programmer's task can be greatly simplified by providing stub procedures (procedures that generate most of the repetitive code) for all services and placing them in a transparent shared library. With this approach, an application programmer can use a service by simply making a procedure call, rather than making a system call or writing code for sending and receiving messages. To facilitate this, Mach provides an interface specification language and compiler called Mach Interface Generator (MIG). MIG generates stub procedures from a service definition.

The MIG language allows interfaces between cooperating computing entities to be specified and maintained independent of specific languages or machine architectures. On the other hand, the MIG compiler translates these specifications into interface code for each of the programming languages supported within the Mach environment, including C, COMMON LISP, Ada, and Pascal. The interface code generated by the compiler has code for communication, runtime support for type checking, type conversions, synchronization, and exception handling.

Over the years, MIG has proved to be a valuable tool because of the following main advantages:

1. It eases the task of programming distributed applications by relieving the programmers from concerns about message data formats, operating system peculiarities, and specific synchronization details.

2. It improves cooperation between programmers working in different languages by allowing both client and servers to be written in any of the languages supported within the Mach environment. The MIG compiler automatically takes care of differences in language syntax, type representations, record field layout, procedure call semantics, and exception-handling semantics.

3. It enhances system standardization by providing a uniform message-level interface between processes.

4. It reduces the cost of reprogramming interfaces in multiple languages whenever a program interface is changed.

## 12.5 CHORUS

Chorus is a microkernel-based distributed operating system that started as a research project in 1979 at INRIA (Institute National de Recherche en Informatique et Automatique), a government-funded laboratory in France. Until now Chorus has passed through four major versions (Versions 0–3). Version 0 (1979–1982) was designed to model distributed applications as a collection of communicating processes called *actors*. Version 1 (1982–1984) was aimed at porting the design of Version 0 from a shared-memory multiprocessor system to a distributed-memory multiprocessor system. It also had additional features of structured messages and some support for fault tolerance. The main goal of Version 2 (1984–1986) was to add the UNIX source code compatibility feature to the system so that existing UNIX programs could be run on Chorus after recompilation. In 1986, the Chorus team left INRIA and formed a new company, named Chorus Systems, to make Chorus a commercial product. They started Version 3 in 1987, with the main goal of changing the research system into a commercial product. For this, the first goal was to provide binary compatibility with UNIX so that UNIX programs could be run on Chorus without the need to recompile them. Many key concepts from other distributed operating systems were also included in Version 3. In particular, a message-based interprocess communication mechanism was borrowed from V-System; some of the concepts of fast interprocess communication, distributed virtual memory, and external pagers were borrowed from Mach; and the idea of using capabilities for global naming and protection was borrowed from Amoeba. Version 3 also has RPC facility, support for real-time operations, and a multithreading feature. It is available as a commercial product for a wide range of hardware, such as the Intel 80x86 family, the Motorola 68000 and 88000 families, and the Inmos Transputer.

The details of Version 3 are presented below. The following description of Chorus is based on [Pountain 1994, Armand et al. 1986, Rozier et al. 1988, Guillemont 1982, Abrossimov et al. 1992, Batlivala et al. 1992, Lea et al. 1991, Lea et al. 1993, Tanenbaum 1995, Coulouris et al. 1994].

### 12.5.1 Design Goals and Main Features

Chorus's design was influenced by the research and design goals given below.

#### UNIX Emulation and Enhancements

One of the main goals of Chorus was to provide a UNIX compatibility feature so that existing UNIX programs could be run on Chorus. This was not an initial goal but was later realized to be important for the commercial success of the system. Therefore, Version 2 of Chorus was designed to provide UNIX source code compatibility. To achieve this goal, the original kernel of Chorus was redesigned and converted to a microkernel by moving as much functionality as possible from it to user address space. Then several processes were added in the user address space to do UNIX emulation. Later, in Version 3, a UNIX emulation subsystem, called Chorus/MiX (MiX stands for Modular UNIX), was built on top of the Chorus microkernel to provide binary compatibility with UNIX System V. The microkernel of Version 2 was further refined by moving out the part added to it for source code UNIX emulation and placing this part in the new UNIX emulation subsystem. A 4.3BSD UNIX emulation is also being currently implemented.

In addition to UNIX emulation, Chorus design also provides UNIX enhancements to allow users of the UNIX emulation to use enhanced facilities provided by Chorus from within UNIX processes. Two such enhancements are the use of multiple threads in a single process and the ability to create a new process at a remote node.

#### Open-System Architecture

Another important feature of Chorus is its microkernel support, which provides a base for building new operating systems and emulating existing ones in a modular way. With this feature, multiple operating system interfaces, such as UNIX System V, BSD UNIX, OS/2, and MS-DOS, can simultaneously exist on the same machine. Therefore, it will be possible to run several existing applications that now are run on different machines on a single machine.

#### Efficient and Flexible Communication

The basic communication paradigm used in Chorus is message passing. Since message passing has a reputation of being less efficient than shared memory, Chorus's designers have made great efforts to optimize the IPC system. The IPC system also provides a high degree of flexibility in handling different types of communications. This IPC system has the following features:

1. It provides both asynchronous message passing and request/reply type interactions.
2. It has RPC facility that provides at-most-once semantics. It also has lightweight RPC facility for communication between two kernel processes.

3. It has group communication facility with the flexibility to choose whether a message should be sent to all members, to any one member, to a particular member, or to any one member with the restriction that the member should not be on a specified node.
4. It ensures secure message communication by using a capability-based access control mechanism that is similar to the one used in Amoeba.
5. When both the sender and receiver of a message are located on the same node, it uses Mach's copy-on-write mechanism to transfer bulk data without doing any copying.

### Transparency

Chorus provides two types of transparency—network transparency and service reconfiguration transparency. Network transparency is implemented by the use of a single global name space and user-level servers called *network managers* that are similar to Mach's network message servers. On the other hand, service reconfiguration transparency, which allows services to be reconfigured dynamically without being noticed by the users interacting with them, is implemented by supporting port group and port migration facilities. Note that Chorus is not perfectly network transparent because some system calls work only for local cases.

### Flexible Memory Management

Two of the main facilities provided in Chorus for flexible memory management are support for multiple user-level memory managers and support for paged distributed shared memory. The former facility is implemented by using Mach-style external pagers, which are called *mappers* in Chorus.

### Support for Real-Time Applications

Another important goal of Chorus was to support real-time applications. To achieve this goal, Chorus provides for flexible allocation of thread priorities and also allows for customized thread-scheduling policies. Moreover, real-time programs can partly run in the kernel mode and can have direct access to the microkernel without any in-between software.

### Object-Oriented Programming Interface

A relatively new goal of Chorus is to provide system-level support for fine-grained object-oriented languages and applications and to do so in such a way that new object-oriented programs and old UNIX programs can be run on the same machine without interfering. To achieve this goal, Chorus designers have designed a subsystem, called Chorus Object-Oriented Layer (COOL), on top of the Chorus microkernel.

### 12.5.2 System Architecture

As shown in Figure 12.12, the Chorus system architecture mainly consists of the following layers:

1. *The microkernel layer.* The lowest layer is the microkernel layer, which is called the "*nucleus*" in Chorus. This layer is present on each node of the system. It consists of four components, three of which are machine independent and one is machine dependent. The machine-dependent part, called the *supervisor*, manages the raw hardware and catches traps, exceptions, and interrupts. It also handles context switching. This part has to be rewritten for each new hardware to which Chorus is ported. Of the three machine-independent components, one is for process and thread management, one is for virtual-memory management, and one is for handling interprocess communications. The four components of the kernel are constructed in a modular way so that any one can be changed without affecting the others.

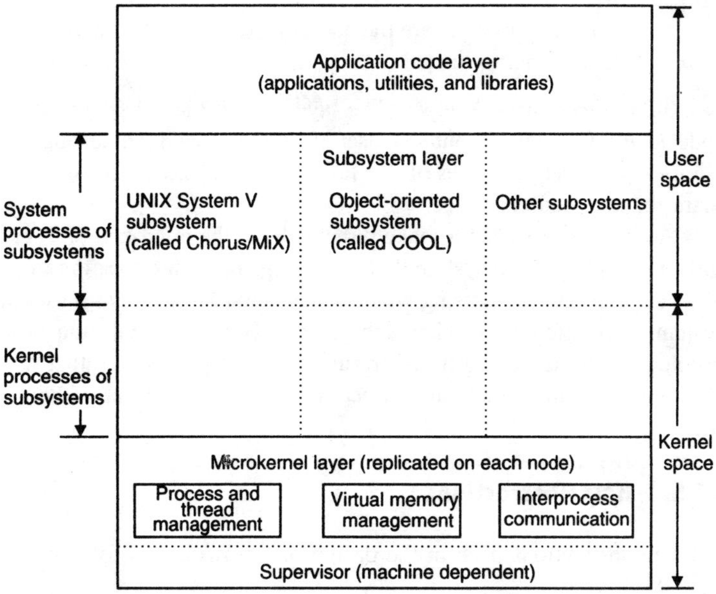


**Fig. 12.12** Chorus system architecture.

2. *The subsystem layer.* The microkernel layer provides a base for building new operating systems and emulating existing ones in a modular way. Each such newly built or emulated system is called a *subsystem*, and all these subsystems together form the subsystem layer on top of the microkernel layer. A subsystem presents a well-defined interface to its users. For example, one such subsystem is the UNIX System-V emulator, called MiX, which provides UNIX interface and allows UNIX programs to

be run on Chorus. Another such subsystem is the object-oriented subsystem, called COOL, which provides system-level support for fine-grained object-oriented languages and applications.

Each subsystem is a collection of Chorus processes. These processes are of two types—*kernel processes* and *system processes*. Kernel processes run in the kernel mode and system processes run in the user mode. Kernel processes can call one another and can invoke the microkernel for obtaining services. On the other hand, system processes can send messages to each other and to kernel processes and can also make calls to the microkernel.

The basic idea behind using kernel processes in the subsystem layer was to provide a way to extend the functionality of the microkernel without permanently increasing its size and complexity. This is achieved by providing the flexibility to dynamically load and remove kernel processes during system execution. With this facility, it is possible to dynamically configure the system software to match the hardware components of a particular node of the system without having to recompile or relink the microkernel. For instance, a disk server, implemented as a kernel process, need not be loaded on diskless workstations.

The kernel processes share the address space with the microkernel. Hence, they must be relocated after being loaded.

3. *Application code layer.* The layer above the subsystem layer is the application code layer. This layer contains user processes that include applications, utilities, and libraries. The user processes of this layer and the system processes of the subsystem layer share the user address space.

A *user process* cannot make direct calls to the microkernel. It can only make system calls offered by the subsystem that it is using. To ensure this, the microkernel keeps track of which user process is using which subsystem and disallows a user process from making system calls offered by other subsystems. However, real-time processes have special privilege in the sense that they can run as system processes rather than as user processes. This allows them to make direct access to the microkernel without any software in the way.

### 12.5.3 Key Abstractions

The key abstractions used in the design of Chorus are as follows:

1. *Actor.* An "actor" in Chorus corresponds to the concept of a "process" presented in this book. It provides an execution environment for one or more threads and has an address space and a collection of ports used to send and receive messages. To avoid any confusion, in the description that follows, the term "process" will be used instead of "actor," except in Chorus system calls.

2. *Thread.* A "thread" in Chorus is the same as the concept of a "thread" presented in this book. In Chorus, threads are managed by the kernel. That is, their creation, destruction, and scheduling are done by the kernel and involve updating kernel data structures.

3. *Region.* Each process has an address space that consists of one or more regions. A region is an area of contiguous virtual address that is associated with some piece of data, such as a program or a file. Regions of a process do not overlap. Only those portions of an address space that are occupied by the regions are accessible by the threads of the owning process. In paged virtual-memory systems, a region is aligned on a page boundary and consists of one or more pages.

4. *Segment.* A segment is a contiguous sequence of bytes identified and protected by a capability. To make the bytes of a segment accessible to the threads of a process, the segment is mapped on to a region of the process's address space. A segment can be simultaneously mapped into multiple regions that may even be in different address spaces. Once mapped, the threads access the segment's bytes simply by reading and writing addresses in the region. Note that to map a segment on to a region, it is not necessary that the segment be exactly the same size as the region. If the segment is larger than the region, only a portion of the segment equal in size to the region will be accessible. An inaccessible portion of the segment can be made accessible by remapping this portion on to the region. On the other hand, if the segment is smaller than the region, the result of reading an unmapped address depends on the mapper (mappers are similar to Mach's external memory managers and are described later). The mapper may be designed to raise an exception, return 0, or extend the segment in this case. Another way to access the bytes of a segment without the need to map it on to a region is to use traditional system calls that are used for I/O operations on files.

5. *Port.* A port is a unidirectional communication channel, logically a bounded message queue. Each port belongs to a single process and only one process can read its messages. To communicate with another process, a process sends a message to a port of the receiver process. The message is queued at the port until the receiver retrieves it from the port. As in Mach, ports can be migrated between processes and can also be grouped together to form port groups.

6. *Message.* In Chorus, the basic communication paradigm is message passing. Hence, two processes communicate with each other by exchanging messages between them. A message is addressed to a port of the receiving process. A message has a header, an optional fixed part (of 64 bytes), and an optional variable-sized body (of maximum 64 kilobytes). For the kernel, both the fixed part and the body are untyped byte arrays. Therefore, the semantics of the contents of a message can be decided by user applications.

7. *User identifier* (*UI*). In Chorus, most kernel resources, such as ports and processes, are assigned a 64-bit UI that is guaranteed to be globally unique within a system in its entire lifetime. For uniqueness, UIs are formed of three fields—(a) the ID of the machine (node) on which the UI was created, (b) an epoch number that is incremented each time the system is rebooted, and (c) a counter that is valid in the epoch. The first field of a UI is used as a hint by the object-locating mechanism to locate the corresponding object (resource). The UIs may be freely passed in messages and files from one process to another.

8. *Local identifier* (*LI*). The systemwide unique UIs are long and expensive to use. Therefore, for efficiency, resources (such as threads and ports) within a single process are identified by LIs, which are 32-bit integers. The LIs are valid only within the process that uses them.

9. *Capability.* Capabilities are used both as resource identifiers and for restricting access to resources. They are mainly used for identifying resources managed by a subsystem, but in some cases they are also used to identify resources managed by the kernel. A capability consists of the following two fields—(a) a 64-bit UI that is normally the identifier of the port to which messages are sent to request operations on the object and (b) a 64-bit key. The key has two fields. The first field serves as an index into a resource table to identify a resource from among multiple resources accessed via the same port. The second field contains a random number that makes it difficult to guess a valid capability. Processes can send capabilities to other processes or store them in files.

10. *Protection identifier* (*PI*). For authentication purposes, each process in Chorus has a PI associated with it. A PI is a bit string having no semantics associated with it. By default, a process's PI is that of the process that created it but can be changed by kernel or system processes. When a process receives a message, it can request the kernel to specify the PI of the process that sent the message. This mechanism can be used in the design of a server process to implement access control for the resources that it manages. For instance, to emulate UNIX protection semantics, the equivalent of a UNIX user identifier (UID) can be associated with each process, and then the Chorus PIs can be used to implement the UIDs.

### 12.5.4 Process Management

Of the key abstractions described in Section 12.5.3, the two basic abstractions used for process management are process (actor) and thread.

#### Types of Processes

In Chorus, processes are classified into the following types:

1. *Kernel processes*. All kernel processes reside in the kernel space and share the same address space with each other and with the microkernel. They execute in the kernel mode. They are trusted, which means that they are allowed to make direct calls to the microkernel. They are also privileged, which means that they are allowed to execute I/O and other protected instructions for making direct access to system resources. For high performance, Chorus provides the facility of lightweight RPC, which kernel processes can use to communicate with each other. This communication facility is not available to the other two types of processes.

2. *System processes*. System processes reside in the user space and execute in the user mode. Each system process has its own address space. These processes are not

privileged but trusted. That is, they can make direct calls to the microkernel but cannot execute privileged instructions meant for direct access to system resources.

3. *User processes.* User processes reside in the user space and execute in the user mode. Each user process has its own address space. These processes are neither privileged nor trusted. Therefore, they are the least powerful ones.

The properties of the three types of processes in Chorus are summarized in Figure 12.13.

| Process type | Space | Execution mode | Private address space | Privileged | Trusted |
|---|---|---|---|---|---|
| Kernel process | Kernel | Kernel | No | Yes | Yes |
| System process | User | User | Yes | No | Yes |
| User process | User | User | Yes | No | No |

**Fig. 12.13** The three types of processes in Chorus.

### Process and Thread States

In Chorus, a process may be in one of the following states:

1. *Active.* A process is in the active state when its threads can change states and can be scheduled to run.
2. *Stopped.* A process is in the stopped state when it is frozen. All the threads of a stopped process are in the stopped state.

On the other hand, a thread may be in one of the following states:

1. *Active.* A thread in the active state is either executing on some processor or eligible for executing and waiting in the run queue for the allocation of a processor to it.
2. *Waiting.* When a thread blocks and has to wait for some event to occur, the thread is put in the waiting state until the event occurs.
3. *Suspended.* A thread that is in the suspended state is neither executing on a processor nor waiting for an event to occur. It has been intentionally suspended by either another thread or itself by issuing a kernel call to suspend the thread.
4. *Stopped.* All threads of a process enter the stopped state when the process's state changes from active to stopped. Note that a thread may simultaneously be in any one of the first three states and the fourth state.

The following system calls affect process and thread states:

- *actorCreate* is used to create a new process. The process type (kernel, system, or user) and the initial state of the process can be specified as parameters. The process's capability is returned to the caller.
- *actorStop* is used to change the state of a process from active to stopped. The state of all the threads of this process is changed to stopped.
- *actorStart* is used to change a process's state from stopped to active. All the threads of this process resume their original states from the stopped state.
- *threadCreate* is used to create a thread. The initial state, priority, and so on, are specified as parameters.
- *threadSuspend* is used to suspend a thread.
- *threadResume* is used to restart a suspended thread.

### Threads Synchronization

Since all the threads of a process share a common address space, the execution of critical regions by the threads must be mutually exclusive in time. The two mechanisms used in Chorus for this purpose are the mutex variable technique and the counting-semaphore technique. The mutex variable technique (described in Chapter 8) is used only for mutual exclusion. It has the advantage that operations that do not cause the caller to block can be carried out entirely in the caller's space without the need for a kernel call. On the other hand, the counting-semaphore technique is used in Chorus for general synchronization of threads. In this technique, system calls are provided for performing UP and DOWN operations on the counting semaphore to increment or decrement its value. The system calls provided for threads synchronization in Chorus are as follows:

- *mutexInit* is used to initialize a mutex variable.
- *mutexGet* is used to perform a lock operation on a mutex variable.
- *mutexRel* is used to perform an unlock operation on a mutex variable.
- *semInit* is used to initialize a counting semaphore.
- *semP* is used to perform a DOWN operation on a counting semaphore.
- *semV* is used to perform an UP operation on a counting semaphore.

### Threads Scheduling

In Chorus, threads are scheduled by the kernel according to individual kernel priorities that can be dynamically changed. Each process is assigned a priority and each thread is also assigned a relative priority within its process. The absolute priority of a thread is the sum of its own priority and the priority of its process. A separate queue of active threads is maintained for each absolute priority level. When a CPU becomes free, the first thread of the highest priority nonempty queue is allocated to it for execution.

We have seen that Chorus provides support for real-time applications. For this, a threshold priority level is used to divide the active threads into two groups, and different scheduling algorithms are used for scheduling of threads in these two groups. That is, threads that belong to a queue having lower priority than the threshold priority level are timesliced and consume CPU time on a quantum basis in a round-robin mode. On the other hand, a thread that belongs to a queue having higher priority than the threshold priority level, once run, will continue to run until either it voluntarily releases its CPU or an even higher priority thread becomes active to run. This mechanism is considered to be good enough for handling most real-time applications.

The system calls for dynamically changing the priorities are as follows:

- *actorPriority* is used to either read or change the priority value of a process.
- *threadPriority* is used to either read or change the relative priority value of a thread.

### Exception Handling

In Chorus, there is a single exception handler kernel thread, and each process may also have its own exception handler thread. When an exception occurs, an attempt is first made to handle it by using the kernel exception handler thread. If this fails, the kernel suspends the thread that caused the exception and sends a message to the exception handler thread of the same process. The faulting thread is killed by the kernel if this method also fails.

## 12.5.5 Memory Management

### Regions and Segments Management

Of the key abstractions described in Section 12.5.3, the two basic abstractions used for memory management are region and segment. They have already been described in Section 12.5.3, and hence only the system calls supported in Chorus for their management and use are presented here. Only the important ones (not all) are given below.

- *rgnAllocate* is used to allocate a region in a process's address space and set its properties. The process's capability, starting address of the region, size of the region, and various initialization options are specified as parameters.
- *rgnInit* is used to allocate a region and to initialize it with the contents of a segment whose capability is specified as a parameter. Several other calls that are similar to *rgnInit* but fill the allocated region in different ways are also provided.
- *rgnSetProtect* is used to change the protection status (read, write, execute bits) associated with a region. It is also used to make a region accessible only to the kernel.
- *rgnStat* is used to get the size and other information about a region.
- *rgnFree* is used to free the space allocated to a region, which can then be used for allocation to new regions.

- *sgRead* is used to read data from a segment. The portion of the data to be read is specified by an offset and number of bytes as parameters. The buffer address to which data is to be copied is also specified as a parameter.
- *sgWrite* is used to write data to a segment. The portion to be written is specified by an offset and number of bytes as parameters. The buffer address from which data is to be copied is also specified as a parameter.

### Mappers

Mappers of Chorus are very similar to external memory managers of Mach. For every segment that is mapped to a region, there is a mapper to control it. A single mapper may control multiple segments. The kernel acts as a cache manager for the mapped segments. That is, the virtual-memory component of each kernel maintains a page cache of memory-resident pages and keeps track of which page belongs to which segment. It also keeps track of which of the cached pages are dirty and which are clean. When a page is selected for replacement to create space for a new page in the cache, the kernel simply discards it if it is clean; otherwise it is sent to the appropriate mapper to be written back to the corresponding segment. On the other hand, when a page fault occurs, the kernel first checks if the page is present in the cache. If not, it makes a request to the appropriate mapper to send the page and suspends the faulting thread until the page is received. The mapper then fetches the page from the segment's storage location if the page is not already present in its address space. The mapper notifies the kernel when the page becomes available with it. The kernel then accepts the page from the mapper, updates the memory management unit (MMU) page tables, and resumes the faulting thread.

Some mapper-related system calls provided in Chorus are as follows:

- *MpCreate* is used by the kernel or a program to request a mapper to swap out a segment and to allocate disk space for it. In response to this call, the mapper allocates a new segment on disk and returns a capability for it to the caller.
- *MpRelease* is used to request a mapper to release a previously created segment.
- *MpPullIn* is used by the kernel to make a request to the mapper for some data from a segment that it controls.
- *MpPushOut* is used by the kernel to send some data of a segment to a mapper that controls that segment. This is needed when the kernel wants to replace a dirty page of the segment from its cache.

### Distributed Shared Memory

The distributed shared-memory mechanism supported in Chorus may be characterized as follows (see Chapter 5 for details of these characteristics):

1. It uses page size as block size. To facilitate this, segments are split up into fragments of one or more pages.
2. It uses the replicated, migrating blocks (RMB) strategy.

3. To simplify the memory coherence problem, it classifies fragments into two types—read only and read-write. Replication of read-write fragments is not performed. Therefore, only read-only fragments are replicated and read-write fragments have only one copy in the entire system.
4. It uses the dynamic distributed-server algorithm for data locating.

### 12.5.6 Interprocess Communication

Of the key abstractions described in Section 12.5.3, the two basic abstractions used for interprocess communication are message and port. Messages are sent to and received from ports, and ports are created and deleted dynamically by processes. The system calls for creating and deleting ports are as follows:

- *portCreate* is used for creating a new port. The capability of the port is returned to the caller, which can be sent to other processes to allow them to send messages to the port.
- *portDelete* is used to delete a port.

#### Sending and Receiving of Messages

Chorus provides the following communication operations to allow threads to send and receive messages in a flexible manner:

1. *Asynchronous send.* The system call *ipcSend* is used to asynchronously send a message to a port. There is no guarantee of successful message delivery and no notification is made to the sender in case of communication failure. This type of communication facility can be used by users to build arbitrary communication patterns on top of the basic communication facility of Chorus.

2. *Receive.* The system call *ipcReceive* is used to receive a message. Two options are available in this case. In the first one, a thread can specify which port it wants to receive on. In the second one, a process can specify that it wants to receive from any one of the ports that it owns. The receive operation of the second option can be made more selective by using the following mechanisms:

(a) By disabling some of the ports by using *portDisable* system call, in which case only enabled ports are eligible to satisfy the request. A disabled port may be enabled by using the *portEnable* system call. Ports can be enabled and disabled dynamically.
(b) By assigning priorities to ports, in which case if more than one enabled port has a message, the enabled port having the highest priority is selected to receive the message. Priorities of ports can be changed dynamically.

If no message is available when the *ipcReceive* system call is made, the calling thread is suspended until a message arrives or a user-specified timer expires.

Chorus uses the copy-on-write mechanism of Mach for efficiency. Therefore, when a message is received, its body is copied to the receiver process's address space only if the sender and receiver processes are on different machines. If the two are on the same machine, the message body is simply mapped to a region of the receiver process's address space, and a page of the message body is copied only when the receiver modifies it.

3. *RPC*. The third type of communication operation supported in Chorus is RPC, which allows request/reply type interactions. The system call for initiating an RPC is *ipcCall*. The process making this call is automatically blocked until either the reply comes in or the RPC timer expires, at which time the sender is unblocked. At-most-once semantics is supported for RPCs.

### Group Communication

Group communication facility is supported in Chorus by allowing multiple ports to be grouped together to form a *port group*. The system calls provided for this purpose are as follows:

- *grpAlloc* is used to create an empty port group. The capability of the newly created port group is returned to the caller. Using this capability, the caller or any other process that subsequently acquires the capability can add or delete ports from the port group.
- *grpPortInsert* is used to add a new port to an existing port group.
- *grpPortRemove* is used to delete a port from a port group.

A sender sending a message to a port group has the flexibility to select one of the following addressing modes:

1. *Broadcast mode*. In this case, the message is sent to all ports in the group. This mode of communication is useful in such cases as sending a file update to all servers having a replica of the file or for requesting an operation upon a resource that is managed by some member of a group of servers, but it is not known which member. In the former example, all members of the group take action on receiving the message, and in the latter example, only the member that manages the resource takes action and the other members simply discard the message.

Note that the broadcast mode of communication does not provide message-ordering guarantees. If this is required, it must be implemented by the user.

2. *Functional mode*. In this case, the message is sent to only one port in the group that is selected by the system. This mode of communication is useful in such cases as where a service is performed identically by a number of servers and a client does not care which server provides the service and may not want to be bothered with the knowledge of the identity of the particular one assigned. In such cases, the client simply sends a request to the group of servers providing the service, and the system selects the most suitable server at that time for servicing the client's request.

An interesting application of the functional mode of communication is to provide reconfigurable services in a system. For instance, all servers providing some service can be grouped together to form a single port group. Now clients send their requests to the group in the functional mode without having to know which servers are available at that time to provide the service. This transparency feature allows new upgraded servers to be added to the group and removal of old servers from the group without disrupting the services and without the clients even being aware that the system has been reconfigured.

3. *Selective functional mode*. In this case also the message is sent to only one port in the group, but the port is selected by the caller and not by the system. A practical use of this mode of communication is in load balancing. An overloaded node may first use the broadcast communication mode to get the current loads of all other nodes. From the replies received, it selects the most lightly loaded node. It then uses the selective functional mode of communication to transfer some of its load to the selected node.

The three modes of group communication are summarized in Figure 12.14. Note that in all three modes messages are sent to port groups by using the asynchronous send and hence the communication is unreliable.

| Communication mode | Message sent to | Member selected by |
|---|---|---|
| Broadcast | All members | — |
| Functional | One member | System |
| Selective functional | One member | Caller |

**Fig. 12.14** Group communication modes in Chorus.

## Port Migration

In Chorus, a system call named *portMigrate* may be used to remove a port from one process and to move it to another process. When a port is moved, all the messages currently in it are moved along with it. As one would expect, ports remain members of port groups when they migrate.

The port migration facility allows the responsibility of providing some service to be dynamically transferred from one server to another without being noticed by the clients who are currently interacting with the server for that service. An interesting application of this facility is for supporting maintenance transparency. For example, a server on a machine that is going down for maintenance can migrate its ports to another server on a different machine that provides the same services. Client requests continue to be processed consistently without any disruption. In this way, server machines can go down for maintenance and come up later without being noticed by their clients.

### Networkwide IPC

For networkwide IPC, Chorus uses *network managers* that are similar to Mach's network message servers. There is a network manager process at each node of the system, and all the network managers work together to extend the communication facilities of the kernel transparently across a network.

When a thread sends a message to a port, the kernel of that machine looks up the port's UI in a list of local ports. If it is not found in the list, the kernel forwards the port's UI to the local network manager. The local network manager then communicates with other network managers to get the location of the port. Once the port has been located, messages sent to the port thereafter are delivered directly to a port of the network manager of the node on which the message port is located. The network manager of that node then forwards the message to the local port to which the message was sent.

## 12.5.7 UNIX Emulation and Extensions

### UNIX Emulation Approach

Chorus designers have built a subsystem called Chorus/MiX (Modular UNIX) for providing binary compatibility with UNIX System V. The basic approach used for designing this UNIX emulation subsystem is briefly described below. Further details can be found in [Gien and Grob 1992, Armand et al. 1989].

The Chorus/MiX subsystem primarily consists of the following processes (see Fig. 12.15):

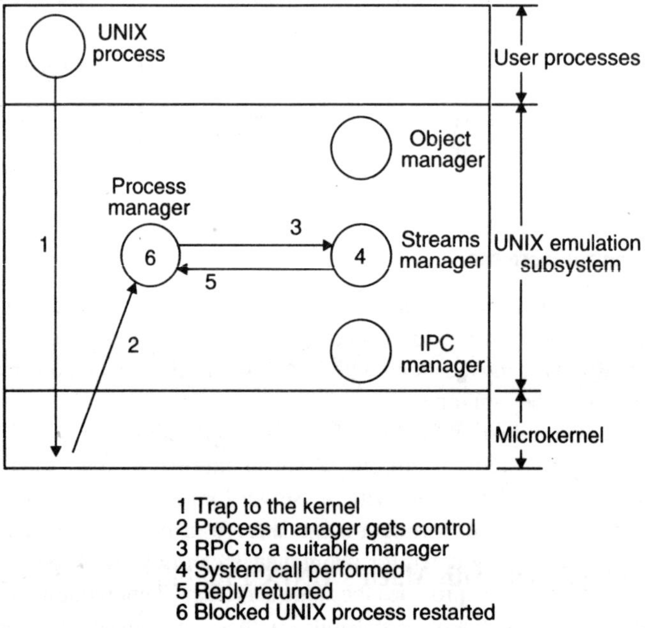


**Fig. 12.15** UNIX emulation in Chorus.

1. *Process manager.* This process is the main component of the emulation subsystem. It catches all system call interrupts and, if necessary, communicates with other processes of the subsystem to handle system calls. In addition, it performs jobs related to process management (including creation and termination of processes), signal handling, and resource naming.

2. *Object manager.* This process mainly performs file management activities and may also contain the disk driver. It also acts as a mapper for the files it controls.

3. *Streams manager.* This process manages pipes, sockets and networking, and stream devices such as keyboard, display, mouse, tape devices, and so on.

4. *Interprocess communication manager.* This process handles system calls related to System V messages, semaphores, and shared memory.

Of these four processes, the process manager contains a large amount of newly written code, while others mostly contain UNIX code itself. Moreover, only the process manager is needed at all nodes having the UNIX emulation subsystem; the other processes are optional and are loaded only where needed. For example, the object manager is not loaded on diskless nodes.

The four processes may be run either in the kernel mode or in the user mode. However, for performance and security reasons, currently they all are run in the kernel mode.

The process manager has multiple threads. Other managers initially start with one thread and additional threads are created as requests come in.

When the system is booted, it inspects its environment and accordingly loads only those optional processes that are needed. As part of their initialization, each of these optional processes send a message to the process manager announcing their ports and telling what system calls they can handle. On the other hand, the process manager informs the kernel that it wants to handle trap numbers that UNIX uses for making system calls. The kernel maintains a table containing the address of a routine for each emulated system call.

With this setup, when a UNIX process makes a system call and traps to the kernel, the thread in the process that handles the corresponding system call automatically gets back control from the kernel. If the system call can be completely handled locally, the process manager performs the requested system call itself. Otherwise, depending on the system call, the process manager does an RPC to either the object manager, streams manager, or interprocess communication manager. The contacted manager process performs the requested system call and sends a reply back to the process manager, which then sets up the proper return value and restarts the blocked UNIX process. The entire process is summarized in Figure 12.15. In the example shown in the figure, the system call is handled by the streams manager.

### Comparison with Mach's UNIX Emulation Approach

The relative advantages and disadvantages of the approaches taken in Mach and in Chorus for supporting UNIX emulation are as follows [Coulouris et al. 1994]:

1. *Modularity.* Chorus design provides better modularity than Mach design because the emulation subsystem uses different server processes to provide different UNIX facilities, as opposed to Mach in which a single UNIX server process is used to provide all UNIX facilities. Since the four manager processes of Chorus do not share any variable or other memory and they communicate exclusively by RPC, any of them can be reimplemented independently of the others, provided the interfaces are not changed.

2. *System state management.* Since Mach uses a single UNIX server process as compared to multiple server processes in Chorus, it is easier to manage the system state in Mach. This is because in Chorus the system state relevant to a single emulated UNIX process is distributed across several server processes that may even be on different machines. If this state is replicated for performance, a mechanism and extra communication overhead will be needed to keep this state consistent. On the other hand, if the state is distributed but not replicated, functionality can be affected because different servers may fail independently of each other. These problems are not associated with Mach's approach because a process's state is confined only to the emulation library's data and the single UNIX server process.

3. *Protection.* In Mach, when a process executes a UNIX system call and traps to the kernel, control is passed back to the emulation library that resides in the address space of the process. Therefore, if the process has buggy code that interferes with the data in the emulation library, this may give rise to nonstandard failure modes causing trouble. Since the approach used in Chorus completely isolates system data structures from user processes, it avoids such problems and provides better protection to the system than Mach's approach.

Further details of the differences between the approaches taken by Mach and Chorus for UNIX emulation can be found in [Dean and Armand 1992].

### Extensions to UNIX

In addition to UNIX emulation, Chorus also provides many extensions to UNIX to allow UNIX processes to use standard Chorus properties that are not available in UNIX. Some of the most important ones are as follows:

1. *Threads.* This extension allows UNIX processes to create and destroy new threads using the Chorus threads package.

2. *Remote process creation.* This extension allows a UNIX process to create a new process on a remote node. In the system call for process creation, it can be specified that the new process is to be created, not on the local node, but on the specified remote node. The new process starts on the local node when forked off, but when it does an *exec* system call, it is started on the specified remote node.

3. *Group communication.* The same group communication facility as that of Chorus can also be enjoyed by UNIX processes. This is because user processes using the UNIX subsystem can create ports and port groups and send and receive messages in the same manner as Chorus processes.

4. *Memory model.* UNIX processes can also enjoy the flexibility of the memory model supported in Chorus. That is, user processes using the UNIX subsystem can create regions and map segments on to them in the same manner as Chorus processes.

### 12.5.8 The COOL Subsystem

In addition to the Chorus/MiX subsystem, another subsystem developed for Chorus is *Chorus Object-Oriented Layer* (*COOL*). Its main goal is to provide system-level support for fine-grained object-oriented languages and applications in Chorus. The basic approach used for designing this subsystem is briefly described below. Its further details can be found in [Lea et al. 1991, 1993].

The COOL (COOL-2, the second version) subsystem that sits on top of the Chorus microkernel is structured into the following layers (see Fig. 12.16):

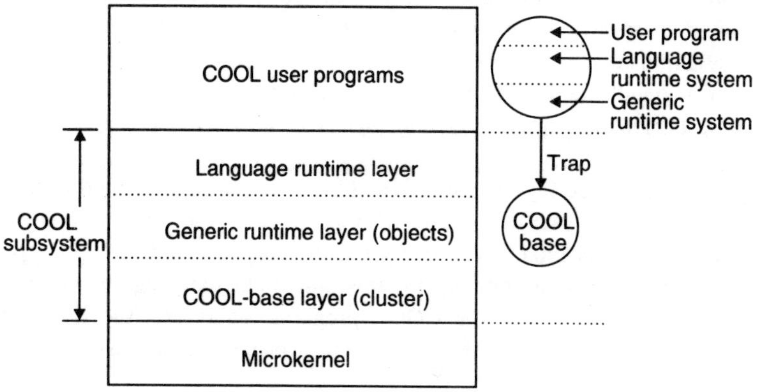


**Fig. 12.16** The implementation structure and layers of COOL subsystem of Chorus.

1. *COOL-base layer.* This layer provides a system call interface that presents the illusion of a new object-oriented microkernel to user applications. It deals with abstractions called *clusters*, which are places where objects exist. A cluster holds a group of related objects, such as objects belonging to the same class. The decision regarding which objects belong to which cluster is made by the upper layers of software.

From the memory model viewpoint, clusters are collections of Chorus regions backed by segments. Therefore, a cluster can be simultaneously mapped into the address spaces of multiple processes, possibly on different machines. However, clusters are not replicated and there is only one physical copy of each cluster at any time. Requests corresponding to remote clusters are serviced either by forwarding the request to the machine that currently holds the cluster for remote invocation or by migrating the cluster to the requesting machine for local invocation. In this manner, the COOL base layer manages clusters, mapping them into multiple address spaces to produce distributed cluster spaces that are visible to all COOL processes without regard to where they are running.

2. *Generic runtime (GRT) layer.* This layer provides support for finer grained objects within clusters. In particular, it provides necessary operations for creating and deleting objects, for mapping them into and out of address spaces, and for invoking their methods. It also provides support for a single-level persistent object store, interobject communications based on Chorus RPC, and protection of objects during application execution.

3. *Language runtime layer.* Programmers may use different object-oriented programming languages, such as C++, Smalltalk, and Eiffel, to define their objects. The language-specific runtime layer maps the object models of several such programming languages on to the GRT's abstractions. It uses preprocessors to generate an up-call table for every type of object created at the GRT level. This mechanism is used to build a standard interface between the generic runtime layer and the language-dependent runtime layer. The generic runtime layer uses this interface to make calls to the language runtime system to obtain language-specific information about the semantics of certain operations. For example, it could find out how to convert in-memory object pointers to persistent pointers for storage or how to handle method dispatch. This mechanism enables COOL to support many different object-oriented programming languages with reasonable efficiency.

Of the three layers, the COOL-base layer is implemented as a Chorus process that runs in the subsystems layer of Chorus. On the other hand, the software in the generic runtime layer is linked with every COOL program, and the appropriate software of the language-specific runtime layer (depending on the language in which a COOL program is written) is linked with the COOL program. Therefore, the language runtime and the generic runtime systems reside in the user program's address space.

## 12.6 A COMPARISON OF AMOEBA, V-SYSTEM, MACH, AND CHORUS

Each of the four distributed operating systems (Amoeba, V-System, Mach, and Chorus) described above have their own strengths and weaknesses that is mainly due to the goals set by their designers and their evolution histories. Amoeba and V-System were designed from scratch as distributed operating systems for loosely coupled distributed memory multiprocessors. From the beginning till now, they have remained university research projects. On the other hand, Mach started as a university research project to build an operating system for tightly coupled shared-memory multiprocessors and was later extended for loosely coupled distributed-memory multiprocessors. It was later selected for commercialization. Finally, Chorus also started as a research project to build a distributed operating system for loosely coupled distributed-memory systems, but its design goals were changed as it evolved from a research project to a commercial system. The consequences of the design goals and evolution histories of these systems are visible in their strengths and weaknesses. To make these differences clearer, let us look at the important aspects of all these four systems together.

### 12.6.1 System Model

Amoeba is based on the processor-pool model whereas V-System, Mach, and Chorus are based on the workstation-server model. Therefore in Amoeba, a user does not log on to a specific machine but to the system as a whole and the selection of CPU (or CPUs) for running a user's job is done automatically by the operating system. In general, a user is not aware of on which CPU his or her job is being processed.

On the other hand, in V-System, Mach, and Chorus, a user logs on to a specific machine (called his or her home machine) on which most of his or her jobs are run by default. Users can request for remote execution of their jobs in these systems. Moreover, V-System also provides automatic load-balancing facility due to which a user's jobs may get processed remotely without his or her knowledge. But in any case, all three systems have the concept of local and remote processing of jobs. This concept does not exist in Amoeba.

### 12.6.2 Kernel

All four systems are based on the microkernel model, in which the kernel is minimal and other functionality and features are supported by user-level servers. However, the complexity of the microkernel and the kernel interface of the four systems differ based on the flexibility offered by them. The microkernels of Amoeba and V-System are simple and have very few system calls. Mach's microkernel is very complex with too many system calls. This is mainly because it attempts to provide greater flexibility in the sense that the same thing can be done in two or three different ways, and the users have the option to select the most convenient or efficient way for a particular circumstance. Chorus's microkernel has fewer system calls than Mach's but more than Amoeba's or V-System's. Therefore, its complexity is moderate.

### 12.6.3 Process Management

Abstractions corresponding to a process in Amoeba, V-System, Mach, and Chorus are process, team, task, and actor, respectively. All four systems support multithreaded processes and in all four threads are managed and scheduled by the kernel.

Mach and Chorus have the flexibility to run the threads of the same process in parallel on different CPUs. This flexibility is not available in Amoeba and V-System. Hence, in these systems, a CPU is time shared by the threads of a process and run in pseudo-parallel.

Amoeba does not provide any type of user control over thread scheduling. V-System and Chorus allow processes to set priorities of their threads. Mach provides maximum flexibility in this case because, in addition to allowing threads priorities to be dynamically changed, it also provides the facility of handoff scheduling. This facility may be used by a thread to hand off the CPU to another thread of its choice when it has finished using the CPU.

Amoeba and V-System support automatic load-balancing facility to spread the workload uniformly over all the machines in the system. Mach and Chorus do not have this facility and by default a user's jobs are executed on his or her home machine. Only on explicit request can a user's job be run remotely.

V-System also has process migration facility. The other three systems do not have this facility.

### 12.6.4 Interprocess Communication

Amoeba, V-System, Mach, and Chorus all provide RPC facility for interprocess communication. Mach and Chorus also provide the facility to send messages asynchronously. Mach packages all forms of message passing in a single system call, whereas Chorus provides alternative calls. The attempt of Mach to package all forms of message passing in a single system call makes its communication interface very complex because of the large number of parameters and options used in the system call to handle all possible different cases.

Chorus makes use of lightweight RPC facility for efficient communication between local kernel processes. The other three systems do not use lightweight RPC.

In Amoeba and V-System, messages consist of a fixed-size header and an optional out-of-line block of data of variable size. In Chorus, messages consist of a fixed-size header, an optional fixed-size in-line data of 64 bytes, and an optional variable-size in-line data of a maximum 64 kilobytes. Mach provides maximum flexibility in this case by allowing multiple variable-size out-of-line blocks of data in a single message.

Mach's messages can be either simple or complex. The contents of simple messages are contiguous sequence of bytes, whereas complex messages contain typed data. Complex messages may be used to transmit capabilities. On the other hand, Amoeba, V-System, and Chorus use simple untyped messages that contain a contiguous sequence of bytes.

Messages are addressed to ports in Mach and Chorus, to processes in Amoeba, and to manager IDs in V-System. A manager ID in V-System may either be a process or a port identifier. All four systems use the mechanism of hint cache plus broadcasting to locate ports or processes.

In local IPC, Mach and Chorus use the copy-on-write mechanism to pass out-of-line data. Amoeba and V-System do not use this mechanism. Therefore, local IPC is faster in Mach and Chorus than in Amoeba or V-System.

Amoeba, V-System, and Chorus support group communication, but Mach does not. The group communication facility of Amoeba provides reliable, ordered broadcast facility; that of Chorus provides unreliable, unordered broadcast facility; and that of V-System provides unordered broadcast facility with the flexibility given to the users to choose the degree of reliability.

In Amoeba and V-System, networkwide IPC is handled by the kernel. On the other hand, in Mach and Chorus, user-level network servers are used for networkwide IPC. Therefore, internode IPC is faster in Amoeba and V-System than in Mach or Chorus.

On the network, all four systems provide support for conventional TCP/IP. In addition, Amoeba supports FLIP, and V-System supports VMTP. These protocols, although not standard and widely used, have been specifically designed for the needs of distributed operating systems and are faster than conventional network protocols for typical RPC usage.

### 12.6.5 Memory Management

Amoeba has a very simple memory management scheme without support for the virtual-memory (demand paging) mechanism. Therefore, when an Amoeba process runs, its entire address space is present in memory. This scheme is simple to implement and has the advantage of high performance. However, it requires that the machines have extremely large memories. A process whose address space is larger than the memory of the machine having the largest memory size among all machines in the system cannot be run on that system. In contrast, V-System, Mach, and Chorus provide support for a paged virtual-memory mechanism. Therefore, any process can be run on these systems no matter how large its address space is.

The virtual-memory management schemes of Mach and Chorus are very powerful and flexible because they allow pages to be shared between multiple processes in various ways. For example, the copy-on-write sharing mechanism allows efficient sharing of pages among multiple processes of a single node, and the external pager mechanism allows virtual memory to be shared even among processes that run on different machines.

Amoeba, V-System, Mach, and Chorus all provide support for distributed shared memory. Amoeba supports an object-based distributed shared memory in which variable-size objects are shared by replicating them on all machines using them. Read operations on an object are performed locally, while write operations on it are performed using the reliable broadcast protocol of Amoeba. On the other hand, V-System, Mach, and Chorus support page-based distributed shared memory. Like Amoeba, V-System allows both read-only and writable pages to be replicated. However, V-System uses problem-oriented approach for solving the memory coherence problem. On the other hand, to solve the memory coherence problem, Mach and Chorus allow only read-only pages to be replicated and there is only one copy of writable pages in the entire system. Due to replication of writable objects and the use of write-all protocol for memory coherence, updates in Amoeba's scheme are more expensive than in V-System's, Mach's, or Chorus's schemes. However, unlike Amoeba's scheme, Mach's and Chorus's schemes suffer from thrashing problem. Thrashing can occur if a writable page is heavily accessed from two machines.

### 12.6.6 File Management

Amoeba's file management scheme is very different from those of V-System, Mach, and Chorus. Amoeba uses the immutable file model, whereas V-System, Mach, and Chorus use the mutable file model. Therefore, a file cannot be overwritten in Amoeba and updates are performed by creating new file versions. In V-System, Mach, and Chorus, a file is modified by overwriting the same file.

In Amoeba, an entire file is always stored contiguously both in memory and on disk. This provides efficient accesses to files but leads to the external fragmentation problem. In V-System, Mach, and Chorus, a file need not be stored contiguously. Storage space is allocated in units of fixed-size blocks or variable-size segments.

All four systems use the data-caching model for remote file accessing. However, in Amoeba the unit of caching is a file, whereas in the other three systems the unit of caching is a block.

Since Amoeba uses the immutable file model, it supports immutable shared file semantics. On the other hand, the file-sharing semantics of V-System, Mach, and Chorus depend on the semantics supported by the user-level file server being used.

Amoeba also supports automatic replication of files. The other three systems do not have this facility.

### 12.6.7 Security

In Amoeba and Chorus, resources are named and protected by capabilities. Therefore, the capability-based access control mechanism is used to control access to resources in these two systems. In Mach, the access control mechanism is based on port rights (port capabilities). That is, Mach servers generally manage many ports, one for every resource, and only processes that own appropriate port rights for a port can access the corresponding resource. Finally, in V-System, the access control mechanism is based on ACLs managed by resource managers.

Capabilities in Amoeba and Chorus are managed in user space, but port capabilities in Mach are managed by the kernel. Amoeba capabilities are protected by using one-way encryption functions. Chorus also provides protection identifiers that may be used to know the actual sender of a message.

### 12.6.8 Some Other Differences

Chorus and V-System provide support for real-time applications. Amoeba and Mach do not provide any special facility for real-time applications.

All four systems provide support for UNIX emulation. However, while V-System, Mach, and Chorus support binary compatibility, Amoeba supports source code compatibility with UNIX.

Chorus also provides system-level support for fine-grained object-oriented languages and applications. The other three systems do not currently provide this facility.

Figure 12.17 presents a summary of the comparison of the four systems presented above.

## 12.7 SUMMARY

This chapter has presented a description of four distributed operating systems to relate the various concepts described in the preceding chapters of this book to real systems. These systems are Amoeba, V-System, Mach, and Chorus. The design goals, system architectures, and the most important and noteworthy aspects of these systems were covered in sufficient detail to consolidate the reader's understanding of the design principles of distributed operating systems. A comparison of the four systems was also presented.

| Feature | Amoeba | V-System | Mach | Chorus |
|---|---|---|---|---|
| System model | Processor pool | Workstation-server | Workstation-server | Workstation-server |
| Kernel model | Microkernel | Microkernel | Microkernel | Microkernel |
| Kernel complexity in terms of system call interface | Simple (few system calls) | Simple (few system calls) | Very complex (too many system calls) | Fairly complex (many system calls) |
| Process abstraction | Process | Team | Task | Actor |
| Supports multiple threads in a single process? | Yes | Yes | Yes | Yes |
| Can threads of a process run on different CPUs? | No | No | Yes | Yes |
| Threads are managed and scheduled by | Kernel | Kernel | Kernel | Kernel |
| Supports user control over threads scheduling | No | Yes (priority assignment) | Yes (priority assignment and handoff scheduling) | Yes (priority assignment) |
| Automatic load balancing facility? | Yes | Yes | No | No |
| Process migration facility? | No | Yes | No | No |
| Basic IPC mechanisms | RPC | RPC | RPC and asynchronous send | RPC and asynchronous send |
| Uses lightweight RPC? | No | No | No | Yes, for communication between local kernel processes |
| Message body | Single variable-size out-of-line block of data | Single variable-size out-of-line block of data | Multiple variable-size out-of-line blocks of data | An optional fixed-size in-line data and an optional variable-size in-line data of maximum 64K bytes |

**Fig. 12.17** A comparison of Amoeba, V-System, Mach, and Chorus. (Continued on next page.)

| Feature | Amoeba | V-System | Mach | Chorus |
|---|---|---|---|---|
| Typed/untyped messages? | Untyped | Untyped | May be typed/untyped | Untyped |
| Messages addressed to | Processes | Manager-IDs (may be a process or a port ID) | Ports | Ports |
| Mechanism used for locating ports or processes | Hint cache and broad-casting | Hint cache and broad-casting | Hint cache and broad-casting | Hint cache and broad-casting |
| Uses copy-on-write mechanism for local IPC? | No | No | Yes | Yes |
| Group communication facility | Reliable, ordered broadcast facility | Unordered broadcast facility with flexibility to choose the degree of reliability | None | Unreliable, unordered broadcast facility |
| Network-wide IPC supported by | Kernel | Kernel | User-level network servers | User-level network servers |
| Supported network protocols | TCP/IP and FLIP | TCP/IP and VMTP | TCP/IP | TCP/IP |
| Supports virtual memory mechanism? | No | Yes | Yes | Yes |
| Supports copy-on-write sharing for objects shared by processes on the same node? | No | No | Yes | Yes |
| Uses external pager mechanism? | No | No | Yes | Yes |
| Provides support for distributed shared memory? | Yes (object-based) | Yes (page-based) | Yes (page-based) | Yes (page-based) |
| Coherence protocol used for distributed shared memory | Write-all | Problem-specific updates | Read-only replication | Read-only replication |
| File model | Immutable files | Mutable files | Mutable files | Mutable files |
| An entire file has to be stored contiguously? | Yes | No | No | No |

**Fig. 12.17** A comparison of Amoeba, V-System, Mach, and Chorus. (Continued on next page.)

| Feature | Amoeba | V-System | Mach | Chorus |
|---|---|---|---|---|
| Remote file-accessing model | Data-caching model | Data-caching model | Data-caching model | Data-caching model |
| Unit of data transfer | File | Block | Block | Block |
| File-sharing semantics | Immutable shared-files semantics | Depends on the user-level file server | Depends on the user-level file server | Depends on the user-level file server |
| Automatic file replication? | Yes | No | No | No |
| Access control mechanism | Resources capabilities that are encrypted using one-way functions | ACLs managed by resource managers | Port rights (port capabilities) | Resource capabilities and protection identifiers |
| Support for real-time applications? | No | Yes | No | Yes |
| UNIX emulation | Source code compatibility | Binary compatibility | Binary compatibility | Binary compatibility |
| Support for object-oriented languages and applications? | No | No | No | Yes |

**Fig. 12.17** A comparison of Amoeba, V-System, Mach, and Chorus.

From the description of these systems, it can be concluded that microkernel-based distributed operating systems with open-system architecture are going to dominate in future. For commercial success, it is important for any newly developed distributed operating system to provide binary compatibility with UNIX. Features such as process migration and load balancing are still restricted to research projects. This is mainly because, with the current state of the art, these features are expensive to implement and use and have not yet proved to give promising results. Therefore, more research work needs to be carried out in these areas.

## EXERCISES

**12.1.** What is an "open distributed system"? What is the most important factor in the design of a distributed operating system that influences this characteristic of the system?

**12.2.** Based on the description of Amoeba, V-System, Mach, and Chorus, what trend are modern distributed operating systems following for kernel design? What are the main reasons for using this approach? Are there any disadvantages in using this approach?

**12.3.** Name the main hardware and software components of Amoeba and describe their functions.

**12.4.** Answer the following questions for the capability-based object-naming mechanism of Amoeba:
(a) How does a subject get a capability for an object? Consider both the case in which the subject is the owner of the object and the case in which the subject is not the owner of the object.
(b) How are capabilities protected against unauthorized access?
(c) How are capabilities made difficult to forge?
(d) When a subject accesses an object, how is the validation check made if the subject is allowed to access the object in the requested mode?
(e) How can the owner of an object who wants to share the object with another subject allow restricted access rights to the subject for its object?

**12.5.** In a capability-based system, an object whose capability is lost can never be accessed but will remain forever in the system. How is this situation prevented in Amoeba?

**12.6.** Describe the process model of Amoeba.

**12.7.** What is a glocal variable in Amoeba? Why is it used?

**12.8.** In the processor-pool model of Amoeba, explain how a processor is selected from the pool for executing a new process.

**12.9.** Describe the policy used in Amoeba for object replication.

**12.10.** Amoeba uses the immutable file model. However, in a file system that uses the immutable file model, every time a file is modified, a new version of the file is created and the old version is deleted. This makes file modifications slow and complicated, especially for a file that is frequently modified. Explain how Amoeba solves this problem.

**12.11.** Describe the group communication facility of Amoeba.

**12.12.** Explain how the following are ensured in Amoeba:
(a) Only genuine clients can request services from a server.
(b) Only genuine servers can receive client requests.

**12.13.** Name the main hardware and software components of V-System and describe their functions.

**12.14.** V-System integrates object-naming and object management mechanisms. What advantages does this approach have in the design of a distributed operating system?

**12.15.** Describe the mechanisms used in V-System to minimize the kernel's job in process management activities.

**12.16.** Describe the UIO interface of V-System. Explain how this facility simplifies device management activities.

**12.17.** Describe the multicast communication facility of V-System. Mention some of the practical applications of this facility in the design of V-System.

**12.18.** In V-System, the sender actions of sending a request and receiving a response are combined into a single *Send* primitive. What advantages does this approach provide? Would it not have been better and simpler to have two calls, *Send_request* and *Get_reply*, one for sending a request and one for receiving a response?

**12.19.** Explain how the copy-on-write mechanism of Mach provides the potential to eliminate much data movement in the system.

**12.20.** In Mach, many kernel activities are moved out of the kernel directly into the client's address space by being placed in a transparent shared library. What advantages does this design provides?

**12.21.** To keep track of the state (suspended/running) of a thread (or process), Mach uses a "suspended" counter that is associated with each thread (or process). Since there are only two possible states (suspended and running), a single bit would have been sufficient for this purpose. Explain the reason for the use of a counter instead of a bit for this purpose.

**12.22.** Describe how threads of a process are synchronized in Mach.

**12.23.** Answer the following questions for the threads-scheduling scheme of Mach:
(a) What is the use of a "hint" variable?
(b) What is the use of a "count" variable?
(c) What is the need to have two run queues instead of a single run queue for each CPU?
(d) What happens if there are no threads waiting to be executed on either of the two queues?
(e) How is it ensured that the system will provide high efficiency when lightly loaded, while providing good response to short requests even when heavily loaded?
(f) How is the monopolization of a CPU by a high-priority thread prevented?
(g) How is fair CPU utilization ensured in a situation in which the system load suddenly increases?
(h) Why is a global run queue locked before being searched for a ready-to-run thread but a local run queue is not locked before being searched?

**12.24.** A commonly used approach to maintain the virtual address space of each process is to keep a linear page table from zero to the highest used page in the kernel. Explain why this approach is not used in Mach. Describe the approach used in Mach for maintaining the virtual address space of each process.

**12.25.** What is an external memory manager in Mach? How is it realized? Describe how an external memory manager and the kernel interact with each other to manage a memory object and to satisfy user access requests for data in the memory object.

**12.26.** Describe how the external memory manager concept of Mach can be used to implement the distributed shared memory facility.

**12.27.** Describe the copy-on-write and controlled inheritance mechanisms used in Mach for memory sharing. Give an example to illustrate the practical use of each of these mechanisms.

**12.28.** Answer the following questions for the port-based IPC mechanism of Mach:

(a) Why are ports kept track of on a per-process basis rather than on a per-thread basis?

(b) An application requires that a sender be allowed to send messages to a port only *n* times. How can this be realized?

(c) What happens when a process having a port capability with *receive* right sends that capability in a message to another process?

(d) How are ports protected?

(e) What happens when a process holding a port capability with *receive* right exits or is killed?

(f) What happens if a sender sends a message to a port whose receiver process has been killed?

(g) What happens if a message arrives at a port whose queue is full?

(h) What is a port-set? Give a practical use of this facility.

(i) Why is message sending to a port-set not allowed?

(j) Why can a port that belongs to a port-set not be used directly to receive messages?

**12.29.** Differentiate between in-line data and out-of-line data in the message-passing mechanism of Mach. Describe how out-of-line data are transferred from a sender to a receiver.

**12.30.** In Mach, explain how messages are exchanged transparently between two processes that are located on different nodes.

**12.31.** What is the role of MIG in Mach? Explain how it simplifies the job of application programmers.

**12.32.** In Mach's UNIX emulation, system calls related to file I/O have been implemented differently than the basic approach described in this chapter. Find out how file I/O system calls are implemented and the reason for using a different approach for implementing them.

**12.33.** Describe how Chorus provides support for real-time applications.

**12.34.** Chorus allows servers (subsystem processes) to reside either in a shared kernel address space or in private user address spaces. Discuss the relative advantages and disadvantages of this feature of Chorus.

**12.35.** Explain how Chorus provides the flexibility to dynamically configure the system software to match the hardware components of a particular node of the system.

**12.36.** What are the various security mechanisms provided in Chorus? What type of security does each of these mechanisms provide?

**12.37.** Explain why three types of processes are used in Chorus.

**12.38.** Describe the threads-scheduling scheme of Chorus. What are its advantages and disadvantages?

**12.39.** Differentiate between broadcast, functional, and selective functional modes of communication in Chorus. Give a practical use of each of these modes of communication.

**12.40.** Explain the port migration facility of Chorus. How does it help?

**12.41.** What is a port group in Chorus? Give two practical uses of this facility.

**12.42.** Explain how UNIX processes can be created on a remote node in Chorus.

**12.43.** Discuss the relative advantages and disadvantages of the approaches taken by Mach and Chorus for UNIX emulation.

**12.44.** Explain how object-oriented facility is supported in Chorus. Can this facility be provided along with UNIX emulation facility on the same machine? Give reasons for your answer.

## BIBLIOGRAPHY

**[Abrossimov et al. 1992]** Abrossimov, A., Armand, F., and Ortega, M., "A Distributed Consistency Server for the CHORUS System," In: *Proceedings of the USENIX SEDMS III Symposium on Experience with Distributed and Multiprocessor Systems*, USENIX Association, Berkeley, CA, pp. 129–148 (1992).

**[Accetta et al. 1986]** Accetta, M., Baron, R., Golub, D., Rashid, R., Tevanian, A., and Young, M., "Mach: A New Kernel Foundation for UNIX Development," In: *Proceedings of the Summer 1986 USENIX Technical Conference*, USENIX Association, Berkeley, CA, pp. 93–112 (July 1986).

**[Almes et al. 1985]** Almes, G. T., Black, A. P., Lazowska, E. D., and Noe, J. D., "The Eden System: A Technical Review," *IEEE Transactions on Software Engineering*, Vol. SE-11, No. 1, pp. 43–59 (January 1985).

**[Andrews et al. 1987]** Andrews, G. R., Schlichting, R. D., Hayes, R., and Purdin, T. D. M., "The Design of the Saguaro Distributed Operating System," *IEEE Transactions on Software Engineering*, Vol. SE-13, No. 1, pp. 104–118 (1987).

**[Armand et al. 1986]** Armand, F., Gien, M., Guillemont, M., and Leonard, P., "Towards a Distributed UNIX System—The CHORUS Approach," In: *Proceedings of the Autumn 1986 EUUG Conference*, USENIX Association, Berkeley, CA, pp. 413–431 (September 1986).

**[Armand et al. 1989]** Armand, F., Gien, M., Herrman, F., and Rozier, M., "Distributing UNIX Brings It Back to Its Original Virtues," In: *Proceedings of the Workshop on Experiences with Building Distributed and Multiprocessor Systems*, pp. 153–174 (October 1989).

**[Babaoglu 1990]** Babaoglu, O., "Fault-Tolerant Computing Based on Mach," *Operating Systems Review*, Vol. 24, No. 1, pp. 27–39 (1990).

**[Bal et al. 1992]** Bal, H. E., Kaashoek, F., and Tanenbaum, A. S., "Orca: A Language for Parallel Programming of Distributed Systems," *IEEE Transactions on Software Engineering*, Vol. SE-18, No. 3, pp. 190–205 (1992).

**[Banino and Fabre 1982]** Banino, J. S., and Fabre, J. C., "Distributed Coupled Actors: A CHORUS Proposal for Reliability," In: *Proceedings of the 3rd International Conference on Distributed Computing Systems*, IEEE Press, New York, NY, p. 7 (October 1982).

**[Banino et al. 1985]** Banino, J. S., Fabre, J. C., Guillemont, M., Morisset, G., and Zimmermann, H., "Some Fault Tolerant Aspects of the CHORUS Distribute System," In: *Proceedings of the 5th International Conference on Distributed Computing Systems*, IEEE Press, New York, NY (May 1985).

**[Baron et al. 1985]** Baron, R., Rashid, R., Siegel, E., Tevanian, A., and Young, M., "Mach-1: An Operating Environment for Large-Scale Multiprocessor Applications," *IEEE Software*, Vol. 2, pp. 65–67 (1985).

**[Batlivala et al. 1992]** Batlivala, N., Gleeson, B., Hamrick, J., Lurndal, S., Price, D., Soddy, J., and Abrossimov, V., "Experience with SVR4 over CHORUS," In: *Proceedings of the USENIX Workshop on Microkernels and Other Kernel Architectures*, USENIX Association, Berkeley, CA, pp. 223–241 (1992).

**[Berglund 1986]** Berglund, E. J., "An Introduction to the V-System," *IEEE MICRO*, pp. 35–52 (August 1986).

**[Bever et al. 1993]** Bever, M., Geihs, K., Heuser, L., Muhlhauser, M., and Schill, A., "Distributed Systems, OSF DCE, and Beyond," In: A. Schill (Ed.), *DCE—The OSF Distributed Computing Environment*, Springer-Verlag, Berlin, pp. 1–20 (1993).

**[Black 1990]** Black, D. L., "Scheduling Support for Concurrency and Parallelism in the Mach Operating System," *IEEE Computer*, Vol. 23, No. 5, pp. 35–43 (1990).

**[Black et al. 1992]** Black, D. L., Golub, D. B., Julin, D. P., Rashid, R. F., Draves, R. P., Dean, R. W., Forin, A., Barrera, J., Tokuda, H., Malan, G., and Bohman, D., "Microkernel Operating System Architecture and Mach," In: *Proceedings of the USENIX Workshop on Microkernels and Other Kernel Architectures*, USENIX Association, Berkeley, CA, pp. 11–30 (1992).

**[Boykin et al. 1993]** Boykin, J., Kirschen, D., Langerman, A., and LoVerso, S., *Programming under Mach*, Addison-Wesley, Reading, MA (1993).

**[Boykin and Langerman 1990]** Boykin, J., and Langerman, A., "Mach/4.3BSD: A Conservative Approach to Parallelization," *Computing Systems Journal*, Vol. 3, pp. 69–99 (1990).

**[Champine et al. 1990]** Champine, G. A., Geer, Jr., D. E., and Ruh, W. N., "Project Athena as a Distributed Computer System," *IEEE Computer*, pp. 40–50 (September 1990).

**[Cheriton 1984]** Cheriton, D. R., "The V kernel: A Software Base for Distributed Systems," *IEEE Software*, Vol. 1, No. 2, pp. 19–42 (April 1984).

**[Cheriton 1987]** Cheriton, D. R., "UIO: A Uniform I/O Interface for Distributed Systems," *ACM Transactions on Computer Systems*, Vol. 5, No. 1, pp. 12–46 (1987).

**[Cheriton 1988]** Cheriton, D. R., "The V Distributed System," *Communications of the ACM*, Vol. 31, No. 3, pp. 314–333 (1988). © ACM, Inc., 1988.

**[Cheriton and Mann 1989]** Cheriton, D. R., and Mann, T. P., "Decentralizing a Global Naming Service for Improved Performance and Fault Tolerance," *ACM Transactions on Computer Systems*, Vol. 7, No. 2, pp. 147–183 (1989).

**[Cheriton et al. 1979]** Cheriton, D. R., Malcolm, M. A., Melen, L. S., and Sager, G. R., "Thoth, a Portable Real-Time Operating System," *Communications of the ACM*, Vol. 22, No. 2, pp. 105–115 (February 1979).

**[Cheriton et al. 1990]** Cheriton, D., Whitehead, G., and Sznyter, E., "Binary Emulation of UNIX Using the V Kernel," In: *Proceedings of the Summer USENIX Conference*, USENIX Association, Berkeley, CA, pp. 73–85 (1990).

**[Coulouris et al. 1994]** Coulouris, G. F., Dollimore, J., and Kindberg, T., *Distributed Systems Concepts and Design*, 2nd ed., Addison-Wesley, Reading, MA (1994).

**[Dasgupta et al. 1991]** Dasgupta, P., LeBlanc, R. J., Ahamad, M., and Ramachandran, U., "The Clouds Distributed Operating System," *IEEE Computer*, Vol. 24, No. 11, pp. 34–44 (1991).

**[Dean and Armand 1992]** Dean, R., and Armand, F., "Data Movement in Kernelized Systems," In: *Proceedings of the USENIX Workshop on Microkernels*, USENIX Association, Berkeley, CA (1992).

**[Douglis et al. 1991]** Douglis, F., Ousterhout, J. K., Kaashoek, M. F., and Tanenbaum, A. S., "A Comparison of Two Distributed Systems: Amoeba and Sprite," *Computing Systems Journal*, Vol. 4, pp. 353–384 (1991).

**[Draves 1990]** Draves, R. P., "A Revised IPC Interface," In: *Proceedings of the USENIX Mach Workshop*, USENIX Association, Berkeley, CA, pp. 101–121 (October 1990).

**[Draves et al. 1989]** Draves, R. P., Jones, M. B., and Thompson, M. R., "MIG—The Mach Interface Generator," Technical Report, Department of Computer Science, Carnegie Mellon University (1989).

**[Duff 1990]** Duff, T., "Rc—A Shell for Plan 9 and UNIX Systems," In: *Proceedings of the Summer 1990 UKUUG Conference*, USENIX Association, Berkeley, CA, pp. 21–33 (July 1990).

**[Finkel et al. 1989]** Finkel, R., Scott, M. L., Kalsow, W. K., Artsy, Y., and Chang, H. Y., "Experience with Charlotte: Simplicity and Function in a Distributed Operating System," *IEEE Transactions on Software Engineering*, Vol. SE-15, No. 6, pp. 676–685 (1989).

**[Fitzgerald and Rashid 1986]** Fitzgerald, R., and Rashid, R. F., "The Integration of Virtual Memory Management and Interprocess Communication in Accent," *ACM Transactions on Computer Systems*, Vol. 4, No. 2, pp. 147–177 (1986).

**[Gien and Grob 1992]** Gien, M., and Grob, L., "Microkernel Based Operating Systems: Moving UNIX on to Modern System Architectures," In: *Proceedings of the UniForum'92 Conference*, USENIX Association, Berkeley, CA, pp. 43–55 (1992).

**[Golub et al. 1990]** Golub, D., Dean, R., Forin, A., and Rashid, R., "UNIX as an Application Program," In: *Proceedings of the Summer 1990 USENIX Conference*, USENIX Association, Berkeley, CA, pp. 87–95 (June 1990).

**[Guillemont 1982]** Guillemont, M., "The CHORUS Distributed Computing System: Design and Implementation," In: *Proceedings of the International Symposium on Local Computer Networks*, pp. 207–223 (April 1982).

**[Jones and Rashid 1986]** Jones, M. B., and Rashid, R. F., "Mach and Matchmaker: Kernel and Language Support for Object-Oriented Distributed Systems," In: *Proceedings of OOPSLA'86*, Association for Computing Machinery, New York, NY, pp. 67–77 (September 1986).

**[Kaashoek and Tanenbaum 1991]** Kaashoek, M. F., and Tanenbaum, A. S., "Group Communication in the Amoeba Distributed Operating System," In: *Proceedings of the 11th International Conference on Distributed Computing Systems*, IEEE Press, New York, NY, pp. 222–230 (May 1991).

**[Keefee et al. 1985]** Keefee, D., Tomlinson, G. M., Wand, I. C., and Wellings, A. J., *PULSE: An Ada-Based Distributed Operating System*, Academic Press, San Diego, CA (1985).

**[Lea et al. 1991]** Lea, R., Amaral, P., and Jacquemot, C., "COOL-2: An Object-Oriented Support Platform Built Above the Chorus Microkernel," In: *Proceedings of the International Workshop on Object-Oriented Systems*, pp. 51–55 (1991).

**[Lea et al. 1993]** Lea, R., Jacquemot, C., and Pillevesse, E., "COOL: System Support for Distributed Programming," *Communications of the ACM*, Vol. 36, No. 9, pp. 37–46 (September 1993).

**[Levine 1987]** Levine, P. H., "The DOMAIN System," In: *Proceedings of the 2nd ACM SIGOPS Workshop on Making Distributed Systems Work, Operating Systems Review*, Vol. 21, No. 1, pp. 49–84 (1987).

**[Miller et al. 1987]** Miller, B. P., Presotto, D. L., and Powell, M. L., "DEMOS/MP: The Development of a Distributed Operating System," *Software—Practice and Experience*, Vol. 17, No. 4, pp. 277–290 (1987).

**[Milojcic 1994]** Milojcic, D. S., *Load Distribution, Implementation for the Mach Microkernel*, Verlag Vieweg, Wiesbaden (1994).

**[Morris et al. 1986]** Morris, J. H., Satyanarayanan, M., Conner, M. H., Howard, J. H., Rosenthal, D. S. H., and Smith, F. D., "Andrew: A Distributed Personal Computing Environment," *Communications of the ACM*, Vol. 29, No. 3, pp. 184–201 (1986).

**[Mullender and Tanenbaum 1986]** Mullender, S. J., and Tanenbaum, A. S., "The Design of a Capability-Based Distributed Operating System," *The Computer Journal*, Vol. 29, No. 4, pp. 289–299 (1986).

**[Mullender et al. 1990]** Mullender, S. J., Van Rossum, G., Tanenbaum, A. S., Van Renesse, R., and Van Staverene, H., "Amoeba: A Distributed Operating System for the 1990s," *IEEE Computer*, Vol. 23, No. 5, pp. 44–53 (1990).

**[Needham and Herbert 1982]** Needham, R. M., and Herbert, A. J., *The Cambridge Distributed Computing System*, Addison-Wesley, Reading, MA (1982).

**[Nelson and Leach 1984]** Nelson, D. L., and Leach, P. J., "The Architecture and Applications of the Apollo DOMAIN," *IEEE Computer Graphics and Applications* (April 1984).

**[Orman et al. 1993]** Orman, H., Menze, E., O'Malley, S., and Peterson, L., "A Fast and General Implementation of Mach IPC in a Network," In: *Proceedings of the 3rd USENIX Mach Workshop*, USENIX Association, Berkeley, CA (April 1993).

**[Ousterhout et al. 1988]** Ousterhout, J. K., Cherenson, A. R., Douglis, F., Nelson, M. N., and Welch, B. B., "The Sprite Network Operating System," *IEEE Computer*, Vol. 21, No. 2, pp. 23–36 (1988).

**[Pike et al. 1990]** Pike, R., Presotto, D., Thompson, K., and Trickey, H., "Plan 9 from Bell Labs," In: *Proceedings of the Summer 1990 UKUUG (UK Unix Users Group) Conference*, USENIX Association, Berkeley, CA, pp. 1–9 (July 1990).

**[Popek and Walker 1985]** Popek, G., and Walker, B., *The LOCUS Distributed System Architecture*, MIT Press, Cambridge, MA (1985).

**[Pountain 1994]** Pountain, D., "The Chorus Microkernel," *BYTE*, pp. 131–136 (January 1994).

**[Presotto et al. 1991]** Presotto, D., Pike, R., Thompson, K., and Trickey, H., "Plan 9, A Distributed System," In: *Proceedings of the Spring 1991 EurOpen Conference*, EurOpen, Hertfordshire, UK, pp. 43–50 (May 1991).

**[Rashid 1986]** Rashid, R. F., "From RIG to Accent to Mach: The Evolution of a Network Operating System," In: *Proceedings of the Fall Joint Computer Conference*, AFIPS, pp. 1128–1137 (November 1986).

**[Rashid 1987]** Rashid, R. F., "Mach: A New Foundation for Multiprocessor Systems Development," In: *Proceedings of COMPCON'87—Digest of Papers*, IEEE Press, New York, NY, pp. 192–193 (1987).

**[Rashid and Robertson 1981]** Rashid, R. F., and Robertson, G., "Accent: A Communication Oriented Network Operating System Kernel," In: *Proceedings of the 8th ACM Symposium on Operating Systems Principles*, Association for Computing Machinery, New York, NY, pp. 64–75 (December 1981).

**[Rashid et al. 1988]** Rashid, R., Tevanian, A., Young, M., Golub, D., Baron, R., Black, D., Bolosky, W. J., and Chew, J., "Machine-Independent Virtual Memory Management for Paged Uniprocessor and Multiprocessor Architecture," *IEEE Transactions on Computers*, Vol. C-37, No. 8, pp. 869–908 (1988).

**[Rozier and Legatheaux 1986]** Rozier, M., and Legatheaux, J. M., "The Chorus Distributed Operating System: Some Design Issues," In: Y. Parker et al. (Eds.), *Distributed Operating Systems: Theory and Practice*, NATO ASI Series, Vol. F28, Springer-Verlag, New York, NY, pp. 261–289 (1986).

**[Rozier et al. 1988]** Rozier, M., Abrossimov, V., Armand, F., Boule, I., Gien, M., Guillemont, M., Herrmann, F., Kaiser, C., Leonard, P., Langlois, S., and Neuhauser, W., "Chorus Distributed Operating System," *Computing Systems Journal*, Vol. 1, No. 4, pp. 305–379 (1988).

**[Satyanarayanan et al. 1990]** Satyanarayanan, M., Kistler, J. J., Kumar, P., Okasaki, M. E., Siegel, E. H., and Steere, D. C., "Coda: A Highly Available File System for a Distributed Workstation Environment," *IEEE Transactions on Computers*, Vol. 39, No. 4, pp. 447–459 (1990).

**[Schantz et al. 1986]** Schantz, R. E., Thomas, R. H., and Bono, G., "The Architecture of the Cronus Distributed Operating System," In: *Proceedings of the 6th International Conference on Distributed Computing Systems*, IEEE Press, New York, NY, pp. 250–259 (1986).

**[Schroeder et al. 1984]** Schroeder, M. D., Birrell, A. D., and Needham, R. M., "Experience with Grapevine: The Growth of a Distributed System," *ACM Transactions on Computer Systems*, Vol. 2, No. 1, pp. 3–23 (1984).

**[Shrivastava et al. 1991]** Shrivastava, S., Dixon, G. N., and Parrington, G. D., "An Overview of the Arjuna Distributed Programming System," *IEEE Software*, pp. 66–73 (January 1991).

**[Silberschatz and Galvin 1994]** Silberschatz, A., and Galvin, P. B., *Operating Systems Concepts*, 4th ed., Addison-Wesley, Reading, MA (1994).

**[Sinha et al. 1991]** Sinha, P. K., Maekawa, M., Shimizu, K., Jia, X., Ashihara, H., Utsunomiya, N., Park, K. S., and Nakano, H., "The Galaxy Distributed Operating System," *IEEE Computer*, Vol. 24, No. 8, pp. 34–41 (1991).

**[Sinha et al. 1994]** Sinha, P. K., Maekawa, M., Shimizu, K., Jia, X., Ashihara, H., Utsunomiya, N., Park, K. S., and Nakano, H., "The Architectural Overview of the Galaxy Distributed Operating System," In: T. L. Casavant and M. Singhal (Eds.), *Readings in Distributed Computing Systems*, IEEE Computer Society Press, Los Alamitos, CA, pp. 327–345 (1994).

**[Swinehart et al. 1986]** Swinehart, D., et al., "A Structural View of the Cedar Programming Environment," *ACM Transactions on Programming Languages and Systems*, Vol. 8, No. 4, pp. 419–490 (1986).

**[Tanenbaum 1995]** Tanenbaum, A. S., *Distributed Operating Systems*, Prentice-Hall, Englewood Cliffs, NJ (1995).

**[Tanenbaum and Van Renesse 1985]** Tanenbaum, A. S., and Van Renesse, R., "Distributed Operating Systems," *ACM Computing Surveys*, Vol. 17, No. 4, pp. 419–470 (1985).

**[Tanenbaum et al. 1990]** Tanenbaum, A. S., Van Renesse, R., Staveren, H. Van, Sharp, G. J., Mullender, S. J., Jansen, J., and Van Rossum, G., "Experiences with the Amoeba Distributed Operating System," *Communications of the ACM*, Vol. 33, pp. 46–63 (1990).

**[Theimer et al. 1985]** Theimer, M. M., Lantz, K. A., and Cheriton, D. R., "Preemptable Remote Execution Facilities for the V-System," In: *Proceedings of the 10th ACM Symposium on Operating Systems Principles*, Association for Computing Machinery, New York, NY, pp. 2–12 (December 1985).

**[Tokuda et al. 1990]** Tokuda, H., Nakajima, T., and Rao, P., "Real-Time Mach: Towards a Predictable Real-Time System," In: *Proceedings of the USENIX Mach Workshop*, USENIX Association, Berkeley, CA, pp. 73–82 (October 1990).

**[Tripathi 1989]** Tripathi, A. R., "An Overview of the Nexus Distributed Operating System Design," *IEEE Transactions on Software Engineering*, Vol. SE-15, No. 6, pp. 686–695 (1989).

**[Wilkes and Needham 1980]** Wilkes, M. V., and Needham, R. M., "The Cambridge Model Distributed System," *Operating Systems Review*, Vol. 14, No. 1, pp. 21–29 (1980).

**[Zimmermann et al. 1981]** Zimmermann, H., Banino, J. S., Caristan, A., Guillemont, M., and Morisset, G., "Basic Concepts for the Support of Distributed Systems: The CHORUS Approach," In: *Proceedings of the 2nd International Conference on Distributed Computing Systems*, IEEE Press, New York, NY, pp. 60–66 (1981).

## POINTERS TO BIBLIOGRAPHIES ON THE INTERNET

Bibliographies containing references on *Amoeba* can be found at:

http:www.cs.vu.nl/vakgroepen/cs/amoeba_papers.html

ftp:ftp.cs.umanitoba.ca/pub/bibliographies/Distributed/amoeba.html

I could not find a bibliography dedicated only to the *V-System*. However, the following bibliographies contain references on this system:

http:www-dsg.stanford.edu/Publications.html

ftp:ftp.cs.umanitoba.ca/pub/bibliographies/Os/IMMD_IV.html

ftp:ftp.cs.umanitoba.ca/pub/bibliographies/Os/os.html

Bibliographies containing references on *Mach* can be found at:

ftp:ftp.cs.umanitoba.ca/pub/bibliographies/Distributed/Mach.html

http:www.cs.cmu.edu/afs/cs/project/mach/public/www/doc/publications.html

A list of books dealing with *Mach* can be found at:

http:www.cs.cmu.edu/afs/cs/project/mach/public/www/doc/books.html

Bibliographies containing references on *Real Time Mach* can be found at:

http:www.cs.cmu.edu/afs/cs/project/mach/public/www/doc/rtmach.html

http:www.cs.cmu.edu/afs/cs/project/art-6/www/publications.html

Bibliography containing references on *Mach-US* (an operating system developed as part of the CMU Mach project) can be found at:

http:www.cs.cmu.edu/afs/cs.cmu.edu/project/mach/public/www/projects/mach_us.html

Bibliography containing references on *Chorus* can be found at:

ftp:ftp.cs.umanitoba.ca/pub/bibliographies/Distributed/chorus.html

# Index

## J



## K



## L



## M

## N



## O

## R



## S

## T

## U



## V